RADAR SYSTEMS FOR SHIPS, HELICOPTERS AND GROUND STATIONS - RADARS FOR NAVIGATION AND AIR-NAVAL SEARCH - DISPLAYS - MISSILE ASSIGNMENT CONSOLLES - HOMING RADARS - SIGNAL PROCESSING AND DATA HANDLING TECHNIQUES.

SMA

SEGNALAMENTO MARITTIMO ED AEREO

P.O. BOX 200 - FIRENZE (ITALIA) - TELEPHONE: 705651 - TELEX: SMARADAR 57622 - CABLE: SMA FIRENZE

Built in 1958 and still going strong, one of SUPRAMAR's PTL 28 Hydrofoils serving SHELL's offshore platforms on the Lake of Maracaibo in Venezuela.

HYDROFOILS=SUPRAMAR

Supramar=Hydrofoil: Simple as it sounds but basically factual ● Hydrofoils came to this world, first by Supramar, both militarily and commercially ● Nearly 40 years of painstaking research, testing, development and accumulated experience in Hydrofoil technology ● Over 20 years of production and licensing major shipyards around the world ● Over 18 years of solid and continuous operations with some 160 Hydrofoils operating the world's rivers, lakes, coastal waters and rough seas ● Over two billion passenger kilometers without a single fatality ● Supramar Hydrofoils could have an important and profitable place in your plan of operation ● They are used by over 100 scheduled ferry services using different types of Supramar Hydrofoils ● Shell Oil have used Supramar hydrofoils for over 15 years to service offshore drilling rigs ● Several Navies use Supramar Hydrofoils for coastal patrol duties ● Supramar Hydrofoils are now fully developed with a simple system of air stabilization, another revolutionary technique exclusively developed and patented internationally by Supramar ● If your business is water transportation, we have an experienced team to handle your purchase, long-term financing, leasing, operational or equity participation requirements ● You should get the facts from Supramar before making any decision ● Write on your letterhead to:

SUPRAMAR AG, DENKMALSTR 2, 6006 Lucerne, Switzerland
Telephone: 041-369636   Telex: 78228

JANE'S
SURFACE SKIMMERS

Hovercraft and Hydrofoils

Compiled and Edited by **Roy McLeavy**

Order of Contents

World Sales Distribution

Jane's Yearbooks,
Paulton House, 8 Shepherdess Walk,
London N1 7LW, England

All the World
except

United States of America and Canada:
Franklin Watts Inc.,
730 Fifth Avenue,
New York, NY 10019, USA

Editorial communication to:

The Editor, Jane's Surface Skimmers
Jane's Yearbooks, Paulton House, 8 Shepherdess Walk
London N1 7LW, England
Telephone 01-251 1666

Advertisement communication to:

Jane's Advertisement Manager
Jane's Yearbooks, Paulton House, 8 Shepherdess Walk
London N1 7LW, England
Telephone 01-251 1666

NAVAL SYSTEMS DIVISION

SELENIA S.p
00131 ROMA   Via Tiburtina km. 12.4
Telex 61106 SELENI

ELETTRONICA SAN GIORGIO S.p
16154 GENOVA SESTRI   Via Hermada
Telex 27660 ELSA

The NA10 mod. 3 System satisfies the intent of filling the requirement peculiar to light vessels which, armed with S/S missiles and one or two gungs, have to perform offensive tasks against surface targets while keeping an adequate self-defence capability.

It is a very light and compact system with minimized above-deck weights so that it may be installed on small craft with stringent stability demands like hydrofoils and fast patrol boats.

Its light weight also allow a high location of the radar antenna for full exploitation of the system's detection capability against low flying tragets, such as S/S missiles.

The most outsanding features of the system are its accuracy, quick-reaction time and flexibility.

The accuracy ensures for the gun battery a high hit probability also against extremely difficult targets such as 2nd generation S/S missiles.

The quick reaction time is also due to the high degree of automation (e.g. acquisition procedures are fully automated), the system requiring only one man.

The main sensor consists of the well known ORION 10X pulse radar which has excellent range and ECM resistance qualities.

As an auxiliary control sensor, use is made of a Low Light Level TV device.

The NA10 mod. 3 System has been chosen by the Italian Navy for its Hydrofoil (PHM) program.

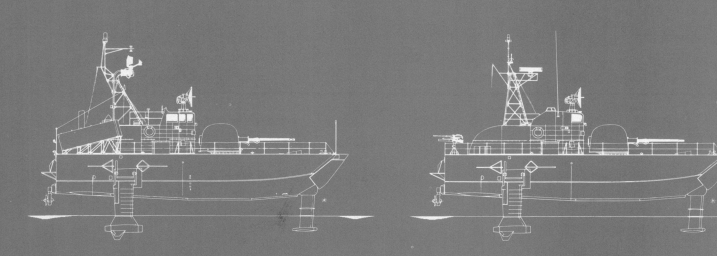

60 Tons "Swordfish" type hydrofoil Missile Gun Boat
Version A   1:76 • 2 OTOMAT

60 Tons "Swordfish" type hydrofoil Patrol Boat
Version A   1:76 • 1·81mm mortar

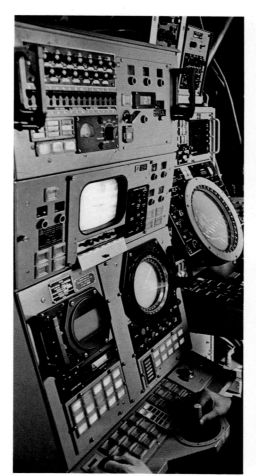

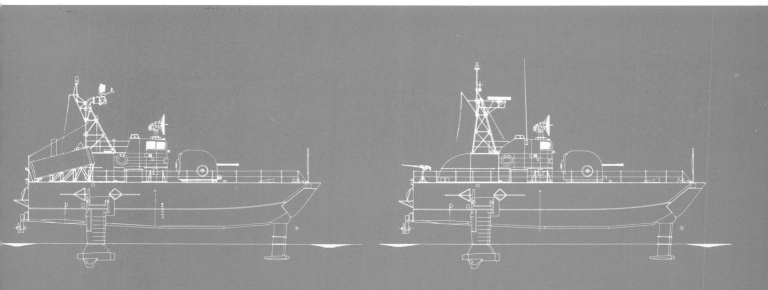

60 Tons "Swordfish" type hydrofoil Missile Gun Boat
VERSION B - 2×40 + 2 OTOMAT

60 Tons "Swordfish" type hydrofoil Patrol Boat
Version B - 2×40 + 1 .50" machine gun

a proven enforcer

What kind of boat is fast enough, tough enough, economical enough and suitable for sustained, open-ocean enforcement?

An evaluation of USCG Cutter **Flagstaff** (WPBH-1), proved the merits of hydrofoils in such missions as enforcement of laws and treaties, search and rescue, marine environmental protection and aids to navigation.

Grumman's **Flagstaff Mark II** — an improved version — offers even greater operating advantages as a missile carrier, coastal patrol, crew boat, gun platform, fast transport or cargo carrier . . . a versatile vehicle for many applications.

FLAGSTAFF MARK II

GRUMMAN AEROSPACE CORPORATION

The companies advertising in this publication have informed us that they are involved in the fields of manufacture indicated below

ACV MANUFACTURERS
Bell Aerospace
British Hovercraft Corporation
Vosper Thornycroft

ACV OPERATORS
Hoverwork

ACV RESEARCH AND DESIGN
Bell Aerospace
British Hovercraft Corporation
Selenia
Robert Trillo
Vosper Thornycroft

DIESEL ENGINES
Mitsui Engineering & Shipbuilding
Motoren-und Turbinen-Union
Zahnradfabrik

ELECTRONIC EQUIPMENT
Selenia

GLASS FIBRE RESINS
British Hovercraft Corporation

GUNS AND MOUNTINGS
Breda Meccanica Bresciana

HOVERCRAFT COMMAND STAFF TRAINING
Bell Aerospace
British Hovercraft Corporation

HOVERCRAFT CONSULTANTS
Bell Aerospace
Hoverwork
Robert Trillo
Vosper Thornycroft

HOVERCRAFT FERRY SERVICE
Hoverwork

HOVERCRAFT INTERIOR DESIGN
Bell Aerospace
British Hovercraft Corporation
Vosper Thornycroft

HOVERCRAFT INTERIOR FURNISHINGS
British Hovercraft Corporation
Vosper Thornycroft

HOVERCRAFT MANUFACTURERS
Bell Aerospace
British Hovercraft Corporation
Mitsui Engineering & Shipbuilding
Vosper Thornycroft

HOVERCRAFT OPERATORS
Hoverwork

HOVERPALLET MANUFACTURERS
British Hovercraft Corporation

HOVER SURVEYORS
Hoverwork

HYDROFOIL BOATS AND SHIPS
Cantiere Navaltecnica
Cantieri Navali Riuniti
Supramar
Vosper Thornycroft

HYDROFOIL INTERIOR DESIGN
Cantiere Navaltecnica
Cantieri Navali Riuniti
Vosper Thornycroft

HYDROFOIL INTERIOR FURNISHING
Cantiere Navaltecnica
Vosper Thornycroft

HYDROFOIL MISSILE/GUN BOATS
Cantiere Navaltecnica
Cantieri Navali Riuniti
Supramar
Vosper Thornycroft

HYDROFOIL MISSILE / GUN BOATS COMBAT SYSTEMS
S.M.A.

HYDROFOIL RESEARCH & DESIGN
Cantiere Navaltecnica
Cantieri Navali Riuniti
Supramar
Vosper Thornycroft

HYDROFOIL SEATING
Cantiere Navaltecnica

INSTRUMENTS—ELECTRONIC
Bell Aerospace
British Hovercraft Corporation

INSTRUMENTS—NAVIGATION
Bell Aerospace

INSTRUMENTS—TEST EQUIPMENT
British Hovercraft Corporation

PATROL BOATS
Bell Aerospace
Cantiere Navaltecnica
Cantiere Navali Riuniti
Mitsui Engineering & Shipbuilding
Supramar
Vosper Thornycroft

PATROL BOATS COMBAT SYSTEMS
S.M.A.

PUBLICATIONS
British Hovercraft Corporation
Robert Trillo
Vosper Thornycroft

RADAR FOR NAVIGATION, WARNING INTERCEPTION, FIRE CONTROL
Bell Aerospace
Selenia
S.M.A.

RADIO NAVIGATION EQUIPMENT
Bell Aerospace
Selenia

REVERSE-REDUCTION GEARS
Vosper Thornycroft

SKIRT MATERIALS
Bell Aerospace
British Hovercraft Corporation
Northern Rubber

TRANSMISSION SYSTEMS
British Hovercraft Corporation

331/396

538

652

956

400 to 6000 horses mtu diesel power

mtu

Motoren- und Turbinen-Union Friedrichshafen GmbH · M. A. N. Maybach Mercedes-Benz · 799 Friedrichshafen · W.–Germany

Design by Rohr Marine Inc. for the US Navy's 3KSES 3,000-ton Surface Effect Ship prototype. Its length of 270 ft, beam of 105 ft and design displacement of 3,000 tons, were selected to provide a high-speed capability in excess of 80 knots and a speed approaching 40 knots in sea state 6. The cushion height of 18 ft was selected to permit operation in open oceans and the beam will permit the vessel to use the Panama Canal. Initially, power will be provided by six GE IM2500 gas-turbines, two driving six centrifugal lift fans and the remaining four driving four waterjet pumps. But the engine space will permit the retrofit of six of the more powerful FT9 gas-turbines during the more advanced stages of its two-year trial period. Helicopters and/or V/STOL aircraft will be carried as well as weapons and sensors for test purposes. The ship is due to be completed during 1982.

JANE'S
SURFACE SKIMMERS
Hovercraft and Hydrofoils

TENTH EDITION

COMPILED AND EDITED BY
ROY McLEAVY

1976-77

I.S.B.N. 0 354 00540 5

JANE'S YEARBOOKS

LONDON

Some things ...like Edo excellence ...never change

In 1935 Edo floats crossed Antarctica with Bernt Balchen on Lincoln Ellsworth's Polar Star. Today, Edo sonar routinely dives under the Polar ice cap aboard the nuclear submarines of the U.S. Navy. In 46 years our standard of excellence has never been lowered...in Edo systems developed for antisubmarine warfare, oceanography, mine countermeasures, strike warfare, airborne navigation, hydrodynamics and airframes, command and control. And speaking of sonar, sonar designed and built by Edo is standard equipment aboard all the nuclear-powered submarines of the U.S. Navy and many of our modern destroyers.

EDO Corporation
College Point, N.Y. 11356

CONTENTS

"JANE'S" is a registered trade mark

FOREWORD

SES—80-KNOT SUB-HUNTER OF THE 1980s

"One swallow does not a summer make . . . ", nor does one 3,000-ton SES frigate prototype make an 80-knot Navy. But the mere knowledge that the first of these incredibly fast warships is now not only within grasp technologically, but is likely to be delivered to the US Navy in mid-1982, must be an enormous morale booster for Western defence strategists.

At last a credible deterrent to the growing menace of the nuclear-powered submarine is on the horizon. Development of the sophisticated technology needed to design and build a seagoing vessel with a top speed of more than 80 knots has taken the US Navy and its contractors nearly ten years and required an investment by the US government of US\$309,000,000 so far. But no one doubts that in terms of providing an effective shield against attack by submarine packs on the Atlantic and other vital international shipping arteries, the final value of the SES programme may well prove inestimable.

One of the chief protagonists of the programme is US Secretary of the Navy, J. William Middendorf II, who was aboard the Bell SES-100B on June 30th, 1976 when it established a new world speed record of 89 knots—about 102.5 mph. Mr. Middendorf sees the SES as the most advanced method of ocean transportation in the world and believes it will revolutionise naval warfare. Commenting on the future of the SES, he said recently; "We did not know the full potential and capacity of the aeroplane when it was first developed. But this did not inhibit the progress of the aeroplane. There were those who felt it would never have any potential other than to carry mail from one town to another. But, as was shown later on, it had a tremendous number of uses and opened up its own areas of application. We believe the SES will do the same."

One of the chief reasons for the sponsorship of the SES by the US government is its concern at being confronted by an adversary armed with more than 250 attack submarines and growing stronger month by month. The country has many major overseas defence commitments which demand that its sea communications remain open in time of conflict. It has been increasing its reliance on imports and currently some 50% of the United States' oil supplies come from overseas sources.

Today's conventional destroyers can barely keep pace with the latest escort carriers, let alone offer adequate protection for a convoy against submarines which, when submerged and operating at 25 knots, have little difficulty in evading any type of displacement craft in medium to heavy seas. Normally a convoy would be screened by about twelve warships, most of them destroyers or ASW frigates. The big advantage of the SES frigates is that they will be able to sprint out well ahead of the convoy at regular intervals, stop, then listen for underwater craft. Their speed, coupled with the increased effectivness of their sonar when operating clear of the convoy, will enable them and their helicopters to detect and destroy submarines long before they have an opportunity to close-in for an attack.

Major studies undertaken to investigate SES weapons, tactics and operations, have shown that the cost/effectiveness of the SES frigate compared with its displacement counterpart is two to three times greater. Naval tacticians suggest, in fact, that four SES's will provide a far more effective shield against attack than twelve displacement warships.

Within the industry it is widely believed that 3,000-ton SES frigates could be in service with the US Navy by 1985 and that by 1990 larger SES's of 6–8,000 tons could be available. These would be employed in "show of force" situations when the Navy needed to deploy troops and equipment to distant parts with the minimum delay to counter local emergencies. As one executive put it: "We envisage a more effective Navy, capable of doing more with fewer ships and smaller crews".

No one doubts that the transition into this exciting new era will introduce sweeping changes in management, planning and operating techniques. Indications as to the extent of these changes will be found in our tenth anniversary feature, "Ten Years Ahead . . .", which includes contributions from executives in the United States actively involved in the SES design, development and acquisition.

A contract for the final design of the 3KSES was awarded to Rohr Marine Inc of Chula Vista, California, on December 9th, 1976. Valued at US\$159.9 million, the contract covers the completion of the final detailed engineering design, which will be undertaken in San Diego, California. Within Rohr's contract is an option for a further contract for US\$155.7 million to construct the prototype, if the design is accepted by the US Navy. Construction of the craft is expected to take about 42 months and it is anticipated that it will be completed during 1982. Two years of naval tests will follow acceptance trials.

The new shape in naval warfare differs radically from any vessel of this tonnage in service today. Compared with the sleek "greyhounds of the sea" so beloved by naval traditionalists, the 3KSES has been described as an "aesthetic zero". But to protect its convoys in a nuclear age, the US Navy requires far more from its warships than a mere trim silhouette.

The craft, which is likely to be the forerunner of a class known as the FFSG (Fleet Frigate Surface Effect Guided Missile), is rectangular in planform. It will ride on an 18 ft deep cushion of air, contained by catamaran-style sidewalls and flexible bow and stern seals. Initially, power will be provided by six GE LM2500 gas-turbines, two driving six lift fans and the remaining four driving four waterjet pumps. But the engine space will permit the retrofit of six of the more powerful P & W FT9 gas turbines during the more advanced stages of its two-year trial period. Its length of 270 ft, beam of 105 ft, and design displacement of 3,000 tons, were selected to provide a high speed capability in excess of 80 knots, and a speed approaching 40 knots in sea state 6. The cushion height of 18 ft was selected to permit operation in open oceans, and the beam will allow the vessel the use of the Panama Canal.

Weapons will include two SH-3H helicopters or one AV-8B Harrier attack aircraft, Standard and Harpoon missiles and Mk 25 and Mk 32 ASW torpedoes. TACTAS towed sonar array, together with its deployment and retrieving system, is located at the stern.

Among the associated objectives of the SES programme is the advancement of the technology on a broader base. Plans for both the Fleet Frigate and SES's of possibly twice and three times its size will be technology-paced and synchronised with the development and testing of the prototype. The next major stage of the programme is likely to be the development of a 6–8,000 ton craft. Payload of an SES of around 8,000 tons would be 2,000 tons. When fully developed, craft of this tonnage are expected to be able to transport freight at a cost per ton mile of about one-third of that of air transport. This is said to be arousing the interest of the US Maritime Administration which foresees a future for SES's of this size as high-speed priority cargo carriers. Rohr Corporation has already undertaken several preliminary design studies for commercial craft based on its overall experience in the design and development of naval SES test craft.

France, too, has recognised that the SES/helicopter combination is the weapon most likely to succeed in anti-submarine warfare. Contracts for preliminary design studies for a 4–5,000 ton craft have been awarded to Sedam and Société des Ateliers et Chantiers de Bretagne by the French Ministry of Defence. Various alternative methods of propulsion are being examined, including four waterjets, four semi-submerged propellers and four turbofans.

In the meantime, the world's largest air cushion vehicle to date, the 240-tonne Sedam N 500-01 mixed-traffic hoverferry, is undergoing tests at Pauillac, near Bordeaux. The first two craft of this type are being built for SNCF (French National Railways), which

Floating wings.

Modern ship designs call for light, high-speed diesel engines and gearboxes to match.

Despite its exacting role, the gearbox must not be heavy. Its range of efficiency should be wide. It should be capable of long service life – dependable to a degree. And for good measure, quiet-running and simple to maintain.

ZF – Europe's No. 1 gearbox specialist – has developed a series of modern marine reversing gearboxes which meet the requirement precisely. They are compact, surprisingly light – give outstanding performance in ratings from 30 to 5000 hp.

Gearboxes of this quality demand first-class materials – backed by uncompromising manu-facturing and inspection standards. For instance, gears are of forged, case-hardened alloy steel with ground tooth flanks. They are inspected with meticulous care.

ZF gearboxes utilise every ounce of engine power in the hydrofoil.
If you'd like the facts,
ZF will be happy to fill you in.

ZF

ZAHNRADFABRIK FRIEDRICHSHAFEN AG
D-7990 Friedrichshafen 1
P.O. Box 307, W.-Germany

will employ them on a service across the English Channel, between Boulogne and Dover, starting in June 1977. The service will be operated in conjunction with British Rail's two SR.N4s.

Figures for the cross-Channel hovercraft services of BR Seaspeed and Hoverlloyd, show that during the first nine months of 1976 they jointly carried 1,459,891 passengers and 231,981 vehicles. These represent increases of 9% and 15.5% over the traffic figures for the same period last year. Market shares obtained by the hovercraft services on the Short Sea routes (Dover, Folkestone and Ramsgate to Boulogne and Calais) during the period January to September 1976 were 30.61% of all passengers and 26.17% of all vehicles. These compare with shares of 27.26% and 23.24% for the same period in 1975. Passengers and vehicles carried by conventional displacement ships operating the same routes both showed a decline on the 1975 figures.

British Government approval was given, during the year, for the stretching of both of British Rail's SR.N4 Mk 1's and the construction of a new, enlarged terminal complex in the inner harbour of Western Dock, Dover. The stretched craft, designated SR.N4 Mk III, will be 185 ft in length, and their increased capacity will enable them to carry up to 55 cars and 420 passengers. The four marine Proteus gas-turbines will each be uprated to 3,800 shp and each will drive a propeller/fan unit with a 21 ft (6.40 m) diameter propeller. By 1978, four of the largest hovercraft in the world—the two SR.N4 Mk IIIs and two Sedam N 500s—will be operating under the Seaspeed banner, providing an annual total capacity of 550,000 vehicles and four million passengers.

Hoverlloyd, which currently operates three BHC SR.N4 Mk II widened Mountbattens, is expanding its capacity also. In June 1977, it will take delivery of its fourth craft, which is of the same type, but with minor modifications.

Today's SR.N4s are expected to reach the end of their operational life in the early 1980's. The question being posed continually by potential mixed-traffic hoverferry operators is what form will its replacement take—and will it be suitable for routes other than the English Channel?

In recent months, Hovercraft Development Limited has been playing a major role in helping to determine the requirements of companies interested in acquiring large third generation craft. Its findings are being incorporated in a draft specification, the basic aim of which is to optimise the design so that it matches as far as possible the requirements of a number of ferry operators.

HDL's specification will be based primarily on the requirements of British Rail Seaspeed and Hoverlloyd Limited, since both operators are already looking to the future and neither wishes to find itself in the unenviable position of facing an indefinite time lag between phasing out the N.4s and introducing its replacement. The advantages of operators reaching an early agreement on a basic design which is acceptable to them are self-evident. By pinpointing requirements for a dozen or so craft of the same basic design before approaching a manufacturer, development costs can be shared over a greater number of units; cost of basic hulls and powerplants can be reduced, and items of maintenance equipment and spares can be ordered ahead so that they are readily available. Operators new to the field would benefit, additionally, by having launched their services with a design based on the tens of thousands of hours of concentrated operational experience, including traffic handling and servicing, gathered by both channel operators over eight years.

ACV technology is gathering momentum in many directions. As it stands today, the N.4 replacement is likely to have a higher speed, improved sea state capability, greater capacity and a longer range than its forebear, thus permitting a far greater choice of routes. Engine time between overhauls is likely to show a significant increase and fuel consumption will be reduced. With its improved economics and greater operating flexibility, the new craft should have a much greater earning potential than any conventional ferries of comparable capacity and is likely to be in wide demand, not only for many existing services, but also for establishing entirely new ones.

While there are no signs that the Soviet Union has built a commercial craft comparable in size to the SR.N4, examples of the Soviet Navy's 220-ton Aist heavy logistics craft are increasingly in evidence. Aists, which are almost certainly in batch production, frequently participate in assault landing exercises, carrying battle tanks and mechanised infantry to simulated beach heads. The first large Soviet amphibious hovercraft, it is now being joined by a smaller, but similar craft which is also capable of transporting a main battle tank. Reports suggest that this new vehicle is a counterpart to the two 160-ton, 50-knot amphibious assault landing craft being built by Aerojet-General Corporation and Textron's Bell Aerospace Division for the US Navy.

Another Soviet design which underlines the emphasis being placed on military applications of ACV technology is Gus, the 27-ton logistic support and amphibious assault craft now entering service in increasing numbers with units of the Soviet Marine Infantry. Series production is underway with, according to reports, more than thirty in service.

Interest in ACVs in the small-to-middleweight class continues to grow around the world. Current leaders in overall sales are BHC's SR.N6 Winchester and Hovermarine's HM.2, but as the market expands, competition from manufacturers in the United States, Canada and, in particular, Japan, is likely to be felt increasingly. BHC has recently supplied to the Egyptian Navy three militarised Winchesters and is negotiating the sale of other military twin-propeller and standard models of the SR.N6 to other countries in both the Middle and Near East.

Well over forty Hovermarine HM.2s are in service or under construction. The most recent requirement for this well-proven sidewall craft has come from the Urban Mass Transportation Administration in the United States, which is to operate three 84-seat HM.2 Mk 4s in the New York City area on the Hudson and East Rivers. The service is described as an "experiment in hovercraft commutation", and will last for two years. Initially the three craft, which will be air-conditioned, will operate a day service between Manhatten and areas such as Riverdale, Co-op City in the Bronx and La Guardia airport. They will also provide a substitute for the night ferry to Staten Island. The HM.2 Mk 4 is 10 ft longer than the 65 passenger Mk 3 and provides capacity for up to 92 passengers. The 50% increase in payload has been achieved with only a minimal increase in costs. A maximum speed of 33 knots is obtained by using two General Motors Type 8V92 diesel engines for propulsion.

The first 177-seat HM.5 Hoverferry is due to be launched in 1977. The prototype will be built to the standard specification but the capacity of production craft is variable from 160-200 passengers, depending upon customer's requirements. Its cruising speed will be 35 knots in waves up to 1 m. A military version can be fitted with either diesel engines or gas-turbines for propulsion giving speeds of up to 50 knots.

An excellent "shop window" for the SR.N6 in North Africa this year was the Algiers Fair, where Hoverwork completed a very successful 32-day charter with an SR.N6 Mk 1S. The craft provided a passenger service between the city centre and the fair, operating seven days a week from 12 am to 12 pm throughout this period, during which well over 10,000 passengers were carried. There was no downtime. Another highly satisfied N.6 operator is the Saudi Arabian Coast Guard and Frontier Force, which has operated eight of these craft from bases in Jeddah and Aziziyah for the past five years. Arab News, the English language daily newspaper published in Saudi Arabia, reports that the experienced smuggler on these hazardous shores has had his confidence shaken. Penetration of isolated beaches in the dead of night no longer goes undetected for the smuggler is aware that his movements can be observed by radar. He can now be pursued on land or sea by a vehicle which moves considerably faster than his in any direction, and when finally intercepted the hovercraft can discharge up to twenty fully-armed policemen.

Development in the hovercraft industry has never been stationary and opportunities for research are seldom overlooked. The experiences gathered from the Saudi Arabian Coast Guard operations and the many varied missions on which amphibious hovercraft have been deployed are too numerous to recount. Logistic support is provided continuously; crash rescue missions are frequently undertaken in areas where no boat or land vehicle can move, and seismic surveys are often conducted where the hovercraft is the

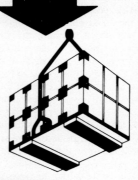

[16]

only vehicle capable of carrying out the various surveys because of the shallow waters of the Red Sea.

Prince Sultan Ibn Abdul Aziz al-Saud, the Saudi Arabian Minister of Defence is now exploring the possibility of employing larger hovercraft for other applications including minesweeping.

Latest military customer for amphibious ACVs is the US Navy which requires a replacement for its ageing logistics support vessels. It has selected a stretched model of the Bell Aerospace Canada Voyageur—the Model 7467 LACV-30. The new Voyageur will give the US Army the ability to move heavy cargo and equipment over water, beaches, ice, snow and marginal areas at speeds up to 56 mph. Although intended primarily as a lighter in support of Logistics Over-the-Shore Operations (LOTS), the craft can also undertake a number of secondary roles including patrol, search and rescue missions and medical evacuation.

Today's world of ACVs is by no means limited to craft designed for scheduled passenger services, the carriage of freight or coastal patrol. Hundreds of small vehicles are now in use for scores of utility applications for which other types of transport are totally unsuitable or too expensive. Variants of the inflatable-hulled Pindair 'Skima' series, Light Hovercraft's 'Fantasy', Surface Flight's 'Sunrider' and a number of others are selling in increasing numbers to areas where there is a steady demand for vessels with a fully-amphibious capability.

Users of the highly successful Skima 4, which was recently demonstrated at the 1976 American Power Boat Show, include an aluminium company in the Persian Gulf, a marine biology research group, missionaries on Lake Chad, a pest research organisation, and flood relief and beach rescue organisations. New clients include civil engineering companies, crop spraying firms, and diving groups. The latest trend is for these craft to be employed as tenders for large air cushion transporters when involved in operations over difficult terrain such as marshland or mud flats. Instead of returning the transporter to solid ground to pick up personnel and supplies, a small inflatable hovercraft operates as a supply tender between the transporter and its shore base. Deflated, and stowed in its box the craft occupies the minimum space aboard the transporter, and when required it can be inflated easily using an on-board air supply.

Before long, transporters are likely to be offered for sale equipped with a small inflatable hovercraft tender as an optional extra.

Latest model of the Skima is the semi-inflatable Skima 12, which is capable of carrying up to 12 people or 1 tonne of freight.

HYDROFOILS

A totally unexpected sight on one of Leningrad's canals this autumn, was a large, new gas-turbine powered hydrofoil in the final stages of construction. Judging from the impressions of a visitor, who encountered the craft while travelling on one of the city's scheduled waterbus services, this is obviously the forerunner of a new class of extremely formidable patrol boats destined for service with the Soviet Navy. Approximately 155 ft long, its displacement is estimated as being in excess of 300-tons, making it the world's biggest operational hydrofoil warship to date. Its armament includes the latest ship-to-ship missiles and a ship-to-air missile system of a new concept. The foil system, which is retractable to simplify hullborne manoeuvring and permit 'laying-up' in shallow coastal waters to avoid detection, comprises a main, split-vee bow foil and a single fully-submerged T-foil aft. Autostabilisation equipment and an autopilot are almost certainly fitted as well as the latest navigation, target detection and fire control systems.

The vessel, which is expected to have a maximum speed of about 55 knots, is the outcome of intensive development over the past thirty years. It illustrates how imaginative thinking, planning on a bold scale and the allocation of adequate resources have put the Soviet Navy ahead of its rivals yet again.

With the exception of the 45-ton Pchela, the small patrol hydrofoil employed by the KGB frontier force, Soviet military hydrofoils in the past have generally been based on existing FPB hulls equipped with a single bow foil only. This arrangement, first introduced on the now obsolete P8 class, and later reproduced on the Chinese "Hu Chwan" class, is also to be found on the more recent Turya ASW torpedo boat. Although an attempt to gain improved sprint

performance at minimum cost, this approach has proved far more effective than it looks.

The appearance of the new 300–350-ton FPB demonstrates the growing confidence being placed by the Soviet Union in its hydrofoil technology and is a significant milestone in the evolution of Soviet sea power.

Restricted funds, inflation and a general manpower shortage have prompted an increasing number of navies to adopt the 'more and smaller' policy for their sea defences. Many are likely to follow the Russian lead. From the cost effectiveness viewpoint, the 50-knot-plus missile-armed hydrofoil is an attractive investment. It costs less than the destroyer or frigate it replaces, and in addition to being much faster, the autostabilised hydrofoil reduces its speed only slightly in the higher sea states. Its speed simplifies the patrolling of long coastlines and the availability of greater numbers provides additional points of fire in the event of a conflict.

The order placed by the Italian Navy for six P 420 Sparviero-class missile hydrofoils is likely to be augmented by an order for a further three or four in 1977. Interest in the operation of hydrofoil patrol craft of between 100–250 tons has been expressed by the navies of Australia, Canada, Columbia, Denmark, France, German Federal Republic, Japan, Libya, the Netherlands, Norway and the United Kingdom. In addition Israel has recently indicated that it would like to co-operate with a US shipbuilder in the design and development of a 100-ton missile-armed craft, which is considered a high priority need in the country's defence planning.

In November 1976, four of the US Navy's initial batch of six Boeing PHMs became victims of a massive reduction in the overall budget for the next five-year defence plan. High technology programmes were those that suffered most. Reports state that the PHMs on order have been reduced to two and that the patrol tender which would have provided a mobile base for their operations has also been 'trimmed' out of the budget. Nevertheless, interest in the acquisition of a number of these excellent craft is being shown by the Italian Navy and others and 1977 could well mark the placing of the first export orders.

Amongst other military hydrofoil designs which are making steady progress are the 250-ton Supramar MT 250 all-weather patrol boat and the 85-ton Supramar MT 80, designed for patrol duties in coastal waters. Both studies are being undertaken in conjunction with Rolls-Royce, which will also provide gas-turbines for the Grumman's projected Flagstaff Mk II and Mk III.

More emphasis is being placed on the design and construction of military hydrofoil by both Navaltecnica, which has recently introduced its Mafius 100, 150, 300 and 600 missilecraft, and Seaflight SpA. In August 1976 Seaflight was taken over by a new Italian financial group. Details of a new range of designs are expected to be available in time for publication in the next edition.

Acceptance of the commercial hydrofoil as one of the most efficient modes of rapid transit on short and medium distance routes is growing everywhere and most manufacturers have full order books. In Italy, Cantiere Navaltecnica is currently building RHS 70s, RHS 140s and RHS 160s. Construction of the company's first RHS 200 was expected to be underway by the end of 1976. Among the latest operators of the company's craft are Aerobarcos de Brasil, and the Rizk Industry and Trade Establishment of Cyprus.

Seaflight's new President Dr Filippo Laudini says that the first craft to be put into production by the reconstituted company will be the 60-ton L90. This will be followed by a 180-seater employing a completely new foil system.

Boeing's 106-ton Jetfoils have been received enthusiastically in both Hong Kong, where two are in service with Far East Hydrofoils, and in the Hawaiian Islands, where three are in service with Pacific Sea Transportation. During the year Boeing operated a six-week experimental service between Seattle and Victoria BC in conjunction with British Columbia Steamship Co. The operation was designed to test the market for such a service and was said to have been a complete success. The Jetfoil employed had a 224-seat commuter configuration and made the 80-mile journey in 1 hour 50 minutes at a fare of US$30 for the return trip or US$16.00 for one way. It left Seattle each morning and returned from Victoria in the early evening. Continental breakfasts, snacks and beverages were served from the galleys on each deck.

40 mm L/70 BREDA TWIN NAVAL MOUNTING

"COMPACT"

Low weight
Maximum compactness
Full remote control with high servo-system performances
Substantial availability of ready-to-use ammunitions (736 rounds)
High rate of fire (600 rounds/min.)
Maximum accuracy
Employ of pre-fragmented shells with proximity fuze

FOR
ANTI-MISSILE DEFENCE (EXPECIALLY SEA-SKIMMERS)
ANTI-AIRCRAFT DEFENCE
SHIP TO SHIP ENGAGEMENTS

AUTOMATIC FEEDING DEVICES FOR 40 mm. L/70 NAVAL MOUNTINGS

MULTIPURPOSE ROCKET LAUNCHER OF "SCLAR" SYSTEM

Boeing's latest Jetfoil clients are Turismo Margarita CA, of Venezuela and Sado Kisen Kaisha of Japan. Turismo Margarita has purchased two Jetfoil 929-100s for a service between Puerto La Cruz and Margarita Island in the Caribbean. Sado Kisen Kaisha has ordered one for services between Niigata on the island of Honshu and Ryotsu on Sado island, in the Sea of Japan.

Supramar, which is now building vessels of its own design in shipyards in Hong Kong and Singapore, has announced details of a totally new concept, the hydrofoil catamaran. The first design in this new range is the Supramar CT 70 powered by two 1,300 hp MTU 331 diesels and seating up to 166 passengers. The craft, which cruises at 31 knots, has been designed especially for operation in shallow, sheltered waters, where draft limitations preclude the use of conventional hydrofoils. About 80-90% of the lift is produced by the foils and the remainder by the partly-immersed hull planing surfaces forward which also provide stability. One advantage of the arrangement is that it permits the placing of the foils below the water surface at a depth generally free of the floating debris. Berthing is possible at any existing pontoon or quay without adaption as the foils are well within the hull beam and therefore fully protected while drawing alongside.

One of the major applications foreseen for this new class of hydrofoil is that of fast waterbus on urban passenger services. Other likely roles include those of oil-rig support vessel and leisure craft. In cases where retractable foils are required a simple method of retraction can be incorporated. Because of the uncomplicated nature of the concept it is felt it could be successfully applied to outboard craft.

In Russia the Cyclone, 140-ton, 250-seat hydrofoil ferry, has completed its trials and preparations are underway for production at a shipyard at Poti, the Black Sea port which is also the centre for Kometa production.

The Cyclone, powered by an 8,000 hp gas-turbine, is propelled by a waterjet system. Its foils are of surface-piercing configuration similar to those of Kometa-M. A stability augmentation system is fitted for greater comfort in high seas. According to reports the craft has a maximum speed of 45-50 knots making it the Soviet Union's commercial hydrofoil.

Other new Soviet passenger hydrofoils being prepared for series production at yards on the Baltic and Black Sea are the Typhoon the Voskhod, Burevestnik and the latest model of the Kometa. Export of the Nevka 14-seat light passenger ferry, which is likely to be in considerable demand in the West, has been delayed further but the new Volga-275 with a semi-enclosed cockpit will be available to overseas buyers from March 1976.

INDUSTRIAL APPLICATIONS

One of the busiest areas of ACV activity is in the construction industry which is purchasing increasing numbers of air cushion transporters, hoverplatforms and hovertrailers to traverse marshy and ice-bound terrain. A leader in this field is Mackley Ace Limited, a wholly-owned subsidiary of J. T. Mackley Limited, a British civil engineering contractor which has specialised for many years in handling contracts in tidal and marshland areas. The major difference between the air cushion transporters built by this company and the more sophisticated high-speed hovercraft is they are designed to meet the needs of the construction industry which requires that they should be simple to operate and of rugged construction. They utilise the air cushion principle to carry plant and materials across otherwise impassable terrain. ·

Mackley Ace helped to build the world's first hoverdredger, built the first range of modular platforms and completed the world's largest hover transporter, the 250-ton capacity Sea Pearl, in the Middle East. It also constructed two 160-ton payload hover transporters which have been in use throughout the arctic summer and winter as chain ferries across the Yukon river.

The company has recently published a feasibility study on ship-to-shore hover systems which is arousing widespread interest in developing nations whose port facilities are unable to cope with the rapidly expanding marine traffic.

As opposed to a port extension, which may take three years, a 160-ton ACT can be delivered in three months. Road and rail links need to be reasonably accessible although this is not critical as the base of the ACT is 4 ft off the ground and can cover even the worst terrain to reach a suitable terminal point. Tidal conditions are irrelevant because the ACT is capable of working 24 hours a day over any surface.

Various techniques can be employed for offloading the ships. Facilities can be provided for taking cargo onto the ACTs from the ship's side. An alternative is to unload onto barges which are brought ashore by the ACTs, and yet another idea is to build a floating pontoon at sea. Cargo is unloaded onto the pontoon ready for transfer to the ACTs. A standard winch, tug or (on land) tractor provide simple, cheap and reliable pulling power. A further attraction is that any crew capable of handling a chain ferry can operate an ACT.

Newcomers to the air-cushion transporter field include British Hovercraft Corporation, Hoverlift Systems Limited, Transhore Ltd, and Vosper Thornycroft. BHC's entry to the field is a 200-ton capacity self-propelled hoverlighter, adapted from the SR.N4. The same basic SR.N4 machinery units will be employed, comprising four Rolls-Royce Proteus gas-turbines, each driving a centrifugal fan and a propeller mounted on a swivelling pylon to provide thrust and heading control. In a typical configuration, the hoverlighter would consist of a flat rectangular platform with a machinery module in each corner. It will carry up to 20 standard containers or equivalent loads up to a maximum of 200 tonnes.

The total capital costs of a large-scale installation, including hoverport, ten hoverlighters, maintenance base and customs facilities would probably be in the region of £150–200 million. Allowing for amortisation of the fleet over a period of ten years and the base facilities over thirty years, the total cost of operating the fleet, including all insurance, fuel and maintenance is estimated to be £12–15 million per year, assuming an annual utilisation (actual running time) of 1,000 hours on each craft. A utilisation of 1,000 hours per year represents an average of about $3\frac{1}{2}$ hours running per day, and is consistent with a one hour cycle on a 4–5 nautical miles ship-to-shore distance.

Working a 10-hour day the fleet would then unload 20,000-tonnes of cargo per day, or approximately 6 million tonnes per year, giving a total cost equivalent of £2–2.5 per tonne. Actual costs would depend on the distance off-shore and the speeds achieved, but would be expected to lie between £1 and £3 per tonne.

Hoverlift Systems of Calgary, Alberta, aims to provide air cushion equipment and services developed especially for companies operating in Canadian arctic and sub-arctic regions, islands, civil engineering, hydro-electric, forestry and mineral exploration projects are hampered by climate and difficult terrain. The company has built a 10-ton air cushion raft designed to be put into emergency operation in remote areas where no support equipment exists. It is now developing a technique of air cushion load assist. The aim is to provide a system which can be quickly attached to standard commercial vehicles to allow them to continue operations during periods of restrictions or load limitations and also to increase their capacity under normal operating conditions.

Vosper Thornycroft's hoverbarges can operate over land and water, carrying goods between a ship anchored off any shelving beach and a simple warehouse nearby, where they can be unloaded by mobile cranes or fork-lift trucks and transferred to an existing road or railway. When a particular loading or unloading operation has been completed in one place, a hoverbarge operation can be transferred almost in its entirety to another location.

Transhore Limited is offering a specialist service for the transportation from ship to site of heavy equipment to major projects as well as the straightforward transhipment of general cargoes from ship-to-shore. It is the owner of the world's largest air cushion transporter, the Sea Pearl, which is capable of carrying indivisible loads of up to 250 tonnes.

Application of the air cushion principle is becoming far broader, more productive and capable of more exploitation than anyone at first imagined. It has already listed some startling successes and will undoubtedly be adding to these in the near future.

Roy McLeavy
January, 1977

A truck skims over water. A ship crosses land. Incredible? No. It's Voyageur.

Voyageur is the rugged air cushion vehicle that is stimulating the imagination of transport experts around the world. In tough ongoing tests, amphibious Voyageur has proved its capability to perform herculean tasks in areas where other machines fall far short. From the frigid ice fields of Alaska and Canada's Northern Shores to the tidal flats of the North American east coast, Voyageur has been performing at speeds in excess of 50 MPH over choppy seas, muskeg, beaches, ice fields and sand bars. Modular construction makes it easily and economically transportable by ship, truck, rail or air. The new stretched version of Voyageur can haul payloads up to 30 tons. Its consistent performance as a cargo carrier, offshore lighter, personnel transport, search and rescue vessel – even ice breaker – are a matter of record. As a military craft the vehicle can haul 30 tons ship to shore and inland at 50 MPH. Cost studies indicate that this Bell craft is the most cost-efficient transportation alternative under many marginal terrain conditions. Voyageur. Look at what it has done. Imagine what it can do for you.

For further information, contact: Bell Aerospace Canada Division of Textron Canada Limited/P.O. Box 160/Grand Bend, Ontario N0M 1T0, Canada

Bell Aerospace Canada TEXTRON
Bell Aerospace Canada Division of Textron Canada Limited

A-3870-INT

ACKNOWLEDGEMENTS

The Editor would like to express his gratitude to his many correspondents for their readiness to supply information and their many helpful suggestions. In particular, he would like to thank:

Baron Hanns von Schertel and Volker Jost, Supramar; Mike McSorley, British Hovercraft Corporation; Leopoldo Rodriquez Jr and Giovanni Falzea, Cantiere Navaltecnica; Albert W. Spindler and Donald J. Norton, Bell Aerospace; Alan Bingham, Arnaud de Cosson and John Brooks, Hovercraft Division, Vosper Thornycroft; Peter Mantle; Capt. T. M. Barry, USN; Dr. William R. Bertelsen, Bertelsen Manufacturing Company; A. Izumi, Mitsubishi Heavy Industries; L. Flammand, Bertin & Cie; M. W. Beardsley, Skimmers Inc; Franklin A. Dobson, Dobson Products Co; Nigel Seale, Coelacanth Gemco; Jacques Beaudequin; Einar Bergström, Aeronautical Research Institute of Sweden; Peter Gooch; T. Akao, Hitachi Shipbuilding and Engineering; Neil MacDonald, Hovercraft Development Ltd; R. V. Taylor, Taylorcraft Transport Pty; A. Bordat, Societe Nationale Industrielle Aerospatiale; Gustav Elm; Admiral J. R. Evenou and Audoin de Dampierre, SEDAM: Charles Brindle, Peter Chennell and C. Palmer, Hovermarine Transport Ltd; C. D. J. Bland and P. H. Winter, Air Vehicles Ltd; Mrs. I. Smith, Novosti Press Agency; Christopher Hook; Vincent Schweizer, Supramar Pacific Shipbuilding; Andre Clodong, United Aircraft of Canada; Leo D. Stolk, Stolkroft Pty Ltd; Chuck Srock, Scorpion Inc; Richard Catling, Rolls-Royce (1971) Ltd; W. G. Eggington, Rohr Marine Inc; B. H. Wright, Rolair; R. C. Fishlock, Canadian Cushion Craft Ltd; Captain C. J. Boyd, SESPO; Kenneth Cook, Hydrofoils Inc; Masahiro Mino, Nihon University; James L. Schuler, Department of the Navy; Mike Pinder, Pindair Ltd; Georges Hennebutte, Ets Georges Hennebutte; Colin Knight, Hoverking; Walter G. Wohleking, Grumman Aerospace, Marine Division; J. F. Baker, Fairey Australasia Pty Ltd; C. F. de Jersey, De Havilland Aircraft of Canada; P. B. Dakan, Boeing; Milton Bade, Arctic Engineers & Constructors; Ralph Wortmann, Airesearch Mfg; W. W. Buckley, Aircushion Boat Co; Christopher Fitzgerald, Neoteric Engineering; Masaya Nakamura, Nakamura Seisakusho Co. Ltd; Judith Jordan, Tiger Equipment & Services Ltd; Geoffrey Parker, Hoverlift Systems Ltd; H. F. Lentge, Seaglide Ltd., John Scarlett, Cilma Holdings Ltd., A. Latham, Air Cushion Equipment (1976) Ltd and Fred Herman, Aerojet-General Corporation.

Grateful acknowledgement is also made for the use of extracts from the following paper;

Commander Jerome J. Fee, USN, Deputy Project Manager PMS 304 and Eugen H. Handler, Assistant for Subsystem Tests—*US Navy SES Program*, Surface Effect Ships Project Office (PMS 304).

Finally he would like to acknowledge the tremendous assistance given by Brenda Perfect and Hope Cohen of Jane's Yearbooks, by Erica Lake for typing the manuscript and to the production team, headed by Glynis Long and Lorraine Hurley, for their enthusiasm and hard work.

TEN YEARS AHEAD . . .

With this new edition, Jane's Surface Skimmers celebrates its tenth year of publication. Reference to our earlier editions will leave no one in doubt as to the spectacular pace at which both ACV and hydrofoil technologies have advanced during the past decade. Today, as manufacturers embark on the design of "third generation" craft, potential operators are posing the following questions: What significant differences will there be between the hovercraft and hydrofoils of today and those of the mid-1980s? What will be their speed, range and load capacity? Will their economics be more competitive with those of their conventional counterparts? In an attempt to answer these and other related questions, we approached a number of the industry's foremost advocates who were invited to contribute their views on the probable trends of "skimmer" design over the coming decade. We are delighted to be able to record their views below.

Capt. T. M. Barry, USN, Manager, US Navy Surface Effect Ships Acquisition Project.

The Surface Effect Ship Acquisition Project, originally the Joint Surface Effect Ship Program Office, was established in 1966. Upon completion of its first decade it is singularly appropriate that this office avail itself of the opportunity to predict its activities and services for the US Navy during the next decade.

The SES development programme is aimed at expanding its technology to ocean-going ships suitable for Navy service. During Phase 1, operation of the water jet-propelled SES-100A and the propeller-driven SES-100B demonstrated the validity of the SES concept and provided verification of the design data base pre-requisite to acquisition of much larger ships.

Phase II, based upon Phase I achievements and extensive mission analyses, focusses on design, development, construction and comprehensive tests in all aspects of a Large Surface Effect Ship of about 3,000 tons (3KSES). This fully-armed developmental prototype, scheduled for completion during 1981, will undergo approximately two years of Navy testing, including fleet operation simulating anticipated ship capabilities in a realistic environment. The development programme includes planning and preliminary design studies for Fleet Frigate Surface Effect Guided Missile Ships (FFSG) as well as subsequent design and construction of much larger vessels, including aircraft carriers, transport, logistics and combat ships. Decisions concerning the FFSG will be made following completion of the 3KSES test and evaluation programme.

SES hydrodynamic resistance is reasonably low in the speed regime below "hump speed" just as a conventional ship's resistance does not become prohibitive until it reaches "hull speed". Towing tank and manned model evaluations of high length/beam air cushion configurations verified analytic predictions of 50-60 knots attainable by high L/B SES with modest power demands as compared with displacement hulls operating at equivalent speeds. Consequently, it is possible that the SES-100B may be stretched from its present $L/B = 2$ to a jumboised $L/B = 6$. Although modifications would be made to lift fan and ducting systems, propulsion would remain basically unchanged. The new configuration would be used for investigation of performance, sea-keeping, stability, control, handling qualities and utility.

The SES-100A and B will continue to serve as test craft for investigations of phenomena which cannot be assessed in towing tanks or water tunnels. Systems and machinery longevity; deterioration due to fatigue, vibration, salt water, and erosion; delamination of bow and stern seal materials and other consequences of extended service will be observed. Improvement in waterjet pump inlets, supercavitating propellers, stabilising devices, ride control systems will continue to be studied and examined for practicability, reliability, and maintainability following installation of the 100A or B.

The SES Acquisition Project, through its coordinated efforts involving analyses, laboratory tests, models, test craft and development prototype is moving swiftly to provide the Navy with 80-100 knot ships during the coming decade.

John B. Chaplin, Director, Engineering, Bell Aerospace Textron.

The development that will take place in the US will depend primarily on the continued expansion of the military interest and associated programmes. Commercial applications in the US have lagged behind the UK progress and, except for some few specialized applications, will probably continue to do so. In the next decade, however, the results of the present US military research and development programmes, such as the amphibious assault landing craft (AALC) and the SES 100-ton test craft, will become evident. The ACV development will see the introduction of operational craft developed specifically for their respective missions in Army logistics and Navy amphibious assault roles, but the final acceptance of these types of craft will depend more on the control of development costs and the influence of cost effectiveness than on any future improvements in performance.

The most significant development in the next decade will be the building and operation of the first US Navy 3,000 ton ocean-going surface effect ship, the 3KSES, together with the development of the technology leading to even larger ships, including high length-to-beam configurations.

Some specific technology developments, which can be anticipated, are as follows:

the continued reliance, at least in the next five years, on the bag and finger bow seal concept, with considerable emphasis on design simplification, manufacturing techniques and improved reliability and maintenance;

a quantum jump in the flexible seal material strengths and a significant increase in operational life;

a 20-30% reduction in high sea state, flexible seal drag;

a 30-40% reduction in cushion power requirements for ACV's and SES;

many more attempts to invent alternative seal system concepts to the bag and finger with only a limited success in the early part of the decade, but the reasonable probability of a successful radical development for large SES in the later years;

the successful operation of waterjet propulsion systems up to 50,000 horsepower;

the development of surface piercing propellers up to 15 feet diameter and capable of absorbing 60-80,000 horsepower;

the development of lightweight, high speed transmission systems up to 80,000 horsepower;

the introduction of super-cooled electrical transmission systems;

initial research and development for lightweight nuclear power systems of 40-80,000 horsepower, weighing 10-16 lbs per horsepower;

the rapid development of ride control systems, simplification of the mechanical design and, in general, application to all sizes of military and commercial SES and ACV's.

Many factors will influence the development of ACV's and SES in the next decade, but no single factor will be more important and have more influence than the need to design to cost and to build competitive and cost effective systems.

Wilfred J. Eggington, Vice-President and General Manager, Surface Effect Systems Division, Rohr Marine Inc.

The last decade has seen two broad accomplishments in surface skimmer developments. Application of the earlier technologies has resulted in a number of successful commercial operations, particularly the European use of hovercraft and hydrofoils. In the United States the main thrust has been to advance the technologies considerably further, with an eye to more ambitious naval applications.

Next Step

From the established base of operational experience and sophisticated technology, I anticipate two major areas of accomplishment during the next decade:

1) an expansion of commercial and military operations, utilising surface skimmers of greater capability,

2) substantial reductions in cost relative to other craft.

Hydrofoils

The development of fully submerged foils, automatic control systems and wave height sensors have made the hydrofoil a stable platform in critical seas. Craft which successfully embody these developments are the US Navy's Patrol Hydrofoil Missile (PHM) and the Boeing Jetfoil. During the next decade we should see this type of coastal craft in greater numbers, and in displacements of up to perhaps 500 tons, operating in both commercial and military fields. Coupled with this should be significant advances made in reducing the relative production cost.

Air Cushion Vehicles

Even more significant developments are predicted for the amphibious air cushion vehicle and the waterborne surface effect ship. In 1977 the US Navy will begin test and evaluation of the two amphibious assault landing craft (AALC), JEFF-A and JEFF-B. Successful completion of testing will lead to the development of a landing craft, air cushion (LCAC), for production by the early 1980s. This craft will benefit from the development of low-cost production techniques without sacrificing performance or payload capabilities. LCAC's will represent the largest number of surface skimmers deployed for a single purpose.

The launching of the 3,000 ton surface effect ship will mark the world's first ocean-going surface skimmer. This high-performance ship, designated the 3KSES, will demonstrate the effectiveness of the SES platform, equipped with aircraft, weapons and sensors, in the fleet environment. Data obtained from the test and evaluation of the 3KSES will provide a basis for the design and production of SESs having similar or larger displacements. It is conceivable that the design of a nuclear-powered SES aircraft carrier could be well advanced by 1986.

In the commercial field of air cushion vehicles emphasis will be placed upon design simplicity, operational reliability and minimal cost. This will be a continuation of the trend over the last ten years with a blossoming of applications beyond the passenger ferry which currently dominates. Typical commercial applications are workboats for the oil industry and high speed fire control boats.

W. A. Graig, Mast. Eng'g (École Nationale Supérieure de l'Aeronautique, France).

Congratulations on your coverage of a momentous decade of the blossoming and ripening of new locomotion concepts. Though ostensibly limiting itself to the recording of developments and achievements that have taken place, Jane's Surface Skimmers has actually contributed to the progress of the Art by unbiased reporting and by collecting, centralising and disseminating 'hard-to-get', much needed information. We have all benefited from your labours. More power to you!

It is difficult to be specific in foretelling the rate of growth of the field of surface skimmers. It depends not on technology alone, but on unforeseeable shifts in military requirements, on capricious economic and even political factors. We can make only tentative projections. This remark dispenses me from qualifying each of my further assertions. To save space, I must use dogmatic and almost aphoristic language.

Barring the emergence of new contestants in an already crowded field, the heroic era in the life cycle of skimmers draws to a close. I expect evolution rather than revolution; refinements and possibly hybridisations; improved subsystems, gains in performance and improved cost effectiveness.

Two forms of skimmer—the hovercraft and hydrofoil—have already reached adulthood, if not complete maturity. But their base of support is narrow. In the coming decade their many variants will seek to expand their spheres of application and gain preponderance in at least one area within a widened spectrum of applications. There will be overlaps. The fittest will survive. There can be more than one survivor.

To categorise, *the inherently stable*, and the assimilated simple *mechanically stabilised* skimmers should conquer at last (if properly promoted) the refractory pleasure-and-sport boating market. Inherently stable craft will accelerate their penetration into the river, ferry, cabotage arena. Higher speed and superior (size-for-size) seakeeping capability gives them an edge over the traditional modes of transportation. Where prevailing sea conditions render employing inherently stable craft on ferry services impractical, fully-submerged hydrofoils may take over the task. Additionally, the hovercraft will gain recognition as overland and amphibious, working horses in certain regions. But in our euphoria let's not overlook other factors: "life cycle cost", development, production, operation, maintenance, time spent in servicing; reliability; etc. Before the inherently stable skimmer's ascendency over displacement craft is conceded, innumerable parameters will be weighed and computerised. In the military field, inherently stable skimmers should expand their hold on subsidiary tasks.

Fully submerged hydrofoils have excellent prospects. Subject to ratification by parametric studies, their missions will expand. Limitation: their speed advantage over displacement craft is relatively modest. Hopefully, it will grow.

The same comments apply to *hovercraft*, but improvements of seakeeping capability presents a problem. At increased speeds, banking inability will create another.

Other concepts, in less advanced development stages hold promise. Particularly intriguing:

Hull supported hydrostatically by fully submerged bodies, with hydrodynamic assist (eg "Swath" etc.).

Aerofoil boat, my outstanding favourite, though obsessive pursuit of inherent stability had diverted effort from higher priority objectives. Critics pretend that waves, even of modest size, inhibit flight in ground effect. There is hope for some untested configurations heavier than those at present envisaged, to take advantage of ground effect over seas, ie automatically stabilised airfoils boats will emerge. For these, moreover, terrain following capability, even out of ground effect, will find strong advocates.

Stanley Ho, Managing Director, Far East Hydrofoil Co. Ltd., Hong Kong.

To invite an operator of surface skimmer craft to forecast the possible development of such craft over the next ten years is hazardous in the extreme, for his sphere is basically the economic operation of proven existing craft, and not designing for the future.

However, our operation between Hong Kong and Macau has seen a number of "firsts", in that we introduced the RHS 110, RHS 160, PT 75 and the Boeing Jetfoil to commercial service, and from our initial experiences have contributed considerably to their development and improved performance and reliability.

The pressure of passenger movement by traditional means in urban areas of large cities, which have extensive waterways, has prompted many a city transport authority to examine the possibility of utilising fast commuter waterborne craft. Obviously, ability to compete with road or rail transport is essential, thus speed is vital, with the creation of minimum wake to affect other craft or the environment. Thus the surface skimmer type of vessel is the logical solution.

There is little doubt that the world is looking more and more to the marine element to meet the increasing needs of the expanding world population, oil, minerals, food etc and the technical spin off from the space exploration programme will contribute to the future design of sea going vessels to meet these needs.

The design of the gas-turbine has already reached the stage where horsepower output per pound weight has increased substantially thus we can expect the gradual replacement of diesel engines by the gas turbine giving greater speed and cleaner air.

Besides speed between two points, the commuting passenger demands a smooth passage in all kinds of sea conditions and it is in the stabilisation systems that the greatest advance may be achieved over the next decade.

There is evidence that the traditional surface-piercing foils do not lend themselves to providing the best form of stable platform. Even with modern stabilisation systems the future lies in the submerged foil or possibly catamaran type hulls.

Our knowledge of hydrodynamics and marine materials will advance to the stage where sea and wind friction, as well as weight, will be drastically reduced, requiring less power to achieve the same through-the-water-speed, thus being able to increase the payload and improve the overall economics of more sophisticated craft.

In addition, their operating hours will be extended by the use of laser beams, ultra violet and other scanners so that on the darkest of nights the crew will have a clear image of any hazards displayed on a three-dimensional screen, thus effectively turning night into day.

[24]

Thus I can envisage that 1980s will see safe, stable streamlined craft, speeding through the seas, day or night, at up to 80 knots carrying a payload, per horsepower output, far in excess of today's skimmers. But will our regulatory bodies, controlled so often by outmoded traditional outlooks, be able to adapt and accept the future skimmers? This is perhaps the main handicap to a golden decade in high speed, novel craft of the future.

Christopher Hook, Managing Director, New Hydrofin Ltd.

It is indeed remarkable how the old sacred monopoly of the displacement ship has been shattered in twenty years by new principles of interface support over water, and how the very severe control problems have gradually been solved. Now that the safety record of both hydrofoil and hovercraft are seen to be without precedent in transport history, it is only a matter of time before they take over a growing proportion of airline traffic where safety is still beset with problems. However, while this trend will be confined to the short haul end of the spectrum, and exception to this rule is the oil rig protection craft which is definitely a hydrofoil role.

For the same reasons, ie long range, small drop in speed in large waves and great comfort on station, the hydrofoil will eventually find a place in the pleasure and fishing boat markets, but a special effort of information dissemination is required before this can come about. This is a chicken and egg problem. Which comes first?

The finished and mass produced small hydrofoil or the bookstall distributed magazine which explains to the general public in simple language what it costs and what it can do that the speed boat cannot do?

Having more recently gained a lot of first-hand experience of sailing foils my present thinking about them is that this is possibly a subconcious attempt to solve the general hydrofoil problem by a cheaper but unsuitable application of foils, with a much too restricted market or no market at all.

With greatly increased research efforts some of the problems of a practical every-day rig could be solved but only greatly increased sizes would possibly find a market. However, I would hope to be found completely wrong since much has been learned which stimulates the imagination and provides a very healthy sport any way.

Leslie A. Hopkins, Director, Air Cushion Equipment Ltd.

It is the air cushion industry's firm belief that, within the next two years, four already proven systems will make their impact. The well-known development of the hovertrailer for the recovery of disabled aircraft will soon be accepted, for the simple reason that high cost secondary damage to the aircraft is nil.

Work is now well in hand for the use of hoverbarges with payloads of 250 to 500 tonnes for transferring loads to the shore from ships unable to use the present harbours, particularly those in the Middle East.

One of the most exciting discoveries over the last three years has been the ease with which a hoverplatform fitted to the bow of a ship converts the ship into the world's most efficient and the cheapest ice breaker. The Canadian Coast Guards have already picked up this development and have issued the specification for a hoverplatform which can be fitted to any ship and used to keep all Canadian harbours open throughout the year.

The fourth development, just on the market, is the pallet fitted with a segmented skirt and using water instead of air at 6 bar to lift loads 75 mm. The current pallet, 2.5 m $\times$ 1.25 m, will lift a load of 100 tonnes and cross uneven surfaces with irregularities as deep as 75 mm. One well known problem this could solve is the barge loading of freight of any weight or C.G. position. For pallets to lift loads greater than 100 tonnes is simply a matter of increasing the pallet area. Known uses for these pallets are in shipbuilding, launching barges and ships down extremely simple launching ramps, launching under water tunnel sections and concrete caissons without the need for dry docks and axle relief for transporters moving over unprepared ground. One possible use worth considering, because of the wasted time in unloading and loading container ships, is to assemble the containers on a loading platform on the dockside before the roll-on, roll-off ship arrives, then unload and reload the complete container cargo in one simple movement on water pallets.

These are known uses for recent developments. There must be many additional applications once these systems are accepted. Given a market this side of the hovercraft industry could lead to new production methods and the marketing of complete systems for the movement of heavy loads.

Robert J. Johnson, Technical Director, Advanced Hydrofoil Systems, US Navy.

When asked to comment on the expected development of hydrofoils in the coming decade, it reminded me of a related story between a banker and a troubled businessman. The banker asked the man, who needed additional financing for his company, why the company had failed in the past to be profitable. His response was that he could predict the future much more readily than he could explain the mistakes of the past.

Looking at the measurable trends over the past ten years several certain facts are apparent:

the number of hydrofoils has increased in total;
the number of countries interested in military hydrofoils has increased;
the costs have increased with improved performance;
the cruise speeds have stayed about constant;
the size has increased;

From these observations, certain indications are available as a basis for using the crystal ball.

The interest in both commercial and military hydrofoils can be expected to grow. In the military arena the capability to pack a lot of punch in to a small package is economically attractive. The number of small gunboats in the world is increasing. The interest of developing nations in using small hydrofoils as gunboats is growing. All this combines to say that the number of operational military hydrofoils will continue to increase.

Commercially that matter has a different aspect. Hydrofoils are now experiencing their first test of proving the saleability of improved performance. A reluctance is evident to pay for improved performance when the only dividend is passenger comfort or convenience. When the improved performance results in higher profits for the operator the willingness to pay for improved performance is evident. When passengers recognise that a more comfortable ride can be obtained at a reasonable price, the demand for better performance will prevail. Based on passenger and operator demands and a belief that producers can control costs, the next ten years will see a growth in high performance, commercial hydrofoils.

As to the growth in speed and size of hydrofoils, some conclusions can be drawn regarding military hydrofoils. It is not anticipated that there will be any appreciable increase in open-ocean cruising speeds. Hydrofoils, while having inferior smooth water speeds compared with some types of advanced surface craft, are speed competitive in the open sea. Generally speaking, the same speed can be attained in rough water as any advanced craft with smaller craft motions using the submerged hydrofoil principle. With the interest for military operation favouring the open sea performance, there is no big incentive to increase the smooth water speed of hydrofoils.

On the other hand, the feasibility of building larger, military hydrofoils has been established. The potential of accomplishing tasks of larger conventional ships in smaller packages is economically attractive. With the continued pressure for lower military expenditure and lower manning levels, the large hydrofoil represents an attainable alternative to conventional warships. With this pressure on the hydrofoil designer, it can be expected that larger hydrofoils will be listed in the future military arsenal of naval warships.

John M. Lefeaux, Managing Director, British Rail Hovercraft Ltd (Seaspeed Hovercraft)

The ten years during which both Jane's Surface Skimmers and Seaspeed have been in existence have seen many developments of varying success in the fast ferry scene, which the former has duly recorded for posterity. The financial climate during the latter part of the decade has undoubtedly slowed the rate of progress, yet things have been happening.

Jane's (1972-73 edition) has recorded the reasons why Seaspeed has sought to stretch its SR.N4s and the new decade opens with the stretching programme going ahead, major new hovercraft terminals being built at Dover and Boulogne and the Sedam N 500s about to join the N4s on the route.

For a long time I have held the view that the first step to the way ahead for big hovercraft would be to stretch the N4s and thereby not only improve their performance in rough weather conditions, and thus the reliability of the service that they offer, but at the same time transform the economics of their operation by increasing their revenue earning potential to far greater degree than the increased cost of operation. The stretched N4 Mk 3 will become a viable commercial vehicle on the short sea cross-Channel routes. Real commercial success in terms of substantial profit has eluded the industry thus far, although there is no doubt that from the point of view of the travelling public they are now wholly acceptable as a means of crossing the Channel. The N4s of Seaspeed and Hover-lloyd have carried over 30% of the passengers and accompanied cars of the short sea routes for several years now and would carry more if they had the capacity to do so. This bodes well for the future.

In terms of ton miles per hour the cost of operation of the stretched N4 Mk 3 will be almost on a par with modern ferries and given their advantages to the travelling public, in terms of speed of crossing, personal service and lack of fuss, real commercial success is just around the corner. Once this is achieved, further major investment in a new generation of big commercial hovercraft will follow, and those craft will incorporate design refinements to greatly improve both their mechanical efficiency and their economics.

I see this happening within the next decade and with it new hovercraft services on several new routes. However, I know all too well that setting up and running hovercraft services is an expensive business and that it will only be justified where there is sufficient traffic to satisfy the voracious appetite of hovercraft for customers spread reasonably evenly in time. A steady base load throughout the year, or day for commuter services, will be necessary to get the economics right, and these factors may well tend to govern the rate at which new services start. It seems probable that some of the new services may well be on longer routes than the present ones, where speed and saving of journey time will be very significant in attracting traffic.

The next decade will see the industry get beyond commercial hump speed!

M. A. Pinder, BSc, CEng, MIMechE, Managing Director, Pindair Ltd.

During the last decade the best light hovercraft have been developed to the point where they can be seriously considered as a reliable form of amphibious transports. The next decade should produce further technological improvements, but my guess is that the learning curve has started to flatten and that the light hovercraft is about where the car was in 1910. The first Model T Ford of hovercraft, therefore, has either just been built or is just about to be. The motor car and the internal combustion engine and other associated technology were developed together so we do not have to wait sixty years to get to the stage that cars have now reached. Cars of ten years ago were not that different from the cars of today. Many believe that cars are approaching as near perfection as is possible to get for the price. The same argument applies for boats and for aircraft. The light hovercraft has yet to catch up, but could achieve this stage technically by the end of the next decade.

The components and materials necessary to build light hovercraft were available thirty years ago. What a pity Sir Christopher did not play with coffee tins a little earlier for the world is now entrenched in its attitude and committed to traditional forms of transport and it is most unlikely that the light hovercraft will, to any great extent, replace any existing forms of transport. Nevertheless, there are still many parts of the earth's surface which are inaccessible by other forms of surface transport and where large hovercraft are impractical or uneconomic. Half the world's rivers and many of its lakes and swamps are unnavigable and these are areas which must be explored and exploited in order to support our population, to provide them with recreation or to ensure that they are defended from one another.

Commercially the light hovercraft cannot so far be considered a success. Most of the world's population have not heard of hovercraft or they think that they are all big. Of those that have heard of hovercraft, very few understand them or the principles, so there is still a tremendous education job to do. Fortunately the younger generation, with their thirst for knowledge, are aware of the capabilities of hovercraft, but we may have to wait for them to become buyers before large quantities of craft are sold.

Unfortunately the press would rather knock than praise. The transport press especially seem to look down on small hovercraft, just as sail looks down on power, and there seems to be almost a closed shop attitude. The hovercraft press has not yet reached the bookstalls and is therefore teaching to the converted subscriber.

As far as light hovercraft are concerned money does not talk, although adequate capitalisation is essential. The brief history of the hovercraft is littered with companies that have failed, even though millions of pounds and dollars had been injected. Financial help is needed both for further development and marketing. But all that glitters is not gold and a good track record must be the main qualification if this is to be given. One would have expected universities to take a deeper interest in the technical design and business progress of hovercraft, especially in Britain where most of the key patents are held.

When the Editor asked me to write this I think he expected a list of technical prophecies. I believe that most of the principles that are to be discovered have been discovered, and that what is needed is painstaking and perhaps costly development, although generally the best of what we have now is good enough. Of course, there will always be room for better skirts with more obstacle clearance, better wear and tear characteristics, more efficient and quieter lift and propulsion systems, lighter, stronger structures, improved transmissions, better speed and payload. But the main technical emphasis now must be on simplification and design for low cost quantity production.

The best light hovercraft are no longer amusing freaks and can do a useful job of work, but the bonanza is still around the corner and by the very nature of the problem, potential customers are the last to hear about the product and can least afford it!

Baron Hanns von Schertel, Director, Supramar AG

Speed and comfort are primary targets in the development of vehicles that operate on road, rail, water and in the air. The hydrofoil designer cannot ignore these objectives if his craft are to remain competitive. Most shipowners, however, are of the opinion that the speed of hydrofoils in current use is sufficient for some time to come. This view is based on the assumption that the direct competitor, the displacement passenger ferry, is incapable of increasing its speed to any great extent, without impairing its economy. Moreover, preference is given to safety and reliability of operation over comfort, and there is a general unwillingness to accept costly and unreliable systems which could raise maintenance costs.

The outstanding success of Jetfoil, the speed and comfort of which has considerable praise from the travelling public, will encourage a revision of this philosophy, although the new concept does not match the profitability of hydrofoils currently in service.

In consequence we can anticipate that during the next decade the trend will be towards second generation craft with greater structural simplicity, and an avoidance of sophisticated components in order to increase reliability and productivity. They will, be the product of shipyards rather than of the aircraft industry.

The surface-piercing foil system is about to be provided with important improvements in respect of seaworthiness and comfort, thus strengthening its viability. For the coming decade, at least, this type will be favoured for use in areas with moderate sea states, as long as it ensures better dependability and a higher return on investments than its fully-submerged-foil competitor.

The question arises as to what growth in size can be anticipated in the next ten years for the hydrofoil ship. The author refers to his lecture presented in May 1976 to the Hovering Craft & Hydrofoil Conference, in which he predicted that a vessel in the range of 250 tons is already the largest size of commercial hydrofoil from which successful operation can be expected. The reason is that size limit is determined by productivity and not by technical feasibility.

However, if technical development advances at the same rate as before we shall see military vessels of 1,000 tons or more by the middle of the 'eighties.

R. Stanton-Jones, MA, DCAe, CEng, AFRAes, Managing Director, British Hovercraft Corporation.

It is now some years since the feasibility of the basic hovercraft principle was proved and the first commercial and military craft established regular operations.

Excluding the small two to five seater sports craft and the activities in the Communist world, we estimate that there are now one hundred to one hundred and twenty craft in regular use. Their operations include Coastguard and Airfield Fire Fighting, using the 7-ton SR.N5 class of craft, naval operations using the 50-ton BH.7 craft, and worldwide commercial operations with Hovermarine sidewall craft and stretched SR.N6s, and Cross-Channel operations with the 200 ton SR.N4s which are likely to increase substantially over the next three years.

Hovercraft cannot yet be considered to be big business. At a rough guess the total turnover of all the hovercraft manufacturers put together is probably of the order of £20 million a year, while the sum total of revenues of all commercial operations is probably in the region of £25 million a year.

However, there are clear signs that hovercraft are on the threshold of a significant forward step in technology, and we at British Hovercraft Corporation are very hopeful that the research and development programmes, which have been proceeding steadily for the past few years, will lead to improvements in craft efficiency and operating costs, which will make the hovercraft a great deal more cost-effective in both commercial and military operations. The next two/three years will see the introduction of the first craft to incorporate some of these improvements: the lengthened version of the SR.N4 (SR.N4 Mk 3) which will be coming into service on the Channel with a substantially reduced seat mile cost relative to a standard SR.N4.

In addition, we are already preparing project designs aimed at a completely new craft incorporating further improvements which we believe could achieve a reduction of the order of 40% in the present operating costs.

If these predicted technical improvements can be established in practice at full scale, it would enable the new hovercraft of the 1980s to compete directly with conventional ships, as regards operating costs on the longer sea routes in the region of one hundred to two hundred miles.

Given these improvements in technology, it should be possible to achieve comparable performances in rough water with craft that are smaller than those of the present day. However, we believe that there is still a minimum practical size in the region of 10 to 20 tons all-up weight for a safe and adequate performance in the minimum of wave heights (around three to five feet) which are encountered in practice. Hence, we are considering the incorporation of these new technical improvements into a craft about the size of the SR.N6, which we hope will meet with even greater success than its widely used predecessor.

In the military field there is continuing interest in the Royal Navy in the use of relatively large hovercraft (the size of the SR.N4) for the mine countermeasure role, which we hope will eventually lead to substantial overseas sales, bringing with it the cost advantages of larger batch production.

Our market surveys indicate that almost every navy in the world is giving serious consideration to the use of hovercraft and that, before long, hovercraft units are likely to become established as an important element in every fleet.

The considerable improvements that the technology will bring to the range and payload capability of hovercraft are of particular importance in the fast attack craft role, and a new 100-200 ton hovercraft will be very competitive in performance with a 600-ton conventional fast patrol boat.

One of the commercial applications of hovercraft that is generating a great deal of interest is the use of large amphibious craft for ship-to-shore off-loading of containers. This has already been done on a small scale in various parts of the world, but this new concept envisages a policy to decentralise complex port installations and to take care of further expansion of port facilities by laying down a number of small and cheap hover ports in areas where they are required in order to avoid the loading and unloading congestion of both ships and trucks in the conventional ports.

This proposal is well within the capability of current technology but the new technological developments would make the hovercraft 'Lighter' a considerably more attractive and economic proposition.

At the forefront of this technological development during the next decade will be the American Navy's LSES programme which will inevitably generate considerable improvements in skirt, lift system and ride control technology. Many of these improvements will undoubtedly be applicable to the further development of the smaller sizes of craft.

William A. Zebedee, Chairman of the Board, Hovermarine Corporation.

Since their commercial beginnings a decade ago, hovercraft have fallen short of the expectations of their backers. Yet, there exists a substantial weight of evidence to support the theory that the backers may have in fact been too conservative in their expectations— although their time horizons were unquestionably too ambitious.

Why has the technology been so slow to develop? What is the evidence that gives encouragement to those who have had the patience to stay with the industry? While disqualifying myself from judging the effectiveness of management in the industry, I would suggest the answer to the first question lies in three areas.

First, hovercraft and hydrofoils are referred to in many circles as "unconventional" vessels, a term which bespeaks the (perceived) revolutionary aspects in a marketplace which has seen relatively few technological advances in two centuries. In short, the market has been and continues evolutionary, and absorption of significant advances simply takes time.

Second, the commercial builders have concentrated to date on the movement of people. This is analogous to focusing on the tip of an iceberg; the vast bulk of the market is engaged in moving things (cargo) and not people.

Finally, the pace of life in general in the twentieth century has outstripped the speed of conventional marine passenger transport, particularly for urban commuters. In the Tri-State region of New York City, for example, travel by ferry has diminished from a peak of over two hundred million annually to just twenty-seven million passenger-trips by water in 1974.

As for encouragement regarding the future, the mere fact that the tenth edition of *Jane's Surface Skimmers* is being published attests to an industry advance from infancy to adolescence. In the next ten years, there is evidence of an advancing market maturity —witness the following:

Urban Mass Transit

The costs of relieving urban transit congestion by means of advanced, land-based systems is proving beyond the means of even the most affluent of nations. Some of these costs arise because urban waterways (which are present in virtually every major city) have become a barrier to transportation. Yet, there is increasing awareness that surface skimmers are suited to the pace of life today, and that the water barriers can represent free and uncongested "highways" for these vehicles.

Freight Transport

Surface skimmers are growing in size; coming closer to being intermediate-distance freight carriers. The United States Navy is proceeding with plans to build a 3,000 ton surface effect ship with trans-oceanic capabilities. Unconventional vessels are definitely moving towards this bigger commercial marketplace.

Market Evolution

If speed could not command a premium, there would be no 25 knot-plus container ships. The next ten years will see further evolution towards higher speeds and economic unconventional vessels.

Military Applications

The recent advent of the two hundred mile territorial waters limit demands an advance in marine hardware for military purposes. In terms of the future, this development may be the most significant in the first decade of our "unconventional" history.

Faster and faster by the sea

MITSUI HOVERCRAFT

52—seater Mitsui hovercraft are already plying regular coastal routes around Japan. Mitsui, pioneer and sole manufacturer of hovercraft in Japan, has also developed a 155—seater, large type hovercraft which will provide further contributions to regular coastal passenger services.

MITSUI HOVERCRAFT MV-PP15
- Overall length: 24.7m
- Overall breadth: 12.7m
- Overall height: 7.9m
- Gross weight abt. 50 tons
- Crew: 5 (including 3 stewards)
- Passenger capacity: 155
- Maximum speed abt. 65 knots
- Service speed abt. 50 knots
- Cruising range abt. 4 hours

MITSUI SUPER WESTAMARAN

Mitsui has now developed a new type of asymmetrically shaped catamaran capable of amazingly high speeds and which is remarkably seaworthy. It is based on a prototype of Westamaran W86 of the Westermoen & Westamaran Hydrofoil A/S, under license from Westamaran A/S of Norway. Now in regular passenger service in Japan.

MITSUI SUPER WESTAMARAN CP20
- Overall length: 26.465m
- Overall breadth: 8.800m
- Depth: 2.488m
- Gross weight abt. 200 tons
- Passenger capacity: 160—200
- Crew: 3
- Maximum speed abt. 28.5 knots
- Cruising range abt. 9 hours

MITSUI ENGINEERING & SHIPBUILDING CO., LTD.

Head Office: 6-4, Tsukiji 5-chome, Chuo-ku, Tokyo, Japan Telex: J22821, J22924
Overseas Offices: New York, Los Angeles, London, Duesseldorf, Hong Kong, Singapore, Rio de Janeiro

[28]

ACV MANUFACTURERS AND DESIGN GROUPS

ARGENTINA

BRUZZONE

ADDRESS:

Peru 327, Buenos Aires, Republic of Argentina, South America

EXECUTIVES:

Jorge O. Bruzzone, Designer

Larry Baqués, Production

Jorge Oscar Bruzzone, an Argentinian aeronautical engineer, designed an amphibious craft, the Guaipo BMX-1, which was built and tested by the Argentine Navy. (Described in JSS 1971-72 edition).

Mr. Bruzzone has experimented with ACVs for nearly fifteen years. At the present time he is building, privately, a light two-seater and a three-seater. Preliminary details of his Yacare JOB-3 two-seat recreational craft and the Yacare II twelve-seater are given below.

YACARE JOB-3

The prototype of this fibreglass-hulled amphibious two-seater is undergoing trials. It has a maximum speed over water of 68·5 mph (110 km/h).

LIFT AND PROPULSION: Lift air is provided by a 1,200 cc Volkswagen air-cooled, four-cylinder four-stroke automotive engine driving a 2 ft 11½ in (90 cm) diameter centrifugal fan. Propulsive thrust is supplied by a 1,600 cc Volkswagen automotive engine driving a 4 ft 3 in (130 cm) diameter ducted, two-bladed propeller.

CONTROLS: Twin aerodynamic rudders control craft heading.

HULL: Moulded glass reinforced plastic structure.

ACCOMMODATION: Side-by-side seating for two in an open cockpit.

DIMENSIONS:

Length	14 ft 5¼ in (4·40 m)
Beam	7 ft 10½ in (2·40 m)
Height	3 ft 11¼ in (1·20 m)

WEIGHT:

Normal all-up weight	1,149 lb (520 kg)
Normal empty weight	595 lb (270 kg)
Normal payload	441 lb (200 kg)

PERFORMANCE:

Max speed	68·5 mph (110 km/h)
Vertical obstacle clearance	11¾ in (0·30 m)

YACARE II

The Yacare II is a single-engined fully amphibious ACV designed to carry payloads of up to 3,528 lb (1,600 kg) on its load deck in containers or modules. The passenger module seats twelve.

LIFT AND PROPULSION: Integrated system powered by a single 300 hp engine. This drives a centrifugal lift fan and a variable-pitch propeller for propulsion.

CONTROLS: Craft heading is controlled by twin aerodynamic rudders hinged to fins located at the rear of the propeller. Side located thrust ports aid low-speed manoeuvring.

HULL: Moulded glass reinforced plastic and aluminium structure.

ACCOMMODATION: The control cabin, forward, has seats for the two-to-three, man crew. Passenger module seats twelve passengers.

DIMENSIONS:

Length overall, power off	36 ft 1 in (11 m)
skirt inflated	36 ft 1 in (11 m)
Beam overall, power off	19 ft 8 in (6 m)
skirt inflated	19 ft 8 in (6 m)

Prototype of the JOB-3 amphibious two-seater prior to final completion. During 1976 the craft attained a speed of 68·5 mph over water. Volkswagen air-cooled four-cylinder engines are employed for both lift and propulsion

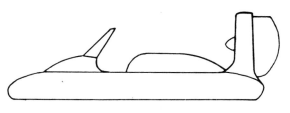
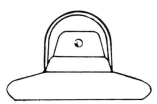
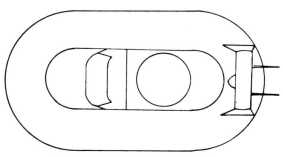
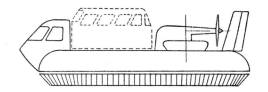
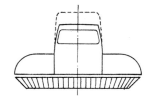
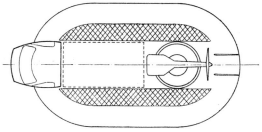

Yacare II, a projected 36 ft (11 m) utility ACV. A 12-seat passenger module can be carried on the flat load deck aft of the control cabin

Height overall on landing pads, power off		9 ft 10 in (3 m)
Height overall, skirt inflated		12 ft 6 in (3·80 m)
Skirt depth		2 ft 7½ in (0·80 m)

DIMENSIONS, INTERNAL, CONTROL CABIN:

Max width	7 ft 6½ in (2·30 m)
Floor area	58 sq ft (5·30 m²)
Passenger cabin, floor area	93 sq ft (8·74 m²)
Freight deck area	226 sq ft (21 m²)

WEIGHTS:

Normal empty weight	4,851 lb (2,200 kg)
Normal all-up weight	7,717 lb (3,500 kg)
Normal payload	2,866 lb (1,300 kg)
Max payload	3,528 lb (1,600 kg)

PERFORMANCE:

Max speed, calm water, max power	60 knots
Max speed, calm water, max cont power	55 knots
Cruising speed, calm water	40 knots
Max wave capability, scheduled runs	3 ft 3 in (1 m)

AUSTRALIA

FAIREY AUSTRALASIA PTY LTD

HEAD OFFICE:
Box 221, Elizabeth, South Australia 5112
TELEPHONE:
(08) 255192
CABLES:
Fairey, Adelaide
DIRECTORS:
F. R. Green, BE, CEng, FRAeS, FAIM, Chairman and Managing Director
A. Moffatt, FASA, ACIS

Fairey Australasia, incorporated in New South Wales, was founded in August 1949. Its Operations Division is located within the Weapons Research Establishment area in Salisbury, South Australia.

The primary activities of the Company are the design, development and manufacture of mechanical, optical, electro-mechanical, and electronic equipment for the aircraft and missile industry and the armed services.

Under a licencing agreement concluded in the autumn of 1972 between the company and Taylorcraft Transport Pty Ltd, it will build, develop and market the Skimaire range, which currently includes the Skimaire I 3-seater, the Skimaire II, a 6-seat, twin-engined craft, and the Skimaire III, a utility version of the Mk II with a 1,000 lb (453·59 kg) load capacity.

The company is currently involved in a major re-design and development programme. Fresh specifications are expected to be available in 1977.

SKIMAIRE I

A small amphibious ACV of glass fibre and ply construction, the Skimaire seats three in an enclosed, pressurized and ventilated cabin. Power is supplied by an adapted Volkswagen industrial engine and the maximum speed over calm water is 50 mph (80·46 km/h).

The production prototype Skimaire was completed in September 1969, and trials were completed in February 1970. The craft is in production. Skimaires have been supplied to purchasers in Australia, Canada, Taiwan, Indonesia and Japan.

LIFT AND PROPULSION: Immediately aft of the cockpit is a single, internally mounted 68 bhp Volkswagen 127V air-cooled four-cylinder, four-stroke petrol engine which drives via a gearbox a 2 ft (609 mm) diameter aluminium alloy centrifugal lift fan, and a 4 ft 2 in (1·27 m) diameter, 4-bladed, fixed-pitch propeller. The propeller is surrounded by a metal guard.

Fuel is carried in two external 5 gallon tanks with amidships refuelling points. Recommended fuel is super grade automotive gasoline.

CONTROLS: Twin rudders mounted on the propeller guard are operated via Bowden cables by the steering wheel. A set of louvre doors mounted below the lift fan controls the supply of air to the plenum and these can be employed as a braking control. Engine speed is controlled by a hand throttle linked to a foot pedal set so that the hand throttle sets the lower limit of engine speed.

HULL: Built in three grp sections—cabin top and deck, hull bottom and cabin interior —bonded together to form a rigid cell. The lower part of the hull is filled with closed cell structure foam and is reinforced below the cabin by a corrugated section. All mechanical components are mounted on a tubular steel frame which can be removed for major servicing.

A Fairey Australasia Pty Ltd Skimaire I on the Coorong. The vehicle, a fully amphibious three-seater is powered by a single 68 bhp Volkswagen 127V air-cooled engine, and has a top speed over calm water of 50 mph (80·46 km/h)

Above and below: The Fairey Australasia Skimaire II is a "scaled-up" model of the Skimaire I with twice the seating capacity. Seen in these photographs is the latest variant of this amphibious six-seater, with revised cabin entry doors/windows and various other refinements

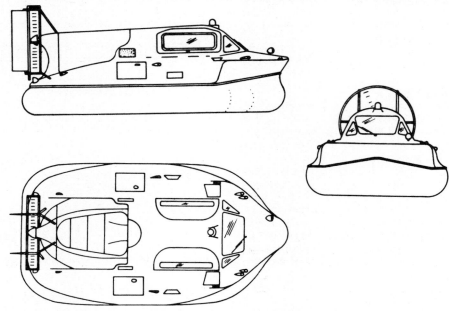

The Skimaire I light amphibious ACV

SKIRT: Closed bag type, attached around the hull periphery where the outer flange joins top and bottom components. Drainage holes provided at rear.

ACCOMMODATION: Access to the cabin is through either of two gullwing doors, located amidships, one each side. The normal seating arrangement places the driver forward, centrally, and there are removable seats for two passengers at the rear. 300 lb (136 kg) of cargo can be carried with the passenger seats removed. The cabin is heated and ventilated.

SAFETY EQUIPMENT: 2 lb fire extinguisher amidships and Spot-a-Fire system.
SYSTEMS: Electrical: 12 volt, 77Ah battery, with 240 w generator for starting and lights.
COMMUNICATIONS: Provision is made for the installation of a marine type transmitter/receiver.

DIMENSIONS, EXTERNAL:
Length	17 ft 0 in (5·18 m)
Beam	8 ft 0 in (2·43 m)
Height overall, power off	5 ft 10 in (1·77 m)
Height overall, skirt inflated	6 ft 0 in (1·82 m)
Draft afloat	2½ in (63 mm)
Skirt depth	1 ft (304 mm)

WEIGHTS:
Normal empty weight	1,200 lb (544·28 kg)
Normal all-up weight	1,850 lb (839·10 kg)
Normal payload	650 lb (294·82 kg)

PERFORMANCE:
Max speed over calm water	50 mph (80·46 km/h)
Cruising speed over calm water	35 mph (56·32 km/h)
Turning circle diameter at 30 knots	130 ft (39·62 m)
Max wave capability	2-3 ft waves (·609 ·914 m)
Still air range and endurance at cruising speed	170 miles (273·58 km)
Max gradient, static conditions	6 in 1
Vertical obstacle clearance	1 ft 0 in (304 mm)

PRICE AND TERMS:
Approximate cost of craft, ex works, Aust. $22,000·00.

SKIMAIRE II

This is a 60 mph (96·60 km/h) twin-engined six-seat derivative of the Skimaire Mk I. Trials were in progress as this edition went to press.

LIFT AND PROPULSION: Motive power for the integrated lift/propulsion system is supplied by two internally-mounted 68 hp Volkswagen 127V air-cooled four-cylinder, four-stroke piston engines, each of which drives a 2 ft 0 in (·61 m) diameter centrifugal lift fan and a 4-bladed fixed pitch propeller. Two 4-bladed reversible-pitch propellers can be supplied as optional extras. Each propeller is surrounded by a metal guard. Cushion area is 190 sq ft (17·65 m²), and cushion pressure is 21 lbs/sq ft. Fuel capacity is 27 Imp gallons (122·85 l). Recommended fuel is super grade automotive gasoline.

CONTROLS: Twin rudders hinged to the rear of the two propeller guards and differential thrust control craft heading. A set of louvre doors mounted below the lift fans controls the supply of air to the plenum and these can be employed as a braking control.
HULL: Basically glass reinforced plastic with aluminium and stainless steel reinforcement.

DIMENSIONS:
Length overall	23 ft 3 in (7·086 m)
Beam, power on	13 ft 9 in (4·19 m)
power off	12 ft 9 in (3·89 m)
Height overall, power on	6 ft 6 in (1·98 m)
power off	5 ft 6 in (1·68 m)

WEIGHTS:
Empty weight, with fuel	2,800 lb (1,271·2 kg)
Payload	1,200 lb (544·8 kg)
Gross weight	4,000 lb (1,816 kg)

Fairey Skimaire II amphibious six-seater, powered by two 68 bhp Volkswagen air-cooled engines and capable of 60 mph (96·60 km/h) over land and 50 mph (80·50 km/h) over water

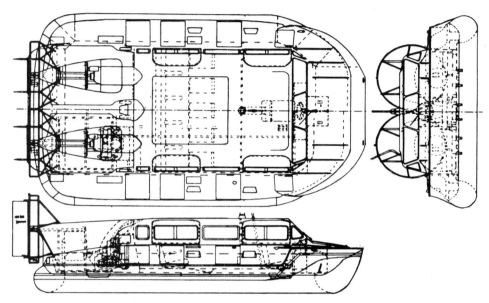

Skimaire II amphibious six-seater

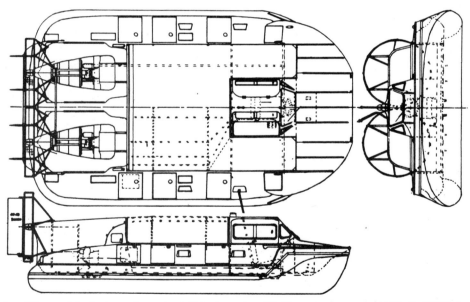

A utility model of the twin-engined Skimaire, the Mk III carries up to a 1,200 lb (544.8) kg payload on its amidship load deck

PERFORMANCE:
Max speed over land	60 mph	(96·60 km/h)
over calm water	50 mph	(80·50 km/h)
Max gradient		1 in 8
Vertical clearance	1 ft 6 in	(457 mm)
Range and endurance	app 220 miles (355 km), 4 hours	

PRICE: Ex works, standard fittings, Aust. $44,000·00.

SKIMAIRE III

This light utility ACV has a cargo deck aft of the driver and is designed to transport general freight loads weighing up to 1,200 lb (544·8 kg).

The amidship load deck has a large removable hatch to facilitate loading.

The specification is similar in most respects to that of Skimaire II.

PRICE: Ex works, standard fittings. Aust. $52,000·00.

NEOTERIC ENGINEERING AFFILIATES LTD

HEAD OFFICE:
9 Queen Street, Melbourne, Australia 3000

TELEPHONE:
Melbourne 623917

TEST FACILITY
11 Beach Drive, Long Island, Hastings, Victoria, Australia 3915

EXECUTIVES:
Edward Atkins, General Manager
Arthur Boyd, Operations
Laurie Fair, Production
Sam Cilauro, Electronic Design
Alan Fitzgerald, Accountant
Neoteric Engineering Affiliates Pty Ltd

specialises in the research and development of industrial and commercial ACV systems in addition to the design and marketing of small recreational hovercraft. A number of Neoteric's executives have been active in ACV research in Australia since 1960 and before forming the present company conducted a business under the name of Australian Air Cushion Vehicles Development.

The company is at present concentrating on marketing single and two-seat models of the Neova amphibious hovercraft, which are available in kit or ready-built form. A three-seat sports model, also available in a light utility configuration, is under development.

In 1975 Neoteric-USA Incorporated was established. This is now the corporate headquarters for the Neoteric Group of Companies and is based at the Fort Harrison Industrial Park, Terre Haute, Indiana 47804. Details of the Neova range of light hovercraft will be found in this edition under the entry for Neoteric-USA Inc.

The Neova is suited to production line manufacture and can be substantially scaled-up for increased load capacity.

International patents are pending and the company is seeking licensing agreements with overseas manufacturers.

STOLKRAFT PTY LTD

HEAD OFFICE:
52 Hilltop Road, Clareville Beach, NSW 2107, Australia

TELEPHONE:
918 3620

CABLES:
Stolkraft Sydney

DIRECTORS:
Leo D. Stolk, Managing Director/Designer
Clive M. Backhouse, Chairman
Rhoda Gladys Stolk, Director/Company Secretary

CONSULTANT:
James Eken, Commercial Marine Design, 24, Thomas Street, Chatswood, NSW 2067, Australia

OVERSEAS REPRESENTATIVE:
UNITED KINGDOM:
Richard M. Jones,
61 Grayling Road, Stoke Newington, London N.16

Mr. L. D. Stolk's Stolkraft concept is a new approach to the air-lubricated planing hull. His main objectives have been to overcome the basic pitch instability apparent in some earlier designs and to eliminate bow wash.

Research and development has been undertaken over the past six years, and the company's first commercial design, the 16 ft (4·95 m) Interceptor II, seating seven adults and two children, is now in production. The company is now seeking licencing agreements.

The basic Stolkraft hull is of trimaran configuration and is designed to roll the waves beneath the hull to provide hydrodynamic lift at speeds below 30 mph (40·28 km/h).

At speed an appreciable amount of aerodynamic lift is built up by a ram-air cushion at the bow, and this, combined with air fed through twin bow intakes and vented from a transverse step beneath the hull aft, lifts the craft in order to reduce frictional resistance.

A feature of the concept is the absence of trim variation. During trials undertaken on the torpedo range of the Royal Australian Navy at Pittwater, near Sydney, it was demonstrated that the craft rises bodily, parallel to the surface and has no tendency to porpoise. At speed it creates neither bow-wash nor hull spray.

The aerodynamic lift on the prototype is about 37% and the maximum load draft is reduced by 80%.

The hull design is applicable to a wide range of vessels from passenger ferries for inland waterways to seagoing craft.

INCEPTOR II SKI.16 Mk. I

The prototype of the company's first production runabout, the fibreglass-hulled SKI-16 Mk 1, was completing its trials as this

Interceptor prototype at 50 mph (80 km/h) during trials. The twin bow intakes (*below*) feed pressurised air to a ventilated transverse step and thence to a second air cushion created beneath the hull aft

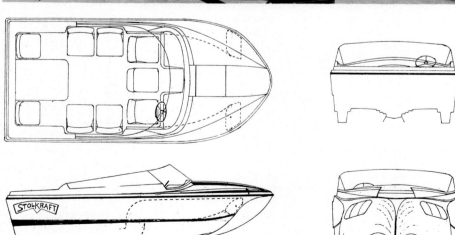

General arrangement of the Stolkraft seven-seat fibreglass-hulled runabout

edition went to press. Location of the air intakes and the vented transverse step is seen in the accompanying drawing.

If, through wave action, a gust of wind or an increase in speed, the forward hull lifts clear of the water as far back as the transverse step, the aerodynamic lifting forces ahead of

the step will rapidly decrease. At the same time, the lifting forces at the rear of the hull will increase because of the greater volume of air being rammed through the step. Because of the decrease in lift forward, and the increased lift aft, the centre of pressure moves towards the rear of the boat. A constant trim angle is maintained automatically in this manner without the use of instrumentation.

PROPULSION: A Volvo Aquamatic stern-drive of either 170 or 225 hp, drives a water screw for propulsion. Alternatively twin outboards can be fitted. Fuel is carried in two 20-gallon tanks located amidships, port and starboard.

HULL: Stepped trimaran configuration. Moulded fibreglass construction with bulkheads in fibreglass-covered seaply. Craft has eight foam-filled airtight compartments for positive buoyancy.

ACCOMMODATION: Open cockpit for driver and six adults and up to two children.

DIMENSIONS, EXTERNAL:

Length overall	16 ft 3 in (4·95 m)
Beam	7 ft 0 in (2·10 m)
Width overall	8 ft 0 in (2·44 m)

WEIGHTS:

Normal payload	1,200 lb (550 kg)
Max payload	1,500 lb (680 kg)
Normal gross weight	3,400 lb (1,550 kg)

PERFORMANCE (Prototype—Inceptor 1)

Max speed, full load	50 mph (80·46 km/h)
Approx cost including seating	A$10,000

Preliminary specifications for two Stolkraft design projects are given below:

HARBOUR FERRY OR RIVER FREIGHTER

Length overall	65 ft 0 in (19·81 m)
Width	26 ft 0 in (7·92 m)

Prototype of Stolkraft's first production runabout, the Inceptor II. Power for this seven-seater is provided by a 170 hp Volvo Aquamatic stern drive engine

Displacement	65 tons	Beam	13 ft 6 in (4·11 m)
Passengers	135	Displacement (payload 30 pass)	9 tons
Powerplant (diesel)	2,650 shp	Speed (full load)	50 mph (80·46 km/h)
Speed	45 mph plus (72·42 km/h)	Powerplant 2 × 300 shp petrol or diesel	600 shp
Draught at 45 mph, waves not exceeding 5 ft (1·52 m)	1 ft 3 in (381 mm)	Draught at rest (full load)	2 ft 6 in (0·76 m)

CRUISER OR WATER TAXI

Length overall	33 ft 0 in (10·05 m)	Draught at approximately 50 mph,	6 in (152 mm)

TAYLORCRAFT TRANSPORT (DEVELOPMENT) PTY LTD

HEAD OFFICE:
Parafield Airport, South Australia 5106

TELEPHONE:
258 4944

DIRECTORS:
R. V. Taylor, Managing Director
J. Taylor

Taylorcraft has been active in ACV research and development since 1966. It is currently developing and marketing machines ranging from the Kartaire, a light single-seater for home builders, to a mixed-traffic sidewall craft designed to carry ten cars and up to 100 passengers.

Other additions to the company's range are the Islander IA for coastal medical work and the Islander IV freighter.

The Skimaire range is licensed to Fairey Australasia Pty Ltd by a holding company, Taylorcraft Transport Pty Ltd.

AIR-BOAT

This light alloy hulled high-speed air-boat is intended for use in shallow or weed-choked rivers and lakes, or for operations in coastal and river waters in general. The planing hull is protected by skids on its bottom. Full-length guard rails and a propeller guard ensure safety when operating near overhanging trees.

The large deck and open cockpit area permit bulky loads to be carried. Seating is provided for four people.

A GM 308 cu in V8 automotive engine drives via a gearbox a 6 ft (1·82 m) diameter propeller, giving the craft sufficient reserve power for riding over reeds and mud banks. A closed cooling system is employed to avoid blocked intakes in weed-choked waters.

Stick-operated rudders and elevators control craft heading and trim.

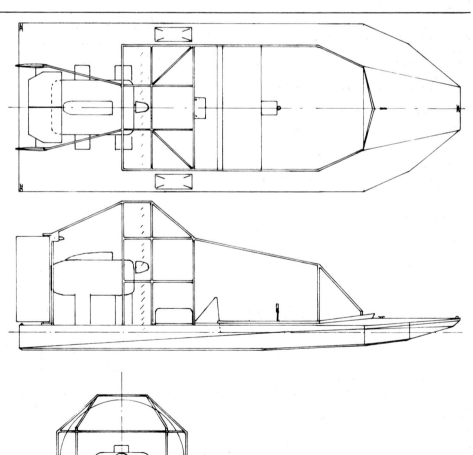

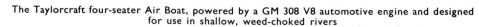

The Taylorcraft four-seater Air Boat, powered by a GM 308 V8 automotive engine and designed for use in shallow, weed-choked rivers

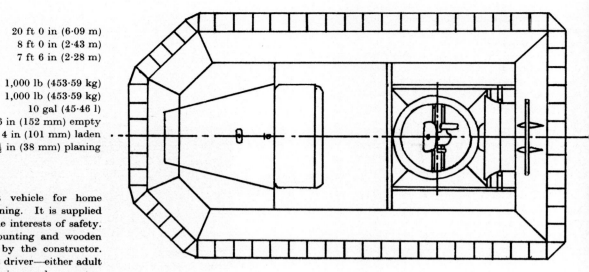

DIMENSIONS:

Length	20 ft 0 in (6·09 m)
Beam	8 ft 0 in (2·43 m)
Height	7 ft 6 in (2·28 m)

WEIGHTS:

Weight empty	1,000 lb (453·59 kg)
Payload	1,000 lb (453·59 kg)
Fuel tank	10 gal (45·46 l)
Draft	6 in (152 mm) empty
	4 in (101 mm) laden
	1½ in (38 mm) planing

Price: A$ 6,250

KARTAIRE Mk I

This is a single-seat vehicle for home builders and initial training. It is supplied in partial kit form in the interests of safety. The engines, engine mounting and wooden components are found by the constructor.

The craft will carry its driver—either adult or child—over flat terrain, sand or water, and if required to traverse deep water, the hull can be fitted with an expanded polystyrene buoyancy block.

LIFT AND PROPULSION: Lift power is furnished by a Victa 160cc two-stroke driving a 1 ft 6 in (457 mm) diameter centrifugal, alloy lift fan. Propulsive thrust on both versions is supplied by a second Victa 160cc two-stroke driving a 3-bladed fixed-pitch, 2 ft 10 in (863 mm) diameter Taylorcraft propeller.

CONTROL: An aircraft-type control column operates twin aerodynamic rudders set in the airscrew slipstream for directional control.

HULL: Kit parts are in ¼ in (6·35 mm) marine plywood; in assembled form the components are in marine ply and glassfibre reinforced plastics.

SKIRT: Bag type skirt in Linatex rubber or Neolon.

The following details apply to the Kartaire Mk. II.

DIMENSIONS:

Length overall	9 ft 0 in (2·74 m)
Beam overall	4 ft 0 in (1·21 m)
Height overall	4 ft 0 in (1·21 m)

WEIGHTS:

Normal empty weight	120 lb (54·42 kg)

PERFORMANCE:

Max speed over calm water	35 mph
Max gradient	1 in 8
Vertical obstacle clearance	6 in

PRICES:

Kartaire I, single-seat ultra-light recreational craft in kit form, A$200.

KARTAIRE III

A lightweight, aluminium-hulled, single-seater, the Kartaire III is intended for recreational and light liaison duties. It is fully amphibious and capable of operating over light vegetation as well as over water, mudflats and sand.

LIFT AND PROPULSION: Lift power is supplied by a single 172 cc Fuji two-stroke, driving a 2 ft (609 mm) diameter, 6-bladed axial fan. The lift fan duct is of light alloy and is located behind the driver's seat to provide a clear load space at the front. Thrust is furnished by a second Fuji engine of the same type driving a 6-bladed, fixed-pitch 2 ft (609 mm) diameter ducted fan. The thrust unit is carried on light alloy members above the rear of the hull and can be detached if required to simplify storage or transport.

CONTROLS: An aircraft type control column operates twin aerodynamic rudders set in the thrust fan slipstream for directional control. The engines are fitted with pull

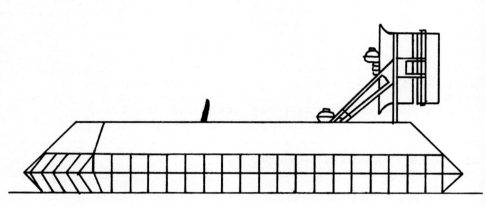

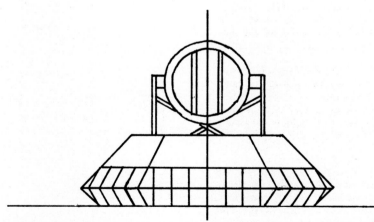

Kartaire III an enlarged version of Kartaire I, powered by two 172cc engines. It will carry one adult and a child

starters and each engine has its own fuel tank.

HULL: Light aluminium alloy construction, rivetted and caulked at the seams. Watertight buoyancy box amidship serves as the seat.

DIMENSIONS, Hardstructure:

Length	11 ft 0 in (3·35 m)
Beam	6 ft 0 in (1·82 m)
Height	4 ft 6 in (1·37 m)

WEIGHTS:

Empty	160 lb (72·57 kg)
Gross	350 lb (158·75 kg)

PERFORMANCE (with 170 lb (77·10 kg) driver only):

Still air speeds:

Land	45 mph (72·42 km/h)
Water	40 mph (64·37 km/h)
Hard structure clearance	6 in (152 mm)
Gradient from standstill	1 : 9

Price: A$1,250

KARTAIRE IV

The Kartaire IV is an ultra-light air cushion vehicle designed for use over water, mud flats and sand. It may be used as emergency transport in flooded areas or as a dinghy in sheltered waters. Its useful hard-structure clearance allows it to operate over fairly rough surfaces.

LIFT AND PROPULSION: Lift power is supplied by a single Fuji 172 cc two-stroke driving a 2 ft (609 mm) diameter 6-bladed axial fan. Propulsive thrust is furnished by a similar engine, driving a 6-bladed, fixed-pitch 2 ft (609 mm) diameter axial fan. The lift and thrust fan ducts are of alloy construction.

CONTROLS: Stick-operated rudder and throttle levers for lift and thrust engines. Both engines are fitted with pull starters.

HULL: The hull is a simple inflatable raft, from which is suspended a finger type skirt. All fabric parts are made from neoprene and hypalon-coated nylon. The hull side and end members are inflated by hand bellows. A light alloy frame with plug-in side stringers supports the two engines.

ACCOMMODATION: The open cockpit is 5 ft (1·52 m) long and 1 ft 10 in (0·55 m) wide and is provided with a single inflated seat which is adjustable to ensure correct trim. Although designed as a single-seater, a passenger may be carried under overload conditions.

DIMENSIONS:

Length, hardstructure	10 ft 0 in (3·04 m)
Beam	5 ft 0 in (1·52 m)
Height	4 ft 6 in (1·37 m)

WEIGHTS:

Empty	100 lb (45·35 kg)
Gross	280 lb (127·00 kg)

PERFORMANCE (Still Air):

Max speed over land	45 mph (72·42 km/h)
over water	40 mph (64·37 km/h)

SPORTAIRE

An inflatable-hulled three-seater, the Sportaire was designed as a light recreational craft, but the large open cockpit makes it suitable for a number of utility roles ranging from skin-diving support to flood rescue and light patrol duties. Deflated and folded for transport or storage the Sportaire measures 6 × 4 × 4 ft (1·8 × 1·2 × 1·2 m). It can be carried by two people or towed behind a vehicle on a small trailer.

LIFT AND PROPULSION: Two ducted fans provide forward or reverse thrust while a third ducted fan is employed for lift. All three fans are driven by a single 30 hp 2-cylinder two-stroke engine, via belts. Cushion area is 127 sq ft (11·78 sq m); cushion pressure is 6·5 lb/sq ft (311 Pa). Static thrust is 120 lb (533 N). Recommended fuel is 25 : 1 two-stroke mixture.

CONTROLS: Steering is by conventional wheel which controls twin aerodynamic rudders. Levers control thrust reversal mechanism.

HULL: Simple inflatable multi-compartment hull, from which is suspended a segmented skirt. Hull has built-in handgrips. A simple drainage system and a bow canopy are provided. The hull can be inflated by a car vacuum cleaner. Special bellows are provided to bring the hull up to its operating pressure of 2½ lb psi.

DIMENSIONS:

Hull length, overall	17 ft (5·18 m)
Hull beam, overall	9 ft (2·74 m)
Height on landing pads	3 ft 6 in (1·06 m)
on cushion	5 ft 0 in (1 m)

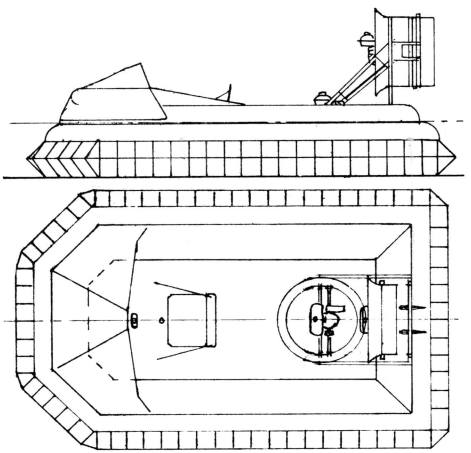

Taylorcraft Kartaire IV, a single-seater with an inflatable hull. Power is supplied by two 172cc Fuji two-strokes, one for lift and one for propulsion

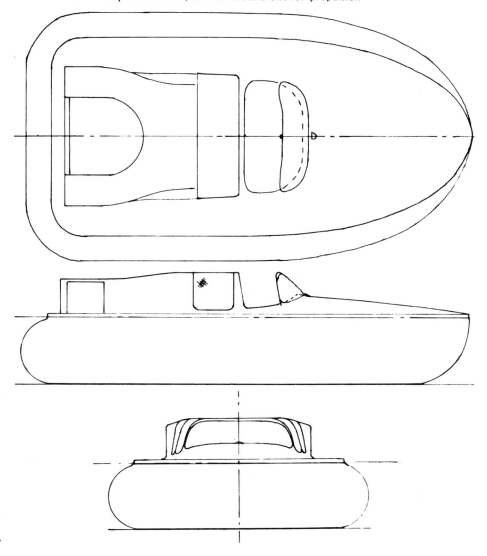

Sportaire, an inflatable-hulled leisure or utility craft with a 350 lb payload

WEIGHTS:

Tare	280 lb (127 kg)
Payload	350 lb (158·9 kg)
Driver and fuel	190 lb (86 kg)
Gross	800 lb (363 kg)

PERFORMANCE (calm water):

Cruising speed	40 mph (64·37 km/h)
Range	60 miles (96 km)
Gradient	1 in 6
Clearance height	1 ft 6 in (45 cm)
Price: A$3,000	

INTERCEPTAIRE

The Interceptaire is a two-seat sports craft intended for use on rivers and sheltered waters. The standard model is powered by a 60 bhp (45 kw) Volkswagen automotive engine, but with a more powerful engine of up to 90 bhp (68 kw), it will perform well as a three-seater.

LIFT AND PROPULSION: Integrated system powered by a single 60 bhp (45 kw) Volkswagen 1600 cc air-cooled automotive engine, located aft of the cockpit, and mounted on a steel frame which is bonded and bolted to the bottom of the hull. The fan is driven directly, avoiding the use of gears or belts.

CONTROLS: Centrally-mounted control stick operates flaps and valves in the duct outlets, enabling all the thrust air to be ejected aft, reversed for braking or applied differentially for turning. With the stick in the central position static hover can be maintained.

HULL: Monocoque construction in grp with reinforcing bulkheads.

ACCOMMODATION: Open cockpit, with bench-type seat for driver and up to two passengers.

DIMENSIONS:

Length overall, on cushion	17 ft 3 in (5·25 m)
Beam overall, or cushion	10 ft 0 in (3·05 m)
Height on cushion	3 ft 5 in (1·03 m)
Draft, displacement	9 in (229 mm)

WEIGHTS:

Empty	1,000 lb (454 kg)
Gross	1,410 lb (635 kg)

PERFORMANCE:

Cruising speed over water	35 mph (55 km/h)
Cruising speed over land	45 mph (70 km/h)
Hard structure clearance	12 in (305 mm)
Range	120 miles (195 km)

PUFFAIRE II

This small, sturdily built utility vehicle is intended for operation over land, rivers and sheltered waters. It has an open cockpit with two seats and an open deck which can accommodate bulky loads of up to 1,000 lb (453 kg). Various alternative accommodation arrangements can be made, including the installation of a folding awning to protect both the crew and cargo, or a 5-seat modular passenger cabin, which fits into the well deck immediately aft of the control cabin A Trailaire VII ACV trailer unit (see company's entry in section covering ACV Trailers, Tractors and Heavy Lift Systems) can be towed by the craft, increasing the payload capacity to two tons.

LIFT AND PROPULSION: Integrated system powered by a Ford 350 V8 water-cooled automotive engine developing 205 hp (153 kw) at 3,800 rpm. Fuel is premium grade petrol. Mounted inboard, the engine drives two centrifugal fans through a torque convertor. Both fans are totally enclosed in ducts to eliminate any danger from rotating

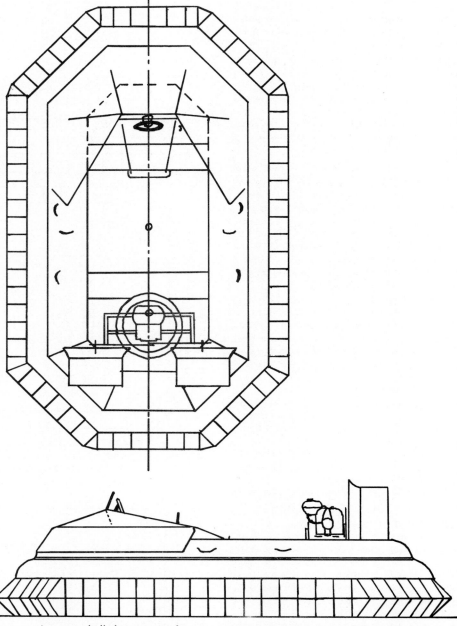

Interceptaire, a grp-hulled two-seater for use on rivers and sheltered waters. Power is supplied by a single 60 bph VW automotive engine

Model of the Taylorcraft Puffaire II, showing the location of the centrifugal fans and load deck. The removable passenger module has five seats

parts. A high thrust unit can be supplied for special applications.

SKIRT: 1 ft 6 in (457 mm) high skirt with 100% segments. Fingers and groups of fingers are easily replaced when necessary.

CONTROLS: Directional control is effected by a skirt shift system and supplemented by differential use of airjet thrust. A single control column, on which is mounted the throttle lever, is located on the right hand side of the cockpit. This also controls reverse thrust.

DIMENSIONS:

Length overall:	
on cushion	22 ft 0 in (6·7 m)
hard structure	19 ft 0 in (5·8 m)
Beam overall:	
on cushion	14 ft 0 in (4·27 m)
hard structure	8 ft 2 in (2·09 m)
Height overall:	
on cushion	7 ft 0 in (2·13 m)
hard structure	5 ft 7 in (1·69 m)
Draft afloat	9 in (229 mm)
Cargo deck size	
7 ft 0 in × 6 ft 3 in (2·13 m × 1·83 m)	

WEIGHTS:

Empty	2,630 lb (1,193 kg)
Payload	1,000 lb (453 kg)
Fuel and driver	370 lb (168 kg)
Gross weight	4,000 lb (1,814 kg)

PERFORMANCE:

Max speed over land	45 mph (70 km/h)
over water	35 mph (55 km/h)
Max gradient	1 : 6
Hump speed	12 mph (20 km/h)
Hard structure clearance	1 ft 6 in (457 mm)
Max wave height	3 ft 0 in (·914 m)
Range	250 miles (400 km)

PUFFAIRE IIS

This new model of the Puffaire features a 6 ft (1·82 m) longer hull, enabling it to carry loads of greater bulk or a lengthened cabin module containing seats for 12 passengers. Compared with Puffaire II, Puffaire IIS has a payload capacity of 2,150 lb (975 kg), an increase of 1,150 lb (521·60 kg).

The overall load space measures 14 ft 7 in × 6 ft 0 in (4·42 m × 1·83 m). Lift, propulsion and control arrangements are identical or similar to those of the Puffaire II.

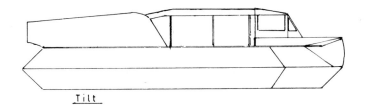

Tilt

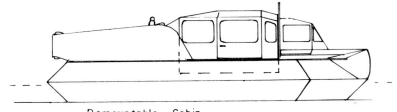

Demountable Cabin

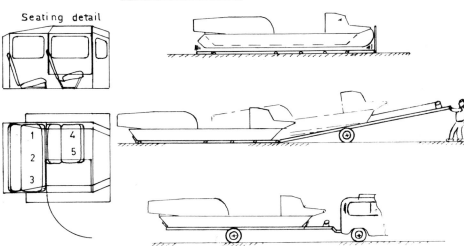

Seating detail

TRAILER LOADING

General arrangement of the Taylorcraft Transport Puffaire II open deck utility vehicle, showing optional configurations including the addition of a 5-seat cabin module

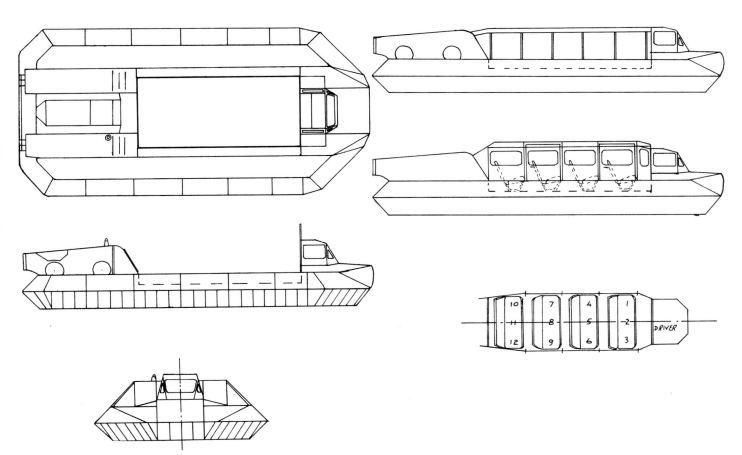

Stretched model of the Puffaire open-deck utility vehicle, the Puffaire IIS, with a payload capacity of 2,150 lb (975 kg)

DIMENSIONS:

Length, hardstructure	30 ft 4 in	(9·24 m)
on cushion	30 ft 4 in	(9·24 m)
Beam, central hull	8 ft 2 in	(2·09 m)
Beam, sidebodies extended		
	15 ft 0 in	(4·57 m)
Height, on landing pads	5 ft 2 in	(1·69 m)
cushionborne	6 ft 0 in	(1·82 m)
Draft, afloat	9 in	(229 mm)
Deck load space		
	14 ft 7 in × 6 ft	(4·42 m × 1·83 m)
Deck loading height	13 in (330 mm) with	
	20 in (508 mm) sill	

WEIGHTS:

Empty	1,990 lb (902 kg)
Payload	2,150 lb (975 kg)
Fuel and Driver	370 lb (168 kg)
Gross weight	4,550 lb (2,063 kg)

PERFORMANCE:

Speed over land	45 mph (70 km/h)
Speed over water	35 mph (55 km/h)
Hard structure clearance	18 in (457 mm)
Max wave height	3 ft (1 m)
Gradient	1 in 8

ISLANDAIRE SERIES

This is a new series of multi-purpose, amphibious ACVs, each of which is powered by four automotive engines. Passenger, freight, fast patrol and ambulance versions are projected. The passenger versions—the Islandaire I, II and III, vary in length only, the cabins being arranged to seat 15, 20 and 25 respectively. An ambulance version, with an 8 ft wide cabin to accommodate four stretcher cases, is designated Islandaire IA, and a fast patrol version, with more powerful engines, is designated IIIM. The freight model is the Islandaire IV, with a cargo deck measuring 7 ft 6 in × 14 ft 0 in (2·28 m × 4·26 m).

The Islandaire series is designed to comply with the British Hovercraft Safety Requirements and the Australian ACV Code. Construction is closely supervised by qualified personnel at all stages and is generally subject to survey requirements.

Though differing in size, superstructure and equipment, vehicles in the Islandaire series are almost identical in terms of overall design. Dimensions, weights and performance figures are given at the end of this summary. The following characteristics apply to all designs:

LIFT AND PROPULSION: Cushion air is supplied by two V8 water-cooled automotive engines driving two 3 ft 4 in diameter centrifugal, double-intake fans through bevel gears. Propulsive thrust is furnished by two pylon-mounted V12 automotive engines, each driving a 6 ft (1·82 m) diameter reversible-pitch propeller through reduction gearboxes on the engine blocks. Lift and thrust engines have closed coolant systems and standard automotive radiators. The lift engines have flexible mountings to reduce interior noise.

CONTROLS: Directional control is effected by twin aerodynamic rudders operated by a rudder bar, differential propeller thrust and a plenum discharge system. The craft can be reversed into confined spaces and can be moved forward or turned without the use of its propellers.

HULL: The hull is divided into three longitudinal structures; the centre section, containing the accommodation, lift system, controls and main beams, and the two outer sections which serve as buoyancy tanks and extend the structure to the required width. Aluminium alloy is used throughout. Most frames, ribs and stringers are fabricated

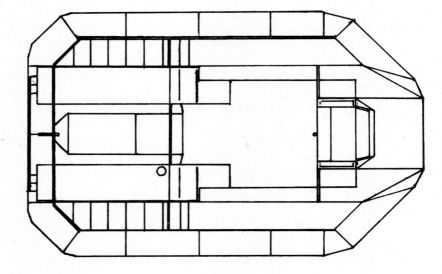

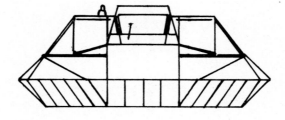

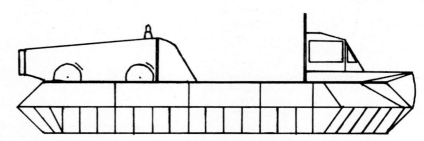

Puffaire open-deck utility vehicle

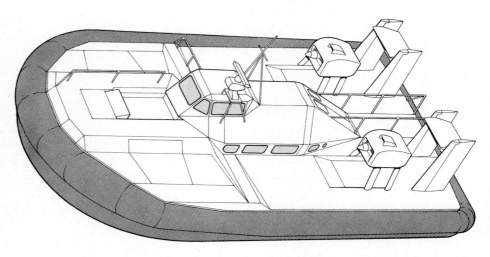

Islandaire IA ambulance and casualty evacuation craft

from alloy sheet to ensure lightness and strength. All parts are treated during assembly and exposed surfaces are finished in polyurethane paint. Foam-filled bottom sections and watertight compartments provide buoyancy.

SKIRT: Tapered bag and segment type skirt with a high outer hinge line around the hull. Skirt is fabricated in nylon neoprene with reinforced lower members. Nylon and corrosion resistant alloy fasteners are fitted. Skirt segments can be indivudually replaced for maintenance. Bag pressure

is variable for maximum stability and anti-plough-in characteristics.

ACCOMMODATION: CREW CABIN: The control cabin is located in a raised position forward to provide the operating crew with a 360° view. Access to the forward deck for craft handling is provided by a hatch on the starboard side. A walkway and rail allow the cabin to be reached from a side boarding point. The rear of the control cabin is open to the main cabin, which is located amidships at a lower level. Forced air ventilation is provided.

PASSENGER VERSIONS (ISLANDAIRE I, II AND III)

The Islandaire I, II and III vary only in length, the cabins being arranged to provide 15, 20 and 25 seats respectively.

Seats are arranged in rows of two and three with a central aisle. Space is provided at the rear of the cabin for toilet, galley and bar facilities. There is standing headroom in the cabin and the wide rear entry doors simplify access.

Emergency exits are provided in the cabin sides and space is available for rafts on the after deck.

Fire extinguisher stations are fitted at several points inside and outside the hull.

AMBULANCE FACILITIES (ISLANDAIRE IA)

The main cabin is 8 ft (2·43 m) wide at window level and 6 ft (1·82 m) high with 36 in (914 mm) wide doors. Bench seats each side of the central aisle will take a total of eight seated passengers or four stretcher cases. Space is provided for toilet and washing facilities. The attendant's seat is positioned to give access to both driver and passengers. An extendable gangway on the rear deck provides access to the cabin, whether the craft is on land or at a jetty. Space is available for the installation of any ambulance equipment required. Blanket lockers and stretchers are located beneath the seats.

FREIGHT VERSION (ISLANDAIRE IV)

The Islandaire IV has a freight deck measuring 7 ft 6 in × 14 ft (2·28 m × 4·26 m) (enclosed by a tilt and canopy if required) and a two-seat control cabin. Loading is over the stern and down a ramp, with a side entry to the cabin. Loads may be laid fore and aft alongside the offset control cabin to a limit of 20 ft (6·09 m) in length.

FAST PATROL VERSION (ISLANDAIRE IIIM)

The combined control and main cabin area is available for rearrangement to suit specific military requirements. Providing the centre of gravity (vertical and horizontal) limitations are met, a variety of military weapons systems or other equipment can be carried within the gross weight of 11,000 lbs (4,989 kg). The thrust engines are of larger cubic capacity and drive three-bladed propellers, allowing performance to be maintained at the increased weight.

SYSTEMS: ELECTRICAL: Normal automotive engine electrical systems are used, with a central fuel control and starting system Power at 12 v is available for navigation lights, radio, radar, cabin lights and auxiliary items from pairs of 45 Ah batteries. All circuits are fused and warning lights are arranged so that they can be checked during starting procedures.

ISLANDAIRE I

DIMENSIONS, EXTERNAL:
Length overall, on cushion
42 ft 6 in (12·95 m)
Width overall, on cushion
24 ft 0 in (7·31 m)
Height (excluding mast) on cushion
12 ft 0 in (3·65 m)
Hard structure clearance
3 ft 6 in (1·06 m)
Height on landing pads
8 ft 6 in (2·59 m)
DIMENSIONS, INTERNAL:
Main Cabin (15 seats)
Height   6 ft 0 in (1·82 m)
Width   7 ft 0 in (2·13 m)

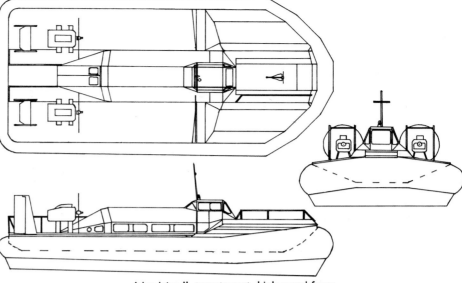

Islandaire II, twenty-seat, high-speed ferry

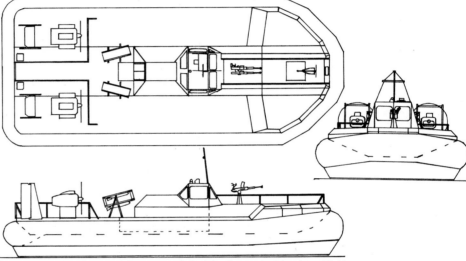

Fast patrol version of the Islandaire, the Islandaire III M

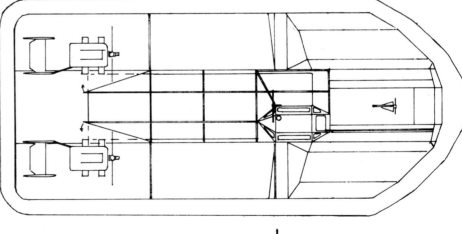

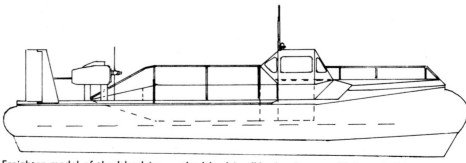

Freighter model of the Islandaire — the Islandaire IV. Loads up to 20 ft (6.09m) long may be carried

Length	9 ft 0 in (2·74 m)	Length	6 ft 0 in (1·82 m)
Control cabin (2 seats)		Rear gangway and Doors	
Height	7 ft 9 in (2·36 m)	Width	3 ft 0 in (0·914 m)
Width	8 ft 0 in (2·43 m)	Toilet and galley/bar at rear of cabin.	

WEIGHTS:

Gross	10,000 lb (4,535 kg)
Fuel and Payload	4,200 lb (1,904 kg)
Maximum freight	2,100 lb (952 kg)

PERFORMANCE:

Cruising speed	45 mph (72·42 km/h)
Maximum speed	65 mph (104·60 km/h)
Fuel consumption	
25 gph at cruising speed (113 lph)	
Endurance	5 hours at cruising speed
Gradient	1 in 7·5, standing start
Bank/single step	4 ft 0 in (1·21 m)
Wave height	
6 ft 0 in—8 ft 0 in long sea (1·82—2·43 m)	
Isolated obstacle	3 ft 0 in (0·914 m)

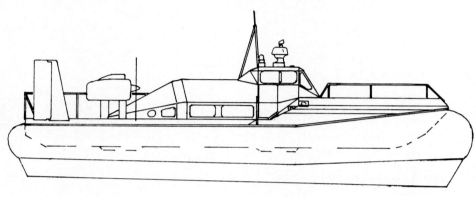

ISLANDAIRE IA AMBULANCE

DIMENSIONS, EXTERNAL:

Length overall on cushion	
42 ft 6 in (12·95 m)	
Width overall on cushion	
24 ft 0 in (7·31 m)	
Height (excluding mast) on cushion	
12 ft 0 in (3·65 m)	
Hard structure clearance 3 ft 6 in (1·06 m)	
Height on landing pads 8 ft 6 in (2·59 m)	

DIMENSIONS, INTERNAL:

Main cabin (8 seats or 4 stretchers)

Height	6 ft 0 in (1·82 m)
Width	7 ft 0 in (2·13 m)
Length	8 ft 0 in (2·74 m)

Control cabin (Driver & Attendant/Deck-hand)

Height	7 ft 9 in (2·36 m)
Width	8 ft 0 in (2·43 m)
Length	6 ft 0 in (1·82 m)

Rear gangway & doors

Width	3 ft 0 in (0·914 m)

WEIGHTS:

Gross	9,000 lb (4,082 kg)
Fuel	2,500 lb 325 gal (1,477·43 litres)
6 persons	1,000 lb (453 kg)

PERFORMANCE:

Cruising speed	45 mph (7·242 km/h)
Maximum speed	65 mph (104·60 km/h)
Fuel consumption	
25 gph (113 lph) at cruising speed	
Endurance	11 hours at cruising speed
Gradient	1 in 7·5, standing start
Bank/single step	4 ft 0 in (1·21 m)
Wave height	
6 ft 0 in—8 ft 0 in (1·82—2·43 m) long sea	
Isolated obstacle	3 ft 0 in (0·914 m)

ISLANDAIRE II

DIMENSIONS, EXTERNAL:

Length overall on cushion	
46 ft 0 in (12·95 m)	
Width overall on cushion	
24 ft 0 in (7·31 m)	
Height (excluding mast)	
12 ft 0 in (3·65 m)	
Hard structure clearance	
3 ft 6 in (1·06 m)	
Height on landing pads 8 ft 6 in (2·59 m)	

DIMENSIONS, INTERNAL:

Main cabin (20 seats)

Height	6 ft 0 in (1·82 m)
Width	7 ft 0 in (2·13 m)
Length	11 ft 0 in (3·35 m)

Control cabin (2 seats)

Height	7 ft 9 in (2·36 m)
Width	8 ft 0 in (2·43 m)
Length	6 ft 0 in (1·82 m)

Rear gangway & doors

Width	3 ft 0 in (0·914 m)

Toilet and galley/bar at rear of cabin
Cabin layout—4 rows of five seats facing
   forwards, centre aisle

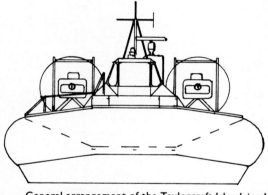

General arrangement of the Taylorcraft Islandaire I, fifteen-seat amphibious passenger ferry

WEIGHTS:

Gross	12,000 lb (5,443 kg)
Fuel and payload maximum	
4,600 lb (2,076 kg)	
Maximum cabin freight 2,800 lb (1,270 kg)	

PERFORMANCE:

Cruising speed	45 mph (72·42 km/h)
Maximum speed	65 mph (104·60 km/h)
Fuel consumption	
25 gph (113 lph) at cruising speed	
Endurance	5 hours at cruising speed
Gradient	1 in 7·5, standing start
Bank/single step	4 ft 0 in (1·21 m)
Wave height	
6 ft—8 ft long sea (1·82—2·43 m)	
Isolated obstacle	3 ft 0 in (0·914 m)

ISLANDAIRE III

DIMENSIONS, EXTERNAL:

Length overall on cushion	
49 ft 6 in (15·08 m)	
Width overall on cushion	
24 ft 0 in (7·31 m)	
Height (excluding mast)	
12 ft 0 in (3·65 m)	
Hard structure clearance 3 ft 6 in (1·06 m)	
Height on landing pads 8 ft 6 in (2·59 m)	

DIMENSIONS, INTERNAL:

Main cabin (25 seats)

Height	6 ft 0 in (1·82 m)
Width	7 ft 0 in (2·13 m)
Length	17 ft 0 in (5·18 m)

Control cabin (2 seats)

Height	7 ft 9 in (2·36 m)
Width	8 ft 0 in (2·43 m)
Length	6 ft 0 in (1·82 m)

Rear gangway and doors

Width	3 ft 0 in (0·914 m)

Toilet and galley/bar at rear of cabin

WEIGHTS:

Gross	16,000 lb (7,257 kg)
Fuel and Payload	6,020 lb (2,730 kg)
Maximum cabin freight 3,500 lb (1,586 kg)	

PERFORMANCE:

Cruising speed	45 mph (72·42 km/h)
Maximum speed	65 mph (104·60 km/h)
Fuel consumption	
25 gph (113 lph) at cruising speed	
Endurance	5 hours at cruising speed
Gradient	1 in 7·5, standing start
Bank/single step	4 ft 0 in (1·21 m)
Wave height	
6 ft—8 ft long sea (1·82—2·43 m)	
Isolated obstacle	3 ft 0 in (0·914 m)

ISLANDAIRE IV

DIMENSIONS, EXTERNAL:

Length overall on cushion

49 ft 6 in (15·08 m)

Width overall on cushion

24 ft 0 in (7·31 m)

Height (excluding mast) 12 ft 0 in (3·65 m)

Hard structure clearance 3 ft 6 in (1·06 m)

Height on landing pads 8 ft 6 in (2·59 m)

DIMENSIONS, INTERNAL AND FREIGHT DECK:

Control cabin

Height 7 ft 9 in (2·36 m)

Width	4 ft 0 in (1·21 m)
Length	6 ft 0 in (1·82 m)

Freight deck

Width	7 ft 0 in (2·13 m)
Length	14 ft 0 in (4·26 m)

Loads up to 20 ft (6·09 m) long may be carried subject to weight distribution requirements

Freight area is half enclosed at 3 ft height; remainder may be closed by canpoy

WEIGHTS:

Gross 13,420 lb (6,087 kg)

Fuel and payload	6,020 lb (2,730 kg)

PERFORMANCE:

Cruising speed	45 mph (72·42 km/h)
Maximum speed	65 mph (104·60 km/h)

Fuel consumption

25 gph (113 lph) at cruising speed

Endurance	5 hours at cruising speed
Gradient	1 in 7·5, standing start
Bank/single step	4 ft 0 in (1·21 m)

Wave height

6 ft—8 ft (1·82—2·43 m) long sea

Isolated obstacle 3 ft 0 in (0·914 m)

BRAZIL

FEI
FACULTY OF INDUSTRIAL ENGINEER-ING

ADDRESS:

Research Vehicle Department (DEPV), Faculty of Industrial Engineering, São Bernado do Campo, Avenido Oreste Romano 112, São Paulo

TELEPHONE:

443 1155

SENIOR EXECUTIVE:

Eng. Rigoberto Soler Gisbert, Director of Vehicle Research

The Vehicle Research Department of the FEI was founded in 1968. Its first major task was to conduct a full-scale investigation into Brazil's transport problems and its likely future requirements. An outcome of this was the design and construction by students and faculty of a 51 ft (15·54 m) long prototype of a tracked ACV, the TALAV, which was exhibited during the 150th anniversary of Brazilian Independence in August 1972 (see Tracked Skimmers).

Since then the Department, under the direction of Eng. Rigoberto Soler Gisbert, has designed, built and tested a number of light amphibious ACVs, including the VA and the VA-1, which it is expected, will be put into production by a Brazilian industrial concern.

VA

A glassfibre-hulled amphibious two-seater, the VA is powered by a single Volkswagen VW 1300 automotive engine and has a top speed of about 50 mph (80 km/h).

LIFT AND PROPULSION: Integrated system powered by a single 50 hp VW 1300 automotive engine driving a ducted fan. Air from the fan feeds into the plenum below for lift and aft propulsion. Total fuel capacity is 6·6 gals (30 litres).

CONTROLS: Single aerodynamic rudder, hinged to rear of fan duct, provides heading control.

HULL: Moulded grp structure.

SKIRT: Bag-type, 6 in (15 cm) deep.

ACCOMMODATION: Open cockpit with seating for two, side-by-side.

DIMENSIONS:

Length overall	13 ft 5⅜ in (4·10 m)
Beam	6 ft 10⅝ in (2·10 m)
Height	4 ft 11 in (1·5 m)

WEIGHTS:

Empty weight	882 lb (400 kg)
Loaded weight	1,654 lb (750 kg)

PERFORMANCE:

Maximum speed:

over land	50 mph (80 km/h)
over water	31 mph (50 km/h)

Maximum gradient, static conditions 1 : 10

Vertical obstacle clearance 6 in (15 cm)

Top: Power for the VA is supplied by a single 50 hp VW 1300 automotive engine which gives it a top speed over water of 43.5 mph (70 kmh)

Centre: FEI VA two-seat light sports ACV during trials

Bottom: A model of VEI's VAI four-seat utility vehicle for operation over land, rivers and sheltered water.

VA-1

The VA-1 is designed for use in a variety of projects aimed at opening up and develop-

ing areas of the Amazon and traversing the swamps of the Matto Grosso.

LIFT AND PROPULSION: Cushion lift is

provided by a single 40 hp Volkswagen 1300 automotive engine driving twin fans located on the centre line, one each end of the open load deck. Thrust is supplied by two 90 hp Volkswagen 2000 engines, each driving a ducted 2-bladed propeller aft. Cushion area is 13·5 m², and cushion pressure 11 gr/cm². Total fuel capacity is 22 gal (100 litres).

CONTROLS: A single aerodynamic rudder provides directional control.

HULL: Moulded fibreglass.
SKIRT: Bag type flexible skirt, 10 in (25 cm) deep.
ACCOMMODATION: Enclosed cabin, forward, seats a driver and three passengers. Access is via two hinged doors, one port, one starboard.
DIMENSIONS:

Length overall	21 ft 7⅞ in (6·60 m)
Beam	10 ft 1⅛ in (3·05 m)

Height	7 ft 8½ in (2·35 m)
WEIGHTS:	
Empty weight	1,764 lb (800 kg)
Loaded weight	3,308 lb (1,500 kg)
PERFORMANCE:	
Maximum speed:	
over water	43·5 mph (70 km/h)
over land	74·5 mph (120 km/h)
Max gradient, static conditions	20%
Vertical obstacle clearance	10 in (25 cm)

BULGARIA

OKRUJNAYE POLYTECHNIC
Plovdiv, Bulgaria
ICARUS II
Relatively little news has been forthcoming over the years on hovercraft activities in the smaller countries of the Eastern bloc. That interest is probably just as keen in these parts as it is in the West, is indicated by the accompanying photograph. Described as "an automobile that rides on an air-cushion", Icarus II was designed and built by students of the Okrujnaye Polytechnic, Plovdiv, Bulgaria, under the guidance of Mr. Christel Christov.

The vehicle has been demonstrated extensively at exhibitions dedicated to the achievements of engineering students and is reported to have made an appearance in the Soviet Union.

Icarus II

CANADA

BELL AEROSPACE CANADA TEXTRON
(A division of Textron Canada Ltd)
DIRECTORS:
William G. Gisel, President
Norton C. Willcox, Vice-President
Joseph R. Piselli, Vice-President
James G. Mills, Managing Director
HEAD OFFICE:
PO Box 160, Grand Bend, Ontario, NOM 1TO, Canada
TELEPHONE:
Area Code 519 238-2333

In January 1971, Bell Aerospace Canada Textron acquired facilities at Grand Bend, Ontario, for the development and production of its Voyageur heavy haul ACV, and the smaller 17-ton Viking multi-duty craft

The facilities at Grand Bend Airport include two buildings with a total of 30,000 sq ft (3,350 m²) of floor space on a 52-acre (21 Ha) site.

The company has worked closely with the Canadian Department of Industry, Trade and Commerce in planning a programme which has led to the establishment in Canada of a commercially viable air cushion industry to meet the growing requirements for Coast Guard, remote area cargo hauling, high speed passenger ferry services and other specialised applications.

The first two 40-ton Voyageurs were built under a joint agreement between the company and the Canadian Department of Industry, Trade and Commerce. The prototype, Voyageur 001, differs from later craft insofar as it is fitted with two GE LM-100 engines, as opposed to the ST6T-75 Twin-Pac gas-turbines which are now standard.

The newer Viking, a smaller but similar multi duty craft was completed under a one-prototype cost-sharing programme similar to that under which the Voyageur was developed.

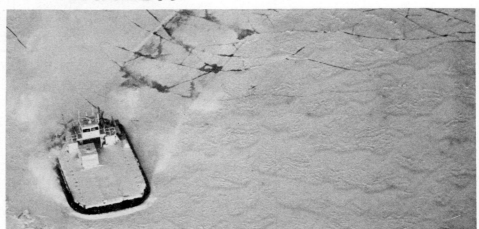

Above: Voyageur 002, operated by the Canadian Coast Guard, breaking up a 3½-mile long ice jam on the Riviere des Prairies, north of Montreal. The craft was operated at a speed of 10 knots to create a series of trailing waves, one of which was allowed to precede the Voyageur into the ice pack, breaking the surface ice into pieces
Below: The Voyageur compressing and cracking the jammed ice into smaller segments. The gaps between the segments increase as they move downstream, carried by the river's three-knot current

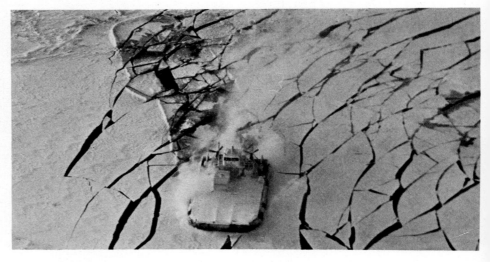

Both Voyageur and Viking feature a basic flatbed hull of all-welded extruded marine aluminium that can be adapted to a variety of operational needs by adding the required equipment and superstructure.

Construction of Voyageur 001 started in March 1971. It began operational trials and certification testing in November 1971.

Since early 1973, Voyageur 001 has been operating extensively in the Mackenzie Delta region of Northern Canada on oil industry exploration logistics support. Voyageur 002 is owned and operated by the Canadian Coast Guard and since March 1975 has been undergoing trials as an ACV icebreaker. Ice in excess of 1 ft 5 in (431 mm) thick has been successfully broken.

MODEL 7380 VOYAGEUR

The Bell Model 7380 is a twin-engined fully amphibious hovercraft designed to haul payloads of up to 25 tons over Arctic and other terrain at speeds up to 87 km/h (54 mph).

The 25 ton payload is equal to that of most transport aircraft engaged in regular supply operations in the North and other remote regions, including the C-130 Hercules. The Model 7380 therefore provides a direct transport link from the airstrips to settlements and support bases for the movement of men, equipment and supplies.

The craft has been tested extensively by the Canadian Coast Guard and the US Army for a variety of high speed amphibious missions.

Modular construction is employed and the craft can be dismantled into easily handled units, plus skirts, for ease of transportation by road, rail or air.

Estimates indicate that ton-mile operating costs will be less than 25% of those experienced with heavy lift helicopters and 50% that of existing small ACVs.

By adding superstructure to the basic flatbed hull, the craft can be used for various alternative roles from a 140 seat passenger ferry to military weapons platform.

LIFT AND PROPULSION: Two 1,300 hp Pratt & Whitney ST6T-75 Twin-Pac gas-turbines mounted aft, one each side of the roll-on/roll-off cargo deck, power the integrated lift/propulsion systems, which employ fans, propellers and transmissions similar to those of the Bell SK-5 and BHC SR-N6. Each engine has two separate gas-turbine sections which drive into a combining gearbox, providing twin-engine reliability for each integrated lift fan and propeller. The second gearbox employed in the Twin-Pac installation is a strengthened version of the integrated drive used in the SR.N5, developed by the SPECO Division of Kelsey-Hayes. The output of each engine is absorbed by a three-bladed Hamilton Standard 43D50 reversible-pitch propeller of 9 ft (2·74 m) diameter and by a 12-bladed 7 ft (2·13 m) diameter light alloy centrifugal lift fan. The fans deliver air to the cushion via a 4 ft (1·21 m) deep peripheral skirt which incorporates stability trunks. Air drawn by the engines first enters a Donaldson filter that traps and removes dust particles. It then passes through a fine knitmesh filter and into a Peerless Vane filter that gathers water droplets. Lift fans and propellers are linked mechanically and the power output of each engine can be apportioned between the propellers and lift fans allowing speed and hoverheight to be varied to suit prevailing operating conditions. The engines have

Voyageur, in the foreground, accompanied by the Viking prototype during a patrol mission with the Canadian Coast Guard

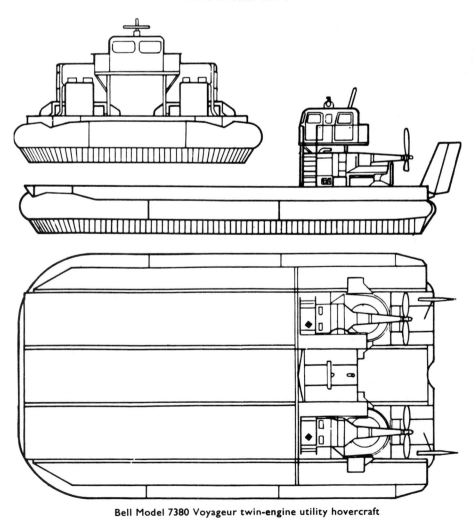

Bell Model 7380 Voyageur twin-engine utility hovercraft

multifuel capability and can be started in extremely low temperatures (—65°F). Two fuel tanks, each consisting of three interconnected bays containing flexible rubber

Upper left and right: For two years, Voyageur 001 was operated by KAPS transport in the Mackenzie Delta region of Northern Canada on oil exploration logistics support missions. Typical loads were a caterpillar tractor and a Nodwell seismic driller weighing 46,000 lbs, a 3,300 Imp gallon fuel tank (filled) and miscellaneous items of earth moving equipment. *Bottom left:* Voyageur 004 hauls a cargo container from a freighter to ice-locked communities along the St. Lawrence river in Quebec. *Bottom right:* Voyageur 003 carrying oil tanks to a drilling site in North Alaska

cells, are built into the aft end of the port and starboard forward flotation boxes. Total fuel capacity is 15,000 litres (3,300 Imp gal), sufficient for a range of approximately 550 nautical miles with a 15-ton payload. Types of fuel which may be used are kerosene, AVTUR, JETA, JP4, JP5 and Arctic diesel.

CONTROLS: Steering is by means of two aerodynamically-balanced rudders hinged to the rear of propeller, supplemented by the use of differential propeller pitch control. Side-located bow thrusters aid low-speed manoeuvring. All controls are located in the raised cab, which seats a crew of two plus four passengers. Propeller pitch controls are located on the starboard side of the operator's seat, so that they can be operated by the right hand, while power can be controlled with the left hand. A conventional foot-operated control bar is provided for rudder actuation.

HULL: Exceptionally rugged all-metal structure, fabricated in corrosion-resistant 6,000 series extruded aluminium alloys, with double wall skinning and multiple watertight compartments. The design of the modular structure incorporates hollow-core, thin-walled aluminium extrusions similar to those employed in the superstructures of commercial and naval ships. Use of this material, with extruded corners for constructing joints, produces a structural box of great strength and stiffness. The hull design is based on flat surfaces, thus eliminating the need for formed parts and simplifying repairs. The structural modules are welded using gas-shielded metal arc and gas shielded tungsten arc processes.

The basic craft hard structure is broken down for transportation into twelve sections. These consist of three forward flotation boxes. two forward and two aft side decks, two

The Viking on patrol near Parry Sound, Ontario

power modules, an aft centre flotation box, a cabin support pedestal and the control cabin.

The three forward flotation boxes are almost identical in appearance and measure 40 ft long, 8 ft wide and 3 ft 1½ in deep (12·19 × 2·43 × 0·952 m). The port and starboard boxes each contain a fuel tank and a landing pad support structure.

The aft centre flotation box is of similar construction, but shorter in length. Scallops are formed in each side to prevent airflow blockage around the perimeter of the lift fans, which are contained in the power modules located on either side of the centre box. This module, together with the three forward boxes, forms the structural backbone of the

craft. Loads from the side decks and power modules are transmitted into this primary structure.

The main deck is designed to accept loadings of up to 4,882 kg/m² (1,000 lb/sq ft.) Cargo tiedown-rings and craft handling gear are provided. Off-cushion, the cargo deck is sufficiently low to permit rapid loading and unloading from trucks and fork lifts.

The craft is completely amphibious and has a reserve buoyancy in excess of 100%.

SKIRT: 1·22 m (4 ft) deep neoprene nylon skirt developed from that of BHC SR.N6. 50% peripheral fingers. High attachment line at bow, similar to that employed on the BH.7. Airflow to the side and bow skirts is supplied through the duct formed by the side hulls. The transverse stability trunks are also supplied from the side hull airflow, via a duct built into the outboard forward flotation boxes immediately forward of the fuel tanks. The port and starboard rear trunks are supplied by rearward airflow from the respective fans. The longitudinal keel is fed by ducts leading from each fan forward to the centre of the aft centre flotation box, then downwards into the keel bag.

ACCOMMODATION: The control cabin is supported on a raised platform aft of the deck between the power modules. It is raised sufficiently to provide 1·93 m (6 ft 4 in) of headroom for personnel or cargo and provides the operator with a 360 deg view. The unit is basically a modified four door truck cab, measuring 2·64 × 2·38 m (8 ft 8 in long by 7 ft 10 in wide). The operating crew of two are seated forward. The operator's position is on the starboard side, and the relief driver or radar operator is at the port position. The control console is located between the two seats and contains the control levers for the engines.

A full-width bench seat is located across the back of the cab, with access provided by the two rear doors. Seat belts are provided for four passengers. Cabin heating and window defrosting is provided by a dual heater, operating on vehicle fuel, and located at the forward end, beneath the port walkway to the control cabin. Electronically heated windows are also installed. Thermal insulation and double glazing are provided throughout the cab and this also attenuates engine noise.

Additional features provided in the cab design are structural provisions for roof mounted radar, air-conditioning and the provision of space in the control console for radio communications and navigation equipment.

SYSTEMS: Electrical: Four gearbox-driven brushless generators, each supplying 28 volts dc, and two 28 volt Nickel-Cadmium batteries. External power: 28 volts dc.

DIMENSIONS:
Length overall	20 m (65·7 ft)
Beam overall	11·2 m (36·7 ft)
Height overall, power on	6·7 m (22·0 ft)
Height overall, power off	5·74 m (18 ft 10 in)
Height of cargo deck, power off	1·17 m (3 ft 10 in)
Skirt height	1·22 m (4 ft 0 in)
Cushion area	166 m² (1,789 sq ft)
Cushion loading at 41,277 kg (91,000 lb)	248·92 kg/m² (50·88 lb/sq ft)
Buoyancy reserve at 41,277 kg (91,000 lb)	125%
Cargo deck size	40 × 32 ft (1,280 sq ft) (12·19 m × 9·75 m) (119 m²)

WEIGHTS:
Basic weight, empty	16,202 kg (35,720 lb)
Design gross weight	40,823 kg (90,000 lb)
Max permissible gross weight	41,277 kg (91,000 lb)

PERFORMANCE:
Max speed over calm water, still air conditions, at a sea level standard day temperature of 59 deg F (15 deg C) with a 20 ton payload.
At 78,000 lb (35,381 kg) gross, 2,600 shp 54 mph (87 km/h)
Endurance at cruise power with 600 US gallons (2,280 l) and 30-ton payload 3 hours
Endurance can be extended to 10-13·5 hours by trading off payload for fuel, with max-

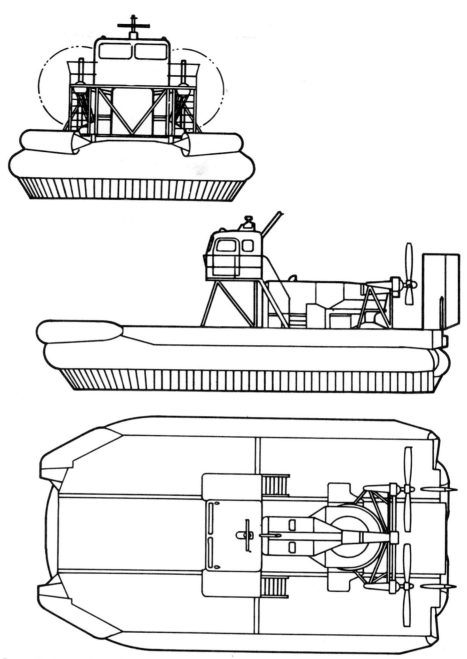

Power for the Viking multi-purpose ACV is provided by a single 1,300 hp Twin-Pac T75, coupled to two variable-pitch propellers via a V-drive transmission. Maximum speed, calm water, is 92 km/h (57 mph)

imum fuel of 15,000 litres (3,300 Imp gal) the payload will be in the region of 18 tons at the maximum permissible gross weight of 41,277 kg (91,000 lb).

MODEL 7467 LACV-30

This stretched version of the Voyageur has been designed to meet the US Navy's requirements for a high-speed amphibious vehicle for LOTS (Logistics-Over-The-Shore) operations.

The chief modifications are an 11 ft (3·35 m) lengthening of the deck ahead of the raised control cabin to facilitate the carriage of additional 10-ton Milvan containers; the siting of a swing crane at the bow, also the provision of a surf fence and a bow loading ramp.

The LACV-30 is intended to replace conventional vessels of the LARC-5 and the LARC-15 types by 1980. It will provide the US Army with a rapid lift capability enabling it to move cargo and equipment over water, beaches, ice, snow and marginal areas. A range of military cargoes can be carried, from containers, wheeled and tracked vehicles, to

engineering equipment, pallets, packs and barrels.

Endurance at cruising speed depends upon the configuration/role in which the craft is used. For the drive-on cargo and Milvan cargo roles the craft can carry payloads of 30 tons with an endurance of 2 hours. In the self-unload Milvan cargo role the payload is reduced to 26·5 tons for the same endurance. Other configurations give endurance figures of between 5 and 9·1 hours with varying payloads.

Although intended primarily for use as a lighter in support of LOTS operations, the craft is also suitable for a number of secondary roles such as coastal, harbour and inland water inspection; patrol, search-and-rescue missions and medical evacuation.

Two pre-production craft have been sold to the US Army for evaluation as ship-to-shore lighters.

LIFT AND PROPULSION: Integrated system, powered by two United Aircraft of Canada Ltd/Pratt and Whitney ST6T Twin-Pac gas-turbines mounted aft, one at each side of the raised control cabin. Each engine is rated at 1,800 shp maximum and 1,400 shp at normal output. The output of each is absorbed by a three-bladed Hamilton Standard 43D50-363 reversible-pitch propeller and a 7 ft (2·13 m) diameter, twelve-bladed, fixed-pitch light aluminium alloy, centrifugal lift fan.

FUEL SYSTEM: Recommended fuel is standard aviation kerosene-Jet A-1, JP4, JP5 or light diesel fuel oil. Main fuel usuable capacity is 2,272 gal (9,419 litres). Fuel ballast/emergency fuel capacity 1,531 gal (6,960 litres).

ELECTRICAL SYSTEM: Starter generators: Four gearbox-driven, brushless, 28 vdc, 200 amp each. Batteries: Two nickel cadmium, 28 vdc, 40 amps hr each.

DIMENSIONS:

Length overall, on cushion
76 ft 6 in (23·3 m)
Beam overall, on cushion 36·7 ft (11·2 m)
Height overall, on cushion
29 ft 0 in (8·83 m)
Height overall, off cushion
25·8 ft (7·86 m)
Skirt height, nominal   4 ft 0 in (1·21 m)
Height, cargo deck, off cushion
4 ft 0 in (1·21 m)
Cargo deck
51 ft 6 in × 24 ft 2¼ in (15·69 m × 7·37 m)

WEIGHTS:
Gross weight   115,000 lb (52,163 kg)

PERFORMANCE (Estimated):
Standard day, zero wind, calm water, at gross weight of 115,000 lb (52,163 kg)
Normal rating   46 mph (74 km/h)
Maximum rating   56 mph (90 km/h)
Estimated fuel consumption at cruising speed   255 gal/hr (1,159 l/hr)

MODEL 7501 VIKING

Evolved from the 40-ton Voyageur, the 17-ton Viking has been designed to meet the need for a smaller but similar multi-purpose **craft capable of hauling a 6-7-ton payload at a speed of 92 km/h (57 mph).**

Above: Voyageur 01 demonstrating its logistics-over-the-shore capability during the OSDOC II joint exercises conducted by the US Army and Navy during 1972

Below: LACV-30-I after modification at Bell Aerospace. Note the swing crane for positioning the Milvan containers and the surf fence

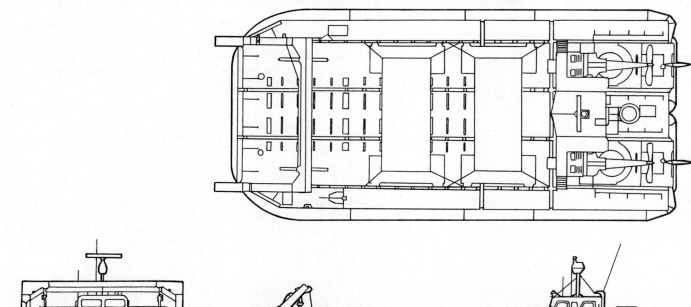

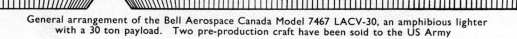

General arrangement of the Bell Aerospace Canada Model 7467 LACV-30, an amphibious lighter with a 30 ton payload. Two pre-production craft have been sold to the US Army

The Viking prototype, equipped to meet Canadian Coast Guard requirements for an inshore search-and-rescue craft, was completed in early 1974. A study has been made of a lighterage variant for the US Marine Corps and the craft also has applications as a seismic survey/hydrographic vehicle.

A feature of the Viking is a vee-drive transmission operable collectively and differentially to provide a high degree of manoeuvrability. Most of the mechanical components are interchangeable with those of the Voyageur, simplifying maintenance and and spares holdings. Modular construction features of the Voyageur have been retained to facilitate transport by road, rail and air, and speedy reassembly and maintenance on site.

LIFT AND PROPULSION: A single UACL ST6T-75 Twin-Pac gas-turbine, delivering 1,300 shp continuous and 1,700 shp intermittent, powers the integrated lift/propulsion system, which employs a number of components identical to those used on the Voyageur. Engine output is transferred to a single 2·13 m (7 ft 0 in) diameter light alloy centrifugal lift fan and, via a V-drive transmission, to two 2·74 m (9 ft 0 in) diameter Hamilton Standard 3-blade variable-pitch propellers for thrust. Maximum cushion pressure is 193·2 kg/sq m (39·6 lb/sq ft). Total fuel capacity is 6,954 l (1,530 Imp gals. 1,837 US gals). Types of fuel allowed are kerosene, JP4, JP5, JETA, AVTUR or Arctic diesel.

CONTROLS: Craft heading is controlled by twin aerodynamically balanced rudders, supplemented by differential propeller thrust. Bow thrust-ports, port and starboard, assist directional control at low speeds.

HULL: All-metal structure fabricated in 6,000 series corrosion-resistant extruded marine aluminium. Basic craft hard structure comprises six modules which are unbolted

Viking crossing a sandbar while on a Canadian Coast Guard rescue operation

for transportation. Cargo deck has a total area of 76·2 sq m (820 sq ft).

SKIRT: 1·22 m (4 ft 0 in) deep neoprene-nylon tapered skirt developed from that of BHC SR.N6. with 50% peripheral fingers and a high attachment line at the bow.

ACCOMMODATION: Operating crew of two (commander/operator; navigator/relief operator), seated in a cabin supported on a raised platform amidships. Basic flat-deck configuration will accommodate a wide range of payloads, or superstructure and/or special equipment.

SYSTEMS:

ELECTRICAL: Two gearbox-driven brushless generators, each supplying 28 volts dc, and two 28 volt Nickel-Cadmium batteries. External power 28 volts dc.

DIMENSIONS:

Length overall	13·6 m (44·5 ft)
Beam overall	7·9 m (26·0 ft)
Height overall	6·1 m (20·0 ft)
Cargo deck area	76·2 sq m (820 sq ft)
Deck height, off cushion	1·2 m (3·9 ft)

WEIGHTS:

Empty weight	9,894 kg (21,811 lb)
Max permissible gross weight	14,742 kg (32,500 lb)

PERFORMANCE:

Max speed, calm water	92 km/h (57 mph)
Continuous gradient capability, standing start	10%
Vertical obstacle clearance	1·2 m (4 ft)
Ditch crossing width	2·1 m (7 ft)
Endurance with maximum fuel	13 hours
Max wave height	in excess of 1·8 m (6 ft)
Max range	680 n miles

MODEL 7505 STRETCHED VIKING

Bell engineers have determined that the overall performance and seakeeping characteristics of the basic Viking can be improved by stretching the hull. Design work on the new model is now in hand. The following details apply to the baseline configuration, with the hull stretched by 11 ft (3·35 m) to 55·5 ft (16·9 m).

DIMENSIONS:

Length overall	16·9 m (55·5 ft)
Beam overall	7·9 m (26·0 ft)
Height overall	6·1 m (20·0 ft)
Cargo deck area	102·2 m² (1,100 sq ft)
Deck height, off cushion	1·2 m (3·9 ft)

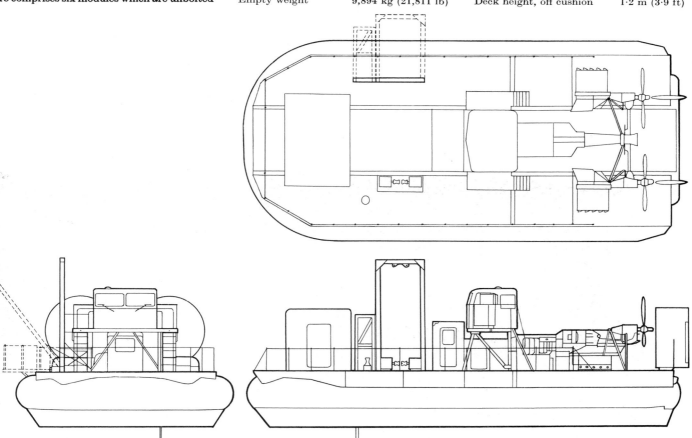
Provisional three-view drawing of the projected Bell Model 7505. Stretched Viking showing the A frame gantry, walkout platform and passenger and laboratory modules

WEIGHTS:		PERFORMANCE:		Endurance with maximum fuel 10·5 hours
Empty weight	11,475 kg (25,299 lbs)	Calm water	94 km/h (58 mph)	Maximum wave height
Maximum permissible gross weight		Continuous gradient capacity 11 deg		in excess of 1·8 m (6 ft)
	19,051 kg (42,000 lb)	Ditch crossing width	2·7 m (9 ft)	Maximum range 550 nm

CANADIAN CUSHION CRAFT LTD

HEAD OFFICE:
Octagon Pond, PO Box 8534, Station A,
St. John's, Newfoundland A1B 3N9,
Canada

TELEPHONE:
(709) 368-1023

TELEX:
016-4675

WORKS:
Beclin Building, Topsail Road, St. John's,
Newfoundland

DIRECTORS:
R. E. Good, President
R. C. Fishlock, Vice-President, Technical
Director
J. Halley, Secretary-Treasurer

In August 1975, Canadian Cushion Craft Ltd began the series production of the Canair 2, an amphibious two-seater intended for a range of utility applications, from patrol and survey to light transport duties. A feature of the company's marketing is the offer of free basic training in the operation of the craft by a qualified ACV instructor.

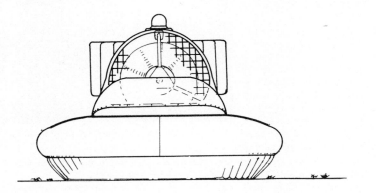

CANAIR 2

Development of the Canair 2 has been supported by the Newfoundland and Labrador Development Corporation, which may participate in the production and marketing of the machine. Its features include a planing hull to reduce the risk of overturning, a single engine and fan installation for reduced maintenance and an HDL skirt with easily replaceable segments.

LIFT AND PROPULSION: Power for the integrated lift/propulsion system is provided by a single Kohler 440 2AS air-cooled 2-cycle engine delivering 35 bhp at 6,000 rpm. Power is transmitted to a 2 ft 6 in (0·726 m) diameter, 10-bladed multi-wing fan aft. The primary air flow is directed aft, and the secondary, for cushion lift, passes down into the plenum. The engine is completely enclosed to reduce the intake of dust, sand and salt-water spray. The engine is cooled by its own fan, in addition to which a main drive fan extracts air out of the compartment via side ducts and forward intake vents. Total fuel capacity is 5 gallons.

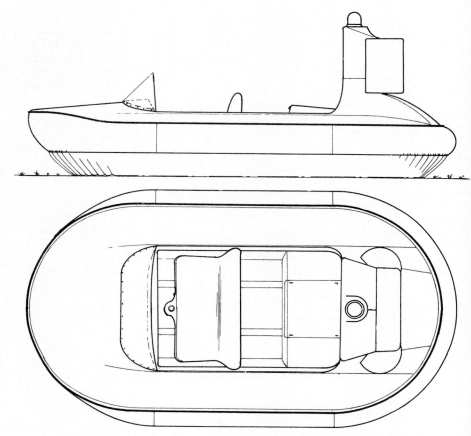

General arrangement of the Canair 2, two-seat, light amphibious hovercraft

Canair 2, an amphibious two-seater designed for a range of utility applications. Development of the vehicle, which is powered by a single 35 bhp Kohler air-cooled engine, was supported by the Newfoundland and Labrador Development Corporation

CONTROLS: A simple twist grip mounted on a central control stick operates the engine throttle. Movement of the stick operates twin rudders hinged to the rear of the fan duct to control craft heading.

HULL: Built in moulded grp. Buoyancy is provided by six watertight compartments, each with an individual inspection hatch.

SKIRT: HDL type loop and segment skirt fabricated in lightweight neoprene-coated nylon. All segments are readily replaceable with simple plastic stud and strap fasteners designed to fail under execessive snatch loads, leaving the segments undamaged.

ACCOMMODATION: Side-by-side seating for driver and passenger in an open cockpit. Room provided behind the seat for baggage or equipment. Seat moves forward or backward for trim change.

DIMENSIONS (engine off):

Length	14 ft 0 in (4·26 m)
Width	7 ft 3 in (2·20 m)
Height	4 ft 6 in (1·37 m)
Cushion depth	10 in (254 mm)

WEIGHTS:

Dry weight	450 lb (204·10 kg)
Normal payload (including two occupants)	450 lb (204·10 kg)

PERFORMANCE:

Max speed	30 mph (48·28 km/h)
Cruising speed	25 mph (40·23 km/h)
Endurance at 80% full power	2 hours

The craft has operated successfully in 25 mph (40·23 km/h) winds, and seas slightly in excess of 1 ft 6 in (0·457 m) high with a payload of 400 lb (181·429 kg).

HOVERJET INC

HEAD OFFICE:
55 Glen Cameron Road, No. 2, Thornhill, Ontario, Canada L3T 1PZ

TELEPHONE:
(416) 881-0737

DIRECTORS AND SENIOR EXECUTIVES:
Ralph Schneider, President
E. De Asis, Chief Engineer
R. Bittner, Chief Technician

SUBSIDIARIES AND AFFILIATED COMPANIES:
Alpha Aerospace Corporation Ltd, Canadian Airships Development Corpn.

Hoverjet Inc is currently producing the HJ-1000, 5-seat passenger and utility craft, the prototype of which completed its trials in April 1974. The company is engaged primarily in ACV research and development and undertakes contract design, consultancy and prototype construction for other companies. Ralph Schneider, formerly director of research and development at Hoverair Corporation and Airfloat Ltd, is responsible for Hoverjet's development and engineering programmes.

HOVERJET HJ-1000

An amphibious "workhorse" designed to meet the needs of exploration parties, the HJ-1000 is of frp construction and carries a payload of up to 800 lb (362·85 kg). The vehicle can be modified to suit a variety of applications ranging from ambulance or rescue craft to water taxi and pilot boat. Power is provided by three 42 hp Kohler engines.

The craft has been designed to permit transport by air, sea and road. It will fit into a transport aircraft with an 8 ft (2·43 m) door opening; it can be accommodated in a standard 8 ft × 8 ft × 20 ft (2·43 m × 2·43 m × 6·09 m) container for delivery by sea, or it can be loaded onto an 8 ft × 20 ft (2·43 m × 6·09 m) boat trailer.

LIFT AND PROPULSION: Lift is supplied by a single 42 hp Kohler K440-2AS two-cycle aircooled engine driving two 1 ft 8 in (0·50 m) diameter 10-bladed aluminium fans mounted vertically at the opposite ends of a transverse shaft. Cushion pressure is 15·9 lb sq ft. Propulsive thrust is supplied by two duct-mounted, 42 hp Kohler K440-2AS two-cycle aircooled engines, each driving a single 2 ft 6 in (0·762 m) diameter 10-bladed axial fan. For manoeuvring and hullborne operation over water a 7 hp outboard motor on a remotely-operated swing mount can be fitted as an optional extra. Fuel is carried in two 10-gallon (45·46 litre) tanks, one port, one starboard, each with a refuelling neck located on deck. Recommended fuel is 2-cycle mix, 40 : 1.

CONTROLS: Craft heading is controlled by an aircraft type control stick which activates twin rudders at the rear of the thrust ducts via push-pull cables. Separate throttles are supplied for each engine, providing differential steering control. Complete engine instrumentation is provided.

HULL: Two-piece construction, comprising upper and lower bodies in colour impregnated fibreglass plastic on welded steel inner frame. Engine and fan mounts are of tubular, welded steel construction.

SKIRT: Segmented loop in laminated 16 oz nylon/neoprene.

ACCOMMODATION: Driver sits forward and up to four passengers are accommodated in a wide cabin aft. Access is via a large door and roof opening on the port side. The passenger seats fold against the sides of the cabin to provide a cargo hold measuring 4 ft wide × 8 ft 0 in long by 4 ft 4 in high (1·21 m × 2·43 m × 1·32 m). Safety equipment includes "pop-out" emergency exit windows, built-in buoyancy, a fire extinguisher and an electric bilge pump.

STANDARD EQUIPMENT: Electric starters, battery, navigation lights, flashing beacon, spotlight, horn, tie-up cleats and fire extinguishers.

OPTIONAL EQUIPMENT: Navigation lights, flashing beacon, spotlight, radio, lifejacket.

Above and Below: Hoverjet's HJ-1000 workhorse hovercraft, designed for freight and passenger applications over marginal terrain. Power is supplied by three 42 hp Kohler K440-2AS two-cycle aircooled engines, one for lift and two for propulsion. Normal cruising speed is 35 mph depending on surface and wind conditions

DIMENSIONS:

Length overall:	
power off	17 ft 10 in (5·43 m)
skirt inflated	18 ft 10 in (5·74 m)
Beam overall:	
power off	7 ft 10 in (2·38 m)
skirt inflated	8 ft 10 in (2·69 m)
Height overall:	
power off	5 ft 10 in (1·77 m)
power on	6 ft 10 in (2·08 m)
Draft afloat	4 in (101 mm)

DIMENSIONS, INTERNAL:

Main cabin:	
Length	8 ft 0 in (2·43 m)
Max width	4 ft 0 in (1·21 m)
Max height	4 ft 4 in (1·32 m)
Floor area	32·5 sq ft (3·01 sq m)

PERFORMANCE:
Normal cruising speed 35 mph (56·32 km/h)
Vertical obstacle clearance
1 ft 1 in (330 mm)

PRICES AND TERMS:
C\$ 17,500, completely equipped, fob, Toronto, Canada.

HOVERLIFT SYSTEMS LTD.

HEAD OFFICE:
1201, 603 Seventh Avenue, S.W. Calgary, Alberta T2P 2T5

TELEPHONE:
403-263-3983

OFFICERS:
R. D. Hunt, P.Eng. President
Dale M. Simmons, P.Eng, Executive Vice-President
K. W. Crowshaw, Vice-President
V. H. Redekop, Treasurer

Hoverlift Systems Ltd was incorporated in April 1975 as a member of the Simmons Group of Companies which is active in the resource and energy fields. Its member companies are: Simmons Drilling Ltd., Kandex Research and Development Ltd., McMurray Operators, Ltd., Rudale Resources Ltd., Western Underground Contractors Ltd. and Hoverlift Systems Ltd. Simmons Drilling in particular has worked for fifteen years in the Canadian North, and is well aware of the many problems posed by operation and maintenance of equipment in the intense cold and darkness of the Canadian Winter.

Hoverlift Systems Ltd. aims to provide air cushion equipment and services developed especially for these conditions, to those companies operating in the Canadian Arctic and Sub-Arctic regions where mineral exploration, civil engineering, construction, hydro-electric, forestry and manufacturing projects are hampered by climate and difficult terrain.

Hoverlift Systems Ltd. has built a ten ton air cushion raft designed to be rapidly despatched and put into emergency operation in remote areas where no support equipment exists. A description of this craft appears in the section devoted to ACV Trailers and Heavy Lift Systems.

During 1976 the company began a programme of basic research to develop the technique of air cushion load assist. The objective is to provide a load assist package which can be readily attached to existing commercial road vehicles to allow them to continue operations during periods of restriction or load limitation and to increase the capacity of existing vehicles under normal operating conditions.

HOVERTEC INC

HEAD OFFICE:
Unit One, 250 Rayette Road, Concord, Ontario, L4K 1BI

TELEPHONE:
416-669-9801

DIRECTORS:
Jim McCurdy, President
Peter Roberts, Works Director

The first craft to be marketed by Hovertec Inc is the Chinook miniature ACV runabout. The vehicle is in production and is being sold through a national dealer network. Sales began in the USA in late 1974. By March 1975, 150 of the Mk 1 version and five Mk 2s had either been built or were on order.

The company is at present completing a new amphibious runabout seating two side-by-side.

CHINOOK I

This is a lightweight amphibious single seater with a maximum payload capacity of about 325 lb (147·41 kg). Built in fibreglass reinforced plastics it is 11 ft 3 in long and sufficiently small and light to be transported on the roof of a family car.

Maximum speed over water is 30 mph (48·28 km/h).

LIFT AND PROPULSION: Cushion air is supplied by a 5 hp Tecumseh 2-cycle engine driving a 2 ft 0 in (0·60 m) diameter ten bladed polypropelene fan. A 20 hp Kohler 295-1, 2 cycle engine drives a 2 ft 0 in (0·60 m) diameter, 10-bladed ducted fan for thrust. Fuel capacity is 5 Imp gallons (22 litres). Fuel recommended is high octane automotive spirit.

HULL: Moulded in fibreglass reinforced plastic.

SKIRT: Bag type in neoprene impregnated nylon.

ACCOMMODATION: Open cockpit with single-seat for driver.

DIMENSIONS:

Length overall	11 ft 3 in (3·42 m)
Beam overall	5 ft 0 in (1·52 m)
Height overall	3 ft 7 in (1·09 m)
Hoverheight, hard structure to ground	8 in (203 mm)

WEIGHTS:

Normal empty weight	285 lb (129·26 kg)
Normal payload	325 lb (147·41 kg)

PERFORMANCE (at normal operating weight):

Max speed over calm water	30 mph (48·28 km/h)
Max speed overland	up to 40 mph (64·37 km)
over ice and snow	up to 45 mph (72·42 km)

Hovertec's light amphibious single-seater, the 30 mph (48 km/h) Chinook,   The craft measures 11 ft 3 in (3·42 m) by 5 ft (1·52 m) and can be carried on the roof of a family car

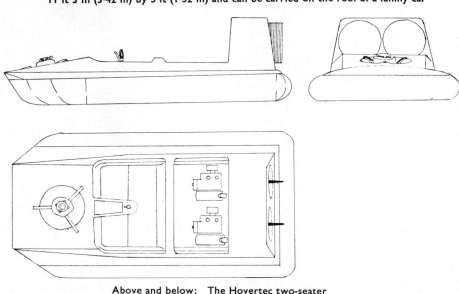

Above and below: The Hovertec two-seater

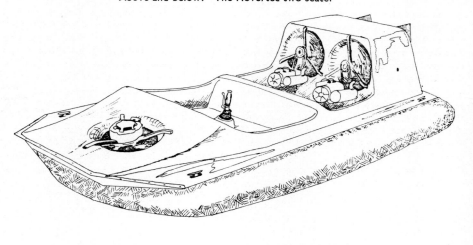

Still air range and endurance at
cruising speed 4·5-5 hours
Max gradient, static conditions 20°
Vertical obstacle clearance 8 in (203 mm)
PRICE: Mk 1: C$1,550.00, COD. (FOB for
overseas orders).

CHINOOK II

The prototypes of the Chinook II completed
trials in March 1975. The chief difference
between the model and its predecessor is in
the installation of a more powerful propulsion
engine, the 26 hp Kohler 295-2AX, for
improved performance. Basic hull structure,
weights and dimensions are unchanged.

PERFORMANCE:
Max speed over calm water
40 mph (64·37 km/h)
Still air range and endurance 4·5-5 hours
Max gradient, static conditions 30 degrees
Vertical obstacle clearance 8 in (203·20 mm)

PRICE AND TERMS:
C$1,750·00 COD (FOB for overseas orders).

HOVERTEC TWO-SEATER

Construction of this amphibious fibreglass-
hulled two-seater, derived from the earlier
Chinook, began in April 1975. Trials were
due to start in the late summer of 1975.
LIFT AND PROPULSION: A single 8 hp
Chrysler engine installed immediately ahead
of the cockpit drives a 5-bladed polypropelene
axial-flow fan for lift. Thrust is supplied by
two 26 hp Kohler 2AX 295 engines mounted
aft and driving two, 10-bladed polypropelene
ducted fans. Fuel is carried in a single 10
Imp gallon (45·46 l) capacity tank located
in the engine compartment aft of the cockpit.
CONTROLS: Craft heading is controlled by
twin aerodynamic rudders hinged to the
rear of the propulsion fan ducts. Tabs are
provided for pitch and roll trim.
HULL: Monocoque structure in moulded
fibreglass reinforced plastics.
SKIRT: Bag type, in neoprene impregnated
nylon.
ACCOMMODATION: Open cockpit with

bench seat for driver and passenger side-by-
side.
DIMENSIONS:
Length overall 12 ft 6 in (3·81 m)
Length overall, skirt inflated
14 ft 0 in (4·26 m)
Beam overall, power off 6 ft 6 in (1·98 m)
Beam overall, skirt inflated
8 ft 9 in (2·66 m)
Height overall on landing pads,
power off 3 ft 9 in (1·14 m)
Height overall, skirt inflated
4 ft 6 in (1·37 m)
Draft afloat 12 in (304·80 mm)
WEIGHTS:
Normal empty weight 350 lb (158·75 kg)
Normal gross weight 900 lb (408·21 kg)
Normal payload 550 lb (249·46 kg)
PERFORMANCE:
Details not available
PRICE AND TERMS:
Retail prices, standard model C $2,500;
de luxe model C $2,900·00.

TRANSPORT CANADA
AIR CUSHION VEHICLE DIVISION

HEAD OFFICE:
Tower A, Place de Ville, Ottawa, Ontario,
K1A 0N5, Canada
OFFICIALS:
J. Doherty, Chief ACV Division,

The Air Cushion Vehicle Division, Transport Canada, was established in 1968 as
part of the Marine Administration. The
Division is responsible to the Director
Canadian Coast Guard Ship Safety Branch
for all aspects of air cushion vehicle regula-

tions. This includes the establishment of
vehicle fitness standards, certification of
pilots and maintenance engineers and registration of air cushion vehicles.

On the operations side, the Division has
direct responsibility to the Director Canadian
Coast Guard Fleet Systems Branch to advise
and assist Coast Guard in its air cushion
vehicle activities. Included in this, is the
use of air cushion technology for ice-breaking
and the Division has been instrumental in
developing this new air cushion technology.

The Canadian Coast Guard Air Cushion
Vehicle Evaluation and Development Unit
is also a responsibility of the ACV Division.
There is also close collaboration with Trans-
port Canada's Policy and Planning Branch,
Surface Administration and the Transport
Development Agency. The advice of the
Division is constantly sought by other federal
departments and provincial governments.

The division also participates actively on
the National Research Council Associate
Committee of Air Cushion Technology.

CHANNEL ISLANDS

T. S. GOOCH

ADDRESS:
La Genètière, Route Orange, St. Brelade,
Jersey, C.I.
TELEPHONE:
Central (0534) 42980

Mr T. S. Gooch has designed and built a
number of lightweight air cushion vehicles,
the latest of which is the J-5. In May 1969,
his J-4 became the first home-built ACV
to make a Channel crossing to France under
its own power. The craft completed the
18-mile (28·96 km) outward crossing from
Gorey, C.I., to Carteret in Brittany in 65
minutes and the return journey in 40 minutes.

The J-4 won first place in the Thames
Hover Race in 1970 in the under 500 cc class,
and has since been acquired by Hovercraft
Development Ltd for research and development applications.

Mr Gooch is now concentrating on the
development of the J-5 four-seater with
almost double the cushion area of the J-4.

Plans of the J-4 are available for amateur
construction and are selling well.

GOOCH J-4

This distinctive 13 ft (3·96 m) long amphibious two-seater has been designed with quiet
operation and safety in mind. Instead of
the more usual propeller, therefore, two axial
fans mounted in a transverse duct across
the stern are employed for propulsive
thrust. The craft is of ply and aluminium
construction and cruises at 40 mph (64·37
km/h). To facilitate storage or towing,
the two ply sidewings carrying the skirt
periphery and running the full length of the
main hull structure hinge upwards to reduce

The Gooch J-4 air-jet propelled, two-seat recreational hovercraft

the overall beam (power off) from 7 ft (2·13
m) to 4 ft (1·21 m).

The prototype J-4 was finished in June
1968 and the craft completed its trials in
July of that year. No variants of the
basic design are being contemplated at
present, but alternative engines may be
fitted.

LIFT AND PROPULSION: Lift is supplied
by a Villiers 8E 197 cc two-stroke motor-cycle
engine mounted in the bow and driving a
24 in (0·609 mm) diameter 10-blade axial
multiwing fan attached directly to its
crankshaft. The propulsion engine is a
250 cc Ariel Arrow, twin two-stroke which
drives, via a timing belt or vee belt, two
24 in (0·609 mm) diameter 5-bladed Multi-

wing axial fans mounted vertically on a
common shaft inside a transverse duct.
Propulsive air is drawn in by the fans from
each side of the duct and expelled through
a rectangular outlet at the stern. An
aluminium reverse thrust/braking bucket is
fitted above the air-jet aperture. Total
fuel capacity is 4 gallons, carried in two 2-
gallon tanks, one each side of the craft on
the CG. A filter cap is fitted to each tank.
Recommended fuel is two-stroke mixture
or regular grade petrol with 20 : 1 fuel/oil
ratio.
CONTROLS: Craft direction is controlled
by deflection of the thrust from the air-jet
propulsion system by four rudders which are
operated by a tiller in the cockpit. A foot

pedal controls the raising and lowering of the braking/reverse thrust bucket.

HULL: Construction is primarily of 4 mm exterior grade ply skinning with spruce frame members. Buoyancy compartments are provided fore and aft. Fan intakes are in glass fibre and the reverse/braking bucket is constructed in aluminium. A 9 in (228·6 mm) deep segmented skirt in 4 oz (124 gr) neoprene-coated nylon is attached to the hull periphery.

ACCOMMODATION: Side-by-side seating is provided for two on a bench type seat with foam rubber cushions. A small fire extinguisher is carried in the cockpit.

SYSTEMS: ELECTRICAL: 6V battery, charged by an alternator on the propulsion engine via a rectifier for starting.

DIMENSIONS, EXTERNAL:
Length overall, power off
　　　　　　　　　　13 ft 0 in (3·96 m)
Length overall, skirt inflated
　　　　　　　　　　13 ft 0 in (3·96 m)
Beam overall, power off　7 ft 0 in (2·13 m)
Beam overall, skirt inflated
　　　　　　　　　　7 ft 10 in (2·38 m)
Height overall, power off　3 ft 4 in (1·01 m)
Height overall, skirt inflated
　　　　　　　　　　4 ft 0 in (1·21 m)

DIMENSIONS, INTERNAL:
Cabin
　　4 ft × 4 ft × 1 ft 9 in
　　　　　　(1·21 m × 1·21 × 0·533 m)

WEIGHTS:
Normal empty weight　　310 lb (140·60 kg)
Normal all up weight　　470 lb (213·17 kg)
Normal gross weight　　630 lb (285·75 kg)
Normal payload　　　　320 lb (145·14 kg)
Max payload　　　　　680 lb (308·42 kg)

PERFORMANCE:
Max cruising speed over land and water
　　　　　　　　　　40 mph (63·74 km/h)
Endurance　　　　　　　　　2 hours
Max survival sea state 1 ft waves (304 mm)
Max gradient, static conditions　　1 in 8
Vertical obstacle clearance　8 in (203 mm)

PLANS:
Plans available, price £10.00 Cash with order.

J-5

This new four-seat recreational craft, a derivative of the J-4, is under development. The new design may be made available either in plan or kit form.

At the time of going to press, the craft was partially dismantled and was being re-engined with a 1200 cc VW engine. The two centrifugal impellers were being replaced with three multiwing axial fans for easier construction.

LIFT AND PROPULSION: Motive power for the integrated lift/propulsion system is

Bow on view of the new Gooch J-5 showing the bow thrust ports and the 3 ft (0·91 m) wide sidewings which hinge upwards to reduce the overall beam for transport

One application forseen for the J-5 is that of beach rescue craft. The cockpit, which can be enclosed by a plexiglas canopy, is large enough to accommodate a standard stretcher

provided by a single 1200 cc VW engine. Power is transmitted via a chain drive to two pairs of 1 ft 11 in (0·58 m) diameter, double-entry centrifugal fans, mounted on a common shaft, with each pair located in a transverse duct aft of the cockpit. Air is drawn from both sides of each fan housing and expelled forward through the side bodies to pressurise the cushion, and aft through rectangular ducts for propulsion. Cushion pressure is about 10 lb/sq ft. Air can also be ejected through thrust ports forward for braking and manoeuvring at low speeds. Two pedal-operated, aluminium braking/reverse buckets are fitted above each air-jet duct. Total fuel capacity is 10 gallons (45·56 l) carried in tanks under the rear passenger seats on C/P.

CONTROLS: Heading is controlled by differential thrust and by twin sets of rudders operating in the air-jets.

ACCOMMODATION: Seats are provided for an operator and three passengers. The cockpit, which can be open or closed, is sufficiently large to accommodate a standard hospital stretcher, should craft of this type be employed for beach rescue.

HULL: Wooden construction, similar to that employed for J-4. Structure consists primarily of 1 in square spruce frame members

glued and screwed to 4 mm marine ply sheet. Hull base is in 6 mm ply sheet. Buoyancy compartments are provided fore and aft. Fan intakes are in glassfibre and the braking buckets are in aluminium.

SKIRT: Loop-and-segment type in 4 oz Briflon. The skirt is attached to the outer edges of the two 3 ft (0·91 m) wide ply sidewings which run the full length of the hull structure and hinge upwards to reduce the overall beam for transport.

UNDERCARRIAGE: Two retractable, independently sprung trailing wheels can be fitted. In the retracted position they can be employed as landing skids.

DIMENSIONS:
Length overall, skirt inflated
　　　　　　　　　　15 ft 0 in (4·57 m)
Beam overall:
　skirt inflated　　　12 ft 4 in (3·75 m)
　sideways folded　　　6 ft 2 in (1·87 m)
Height overall, skirt inflated
　　　　　　　　　　4 ft 6 in (1·37 m)

WEIGHTS:
Empty weight　　　　410 lb (185·96 kg)

PERFORMANCE:
Maximum speed:
　over water　　　　about 35 knots
　over land　　　　40 mph (64·37 km/h)

CHINA

An ACV research programme is being undertaken by a shipyard in the Shanghai area. Two small amphibious ACVs are currently employed as test craft, it is reported, one imported from Australia, the other built at the yard. In 1976, the Chinese government announced that its shipyards were now in a position to design and build advanced marine vehicles, including air cushion vehicles and hydrofoils.

FRANCE

BERTIN & CIE
OFFICE AND WORKS:
　BP No. 3, 78370 Plaisir, France
TELEPHONE:
　462.25.00

TELEX: Aviatom 692471 F
DIRECTORS:
　Fernand Chanrion, President, Director General
　Michel Perineau, Director General

Georges Mordchelles-Regnier, Director General

Société Bertin & Cie has been engaged in developing the Bertin principle of separately fed multiple plenum chambers surrounded by flexible skirts since 1956. A research and design organisation, the company employs a staff of more than 500, mainly scientists and design engineers who are involved in many areas of industrial research, including air cushion techniques and applications.

Société de l'Aérotrain is responsible for the construction and development of Bertin tracked air cushion vehicles (Aérotrain) and the SEDAM is responsible for developing the Naviplane and Terraplane vehicles. Designs based upon the Bertin technique are described under the entries for these two companies in this volume.

The Bertin principle for air cushions has also led to numerous applications in the area of industrial handling and aeronautics. These applications, developed by Bertin, are described in the sections devoted to Air Cushion Applicators, Conveyors and Pallets; and Air Cushion Landing Systems.

The company's designers are also undertaking studies in the field of long-range, transocean marine vehicles combining the features of freightplanes and wing-in-ground-effect machines. Preliminary details of the Bertin Cygn concept are given below:

CYGNE PROJECT

Studies conducted by Bertin designers for a number of years have led to the design of a new form of low-flying, transoceanic freighter which will combine the speed of a freight plane with the cargo space and low operating costs of a conventional ship.

The project involves two machines, Cygne 10 and Cygne 14, of 1,000 and 1,400 tonnes all-up weight, and gross payloads of 550 tonnes and 867 tonnes, respectively. They will be capable of operating at any height from zero level up to 10,000 ft at a speed of 200 knots. Much of their journey would be completed while operating in ground effect. They would complete Atlantic crossings in about 20 hours.

Landing or alighting on water becomes economically feasible with this type of machine, and since refuelling in mid-route is possible, they could totally revise the economics of airfreighting by reversing the payload/fuel ratio. Thus freight aircraft, in the opinion of the Bertin design team, would no longer be flying tankers but would become freighters in the full sense of the word, with payload rather than fuel becoming preponderant.

One of the limits on the tonnage increase for conventional aircraft is caused by the limitations of the wheeled undercarriage. The Bertin designs would overcome this by

Above: The Bertin Cygne 14, a project for a combined aircraft, wing-in-ground-effect freight plane with an all-up weight of 1,400 tonnes. Cruising speed would be 200 knots and the payload 867 tonnes. *Below:* Based on an alternative configuration, the Cygne 10 is a flying-wing with an all-up weight of 1,000 tonnes. Due to the limited output of today's gas-turbines, multiple engines will be installed in the manner of the pre-war Do.X

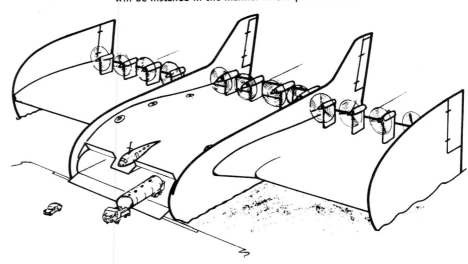

the use of an air-cushion landing system, which would have the additional advantage of permitting these machines to operate from land or water. The Bertin philosophy has been to build the aircraft around the idea of a giant truck, moderate in speed, but still ten times faster than a ship. For this reason, and also because of the relatively limited output of the turbojets at the present time, it seemed essential to return to propellers.

Each craft will have either eight or twelve propeller turbines, some mounted forward above the mainplane and the remainder above an aerofoil-shaped hull.

Bertin compares the use of multiple engines with the formula employed by many large seaplanes and flying boats in the late 'twenties and early 'thirties, particularly the Dornier Do. X, which several times, carried remarkably high payloads over long ranges while flying in its ground cushion.

CLUB FRANCAIS DES AEROGLISSEURS

HEAD OFFICE AND WORKS:
85 Rue Republique, 92150 Suresnes, France
WORKS:
41 and 43 Rue Aristid Briande, 95130 Meung sur Loire, France
OFFICERS:
Jacques Beaudequin, Director
Gabriel Vernier, Chief Designer

M. Jacques Beaudequin, President of the Club Francais des Aeroglisseurs has designed a number of successful lightweight amphibious ACVs, including the Moise III and the Skimmercraft, described in the 1971-72 edition.

His latest design is the Motoglisseur V Beach, preliminary details of which are given below.

MOTOGLISSEUR V BEACH

Derived from the earlier Skimmercraft, the V Beach is a lightweight amphibious two-seater with an inflatable catamaran hull.

LIFT AND PROPULSION: Cushion lift is supplied by a 22 hp 425 cc Citroen air-cooled 4-stroke driving a 24·4 in (620 mm) Multiwing fan.

Propulsive thrust is provided by an adapted Citroen AMI 8 602 cc 4-stroke driving a 4 ft 7¼ in (1·40 m) diameter four-bladed Merville

propeller via a reduction and reverse gearbox.

CONTROLS: Craft direction is controlled by twin aerodynamic rudders aft and operated by a steering wheel. Elevators operating in the propeller slipstream provide trim.

HULL: Basic structural member is the central load carrying deck on which the lift and propulsion units are mounted. The inflatable hull is of catamaran configuration and features flexible bow and stern skirts.

The two inflatable hulls are in polyester coated with neoprene and hypalon.

ACCOMMODATION: Open cockpit for three side-by-side with individual seats.

DIMENSIONS:

Length overall	21 ft 0 in (6·40 m)
Beam overall	9 ft 4¼ in (2·85 m)
Height	5 ft 11 in (1·80 m)

WEIGHTS:

Loaded weight	926 lb (420 kg)
Payload	529 lb (240 kg)

PERFORMANCE:

Max speed	62 mph (100 km/h)
Range	124 miles (200 km)
Turning radius	
	82 ft at 37 mph (25 m at 60 km/h)

Club Francais des Aeroglisseurs is to build this new amphibious two-seater in series. The production model will be powered by two Citroen engines and have a top speed of 62 mph (100 km/h)

GEORGES HENNEBUTTE
Societe d'Exploitation et de Development des Brevets Georges Hennebutte

HEAD OFFICE:
43 Avenue Foch, 64 Biarritz

WORKS:
23 Impasse Labordotte, 64 Biarritz

TELEPHONE:
24.22.40

SENIOR DIRECTOR:
M. Ellia

CHIEF EXECUTIVE.
G. Hennebutte

Ets G. Hennebutte was founded in 1955 to design and build inflatable dinghies. Its Espadon series of sports craft is used extensively by French lifeguard patrols and the French Navy.

The Espadon 422 is the only inflatable craft to have crossed the Etal Barrier.

Development of the Espadon to meet a range of special requirements led to the construction of a number of experimental craft, including one equipped with foils, one with hydroskis and a third with an inflatable parasol delta wing for aerodynamic lift.

The success of the latter has resulted in a series of experimental craft, the latest of which is the Hennebutte 255. a preliminary description of which is given below.

HENNEBUTTE PROTOTYPE 255

This is one of a series of lightweight ACVs based on the range of inflatable craft built by Est. Georges Hennebutte. The company's principal objective is the development of a small, high-speed marine craft for offshore and inter-island travel, able to match the average family car in price and cruising speed.

Features of the latest design are seen in the accompanying photographs.

LIFT AND PROPULSION: At cruising speed and above, aerodynamic lift is provided by a flexible parasol sailwing. The low-speed lift system is powered by a Salle 200 engine. Thrust is supplied by a Fokker WSG 85 fan-thrust pod, combining a 50 hp Wankel rotary engine with a ducted fan.

CONTROLS: Craft heading is controlled by a combined aerodynamic and water rudder aft. Pitch and roll trim is provided by movement of the sailwing.

HULL: Catamaran type hull, with rigid central hull frame and inflatable, nylon-coated neoprene outer sections.

Above: Hennebutte 255 prototype undergoing trials in May 1976. Thrust is supplied by a 50 hp Fokker WSG 85 fan thrust pod, which combines a Wankel rotary engine with a ducted fan. *Below:* Hennebutte 255 with its parasol sailwing folded. The catamaran hull is based on one of the company's range of inflatable sports and rescue craft

ACCOMMODATION: Open cockpit for driver and three passengers.

DIMENSIONS:

Length overall	15 ft 0 in (4·57 m)
Beam overall	9 ft 6 in (2·89 m)
Draft Afloat	8 in (228 mm)

WEIGHT:

Normal empty weight	331 lb (150 kg)

PERFORMANCE:

Max speed over calm water, max power	74 mph (120 km/h)
Max speed over calm water, max continuous power	55 mph (90 km/h)
Cruising speed, calm water	31 mph (50 km/h)

Z. O. ORLEY

ADDRESS:
21 Rue Mademoiselle, 75 Paris 15ème
TELEPHONE:
828-2949
350-9313

Mr Z. O. Orley and Mr Ivan Labat have designed a range of lightweight recreational craft employing the glider-craft air cushion system invented by Mr Orley. The object of the system is to reduce the loss of cushion air by fully skirted vehicles when crossing uneven surfaces.

Beneath the hard structure of the glider craft is an air cushion chamber in rubberised fabric, the base of which is divided into a number of small cell compartments.

Each cell is equipped at the lower end with a perforated shutter.

A short surface sensor protruding beneath each shutter is designed to open up, to deliver cushion air fully, whenever the cell encounters an obstacle rising above the general plane of the reaction surface, and reduce cushion air delivery when crossing a hollow.

A design study is being undertaken for a small commercial craft for operations in South America to carry 12 passengers and freight.

Mr Orley and his partner will build to order commercial and military prototypes employing his system for use over arctic and tropical terrain. Illustrations of a dynamic model incorporating the glider-craft air cushion system appears in JSS 1973-74 and earlier editions.

ESCAPADE

Recently Mr Orley and Mr Labat, who was a member of the N 500 design team, have projected a 62 mph (100 km/h) two-seater —the Escapade.

A feature of the design is the combination of a petrol engine for thrust and a hydraulic drive for the lift fan. This arrangement allows a continuous sharing of the power output between the lift and propulsion systems.

Aircraft-style seating and furnishing is provided for the driver and passenger.

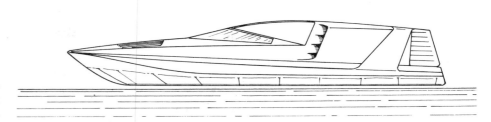

Inboard and outboard profiles of the two-seat Orley Escapade

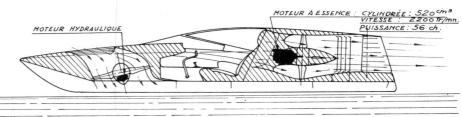

A projected 4-5 seat amphibious ACV with retractable wheels and water rudder

DIMENSIONS:

Height overall	18 ft 0 in (5·50 m)
Hull beam	8 ft 10¼ in (2·70 m)
Folded width for transport	6 ft 2¾ in (1·90 m)
Height overall, on cushion	3 ft 9¼ in (1·15 m)

WEIGHTS:

Craft weight, with fuel	529 lb (240 kg)
Loaded weight, for operation on air cushion	860 lb (390 kg)
Loaded weight for operation as hydroplane	926 lb (420 kg)

PERFORMANCE:

Max speed, calm water	55 mph (90 km/h)
over land	62 mph (100 km/h)
Cruising speed over calm water	43·5 mph (70 km/h)
Max gradient static conditions	15%
Vertical obstacle clearance	1 ft 0 in (0·30 m)

SEDAM
SOCIETE D'ETUDES ET DE DEVELOPPEMENT DES AEROGLISSEURS MARINS, TERRESTRES ET AMPHIBIES

HEAD OFFICE:
80 Avenue de la Grande Armée, 75 Paris 17eme
TELEPHONE:
380-17-69
TELEX:
290124 Sedam Paris
OFFICERS:
Bernard Guillain, President Director General
Benjamin Salmon, Director General
Paul Guienne, Director Technique
Admiral J. R. Evenou, Conseil de Direction
P. Naudin, Secretary General
R. Anger, Works Director
A. de Dampierre, Sales Director

SEDAM was incorporated on July 9th 1965, to study, develop and test the Naviplane series of amphibious ACVs based on principles conceived by Bertin & Cie. In April 1968, the company was vested with similar responsibilities for the Terraplane

Naviplane N 102C 14 seat ferry or light utility craft, powered by a single 700 hp Astazou XIV gas-turbine. Pitch trim is provided by a variable incidence elevator mounted on the fin

wheeled ACVs based on identical principles. The company holds the exclusive world licence for Bertin patents involving both the Naviplane and Terraplane series.

In 1965, the 5-ton Naviplane BC 8 was completed, after which SEDAM built several small research craft, including the N 101, a quarter-scale manned research model of the 30 ton 90-passenger N 300. Two N 300s were completed in the winter of 1967/68 and operated along the Cote d'Azur up to the summer of 1971. One has since been operated by the Department of Gironde as a passenger/car ferry across the Gironde estuary and is available for charter operation.

Following its reorganisation in late 1972, the company has been concentrating on three main objectives: the final design, construction and marketing of the 240t N 500 Naviplane series: incorporation of improvements on the N 300; and the introduction of a series of air cushion barges. Details of the latter are to be found in this edition in the section devoted to ACV Trailers and Heavy Lift Systems.

Two firm orders have been received for the N 500 from SNCF, who will operate the first two craft across the English Channel on the route Boulogne-Dover. The craft, which are being assembled in a new plant at Pauillac, on the Gironde estuary near Bordeaux, are due to enter service in July 1977. SEDAM is responsible for all design studies (lift, stability, manoeuvrability etc) and for the trials. It will also undertake the assembly of the craft. Major sub-contracts have been let to Lorient Dockyard (main hull structure) and UTA at Le Bourget (tail unit). Options on two more craft are held by Compagnie Générale Transmediterranée.

The aim of the new N 300 programme is to design a production model which will incorporate various improvements felt necessary in the light of the operations conducted by the two prototypes since 1969. Modification will be introduced in the interests of both economy and ease of production.

A completely new Terraplane, based on the T3S, was completed in 1973. A combined ACV and wheeled vehicle, it is designed for use in under-developed territory, regardless of season or state of the soil. The primary market is French-speaking Black Africa.

In September 1972, Sedam and Fiat SpA. Turin, signed an agreement under which Fiat received exclusive rights for the manufacture in Italy of Naviplane vehicles employing patents evolved by Bertin et Cie and Sedam. Within the agreement is the right to market these craft in Italy, the Soviet Union, Poland, Yugoslavia, Egypt and other countries in the Near East, Africa and South America.

The company is also undertaking feasibility studies for surface effect warships of 4-5,000 tons and more for the French Navy.

In July 1972, in response to an E.E.C. request, Sedam completed a study for a 4-5,000 metric ton mixed-traffic sidewall vessel propelled by hydrojets.

NAVIPLANE N 102C

A 13-14 seat, single engine ACV employing a plenum chamber enclosed by a labyrinth skirt developed from Bertin's patents, the Naviplane 102C is designed for a wide range of civil and military applications, including customs and police patrol, water-taxi, light cargo and ambulance work, military reconnaissance and dual-control training for the commanders of large Naviplanes.

Two prototypes were completed during 1959 and the first N 102C production craft was launched in 1970. In June 1970 the craft was flown to Kinshasa, in the Congo, for trials and demonstrations. Ten N 102s have since been built, including one 'stretched' variant, the Naviplane N 102L, with its length increased from 33 ft 6 in (10·20 m) to 35 ft 9 in (10·90 m). Two are being employed by the Departments of Montpellier and Perpignan, two have been supplied to the French Navy, one has been sold to Fiat, two are being used by Sedam for research, and

Stretched variant of the Sedam N.102—the N.102L

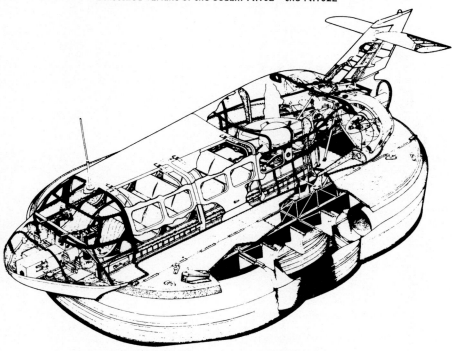
Cutaway of the N102L showing internal arrangements

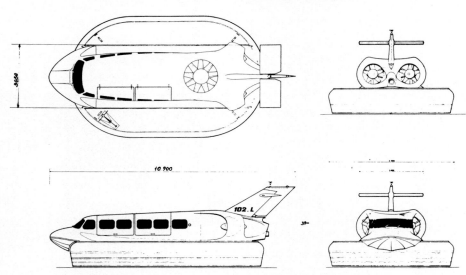
"Stretched" version of the N102—the model L—with revised planform

the remaining craft are for sale.

LIFT AND PROPULSION: A single 700 hp Turboméca Astazou XIV or 565 hp Astazou II shaft turbine powers the integrated lift propulsion system. Mounted at the rear of the cabin, the engine drives a 5 ft 3 in (1·60 m) variable-pitch axial lift fan and two five-bladed variable and reversible pitch shrouded propellers for propulsion.

CONTROL: Directional control at cruising speed and above is maintained by an aero-

dynamic rudder hinged to the rear of the tail fin and differential pitch of the two propellers. At low speeds, steering is assisted by pneumatically-operated side thrust ports. Pitch trim at cruising speed is controlled by a manually operated variable-incidence elevator mounted on the fin.

HULL: The basic hull structure comprises a doughnut-shaped inflated buoyancy chamber in neoprene nylon fabric, surrounding a corrosion resistant light alloy sandwich platform. The buoyancy chamber is divided into twelve watertight compartments for safety. Reserve buoyancy is in excess of 200%. The main components of the super-structure—the shaped bow, cockpit, passenger/freight cabin, engine housing, fan and propeller ducts—are in moulded glass reinforced plastics. The sidewings can be removed to facilitate transport by road, rail or air.

The cabin seats a crew of either one or two and either thirteen or twelve passengers. There are two bucket seats forward and three bench-type seats behind accommodating three or four passengers each, according to traffic requirements. Access is through two wide gull-wing doors. The central section of the cabin superstructure can be quickly removed to provide a freight deck for pallets, containers or military equipment.

OVERLAND USE: Provision is made on the underside of the main hull structure for the attachment of a three-legged, retractable undercarriage. The front wheel is steered hydraulically to provide precise directional control. Lowering of the under-carriage facilitates repairs to the hull under-side and skirt maintenance. The arrange-ment also allows an extra 1 ton payload to be carried over land. Speed over rela-tively smooth ground, with undercarriage lowered, is close to 40 mph (64·37 km/h).

DIMENSIONS, EXTERNAL (N 102C):

Length overall	33 ft 5⅞ in (10·20 m)
Beam	25 ft 3⅛ in (7·70 m)
Height overall on landing pads	
	13 ft 1½ in (4·00 m)
Skirt depth	2 ft 7½ in (0·80 m)

DIMENSIONS, INTERNAL:

Cabin length	11 ft 9¾ in (3·60 m)
Max width	7 ft 3 in (2·20 m)

Size of gull-wing doors, one each side:

Height	2 ft 9½ in (0·85 m)
Width	6 ft 2 in (1·90 m)

WEIGHTS:

Empty weight	6,600 lb (3,200 kg)
Normal gross weight	8,800 lb (4,200 kg)
Normal payload	2,200 lb (1,000 kg)
Fuel load	1,100 lb (600 l)

Normal load over water

2-2,400 lb (900-1,100 kg)

over land   4,200-4,600 lb (1,900-2,100 kg)

PERFORMANCE: (Normal all-up weight):

Max speed, max power, over calm water
54 knots

Max speed, max continuous power 55 knots

Cruising speed (IAS) in 2 ft 6 in (0·75 m)
waves   40-45 knots

Endurance (max continuous power)

3-4 hours

Max gradient	12-18%
Acceptable wave height	3 ft (1 m)

DIMENSIONS, EXTERNAL (N 102L):

Length overall	35 ft 9 in (10·90 m)
Beam overall, on cushion	19ft 4¼ in (5·90m)

Beam overall, hardstructure

10 ft 0 in (3·05 m)

Height overall, on cushion

12 ft 9½ in (3·90 m)

NAVIPLANE N 300

A 27-ton multi-purpose transport for amphibious operation, the N 300 was the first full-scale vehicle in the Naviplane series designed for commercial use.

The first two N 300s were built at Biarritz at the Breguet factory and started tethered hovering and preliminary handling trials in December 1967. Afterwards they were transported by sea to the Sedam test centre at l'Etang de Berre. In September 1968

N 300 Naviplane, multi-purpose hoverferries

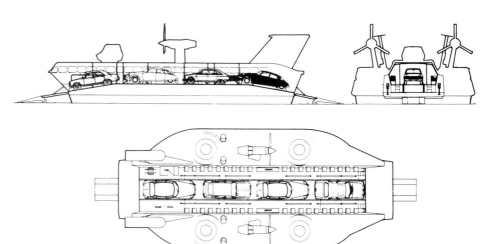

Mixed ferry version of the N 300, accommodating thirty-eight passengers and four cars

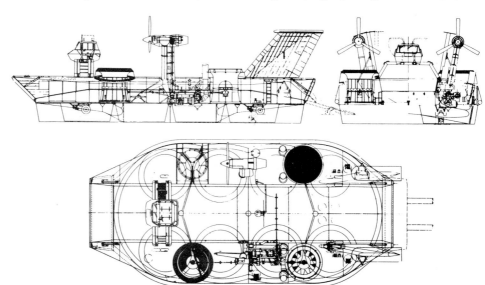

Internal arrangements of the N 300. The drawings show the craft in open deck freighter con-figuration. The all-passenger version seats 90 in a lightweight cabin structure which is attached to the freight deck

N 300-01 and -02 went to Nice for a series of experimental services and tests conducted by the French armed services.

During the summer of 1970 the two craft operated a scheduled passenger service along the Cote d'Azur. One N 300 was later acquired by the Gironde Department for the operation of a passenger/car ferry service across the Gironde estuary between Blaye and Lamarque. The craft, which was operated by the Bordeaux Port Authority carried up to four cars and thirty-five passen-gers per crossing. It operated thirty crossings per day, seven days a week.

The passenger version seats 90 in a light-weight cabin structure above the open deck. Possible military uses of the N 300 include coastal patrol, salvage, rescue, landing craft, assault craft and logistic supply vehicle.

A production model is under development one variant of which has its wheelhouse built onto the cabin superstructure forward instead of being located on a bridge structure spanning the foredeck.

LIFT AND PROPULSION: Motive power is provided by two Turboméca Turmo IIIN3 gas turbines located in separate engine rooms, port and starboard and drawing filtered air from plenum compartments behind the forward fan ducts. Each engine is coupled via a main gearbox located directly beneath each propeller pylon to a 3-bladed Ratier-Figeac 11 ft 10 in (3·60 m) diameter, variable and reversible pitch propeller and via a secondary gearbox to a two 11-blade 6 ft 3 in (1·90 m) diameter axial lift fans. The main gearboxes are cross-connected by a shaft so that in the event of one engine failing or malfunctioning the four fans and two propellers can all be driven by the remaining engine. The fans deliver air to eight individual Bertin skirts, each 6 ft 7 in (2 m) deep and with a hemline diameter of 10 ft 2 in (3·09 m). These are in turn surrounded by a single wrap-round skirt.

CONTROLS: The wheelhouse, which seats a captain and navigator, is located above a bridge spanning the foredeck to provide a 360° view. The main driving controls and the instrumentation are positioned in front of the port seat.

The wheel of a control column varies the pitch of the two propellers differentially and fore and aft movement of the column alters pitch collectively.

HULL: The hull is a raft-like structure built in marine corrosion resistant aluminium alloys. Main buoyancy compartments are beneath the freight deck. Fans and machinery are installed in separate structures on either side of the freight/passenger deck, port and starboard.

ACCOMMODATION: Aircraft-type seats are provided for 100-120 passengers. Baggage areas are provided in the centre of the passenger saloon, port and starboard, and at the rear of the saloon where there is also a dinghy stowage area. Access to the passenger compartment is by steps built into the bow and stern ramp/doors.

DIMENSIONS:

Length overall	78 ft 9 in (24 m)
Beam	34 ft 5 in (10·5 m)
Height overall	24 ft 7 in (7·5 m)
Skirt depth	6 ft 7 in (2·0 m)
Cabin floor area	861 sq ft (80 m²)
Cushion area	1,722 sq ft (160 m²)

WEIGHTS:

Basic weight	14 tons
Passenger version	100-120 passengers
Freight version	13 ton
Normal all-up weight	27 ton

PERFORMANCE:

Max speed	57/62 knots
Cruising speed	44/50 knots
Endurance	3 hours

NAVIPLANE N 500

Two firm orders have been placed for the N 500, a 240-tonne, mixed-traffic hoverfrery with a payload capacity of 85 tonnes and a maximum speed of 70 knots (130 km/h) in calm conditions. The first two craft will be built for SNCF (French National Railways) which will operate them under the name Seaspeed on a service across the English Channel, between Boulogne and Dover, starting in 1977.

Above: First N 500 under assembly at the Sedam works at Pauillac, Bordeaux on July 1st, 1976. At this stage, the lift engines APU and fin and stabiliser had been fitted
Below: View of the N 500 showing the aperture for the rear entry doors for vehicles and the main longitudinal girder which forms the coach passage.   Compartments for the lift engines and fans can be seen forward, one on each side of the coach passage

The French government is contributing half the development and production costs of the first two craft, a total of Fr. 74 million.

An option on two further craft is held by Compagnie Générale Transmediterranée, which plans to operate a service between Nice and Corsica. Interest in the N 500 is also being shown by Hoverlloyd.

Assembly of the first N 500 started at Pauillac, near Bordeaux, on the Gironde estuary, at the end of 1975. The assembly shop, currently nearing completion, is of sufficient size to permit the construction of up to four craft a year. Trials will also be conducted from the base at Pauillac. The first craft is due to be completed at the end of 1976 and will be delivered to SNCF Seaspeed in July 1977.

LIFT AND PROPULSION: Motive power is supplied by five Avco Lycoming TF 40 marinised gas-turbines, two for lift and three for propulsion. Max output of the TF 40 is 3,000 hp; max intermittent output is 3,400 hp and max continuous is 3,200 hp Specific fuel consumption is 247 gal/hr. Each lift engine drives via a reduction system and bevel gear a 13 ft 1½ in (4 m) diameter, 13-bladed, axial-flow fan of laminate construction. The fans, built by Ratier-Forest, are based on experience gained with the N 300 series, and the blades can be adjusted, when stopped, to suit flight conditions. Revolution speed is 900 rpm and the tip speed is limited to 200 m/s to avoid excessive noise. Each fan weighs 1,764 lbs (800 kg) and their rated input power is 2,150 kW.

Fan air intakes are located immediately aft of the wheelhouse, one each side of the longitudinal centreline. Cushion air is drawn into two wells reaching down through the passenger and car decks, into a plenum beneath the latter, from which it is fed to the multiple skirts. The flow of air to each group of skirts is controlled by air valves.

Both fans deliver air to a common plenum and in the event of either having to be shut

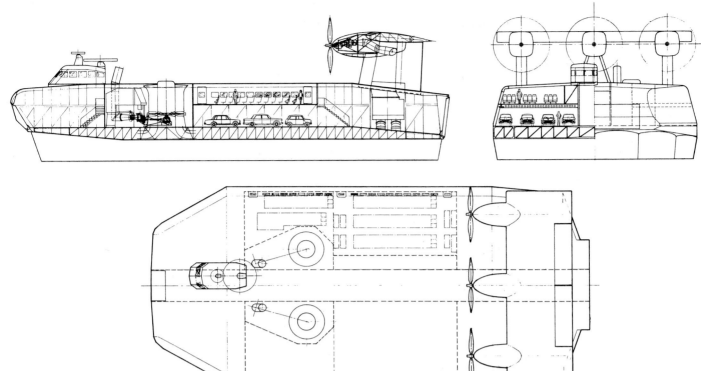

General arrangement of the N 500 powered by five 3,200 hp Avco Lycoming TF 40 marinised gas-turbines, two for lift and three for propulsion

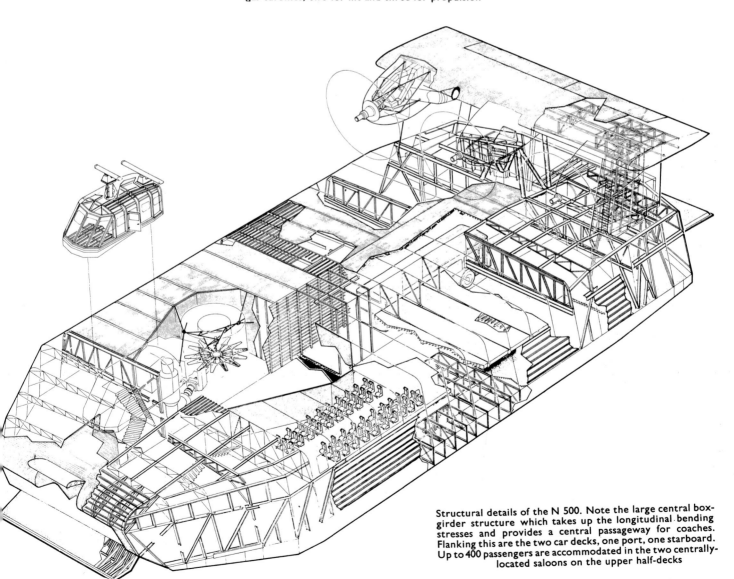

Structural details of the N 500. Note the large central box-girder structure which takes up the longitudinal bending stresses and provides a central passageway for coaches. Flanking this are the two car decks, one port, one starboard. Up to 400 passengers are accommodated in the two centrally-located saloons on the upper half-decks

down, the remaining unit has sufficient capacity to enable the craft to take-off and operate in waves up to 8 ft 3 in (2·5 m) high.

Lift and propulsion systems are totally independent of each other in order to reduce gearing to a minimum. The three propulsion engines, each contained in a separate nacelle, are mounted on a horizontal stabiliser aft, where each TF40 drives a 20 ft 8 in (6·3 m) diameter, 4-bladed variable- and reversible-pitch propeller at a maximum rotation speed of 640 rpm. Three reduction units reduce the nominal engine speed of 15,400 rpm to 622 rpm at the propeller. The second of these units is equipped with a brake to stop propeller rotation in case of engine failure. The propellers, designed and built by Hawker-Siddeley Dynamics, are similar to those used on the BH.7. The blades consist of a duralumin spar, forged and machine-finished, and covered with a glass fibre and epoxy resin shell to NACA Series 16 and 64 modified profiles. Tractive power is 15 t at zero speed and 11·5 t at 36 m/s.

The horizontal stabiliser is designed to counteract pitching during take-off and create sufficient lift to compensate the tail-load moment induced by the aerodynamic forces acting on the craft.

The craft can take-off and operate with one propulsion unit out of action in waves 8 ft 3 in (2·5 m) high.

CONTROLS: Craft directional control is provided by pedal-operated aerodynamic rudders and differential propeller pitch. In the event of either outboard propeller being stopped, yawing moment is compensated by the use of rudders. Pitch control is provided by elevators on the horizontal

stabiliser, and fuel is transferred between forward and aft tanks to adjust fore and aft static trim.

HULL: Modular structure built in simple light alloy units. The main platform structure is made up of welded longitudinal and transverse girder boxes which also form buoyancy chambers. The main longitudinal box girder is the central lane for coaches and heavy vehicles. Beneath each car deck is a structure made up by welded trellis-type lateral beams. The main hull platform supports the box-like coach compartment on the longitudinal centreline and the two car decks, one each side of the coach deck. On land, off-cushion, the craft rests on small cylindrical inflated pads. Lifting jacks are employed to raise the craft off the ground for inspection and servicing. Both the forward and aft load door/ramps can accommodate three vehicles abreast for loading and off-loading.

SKIRTS: Arrangement based on that adopted for the N 300. Planform of the N 500's hull is a rectangle, elongated at the bow by a semicircle. The skirt system comprises 48 identical skirts, each of 13 ft 1½ in (4 m) diameter, arranged around the outer perimeter of the hull base in a continuous double ring. The skirts are in Tergal (Terylene) covered with synthetic rubber. Air is fed to the skirts in groups, giving a labyrinth effect. It is also fed into the central cushion area direct.

ACCOMMODATION: In the mixed-traffic version, passengers are accommodated in two saloons on two upper half-decks on either side of the box structure containing the coach passageway. The arrangement is claimed to give passengers greater safety,

since they are on a different level from the vehicles; as well as greater comfort as their location is in the centre of the craft. Since their seats are sited above the spray they will also have a better view. The payload of 85 tonnes would comprise 400 passengers and 45 medium-size cars, or 280 passengers, 10 cars and 5 coaches. The wheelhouse, located above the forward end of the longitudinal coach box, accommodates a crew of three—captain, co-pilot and radio operator/navigator. Access is via a companionway at the base of the starboard lift engine compartment and a vertical ladder from the passenger saloon.

SYSTEMS, ELECTRICAL: Electrical supply is provided by two turbo-alternators, each comprising a Deutz T216 gas-turbine driving an Auxilec 1602 alternator.

NAVIGATION: Two Decca radars, one 10 cm, one 3 cm plus one gyro and one magnetic compass.

DIMENSIONS, EXTERNAL:

Length overall	164 ft 1 in (50 m)
Beam overall	75 ft 1½ in (23 m)
Height overall, on cushion	55 ft 9 in (17 m)
Cushion length	147 ft 8 in (45 m)
Cushion beam	72 ft 2 in (22 m)

DIMENSIONS, INTERNAL:

Cargo deck length, inboard	150 ft 11 in (46 m)
Cargo deck width, inboard	72 ft 2 in (22 m)
Cargo deck area	10,332 ft² (960 m²)

WEIGHTS:

Hull	93 tons
Powerplant	19·5 tons
Equipment	6·75 tons
Empty weight	118·25 tons

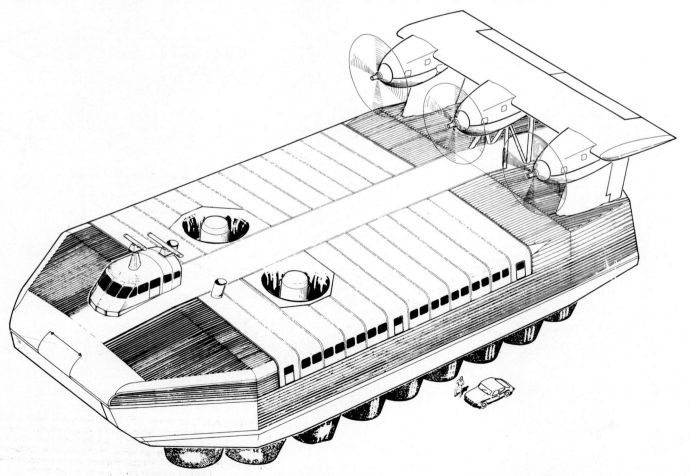

Perspective drawing of the N 500, showing the two fan air intakes, the forward location of the wheelhouse and the three underslung propulsion engine nacelles mounted on the horizontal stabiliser aft. The skirt system comprises 48 identical, individual skirts, each of 13 ft 1½ in (4 m) diameter, arranged around the outer perimeter of the hull base in a continuous double ring

Commercial equipment for 385 passengers	
and 65 cars	15 tons
Crew	0·25 tons
Fuel and oil	20·50 tons
Payload	85 tons
Total gross weight	240 tons

PERFORMANCE:

Max speed, calm water
75 knots, attainable in less than 200 secs.

Cruising speed, 1·50 m waves	58 knots
Cruising speed, 2·50 m waves	48 knots
Endurance over 2·5 m waves	5 hours
Max wave height	13 ft 2 in (4 m)

Normal stopping distance from

70 knots	1,000 m
Emergency	500 m
Vertical acceleration	0·15g

MN.2 RESEARCH CRAFT

While conducting design studies for the N 500, SEDAM made extensive use of data gathered from models. Wind tunnel tests were undertaken at the Eiffel research centre with a 1 : 50 scale model, and a 1 : 20 model was tested at the Carèsnes tank to measure aerodynamic and hydrodynamic resistance.

Two manned, dynamic research craft employed were the MN.1 and the MN.2. The former, a 1 : 9 scale, 19 ft 8 in (6 m) long model was designed for testing the fans and multiple skirt system, while the latter was built for handling and manoeuvrability trials. In addition, a number of tests were conducted with scale model skirts, singly and in groups.

4-5,000 ton SES

A study for a 4,000-5,000 ton surface effect ship for the French Navy is being undertaken by Sedam in conjunction with Société des Ateliers et Chantiers de Bretagne (ACB). The study has been requested by the Centre de Prospective et d'Evaluations (CPE) of the Ministry of Defence.

The configuration selected is known as the AQL, an abbreviation of the French term for sidewall craft—aeroglisseur à quilles latérales.

The studies are being undertaken at the Bassin des Carènes, Paris, with the aid of models equipped with rigid sidewalls integral to the hull structure and flexible seals fore and aft to contain the air cushion.

Several versions of the projected vessel

The SEDAM MN.2 manned, 1:7 dynamic model of the N.500, undergoing tests on the Berre flats. The propellers and fans are driven by piston engines. This particular model has been used chiefly for gathering data on handling and manoeuvrability

Dynamic model of the 4-5,000 ton SES undergoing tank tests at the Bassin des Carenes, Paris

are envisaged. An ASW variant appears to be high on the list of the French Navy's requirements. In ASW configuration, the craft would carry VDS and could also be fitted with auxiliary medium depth sonar enabling it to conduct attacks with its own weapons. In addition it could carry ASW helicopters on its aft deck which could locate

One of the configurations of a 5,000 ton SES for the French Navy being studied by Sedam in conjunction with Societe des Ateliers et Chantiers de Bretagne (ACB). Alternative propulsion systems under consideration include four turbofans, four hydrojets and four semi-submerged propellers

distant targets and conduct attacks on their own.

All versions of the projected vessel would be equipped with defensive armament based on naval automatic guns, surface-to-air missiles and electronic warfare systems.

Long range offensive patrols, the transport of helicopter-borne assault forces and escort destroyer are among the other applications foreseen.

PROPULSION: Various alternative methods of propulsion are being examined, including four hydrojets, four semi-submerged propellers and four turbofans. The power output necessary to operate the vessel is estimated as follows:

Operation hullborne	11,500 CV 84 mW
Operation on air cushion	190,000 CV 140 mW
Power to operate lift fans and generate cushion	30,000 CV 22 mW
Electricity	4,000—22,000 3—16 mW

The specification below applies to the hydrojet-propelled variant.

DIMENSIONS:

Length overall	119·4 m
Beam overall	47 m
Beam across sidewalls	31 m
Width of each sidewall	8 m
Cushion length	100 m
Cushion width	37 m
Cushion height	10 m
Cushion area	3,700 m²

WEIGHTS:

Empty weight	2,900 tons
Fuel	1,500 tons
Weapons and equipment	600 tons
Total gross weight	5,000 tons

PERFORMANCE:

Max speed hullborne	16 knots
Max speed on cushion in force 3 winds, wave height 1-1·5 m	60 knots
Max speed, force 3, wave height 3 m	55 knots

In waves higher than 5 m, the vessel would operate in displacement condition.

TERRAPLANE T3S

The Terraplane T3S is a combined ground effect machine and wheeled vehicle, driven

The Terraplane T3S, combined ground effect machine and wheeled vehicle for off-the-road transport in underdeveloped areas

like a car or truck, but with the essential difference that it can be run at speeds up to 31 mph (50 km/h) over uneven ground, water or liquid mud.

It is designed for use over unprepared land in underdeveloped territories regardless of the season or the state of the soil. A hydraulic system allows selection of weight transference to the road wheels ranging from 20-50% of the total weight of the ground surface and gradient.

On roads the entire weight can be supported by the wheels and the vehicle is then operated in a similar way to the traditional lorry. The air cushion only can be employed when crossing rivers and when manoeuvring the craft in a confined space.

LIFT AND PROPULSION: The front wheels are fitted with heavy duty tyres and are steered by a normal steering wheel from the driver's cab.

Motive power for the lift/propulsion system is provided by an adapted 250 hp Chevrolet V8 petrol engine. This drives an axial fan for lift and a hydrostatic trans-

mission circuit which provides either two- or four-wheel drive. Cushion air is ducted into seven individual neoprene-coated tergal skirts, six of which are surrounded by a lightweight wrap-round skirt. Transmission to the four wheels is via an engine-mounted pump circulating fluid through lines to four hydraulic motors which drive the wheels.

Special paddle vanes which can be attached to the wheels allow travel over water at speeds up to 4·35 mph (7 km/h).

WEIGHTS:

Weight empty	2 tons
Weight loaded	3·6 tons

DIMENSIONS:

Length	20 ft 8 in (6·3 m)
Width	8 ft 2¼ in (2·5 m)

PERFORMANCE:

Speed over flat surfaces	43·5 mph (70 km/h)
Speed over uneven ground	31 mph (50 km/h)
Speed over water	4·35 mph (7 km/h)
Endurance	3 hours
Gradient capability	8-20%
Vertical obstacle clearance	1 ft 4 in (0·40 m)

GERMAN FEDERAL REPUBLIC

Rhein-Flugzeugbau GmbH (RFB)
(Subsidiary of VFW-Fokker GmbH)

HEAD OFFICE AND MAIN WORKS:
   D-4050 Mönchengladbach 1, Flugplatz,
   P.O. Box 408
TELEPHONE:
   (02161) 662031
TELEX:
   08/52506
OTHER WORKS:
   D-5050 Porz-Wahn, Flughafen Köln-Bonn,
   Halle 6;
   and D-2401 Lübeck-Blankensee, Flugplatz
EXECUTIVE DIRECTORS:
   Dipl-Volkswirt Wolfgang Kutscher
   Dipl-Ing Alfred Schneider

Founded in 1956, this company holds 100% of the stock of Sportavia-Pützer.

RFB is engaged in the development and construction of airframe structural components, with particular emphasis on wings and fuselages made entirely of glassfibre-reinforced resins. Research and design activities include studies for the Federal German Ministry of Defence.

Current manufacturing programmes in-

RFB X-113 Am during a flight demonstration over the Wattenmeer

clude series and individual production of aircraft components and assemblies made of light alloy, steel and glassfibre-reinforced resin for aircraft in quantity production, as well as spare parts and ground equipment. The company is also active in the fields of shelter and container construction.

Under contract to the German government, RFB services certain types of military aircraft, and provides target-towing flights and other services with special aircraft.

It operates a factory-certificated service centre for all types of Piper aircraft and the Mitsubishi MU-2 utility transport aircraft. General servicing of other types of all-metal aircraft is undertaken, together with the servicing, maintenance, repair and testing of all kinds of flight instruments, engine instruments and navigation and communications electronics.

In the aircraft propulsion field, RFB has been engaged in the development of specialised applications for ducted propellers, leading to the Fantrainer AWI 2 project. As a variation for civil use, RFB started in 1972 the Fanliner project; the first flight of a prototype took place in December, 1973. In April, 1974 it was announced that RFB and Grumman American Aviation had decided to collaborate in the development of this new two-seat light aircraft, which utilises the ducted-fan propulsion system evolved by RFB.

In the course of the further development of the Fantrainer AWI-2 project, preperation of two demonstrators of this military multi-purpose training aircraft was started by the end of 1974. First flight will be beginning 1977.

Under the scientific direction of the late Dr A. M. Lippisch, the all-plastics X-113 Am Aerofoil Boat has been built and tested. Fight testing of the six-seat Aerofoil Craft X-114 started in the autumn of 1976.

RFB (LIPPISCH) X-113 Am AEROFOIL BOAT

The Aerofoil Boat was conceived in the United States by Dr A. M. Lippisch. The first wing-in-ground-effect machine built to Lippisch designs was the Collins X-112, which was employed by Lippisch to examine the stability problems likely to be encountered in the design of larger machines of this type.

Since 1967 further development of the concept has been undertaken by RFB, with government backing. The single-seat X-113 has been built as a test craft to provide data for the design of larger craft of the same type.

The X-113 Am underwent its first airworthiness test from Lake Constance in October 1970.

During the first series of tests, the craft demonstrated its operating ability on water as well as flight capability at very low altitudes. These tests were followed in the autumn of 1971 by a second series of trials during which performance measurements were taken. A cine camera built into the cockpit recorded instrument readings and a camera built into the lateral stabilisers took pictures of small threads on the upper wing surface for current flow analysis.

The earlier trials on the Bodensee were followed in November/December 1972 by a third series of tests in the North Sea in the Weser estuary area.

Apart from various performance measure-

Underside of the X-113 Am, showing the anhedral reversed delta wing which overcomes the problem of pitch instability during the transition from surface effect to free- flight and back again

Model of the new six-seat RFB X-114 Aerofoil Boat. A 200 hp engine drives a ducted fan designed by Rhein-Flugzeugbau

RFB X-114 six seater during final assembly. Flight trials were due to begin in August 1976

ments, the aim of these trials was to investigate the machines' capabilities in roughish weather conditions. Although the machine was originally designed only for a brief general demonstration on calm water, the intention undertook take-offs and landings in a moderate sea.

Remarkably good sea behaviour was shown from the outset. Taking-offs and

landings in wave heights of about 2 ft 6 in (0·75 m) presented no problem. During the course of these tests, flights were made in the coastal region, and sometimes on the Wattenmeer, in wind forces of up to 25 knots, without any uncontrollable flying tendencies being observed in low-level flight.

The flight performance measurements gave a gliding angle of 1:30, which cannot be greatly improved by enlarging the machine. It is also of interest to note that the relatively thin outer laminate of the GFR wing sandwich, with a thickness of 0.4 mm, stood up to the loads involved in taking off in a roughish sea and also remained watertight throughout the whole period of trials.

Towards the end of the trials, in order to reduce noise and give the airscrew better protection from spray, the machine was converted to pusher propulsion.

The company envisages a range of Aerofoil craft for a variety of civil and military purposes, from single-seat runabouts to cargo transporters with payloads of up to 10 tons. As transports they could be employed on coastal, inter-island and river services. Military variants could be used as assault craft, FPBs and ASW vessels.

Flight tests, including a series performed over rough water in the North Sea near Bremmerhaven, have established that 50% less power is required in ground effect, enabling operations in excess of 50-ton-miles per gallon of fuel at speeds in the 90-180 knot range.

RFB X-114 AEROFOIL BOAT

Evolved from the X-113, this new six-seater has a maximum take-off weight of 2,977 lb (1,350 kg) and is fitted with a retractable wheel undercarriage, enabling it to operate from land or water.

Power is provided by a 200 hp engine driving a specially-designed Rhein-Flugzeugbau ducted fan. Range, with 220 lb (100 kg) of fuel is more than 621 miles (1,000 km). Operational speed is 46-124 mph (75-200 km/h).

The prototype is due to make its first flight in August 1976.

The vehicle is designed to operate over waves up to 1·50 m (4 ft 11 in) in ground effect and can therefore be used without restriction during 80% of the year in the Baltic Sea area and 60% of the year in the North Sea. On days with high seas of more than 1·50 m (4 ft 11 in) takeoff and landing takes place in waters near the coast. Flying is vertually unrestricted, providing due allowance is made for the loss in economy.

Fuel consumption costs, while flying in ground effect, are lower than those for cars. RFB states that its economics cannot be matched by any other form of transport aircraft.

Without any significant new research the construction of a vehicle with a takeoff weight of approximately 18,000 kg is possible. On a vehicle of this size, the ratio of empty weight to takeoff weight is less than 50%

ITALY

FIAT SpA

HEAD OFFICE:
Centro Ricerche Fiat, Strada Torino 50, Orbassano, Torino

TELEPHONE:
011 90 11 401

TELEX:
22289 FIATLABS

OFFICERS:
Prof. Ugo Lucio Businaro

Fiat has been licensed by Sedam, the French ACV company, for the manufacture of Sedam Naviplane vehicles, and has been granted exclusive rights for their sale in Italy, Argentina, Egypt, Yugoslavia, Poland, Turkey, the Soviet Union and other countries.

Fiat's "Centro Ricerche", is currently undertaking a research programme in this field.

JAMAICA

CILMA HOLDINGS LTD

HEAD OFFICE:
10 Glendon Drive, Kingston 10, Jamaica

DIRECTORS:
J. Scarlett, Managing Director
C. Scarlett

Cilma Holdings Limited was formed in February 1976 to investigate the feasibility of hovercraft application in Jamaica. Areas to be investigated include recreational vehicles for the tourist industry, rapid transit ferry services and industrial and military applications.

CILMA V

First hovercraft to be designed and built in Jamaica, Cilma V is being employed as a test vehicle and also to undertake feasibility studies. The data provided will be used in determining the design of future production hovercraft.

LIFT AND PROPULSION: Lift air is provided by a 30 hp, 1,200 cc Volkswagen engine driving a 2 ft 6½ in (0·774 mm) diameter, 45° pitch multi-wing fan fitted directly to the crankshaft. Thrust is supplied by a 1,500 cc 65 hp Volkswagen engine, geared to a 7 ft 6 in (2·28 m) diameter propeller, which has been fabricated from the main rotor of a Sikorsky helicopter. Chord of the propeller is 12 in (304 mm) and pitch 15°. Maximum engine speed is 3,000 rpm.

CONTROLS: Craft heading is controlled by twin aerodynamic rudders hinged to the tubular metal guard aft of the propeller. The control stick is connected to the rudders via a torsion rod running the length of the craft. Fore and aft movement of the control stick operates the throttle of the propulsion engine.

HULL: Wooden frame, with top and bottom skins of ¼ in marine ply separated by stringers and ribs. All spaces within the hull are filled with polyurethane foam, which supplies buoyancy in the event of the marine ply skin being ruptured.

Above and below: The Cilma V three-seater research craft during trials. Thrust is supplied by a 65 hp Volkswagen engine driving a 7 ft 6 in (2.28m) diameter propeller fabricated from the main rotor of a Sikorsky helicopter

SKIRT: Bag type, in neoprene impregnated fabric.

ACCOMMODATION: Seats are provided for a driver and two passengers in an enclosed cabin. Access is via two gullwing doors, one on each side. Lifebelts are stored in the forward compartment. A 1½ hp outboard engine, intended for emergency use, and anchors are stowed behind the seats. A fire-extinguisher is attached to the dashboard and safety belts are provided.

DIMENSIONS:

Length	10 ft 0 in (3·04 m)
Beam	8 ft 0 in (2·43 m)
Height to prop tip, off cushion	9 ft 0 in (2·74 m)
Height to prop tip, cushionborne	10 ft 0 in (3·04 m)

WEIGHTS:

Empty	1,300 lb (589·64 kg)
Loaded	1,800 lb (816·42 kg)

PERFORMANCE:

Maximum speed, calm water	75 mph (120·70 km/h)
Normal cruising speed	50 mph (80·46 km/h)
Vertical obstacle clearance	10 in (254 mm)

JAPAN

AOYAMA GAKUIN UNIVERSITY

LN 360

This combined ground effect machine and wheeled vehicle was developed jointly by the Traffic Engineering Department at Aoyama Gakuin University, under the direction of Eigi Tonokura and the Aerodynamics Laboratory at Nihon University, under the direction of Masahiro Mino.

The test vehicle illustrated, which has front-wheel drive only, represents the first stage in the development of a vehicle with air cushion assist and a four-wheel drive. The objective is to design a plenum-type vehicle capable of operating over both rough tracks and unprepared terrain while carrying heavy loads.

Combined ground effect machine and wheeled vehicle under development at Aoyama Gakuin University, Japan. Designated LN 360, the vehicle has a plenum left system powered by either a 14.5 hp Yamaha YD-2 or 12 hp Daihatsu ZD 305 petrol engine. The front wheels are fitted with agricultural tyres and are steered by normal steered wheel.

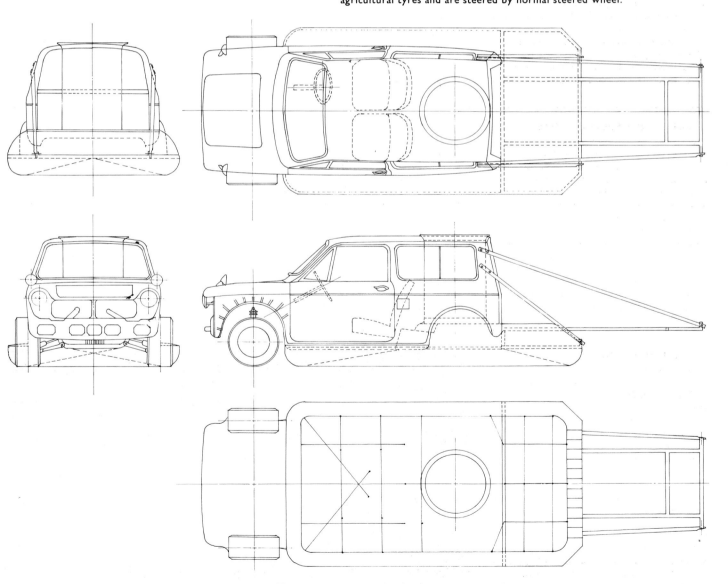

General arrangement of the LN 360 air cushion assist research vehicle developed jointly by Aoyama and Nihon Universities

DIMENSIONS (ACV conversion):

Length	4,950 mm
Width	1,700 mm
Height	1,390 mm

WEIGHTS (With Driver only):

All up weight	580 kg
Cushion area	3·92 m²
Cushion length	8·30 m

Thrust engine:
  Honda N360E 354 cc 31 hp at 8,000 rpm
Lift engine
  (1) Yamaha YD-2 247 cc 14·5 hp at 6,100 rpm 2-cylinder, air-cooled, 2-cycle.
  (2) Daihatsu ZD305 305cc 12 hp at 4,500 rpm 1-cylinder air-cooled, 2-cycle.
Lift fan:
  570 mm dia, 6 bladed axial fan. Weight 2·5 kg
Tire:
  Agricultural type tire AL-3 (19 × 10,000 -10) Ohtsu Tire Co. Ltd.

ASHIKAGA INSTITUTE OF TECHNOLOGY
ADDRESS:
  Mechanical Design Study Group, Institute of Technology, 268 Ohmae cho, Ashikag-ishi, 26326, Japan
DIRECTORS:
  T. Imamura
  E. Sakai
  S. Suzuku

The Mechanical Design Study Group at the Ashikaga Institute of Technology is conducting an ACV research programme in conjunction with the Aerodynamics Section of the Physical Science Laboratory, Nihon University. It has recently taken over the Pastoral 1, constructed at Nihon University in 1970, and introduced various modifications. In its new form the craft is some 35% lighter, and has been redesignated Pastoral 2.

PASTORAL 2
This is a light amphibious single-seater employed to gather data for research and development projects. At the time of going to press the modified craft had completed nearly five hours of tests over sand, grass and mud and had attained a speed of 55 mph (98 km/h).

LIFT AND PROPULSION: A single 8 hp Fuji Heavy Industries 2-cycle single-cylinder

Pastoral single-seat research ACV

air-cooled engine installed immediately aft of the cockpit drives a 5-bladed 1 ft 9¼ in (540 mm) diameter axial-flow fan for lift. Propulsion is supplied by a 36 hp Toyota 2U-B 4-cycle, 2-cylinder engine driving a 3 ft 11¼ in (1,200 mm) diameter two-bladed propeller.

CONTROLS: Twin aerodynamic rudders operated by a wheel in the cockpit control craft heading .

HULL: Moulded glassfibre, with inflatable

fabric-reinforced neoprene sidebody/skirt.
DIMENSIONS:
  Length overall, skirt inflated
                    13 ft 9½ in (4·20 m)
  Beam overall, skirt inflated
                    5 ft 11 in (1·80 m)
  Height, skirt inflated   5 ft 1 in (1·55 m)
WEIGHTS:
  Normal all-up weight   706 lb (320 kg)
PERFORMANCE:
  Max speed over land   56 mph (90 km/h)
     over water   37 mph (60 km/h)

HOVERMARINE PACIFIC LIMITED

In July, 1975, it was announced that Hovermarine Transport Limited, the UK subsidiary of Hovermarine Corporation, is to begin manufacturing and marketing Hovermarine products in Japan and other nearby areas in the Far East through a new company, Hovermarine Pacific Limited.

Hovermarine Pacific is a joint venture by Hovermarine Corporation, Taiyo Fishery Co Limited, Sasebo Heavy Industries Ltd and Fairfield-Maxwell Limited. Taiyo is the world's biggest fish processing company, with an annual sales revenue in excess of US $82 billion and Sasebo is the world's tenth

largest shipbuilder. Fairfield-Maxwell, based in New York, is a private company with extensive interests in shipping.

Initial activities of Hovermarine Pacific will be focussed on the marketing of the Hovermarine HM.2, 60 passenger, 35 knot sidewall hoverferry. The company has received orders for four HM.2 craft to be supplied to the Philippines and at the time of going to press is expecting to achieve the first orders from the Japanese home market. These will be met from Hovermarine's existing facilities in Southampton, England and Titusville, Florida. HM.2 manufacturing facilities are being established at Sasebo, on

the Japanese Island of Kyushu. These manufacturing facilities will initially produce HM.2 Mark IV in 1977 and will plan to expand production to include HM.5 during 1978.

Hovermarine is licenced by Hovercraft Development Limited an agency of the National Research Development Corporation, under various world-wide patents relating to air cushion technology. The licence excludes the Japanese market, and therefore Hovermarine products have not previously been available there. However, recent negotiations have now resulted in Hovermarine Pacific being licenced directly by HDL.

FANBIRD HOVERCRAFT
HEAD OFFICE:
  305 Kyuwa Bissidense, 3-2-1 Mita Minato-Ku, Tokyo, Japan
DIRECTORS:
  Jiichiro Yokota
  Yoshimichi Kushida
CONSULTANTS:
  Masahiro Mino

Fanbird Hovercraft was formed in May 1976. It is currently engaged in the design, development and manufacture of light hovercraft, several of which are available in plan and kit form to Japanese amateur hovercraft constructors.

Design consultant to the company is Mr Masahiro Mino, Senior Director of the Aerodynamics Department at Nihon University, which has been conducting an extensive ACV

Fanbird FB 36 two seat sportscraft

research programme for a number of years.

Abbreviated specifications of five of the company's designs, appear in the accompanying table.

Fanbird FB 30 single seater. Top speed is 31 mph (50 km/h)

Fanbird FB 26 Mini, single-seat hovercraft

Fanbird FB 32 STD single-seat hovercraft

Fanbird FB 32, a 37 mph single-seat sportscraft

	$L \times W$	Seats	Dry Wt.	Payload	Engine (HP)		Max. Speed	Skirt	Form Available
	(m)		(kg)	(kg)	**L	T	(Km/h)		
FB26 MINI	2·1 × 1·6	1	110	43	9-20	*L/P	35	Bag	Plan, parts, kit
FB32 STD	3·2 × 1·8	1	180	110	25-40	*L/P	50	Bag	Plan, parts
FB32 SPORT	3·2 × 1·8	1	205	135	7 + 36		60	Bag	Plan, parts
FB36 SPORT	3·6 × 1·8	2	280	165	7 + 36		55	Bag	Plan, parts
FB30	3·0 × 1·8	1	170	110	34 L/P		50	Bag	Complete craft. In production.

* L/P Integrated lift and propulsion system   ** L—Lift T—Thrust

Mitsui Shipbuilding & Engineering Co. Ltd.

HEAD OFFICE:
6-4, Tsukiji 5-chome, Chuo-ku, Tokyo, Japan
TELEPHONE:
544-3450
TELEX:
J22821, J22924
CABLE:
Mituizosen Tokyo
BOARD OF DIRECTORS:
Isamu Yamashita, President
Sobei Kudo, Senior Managing Director
Masami Fukuyama, Senior Managing Director
Jiro Komatsu, Senior Managing Director
Kyoichi Kato, Managing Director
Shoji Massaki, Managing Director
Kazuo Hamano, Managing Director
Kazuo Nagai, Managing Director
Kazuo Maeda, Managing Director
Ryoji Kawazura, Managing Director
Teiji Asano, Director
Yasuhisa Sawada, Director
Tatsuhiko Ueno, Director
Masahiko Irie, Director
Michio Sugimoto, Director
Takeharu Sueoka, Director
Takeo Takayanagi, Director
Hiromasa Kikuchi, Director
Hideo Matsushima, Director
Masataro Takami, Director
Yoshio Ishitani, Director

Kakuro Tsukamoto, Director
Koji Arase, Director
Saburo Sakamoto, Auditor
Nobuo Yashima, Auditor
Yoshinori Takahashi, Auditor
Tetsujiro Tomita, Deputy Director
Masatomo Ishibashi, Manager, Hovercraft Department

Mitsui's Hovercraft Department was formed on May 1st 1964, following the signing of a licencing agreement in 1963 with Hovercraft Development Ltd and Vickers Ltd, whose ACV interests were later merged with those of British Hovercraft Corporation. In addition, the company was licenced by Westland S.A. in 1967, following the formation of BHC.

The company has built two eleven-seat MV-PP1s, one of which has been supplied to the Thai Customs Department, fourteen MV-PP5s and four MV-PP15s.

The MV-PP5 is now in production at the initial rate of four craft a year. In the summer of 1969 the craft was put into service by Meitetsu Kaijo Kankosen Co, Ltd, between Gamagoori and Toba, Ise Bay.

Since October 1971 three MV-PP5s designated Hobby 1, 2 and 3 have been operated by Oita Hoverferry Co, Ltd on a coastal route linking Oita airport with the cities of Oita and Beppu. The three craft complete a total of sixteen round trips per day to link with flight schedules at the airport.

Other PP5 operators include Japanese

National Railways (two craft), Kagoshima Airport Hovercraft Co Ltd (four craft), Yaeyama Kanko Ferry Co Ltd (one craft) and Nippon Hoverline (two craft). The craft has now been joined in production by the bigger, 155-seat MV-PP15.

The company is also building the prototype MV-PP05, a 5-seater, and has started the design of a 200-ton mixed-traffic ferry.

MV-PP15

Developed from the earlier PP5, the Mitsui MV-PP15 is designed for high speed passenger ferry services on coastal and inland waterways. Accommodation is provided for 155 passengers and a crew of 5.

The prototype was completed in the autumn of 1972.

LIFT AND PROPULSION: Two Avco Lycoming TF25 gas-turbines, each with a maximum continuous output of 2,200 hp at 15°C, drive the integrated lift/propulsion system. Each turbine drives a 7 ft 6 in (2·3 m) diameter, 13-bladed centrifugal fan and a 10 ft 6 in (3·2 m) diameter, 4-bladed variable-pitch propeller. Power is transmitted via a main gearbox, propeller gearbox, fan gearbox and an auxiliary gearbox, all connected by shafting and flexible couplings. Auxiliary systems, such as hydraulic pumps for propeller pitch and lubricating oil pumps, are driven directly by auxiliary gears. Fuel is carried in two flexible tanks located immediately ahead of the lift fan assemblies. Total volume of the fuel tanks is 21·2 ft³ (6 m³).

CONTROLS: Twin aerodynamic rudders in the propeller slipstream and differential propeller pitch provide directional control. The rudders are operated hydraulically by a wheel from the commander's position. In addition, two retractable wheels, located aft, one each side of the main buoyancy tank, can be extended downwards into the water to prevent drift when turning and assist braking at high speeds. On land, the wheels assist manoeuvring and help to reduce skirt wear.

A thrust port air bleed system provides lateral control at slow speeds. Four ports are located beneath the passenger door entrances, port and starboard. A water ballast system is provided for longitudinal and transverse cg adjustment.

HULL: Construction is primarily in corrosion resistant aluminium alloy. The basic structure is the main buoyancy chamber which is divided into watertight sub-divisions for safety, and includes the fore and aft ballast tanks. Overall dimensions of the main buoyancy raft structure are 64 ft 10½ in (19·8 m) long by 23 ft 3½ in (7·1 m) wide by 2 ft 4 in (0·7 m) high. Sidebodies of riveted construction are attached to the sides of the main buoyancy structure. The outer shell of the main buoyancy chamber. machinery deck space, the forward deck and passageways around the cabin interior, are all constructed in honeycomb panels with aluminium cores. The lift fan air intake, inner window frames and hood for the electric motor that rotates the radar scanner are in glassfibre reinforced plastics.

Six rubber-soled landing pads are fitted to the hull base, together with jacking pads. Four lifting eyes for hoisting the craft are provided in the buoyancy chamber.

SKIRT: 5 ft 3 in (1·60 m) deep fingered-bag skirt of Mitsui design, fabricated in nylon-based sheet and coated both sides with synthetic rubber. Two transverse stability bags are included in the skirt system to minimise pitch and roll.

ACCOMMODATION: The passenger cabin, containing 155 seats, is located above the forward part of the main buoyancy chamber. The seats are arranged in three groups and divided by two longitudinal aisles. Seats in the two outer sections are arranged in rows of three abreast, and in the centre section, six abreast.

The four cabin entrance doors, two port, two starboard, are divided horizontally, the top section opening upwards and the lower section opening sideways. A lavatory, toilet unit, pantry and luggage room are provided aft, and a second luggage room is located forward. Lockers are sited close to the forward entrance doors. The control cabin is located above the passenger cabin superstructure and provides a 360 deg. view. It is reached from the passenger saloon by a companion ladder. An emergency exit is provided on the starboard side.

The cabin has a total of four seats, one each for the commander and navigator, plus two spare ones of the flip-up type. The wheel for the air rudders, the two propeller pitch-control levers, instrument panel and switches are arranged on a console ahead of the commander; and the radio, fuel tank gauge,

Mitsui's MV-PP15 50-ton passenger ferry, powered by twin 1,950 hp Avco Lycoming TF25 gas turbines. The craft seats 155 passengers and has a top speed of 65 knots. Seen in these photographs are the raised control cabin, the pylon mounted propellers, lift fan air intakes and the thrust ports beneath the passenger door entrances, port and starboard

water ballast gauge and fire warning system are arranged ahead of the navigator.

On the cabin roof are the radar-scanner, mast for navigation lights, a siren and a searchlight.

SYSTEMS:

ELECTRICAL: 28·5 volts dc. Two 9kw generators are driven directly by the main engines. One 24 volt 175 Ah battery is employed for starting, and another for control. Both are located in the engine room and are charged by the generators when the main engines are operating. A shore-based power source is used for battery charging when the main engines are not in use.

RADIO/NAVIGATION: Equipment includes one 10 in radar, compass, radio and one 20 cm, 250 W searchlight.

AIR CONDITIONING: Two Daikin RKA 1000R-PP15 air coolers, each with a capacity of 20,000 Kcal/hr. Compressors are driven by belts from the auxiliary gearboxes and cooled air is supplied via air-conditioning ducts. Four ceiling ventilators are provided, each equipped with a 40W fan.

SAFETY: Remotely-controlled BCF or BTM fire extinguishers provided in the engine room.

Portable extinguishers provided in the passenger cabin. Inflatable life boats, life jackets, automatic SOS signal transmitter and other equipment carried according to Japanese Ministry of Transport regulations.

DIMENSIONS, EXTERNAL:

Length overall on cushion	86 ft 8 in (26·40 m)
Length overall on landing pads	82 ft 4 in (25·09 m)
Beam overall on cushion	45 ft 7 in (13·90 m)
Beam overall on landing pads	36 ft 5 in (11·10 m)
Height on cushion	25 ft 11 in (7·90 m)
Height on landing pads to tip of propeller blade	22 ft 8 in (6·90 m)
Skirt depth	5 ft 3 in (1·60 m)

DIMENSIONS, INTERNAL:
(Passenger cabin including toilet, pantry and locker rooms):

Length	46 ft 5 in (14·14 m)
Maximum breadth	23 ft 2 in (7·06 m)
Maximum height	6 ft 11 in (2·10 m)
Floor area	1,001 sq ft (93 m²)

WEIGHTS:

All-up weight	about 50 tons

PERFORMANCE:

Max speed	about 65 knots
Cruising speed	about 50 knots
Fuel consumption	
	about 280 gr/shp/hr at 15 deg C
Endurance	about 4 hours

MV-PP5

Mitsui's first large hovercraft, the 50-seat MV-PP5, is a gas-turbine powered craft intended primarily for fast ferry services on Japanese coastal and inland waters.

LIFT AND PROPULSION: All machinery is located aft to reduce to a minimum the noise level in the passenger cabin. A single IHI IM-100 gas-turbine (license-built General Electric LM100) with a maximum continuous rating of 1,050 hp at 19,500 rpm drives the integrated lift/propulsion system. Its output shaft passes first to the main gearbox from which shafts extend sideways and upwards to two 3-bladed Hamilton/Sumitomo variable-pitch propulsion propellers of 8 ft 6 in (2·59 m) diameter. A further shaft runs forward to the fan gearbox from which a drive shaft runs vertically downwards to a 7 ft 7 in (2·27 m) 13-bladed lift fan mounted beneath the air intake immediately aft of the passenger saloon roof. The fan is constructed in aluminium alloy and the disc plate is a 1½ in (40 mm) thick honeycomb structure.

To prevent erosion from water spray the propeller blades are nickel plated.

Fuel is carried in two metal tanks, with a total capacity of 416 gallons (1,900 litres), located immediately ahead of the lift fan assembly.

CONTROLS: Twin aerodynamic rudders in the propeller slipstream and differential thrust from the propellers provide directional control. The rudders are controlled hydraulically from the commander's position. In addition two retractable water rods, located slightly aft of amidships on each side of the main buoyancy tank, can be extended downwards to prevent drift when turning and

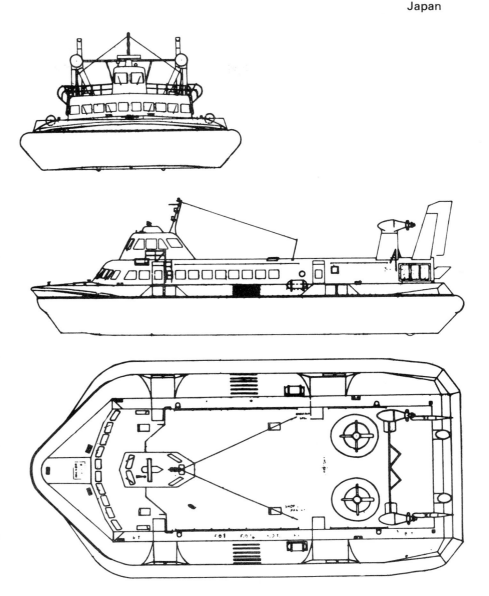

Mitsui MV-PP15 155-seat hoverferry. Twin Avco Lycoming TF25 gas-turbines power the integrated lift propulsion system and give the craft a maximum speed of 60 knots

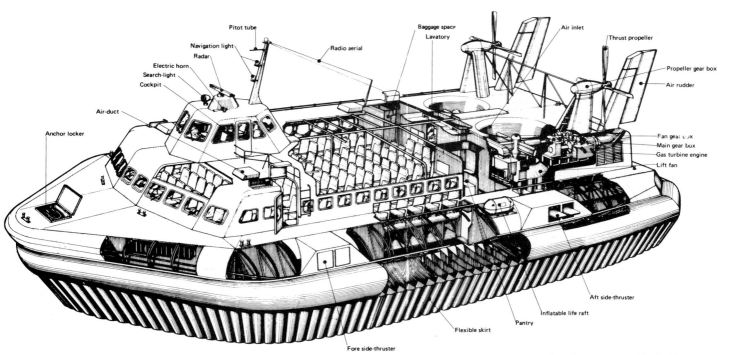

Cutaway of the Mitsui MV-PP15, showing the seating arrangements for the 155 passengers. Seats are arranged in three groups, divided by two longitudinal aisles. In the two outer sections they are arranged in rows of three abreast, and in the centre, six abreast

these also assist braking at high speeds. The water rods are operated hydraulically by foot-pedals. When used in conjunction with the rudders, the turning radius is reduced to about a third of that taken when only air rudders are used.

A thrust-port air bleed system provides lateral control at slow speeds. The thrust ports are actuated by air extracted from the engine compressor and are located beneath the passenger door entrances, port and starboard.

HULL: Construction is primarily of high strength AA502 aluminium alloy suitably protected against the corrosive effects of sea water. The basic structure is the main buoyancy chamber which is divided into eight watertight sub-divisions for safety, and includes fore and aft trimming tanks. Two further side body tanks, each divided into three watertight compartments, are attached to the sides of the main buoyancy chamber. To facilitate shipment the side body. tanks can be removed, reducing the width to 12 ft 4 in (3·75 mm).

The outer shell of the main buoyancy chamber, the machinery deck space, the forward deck and the passage decks around the cabin exterior are all constructed in honeycomb panels with aluminium cores.

The lift fan air intake, radar cover, part of the air conditioning duct, and inside window frames are in glass-fibre reinforced plastic.

Design loads are as required by the Provisional British ACV Safety Regulations.

SKIRT: The flexible skirt was designed by Mitsui in the light of research conducted with aid of the RH-4 (MV-PP1 prototype) It is made of $\frac{1}{32}$ in (0·8 mm) thick chloroprene-coated nylon sheet. A fringe of finger type nozzles is attached to the skirt base at the bow and on both sides. At the stern a D-section bag skirt is used to avoid scooping up water.

Two transverse and one longitudinal stability bags are fitted.

ACCOMMODATION: The passenger cabin is sited above the forward end of the main buoyancy chamber. Seats for the two crew

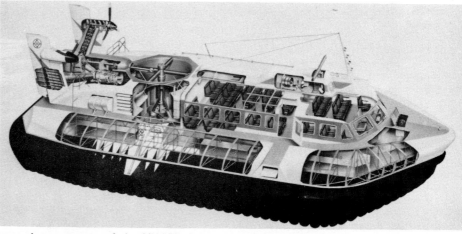

Internal arrangement of the MV-PP5 showing passenger accommodation and the gas-turbine powered lift/propulsion system aft of the cabin

members are on a raised platform at the front of the cabin. All controls, navigation and radio equipment are concentrated around the seats. The windows ahead are of reinforced tempered glass and have electric wipers.

The two cabin entrance doors are divided horizontally, the lower part opening sideways, the top part upwards. The standard seating arrangement is for 42 passengers but ten additional seats can be placed in the centre aisle.

In accordance with Japanese Ministry of Transport regulations a full range of safety equipment is carried, including two inflatable life rafts, 54 life jackets, one automatic, manually activated fire extinguisher for the engine casing and two portable fire extinguishers in the cabin. Other standard equipment includes ship's navigation lights, marine horn, searchlight and mooring equipment, including an anchor. The twelve side windows can be used as emergency exits and are made of acrylic resin.

SYSTEMS:
ELECTRICAL SYSTEM: Two 2 kW, 28·5 volt ac/dc generators driven by belts from the main gearbox. One 24 volt, 100 Ah battery for engine starting.

HYDRAULIC AND PNEUMATIC SYSTEM: A 99·56 lb/in² (7·0 kg/cm²) hydraulic system pressure for water rods and 56·8-99·5 lb/in² (4·7-7 kg/cm²) pneumatic system for thrust port operation.

COMMUNICATION AND NAVIGATION: Equipment includes a radio and radar.

DIMENSIONS, EXTERNAL:

Length overall	52 ft 6 in (16·0 m)
Beam overall	28 ft 2 in (8·6 m)
Height overall on landing pad	
	14 ft 5 in (4·4 m)
Skirt depth	3 ft 11 in (1·2 m)
Draft afloat	11 in (0·2 m)
Cushion area	741 sq ft (88· m²)

DIMENSIONS, INTERNAL:

Cabin:	
Length	23 ft 4 in (7·1 m)
Max width	12 ft 6 in (3·8 m)
Max height	6 ft 3 in (1·9 m)
Floor area	280 sq ft (26 m²)
Doors:	
Two (0·65 m) × (1·4 m), one each side of cabin	
Baggage-hold volume	24 cu ft (0·6 m³)

WEIGHTS:

Normal all-up weight	14 tons
Normal payload	5·5 tons

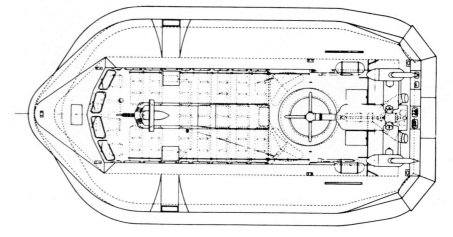

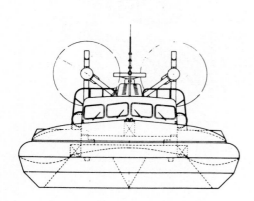

Mitsui MV-PP5 50-seat hovercraft, designed for fast ferry services on Japanese coastal and inland waters

PERFORMANCE:

Max speed, calm water 55 knots (102 km/h)

Cruising speed, calm water
45 knots (83 km/h)

Still air range and endurance at°cruising speed of about 160 nautical miles, 4 hours approximately

Vertical obstacle clearance 2 ft (0·6 m) approximately.

MV-PP1

The MV-PP1 is a small peripheral jet ACV built for river and coastal services and fitted with a flexible skirt. It seats a pilot and ten passengers and cruises at 40 knots.

Two craft of this type have been built to date—the prototype, which was completed in July 1964 and has been designated RH-4, and the first production model, the PP1-01.

The latter was sold to the Thai Customs Department, for service in the estuary of the Menam Chao Phya and adjacent waters, and has been named Customs Hovercraft 1. It has been in service with the Thai Customs Department since September 1967.

Details of construction weights, performance, etc will be found in JSS for 1970-71 and earlier editions.

Mitsui has built fourteen MV-PP5s, eleven of which are currently in service. The three craft above are operated by Kagoshima Airport Hovercraft Co Ltd (*left*), Yaeyama Kanko Ferry Cc Ltd (*centre*) and Japanese National Railways

NAKAMURA SEISAKUSHO CO LTD

HEAD OFFICE:

2-13 2-Chome, Tamagawa, Ota-ku, Tokyo
144, Japan

TELEPHONE:

03-759-2311

CABLES:

Gamecreator, Tokyo

DIRECTORS:

Masaya Nakamura, President
Hazime Yamauchi, General Director
Takeharu Daira, Sales Director
Tadashi Manabe, Director
Shigeru Yamada, Director

SENIOR EXECUTIVES:

Tadanori Yanagidaira, General Manager, NAMCO Group
Tatuo Ichisi, Sales Manager
Hiromichi Kuroda, Designer
Noboru Horii, Designer
Fumio Tatumi, Designer

Nakamura Seisakusho Co of Tokyo is a leading Japanese manufacturer of amusement and recreational equipment. The company's first venture into the ACV field is a battery-powered single-seater, the Namco-1. Designed initially as an amusement novelty, the vehicle is now undergoing development as a hand-propelled pallet, capable of lifting loads of up to 120 kg (265 lb).

NAMCO-1

This novel, battery-powered single-seater is intended for amusement only and is designed for use over relatively smooth surfaces. A feature of the craft is the use of a diaphragm-type industrial air bearing system for lift.

A pedestrial-propelled pallet version has been built.

LIFT AND PROPULSION: Motive power is supplied by five Hitachi 12v 50AL automobile storage batteries. Three of the batteries power three National 12v dc 0·125W blowers which operate at 19,000 rpm to provide pressurised air to inflate the diaphragm, which is in 0·04 in thick neoprene rubber. Air then passes through holes in the base of the diaphragm to form a continuous air film between the diaphragm and the surface beneath.

Thrust is supplied by two National 24v dc, 0·6 kW electric motors (powered by the remaining two batteries) each driving a 1 ft

Above and below: Nakamura Seisakusho's battery-powered Namco-1 amusement ACV is raised above its supporting surface on a diaphragm-type industrial air bearing

11 in (0·6 m) diameter, 5-bladed, 30° pitch Multi-wing fan made by Yashima Kogyo. Total propulsive thrust available is 22·05 lb (10 kg).

CONTROL: Craft heading is controlled by differential use of the thrust fans. It can travel forward, backwards or sideways, or spin around on its own axis.

HULL: Hull of prototype is in steel plate with bumper in polyethylane. Production models will be in fibreglass with pneumatic bumpers.

DIMENSIONS:

Height overall on landing pads, power off
                        3 ft 1 in (0·94 m)
Height overall, diaphragm inflated
                        3 ft 3·4 in (1·00 m)
Diameter overall   5 ft 3 in (1·60 m)
Diameter of diaphragm 3 ft 1·2 in (1·20 m)
Cushion area   11·02 sq ft (0·95 m²)

WEIGHTS:

Normal empty weight   264·6 lb (120 kg)
Total battery weight   137·3 lb (60 kg)

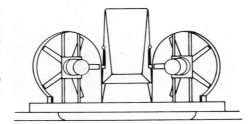

General arrangement of the Namco-1

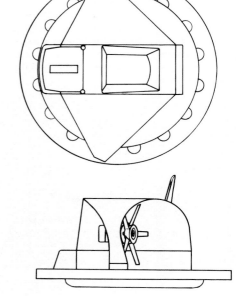

NIHON UNIVERSITY, NARASHINO

ADDRESS:

Aerodynamics Section, Nihon University at Narashino, 7-1591 Narashinodai; Funabashi, Chiba-Ken, Japan

TELEPHONE:

0474-66-1111-4

EXECUTIVES:

Masahira Mino, Senior Director
Toyoaki Enda, Director

The Aerodynamics Section of the Physical Science Laboratory, Nihon University, is conducting an extensive ACV research programme, which includes the construction and test of four small experimental craft: the Pastoral light amphibious single-seater, the Mistral, propelled by either water-screw or waterjet, the Floral, a two-seat sidewall craft and the N73.

An air boat, the Ripple, is employed as a "chase" craft to record on film the behaviour of these light ACVs over water.

Nihon University's ACV design group works in close co-operation with similar groups at the Institute of Technology, Ashikaga, and the University of Aoyama-Gakuin. Pastoral, in modified form, is now being employed in a research programme conducted by the Institute of Technology, Ashikaga.

A new design, the LJ-10 Jimny, a combined ground effect machine and wheeled vehicle, has been completed by Nihon in conjunction with Aoyama Gakuin University.

FLORAL 1

This experimental two-seater was completed in February 1971, and was the first sidewall craft to be built in Japan. In calm water the performance has proved to be superior to that of standard displacement runabouts of similar size and output. The craft was reconstructed in 1972 when the twin outboard propulsion units were replaced by a single unit, and a new stern skirt and trim flaps were introduced. Instrumentation includes trim, roll angle and speed indicators and gauges for measuring pressure in the plenum chamber.

LIFT AND PROPULSION: Lift is provided by a single 8 hp ZD-305 2 cycle single-cylinder air-cooled engine, located aft of the

Floral I, two-seater sidewall ACV, built by students of the Aerodynamics Section of Nihon University, Narashino, Japan

Mistral 2 single seat-research ACV

open cockpit and driving an F. S. Anderson 710-20-3L plastic fan. Propulsion is provided by a single Penta 550 outboard engine driving a waterscrew.

CONTROL: Engine/propeller unit turns for steering.

DIMENSIONS:

Length overall	17 ft 1 in (5·2 m)
Beam overall	5 ft 11 in (1·8 m)
Height overall	2 ft 7½ in (0·8 m)

WEIGHTS:

Normal gross weight	1,191 lb (540 kg)

PERFORMANCE:

Max speed over calm water	39 mph (62·7 km/h)
Max speed, 16 in (·40 m) waves	32 mph (52·1 km/h)

MISTRAL 2

Developed jointly by Nihon University, Masahiro Mino and the Institute of Technology, Ashikaga, the Mistral 2 is an experimental water-screw propelled single-seater derived from the SEA-NAC.

LIFT AND PROPULSION: A single 8 hp Fuji ES-162DS- 2-cycle single-cylinder air-cooled engine mounted immediately aft of the cockpit drives a 22⅞ in (580 mm) S11-03-FS03 5-bladed aluminium alloy fan for lift. Propulsion is supplied by either a 22 hp Fuji KB-2 or 50 hp Mercury 500 driving a waterscrew.

HULL: Moulded glass fibre, with inflated fabric-reinforced neoprene side-body/skirt.

CONTROLS: Engine/propeller unit turns for steering.

DIMENSIONS:

Length overall	13 ft 5 in (4·10 m)
Beam overall	5 ft 11 in (1·80 m)
Height overall	3 ft 7 in (1·09 m)

WEIGHTS:

Normal gross weight	664 lb (310 kg)

PERFORMANCE:

Max speed over calm water	42 mph (67·5 km/h)
Max speed, 2 ft (0·6 m) waves	28 mph (45·5 km/h)

LJ-10 JIMNY

Based on a reconditioned Suzuki Auto Co LN-360 Jimny—a jeep counterpart—this is a combined ground effect machine and wheeled vehicle, and can be driven like a car or truck. It was built by the Aerodynamics Section of Nihon University, headed by Masahiro Minot, in conjunction with the Traffic Engineering Dept, Aoyoma Gakuin University, headed by Eiji Tonokura. The vehicle is designed for use over uneven ground, and, marshes, and other terrain which cannot be traversed by wheeled or tracked cars and trucks. During 1973, the craft successfully completed running tests over normal road surfaces, unprepared tracks and stretches of water.

LIFT AND PROPULSION: Motive power for the lift system is provided by a single 55 hp Nissan A-10 988 cc engine which drives two 23½ in (595 mm) diameter 10-bladed centrifugal fans mounted on a common shaft to the rear of the driving position. Air is drawn through two inward facing metal ducts and expelled downwards into a fingered-bag skirt system. The vehicle has a four wheel drive system, powered by a Suzuki FB 395 cc petrol engine developing 27 hp at 6,000 rpm. Heading is controlled by a normal steering wheel located ahead of the driver.

DIMENSIONS

Length	17 ft 8 in (5,390 mm)
Width	10 ft 11 in (3,440 mm)
Height	5 ft 11 in (1,820 mm)

WEIGHTS:

All-up weight	2,200 lb (998 kg)

LJ-10 Jimny a combined ground effect machine and wheeled vehicle. Designed for use over terrain normally impassable to wheeled or crawler-equipped tractors the vehicle comprises a Suzuki Auto Co LN-360 Jimny—a counterpart to the US Army's jeep—equipped with a sidebody to support the skirt system and two lift fan assemblies. Cushion air is supplied by a 55 hp Nissan engine driving two 10-bladed centrifugal fans

N 73 amphibious runabout during trials. Built by the Aerodynamics Section, Nihon University, the craft has attained 55 mph (90 km/h) over water

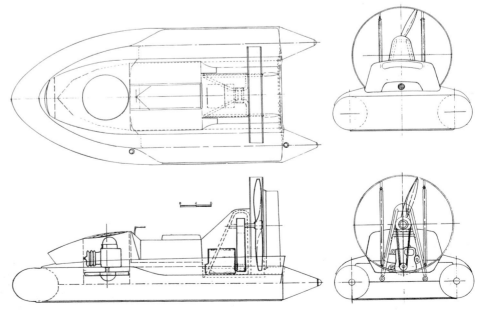

General arrangement of the N 73 single-seat amphibious runabout

PERFORMANCE:

No details received

N 73

This experimental single-seater has attained 55 mph (90 km/h) over water and 37 mph (60 km/h) during trials over land.

LIFT AND PROPULSION: A single 13 hp Daihatsu 2-cycle, single-cylinder air-cooled engine immediately ahead of the cockpit drives a 22 in (560 mm) diameter Multiwing fan for lift. Propulsion is supplied by a 40 hp Xenoax G44B 2-cycle twin-cylinder engine driving a 3 ft 11¼ in (1,200 mm) diameter 2-bladed propeller.

CONTROLS: Craft heading is controlled by twin aerodynamic rudders hinged to the rear of the propeller shroud and operated by a handlebar.

HULL: Moulded glass fibre with inflated fabric-reinforced neoprene sidebody/skirt.

DIMENSIONS:

Length overall   14 ft 9 in (4·50 m)

Beam overall	5 ft 10⅞ in (1·80 m)
Height	5 ft 1 in (1·55 m)
WEIGHTS:	
Normal empty weight	750 lb (340 kg)
Normal payload	474 lb (215 kg)
PERFORMANCE:	
Max speed over water	55 mph (90 km/h)
Max speed over land	37 mph (60 km/h)
Range	93·2 miles (150 km)

KUWAIT

AL-RODHAN TRADING AND CONTRACTING EST

HEAD OFFICE:

P.O. Box 5020, Kuwait, Arabian Gulf

Al-Rodhan is the representative for Eglen Hovercraft Inc in Kuwait, United Arab Emirates, Bahrain, Oman and Muscat, Yemen and Saudi Arabia.

NETHERLANDS

MACHINEFABRIEK ENBE BV

Air Cushion Vehicle Design and Manufacturing Subsidiary:

B. V. LUCHTKUSSENVOERTUIGEN FABRIEK

HEAD OFFICE:

Industrieterrein, Asperen, Netherlands

TELEPHONE:

03451-2743/2744

TELEX:

ENBE NL 47864

WORKS:

LKV Fabr. Industrieterrein, Asperen

DIRECTORS:

W. A. G. v. Burgeler

N. C. Nap

SHAREHOLDERS, (BV ENBE)

N. C. Nap

A. H. Nap

W. A. G. v. Burgeler

ENBE has built three light amphibious ACV prototypes, the B-1, B-2 and B-3, all designed by Mr. W. A. G. v. Burgeler.

Since January 1st, 1974, the company has been the distributor in the Netherlands for the Air Vehicles AV.2 light utility ACV.

NEW ZEALAND

HOVER VEHICLES (N.Z.) LTD

ADDRESS:

PO Box 10, Ohau, New Zealand

TELEPHONE:

80792 LEVIN

EXECUTIVES:

Roy Blake

David Clemow

Jim Pavitt

Ron Wadman

Brian Shaw

Mel Douglas

D. Hammond Murray, Managing Director

Hover Vehicles (N.Z.) Ltd has been formed by a group of New Zealand pilots, engineers and businessmen in association with Roy Blake, winner of the "Hovernaut of the Year" title in the United Kingdom in 1968, who afterwards emigrated to New Zealand.

The company plans to build vehicles which can be employed either on light utility applications or as recreational craft. The first craft under development is the H.V.4, a 6·4 m (21 ft) long amphibious six-seater, the final design for which has been completed. Initial tests of the prototype began in May 1975, when speeds of up to 50 mph (80·46 km/h) were recorded over land. Good stability and handling qualities were observed.

It is envisaged that several pre-production models will be built before consideration is given to putting the craft into full-scale production.

Apart from the design and construction of the H.V.4 the company has built and tested its own variable- and reversible-pitch fibreglass airscrew which will be used for ACV propulsion.

Government financial assistance was provided for the first prototype. Preliminary details of the company's first craft are given below.

During initial trials, Hover Vehicles H.V.4 attained speeds of up to 50 mph (80·46 km/h) over land

Power is supplied by a single 185 hp Rover V8 automobile engine which drives a 3 ft (914 mm) diameter centrifugal lift fan and two 3 ft (914 mm) diameter variable-pitch ducted propellers

H.V.4

The prototype of this attractive six-seat recreational ACV is complete. It is intended as a quiet, easily controlled craft which can be driven by an "above average" car driver after two hours training. The craft can be towed on a trailer behind most 6-cylinder cars.

LIFT AND PROPULSION. Power for the integrated lift/propulsion system is provided by a single 185 hp Rover V8 automobile engine which drives a 3 ft (914 mm) diameter centrifugal lift fan and two 3 ft (914 mm) diameter variable-pitch shrouded airscrews.

ACCOMMODATION: Seats are provided for a driver and five passengers in a fully enclosed cabin.

WEIGHTS:
Normal loaded weight
1,360·77 kg (3,000 lb)

DIMENSIONS:
Length overall   6·4 m (21 ft 0 in)
Beam overall   3·04 m (10 ft 0 in)
Reduced for transport by road
2·43 m (8 ft 0 in)
Ground clearance   609 mm (2 ft 0 in)
PERFORMANCE:
Max speed   80·46 km/h (50 mph)

Seats are provided for a driver and up to five passengers

SWEDEN

FLYGTEKNISKA FORSOKSANSTALTEN THE AERONAUTICAL RESEARCH INSTITUTE OF SWEDEN

HEAD OFFICE:
PO Box 11021, S-161 11 Bromma 11
TELEPHONE:
08.26 28 40
TELEX:
107 25
TELEGRAMS:
Flygtekniska
EXECUTIVE RESPONSIBLE FOR ACV DEVELOPMENT:
Einar Bergström,

FAA has conducted an ACV research programme for several years and is now working on designs for a series of full-size craft.

The FAA concept, described as a "semi-hovercraft", has three flexible, inflated rubber keels, a bow cushion seal and one or more fans situated aft.

The fans produce both propulsive thrust and cushion pressure. Air from the fans is blown rearwards beneath two adjustable flaps. These control the pressure in the two halves of the cushion, which is divided into two by a central keel. The hover gap is

FFA's test vehicle at 34 knots, while accelerating at 1·3 knots per second. Powered by a 57 hp Volkswagen engine, it has attained 56 knots on half-power

normally zero, hovering being limited to that necessary to clear stretches of ice and shallow water, and for parking on concrete terminals, beaches and pontoons. Hovering, turns, side thrust and reverse thrust are controlled by the operation of two adjustable side keels aft and the bow seal.

The concept is aimed towards lower initial and operating costs, reduced noise, and improved manoeuvrability.

A small dynamic test vehicle with a 10 hp engine was followed in 1971 by a larger test craft which has successfully completed a

major trials programme. Development of a 4-seat recreational ACV based on the test craft and a 41-seat hoverferry started in 1972. Prototype development is continuing successfully, the institute reports, and was due to be completed in 1976. Since FFA's activities are devoted purely to research, it is anticipated that further development and production will be undertaken by a commercial concern in Sweden.

Details of FFA's test vehicle, sportscraft and its projected 41-seat Hover Bus can be found in JSS 1975-76 and earlier editions.

TRINIDAD

COELACANTH GEMCO LTD

HEAD OFFICE:
1 Richardson Street, Point Fortin, Trinidad, W.I.
TELEPHONE:
Point Fortin 2439
CABLES:
Coelacanth, Trinidad
DIRECTORS:
Nigel Seale
Kelvin Corbie
SECRETARY:
R. Varma

Coelacanth Gemco Ltd, the first company to specialise in the design and construction of air cushion vehicles in the West Indies, has been granted Pioneer Status for the manu-

facture of hovercraft in Trinidad by the government-controlled Industrial Development Corporation. The company has obtained the approval of the Town and Country Planning Commission to construct an ACV factory and a hoverport at Guapo beach, Trinidad. Guapo Bay and the neighbouring Antilles Bay will be used by the company for sea tests and a disused runway adjacent to the site will be used for overland tests.

The company also plans to build a two-mile long, 100 ft wide ACV roadway between Guapo Beach and the Point Fortin Industrial Estate.

Meetings have been held with the Trinidad Government to negotiate a right-of-way over Government owned land.

A freight operation is planned with ACVs taking aboard finished goods from the factories, and delivering them to Port of Spain, 40 minutes away at a speed of 60 knots.

Craft at present under development by the company are the Pluto, Jupiter, Venus, Arcturus and Mars, and a military ACV.

Progress is also being made with the development of a hover truck, with a payload of 3 tons, for carrying sugar cane from the Trinidad cane fields in wet weather.

PLUTO Mk I AND II

The Pluto is a two-seat test vehicle, built in marine ply, and designed to provide data for a sport and recreational craft which will be marketed under the same name.

The production prototype, which is based

on the existing hull and designated Pluto Mk II is undergoing trials. A four-seat version, Pluto Mk III, is due to go into production.

Two and four-seat versions are planned. A standard feature of the production models will be a two-berth cabin and cooking facilities, which will allow the craft to be used for cruising to the northwest of Trinidad in the Gulf of Paria.

LIFT AND PROPULSION: Lift power on Pluto Mk II is supplied by two 6 hp Briggs and Stratton motor-mower engines driving two Rotafoil fans. Thrust is supplied by two 250cc Velocettes driving two 2 ft 3 in (0·685 m) diameter ducted Hordern-Richmond propellers at 5,000 rpm.

DIMENSIONS, EXTERNAL:

Length	16 ft 0 in (4·87 m)
Width	7 ft 10 in (2·38 m)
Height	6 ft 0 in (1·82 m)

WEIGHTS:

Empty weight	1,100 lb (498·92 kg)
Loaded weight, 2 seat model	1,500 lb (680·35 kg)

PERFORMANCE:

Speed over water	22 mph (35·40 km/h)
Speed over land (with one person)	39 mph (62·76 km/h)
Vertical obstacle clearance	8 in (203 mm)

PLUTO Mk III

Developed from Pluto Mk. II, Mk. III is a four-seater runabout and yacht.

The production prototype was launched on July 26th, 1975 at Point Fortin beach.

LIFT AND PROPULSION: Lift is provided by a single 20 hp Sachs Wankel rotary engine driving two Rotafoil fans, and propulsion by two 250cc Velocettes driving two 2 ft 3 in (0·685 m) diameter ducted Hordern Richmond propellers at 5,000 rpm.

All series production craft will be powered by three Sachs Wankel engines—one for lift and two for propulsion. Fuel is carried in two standard marine power boat tanks, mounted amidships on the outer hull periphery.

Plans are being made to power a de luxe model with a 120 hp engine driving a hydraulic pump which will, in turn, drive three hydraulic motors. Two of these will power the propulsion system and the third will power the lift system.

CONTROLS: Craft heading is controlled by twin rudders aft operating in the slipstreams of the two propellers. Thrust ports are fitted port and starboard, fore and aft, to provide additional control at slow speeds when approaching and leaving jetties.

HULL: First production craft will be in ³⁄₁₆ in mahogany marine ply, with the bottom and sides sheathed to 6 in (152 mm) above the waterline in glassfibre.

ACCOMMODATION: The cabin accommodates a family of four—two adults and two children—and stores for an overnight stay. The seats are removable and can be used on the beach. On board the craft, the position of the seats can be altered if necessary to adjust craft trim. Built-in steps are provided on each side of the hull to simplify access to the craft after bathing. A hatch is provided aft for baggage items and stores and another forward to facilitate the handling of mooring lines and the anchor. The cabin windows, in ³⁄₁₆ in plexiglass, slide rearwards in their frames for access to the cabin.

Pluto Mk II, a manned test model of Coelacanth Gemco Pluto series, puts to sea for a test run off Point Fortin, Trinidad

Above: Pluto III immediately after launching at Point Fortis beach. A submerged obstruction ripped a 2 m gash in the starboard skirt preventing the craft from riding on its cushion. *Below:* Pluto III undergoing tests in displacement condition

DIMENSIONS, EXTERNAL:

Length	18 ft 0 in (5·48 m)
Width	7 ft 10 in (2·38 m)
Height, inflated skirt	6 ft 0 in (1·82 m)
Cushion depth	1 ft 3 in (381 mm)
Freeboard in displacement mode	2 ft 6 in (0·76 m)

DIMENSIONS, INTERNAL:

Cabin floor area (total usable area)	40 sq ft (3·71 m²)

WEIGHTS:

Normal gross weight (4 passengers and 20 gallons of petrol)	1,950 lb (884·5 kg)
Empty weight	1,250 lb (566·90 kg)

PERFORMANCE:

Speed over water	25 mph (40·23 km/h)
Speed over land	40 mph (64·37 km/h)

COST: Estimated price, g.r.p. model £3,500 (West Indies $16,800).

VENUS

This craft has been designed principally for carrying oil company executives to and from wells in the Gulf of Paria, in Soldado and other areas in the West Indies. Ten and fifteen seat versions will be built, and like the Jupiter, the craft will be available in either amphibious form with a continuous skirt or as a rigid sidewall type with bow and stern skirts.

A manned scale model hull of the craft was completed in November 1968. This craft is also being used as a test bed for the two and four-seat Pluto series.

JUPITER

A projected four-seat ACV runabout, Jupiter is designed around the basic hull of the company's Super Bee cabin cruiser, and will be available either as an amphibious craft, with a continuous peripheral skirt, or as a rigid sidewall type with bow and stern skirts.

Lift will be provided by a 75 hp modified outboard driving two Rotafoil fans, and propulsive thrust by a 90 hp modified outboard driving a reversible pitch-ducted propeller.

DIMENSIONS:

Length	18 ft 0 in
Beam	10 ft 0 in
Height	7 ft 0 in

WEIGHT:

Weight, incl fuel	2,810 lb

PERFORMANCE:

Max speed (est)	50 knots

ARCTURUS

The Arcturus is a 35-seat amphibious ACV designed by Nigel Seale. Motive power for

Nigel Seale, designer of Pluto III, stands at the side of the craft as it is put through static hovering trials in Coelacanth Gemco's workshop. Hatches in the cabin roof and at the bow enable mooring lines to be handled more easily

the lift and propulsion system will be supplied by high speed diesel generators driving Lear Siegler Electric Motors.

Work has started on a manned scale model but activity has been suspended temporarily while the company concentrates its resources on the development of the Pluto series.

MARS

Coelacanth Gemco's first military design is the 35 ft (10·66 m) long Mars, a 10-ton patrol craft designed to operate in sheltered waters. It will carry seven fully armed men.

A manned scale model capable of testing hovering performance is being built and is expected to be ready for trials in late 1977.

Construction will be in g.r.p., with aluminium extrusions and panels. Six Rotafoil fans will be employed in the integrated lift/propulsion system.

A feature of the craft will be the employment of stabilisers to reduce drift.

DIMENSIONS:

Length	35 ft 0 in (10·66 m)
Beam	15 ft 0 in (4·57 m)
Height	15 ft 0 in (4·57 m)

WEIGHTS:

Normal all-up weight	10 tons

PERFORMANCE:

Cruising speed	35 knots

UNITED KINGDOM

AIR BEARINGS LTD

HEAD OFFICE AND WORKS:
Quay Lane, Hardway, Gosport, Hampshire PO12 4LJ

TELEPHONE:
(070) 17-87421

TELEX:
47674

TELEGRAMS:
AIR BEAR—GOSPORT

DIRECTORS:
E. D. Wilkinson, Chairman
J. E. Cook, Managing
R. H. Arrow, Engineering
J. J. Eadie, Commercial

Air Bearings Ltd was formed in March 1965 to manufacture light ACVs employing the company's own integrated lift/propulsion system and skirt design. Production of the AB 11 Crossbow three-seater is underway and sales have been made to a number of overseas customers including Mitsui and King Hussein of Jordan.

Design of the AB 12 Longbow, a 'stretched' version is nearing completion. A 10-12 seat vehicle, it retains the same ease of handling as Crossbow and employs a similar system of controls and reverse thrust. Twin engines are fitted to provide an adequate power reserve to cope with high winds and adverse sea conditions. Civil and lightly armed military versions are available.

AB 11 CROSSBOW

This general purpose amphibious ACV is based on the company's experience with the HC 10, and earlier prototypes. Commercial and lightly armoured military variants are available.

Above: The Air Bearings Crossbow, a three-seat general purpose amphibious ACV
Below: Impression of the AB 12 Longbow, a twin-engined development of Crossbow

LIFT AND PROPULSION: Motive power for the integrated lift/propulsion system is provided by a 135 hp Johnson (OMC) ESL 74 V4 two-stroke, driving a single Dowty Rotol axial fan mounted above the engine and inclined at a slight angle forward to the horizontal. Thrust is provided by ejecting fan air horizontally from the rear of the hull. Lift air passes directly into the cushion. Fuel is carried in two bagged tanks located in the sides of the hull close to the c of g. Refuelling points are provided port and starboard, amidships. Fuel recommended is 4 star petrol/oil mix 45:1.

CONTROLS: Directional control is provided by rudders in the airjet exit and movable vanes, linked to the rudders, in the reverse thrust ducts on either side. A double elevator aft of the thrust duct provides fore and aft trim. Reverse and braking thrust while cushion borne is achieved by a shutter and vane system. Driving controls comprise a steering yoke and wheel and three hand-operated levers which control throttle, reverse thrust and fore and aft trim.

INSTRUMENTATION: Instrumentation includes a tachometer, fuel contents gauge, engine water temperature and battery condition indicators and a clock and hours-run counter. Switches operate navigation lights, flashing beacon, headlights, cabin interior light and other electrical accessories. Airspeed and yaw indicators are optional extras.

HULL: Hull, longitudinal members, most bulkheads and superstructure are constructed in grp. For added strength grp tubes are bonded into the hull. A continuous 100% finger skirt of HDL design in polyurethane/nylon is fitted, giving a hard structure clearance of 12 in (30 cm).

ACCOMMODATION: Entry to the cabin is via two gull-wing doors. In the casualty evacuation role, two stretchers can be carried, one either side of the driver.

SYSTEMS, ELECTRICAL: Two 12 v alternators, 35 amp/hr and 6 amp/hr. Two 12 v batteries, 60 amp/hr.

COMMUNICATIONS: Radio, optional extra.

DIMENSIONS:

Length overall	18 ft 9 in (5·72 m)
Beam (skirt inflated)	11 ft 6 in (3·50 m)
Beam (power off)	7 ft 8 in (2·33 m)
Height on landing pads	4 ft 3 in (1·27 m)
Cushion area	147 sq ft (13·65 m²)

DIMENSIONS, INTERNAL:
Cabin:

Length	4 ft 8 in (1·42 m)
Max width	4 ft 8 in (1·42 m)
Max height	3 ft 2 in (91·5 cm)
Floor area	22 sq ft (2·04 m²)

WEIGHTS:

Normal empty weight	1,600 lb (714 kg)
Normal all-up weight	2,325 lb (1,038 kg)
Maximum payload	600 lb (272·14 kg)

PERFORMANCE (normal operating weight, calm water):

Max speed	35 knots
Cruising speed	30 knots
Endurance at cruising speed	4 hours
Vertical obstacle clearance	1 ft (30 cm)

AB 12 LONGBOW

An enlarged and more powerful version of Crossbow, Longbow incorporates a similar, integrated lift/propulsion arrangement and reverse thrust system. Twin engines are fitted, providing reserve power to cope with adverse wind and sea states and at the

Interior of Crossbow's cabin showing the instrument layout and controls. The bench seat accommodates the driver and two passengers

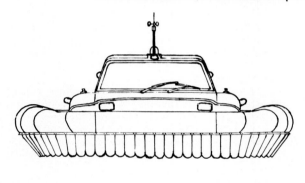

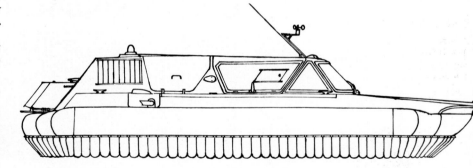

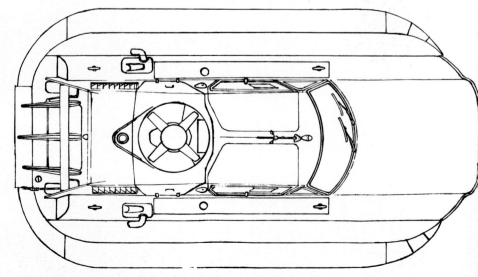

General arrangement of the AB II Crossbow

same time permitting the craft to operate on one engine at reduced performance.

Bow thrust ports, combined with a steerable reverse thrust system, ensure a high degree of control at low speeds.

Features include a large cabin with a raised wheelhouse position for the driver and navigator.

LIFT AND PROPULSION: Power for the integrated lift/propulsion system is provided by two 200 hp marine engines mounted aft of the main cabin. Power is transmitted from each engine to two Dowty Rotol axial flow fans. Split ducts channel fan air aft to the airjet aperture for thrust and down through the radiator matrices for lift. Shutters close off one lift duct in the event of single engine operation. Fuel is carried in three bag tanks, amidships. Total fuel capacity is 1,000 lb (446 kg).

CONTROLS: Rudders operating in each of the twin airjet thrust ducts provide directional control. Additional directional control at low speeds is provided by reverse thrust ducts and bow thrust ports. Elevators aft of the thrust apertures provide trim control. Reverse thrust is obtained by closing sets of balanced shutters across the thrust ducts, thus re-directing air through the controllable vanes in the port and starboard ducts. Operating controls comprise a rudder bar, twin throttle levers, and levers controlling trim, reverse thrust and bow thrust ports.

HULL: Hull and superstructure consist of three primary grp mouldings. Longitudinal members and bulkheads are either in grp or aluminium aeroweb and are bonded into place.

SKIRT: 3 ft (0·914 m) deep loop and segment skirt of HDL design giving a hard-structure clearance in excess of 2 ft 0 in (60 cm).

ACCOMMODATION: Enclosed cabin with 11 ft 7 in × 4 ft 2 in (3·53 × 1·27 m) floor

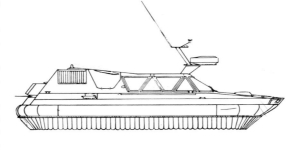

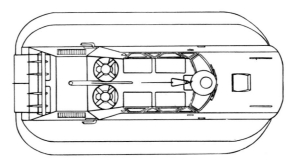

AB 12 Longbow (two 130 hp Wankel rotary engines)

space. Alternative seating layouts can be provided including one for 12 passengers. Floor can be strengthened for point loading to enable fire pumps, stretchers and items of military equipment to be carried. Access to the main cabin is by gull wing doors, port and starboard. Separate access is provided for the wheelhouse. The standard version is heated and ventilated. Full air conditioning is an optional extra.

DIMENSIONS, EXTERNAL:

Length overall	34 ft 9 in (10·59 m)
Beam, skirt inflated	18 ft 6 in (5·63 m)
Beam, packed for shipment	8 ft 0 in (2·43 m)
Height overall on landing pads	8 ft 6 in (2·59 m)

DIMENSIONS, INTERNAL:

Cabin length	11 ft 7 in (3·53 m)
Cabin width	4 ft 2 in (1·27 m)

WEIGHTS:

Normal empty weight	4,200 lb (1,875 kg)
Normal payload	2,200 lb (982 kg)
Fuel, normal	1,000 lb (446 kg)
Total laden weight	7,800 lb (3,482 kg)

PERFORMANCE (at normal operating weight, calm conditions):

Max speed	35 knots
Cruising speed	30 knots
Endurance at cruising speed	6 hours
Vertical obstacle clearance	2 ft 4 in (71 cm)

AIRHOVER LTD

HEAD OFFICE:
Hoverplane Works, Main Road, Arlesford, Colchester, CO7 8DB Essex, England
TELEPHONE:
Boxted 356
DIRECTORS:
R. P. Wingfield, Managing Director
V. A. Johnson
V. E. Andrews, Secretary

Airhover Ltd is marketing the Aero Sabre Mk I and Mk II light hovercraft—both open single or two seaters—and the more sophisticated Aero Sabre III, high performance sports ACV.

Latest addition to the line is the Mk IV, a luxury 4-seater with ducted fan propulsion.

AERO SABRE Mk I

The new Aero Sabre Mk I is a high performance amphibious light sports hovercraft. It is in production and is available either complete or in kit form. Two models are offered: Mk 1, with a single engine and lift/propulsion duct assembly, and Mk 1SP, a modified version, produced for youth training organisations and schools with workshop facilities as an educational project machine.

LIFT AND PROPULSION: Power for the integrated lift/propulsion system can be provided by a wide choice of engines ranging from a 9 bhp or 13 bhp Stihl to a 12 bhp Kyoritsu. The primary airflow from the eight-bladed axial-flow fan is ejected through a propulsive slot aft of the fan duct, and the

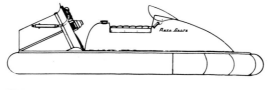

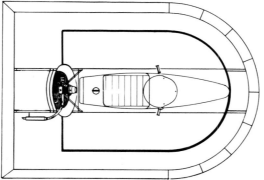

General arrangement of the Aero Sabre Mk I

secondary airflow, for the cushion, passes downwards into the plenum chamber.

HULL: Mixed aluminium, glassfibre and wooden construction. Laminated wooden outer frame amd similar inner frame. The engine, aluminium duct and outlet, moulded glassfibre seat and streamlined nose fairing are all carried on the two longitudinals and can be detached as one separate unit. Upper surface covered with lightweight nylon,

impregnated on both sides with pvc. Fuel tank is integral with glassfibre superstructure with filler neck aft of driver's seat. Fuel capacity is 2 gals (9·09 1).

SKIRT: Made in extra strong nylon fabric and reinforced with double skin of pvc. Skirt is in eleven segments and is stitched with rot-proofed thread. Skirt attachment rails provided.

ACCOMMODATION: Open motor-cycle type upholstered seating for one or two in tandem.

CONTROLS: Throttle twist grip control, with dummy grip opposite and ignition cut-out switch. Steering is by kinesthetic control (body movement). The manufacturer points out that as the performance is "very lively," experience at low speeds is desirable before attempting high speed runs.

DIMENSIONS:

Length	9 ft (2·74 m)
Beam	6 ft (1·82 m)
Height	3 ft (91·44 m)

WEIGHTS:

Unladen	100 lb (45·35 kg)
Max payload	400 lb (181·43 kg)

PERFORMANCE:

Designed speed,	
land	35 mph (56·33 km/h)
water	20 mph (32·18 km/h)
Fuel consumption	1 gph (4·5 lph)
Obstacle clearance	6 in (15·24 cm)

AERO SABRE Mk 1 SP

This is a modified version of the Mk 1, produced for Education Authorities which are planning to include hovercraft design theory among their educational projects. Export orders for the machine have been received from overseas authorities, including one from the Government of Western Australia.

The company was approached with the suggestion that the Aero Sabre Mk 1 would be ideal for such projects, and as a result, a special kit has been developed from which it can be constructed without complicated equipment. It can be completed with simple hand tools and some assistance from a small engineering workshop.

The full kit is divided into seven individual assemblies, five of which are supplied complete. The remaining two, the airframe and the engine, occupy about 60% of the construction time.

The materials used in the airframe are normally available in the school stock room or are readily available locally. Any small two-cycle industrial or motor cycle engine can be installed, providing it develops a minimum of 7 bhp.

If difficulties are experienced in obtaining either materials for the airframe or a suitable engine, these items can also be supplied by Airhove Ltd.

AERO SABRE Mk III

The prototype of this exceptionally elegant two-seater is undergoing tests. One of the aims of the designers has been to produce a high-performance light ACV which combines the lines of a racing aircraft with the comfort of a modern sports car. Various alternative layouts are available to suit commercial applications. Performance depends upon the power installed: but the designed maximum speed is 60 mph (95·56 km/h)

LIFT AND PROPULSION: The lift engine, a 20 hp MAG type 1031 two-stroke is located forward of the cabin beneath a protective metal mesh panel and drives a 1 ft 9 in (0·53 m) diameter fan with blades set at 30 deg. Each blade is detachable to facilitate replacement. Located aft of the cabin, the propulsion engine, a 33 hp MAG 2062-SRB twin cylinder two-stroke, drives a 3 ft 0 in (0·914 m) diameter two-bladed variable-pitch propeller. The entire thrust unit will be surrounded by a plated protective mesh guard. Both engines have electric starters.

Above: The Aero Sabre Mk I SP, now available in partially assembled kit form for education authorities for school educational projects including hovercraft theory. *Below:* The standard Aero Sabre Mk. I high performance light sports ACV

Aero Sabre, Mk III a 60 mph (96-56 km/h) amphibious two-seater, combines elegance and high performance with the comfort of a modern sports car

CONTROLS: Heading is controlled by a single, swept back aerodynamic rudder operating in the propeller slipstream. Aircraft-type wheel, instrumentation, switches and throttles.

HULL: Built in high grade marine ply and incorporating three watertight buoyancy compartments. In the event of either one or two of these sustaining damage, the remaining compartments will keep the craft afloat. The superstructure, which includes the canopy, forward, decking and air intake is a one-piece moulding in grp. Windows and windshields are in perspex. Cabin access is via two light alloy gull-wing doors which are raised electrically.

SKIRT: Conventional bag-type, 1 ft 0 in (304 mm) deep.

CABIN: Access is via gull-wing doors. Semi-reclining, upholstered seats are provided side-by-side for driver and passenger. Panels and pillars are finished in matching colours.

DIMENSIONS:

Length overall	17 ft (5·18 m)
Beam overall	8 ft (2·43 m)
Height to top of rudder (on landing pads)	5 ft (1·52 m)
Skirt depth	1 ft 4 in (406 mm)

WEIGHTS:

Unladen	680 lb (308·42 kg)

Payload	600 lb (272·14 kg)
PERFORMANCE:	
Obstacle clearance	12 in (304 mm)
Max speed	60 mph (96·56 km/h)

AERO SABRE Mk IV

Work on the prototype of this luxury four-seater is currently in progress. Trials are expected to be begin early in 1977.

One of the main objectives has been to provide a fast, amphibious vehicle suitable for business executives working in countries with a dry and dusty environment. Simplicity of construction and ease of maintenance are two of the design keynotes.

LIFT AND PROPULSION: Power for the integrated lift/propulsion system is provided by a single Rolls-Royce Continental aero-engine rated at 100 hp. This drives a single 3 ft 10 in (1·16 m) diameter, 4-bladed ducted fan, the primary airflow from which is ejected through a propulsive slot aft, while the secondary airflow is ducted downwards into the plenum chamber for lift. Fuel is carried in two tanks of 7·7 gal (35 l) capacity.

CONTROLS: Craft heading is controlled by triple rudders in the airjet outlet aft. The two outer units are uncoupled for braking and reverse thrust.

HULL: Mixed grp and light alloy construction.

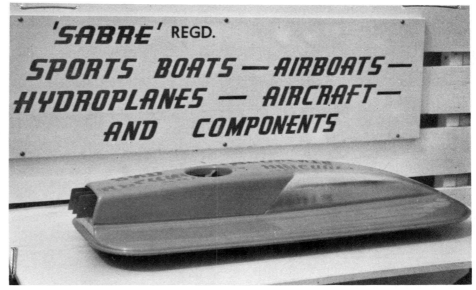

One-seventh scale model of the new Aero Sabre Mk IV four-seater. Power for the integrated lift/propulsion system is provided by a 100 hp Rolls-Royce Continental aero-engine

ACCOMMODATION: Totally enclosed cabin fitted with four semi-reclining seats. Aircraft-style instrumentation.

DIMENSIONS:

Length	21 ft 0 in (6·40 m)	Beam	9 ft 0 in (2·74 m)
		Height	4 ft 0 in (1·21 m)
		WEIGHTS:	
		All-up weight	1,150 lb (521·50 kg)
		Payload	650 lb (294·82 kg)

AIR VEHICLES LIMITED

HEAD OFFICE AND WORKS:
  1 Sun Hill, Cowes, Isle of Wight
YARD:
  Dinnis' Yard, High Street, Cowes, Isle of Wight
TELEPHONE:
  Cowes 3194 and 4739
TELEX:
  86513 (Hoverwork, Ryde)
DIRECTORS:
  P. H. Winter, MSc
  C. D. J. Bland
  C. B. Eden

Air Vehicles Ltd was founded in 1968 and has concentrated on the development of small commercial hovercraft and various systems including skirts and ducted propellers, for larger craft.

Three machines of the AV2 type have been built and have accumulated many hours of operation both on test and on charter. Two have been sold to LKV in Holland. A development, the AV Tiger, was completed in November 1975. Features include a new ducted propeller, increased payload and better fuel economy. This craft is now offered both for charter and sale.

Air Vehicles Ltd is approved by the Civil Aviation Authority and undertakes design and manufacture of major modifications to larger craft. These have included flat-deck freight conversions for the SR.N5 and SR.N6 and power-assisted rudder packs for both types.

The company is now a leader in the design of low-speed ducted propeller systems and, following the success of the propeller duct fitted to an SR.N6, a smaller unit with integral controls was made for the AV Tiger. Two larger units have been supplied to the US for a military hovercraft.

Several studies involving the use of hoverbarges have been completed particularly for ship-to-shore operation, and an on-site survey has recently been undertaken in Indonesia. Capt B. Goldsmith has been appointed Marine Advisor for these applications.

SR.N5 modified by Air Vehicles on charter to the Department of Aboriginal Affairs, Australia

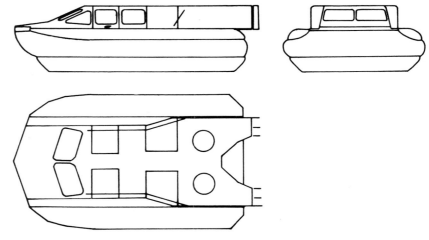

General arrangement of the Air Vehicles Ltd. AV 2

Air Vehicles Ltd designed and commissioned the first hoverbarge to operate on the Yukon River-the 'Yukon Princess'.

The company has a major interest in two SR.N5 craft, GH 2009 and GH 2041. These craft have both been on charter for a year, GH 2009 in Australia and GH 2041 on the Wash in England.

AV2

A feature of this twin-engined amphibious 5-6 seater is the use of fan-jet propulsion to minimise noise. The prototype, built in 1970, has completed several hundred hours of development testing to prove the basic reliability of the machine and its components. This was followed by various operations, charters and tests undertaken with AV2-002. As a result production craft—AV2-003 and subsequent machines—embody various improvements in terms of construction, payload and control. The craft is suitable for both civil and para-military roles. It can operate on either of its two engines enabling it to return to base in the event of one engine failing.

AV2-003 completed a charter to take pilots to and from ships across the ice in Sweden during the winter of 1975-76.

LIFT AND PROPULSION: Two converted outboard engine powerheads drive two centrifugal fans for lift and propulsion. Kits will be available to convert the engines from petrol to kerosene fuel.

CONTROLS: Rudder vane control and throttles for the two engines, auxiliary control systems for trim and reverse thrust.

HULL: 001 and 002, robust foam/fibreglass structure. 003 and subsequent craft, fibreglass internal and external production mouldings. Hull sidebodies are inflated for buoyancy but can be deflated for transport.

ACCOMMODATION: Enclosed cabin for driver and up to five passengers.

SKIRT: Pressurised bag with separate segments.

DIMENSIONS:

Length overall	19 ft 0 in (5·79 m)
Beam overall	11 ft 2 in (3·40 m)
Beam, sidebodies deflated for transport	7 ft 10½ in (2·39 m)

WEIGHTS:

Empty weight	200 lb (907·12 kg)
Loaded weight	3,000 lb (1,360·8 kg)

PERFORMANCE:

Cruising speed, calm water	35 knots
Fuel consumption (petrol) at full throttle	15 gal/hr (68 l/hr)
Fuel consumption, cruising	10 gal/hr (45 l/hr)

AV TIGER

This craft is a development of AV2 and use the well-tried hull, skirt and inflated sidebodies system but has increased length with a larger cab and room for 8-10 passengers. It uses a single Rover V8 3·5 litre engine and the ducted propeller gives very high thrust enabling it to operate in difficult wind and wave conditions. Low propeller tip speed keeps the craft quiet and the integrated control surfaces on the duct gives it a high degree of manoeuvrability.

LIFT AND PROPULSION: Motive power for integrated lift/propulsion system is provided by a single 3·5 litre Rover V.8 petrol engine. Engine output is transferred to the lift fan and a four-bladed, ducted propeller through a notched belt system.

CONTROLS: Multiple rudder vanes hinged at the aft end of the propeller duct provide directional control. Elevators provide trim, and when raised fully, assist braking by reducing thrust by 75%.

HULL: Laminated grp with metal strengthening members. Side members are inflatable, giving additional buoyancy and protection for the craft when mooring. By deflating the side members the vehicle can be trailed behind any large car or small truck. Built-in jacking system provided for loading.

ACCOMMODATION: Enclosed cabin for driver and up to nine passengers. Access via hinged doors, one port, one starboard.

SKIRT: Pressurised bag skirt with separate segments.

DIMENSIONS:

Length	22 ft 9 in (6·94 m)
Width (inflated)	11 ft 6 in (3·5 m)
Transport width	8 ft 0 in (2·44 m)
Height (static)	8 ft 3 in (2·5 m)
Hoverheight	15-18 in (38-46 cm)
8 place cabin	10 × 6 ft (3 × 1·8 m)

WEIGHTS:

Empty weight	2,200 lb (1,000 kg)
Max. weight	3,700 lb (1,680 kg)
Disposable load	1,500 lb (680 kg)

PERFORMANCE:

Max speed	35 knots (65 km/h)
Cruise speed	25 knots (46 km/h)
Max conditions	25 knot wind (46 km/h wind)
	3 ft sea (1 m sea)
Speed in 25 knot wind	20 knots (37 km/h)
Gradient climbing	1 : 7 (standing start)

AV Tiger, an 8-10 seat light hovercraft powered by a 3.5 litre Rover V.8. Top speed is 35 knots (65 km/h)

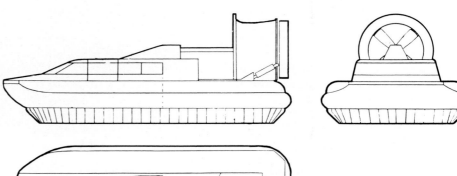

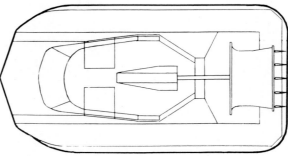

General arrangement of the AV Tiger 8-10 seat light hovercraft

Fuel consumption cruise

4·6 Imp. gall/hr (21 l/hr)

Fuel consumption max

9·8 Imp. gall/hr (45 l/hr)

DUCTED PROPELLERS

SR.N6:

The first ducted propeller unit designed for the N6 has been operating for almost two years and has proved capable of reducing noise by up to 12 dBA. During extensive trials, it was demonstrated that it would also augment static thrust, enabling the craft to negotiate steeper slopes. The propeller was that of the standard N6 but cropped to 6 ft 10 in diameter. The shape of the duct ensures that thrust is maintained at high angles of yaw. A set of integral rudders is being constructed which will give improved control over the standard N6 and dispense with the existing tail unit.

AV Tiger:

Following the success of the N6 duct, a smaller one of 4 ft 6 in diameter was designed for the new Tiger hovercraft. This unit incorporates integral rudders and elevators. The propeller is made from a balsa core with fibreglass skin and was designed and manufactured by AVL.

SR.N6 undergoing trials with a ducted propeller manufactured by Air Vehicles.

Ducts for USA:

Early in 1976 two large ducts were designed and constructed for a US hovercraft. These are nearly 9 ft in overall diameter and made on the same structural principles as the N6 duct, The ducts were delivered in April and tested in June.

New Ducts:

With the accummulated practical experience of the units so far made, Air Vehicles is designing new units which will power a new low-cost, diesel-engined hovercraft, similar in size to the successful SR.N6.

BRITISH HOVERCRAFT CORPORATION

Head Office:

East Cowes, Isle of Wight

Telephone:

Cowes 4101

Telex:

86190

Telegrams:

BRITHOVER COWES TELEX

Directors:

Sir Christopher Hartley, KCB, CBE, DFC, AFC, BA, Chairman

R. Stanton-Jones, MA, DCAe, CEng, AFRAeS, Managing Director

R. L. Wheeler, MSc, DIC, CEng, AFRAeS, Technical Director

J. M. George, BSc(Eng), DCAe, Sales Director

J. McGarity, Works Director

T. Bretherton, Finance and Secretary

W. A. Oppenheimer, FCA

G. S. Hislop, PhD, BSc, ARCST, CEng, FIMechE, FRAeS, FRSA

B. D. Blackwell, MA, BSc(Eng), CEng, FIMechE, FRAeS, FBIM

The British Hovercraft Corporation is the world's largest hovercraft manufacturer. It was formed in 1966 to concentrate the British hovercraft industry's major technical and other resources under a single management.

The corporation deals with a wide variety of applications of the air cushion principle, the emphasis being on the development and production of amphibious hovercraft. Other activities include the investigation of industrial applications of the air cushion principle.

The capital of the corporation is £5 million, which is wholly owned by Westland Aircraft Ltd.

BHC established the world's first full-scale hovercraft production line in 1964. Currently it is producing the 10-ton Winchester (SR.N6) Class craft, the 50-ton Wellington (BH.7) Class craft and the 190-ton Mountbatten (SR.N4) Class craft at East Cowes.

At present five Mountbatten Class craft are in service as passenger/car ferries on the Dover/Boulogne and Ramsgate/Calais routes; two with British Rail Hovercraft, and

Swift, the first 200-ton SR.N4 Mk 2 mixed-traffic hovercraft. Converted by BHC from a standard craft for Hoverlloyd Limited, the Mk 2 carries up to 278 passengers and 37 vehicles compared with 254 passengers and 30 vehicles on the standard craft

three with Hoverlloyd Ltd. An additional craft is under construction for Hoverlloyd and will enter service in June 1977.

One BH.7 is in service with the Royal Navy's Naval Hovercraft Trials Unit and six have been delivered to the Imperial Iranian Navy.

Military and general duty variants of the Warden and Winchester Class hovercraft are now in service with the Naval Hovercraft Trials Unit, Imperial Iranian Navy, Italian Interservice Hovercraft Unit and the Canadian and Saudi Arabian Coast Guard.

Winchesters have been employed since 1967 in trials and sales demonstrations in Africa, Canada, Denmark, Finland, India, South America and the Middle and Far East, logging well over 160,000 operating hours.

Commercial general purpose variants of the Warden and Winchester are in service with Solent Seaspeed Ltd, Department of Civil Aviation, New Zealand, Department of Transport, Canada, Hovertravel Ltd, Hoverwork Ltd and Mitsubishi Heavy Industries Ltd. In recent years the Winchester has been used increasingly for general purpose roles including hydrographic and seismic survey, freighting and search and rescue duties.

MOUNTBATTEN (SR.N4) CLASS Mk. 1

The world's largest hovercraft, the Mountbatten is a 200-ton passenger car/ferry designed for stage lengths of up to 100 n miles (184 km) on coastal water routes. It has an average service speed of 40-50 knots in waves up to 10 ft (3·04 m) in height and is able to operate in 12 ft (3·7 m) seas at a speed of about 20 knots.

The first craft entered commercial service with British Rail Hovercraft Ltd. in August 1968 on the Dover/Boulogne route and British Rail took delivery of a second craft for service on the same route late in the summer of 1969.

Two further craft entered service with Hoverlloyd Limited in April 1969 on the Ramsgate/Calais route—and a third craft joined this operation in 1972.

LIFT AND PROPULSION: Power is supplied by four 3,400 shp Rolls-Royce Marine Proteus free-turbine, turboshaft engines located in pairs at the rear of the craft on either side of the vehicle deck. Each has a maximum rating of 4,250 shp, but usually operates at 3,400 shp when cruising. Each engine is connected to one of four identical propeller/fan units, two forward and two aft. The propulsion propellers, made by Hawker Siddeley Dynamics, are of the 4-bladed, variable and reversible pitch type 19 ft (5·79 m) in diameter. The lift fans, made by BHC, are of the 12-bladed centrifugal type, 11 ft 6 in (3·5 m) in diameter.

Since the gear ratios between the engine, fan and propeller are fixed, the power distribution can be altered by varying the propeller pitch and hence changing the speed of the system, which accordingly alters the power absorbed by the fixed pitch fan. The power absorbed by the fan can be varied from almost zero shp (i.e. boating with minimum power) to 2,100 shp, within the propeller and engine speed limitations. A typical division on maximum cruise power would be 2,000 shp to the propeller and 1,150 shp to the fan; the remaining 250 shp can be accounted for by engine power fall-off due to the turbine rpm drop, transmission losses and auxiliary drives.

The drive shafts from the engines consist of flanged light-alloy tubes approximately 7 ft 6 in (2·28 m) long supported by steady bearings and connected by self-aligning couplings. Shafting to the rear propeller/fan units is comparatively short, but to the forward units is approximately 60 ft (18·27 m).

The main gearbox of each unit comprises a spiral bevel reduction gear, with outputs at the top and bottom of the box to the vertical propeller and fan drive shafts respectively. The design of the vertical shafts and couplings is similar to the main transmission shafts, except that the shafts above the main gearbox are of steel instead of light alloy to transmit the much greater torque loads to the propeller. This gearbox is equipped with a power take-off for an auxiliary gearbox with drives for pressure and scavenge lubricating oil pumps, and also a hydraulic pump for the pylon and fin steering control.

The upper gearbox, mounted on top of the pylon, turns the propeller drive through 90° and has a gear ratio of 1·16 : 1. This gearbox has its own self-contained lubricating system.

Engines and auxiliaries are readily accessible for maintenance from inside the craft, while engine, propellers, pylons and all gearboxes can be removed for overhaul without disturbing the main structure.

The fan rotates on a pintle which is attached to the main structure. The assembly may be detached and removed inboard onto the car deck without disturbing the major structure.

During 1975, British Rail's two SR.N4s carried between them 600,000 passengers and 86,000 cars on the Dover-Boulogne and Dover-Calais services

Hoverlloyd's SR.N4 Mk.2 Swift, en route to Calais in sea state 4. Currently SR.N4s in cross-channel service are limited to operation in seas of up to 8 ft (2·43 m) significant wave height (12 ft (3·65 m) maximum), when the waves are shorter than 1½ times craft length (200 ft (60·96 m). It is anticipated that the corresponding sea state limitation on the SR.N4 Mk. 3 will permit operation in waves up to 10 ft (3·04 m) significant wave height (15 ft (4·57 m) max)

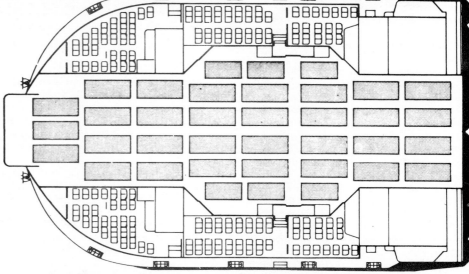

In most respects, the SR.N4 Mk 2 is identical to the standard version. The increased capacity of 282 passengers and 37 cars was achieved by removing two inner passenger cabins to increase the car deck area and by widening the outer passenger cabins

CONTROLS: The craft control system enables the thrust lines and pitch angles of the propellers to be varied either collectively or differentially. The fins and rudders move in step with the aft pylons. The pylons, fins and rudders move through $\pm 35°$, $\pm 30°$ and $\pm 40°$ respectively. On Hoverlloyd's craft the rudders have been deleted and on Seaspeed's craft the rudders have been locked relative to the fins.

Demand signals for pylon and fin angles are transmitted from the commander's controls electrically. These are compared with the pylon or fin feed-back signals and the differences are then amplified to actuate the hydraulic jacks mounted at the base of the pylon or fin structure. Similar electro-hydraulic signalling and feed-back systems are used to control propeller pitches.

The commander's controls include a rudder bar which steers the craft by pivoting the propeller pylons differentially.

For example, if the right foot is moved forward, the forward pylons move clockwise, viewed from above, and the aft pylons and fins move anti-clockwise, thus producing a turning movement to starboard. The foregoing applies with positive thrust on the propellers, but if negative thrust is applied, as in the case of using the propellers for braking, the pylons and fins are automatically turned to opposing angles, thus maintaining the turn. A wheel mounted on a control column enables the commander to move the pylons and fins in unison to produce a drift to either port or starboard as required. The control of the distribution of power between each propeller and fan is by propeller pitch lever. The pitch of all four propellers can be adjusted collectively over a limited range by a fore-and-aft movement of the control wheel.

HULL: Construction is primarily of high strength, aluminium-clad, aluminium alloy, suitably protected against the corrosive effects of sea water.

The basic structure is the buoyancy chamber, built around a grid of longitudinal and transversal frames, which form twenty-four watertight sub-divisions for safety. The design ensures that even a rip from end-to-end would not cause the craft to sink or overturn. The reserve buoyancy is 250% the total available buoyancy amounting to more than 550 tons.

Top and bottom surfaces of the buoyancy chamber are formed by sandwich construction panels bolted onto the frames, the top surface being the vehicle deck. Panels covering the central 16 ft (4·9 m) section of the deck are reinforced to carry unladen coaches, or commercial vehicles up to 9 tons gross weight (max axle load 13,000 lb (5,900 kg)), while the remainder are designed solely to carry cars and light vehicles (max axle load 4,500 lb (2,040 kg)). An articulated loading ramp, 18 ft (5·5m) wide, which can be lowered to ground level, is built into the bows, whilst doors extending the full width of the centre deck are provided at the aft end.

Similar grid construction is used on the elevated passenger-carrying decks and the roof, where the panels are supported by deep transverse and longitudinal frames. The buoyancy chamber is joined to the roof by longitudinal walls to form a stiff fore-and-aft structure. Lateral bending is taken mainly by the buoyancy tanks. All horizontal surfaces are of pre-fabricated sandwich panels with the exception of the roof, which is of skin and stringer panels.

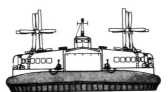 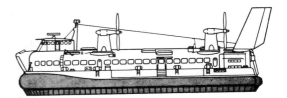 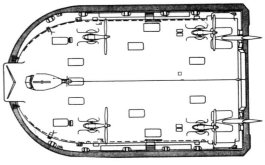

Typical internal arrangements of the SR.N4 include an all-passenger layout, seating 609, and mixed traffic ferries for either 174 passengers and 34 cars, or 254 passengers and 30 cars.   Average service waterspeed is 40-60 knots

Cars being unloaded from the SR.N4 via the 31 ft (9.45 m) wide stern doors

Panels covering the central 16 ft (4·9 m) of the vehicle decks are reinforced to carry unladen coaches or commercial vehicles up to 9 tons gross weight while the remainder is designed solely to carry cars and light vehicles

Double curvature has been avoided other than in the region of the air intakes and bow. Each fan air intake is bifurcated and has an athwartships bulkhead at both front and rear, supporting a beam carrying the transmission main gearbox and the propeller pylon. The all-moving fins and rudders behind the aft pylons pivot on pintles just ahead of the rear bulkhead.

The fans deliver air to the cushion via a peripheral fingered bag skirt.

The material used for both bags and fingers is nylon, coated with neoprene and/or natural rubber, the fingers and cones being made from a heavier weight material than the trunks.

ACCOMMODATION: The basic manning requirement is for a commander, an engineer/radio operator and a radar operator/navigator. A seat is provided for a fourth crew member or a crew member in training. The remainder of the crew, i.e. those concerned with passenger service or car handling, are located in the main cabins. The arrangement may be modified to suit individual operator's requirements.

The control cabin is entered by either of two ways. The normal method, when the cars are arranged in four lanes, is by a hatch in the cabin floor, reached by a ladder from the car deck. When heavy vehicles are carried on the centre section, or if for some other reason the ladder has to be retracted, a door in the side of the port forward passenger cabin gives access to a ladder leading onto the main cabin roof. From the roof an entrance door gives access into the control cabin.

The craft currently in service carry 254 passengers and 30 cars but the basic design permits variations from an all-passenger craft (609 seats) to one carrying 174 passengers and 34 cars.

The car deck occupies the large central area of the craft, with large stern doors and a bow ramp providing a drive-on/drive-off facility.

Separate side doors give access to the passenger cabins which flank the car deck. The outer cabins have large windows which extend over the full length of the craft. The control cabin is sited centrally and forward on top of the superstructure to give maximum view.

DIMENSIONS, EXTERNAL:

Overall length	130 ft 2 in	(39·68 m)
Overall beam	78 ft 0 in	(23·77 m)
Overall height on landing pads		
	37 ft 8 in	(11·48 m)
Skirt depth	8 ft 0 in	(2·44 m)

DIMENSIONS, INTERNAL:

Passenger/vehicle floor area
5,800 sq ft (539 m²)
Vehicle deck headroom-centre line
11 ft 3 in (3·43 m)
Bow ramp door aperture size (height × width) 11 ft 6 in × 18 ft (3·51 × 5·48 m)
Stern door aperture size (height × width)
11 ft × 31 ft (3·51 m × 9·45 m)

WEIGHTS:

Normal gross weight 180 tons
Fuel capacity
4,500 Imp gallons (20·456 litres)

PERFORMANCE (at normal gross weight at 15°C):

Max waterspeed over calm water, zero wind (cont power rating) 70 knots
Average service waterspeed 40-60 knots
Normal stopping distance from 50 knots
525 yards (480 m)
Endurance at max cont power on 2,800 Imp gallons 2·5 hours
Negotiable gradient from standing start
1 : 11

SR.N4 Mk. 2

To cope with the increasing public demand for its cross-Channel service, Hoverlloyd has increased the capacity of its craft from 254 passengers and 30 vehicles to 278 passengers and 37 vehicles.

Modification of the first of these craft was completed in January 1973, and the remaining two craft underwent similar conversions during the winter 1973/74. An additional craft is now under construction for Hoverlloyd and will enter service in June 1977.

This increase in capacity has been achieved by the removal of the two inner passenger cabins on the car deck level to accommodate more vehicles. Passenger capacity has been increased by widening the outer cabins to the periphery of the craft structure.

At a maximum gross weight of 200 tons, the SR.N4 Mk. 2 is heavier than the standard craft, but the effect of this increase in weight on performance is minimal ensuring that high frequency schedules continue to be met. The craft is also fitted with a "tapered" skirt which is now standard for all SR.N4 craft.

SR.N4 Mk. 3

A contract was signed on April 2nd, 1976 for the conversion of the two British Rail

Passenger seating in one of the side cabins flanking the car deck on a Hoverlloyd SR.N4

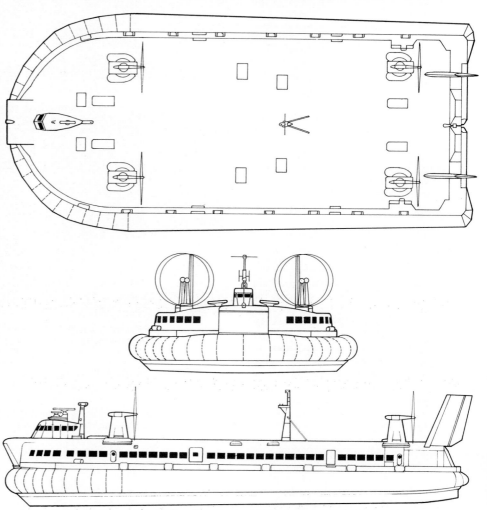

General arrangement of the SR.N4 Mk 3. A contract was signed on April 2nd 1976 for the conversion of the two British Rail SR.N4 Mk.1 craft to Mk.3 standard. The first converted craft is due to enter service in the Spring of 1978 and will carry up to 416 passengers and 60 vehicles. It is anticipated that the SR.N4 Mk 3 will be able to operate in waves of up to 10 ft significant wave height (15 ft maximum)

Impression of a BHC SR.N4 Mk 3 Mountbatten-class hovercraft

SR.N4 Mk. 1 craft to Mk. 3 standard. The first of these converted craft will enter service in the Spring of 1978 and will be capable of carrying up to 416 passengers and 60 vehicles.

The four marine Proteus gas-turbines will be up-rated to 3,800 shp each, and each will drive a propeller/fan unit with a 21 ft (6·40 m) diameter propeller. The additional power will ensure that the performance of the current craft is maintained.

Craft motion will be less than that experienced on the standard SR.N4, and for similar comfort levels the larger craft should be capable of operating in waves up to 2 ft (0·61 m) higher than the present craft.

DIMENSIONS:

Length overall	186 ft 0 in (56·69 m)
Beam, hard structure	87 ft 0 in (26·52 m)
Cushion depth, mean	10 ft 0 in (3·05 m)
Height on landing pads	44 ft 0 in (13·41 m)

WEIGHTS:

Basic weight	168 tons
Max disposable load (incl. fuel etc)	112 tons

WINCHESTER (SR.N6) CLASS

Designed primarily as a fast ferry for operation in sheltered waters, the Winchester can accommodate either 38 passengers or 3 tons of freight.

Fully amphibious, it can operate from relatively unsophisticated bases above the high water mark, irrespective of tidal state.

Directional control is achieved by twin rudders and a thrust port system. Two manually actuated elevators provide pitch trim at cruising speed.

Winchesters have been in regular commercial service since 1965 and current operators include: British Rail Hovercraft Ltd., Hovertravel Ltd, Hoverwork Ltd, and Mitsubishi. A further Winchester is in service with the Civil Aviation Department, Ministry of Transport, New Zealand, as a crash rescue craft at Auckland International Airport. Its smaller, 7-ton predecessor, the SR.N5 (see JSS 1971-72 and earlier editions) is in service with the Canadian Coast Guard.

Military variants are in service with the Royal Navy's Hovercraft Trials Unit, the

One of three SR.N6s operated by the Royal Navy's Hovercraft Trials Unit, Lee-on-Solent. This particular variant is a Mk.2

Imperial Iranian Navy and the Saudi Arabian Frontier Force and Coast Guard.

LIFT AND PROPULSION: Power for the intergrated lift/propulsion system is provided by a Rolls-Royce Marine Gnome gas turbine with a maximum continuous rating at 15°C of 900 shp. This drives a BHC 12-blade centrifugal 7 ft (2·13 m) diameter lift fan, and a Dowty Rotol 4 blade variable pitch 9 ft (2·14 m) diameter propeller for propulsion.

DIMENSIONS, EXTERNAL:

Overall length	48 ft 5 in (14·76 m)
Overall beam (solid structure)	23 ft (7·01m)
Overall height on landing pads	15ft (4·57m)
Skirt depth	4 ft (1·22 m)

DIMENSIONS, INTERNAL:

Cabin size (length × width)
21 ft 9 in × 7 ft 8 in (6·62 m × 2·34 m)
Cabin headroom-centre line 6 ft (1·83 m)

Door aperture size (height × width)
5 ft 9 in × 3 ft 3 in (1·75 m × 0·99 m)

WEIGHT:

Normal gross weight	10 tons

PERFORMANCE (at normal gross weight at 15°C.):

Max water speed over calm water zero wind (cont power rating) 52 knots (96 km/hr)
Average service waterspeed in sheltered coastal waters 30·35 knots (55·65 km/hr)
Endurance at max cont power rating on 265 Imp gall of fuel 3·6 hours

WINCHESTER (SR.N6) CLASS—
PASSENGER FERRY/GENERAL PURPOSE

Since the SR.N6 first entered service as a passenger ferry in 1965, it has carried well over three million fare-paying passengers and is now firmly established in certain areas as an integral part of surface transportation networks.

The popularity of these services subsequently led to the introduction of an SR.N6 with a larger carrying capacity, designated the SR.N6 Mk. 1S. At 58 ft in length, the Mk. 1S is 10 ft longer than the standard craft and can carry up to 58 passengers as opposed to 35-38 in the standard SR.N6.

Other modifications to this craft include additional baggage panniers, emergency exits and improved cabin ventilation. An additional bonus is a significant increase in ride comfort. To ensure that performance is maintained, the rating of the Rolls-Royce Marine Gnome gas turbine engine has been increased by 100 shp to 1,000 shp.

Two Mk. 1S craft are in service with Solent Seaspeed Ltd, linking Cowes and Southampton, and one Mk. 1S is in operation on the Ryde/Southsea route with Hovertravel Limited.

Apart from passenger services, commercial SR.N6s have also made successful inroads into other fields of operation in recent years and typical examples of such applications include freight-carrying, hydrographic/seismographic survey, offshore support operations, general communications, crash rescue and firefighting.

To undertake these duties, craft have been modified either with the fitting of specialised equipment or by structural alterations such as flat-decks.

WINCHESTER (SR.N6) CLASS— MILITARY

Currently, variants of the SR.N6 are in service with a growing number of the world's military and paramilitary forces on coastal defence and logistic support duties.

The SR.N6 Mk. 2/3, for logistic support, features a roof loading hatch and strengthened side-decks for carrying long loads of up to ½-ton. Lightweight armour may be fitted to protect troops being carried in the cabin; the engine; and other vital systems. Defensive armament is provided by a roof-mounted light machine gun (7·62 mm or 0·05 in).

The craft can carry upwards of 20 fully-equipped troops or supply loads of up to 5 tons. A small auxiliary generator is installed to provide power when the main engine is stopped.

The SR.N6 Mk. 4 for coastal defence duties may be fitted with 20 mm cannon or short-range wire-guided surface/surface missiles. Communications equipment is concentrated behind the rear cabin bulkhead.

The SR.N6 Mk. 5A, with a length of 60 ft 8 in (18·5 m) is 10 ft longer than the standard SR.N6 and differs greatly externally. It is a projected development of the SR.N6 Mk. 5 which was extensively tested under operational conditions on both the northern and southern flanks of NATO by 200 Squadron, Royal Corps of Transport. Its main feature is a long central well-deck, strengthened for carrying vehicles including BV 202 Snocats and Landrovers and weapons including howitzers. A bow ramp is provided for loading. Twin cabins flank the well-deck; that on the starboard side housing the captain, navigator and controls, and that on the port the observer and vehicle driver.

To maintain high performance at the heavier loading—33,000 lb maximum gross weight—the Marine Gnome gas turbine has been uprated to 1,400 shp

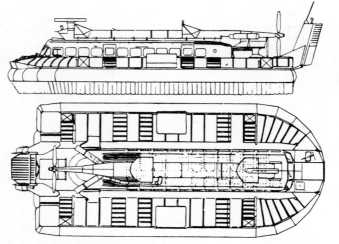

General arrangement of the SR.N6 Mk. 1S (one 1,000 shp Rolls-Royce Marine Gnome gas-turbine)

One of two SR.N6 Mk 1S hovercraft operated on the Solent Seaspeed service between Cowes and Southampton. The "stretched" variant, which is 10 ft longer than the standard craft seats up to 58 passengers compared with the 35/38 in earlier models

Prototype of the SR.N6 Mk 6

SR.N6 Mk. 5A, leading particulars:

DIMENSIONS:

Overall length	60 ft 8 in ((18·5 m)
Overall beam	25 ft 4 in (7·7 m)
Overall height (on landing pads)	
	14 ft 2 in (4·3 m)
Engine	R.R. Gnome GN 1301
Maximum power	1,400 shp
All-up weight	33,000 lb (15,000 kg)
Capacity	Up to 4 persons and 1 vehicle and trailer; 1 m/c gun
Maximum speed	47 knots
Endurance	3 hr
Long range endurance	6 hr

WINCHESTER (SR.N6) CLASS—Mk. 6

The SR.N6 Mk. 6 is the latest development of the successful Winchester series and represents a significant step forward in terms of increased payload, all weather performance and a substantial reduction in external noise. These advances have been achieved by the introduction of twin-propeller propulsion, a more powerful engine, a redesigned skirt and an increase of 10 ft (3·04 m) in overall length.

The twin 10 ft (3·04 m) diameter propellers with which the craft is fitted turn at reduced rpm, resulting in lower external noise levels. The pitch of each can be varied independently giving the pilot greatly improved directional control at high and low speeds.

Power is supplied by a Rolls-Royce Gnome 1301 gas-turbine rated at 1,400 shp maximum and 1,285 shp continuous.

SR.N6 Mk. 6A FAST INTERCEPTOR

A fast patrol version of the SR.N6, the Mk. 6A is designed primarily for coastal defence, but alternative roles include coastal patrol, fast escort and search and rescue. A full range of navigation aids provide it with 24-hour operating capability.

The craft is amphibious, with good rough water performance and has low-speed propellers to ensure low external noise.

Dependent upon the role for which it is required, the craft can either be fitted with a 20 mm GAM B.O.1 mounting, or a 30 mm A32 mounting. With the former weapon, which is manually operated and independent of electrical supplies, the vessel is capable of fulfilling all coastguard duties. With the latter, it is able to engage targets while operating at high speeds in rough water. It can also track fast-moving targets.

Each system can be augmented by small arms operated from the cabin top, providing covering fire for boarding parties.

If required, the craft can be adapted for various armed logistic support roles, including that of vehicle carrier, with troops in the main cabin, or troop-carrier with a soft extension above the well deck. Capacity is provided for up to 11 persons and one vehicle and trailer.

LIFT AND PROPULSION: Motive power is supplied by a single 1,400 shp Rolls Royce Gnome GN.1301 gas-turbine driving a single centrifugal lift fan and two 10 ft (3·05 m) diameter variable-pitch propellers.

HULL: Marine corrosion-resistant aluminium alloys. Flat side decks accommodate auxiliary power units air-conditioning system and servicing equipment.

SKIRT: Tapered, BHC fingered bag type.

ACCOMMODATION: Cabin access is from the well deck via a watertight door in the forward bulkhead. Radio racks, power generation equipment and small arms lockers are located in the forward cabin areas. Seating is provided on each side of the central area. Above are the command and

SR.N6 Mk 6 prototype, showing the twin-propeller arrangement and tapered skirt

Impression of the 50-knot SR.N6 Mk 6A gunship, equipped with a BMAR3 30 mm twin gyro-stabilised cannon. The craft will be capable of engaging targets at high speeds in rough water

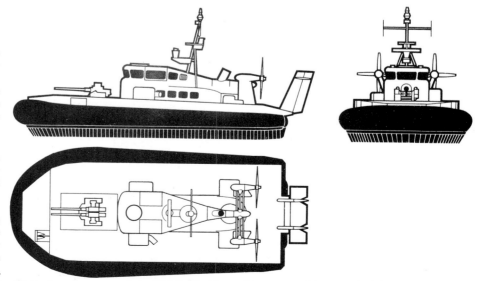

General arrangement of the SR.N6 Mk 6A gunship, powered by a single 1,400 shp Rolls-Royce GN.1301 gas-turbine

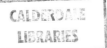

navigation stations. All accommodation is air-conditioned. A galley and toilet are located aft, with doors separating them from the main cabin area.

SYSTEMS, WEAPONS: Alternative arrangements: Single Oerlikon 20 mm manually operated G.A.M.-B.O.1 rapid fire cannon operated by one man. Twin B.M.A.R.C. 30 mm gyro-stabilised type A32 Mounting—this weapon system incorporates two-axis gyro stabilisation which gives high accuracy in adverse weather conditions.

APU: A Lucas 15/90 gas-turbine APU provides electrical power for full air conditioning and all equipment when engine is stopped.

COMMUNICATIONS: HF, VHF and UHF radio installed, together with radar and Decca Navigator.

DIMENSIONS:

Craft length over hard structure	
	63 ft 0 in (19·2 m)
Beam, skirt inflated	26 ft 0 in (7·92 m)
Height on landing pads	21 ft 9 in (6·63 m)
Height hovering	29 ft 2 in (8·89 m)

WEIGHTS:

Max A.U.W.	38,000 lb (17,240 kg)

With Oerlikon single 20 mm cannon on manually operated GAM-BO1 mounting:

Craft basic weight	27,000 lb (12,250 kg)
Normal max operating weight	35,000 lb (15,880 kg)
Disposable load	8,000 lb (3,630 kg)
Total fuel	5,300 lb (2,400 kg)
Ammunition	500 lb (227 kg)
Boarding Party (Seven Troops)	1,400 lb (635 kg)
Overload Capability	3,000 lb (1,360 kg)
Maximum Operating	38,000 lb (17,240 kg)

With B.M.A.R.C. twin 30 mm cannon on gyro-stabilised type A32 mounting:

Craft basic weight	31,200 lb (14,150 kg)
Normal max operating weight	38,000 lb (17,240 kg)
Disposable load	6,800 lb (3,080 kg)
Total fuel	3,400 lb (1,540 kg)
Ammunition	900 lb (408 kg)
Boarding party (Seven troops)	1,400 lb (635 kg)

PERFORMANCE:

Max speed, calm water	50 knots
Endurance	3 hours
Long range endurance	8 hours

SR.N6 6B LOGISTIC

The Mk. 6B is designed for the fast transport of military loads. It is fitted with a bow ramp for vehicle 'drive on/drive off' to a strengthened well-deck (9·44 m × 2·33 m) which provides unobstructed stowage space. There are two cabins, one on each side deck. The starboard cabin is for the commander and navigator, the port for additional crewman. Defensive armament consists of a ring-mounted machine gun mounted in the port cabin roof.

This craft has a carrying capacity of 45 fully equipped troops or one ¾ ton Land Rover with trailer or a Land Rover and 105 mm field gun. Alternatively it can be loaded with up to 6 tons of mixed stores.

DIMENSIONS:

Overall length	63 ft (19·2 m)
Overall beam	26 ft (7·92 m)
Overall height (on landing pads)	21 ft 9 in (6·63 m)
Engine	R.R. Gnome GN 1301
Maximum power	1,400 shp
All-up weight	38,000 lb (17,237 kg)
Capacity	Up to 7 persons and 1 vehicle and trailer; 1 m/c gun

SR.N6 Mk 5, with a central well-deck for small armoured vehicles and weapons, including howitzers The starboard cabin houses the controls and hovercraft crew and the port cabin accommodates the vehicle crews.   Payload is 7 tons

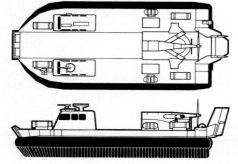 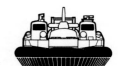

SR.N6 Mk 5A

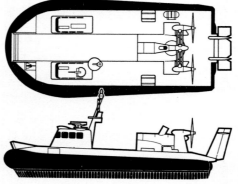 

The twin-propeller version, the Mk.6B.

Maximum speed	50 knots
Endurance	3 hours
Long range endurance	8 hours

SR.N6 MK. 6C GENERAL PURPOSE AND COMMAND VEHICLE

The Mk. 6C is a development of the Mk. 1.

It is suitable for military and paramilitary roles and general coastal security work, and can carry up to 40 fully equipped troops or 5 tons of military stores.

WELLINGTON (BH.7) CLASS

BH.7 is a 50-ton hovercraft which was

designed specifically for naval and military roles. The prototype, designated BH.7 Mk. 2, has been in service with the Royal Navy since 1970 where it has been evaluated in a number of roles including Fishery Protection, ASW and MCM work.

The second and third craft, designated Mk. 4 and a further four Mk. 5As, are all in service with the Imperial Iranian Navy.

LIFT AND PROPULSION: Power for the integrated lift propulsion system on the Mk. 2 and Mk. 4 is provided by a Rolls Royce/BS Marine Proteus 15M541 gas-turbine with a maximum rating at 23°C of 4,250 shp. On the Mk. 5A, a 15M549 is installed with a maximum rating of 4,250 shp. In both types the engine drives, via a light alloy driveshaft and bevel drive gearbox, a BHC 12-blade, centrifugal 11 ft 6 in (3·5 m) diameter lift fan and an HSD 4-blade, variable-pitch pylon-mounted propeller. Propeller diameter on the Mk. 4 is 19 ft (5·79 m) and 21 ft (6·40 m) on the Mk. 2 and Mk. 5A. Normal fuel capacity is up to 3,000 Imp gallons.

CONTROLS: Craft direction is controlled by swivelling the propeller pylon angle by a footpedal. Thrust ports are fitted at each quarter to assist directional control at low speed, and a hydraulically-operated skirt-shift system helps to bank the craft into turns, thereby reducing drift.

Fuel is transferred between forward and aft tanks via a ring main to adjust for and aft trim.

HULL: Construction is mainly of corrosion resistant light alloy. Extensive use is made of components which were designed for the N4. The bow structure is a Plasticell base covered with glass fibre.

SKIRT SYSTEM: The fan delivers air to the cushion via a continuous peripheral fingered bag skirt made in neoprene coated nylon fabric. The skirt provides an air cushion depth of 5 ft 6 in (1·68 m). The cushion is divided into four compartments by a full length longitudinal keel and by two transverse keels located slightly forward of amidships.

ACCOMMODATION: The raised control cabin, located slightly forward of amidships on the hull centre line, accommodates a crew of three, with the driver and navigator/radar operator in front and the third crew member behind. The driver sits on the right, with the throttle and propeller pitch control lever on his right, and the pylon angle foot-pedal and skirt-shift column in front.

The navigator, on the left, has a Decca radar display (Type 914 on the Mk. 5) and compass in front and Decometers in an overhead panel.

The large main cabin area permits a variety of operational layouts. In a typical arrangement, the operations room is placed directly beneath the control cabin and contains communication, navigation, search and strike equipment and associated displays.

The craft has an endurance of up to 11 hours under cruise conditions but this can be extended considerably as it can stay 'on watch' without using the main engine.

Provision can be made for the crew to live aboard for several days.

SYSTEMS: Electrical: Two Rover IS/90 APUs provide via two 55kVA generators 3-phase 400Hz ac at 200 volts for ac and dc supplies.

One of two BH.7 Mk. 4s operated by the Imperial Iranian Navy. The craft are employed on logistics duties and have bow loading doors.

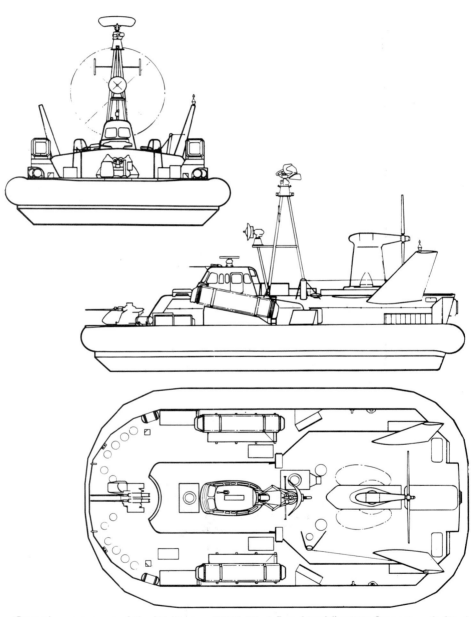

General arrangement of the Wellington (BH.7) Mk 5 Fast Attack/Logistic Support craft fitted with Exocet launchers and a twin 30 mm dual purpose mounting

DIMENSIONS, EXTERNAL:

Length overall	78 ft 4 in (23·9 m)
Beam overall	45 ft 6 in (13·8 m)
Overall height on landing pads	
	34 ft 0 in (10·36 m)
Skirt depth	5 ft 6 in (1·67 m)

DIMENSIONS, INTERNAL (Mk 4 only):

Bow door size	
13 ft 9 in × 7 ft 3 in (4·18 m × 2·20 m)	
Headroom centre line ·	7 ft 10 in (2·38 m)

WEIGHT:

Normal gross weight	50 tons
Payload	14 tons

PERFORMANCE (at max operating weight at 15°C)

Max waterspeed over calm water (cont power rating)	60 kts
Average water speed in 4½ ft (1·37 m) seas	35·50 knots

WELLINGTON (BH.7) Mk. 4 LOGISTIC SUPPORT

ACCOMMODATION: In this role, the main hold floor area of 600 sq ft (56 m²) of the Mk. 4 provides an unobstructed space suitable for loading wheeled vehicles, guns and military stores.

Two side cabins, filled with paratroop-type seats, can accommodate up to 60 troops and their equipment.

Access at the bow is through a "clamshell" door.

Machine guns can be fitted in gun rings on the roof on either side of the cabin and provision can be made for armour plating to protect personnel, the engine and vital electrical components.

SYSTEMS: Two Rover IS/90 gas turbine APUs provide electrical power independently of the main engine.

TYPICAL MILITARY LOADS: 170 fully equipped troops or 3 field cars and trailers plus 60 troops or two armoured scout cars or up to 20 NATO pallets.

DIMENSIONS, EXTERNAL:

Overall length	78 ft 4 in (23·85 m)
Overall beam	45 ft 6 in (13·8 m)
Overall height on landing pads	
	33 ft (10·06 m)

DIMENSIONS, INTERNAL:

Main cabin floor area	600 sq ft (56 m²)
Main cabin headroom—centreline	
	7 ft 10 in (2·38 m)
Access door aperture (height × width)	
	7 ft 3 in (2·20 m) × 13 ft 9 in (4·2 m)

WEIGHTS:

Normal gross weight	45 tons
Fuel load at 45 tons AUW	9 tons
Max fuel capacity	12·5 tons

PERFORMANCE (at normal gross weight at 15°C):

Max waterspeed, calm water, zero wind cont power rating   65 knots (120 km/hr)

Rough waterspeed in 4½ ft (1·37 m) seas depending on heading and wave length
                            35-50 knots (65-92 km/hr)

Endurance at max cont power rating with a 9 tons of fuel (with 10% reserve) 8-hours

WELLINGTON (BH.7) MK. 5 FAST ATTACK

Designed for coastal defence operations, the BH.7 Mk. 5 carries medium-range surface/surface missiles, such as Exocet, on its sidedecks. Secondary armament consists of a twin 30 mm surface/AA radar controlled mounting situated on the foredeck forward of the main centre cabin.

The main central cabin, employed on the BH.7 Mk. 4 for load-carrying, is equipped as an operations and fire control room. Since it is fully amphibious, the BH.7 Mk. 5 can be operated from relatively unprepared bases on beaches and can head directly towards its target on interception missions regardless of the tidal state and marginal terrain. Also, since none of its solid structure is immersed, it is invulnerable to underwater defences such as acoustic, magnetic and pressure mines and to attack by torpedoes.

A full range of electronic navigational aids permit the craft to operate by day or night ensuring 'round-the-clock' availability.

WELLINGTON (BH.7) Mk. 5A FAST ATTACK/LOGISTICS

Similar to the Mk. 5 above, with the exception that the bow door is retained, giving the craft a dual fast attack/logistic capability. Secondary armament can consist of 2 roof-mounted single 20 mm guns.

Wellington Mk.5A fast attack /logistic support craft. This particular variant carries medium range ship-to-ship missiles, such as Exocet, on its sidedecks and retains the bow loading door of the Mk.4

Impression of the BH.7 Wellington Mk. 6 fast attack/patrol craft, equipped with a 76 mm Oto Melara cannon and four Exocet ship-to-ship missiles. Maximum speed of the craft, which will have an all-up weight of 90 tons, will be 68 knots under calm conditions

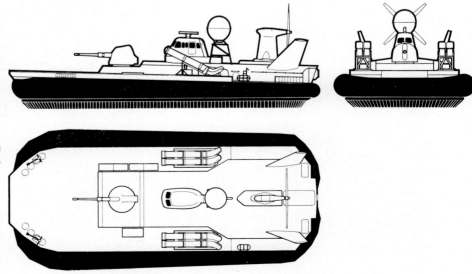

General arrangement of the 108 ft long BH.7 Mk 6, powered by two 3,000 shp gas-turbines

LEADING PARTICULARS:

Overall length	78 ft 4 in (23·9 m)
Overall beam	45 ft 6 in (13·9 m)
Overall height (on landing pads)	
	34 ft (10·7 m)
Engine	R.R. Proteus (15M 549)
Maximum power	4,250 shp
All-up weight	55 ton (55·88 tonnes)
Capacity	Up to 5 persons and 7 ton weapon payload
Maximum speed	58 knots
Endurance	8 hours
Long range endurance	10 hours

WELLINGTON (BH.7) Mk. 6 FAST ATTACK/PATROL

This projected craft is intended to be powered by two 3,000 hp gas turbines driving a centrifugal lift fan and a 21 ft (6·40 m) diameter variable-pitch propeller. The craft illustrated is armed with four General Dynamics ARM (anti-radiation missile) or Active Standard surface-to-surface missiles and a single 76 mm Oto Melara dual-purpose cannon. If required it can be adapted for use as a hunter/killer ASW vessel or for employment as a mine-countermeasures craft in conjunction with the Edo Mk. 105 mine countermeasures system and other similar equipment.

ACCOMMODATION:

Air-conditioned working and living quarters for crew of 12.

WEAPON SYSTEMS:

4 ARM Standard surface-to-surface missiles, plus 76 mm Oto Melara radar-controlled dual-purpose gun. HSA combined fire control and surveillance radar. Alternative systems: Semi-active variant of Standard, Exocet, Harpoon, Penguin or Seakiller, 35 mm twin Oerlikon or 30 mm twin Hispano Suiza.

DIMENSIONS:

Length overall, hard structure	
	108 ft 3 in (33·0 m)
Beam overall, hard structure	
	45 ft 6 in (13·9 m)
Height on cushion	36 ft 6 in (11·5 m)

WEIGHTS:

Starting all-up weight	90 tons
Weapons payload	17 tons
Fuel, including ballast	15 tons

PERFORMANCE:

Both engines running at max continuous rating of 6,000 shp.

Max speed, calm conditions	68 knots
Endurance	10 hours
Range of operation	400-550 n miles

One engine running at 3,000 shp

Cruising speed (depending on weight and conditions)	16-40 knots
Endurance	18 hours
Cruising range	290-700 n miles

BHC MINE CLEARANCE HOVERCRAFT

Minesweeping is one of the most hazardous of all naval activities. Clearance techniques in the past have been very much on a hit or miss basis with craft operating in pairs, one sweeping and the other hunting and destroying the released mines as they surfaced by rifle and machinegun fire. Since the precise location of each mine was unknown, it was not unusual for a released mine to surface in the path of or beneath the hull of the hunter craft.

In the United States in recent years, efforts to reduce the tremendous wastage in lives and craft led to the introduction of the Edo 105 and 106 foil-equipped catamaran minesweeping systems. These not only speed up the process of mine clearance, but since they

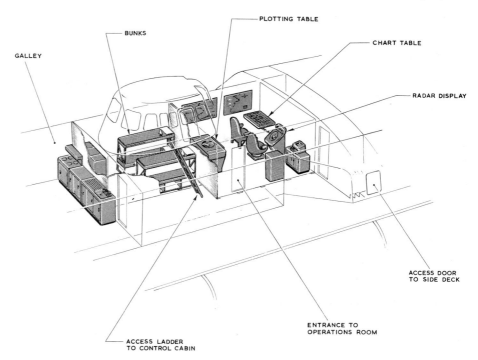

Interior layout of the BH.7 Mk 5A Minesweeper

The 200 ton SR.N4, Sir Christopher, accompanied by the 40 knot patrol craft, "Tenacity", during mine countermeasures trials with the Royal Navy off Portland in May 1976. During these trials the craft reached speeds in excess of 70 knots and covered the 167 nautical miles from Portland back to Ramsgate at an average speed of 51·4 knots

are towed by helicopter, reduce very considerably the risks to the crews involved.

In the United Kingdom, the Ministry of Defence (Navy) has stated that as hovercraft normally operate clear of the water, they are less vulnerable to possible mine explosions than conventional vessels, and with mine countermeasures equipment they have a potential for this type of work.

British Hovercraft Corporation has announced plans for both sweeper and hunter versions of the BH.7 and the SR.N4 Descriptions of these vessels are given below.

BH.7 Mk. 5A MINESWEEPER

Among the advantages offered by the use of this type of fully amphibious hovercraft for MCM, as opposed to a displacement vessel

are four times the transit speed; very low acoustic and magnetic underwater signatures; and virtual immunity to underwater explosions. Additionally, the craft can be used for crew rescue in mined waters. Since the craft is based on the standard BH.7 Mk. 5A, and retains its bow landing door, it has logistic support capability when not being employed for minesweeping.

LIFT AND PROPULSION: Integrated lift/propulsion system powered by a single Rolls-Royce/BS Marine Proteus 15M/549 gas-turbine with a continuous output at 15°C of 3,800 hp at 10,000 turbine rpm. This drives via a light alloy drive shaft and bevel drive gearbox, a BHC 12-blade, centrifugal 11 ft 6 in (3·5 m) diameter, lift fan and an HSD 4-blade, variable-pitch 21 ft (6·40 m) diameter, pylon-mounted propeller.

ACCOMMODATION: Total crew complement is eight men. The raised control cabin accommodates a three-man operating crew, with the captain and navigator in front and the third crew member behind. An off-duty cabin is located immediately beneath, with bunks for four. Ahead of the off-duty cabin is a galley and aft, in the midship cabin, is the operations room with navigation, surface and under surface plotting tables, radar display and data processing equipment. The control cabin is air-conditioned and the rest areas are air-conditioned and soundproofed. Access from the off-duty cabin to the control cabin is via a ladder.

SYSTEMS, MCM EQUIPMENT: Mine-sweeping equipment, including winches and cable reels, are stowed on the side decks and sides of the superstructure forward. Equipment includes floats, depressors, otters and cutters, venturi acoustic sweeping gear, marker buoys and an inflatable dinghy.

SWEEP DEPLOYMENT: Sweeps are deployed from the port side deck and shackled to the primary tow cable which is permanently attached to the destabilising pulley running on the towing bridle.

DIMENSIONS, EXTERNAL:

Length overall	78 ft 4 in (23·9 m)
Beam overall	45 ft 6 in (13·9 m)
Height overall	
on cushion	38 ft 8 in (11·8 m)
on landing pads	34 ft 0 in (10·4 m)

DIMENSIONS, INTERNAL:

Cabin headroom, on centreline
7 ft 10 in (2·4 m)
Bow door opening
13 ft 9 in × 7 ft 3 in (4·1 m × 2·9 m)

WEIGHTS:

Starting all-up weight	53 tons app
Mean operating weight	48 ton app
MCM payload	3 tons app

PERFORMANCE:

Cruising speed, knots

Craft heading	Into wind	Beam wind
Calm water, still air	68	68

Significant wave height/wind speed

1 ft/6 kt	57	59
2 ft/11 kt	47	52
3 ft/15 kt	38	44

ENDURANCE:

Total fuel consumption at max. continuous power (includes both APU's) 1·16 ton/hour
Endurance on a nominal 10 ton fuel load
8·6 hours
Towing capability. A towing force of 3·5 tons is available at speeds of up to 10 knots in significant waveheights up to 3 ft.

BH.7 Mk. 5A MINE HUNTER

This version is identical in practically every respect to the mine sweeper model and can be reconfigured readily to sweeping duties or logistic support roles. It differs from the sweeper only in the mine disposal equipment carried.

SYSTEMS: MCM EQUIPMENT: A 20 mm machine gun mount ahead of the control cabin is optional. Towed or dunking mine detection and classification sonars; remotely piloted mine disposal vehicles; sonar display units; recorders etc; navigation and communications gear.

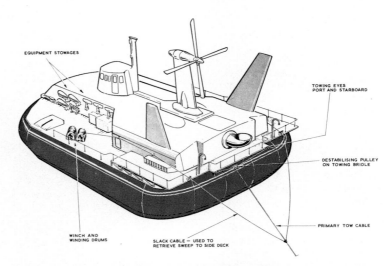

BH.7 Mk 5A equipped for Minesweeping

The Royal Navy's BH.7 Mk.2 as modified by BHC for the mine countermeasures role, to enable the craft to play a more realistic part in naval exercises. The deck extension carries cable rollers and a small davit to assist in deployment and recovery

DEPLOYMENT: Over the sidedecks via davits and swinging A frames. Towing lines are deployed and retrieved by winch and shackled to the primary tow cable which is permanently attached to the destabilising pulley running on the towing bridle.

PERFORMANCE:

Cruising and towing speed
As for minesweeper

Endurance: In the case of a sonar being towed at a speed of 5 knots or less, but with the craft in full hover condition, the estimated fuel consumption (ton/hour) is:

Proteus   0·677 (ISA conditions)
2 Rover APU
               0·111 (assumed requirement)
               0·778 ton/hour total

On a nominal 10 ton fuel-load, endurance would be 12·9 hours

SR.N4 Mk. 4 MINESWEEPER

The SR.N4 Mk. 4 would have a transit speed of up to five times that of conventional minesweepers. It would also retain its logistic capability and operate as a support vessel when required. In most respects the craft would be similar to the SR.N4 Mk. 2.

LIFT AND PROPULSION: Power is supplied by four Rolls-Royce Marine Proteus free turbine turboshaft engines located in pairs at the rear of the craft on either side of the working deck space. Each would operate at 3,800 shp when cruising. Each engine is connected to one of four identical propeller/fan units, two forward, two aft. The propellers, made by Hawker Siddely Dynamics, are of 4-bladed, variable and reversible pitch type, 21 ft (6·40 m) in diameter. The lift fans, made by BHC, are of 12-bladed centrifugal type, 11 ft 6 in (3·5 m) in diameter.

CONTROLS AND HULL: Similar to SR.N4 Mk. 2.

ACCOMMODATION: Crew complement is up to twenty men, with 10-15 on watch. Rest areas and bunks are provided for 10 men.

A typical minesweeper interior places the operations room amidships, at the most advantageous position to minimise the effects of craft motion on the seated operators. Within the operator's room are navigation, surface and below-surface plotting tables and data processing equipment. The operators room and rest areas are ventilated by forced air and the noise level is 65-70 dbA.

Stowed on the works deck aft of the operations room are Oropesa sweeps, otters and floats, acoustic sweep equipment, side scan sonars, short scope buoys and an inflatable dighy. A pulse generator can be installed forward of the accomodation spaces. The entire work deck space is ventilated with forced air draught to prevent the ingress of spray and exhaust fumes.

EQUIPMENT DEPLOYMENT: All equipment is deployed over the stern via two destabilising carriages or davits. A main double warp winch is provided for wire sweeping. Space is available for a magnetic sweep reel.

WEAPONS: Two 20 mm, hand-operated machine guns can be fitted in recesses at main deck level in port and starboard forward quarters.

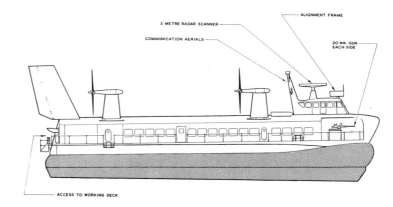

Above and below: Features of the SR.N4 Mk 4 Minesweeper

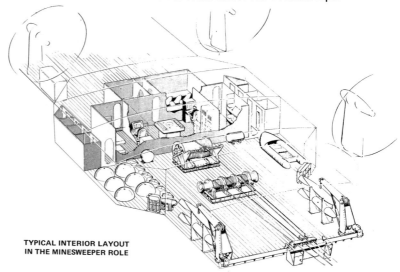

TYPICAL INTERIOR LAYOUT
IN THE MINESWEEPER ROLE

NAVIGATION:

Track: Pilot function, determined by limiting wind and sea conditions.

Position: Derived from external navigation datum.

Course to steer: Derived from navigation system computer.

DIMENSIONS, EXTERNAL:

Overall length   130 ft 2 in (39·68 m)
Beam   78 ft 0 in (23·77 m)
Height on landing pads 37 ft 8 in (11·48 m)

WEIGHTS:

Starting all-up weight   220 tons
Mean operating weight   200 tons
MCM equipment   35 tons

PERFORMANCE:

Cruising speed, knots.

Craft heading	Into wind	Beam and Downwind
Calm water, still air	69	69
Significant wave height/wind speed		
3 ft/15 kt	45	50
6 ft/25 kt	26	36
9 ft/30 kt	19	25

Endurance. Based on a nominal 40 ton fuel load, operation at 3,800 output hp/engine and continuous use of both APUs, endurance would be 9·3 hours.

Towing capability. A towing force of 8-20 tons is available at speeds of up to 10 knots in significant waveheights up to 9 ft.

SR.N4 Mk. 4 MINEHUNTER

This variant of the SR.N4 is identical to the minesweeper model and can be converted readily to this configuration from the minesweeper role. It differs only in the mine disposal equipment carried.

The craft can operate in conjunction with conventional MCM vessels and does not need a separate remote platform for mine disposal equipment employment.

SYSTEMS, MCM EQUIPMENT: Towed or dunking sonar and mine disposal vehicles are deployed over the stern by means of stern davits. The craft can also deploy remote piloted vehicles. Two hand-operated 20 mm machine guns mounts can be installed in the forward port and starboard quarters on the main deck.

BH.88

During the summer of 1975, BHC announced that it was developing a new generation hovercraft, designated BH.88, to replace the SR.N4. The new craft will be able to operate in winds of up to Force 9, have a higher cruising speed and use approximately one third of the fuel per passenger compared with that used the the SR.N4.

BHC has been awarded a contract from British Rail Seaspeed for stretching its two standard SR.N4s. In lengthened form, the SR.N4 Mk. 3 will provide much of the operational data for the projected BH.88, which will be of approximately the same size and carry a similar payload of 400 passengers and 50 cars—considered close to the optimum for cross-Channel routes. Improvements in the overall design will include a new propulsion system, employing either the latest large propellers or ducted fans, the installation of Rolls-Royce Marine Tyne gas-turbines to achieve a 25% improvement in fuel consumption, lift fans of higher efficiency and a modified skirt and hull to reduce hydrodynamic resistance.

The new craft is expected to be about five knots faster than the SR.N4 and it will also show a 40% reduction in power requirements and a 60% saving in fuel. The fuel consumption is expected to be about 2·0 lb/payload ton-mile, some 15% less than orthodox ships per unit of payload.

Estimated cost of the craft is about £6 million at today's prices, but at the same time an initial research and development investment of about £0·5 million is considered necessary. The craft will be suitable for many mixed ferry routes in the Pacific, North and Central America, Canada, Europe and the Mediterranean.

CYCLONE HOVERCRAFT

HEAD OFFICE:
5 Lordsmead, Cranfield, Bedford, MK43 0HP

TELEPHONE:
0234 750765

EXECUTIVES:
N. R. Beale BSc, MSc.
P. J. Beale

Cyclone Hovercraft have developed a plans, components and design service based upon the experience that has won the British National Championships for five consecutive years.

Their latest enterprise is a simple single-engined hovercraft, plans of which are offered for home construction. This craft is designed around the new British-made "Breeza" axial fan, for which Cyclone has been appointed agent. "Breeza" fans employ adjustable pitch blades made from high strength glass-filled polypropylene.

THE SIMPLE CYCLONE

A single-engined design employing a single ducted fan for its integrated lift and propulsion system, "Simple Cyclone" will carry one adult over water at speeds of up to 30 mph (48·28 km/h). Over smooth land its payload may be increased to two adults.

LIFT AND PROPULSION: A single Kyoritsu KEC 225 cc two-stroke engine, rated at 12·5 bhp at 5,500 rpm, drives via a toothed belt a 23⅝ in (600 mm) diameter "Breeza" fan. The unit supplies air for both lift and thrust. Any suitable engine of between 10 and 25 bhp may be used. The one gallon (4·5 litres) fuel tank gives a cruising endurance of more than one hour. A larger capacity tank may be fitted if desired.

CONTROLS: For the utmost simplicity, only two controls are provided, designed for single-handed operation. A lever control for the engine throttle is mounted on the control column which operates the twin rudders.

HULL: The hull is constructed from thin exterior grade plywood with wooden stringers. Polyurethane foam within the hull structure ensures adequate buoyancy. The fan duct unit is laminated from glass reinforced plastic.

SKIRT: The skirt fitted to the Simple Cyclone is a Cyclone-designed extended segment type employing an individual air feed through the hull to every segment.

DIMENSIONS:
Length overall 9 ft 11 in (3,000 mm)
Width overall 6 ft 0 in (1,830 mm)
Height (at rest) 1 ft 11 in (900 mm)
Hard Structure Clearance 7³⁄₃₂ in (180 mm)

WEIGHTS:
Unladen weight 176 lb (80 kg)
Normal Payload 198 lb (90 kg)

PERFORMANCE:
Max speed over land or water
30 mph (48·28 km/h)

Above: Simple Cyclone, a single-engined light hovercraft employing a single ducted fan with adjustable pitch blades for its integrated lift and propulsion system (Photo: Nigel Beale)
Below: Simple Cyclone at speed over water on Loch Lubraigh, Scotland. Maximum speed over land and water is 30 mph (48.28 km/h)

HFL-SEAGLIDE LTD

HEAD OFFICE:
PO Box 33, London N14 7NS
TELEPHONE:
01-368-6013
TELEX:
21879 IMP
DIRECTORS:
H. F. Lentze, Managing Director
R. Bourn
H. V. Lentze

HFL-Seaglide Limited was formed in 1976 to build and market the Seabee series of aerodynamic ram-wings designed by Ronald Bourn. The company's first craft is a prototype 3-seater with an overall length of 17 ft (5·18 m). The machine is based on data derived from an earlier delta wing prototype first flown in 1971. Among the range of designs projected by the company are a 3-seat fast launch, an 8-seat water taxi or freight carrier and a 35-seat water bus or freighter.

SEABEE 3-SEATER

This novel grp-hulled 3-seater was completed in 1972 and is undergoing development in three stages. During the first stage it was fitted with a converted 90 hp General Motors flat six-cylinder air-cooled engine driving a 4-bladed fixed-pitch wooden propeller optimised for 70 knots. For the second stage, this was replaced by a 130 hp flat 4-cylinder aero engine driving a 2-bladed fixed-pitch propeller optimised for 120 knots. The third stage was reached in July 1976 when this engine was replaced by a 130 hp Turbomeca Artouste turbofan.

The vehicle has undergone both preliminary and advanced trials in ground effect, but no attempts to convert to free-flight and back had been made at the time of going to press.
POWER PLANT: 130 hp 4-cylinder horizontally-opposed Rolls-Royce 240A aero-engine driving a 2-bladed De Havilland fixed-pitch propeller.
CONTROLS: Aircraft type, with yoke operating elevon on stabiliser, and foot-operated rudder bar linked to twin rudders.
HULL: Monocoque structure in moulded grp. Conventional hard chine design.
MAINPLANE: Wing tips in grp. Control surfaces in doped fabric. Spruce main spars. RAF 30 section with lift area of approx. 108 sq ft.
DIMENSIONS:

Length overall	16 ft 11 in (5·18 m)
Beam overall	14 ft 11 in (4·57 m)
Height to top of stabiliser	5 ft 9 in (1·75 m)

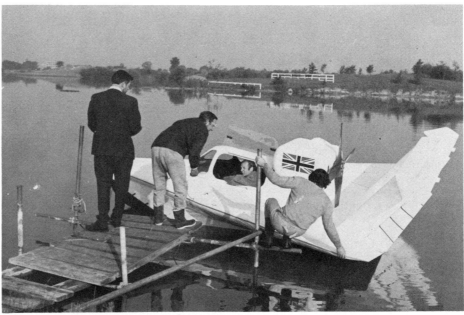

Above and below: The Seabee 3-seat aerodynamic ram-wing prototype. Speeds of up to 70 mph (112 km/h) have been achieved in ground effect during tests

WEIGHTS:
All up weight with operator and one passenger 1,107 lb (502.10 kg)
PERFORMANCE (130 hp Rolls-Royce 240A):

Max speed (design) 120 knots
Craft can be operated at any desired speed between 2 and 100 knots
Take-off speed, depending upon payload and weather conditions 35-40 knots

HOVERCRAFT DEVELOPMENT LTD

HEAD OFFICE:
Kingsgate House, 66-74 Victoria Street, London SW1E 6SL
TELEPHONE:
01-828 3400
TELEX:
23580
DIRECTORS:
T. G. Fellows (Chairman)
M. W. Innes
Prof. W. A. Mair
J. E. Rapson
T. A. Coombs
SECRETARY:
P. N. Randell
TECHNICAL OFFICE:
Forest Lodge West, Fawley Road, Hythe, Hants. SO4 6ZZ
TELEPHONE:
Hythe (Hants) 843178 STD Code 0703

Hovercraft Development Ltd. (HDL) was formed in January 1959 by the National Research Development Corporation (NRDC) to develop, promote and exploit the hovercraft invention. The company uses its large portfolio of patents as the basis of licensing agreements with the principal hovercraft manufacturers in the United Kingdom and overseas, and allows licensees access to work undertaken by its original Technical Group and the current Technical Office at Hythe. HDL may, in certain cases, provide financial backing to assist projects, such as the Hovermarine HM.5, the BHC SR.N4 and the Vosper VT.1.

The small technical team employed by the company makes assessments of new hovercraft designs and projects in addition to regional and route studies for proposed hovercraft operations. HDL's Technical Office at Hythe also provides a source of

unbiased but informed technical information for government departments, official bodies, potential manufacturers, operators and backers of hovercraft enterprises.

Currently, various programmes are being undertaken with a manned test hovercraft, designated HD-4, to evaluate new and improved control and cushion systems for hovercraft of all sizes. This work, together with other investigations, is aimed towards improving the control, skirt and propulsion aspects of modern hovercraft and assist the company's licensees to manufacture increasingly effective products for civil, military and industrial uses.

Patents held by the company largely result from the work undertaken by Christopher Cockerell and the HDL Technical Group, which investigated a wide range of marine, industrial and medical applications. The former Technical Group also operated three research hovercraft.

HD-4

This is a new 14 ft (4·26 m) long two-seat test vehicle employed by HDL to evaluate new and improved hovercraft control and cushion systems. The prototype was completed in July 1975 and further trials of the craft over water were in progress at the time of going to press in July 1976.

LIFT & PROPULSION: Lift is supplied by a single 197cc Villiers 8E two-stroke engine driving a single 24 in (0·609 m) diameter, ten-bladed Multi-wing axial fan. Propulsion is provided by a single Kyoritsu 225cc engine driving a single five-bladed "Breeza" ducted fan of 24 in (0·609 m) in diameter. Fuel is carried in two 2 gallon (9·09 litres) tanks, one each side of the cockpit.

CONTROLS: The craft is controlled by twin rudders in the fan slipstream and a balanced skirt-shift system operating in pitch and roll.

HULL: Wooden construction. Craft has a framework of 1 in sq spruce and ½ in sq Ramin, overlaid with sheets of 4 mm and 1·5 mm exterior grade ply.

SKIRT: HDL loop and segment type in 4 oz/yd² and 2 oz/yd² lightweight coated fabric.

ACCOMMODATION: Open cockpit with seating for driver and one passenger.

DIMENSIONS:
Length overall, power off
                        14 ft 0 in (4·26 m)
Beam overall, power off 6 ft 6 in (1·98 m)
Height overall, power off 3 ft 8 in (1·11 m)
Height overall, hovering 4 ft 7½ in (1·40 m)
Normal All-up weight   690 lb (312·96 kg)

HDL's new research hovercraft, the HD-4 is being employed in the development of a new HDL centre-of-pressure shift system. The system, which is showing considerable promise, permits the adjusting of bow-up or stern-up trim without the use of ballast and also aids low-speed manoeuvring. One design objective is to produce a system which permits hovercraft to make short diameter turns in areas of dense traffic

Top: HD-4 during overwater trials on Southampton Water in May 1976

Bottom: The new HDL CP shift system in operation. The degree of roll to starboard is such that most of the port skirt is clear of the water

HOVERKING LTD

HEAD OFFICE:
  Hoverking, Ullesthorpe, Lutterworth,
  Leics LE17 5AG, England
DIRECTORS:
  C. Knight
  P. M. Knight
  R. T. Jackson
CONSULTANTS:
  F. Cooton
  D. Walters DCAe, C.Eng, AFRAES, MCASI, FBIS
  Cdr. Th. Pellinkhof, C.Eng., FIMarE

Hoverking Ltd was formed in 1970 to design and develop the Ranger series of light hovercraft, initially for the amateur builder. The aim was to produce a luxury sports racing hovercraft that could be manufactured commercially to meet the wide demand for racing ACVs.

Ranger 1 has been intensively tested and developed to achieve the right combination of high performance, reliability, safety and stability. This included a series of tests conducted by Loughborough University which confirmed the machine's outstanding pitch and roll stability.

An amateur-built version of the Ranger 1, built by David Ibbotson, won the Hovercraft of the Year Award and David Ibbotson himself was Joint Hovernaut of the Year in 1973.

The manoeuvrability of the craft was tested to the full on the canals in Birmingham, where it featured locations shots for the film "Take Me High", starring Cliff Richard.

Widespread interest has been shown in the principles embodied in the design of the Ranger 1. A world-wide network of agents with complete spares and technical support is in the process of being established.

Ranger 1, winner of the 1973 Hovercraft of the Year Award, followed by an experimental version of the Ranger with twin Wankel thrust engines

RANGER 1

A single-seater sports/racing hovercraft, Ranger 1 is easy to handle and its components are both simple and functional to ensure low maintenance and running costs.

LIFT AND PROPULSION: Lift air is provided by an 8 hp Sachs Wankel Rotary KM48 engine driving a 22 in (·55 m) diam. 8 blade Multiwing fan. Thrust is provided by a 21 hp Sachs Rotary MK914 engine driving a 27 in (0·68 m) diam. ducted Permali propeller. The fuel capacity is from 2 gal (9·02 litres) (for racing) up to 8 gal (36·3 litres) for cruising. The fuel tank is mounted inboard in a compartment behind the driver.

CONTROLS: Twin rudders mounted in the propeller slipstream provide directional control. The rudders are linked by teleflex cable to an ergonomically designed control column with handgrips set at 45%, permitting single or two-handed control. The thrust throttle lever can be operated by either hand.

HULL: Box-section, wood-laminated internal structure bonded into a light grp external skin. The four corners are foam filled to provide buoyancy and impact resistance.

SKIRT: Twin bag of lightweight polyurethane impregnated terylene/nylon. Skirt system permits safe operation of the craft even with extensive damage to the outer skirt. The lightweight material permits temporary repairs to be undertaken by hand. System maintains a higher pressure in the skirt than in the plenum, combining the advantages of a low cushion pressure with resistance to skirt decay at high speeds.

ACCOMMODATION: Single-seat located just forward of the centre of gravity. Seating position is adjustable from a normal upright to full 'racing prone' position for maximum safety at high speeds. Adjustable footrest provided.

DIMENSIONS:

Length	11 ft 9 in (9·58 m)
Width	6 ft 7 in (2·00 m)
Height	4 ft 0 in (1·21 m)

WEIGHTS:

Weight empty	400 lb (181·42 kg)
Payload	400 lb (181·42 kg)

PERFORMANCE:

Max speed	55 mph (88·57 km/h)
Fuel consumption	1½-2 gal/hr (6·81-9·0 l/hr)
Maximum cont. gradient	1 : 6
Obstacle clearance	9 in (228 mm)

PRICE: £1,400-£1,800 ex works subject to specification.

RANGER II

This is a new version of the Ranger, with a specification similar to that for Ranger I, but with a modified hull and improved guard for the ducted propeller.

COMMODORE 1

The prototype Commodore, a two/three seat, sports/cruising craft, has been sold to a customer in Spain.

LIFT AND PROPULSION: Power is supplied by three 21 hp Sachs Wankel Mk 914 air-cooled rotary engines, one for lift and two for propulsion.

HULL: Box section wood laminate interior, bonded to a grp external skin. Multicell buoyancy and impact resistance. Basic hull is designed to accept various cockpit and engine installations to suit environmental requirements.

SKIRT: Hoverking twin bag skirt.

ACCOMMODATION: Seats for driver and up to two passengers. Wrap round windscreen or detachable hard top with sliding canopy.

Ranger II, showing the modified hull

Prototype of the Commodore, two/three seat sports hovercraft

DIMENSIONS:

Length overall	14 ft 0 in (4·26 m)	Beam overall	7 ft 0 in (2·13 m)
		Height	4 ft 6 in (1·37 m)

HOVERMARINE TRANSPORT LIMITED

HEAD OFFICE AND WORKS:
Hazel Wharf, Hazel Road, Woolston, Southampton, SO2 7GB.

TELEPHONE:
Southampton (0703) 446831

TELEX:
47141

DIRECTORS:
Edward F. Davison, Chairman
M. R. Richards, Managing Director
C. A. Brindle, Marketing Director
D. W. Nicholas, Marketing Services Director
E. G. Tattersall, Technical Director
R. F. Stubbs, Financial Director
E. W. Furnell, Manufacturing Director
J. H. Chapman, Customer Service Director

Hovermarine Transport Limited, a subsidiary of Hovermarine Corporation (U.S.A.) produces the HM.2 Mark III and HM.2 Mark IV rigid sidewall craft and is currently engaged in the manufacture of the HM.5 Hoverferry.

The HM.2 craft are available in a variety of configurations including passenger ferry, general purpose model, armed patrol craft, rapid intervention firefighting craft and a luxury 'Pullman' interior layout. At the

One of three Hovermarine HM.2 Mk. IIIs undergoing trials on the Solent prior to delivery to Tourismo Margarita, Venezuela

time of going to press 40 HM.2 Mk III craft have been sold and several more are under construction. The first HM.2 Mark IV was due to be launched at the time of going to press and has been sold.

HM.2 Mk III

A rigid sidewall craft designed for ferry operations, the HM.2 Mk III carries 62-65 passengers or 4·8 tons of freight at speeds up to 35 knots. The craft has a reinforced plastic hull, and is powered by three marine diesel engines.

Its features include an extended bow skirt which permits operations in waves up to 1·6 m (5 ft), mixed-flow fans to provide improved cushion characteristics, a new propulsion transmission system, modified engine components and the provision of sound insulation in the cabin to reduce internal noise levels.

HM.2 is type approved in the U.K. for Certificates of Construction and Performance and Hovercraft Safety Certificates issued by the Civil Aviation Authority, also for Operating Permits issued by the Department of Trade. In addition, the HM.2 has been certified by Lloyds Register of Shipping as a Class A1 Group 2 Air Cushion Vehicle. Fleets of HM.2 are operating in: Setubal, Portugal; Rio de Janeiro, Brazil; Hong Kong Harbour; Margarita, Venezuela; and Manila Bay, Republic of the Philippines. Elsewhere these craft are operating in Australia, Belgium, Bolivia, Brazil, France, Greece, Italy, India, Japan, U.S.A. and the United Kingdom.

LIFT AND PROPULSION: Two Cummins turbocharged VT8-370M eight-cylinder V marine diesels, each developing 320 bhp at 2,800 rpm provide propulsive power and a single Cummins V8-504M diesel rated at 185 bhp at 2,800 rpm drives the lift fans. The lift engine drives two pairs of forward fans through toothed belts and one aft fan through a hydraulic system. Air for the forward fans is drawn through inlets at each forward cabin quarter and in the base of the wheelhouse structure, while the air for the aft fan is drawn through an inlet in the rear companionway. The lift fans are of glass fibre construction.

The two propulsion engines drive two 15 in (381 mm) diameter stainless steel propellers through a reversing gearbox and 1 : 1 ratio Vee box. Short skegs projecting from the base of the sidewalls protect the propellers from driftwood and grounding. Fuel is carried in reinforced rubber tanks, two beneath the aft companionway, holding 640 litres (140 Imperial gallons) and one under the main lift fan holding 182 litres (40 Imperial gallons). Two refueling points are provided on the transom and one on the starboard side of the main air intakes.
CONTROLS: Craft direction is controlled by twin balanced stainless steel rudders which are operated hydraulically by a car type steering wheel. Additional control is provided by differential use of the water propellers.
HULL: Built in glass-reinforced plastic and grp sandwich panels. Hull is one homogeneous laminate into which are bonded grp panel frames.
ACCOMMODATION: The craft is operated by a crew of two. Controls are all sited in an elevated wheelhouse with a 360° view, located at the forward end of the passenger compartment. The captain is seated on the starboard side with the principal instru-

HM.2s under construction at Hovermarine's plant at Woolston, Southampton

First HM.2 Mk IV during trials. The hull of this new model is 10 ft (3.04 m) longer than that of the 65-passenger Mk.III and can be fitted with either 92 utility seats or 84 aircraft type seats

HM.2 Mk III general purpose sidewall craft equipped for hydrographic survey and operated on the River Scheldt by the Belgian Ministry of Public Works

mentation. Radar and auxiliary equipment is located on the port side.

Accommodation is normally for 62 seated passengers, with a maximum of 65. Seats are normally three abreast in banks of three. Toilet and luggage compartments are located aft.

Passenger access is via a double width door aft. Crew and emergency access is provided forward via two hatch doors, one each side of the wheelhouse.

"Knock-out" emergency windows are provided in the passenger saloon. Safety equipment includes: Beaufort life rafts, aircraft-type life jackets under the seats, and Graviner fire detectors and extinguishers.

Heating for the passenger saloon and wheelhouse is from the fresh water circuits of the engine cooling system, via two heat exchanger blowers through ducts at floor level. Optional air conditioning units can be fitted at the customer's request.

SYSTEMS: Electrical: 24 volt dc from engine driven alternators (2 × 60 amp) with 128 Ah Daganite batteries. Supplies instruments, radio, radar and external and internal lights.

HYDRAULICS: Systems used for the steering and rear fan operate at 800 lb sq in and 2,500 lb sq in maximum respectively.

SKIRT: Front and rear skirts are of loop and segment form and designed for a cushion height of 3 ft (914 mm).

COMMUNICATIONS AND NAVIGATION: Decca Super 101 radar and Redifon GR674 vhf radio. Other navigational equipment includes a Smith E2B compass and remote reading compass.

DIMENSIONS, EXTERNAL:

Length overall	51 ft 0 in (15·54 m)
Beam overall	20 ft 0 in (6·10 m)
Height overall	13 ft 9 in (4·19 m)
Draft floating with water-screws	4 ft 10½ in (1·49 m)
Draft hovering with water-screws	2 ft 10½ in (0·87 m)
Cushion area	627 sq ft (58·4 m²)

DIMENSIONS, INTERNAL:

Cabin (excluding wheelhouse, galley and toilet):

Length	22 ft 0 in (6·7 m)
Max width	16 ft 0 in (4·8 m)
Max height	6 ft 6 in (1·9 m)
Floor area	352 sq ft (32·7 m²)

DOOR SIZES:

Rear door:	4 ft 0 in (1·2 m) wide × 6 ft 3 in (1·9 m) high
Two forward doors:	2 ft 0 in (0·60 m) wide × 6 ft 3 in (1·9 m) high

BAGGAGE HOLDS:

Basic craft   60 cu ft (1·69 m³) aft of cabin

FREIGHT HOLDS:

None on standard passenger version.

Freight carried in main cabin on freight versions.

WEIGHTS:

Normal all-up weight, including normal payload	42,500 lb (19,300 kg)
Normal payload 62 passengers or 4·8 tons	(4,900 kg)
Max gross weight	44,500 lb (20,185 kg)

PERFORMANCE (at normal operating weight):

Max service speed	35 knots
Water speed in- 4 ft waves and 15 knot head wind	25 knots
Max wave capability	5 ft (1·52 m)
Endurance	4 hours

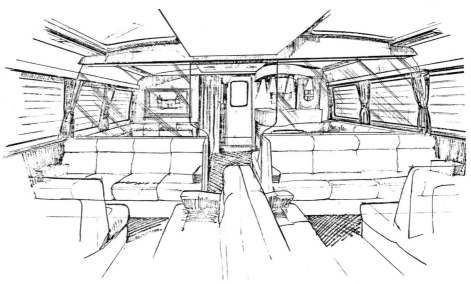

Sketch of the interior of the HM.2 Pullman

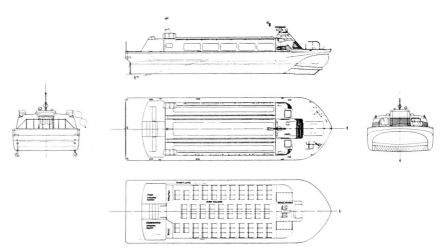

General arrangement of the Hovermarine HM.2 Mk IV. Two GM Type 8V92 diesel engines are employed for propulsion

HM.2 'PULLMAN'

This craft was developed during the latter end of 1974 as a luxury version of the 65 passenger version. Customers had indicated that there would be a ready market for this latest adaptation of the HM.2 high speed ferry, and Hovermarine Transport Limited, in co-ordination with design consultants, developed the 'Pullman' concept to meet this demand.

The interior utilises the same basic saloon area as the HM.2 65-seater craft, but the interior design and fitting gives the craft a much higher degree of comfort. The saloon is divided into two main areas, an aft bar/saloon and a forward lounge, separated by an engraved 'Plexiglas' screen. Luxury seating can be provided for up to 30 passengers and arranged to give maximum all round visibility. Controllable air-conditioning makes temperature control possible giving maximum passenger comfort. Combined with the seating in the aft saloon are free-standing tables. The toilet compartment, fitted with an electric WC and vanity unit, is located at the rear end of this saloon.

The forward lounge has first-class aircraft seating and a film projector can be installed. A stereo sound track is available and can be played through eight room-mounted speakers.

Fitted perspex roof lights and sidelights combined with interior curtains or adjustable louvres allow interior lighting to be adjusted.

In mid-1975 a 30 seat 'Pullman' layout HM.2 was delivered to Lake Titicaca. It is now operating a tourist service on the Lake which is 13,000 ft above sea level in the Bolivian Andes.

HM.2 Mk. III GENERAL PURPOSE CRAFT

Similar in basic design, construction and power plant to the HM.2 passenger craft, this general purpose version is suited to a variety of roles from police and customs patrol to hydrographic survey, and search and rescue duties.

The craft is equipped with a revised superstructure to suit these applications. For para-military roles, the craft can be equipped with a range of conventional automatic weapons.

DIMENSIONS, EXTERNAL:

Length overall	51 ft 0 in (15·54 m)
Beam overall	20 ft 0 in (6·09 m)
Height above hovering water line is	10 ft 8 in (2·35 m) wheelhouse top
Draft hovering	2 ft 10 in (0·86 m)
Draft afloat	4 ft 10 in (1·47 m)

WEIGHTS:

Maximum all up weight (fully equipped)	42,500 lb (19,300 kg)
Normal disposable load	12,300 lb (5,830 kg)

HM.2 TROJAN CLASS—MILITARY SUPPORT

HM.2 Trojan is the military version of the HM.2 Mk III passenger craft, and is similar in basic construction. Designed to undertake a wide variety of support roles, including counter-insurgency, logistic support, troop transport, etc, these craft normally have plastic armour and two machine guns forward.

In the personnel carrier variant, 55 troops may be carried at speeds of up to 35 knots. With the more heavily armed patrol craft layout, however, the main cabin will be sub-divided to provide living accommodation, Extra fuel tanks will be installed if required to increase the vessel's range.

The general specification is as shown for the standard passenger version.

HM.2 Mk. IV

The HM.2 Mk IV is a lengthened version of the Mk III craft and retains many of the systems and design features of that craft.

It is 10 ft (3·04 m) longer than the 65 passenger Mk III and provides capacity for up to 92 passengers. The 50% increase in payload has been achieved with only minimal increase in costs. The 33 knots maximum service speed is obtained by using two General Motors Type 8V92 diesel engines for propulsion.

The craft hull is manufactured in glass reinforced plastic and is built to a standard approved by a number of world authorities including Lloyds Register of Shipping, United States Coast Guard, the Hovercraft Division of the Civil Aviation Authority and the Marine Division of the Japanese Government.

The cabin area may be fitted with either 92 utility seats or 84 aircraft type seats. Five large tinted windows are fitted each side of the saloon. All craft are equipped with air-conditioning. Additional passenger aids include 8-track stereo and a public address system controlled from the stewardess's bay at the aft end. Toilet spaces are provided with an electric w.c. and vanity unit.

HM.5 hull mould under construction

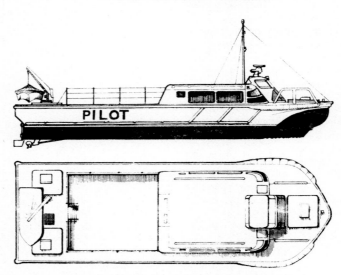

Hovermarine HM.2 Mk. IV in pilot launch configuration

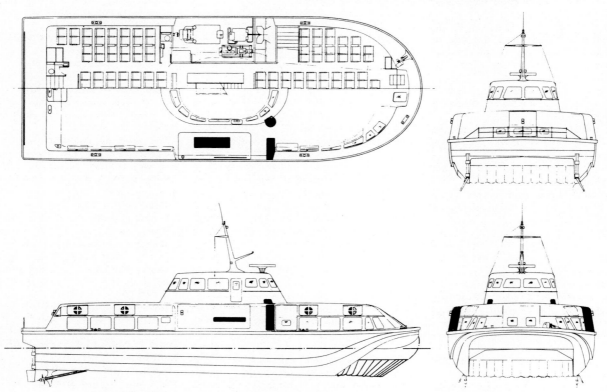

Hovermarine HM.5, 177-seat passenger ferry. Seating arrangements can be varied from 160 to 215 passengers, depending upon customer requirements. In addition a mixed-traffic variant is planned with accommodation for 140 passengers and a vehicle deck for ten cars

DIMENSIONS:

Length overall	18·16 m (59 ft 7 in)
Beam overall	6·1 m (20 ft)
Height overall	5·8 m (19 ft)
Hull depth (base to deck)	1·98 m (6 ft 6 in)
Nominal freeboard	0·91 m (3 ft)
Cabin beam	4·88 m (16 ft)
Cabin length	8·96 m (29 ft 5 in)
Draft floating	1·58 m (5 ft 2½ in)
Approx. draught hovering (aft)	
	0·87 m (2 ft 10½ in)

WEIGHTS:

Normal payload	84/92 passengers
Nominal payload weight	
	6,872 kg (15,140 lb)
Freight capacity	7,350 kg (7¼ tons)
Nominal gross weight (subject to 2% production tolerance)	
	25,966 kg (55,000 lb)
Dry weight	16,856 kg (33,150 lb)
Fuel tank capacity (standard)	
aft	635 litres (140 imp. galls)
forward	182 litres (40 imp. galls)
forward transferable	
	182 litres (40 imp. galls)
Minimum endurance at maximum continuous rating	4½ hours
Range at maximum speed	
	250 km (135 n miles)

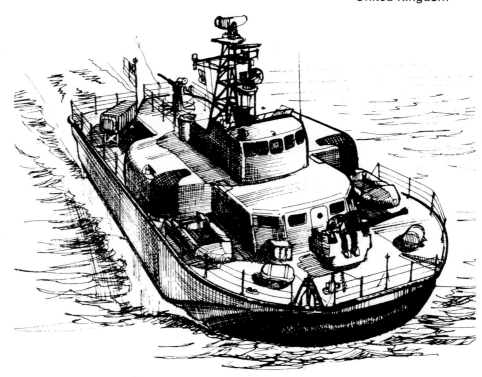

Impression of a fast patrol variant of the HM.5

Mark IV Variants

The HM.2 Mark IV is available in a range of different configurations suitable for a variety of applications such as fireboat, crew/supply vessel and fast harbour/pilot launch. Pullman versions of the Mark IV are also available.

In freight carrying roles the craft has a capacity of 7¼ tons with a standard fuel tank.

HM.2 Fireboat

The use of a high speed craft for fire-fighting duties reduces the time required for the appliance to reach the outbreak of fire and thus significantly increases the chance of dealing with the conflagration before it becomes really serious. The HM.2 fireboat combines a high speed ability with excellent manoeuvrability at all speeds and provides a very stable platform from which to fight the fire.

The HM.2 rapid intervention fire-fighting craft is based upon either the Mk III or Mk IV hull and fitted with a shortened super-structure which permits the fitting of fire control equipment, including a Carmichael C 5000 monitor mounted on a 19 ft (5·8 m) tower. This has a capacity of 5,000 galls./ min. foam and a projection of up to 120-150 ft, dependent upon weather conditions. Diffuser jaws on the monitor enable a foam carpet to be laid 25-40 ft wide at a distance of approximately 50-60 ft. The minitor rotates through 270° with adequate elevation and depression.

The single-stage centrifugal fire pump, powered by the lift engine, has an output of 530 gal per minute. It draws water from the sea by way of a heavy duty hose and filter mounted on the starboard side.

Two smaller hand held branches, fitted on deck to port and starboard of the monitor tower, are suitable for either foam or water delivery.

Crew accommodation is located aft of the wheelhouse. The cabin has four bunks, individual seats and a dining area. A galley is provided on the starboard side and is fitted with gas cooker, sink, water supply, refrigerator and extractor fan. On the port side is a fitted toilet and wash room. If

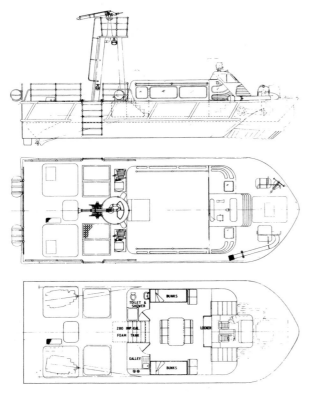

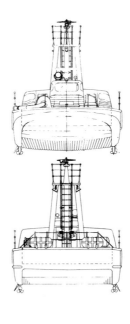

Hovermarine HM.2 Mk. IV rapid intervention fire fighting craft. Height of the monitor above the waterline is 19 ft (5·8 m)

required the accommodation and wheelhouse spaces can be air conditioned.

On the larger Mark IB RIFF craft the accommodation may be extended to make provision for carrying extra personnel or evacuees from a danger area.

HM.5

The first 177 seat HM.5 Hoverferry is due to be launched early in 1977. This craft will be produced to the standard specification but the capacity of future craft is variable from 160 to 215 passengers, depending upon customer requirements. In addition a 140 passenger and 10 car variant is planned for mixed-traffic routes.

Maximum speed of the HM.5 is 40 knots and its cruising speed is 35 knots in 1 m waves. The hull is built in glass reinforced plastic and the machinery and propulsion systems are conventional marine diesel engines and water screws.

A military version of HM.5 will also be available. This craft will utilise either diesel engines or gas turbines for propulsion, giving speeds of up to 50 knots. It will have a capacity for extended patrol at 18 to 20 knots. The military craft will have a disposable load of 20 tons which will allow a comprehensive range of weapons or other equipment to be fitted. A typical fast patrol craft variant will be equipped with two 40 mm cannon and ship-to-ship missiles, complete with full fire control systems.

The basic HM.5 configuration has been the subject of extensive model testing which has demonstrated outstanding seakeeping and ride qualities for a craft of its type. For the military craft these qualities will be further improved by the use of dynamic ride control systems at present under development.

DIMENSIONS:

Length overall	27·20 m (89 ft 3 in)
Beam overall	10·20 m (33 ft 5½ in)
Height off cushion—waterline to wheelhouse top	5·3 m (17 ft 6½ in)
Draft—off cushion	2·55 m (8 ft 4½ in)
Draft—on cushion	1·40 m (4 ft 7 in)
Freeboard—off cushion	1·20 m (3 ft 11¼ in)
Cushion depth (mean)	1·75 m (5 ft 9 in)
Cabin beam	8·2 m (26 ft 11 in)
Cabin length (forward)	6·9 m (22 ft 7½ in)
Cabin length (aft)	7·5 m (24 ft 7 in)

WEIGHTS:

Standard gross weight	77,000 kg (169,754 lb)
Normal, payload	17,600 kg (38,801 lb)
Standard passenger capacity	177
Forward saloon capacity	78
Aft saloon capacity	84
Upper saloon capacity	15
Maximum overload weight	80,000 kg (176,320 lb)

MACHINERY:

Propulsion engines
2 × MTU 12v 331 TC71—1,200 hp (metric) @ 2,000 rpm

Lift engine
2 × MAN D.2530 MTE—352 hp (metric) @ 2,300 rpm

Auxiliary power units
2 × MAN D.0026 ME 69 hp (metric) @ 1,500 rpm

Propellers
2 × 0·73 m. dia. × 1·02 m. pitch (28·7 × 40·2 ins)

FUEL CAPACITY:

Fuel tanks	4 × 833 litres (4 × 205 galls)
Total capacity	3,732 litres (821 galls)

PERFORMANCE:

Maximum speed—still air calm water	40 knots
Cruise speed in 1 m. seas	35 knots
Endurance at cruise speed	6 hours
Range at cruise speed	210 n miles
Emergency stop distance	100 m (328 ft)
Turning circle dia. at max. approach speed	400 m (1,312 ft)

LIGHT HOVERCRAFT COMPANY

HEAD OFFICE:
Felbridge Hotel & Investment Co Ltd, London Road, East Grinstead, Sussex

TELEPHONE:
East Grinstead 24424

EXECUTIVES:
L. H. F. Gatward, Proprietor

Light Hovercraft Company has been active in the field of hoverpallets since 1969. It has entered the light sports ACV field with a fibreglass hulled-variant of Nigel Beale's Cyclone, which won the British National Hovercraft Championships in 1971 and was joint winner of this event in 1972. In August 1972 a production Cyclone crossed the English Channel from Pegwell Bay hoverport to Calais, a total open sea distance of 35 miles (56·32 km).

The company is now concentrating on the production of the Stratus light hovercraft runabout and the two-seat Fantasy.

FANTASY

Light Hovercraft's latest design is the Fantasy, an amphibious two-seater with a top speed of 40 knots (80 km/h). Separate lift and propulsion engines are employed, both of which are rubber-mounted to reduce vibration. Large silencers are fitted for quiet running.

The craft is sufficiently light to be carried by two people. It can be hovered onto a trailer for towing behind a car.

LIFT AND PROPULSION: Lift is provided by an 8 hp engine driving a 1 ft 7 in (482 mm) diameter Multiwing fan. Aft of the passenger seat is a 40 hp engine driving a 2 ft 6in (762 mm) diameter ducted Multiwing fan for propulsion. Fan ducts are covered by safety guards.

CONTROLS: A single rudder hinged to the rear of the thrust fan provides directional control. A lever throttle operates the lift engine and a twistgrip throttle controls propulsion.

HULL: Foam-filled glassfibre hull. High freeboard and full planing surfaces.

Light Hovercraft Fantasy, two-seat amphibious sports craft

SKIRT: Bag type skirt in polyurethane nylon, 1 ft 4 in (0·41 m) deep.
ACCOMMODATION: Padded saddle seat with back rest, accommodates two.
DIMENSIONS:

Length	11 ft 4 in (3·44 m)
Width	6 ft 2 in (1·86 m)

WEIGHTS:

Empty weight	350 lb (160 kg)
Payload	400 lb (200 kg)

PERFORMANCE:

Max speed	40 knots
Endurance	3 hours

STRATUS

This is a new ultralight sports hovercraft, based on the company's experience with the earlier Cyclone. The aim has been to produce a small craft of simple design which is easy to both operate and maintain.

LIFT AND PROPULSION: Integrated system powered by a single 22 hp 331 cc twin-cylinder engine. This drives a 2 ft 0 in (610 mm) diameter axial fan, air from which is used for both lift and propulsion at the ratio of 1 : 3. Engine is rubber mounted. The fan has five replaceable polypropylene blades and is ducted for quietness and thrust efficiency.

CONTROLS: Heading is controlled by a single aerodynamic rudder aft of the fan duct and operated by a handlebar. Engine output is controlled by a twist-grip throttle.

HULL: Single-piece foam-filled glassfibre structure.

SKIRT: Bag-type skirt in polyurethane nylon, 10 in (24 cm) deep.
DIMENSIONS:

Length	9 ft 5½ in (2·88 m)
Width	6 ft 1 in (1·85 m)
Folded	4 ft 0 in (1·22 m)
Height	3 ft 4 in (1·01 m)

WEIGHTS:

Empty weight	200 lb (90 kg)
Payload	350 lb (160 kg)

PERFORMANCE:

Max speed	30 knots
Endurance	2 hours

CIRRUS

This new multi-duty 5-seater was introduced in 1976. Keynotes of the design are reliability ease of maintenance and quiet operation. The fans are large and slow turning in order to maintain as low a noise level as possible. The company states that Cirrus can be operated in residential areas without concern.

LIFT AND PROPULSION: Motive power for the integrated lift/propulsion system is furnished by a 100 hp Ford OHC 2 litre

Cirrus 5 seater, powered by a single 100 hp Ford OHC 2 litre engine. A feature of the design is the mounting of the centrifugal lift fan and axial propulsion fan on a common shaft to simplify the drive system

Light Hovercraft Stratus single-seat runabout

engine. Both the centrifugal lift fan and the axial drive fan are mounted on a common shaft, resulting in a simple drive system. Adequate room is available in the engine bay for an alternative or twin engine installation if required. Total fuel capacity is 30 gal.

HULL: Glassfibre construction, with a backbone of foam buoyancy in the sidebodies. Buoyancy is 7,000 lb (3,175 kg).

SKIRT: 2 ft 6 in (0·762 m) deep skirt of loop segment type. Each segment can be replaced and repaired without difficulty.

ACCOMMODATION: Seats are provided for a driver and up to four passengers in the fully-enclosed cabin.

Cabin can be equipped for ambulance, customs or military duties by installing the appropriate accessories.

DIMENSIONS:

Length	19 ft 0 in (5·79 m)
Beam	9 ft 0 in (2·74 m)
Height	8 ft 0 in (2·43 m)
Skirt depth	2 ft 6 in (0·76 m)

WEIGHTS:

Empty weight	1,600 lb (725·71 kg)
Payload	1,000 lb (453·57 kg)

PERFORMANCE:

Maximum speed	50 mph (80·46 km/h)
Endurance	10 hours

MISSIONARY AVIATION FELLOWSHIP

ADDRESS:
3 Beechcroft Road, South Woodford, London E18 1BJ
TELEPHONE:
01-989 0838
DIRECTORS:
S. Sendall-King
B.Sc., C.Eng., A.F.R.Ae.S., F.S.L.A.E.T.
General Director
T. S. Frank, B.A. UK Director
EXECUTIVE, HOVERCRAFT PROJECT:
T. J. R. Longley T.Eng. (C.E.I.)
A.M.R.Ae.S

The Missionary Aviation Fellowship is an international, interdenominational Christian organisation which operates a total of 75 light aircraft in support of missionary work in some of the world's more remote areas.

In the belief that a suitable hovercraft could make a valuable contribution to missionary work, M.A.F. began the design of a craft to its own specification, early in 1970. Design assistance was given voluntarily by several specialists in the field of hovercraft and aircraft engineering.

As a result of two years of intensive trials, the Missionaire has been developed into an efficient and reliable craft. To demonstrate its capability, it was driven around the Isle of Wight with a 1,100 lb payload in 2 hrs 13 minutes. Block cruising speed was 27 knots and the total fuel consumption was only 2·7 gallons per hour.

The Missionaire prototype is still awaiting shipment to its intended destination on Lake Chad, as drought conditions have caused a large part of the lake to dry up.

MISSIONAIRE Mk I

This is a lightweight amphibious hovercraft powered by two Volkswagen engines. Although originally designed as a five-seater, the craft has a spacious cabin and has demonstrated its ability to carry seven adults over hump speed into a 12 knot headwind without any difficulty. Cruising speed over calm water is 35 knots.

LIFT AND PROPULSION: An air-cooled Volkswagen 1,500 cc automotive engine, developing 53 bhp at 4,200 rpm, drives two 2 ft 0 in (609 mm) diameter aluminium centrifugal impellers for lift. Thrust is provided by a 68 bhp Volkswagen 1,700 cc engine driving a 5 ft 8 in (1·72 m) diameter fixed-pitch Sensenich airboat-type propeller. Power transmission and speed reduction on both units is by Stephens Miraclo-Meteor high-speed belting. Total fuel capacity is 35 Imp gallons (195 l), carried in a single welded aluminium tank located amidships. Recommended fuel is 95 octane automotive grade petrol.

CONTROL: An aerodynamic rudder operating in the propeller slipstream provides directional control under cruising conditions. Forward-located puff-ports are provided for low-speed directional control, though they can be used at high speed. This combination of controls has been found to aid manoeuvrability and facilitate handling. The craft also possesses good high-speed ditching characteristics, with no tendency to plough-in.

Longitudinal trim and a certain amount of lateral trim is provided by two 8 gallon integral water-ballast tanks located side by side in the bows. Water can be pumped aboard while the craft is floating, and can be off-loaded on or off cushion. No ballast is required when maximum payload is carried in the cabin.

HULL: The prototype hull is built in marine ply and spruce. For greater durability and ease of construction, a hull of composite GRP/aluminium alloy construction is planned for future craft. The hull incorporates ample reserve bouyancy.

SKIRT: Segmented type, 1 ft 6 in (458 mm) deep in neoprene/nylon.

ACCOMMODATION: Seats are provided in a fully enclosed cabin for a driver and four passengers. Access is via car-type doors (one each side) hinged to the forward door-posts. The entire cabin roof is hinged at its forward edge, providing unrestricted headroom for entry and loading. The three-place bench-type rear seat can be quickly converted into a stretcher, situated athwartships. A sizeable compartment for hand baggage and medical supplies is located behind the rear bench-seat. Cabin ventilation is provided by cushion air bleed ducts controlled by louvres.

SYSTEMS: Electrical: generator on the lift engine supplies 12 volts to a 60 a/hr battery for engine starting and other services.

Fire-detection and extinguishing: The engine bay is equipped with flame switches giving visual and audible warning on the instrument panel. A Graviner "Swordsman" BCF fire extinguisher adjacent to the driver's seat is plumbed into a distribution manifold in the engine bay. A quick-release connection makes it instantly useable as a hand-held extinguisher in the event of cabin, or other fires.

COMMUNICATIONS AND NAVIGATION: Provision for radio communications equipment. Magnesyn remote-reading compass.

DIMENSIONS, EXTERNAL:

Length overall, power off 22 ft 0 in (6·70 m)
Length overall, skirt inflated
                    22 ft 0 in (6·70 m)
Beam overall, power off 10 ft 6 in (3·20 m)
Beam overall, skirt inflated
                    12 ft 6 in (3·81 m)
*Height overall, on landing pads
                    7 ft 10 in (2·38 m)
*Height overall, skirt inflated
                    9 ft 4 in (2·84 m)
Draft afloat   10 in (254 mm)
Cushion area   170 sq ft (15·79 m²)
Skirt depth   1 ft 6 in (458 mm)

*Propeller horizontal.

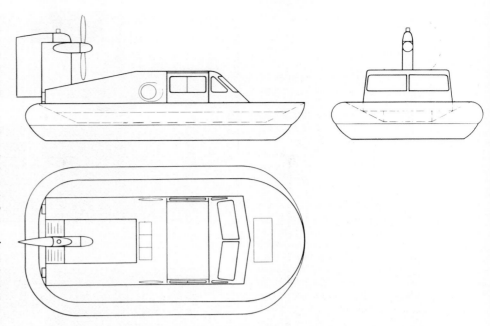

General arrangement of the Missionary Aviation Fellowship hovercraft prototype

Above and below: Missionary Aviation Fellowship's general purpose amphibious five-seater, the Missionaire. Powered by two Volkswagen engines, the craft has a top speed of 38 knots. The rear passenger seats can be replaced by a stretcher carried athwartships

DIMENSIONS, INTERNAL:

Cabin:		
Length	6 ft 3 in	(1·90 m)
Max width	7 ft 0 in	(2·13 m)
Max height	4 ft 2 in	(1·26 m)
Floor area	43·75 sq ft	(4·06 m²)

Baggage hold behind rear seats
               15 cu ft (0·425 m³)

Freight hold (in place of rear seats)
               45 cu ft (1·27 m³)

Door width   3 ft 6 in (1·06 m)

WEIGHTS:

Normal empty weight	2,200 lb	(998 kg)
Normal all-up weight	3,200 lb	(1,451 kg)
Max all-up weight	3,600 lb	(1,633 kg)

Normal payload (with full tank)
1,000 lb (453 kg)
Maximum payload   1,400 lb (635 kg)
PERFORMANCE (at normal operating weight):
Max speed over calm water (max power) at 60 deg F   38 knots
Cruising speed, calm water   35 knots

Turning circle diameter at 30 knots
2,200 ft (670 m)
Max wave capability   2-3 ft (609-914 mm)
Still air range at cruising speed
(without reserves)   280 nm
Max gradient, static conditions   1:10
Vertical obstacle clearance 1 ft 4 in (407 mm)

MAF 5-SEATER
In response to requests from missionaries in various parts of the world, M.A.F. is working on the design of a new 5-seater hovercraft named Riverover.

Primary design considerations are low-cost and good controllability, to enable the craft to follow the courses of winding rivers. Components have to be relatively small so that they can be carried in a single-engined Cessna aircraft.

PINDAIR LIMITED

HEAD OFFICE AND WORKS:
Quay Lane, Hardway, Gosport PO12 4LJ
TELEPHONE:
Gosport (070 17) 87830
DIRECTORS:
M. A. Pinder, Bsc, CEng, MIMechE, (Managing)
A. M. Pinder
J. Holland, FCA
EXECUTIVES:
N. Horn, Design and Development
M. Pinder, Marketing
B. M. Oakley, Production
R. Bagley, Demonstrations
D. McClunan, Testing and Servicing
V. A. Wells, Administration and Accounts
CONSULTANTS:
D. Robertson
E. Gifford

Pindair Limited was formed in May, 1972. It is currently engaged in the design, development, manufacture and sales of a range of inflatable light hovercraft for recreation, commercial and military use as well as designing for outside manufacture ACV trailers of up to 10 t payload. The company also supplies amateur hovercraft constructors in the United Kingdom with engines, fans, ducts, skirt materials and many other specialised components.

Five amphibious models are currently in production; one model is at the prototype stage. Production capacity for the smaller models is currently 10 per week and the larger models are custom built.

The use of folding inflatable hulls for the Pindair Skima range offers a number of advantages including ease of transport and storage, low weight, and resistance to icing. Special attention has been paid to simplicity of owner maintenance and use of components with worldwide spares availability.

The smaller models use Valmet 160 cc 2-stroke engines coupled to ducted multiwing axial fans with replacement polypropylene blades. The larger models use 4-stroke automotive engines. The Skima 12 has been developed with assistance from Hovercraft Development Limited.

In all cases HDL loop segment skirts are used. Pindair hovercraft are in use in more than 35 countries and in all climatic conditions from equatorial heat to arctic cold. Prices generally compare with boats having similar payload and performance.

SKIMA 1
This has been designed as a low cost one-man hovercraft which can be stowed in the luggage compartment of most cars, be light enough for easy portability by one man yet be capable of carrying one man on land or water in reasonable conditions.

In 1972 three single-seat inflatable hover-craft designed by Pindair reached an altitude of 3,000 m in the Himalayas by travelling along turbulent rivers.

SKIMA 2
This was the first craft marketed by the company. It is light enough to be carried by two people and can carry two people under reasonable conditions. It has separate lift and propulsion systems and can be folded to fit onto a car roof rack or into a small estate car.

The Skima 2 can be used as an amphibious yacht tender, runabout, for exploration or for class competition.

SKIMA 3
This is derived from a special version of the Skima 2 which was raced successfully by Barry Oakley in the 1973, 1974 and 1975 Hover Club of Great Britain Championships, winning a number of open races and also speed, manoeuvrability and free style competitions outright.

Although capable of operating as a three-man hovercraft it is mainly used for two

---

SKIMA SPECIFICATIONS

Craft	SKIMA 1	SKIMA 2	SKIMA 3	SKIMA 4	SKIMA 6 (estimated)	SKIMA 12
Length	2·75 m	3·25 m	3·25 m	4·00 m	5·00 m	7·77 m
Width	1·53 m	2·00 m	2·00 m	2·00 m	2·30 m	3·40 m
Height off cushion	1·00 m	1·20 m	1·20 m	1·20 m	1·50 m	2·29 m
Dry weight		90 kg	125 kg	160 kg		
Skirt	HDL	HDL	HDL	HDL	HDL	HDL
Skirt depth	12 cm	15 cm	15 cm	20 cm	20 cm	46 cm
Obstacle clearance	20 cm	30 cm	30 cm	35 cm	50 cm	40 cm
Folded dimensions	76 cm × 90 cm × 35 cm	1·15 m × 1·52 m × 60 cm	1·50 m × 1·50 m × 60 cm	1·22 m × 1·52 m × 60c m		6·48 m × 2·40 m × 2·29 m
Pack dimensions	76 cm × 91 cm × 35 cm	84 cm × 1·07 m × 61 cm	84 cm × 1·07 m × 84 cm	94c m × 1·07 m × 84c m		
Assembly time	15 min	30 min	40 min	40 min	60 min	120 min
Engines	1 Valmet	2 Valmet	3 Valmet	3 Valmet		GM V8
Fans—Lift	1 axial	1 axial	1 axial	1 axial	1 Centrifugal	1 Centrifugal
Thrust		1 axial	2 axial	2 axial	1 axial	1 axial
Total engine power	10	15	25	25	100	220

SKIMA PERFORMANCE DATA

Craft	Units of	SKIMA 1	SKIMA 2		SKIMA 3			SKIMA 4			SKIMA 6 (estimated)		SKIMA 12		
Payload	75 kg. or 1 person	1	1	2	1	2	3	1	2	3	4	3	6	3	6	9	12
Max speed over water	km/h	40	45	40	60	50	40	55	55	50	40	60	50	70	60	55	50
Max speed over grass	km/h	40	45	40	60	50	40	55	55	50	40	60	50	70	60	55	50
Max speed over tarmac	km/h	45	50	45	70	60	45	60	60	50	45	70	60	90	70	60	50
Max speed over ice	km/h	50	65	50	90	70	60	70	70	65	60	100	70	110	90	70	60
Hump speed	km/h	3	5	8	5	6	8	3	5	6	8	3	6	4	6	8	10
Max wind force	Beaufort	3	4	2	6	5	4	6	5	4	3	8	4	8	6	4	2
Fuel consumption	Litre/h	4	7	7	9	9	9	9	9	9	9	25	25	25	25	25	25
Max range	km	50	150	130	150	130	100	150	140	130	100	130	100	300	240	220	200
Turning circle (low speed)	m	3	3	3	5	5	5	6	6	6	6	8	8	10	10	10	10
Turning circle (high speed)	m	25	35	50	25	35	50	35	50	70	90	35	160	35	60	100	120
Max short slope	%	100	100	60	100	70	60	100	80	70	60	100	60	60	45	30	15
Max continuous slope	%	15	20	13	25	20	13	30	25	20	13	30	25	30	25	20	15

people or by one person in competitions.

SKIMA 4

During proving trials in 1973 this hovercraft covered the longest journey so far by a light hovercraft on inland and coastal waters. The Naval Hovercraft Trials Unit has recommended it as an alternative to the Gemini inflatable boat used by the British armed services, particularly in cases where its amphibious qualities would be an advantage.

Examples of the Skima 4 are in use in various parts of the world as amphibious transport for two people plus their equipment in most conditions or four people in good conditions. The rear inflatable seat is instantly removable for stowing freight or equipment. Users include missionaries, an aluminium company in the Arabian Gulf, a pest research organisation, a marine biology research group, defence forces, subaqua organisations, and flood and beach rescue organisations.

SKIMA 6 (Under Development)

A semi-inflatable hovercraft capable of carrying six persons. Suitable for personal transport as well as military, rescue, ambulance, pest control, freight, survey and exploration duties. Capable of being transported complete by road ready for use, but may be reduced in size for shipment. It has a folding hood.

SKIMA 12

A semi-inflatable multirole hovercraft,

A Pindair Skima 12 hovercraft operating off Portchester

Skima 12 is capable of carrying up to 12 people or 1t of freight. It combines features of an off-highway vehicle with those of a high-speed workboat. The Skima 12 is easily transported on a trailer with the inflatable cylindrical tube around the perimeter of the hull furled or detached and can be shipped in a standard 6 m × 2·5 m × 2·5 m shipping container.

The monocoque aluminium hull is extremely strong and built with marine materials. It will not corrode or absorb water and if knocked will dent rather than fracture allowing repairs to be made at a convenient time. Separate compartments contain the accommodation, the engine and propulsor the lift fan, rubber fuel bags, the trim system, batteries, safety equipment,

Pindair's new Skima 12, a semi-inflatable, multi-duty hovercraft capable of carrying 12 people or up to 1 tonne of freight. Power is supplied by a single marinised 220 hp GM 7V automotive engine. Maximum speed over water is 70 km/h (43 mph)

stowage areas and additional buoyancy.

The engine, tooth belt transmission, and ducted propulsor are mounted together on a sub-frame so that the whole assembly can be removed quickly for service or repair. Everything is easily accessible for maintenance.

The marinised car engine is geared to run at relatively low speed for long life and low noise. The centrifugal aluminium lift fan and ducted four blade propulsor are also designed to run at low speed to reduce noise yet provide more than adequate air flow for good payload and performance. Robert Trillo Limited has designed the propulsor

and aerodynamic duct exclusively for Pindair.

The low cushion pressure together with the HDL patented skirt system generate an exceptionally low spray pattern, allowing the Skima 12 to be operated with an open cockpit if desired. Individual skirt segments may be quickly replaced when they become worn or damaged without lifting the craft.

The standard craft has accommodation for 12 passengers and a driver. There are three bucket seats with the driver in the centre at the forward end of the cockpit with two bench seats along each side. The bench seats can be used as bunks or stretchers and are removable to provide a 5 cubic metre

load space. Various arrangements can be specified to provide cover for the accommodation. A cruiser-type folding hood with removable sides can be fitted, or a small cockpit cover or a hard top. Additional equipment such as radio, radar, searchlights, heating and air conditioning can be incorporated. A trailer and lifting gear are available.

The Skima 12 can be built for a wide variety of applications, from police, coastguard, pilot and military uses, to pest control, flood relief, fire fighting; as a passenger ferry or ambulance.

Top Left: Pindair's current production models include the Skima 12, Skima 2, Skima 3 and Skima 4
Top Right: A Skima 4 negotiating turbulent water in the River Severn during endurance trials
Bottom Left: Skima 2 demonstrating its ability to enter water safely from a 45° slope
Botton Right: Skima 2S, a racing variant of Skima 2

QUANTUM HOVERCRAFT LTD

HEAD OFFICE:
31 West Street, Wimborne Minster, Dorset, England

CABLE ADDRESS:
4M104 (QHL)

WORKS:
96 Rempstone Road, Wimborne Minster, Dorset, BH21 1SX, England

TELEPHONE:
Wimborne 887002

DIRECTORS:
J. R. Raymond, Secretary
D. Harmon-Brown
M. Charman
A. G. Field

SENIOR EXECUTIVES:
N. V. Charman, Engineering Manager

Formed in 1972, Quantum Hovercraft Ltd has been concentrating on the development of light amphibious passenger and utility craft. First vehicles to be marketed by the company are the Islesman 1000 six-seater; the Islesman 1500 nine-seater and the Islesman Utility. The prototype of the Islesman 1000 has been completed and the first production craft of this series will be available in 1977.

ISLESMAN 1000

This new glassfibre-hulled amphibious hovercraft is designed for a number of duties from six seat water-taxi to light transport and harbour inspection. The prototype

completed its trials in the autumn of 1976 and the first production machine has been ordered.

LIFT AND PROPULSION: Integrated system powered by a single Lotus 907 two-litre four-cylinder four-stroke aluminium engine rated at 155 bhp at 6,500 rpm. Cushion air is supplied by a 2 ft 0 in (600 mm) diameter 14-bladed Multiwing axial-flow fan located at the rear of the craft behind the cabin. Cushion pressure is 15 psf (22·25 kgm²). Thrust is supplied by two 2 ft 0 in (600 mm) diameter 14-bladed axial-flow fans of the same type mounted singly in two propulsion air ducts. Lift and propulsion fans are driven by the single engine via a hydraulic drive system developed by Volvo Hydraulics of Sweden: High pressure oil is piped to a manifold from whence it is diverted to the appropriate hydraulic fan motor by electric solenoid valves. Fuel is carried in four tanks, each with a capacity of 8 gal (30 l). Engine oil capacity is 9 pints; hydraulic capacity 15 gal (56 l). Engine access is via a large roof hatch and a removable panel in the cabin bulkhead.

CONTROLS: Craft heading is maintained by triple rudder vanes hinged at the rear of each of the propulsion ducts. Reverse thrust for braking is obtained by reversing the rotation of the propulsion fans through the hydraulic drive system, forcing the air forward. A fuel pumping system is used for longitudinal trim.

HULL: Prototype is of wooden construction. Hulls of production craft will be fabricated in coloured, fire retardent glass reinforced plastics. Sidestructure can be detached, bringing width to within 8 ft for towing on roads.

SKIRT: 18 in (0·45 m) deep HDL loop and finger skirt fabricated in neoprene coated nylon fabric supplied by Leyland Rubber of Birmingham, and designed and assembled by Robert Trillo Ltd.

ACCOMMODATION: Basic version seats a driver and up to five passengers. Seats are secured by quick release fastenings that permit the interior to be cleared to carry stretchers, general cargoes and livestock. Full instrumentation is provided, including fan speed indicators. Access is via two large folding doors, one port and one starboard. Air conditioning can be fitted as an optional extra. Electrically-operated fire detectors and extinguishing equipment is fitted.

SYSTEMS: Electrical. 12 and 24 v systems. Engine driven 24 volt, 45 amp alternator.

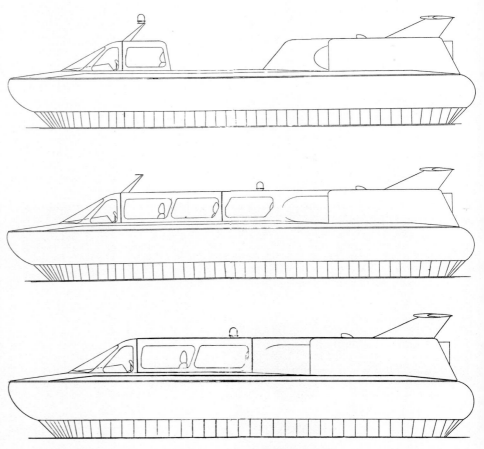

Outboard profiles of the Islesman 1000, *top* the Islesman 1500, *centre* and *bottom* the Utility model

DIMENSIONS, EXTERNAL:

Length overall		
power off	20 ft 1 in	(6·14 m)
skirt inflated	21 ft 0 in	(6·25 m)
Beam overall,		
power off	11 ft 5 in	(3·50 m)
skirt inflated	14 ft 0 in	(4·26 m)
Height overall,		
on landing pads	5 ft 0 in	(1·50 m)
skirt inflated	6 ft 6 in	(1·92 m)
Draft afloat	3 in	(0·08 m)
Skirt depth, prototype	1 ft 6 in	(0·48 m)

DIMENSIONS, INTERNAL:

Cabin length	8 ft 0 in	(2·43 m)
Maximum width	4 ft 9 in	(1·45 m)
Maximum height	3 ft 4 in	(1·00 m)
Floor area	36·8 ft²	(3·5 m²)

WEIGHTS:

Normal empty weight	1,500 lb	(680 kg)
Normal gross weight	2,500 lb	(1,134 kg)
Normal payload	1,000 lb	(454 kg)

PERFORMANCE:

Maximum speed, calm water, maximum power	50 knots
Cruising speed, calm water	35 knots
Maximum wave capacity	3 ft 0 in (1 m)
Still air range and endurance at cruising speed	250 miles (400 km) 6 hours
Maximum gradient, static conditions	1 : 8
Vertical obstacle clearance, prototype	1 ft 6 in (0·45 m)

PRICE: £20,000 ex-works UK

ROTORK MARINE LIMITED

HEAD OFFICE:
Westbury, Wilts, BA13 4JT, England
TELEPHONE:
(0373) 823831
TELEX:
449666 Rotork Westbury
DIRECTORS:
J. J. Fry
J. S. Fry
A. J. F. Garnett
A. J. Percy
G. Ruston
MARKETING COMPANY:
Rotork Technical Services Limited
516 High Street, Reigate, Surrey RH2 9AE
TELEPHONE:
(073 72) 21121
TELEX:
946746 Rotech G
CABLES:
Rotorktech

Rotork Marine is building and marketing a series of fast, flat bottom, multi-purpose workboats, the best known of which is the Sea Truck. A key feature of the design is the use of air lubrication to reduce hydrodynamic

A Rotork 12m logistic support craft at speed

drag. A ram-air cushion, contained by shallow side skegs, raises the bow clear of the water at speed. As the pressurised air flows aft it generates air/foam lubrication for the remainder of the hull, permitting speeds of up to 50 mph (80·46 km/h) to be achieved. The performance depends upon the payload, installed power and sea conditions. A wide choice of power plants is available, and cabin modules can be supplied for passenger and work crew accommodation. Bow loading ramps are fitted for ease of access and operation from beaches.

The company offers a series of fast assault craft and patrol boats, tactical personnel carriers and logistic support craft, together with a range of general purpose short haul passenger and vehicle ferries, 8 m (25 ft 3 in) or 12 m (39 ft 4½ in) in length. Since June 1972, when the Mk 4 Sea Truck was introduced, more than 300 craft have been sold, 90% of which were delivered to overseas markets.

ROTORK 8M SEA TRUCK Mk 4

This is a heavy duty, multi-purpose workboat designed for high performance and low running costs. It can operate safely in only 1 ft (304 mm) of water and is equipped with a bow ramp to facilitate the loading of passengers, freight or light vehicles from beaches. The maximum payload is 3 tons.

POWER PLANT: Dependent upon payload and performance requirements and whether the craft is to be employed for sheltered water or open sea operation. Engines recommended are: Outboard: 135 hp OMC OBMs, or 150 Mercury OBMs. These can be fitted as twin or triple installations. Inboard (diesel): 106 hp Volvo AQD 32/270, installed as either single or twin installations. Supplied as standard with these units are the control console, and depending on the type of power unit, 50 gal (220 l) or 100 gal (440 l) bulwark or saddle tanks in welded mild steel, fuel lines, fittings and batteries.

HULL: Heavy duty glass fibre reinforced plastics. Star frame chassis integral with hull structure. 'Top hat' section. Bottom is in double thickness heavy duty grp and has five reinforced rubbing strips. Buoyancy is provided by closed cell polyurethane foam of TD 1 type. The skegs are in prestressed cold drawn stainless steel tube. The ramp, which is manually operated, is in 1 in (25·4 mm) thick, polyurethane-coated marine ply. It is housed in a galvanised steel frame with galvanised steel capping, and is counterbalanced by a torsion bar.

ACCOMMODATION: Up to four moulded grp cabin modules can be installed, together with passenger seats.

SYSTEMS, ELECTRICAL: Heavy duty 12 volt batteries housed in acid-resistant reinforced plastic battery box mounted at deck level

FUEL: Fuel is carried in one or more 50 or 100 gallon pannier type tanks, carried between the upper and lower fender tubes, port or starboard.

SCUPPERS: Scuppers for the removal of deck water are located in the transom. Discharge capacity is 180 gal/min (818·27 litres/min).

DIMENSIONS:

Length overall	24 ft 2 in (7·36 m)
Length at waterline	20 ft 0 in (6·09 m)
Beam	9 ft 10 in (2·74 m)

Freeboard:

unladen, to deck level	5 in (127 mm)
to top of bulwarks	3 ft 0 in (0·914 m)

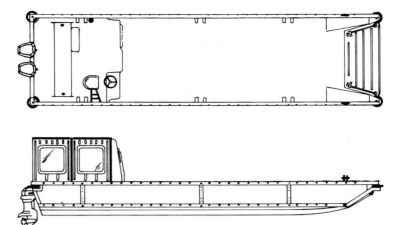

The Rotork 12 Metre Sea Truck in this configuration gives a clear open working deck area of over 6 m × 2·4 m

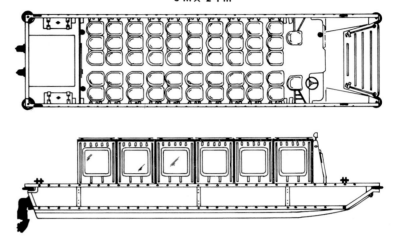

Rotork 12 metre diesel powered shorthaul passenger vehicle with seating for up to 50 passengers plus helmsman and observer. Seating capacity may be reduced according to operational requirements

max load, to deck level	2 in (50·80 mm)
to top of bulwarks	2 ft 7 in (0·787 m)

Deck area (with outboard power)
170 sq ft (15·79 m²)

Draft:

unladen, outboard drive up 7 in (177·8 mm) outboard drive down 1 ft 11 in (0·584 m)

Max load, outboard drive up
11 in (279 mm)

outboard drive down 2 ft 3 in (0·685 m)

WEIGHTS:

Basic hull, less engine	3,200 lb (1,451·49 kg)
Total integral foam buoyancy	11,500 lb (5,216·31 kg)
Payload, inshore	6,000 lb (2,721·55 kg)
sea conditions	3,000 kg

PERFORMANCE (8m):

Performance varies with rig, type of load, installed power and operating conditions. An approximate guide, based on the standard open deck-hull, is provided by the accompanying performance graph. This applies to the STW8 Sea Truck 8m workboat configuration.

ROTORK 12 M SEA TRUCK Mk 4

HULL: Glass-fibre reinforced plastic. Reinforcement: E glass chopped strand mat. E glass woven roving. Silane finish. Matrix: Isophthalic polyester resins meeting Admiralty DG 180 specification for large ships, integrally coloured. Resins: Cellobond A2785 CV or Scott Bader 625 TV.

BUOYANCY: Closed cell polyurethane foam of the TDI type. Nominal density 43·64 kgf/cu m (2·4lb/cu ft) 98% closed cell. Method of manufacture: auto proportioning machine mix foamed in situ.

DECK: Non-slip bonded grit surface applied to special point load resisting composite structure.

CHASSIS: 'Star frame' chassis integral with hull structure. 'Top hat' section.

GLAZING: 6 mm perspex acrylic sheet. Triplex where wipers are used.

FENDER FRAMES: Hop-dip galvanised welded mild steel tube 101·6 mm (4 in) diameter.

SKEGS: Prestressed cold drawn seamless steel tube. Anti-corrosion coated.

FENDERS: Rotating fender wheels are fitted as standard at bow and stern.

RAMP: 25·4 mm (1 in) thick marine plywood ramp. Polyurethane coated and grit bonded. Housed in galvanized steel frame with galvanized steel capping. Ramp counterbalanced by torsion bar.

RAMP LOCK: Ramp opened and closed by galvanized mild steel levers. Manually operated.

RAMP SEAL: 50·8 mm (2 in) diameter neoprene tube in compression.

SCUPPERS: Scuppers for the removal of water from the deck are located in the transom.

TANKS: Welded mild steel, phosphate conversion coated, epoxide primed, 2-pack polyurethane finish enamelled. Pressure tested.

FITTINGS: ¼ in and ⅜ in BSP

FUEL LINES: 9·5 mm (⅜ in) ID rubber hose with integral steel braiding.

CAPACITY AND MOUNTING: Type 1— 220 litre (50 gallon imperial) pannier for bulwark mounting. Type 2—440 litre (100 gallon imperial) saddle tank for athwartship mounting.

DIMENSIONS:
Length
  Overall   11·27 m (37 ft)
  At waterline   9·8 m (32 ft 2 in)
  Beam   2·74 m (9 ft 10 in)
Freeboards:
  Unladen to deck level   127 mm (5 in)
  Unladen to top of bulwarks
               814·4 mm (36 in)
  With max load to deck level
               50·8 mm (2 in)
  With max load to top of bulwarks
               838·2 mm (33 in)
Height:
  Of top rail from deck   787·2 mm (31 in)
  Of metacentre above centre of gravity
               5·51 m (18 ft 1 in)
Deck area:
  overall   30·85 sq m (287 sq ft)
Draft:
  Unladen, outdrive up   177·8 mm (7 in)
  Unladen, outdrive down 584·2 mm (23 in)
  With max load, outdrive up
               279·4 mm (11 in)
  With max load, outdrive down
               685·8 mm (27 in)
Weights:
  Less engine   2405 kg (4,500 lbs)
  Total integral foam buoyancy
               886 kg (1,968 lbs)

ROTORK STW 12 SEA TRUCK WORKBOAT

HULL: Standard Rotork 12 metre hull.
COLOUR: Hull—high visibility orange. Metalwork—bright galvanized finish.
FIXING POINTS: Rotork military pattern eye bolts at modular fixing points on upper and lower mainframe.
ELECTRICAL: Navigation lights, klaxon and searchlight mounted on mast operable from helmsman's position are standard equipment.
FUEL: 445 litre (100 gallon imperial) capacity. Mild steel welded and pressure tested tanks fitted with drain cocks, quick release filler caps and sight gauges.
FIRE FIGHTING EQUIPMENT: 1·1 kg (2½ lb) rechargeable CO_2 hand extinguisher.
TOTAL WEIGHT: 2,045 kg (4,500 lb).
  Optional items include:
NAVIGATION: Illuminated and fully gimballed compass mounted next to helmsman. Approx weight 2.7 kg (6 lb).
COMMUNICATIONS: VHF 8-channel transmitter/receiver. Approx weight 5·7 kg (13 lb). Small ship radar with range of 16 nm at 3kw. Approx weight 40 kg (88 lb).
CREW PROTECTION: GRP covered after-control position with all round vision. Nylon reinforced PVC dropscreen at rear. Approx weight: 143 kg (315 lb).
INSULATION: Heat resistant safari roof for service in particularly high ambient temperatures. Approx weight 25 kg (55 lb).
SUPPLEMENTARY CREW AREA: 4 ft forward extension of control position providing additional covered crew space and GRP stowage lockers. Approx weight 65 kg (143 lb). Additional extension of cabin forming an enlarged crew compartment. Approx weight 130 kg (286 lb).
MOBILITY: Detachable short haul wheels for launching and landing. Approx weight

An 8 metre patrol craft in service with the Medway Ports Authority

12m shorthaul passenger ferries are in service in Africa, the Far East and South America

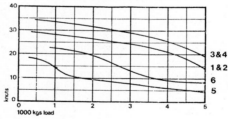
Performance graph for Rotork 12 metre Sea Truck workboat

Propulsion
1 Two 135 hp OMC OBM's 282 kg (620 lb)
2 Two 150 Mercury OBM's 282 kg (620 lb)
3 Three 135 hp OMC OBM's 424 kg (932 lb)
4 Three 150 Mercury OBM's 424 kg (932 lb)
5 One 106 hp Volvo AQD 32/270 inboard
                391 kg (861 lb)

151 kg (333 lb).
PROPULSION: (Alternative power plants and weights)
  1 Two 135 hp OMC OBM's
              282 kg (620 lb)
  2 Two 150 Mercury OBM's
              282 kg (620 lb)
  3 Three 135 hp OMC OBM's
              424 kg (932 lb)
  4 Three 150 Mercury OBM's
              424 kg (932 lb)

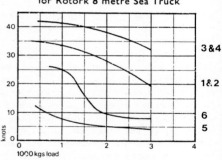
Approximate performance graph for Rotork 8 metre Sea Truck

6 Two 106 hp Volvo AQD 32/270 inboards
          782 kg (1,721 lb)
Payload: Maximum normal loading in the 8 metre Sea Truck Workboat is 3,000 kg. This figure is dependent on choice of optional equipment and propulsion system. Individual weights are as indicated.

5 One 106 hp Volvo AQD 32/270 inboard
          391 kg (861 lb)
6 Two 106 hp Volvo AQD 32/270 inboards
          782 kg (1,721 lb)
PAYLOAD: Maximum normal loading in the 12 metre Sea Truck Workboat is 5,000 kg. This figure is dependent on choice of optional equipment and propulsion system. Individual weights are as indicated.
  See accompanying graph for approximate performance figures.

SURFACE CRAFT LTD.

HEAD OFFICE:
Vale House,
169 Thorpe Road, Peterborough, 1.
TELEPHONE:
(0732) 61376

NIMBUS

This inflatable two/three-seater is intended for leisure, commercial and para-military applications. It can be towed on a specially designed trailer fitted with a remotely controlled electric winch. Loading and unloading is a one-man operation which can be undertaken in a matter of minutes.

LIFT AND PROPULSION: Integrated system powered by a single, 40 bhp Rotax 635 cc air-cooled twin-cylinder engine. The primary airflow from the two axial fans is ejected through a propulsion slot aft of the fan duct and the secondary flow, for the cushion, passes downwards into the plenum chamber. Fuel tank capacity 10 Imp gal (45 litre).

CONTROLS: Fourteen small rudder vanes in the propulsion slot control craft heading.

HULL: Main structure in colour-impregnated glassfibre. Twin, neoprene buoyancy tubes integral with craft structure. Electric bilge pump fitted.

ACCOMMODATION: Open cockpit for 2-4

Nimbus, a 50 mph (80 km/h) 2-3 seater built by Surface Craft Ltd.

passengers, depending on weight and distribution. Access through forward sliding entry door.

DIMENSIONS:
Length overall, power off 15 ft 2 in (4·62 m)

Height, on landing pads 5 ft 2 in (1·57 m)

PERFORMANCE:
Max speed	50 mph (80 km/h)
Cruising speed	35 mph (56 km/h)

STENTON HOVERCRAFT CO LTD

HEAD OFFICE:
West Barns, Dunbar, East Lothian, Scotland

TELEPHONE:
Dunbar 63582
DIRECTORS:
W. Carroll
T. Brady

Stenton Hovercraft is manufacturing and marketing the Hoverfly, a low-cost single-seater, developed and tested in conjunction with two of the most successful designers and builders of light hovercraft in the United Kingdom—Geoff Kent and Nigel Beale.

Hoverfly is a highly-manoeuvrable, amphibious sporting craft, which is capable of crossing land, water, ice and marshland at speeds up to 30 mph (48 km/h).

HOVERFLY

A simple single-seat design Hoverfly meets all the safety requirements of the Hover Club of Great Britain. It is capable of speeds of up to 25 mph (40·23 km/h) over land or water and employs an integrated lift/thrust propulsion system.

LIFT AND PROPULSION: A single JLO 250 cc two stroke engine rated at 15 hp at 5,500 rpm drives via a toothed belt a 24 in diameter, (609 mm) five-bladed, 45° pitch ducted fan. This unit supplies air for both lift and thrust, with about 40% of the fan duct diameter scooping air for the cushion and the remainder being used for thrust. With this system a static thrust of about 45 lb is achieved. Cushion pressure is about 9 lb/sq ft and the craft has a fuel capacity of 1½ gallons.

CONTROLS: A simple twist grip mounted on the steering handlebars operates the throttle for the single engine. An air rudder mounted in the fan duct controls craft heading.

HULL: The complete hull structure is constructed from self-coloured glass-reinforced

Stenton Hoverfly, low-cost amphibious single-seater powered by a 15 hp JLO 250 cc two-stroke

plastics with polyurethane foam, providing about 150% buoyancy, contained in the underside of the hull. It is also possible to fit marine buoyancy bags along the open wells on the sides of the craft to give additional buoyancy if the craft operates with an overload weight.

SKIRT SYSTEM: A simple bag skirt giving about 6 in obstacle clearance is fitted to the hull. The skirt is made from polyurethane coated nylon fabric weighing 4 oz/sq yd.

ACCOMMODATION: Hoverfly is a single-seater with the driver sitting astride a central bench.

DIMENSIONS:
Length overall	9 ft 0 in (2·74 m)
Width overall	5 ft 0 in (1·52 m)
Height overall	3 ft 6 in app. (1·06 m)
Height at rest	3 ft 0 in app. (·91 m)

WEIGHTS:
Weight empty (dry)	120 lb (54·42 kg)
Normal payload	200 lb (90·71 kg)
Normal all-up	350 lb (158·75 kg)

PERFORMANCE:
Maximum speed over land	29·82 mph (48 km/h)
over water	20 kt approx.

PRICE: £650·00.

SURFACE FLIGHT LTD

HEAD OFFICE:
   147/149 London Road, East Grinstead,
   Sussex
TELEPHONE:
   0342 28386
EXECUTIVES:
   G. R. Nichol
   P. V. McCollum
   N. A. Old
Surface Flight Ltd is concentrating on the development of low-cost, two-seat amphibious hovercraft, the first of which, the Sunrider, is now in production. Although designed for recreational use, the craft is suitable for a range of utility roles from light transport and rescue boat, to water-taxi and port and harbour inspection vehicle.

SUNRIDER

The Sunrider is a glass-fibre-hulled two-seater with a maximum speed of 35 mph (56 km/h). Ruggedly constructed, it is easy to operate and has an extremely low noise level.

LIFT AND PROPULSION: A 9·5 bhp Rotax two-stroke, single-cylinder engine located ahead of the open cockpit drives a 7-bladed fan for cushion lift. Thrust is provided by a 38·5 bhp Rotax 2-cylinder two-stroke driving a ducted 20-bladed fan aft of the cockpit. Fuel recommended is 93 octane. Tank capacity is 6 Imp gallons (27 litres).

CONTROLS: Single control column operates twin rudder hinged to rear of fan duct. Column incorporates twist-grip throttle for

Production model of Surface Flight's Sunrider two-seater, which is being employed for a number of light transport and liaison duties

lift fan. Electric starter provided for thrust engine.
HULL: Moulded glass-reinforced plastics.
SKIRT: Loop and segment skirt in polyurethane nylon. Replaceable segments.
ACCOMMODATION: Single, two place bench-type seat in open cockpit
DIMENSIONS:

Length overall	13 ft 4 in (4·06 m)
Beam overall	6 ft 6 in (1·98 m)
Height	3 ft 8 in (1·117 m)
WEIGHTS:	
All up weight	1,060 lb (480 kgs)
Payload	420 lb (190 kg)
PERFORMANCE:	
Max speed	35 mph (56 km/h)
Range	100 miles (160 km)
Endurance	4 hours approximately

VOSPER THORNYCROFT LTD

HEAD OFFICE:
   Vosper House, Southampton Road, Paulsgrove, Portsmouth, England
TELEPHONE:
   Cosham 79481
TELEX:
   86115
CABLES:
   Repsov, Portsmouth
DIRECTORS:
   Sir David Brown, Chairman
   John Rix, MBE, Managing Director
   Commander Christopher W. S. Dreyer, DSO, DSC, RN
   Alan D. Worton
   The Hon. Sir Clive Blossom, Bt
   Kenneth D. C. Ford
   John E. C. Grant, MBE
EXECUTIVE BOARD:
   John Rix, MBE, Chief Executive
   K. D. C. Ford, Financial Director
   J. E. C. Grant, MBE, Secretary
   P. D. P. Kemp, Managing Director Shipbuilding Division
   L. Peacock, Executive Director Personnel
   A. P. Shaw, Director Products Division
   D. P. E. Shepherd, OBE, Sales and Commercial Executive Director
   P. J. Usher, Deputy Managing Director Shipbuilding Division
   J. A. Wilde, CBE, Managing Director Repairs Division
   D. E. Wilson, Executive Director Ship Sales
SENIOR EXECUTIVES (Hovercraft):
   A. E. Bingham, BSc., (Tech), MIMechE, MRAeS, Chief Hovercraft Designer
Vosper Thornycroft Limited is the holding company for a number of companies throughout the world, the most important of which is Vosper Thornycroft Private, Ltd. in Singapore.

A 270-seat Vosper Thornycroft VT 1 hoverferry

Vosper Thornycroft has a high reputation as builder of warships including fast patrol craft, corvettes and frigates powered by diesel and gas-turbine machinery singly or in combination. Warships built by the company are in service with the Royal Navy and the navies of more than a dozen foreign and commonwealth countries. It also has a major ship repair facility in Southampton Docks.

With an annual turnover in the region of £82 million, derived mainly from building warships, Vosper Thornycroft also has a number of prosperous ancillary activities. These include the design and production of ship stabilisers, specialised electrical and electronic control equipment for marine and industrial use, oil burning equipment and furnishing.

In 1968, the decision was taken to enter the hovercraft field and shortly afterwards an order was received for the VT 1—an 87 ton hoverferry designed to carry 146 passengers and ten cars at speeds up to 40 knots. The VT 1 has been subjected to exhaustive trials to evaluate every aspect of its commercial viability and particularly its reliability and seakeeping, both in the English Channel and in the notoriously rough waters between the Channel Islands and the French coast. The first two all-passenger craft built by the company were operated in Scandinavian waters between Malmo, Sweden and Copenhagen, Denmark in 1972.

Operationally, the craft proved extremely successful. They carried more than 310,000 passengers and travelled more than 61,000 miles, with a mechanical reliability of 98·73 per cent.

In 1973 the company announced that it was building the VT 2, the first of a new class of fully amphibious hovercraft intended primarily for military applications. The prototype began trials in late 1975. Design studies have covered a range of larger vessels, including a 170-ton ASW or MCM vessel and a 500-ton convoy escort.

VT 1

The VT 1 is an 87 ton ACV designed for fast, low-cost passenger/car/operation. It is built to the standards required by the British Civil Air Cushion Vehicle Safety Requirements. Power is supplied by two Avco Lycoming TF25 marine gas-turbines each driving four fixed-pitch lift fans and one controllable-pitch water propeller.

Cruising speed is 35-38 knots (65-70 km/h) and the craft will operate in complete safety in wave heights up to 10-12 ft (3-3·7 m). The VT 1 can be operated from existing terminals or alternatively, simple low-cost slipways or pontoon terminals can be established on beaches.

VARIANTS: Typical layouts include a car/passenger version for 146 passengers and 10 vehicles and a 250/270 passenger version which can be fitted with facilities for serving refreshments on route.

LIFT AND PROPULSION: Motive power is provided by two Avco Lycoming TF 25 marine gas-turbines, with power ratings between 1,675 and 2,000 hp for ambient temperatures between 80°—60°F. These are located in separate engine rooms amidships, port and starboard. Each engine is directly coupled via a transfer gearbox to four 5 ft diameter centrifugal lift fans and thence to a skeg-mounted water propeller via a Vee-drive gearbox.

CONTROLS: The control cabin is located above the port side of the superstructure and provides a 360° view. Provision is made for two craft control positions abreast of each other forward, with radar located at a third seat position behind. Engine controls are on a central console within easy reach of both front seat positions.

Directional control is provided by power-operated twin water rudders, controllable-pitch propellers and twin skegs. A water ballast system is provided for longitudinal and transverse CG adjustments.

OPERATING TECHNIQUES: The VT 1 is designed to operate like a conventional ship when at sea and when berthing alongside piers and moles. It can operate from simple concrete ramps or slips laid on any reasonably steep beach, an ideal arrangement for loading and off loading vehicles. By employing this technique for passenger car/ferry services, simple, inexpensive terminals can be built on beaches of suitable gradient (between 1 in 8 and 1 in 12) from which the craft can be operated in all tide states.

At its maintenance base, the beach landing technique is used to land the craft onto a trolley on which it is hauled out of the water for maintenance.

ACCOMMODATION: The car/passenger version has four passenger compartments, one at each corner of the craft, and seats a total of 146 passengers. Each compartment has a toilet/washroom. There are two main entrances to each passenger compartment.

Interior of one of the four corner passenger cabins flanking the VT 1's central deck area

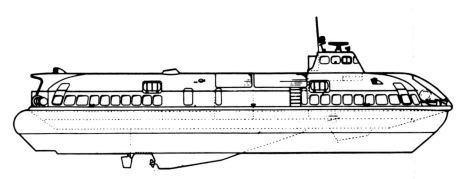

Profile of the VT 1 and interior arrangements of the cruise variant for 270 passengers

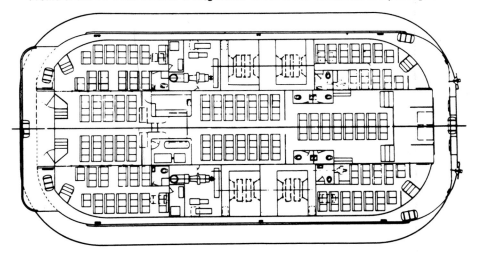

enter over the main ramp or may use the external superstructure doors via mobile embarkation steps.

The car bay, designed for 10 cars, has full width doors at the bow, which form an access ramp for loading and unloading. The craft always beaches bows-to, and cars must be driven off in reverse. To simplify the control and positioning of cars a guide track is provided for each lane of cars and runs the full length of the bay. This enables vehicles to be disembarked quite satisfactorily. As an alternative to cars, up to three ISO 20 ft containers can be carried.

Further details of the VT 1, together with dimensions, weights and performance can be found in JSS 1975-76 and earlier editions.

VOSPER THORNYCROFT VT.2 HOVERCRAFT FOR NAVAL AND MILITARY USE

Based on the VT 1, this gas-turbine powered hovercraft patrol boat has a floating displacement of 100 tons and a speed in excess of 60 knots. In a strike role, armament would comprise Exocet anti-ship missile launchers, and a twin-barrelled 35 mm Oerlikon cannon designed primarily for rapid and accurate fire against aircraft and guided missiles, but which is also extremely effective when directed against surface craft. The missiles and cannon will be controlled by a Contraves or similar fire control system.

The craft offers a number of important advantages over conventional fast patrol boats of comparable size. In particular, due to the depth and flexibility of its fully peripheral skirt, the craft can maintain a high speed and provide a stable weapons platform in rough sea conditions.

A number of variants are available. In addition to the strike version, there is a logistic support variant for carrying troops, vehicles and guns; a general purpose configuration combining both weapons and a logistic capability and a mine countermeasures variant.

LIFT AND PROPULSION: Motive power for the integrated lift/propulsion system is supplied by two Rolls Royce Proteus marine gas-turbines rated at 4,500 shp maximum and 3,800 shp continuous. The gas turbines are installed in port and starboard engine rooms, amidships, and each powers two drive shafts via a David Brown gearbox. One shaft transmits power to a bank of four centrifugal lift fans, which absorbs about one third of the output, the other drives a ducted propulsion fan via an inclined shaft.

The 13 ft 6 in (4·11 m) diameter propulsion fans, made by Dowty Rotol, have variable-pitch blades and are housed in ducts manufactured by Vosper Thornycroft. Each engine/fan unit provides sufficient power to maintain the craft on full cushion and ensure adequate controllability in the event of a single engine failure.

The blade tip speed is low so that the noise commonly associated with open air propellers is substantially reduced.

CONTROLS: The control cabin is located above the superstructure on the longitudinal centreline amidships and provides a 360° view. The control position is forward to port, with an engineer's position to starboard and navigator's and observer's positions behind. Control surfaces for vectoring thrust are fitted aft of the fans for normal steering, but differential pitch is used for steering at low speeds supplemented by a bow thruster which is particularly useful when when manoeuvring in a confined space. Thrust can be varied for manoeuvring the craft without altering the engine speed or cushion depth.

HULL: Construction is mainly in marine corrosion resistant aluminium alloy and comprises a buoyancy raft 2 ft 3 in (0·7 m) deep extending over the whole plan area and sub-divided into thirty watertight compartments which enable the craft to float indefinitely in the event of complete engine failure. Longitudinal bulkheads run the length of the craft and increase the bending strength of the structure; the remainder of the superstructure is non-load bearing and can be adapted as required for the particular role.

SKIRT: VT 2 has a 5·5 ft (1·7 m) deep single-cell flexible skirt. Stability is provided by the edge configuration of the skirt. Hardstructure is chamfered all round so that the inner attachment points of the skirt segments can be reached without jacking the craft up from its off-cushion position, thus simplifying maintenance.

DIMENSIONS (all variants):

Length overall	99 ft 0 in (31·17 m)
Beam overall	43 ft 6 in (13·10 m)
Cushion height	5 ft 6 in (1·67 m)
Hand structure clearance when hovering	3 ft 7 in (1·09 m)
Draft in displacement condition	2 ft 10 in (0·86 m)
Height (hovering to top of propulsion fan ducts)	30 ft 3 in (9·15 m)

Above and Below: Operational bases for the 60-knot plus VT 2 fast patrol hovercraft can be established on any gently sloping beach. Equipped with missiles, it carries an armament load comparable to that of a much larger conventional patrol boat. Armament would normally comprise two or four anti-ship missiles and either an Oto Melara 76 mm general purpose automatic cannon or a Bofors 57 mm cannon, together with their associated control equipment

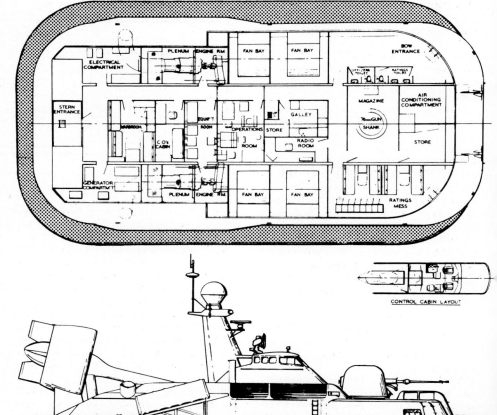

Outboard profile and deck plan of the VT 2 in fast missile hovercraft configuration. The craft illustrated is equipped with two Otomat surface-to-surface missiles and a 76 mm Melara combat gun

PERFORMANCE:

Max speed, calm conditions

in excess of 60 knots

Max speed in 5 ft (1·52 m) waves 55 knots

VT 2 FAST PATROL HOVERCRAFT, HEAVILY ARMED

This version is equipped with two Otomat surface-to-surface missiles and an Oto Melara compact gun. Other armament of similar weight could be fitted to meet individual specifications. Armament and crew weight is 23½ tons, and with 10½ tons of fuel, the endurance is five hours or 300 nm and 60 knots. An additional 10½ tons of fuel for the overload case (giving a half fuel weight of 100 tons) results in a range of 600 nm.

WEIGHTS:

Operating weight	66·0
Armament and crew	23·5
Fuel	10·5
Starting auw	100·0 tons

VT 2 LOGISTIC SUPPORT HOVERCRAFT

Designed to carry a company of 130 fully-armed troops and their vehicles. The vehicle bay is approximately 16½ ft (5·02 m) wide, 9½ ft (2·89 m) high and 70 ft (21·33 m) long. It has a full width bow ramp and door together with an 8 ft (2·43 m) wide stern ramp and door for the through loading and unloading of vehicles. The craft can carry payloads of 30-33 tons, together with fuel for five hours. Considerable overloading of the craft is acceptable at reduced performance so that with suitable deck and entrance ramp reinforcing, a 50 ton Chieftain battle tank could be carried.

The vessels can either be shipped to a theatre of operations, or if required by a NATO country, it could be deployed to any point on the coastline of Europe or the Mediterranean under its own power. The longest 'stage' would be from the United Kingdom to Gibraltar, a distance of approximately 1,100 nautical miles, and to allow an adequate reserve en route for rough seas. the craft would carry an additional 10 tons of fuel, starting out at an all-up weight of 115 tons.

WEIGHTS:

Operating weight	62·5
Payload	32·0
Fuel	10·5
Starting auw	105·0 tons

VT 2 MULTI-ROLE LOGISTIC SUPPORT AND GP PATROL HOVERCRAFT

Fitted with a rear loading door and ramp, enabling four 1-ton Land Rovers and 60 troops to be loaded in the aft section of the central bay. The bow is the same as that of the lightly armed fast patrol version. The forward area of the central bay and the forward cabins on each side would be fitted out as a small operations room and crew quarters.

WEIGHTS:

Operating weight	65·5
Armament and crew	5·0
Payload	19·0
Fuel	10·5
Starting auw	100·0 tons

VT 2 FAST PATROL, LIGHTLY ARMED

Armed with a twin Hispano-Suiza 30 mm cannon. At a starting weight of 100 tons, it has 24½ tons of fuel, providing a range of 700 nm or 11½ hours endurance at a speed of

Top: Impression of an assault force being landed by VT 2 logistic support hovercraft. A typical payload would be a company of 130 troops and their vehicles
Centre: VT 2 prototype during trials on the Solent. The craft can carry a payload of 30-33 tons together with fuel for five hours
Bottom: VT 2 demonstrating its amphibious capability. Power is provided by two 4,500 hp Rolls-Royce Proteus gas-turbines

60 knots. An additional 10½ tons of fuel (a total of 35 tons), increases the range to 1,000 nm.

170-ton ASW OR MCM VESSEL

This design for a 170-ton anti-submarine or mine countermeasures vessel is based on that of the 100-ton fast patrol boat. An increase in installed horsepower and length provides off-shore capability, and the larger deck area permits the installation of a wider range of weapons.

Motive power is supplied by three Rolls-Royce Proteus gas-turbines driving lift fans and three axial-flow waterjet units. Alternatively the designers propose a CODAG arrangement in which diesel engines can be coupled to the integrated lift/propulsion system to provide increased range.

DIMENSIONS:

Length overall	37·1 m
Beam (hard structure)	12·25 m
Height, power on (sea level to top of control cabin)	8·1 m
Cushion depth	2·3 m
Hovering draught	1·0 m
Floating draught (gear retracted)	1·5 m)

WEIGHTS:

All-up weight	170 tonnes
Armament load	29 tonnes

PERFORMANCE:

Range full power	700 nm

With diesels fitted for low speed cruising—
   at AUW 182 tonnes—15 knots 1,500 nm
Speed, maximum continuous
              In excess of 50 knots

VOSPER VT 2 MINE COUNTERMEASURES

Vosper Thornycroft's VT 2 hovercraft, which is aimed primarily at the military market, has been delivered to the Naval Hovercraft Trials Unit (formerly IHU), Lee-on-the-Solent, which is primarily concerned with the development of hovercraft for mine countermeasures duties.

Interest in amphibious hovercraft for this application stems from its relative invulnerability compared to displacement vessels, to underwater explosions and their low magnetic and underwater noise signatures. The accompanying photograph of a model shows one possible arrangement of a VT 2 for this particular role.

As can be seen from the model, the VT 2 is of suitable size for this work. The model shows the sweepdeck space with sweepgear stowed. The gear illustrated is either in current use or readily available commercially.

The VT 2 prototype is powered by two 4,500 shp Rolls-Royce Proteus marine gas-turbines which gives it a maximum speed in excess of 60 knots. Alternative power-plants, such as the more powerful 5,800 shp Rolls-Royce Tyne RM2D, can be installed, if increased performance is required.

500-TON ASW OR CONVOY ESCORT

The main role for which this vessel has been designed is that of ocean convoy escort. Lift fans and waterjet units would be driven by a Rolls-Royce Olympus and two Avco Lycoming TF45 gas turbines.

DIMENSIONS:

Length overall	66 m
Beam (hard structure)	19 m
Height (sea level to top of control cabin—on cushion)	13·5 m
Cushion depth	3·5 m
Hovering draught	1·7 m
Floating draught (skeg folded)	2·8 m

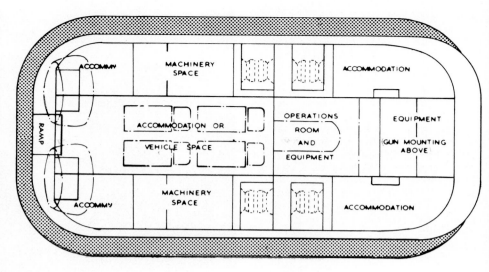

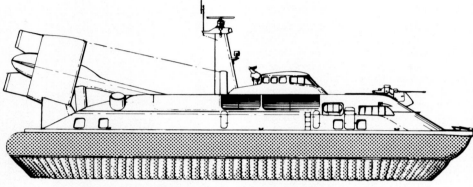

VT 2 equipped for lightly armed patrol and general purpose roles

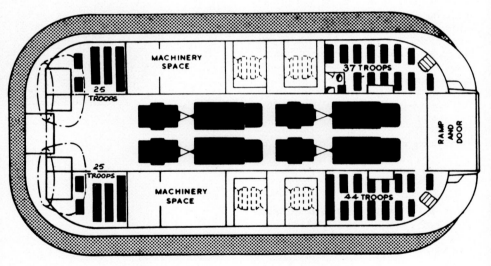

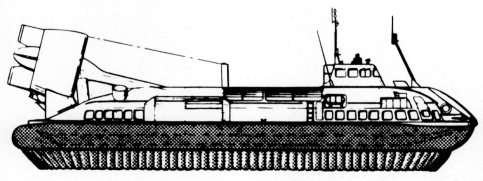

Outboard profile and accommodation plan of the VT 2 in logistic support configuration

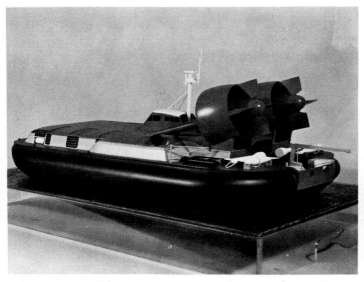

Model of the VT 2 in a possible MCM configuration showing its sweepgear

VT 2 preparing to tow. Note the protection to personnel afforded by the fan ducts and the ample deck space aft

WEIGHTS:

All-up weight	500 tonnes
Armament load	50 tonnes

PERFORMANCE:

Range full power	1,200 nm
Range at 23 kts	2,000 nm
Speed—maximum continuous	
	In excess of 50 knots

2000-TONNE ASW FRIGATE

Designed for anti-submarine warfare, this craft would employ large ducted fans for propulsion. Maximum continuous speed would be 100 knots.

Power would be provided by five Rolls-Royce Olympus gas-turbines, three for lift and two for propulsion

DIMENSIONS:

Length overall	110 m
Beam overall	39 m
Cushion depth	4·5 m

WEIGHTS:

All up weight	2,000 tonnes
Disposable load	1,150 tonnes

PERFORMANCE:

Max continuous speed	
	100 knots (calm conditions)
Range at 75 knots	1,500 nm

VT 1M

Built as a manned scale model of the VT 1 hovercraft, the VT 1M has now completed its programme of development trials, including a test programme with waterjet propulsion.

A 500-ton ocean-going escort designed by Vosper Thornycroft. A helicopter landing pad and hangar can be provided aft of the superstructure

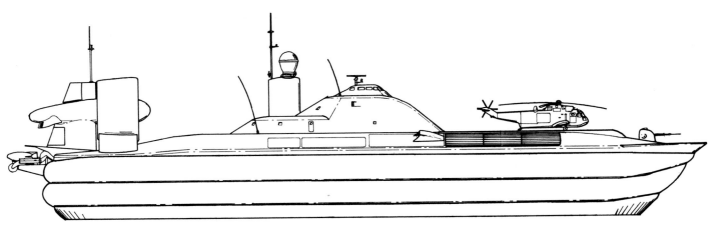

Powered by five Rolls-Royce Marine Olympus gas-turbines this Vosper Thornycroft project for a 2,000 ton ASW vessel would have a maximum continuous speed of 100 knots in calm water

UNITED STATES

AEROJET-GENERAL CORPORATION
(Subsidiary of The General Tire and Rubber Co)

CORPORATE OFFICE:
J. H. Vollbrecht, President
9100 East Flair Drive, El Monte, California 91734
TELEPHONE:
213 572-6000
AEROJET LIQUID ROCKET COMPANY:
J. L. Heckel, President
PO Box 13222, Sacramento, California 95813
TELEPHONE:
916 355-1000
AALC OPERATIONS:
PO Box 2173, Tacoma, Washington 98401
Fred F. Herman, Program Manager
A. E. Rose, Director, Operations

Aerojet-General began research and development programmes on both rigid sidewall and skirted amphibious air cushion configurations in June 1966. The company's research and development programmes include lift system development, skirt and structural materials investigations and development sub-scale and full-scale dynamic model testing, test laboratory development and full-scale vehicle operation. In addition, Aerojet has conducted government and company funded design and application studies on many rigid sidewall and skirted air cushion vehicle designs for military, non-military government and commercial roles. Work is at present concentrated on a US Navy contract for the development of the AALC Jeff(A) amphibious assault landing craft.

SES-100A

Earlier contracts for preliminary design of a "less than 100-ton" SES craft and for the dynamic test programme for the US Navy's XR-3 research craft led to the award of a contract, in January 1969, for the detailed design, construction and test of a 100-ton rigid sidewall testcraft—the SES-100A—under the sponsorship and management of the Surface Effect Ships Programme Office (SESPO), an agency of the US Navy.

Dockside testing began in August 1971 and deep water trials began in May 1972. Official US Navy test and evaluation trials began in September 1972 and were completed in 1974.

Subsequently the craft was moved from the Seattle, Washington, area to the US Navy's SES Test Facility at the Naval Air Station, Patuxent River, Maryland, where tests have been resumed.

A description of the vessel appears in the entry for Rohr Industries, which under navy contract, provides maintenance, engineering, test planning and data handling support for the test programme.

AALC JEFF (A)

In 1970, Aerojet-General was awarded a contract by US Naval Ship Systems Command for the preliminary design of an experimental 160-ton 50-knot amphibious assault landing craft. This was followed in March 1971 by a further contract for the detail design, construction and test of the craft, which is designated AALC Jeff(A) Construction of the hull was initiated by Todd Shipyards Corporation, Seattle, Washington, in 1974. Manufacturer's and US

Above and below: Aerojet-General's SES-100A during a series of high-speed test runs. The craft is powered by four 3,500 hp Avco Lycoming TF 35 gas-turbines and has a maximum speed of about 80 knots. Shown in these photographs are the forward skegs, used for directional control at high speeds, and the two engine air inlets on the topside, aft. The cabin accommodates four crew members and up to six test observers

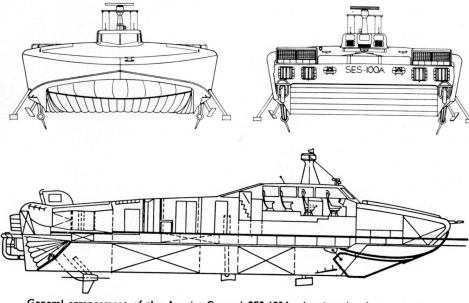

General arrangement of the Aerojet-General SES-100A, showing the loop-and-segment bow seal design

Navy trials will be undertaken during 1977 and 1978.

The craft is designed to operate at a nominal speed of 50 knots in Sea State 2 and accommodate up to 75 tons in palletised supplies and/or equipment. It is designed primarily for use by the US Marine Corps, and will carry tanks, trucks, half-trucks and other equipment from an LPD, LSD or LHA support ship to a point inland.

To ensure adequate world-wide operational capability, the specification calls for operation in temperatures from 0°-100°F.

LIFT AND PROPULSION: Cushion lift is provided by two 3,750 hp Avco Lycoming TF40 gas-turbines, one in each of the two sidestructures, driving two sets of four 4 ft 0 in (1·21 m) diameter fans through lightweight transmission and shafting connections.

Thrust is supplied by four 3,750 hp Avco Lycoming TF40 gas-turbines each driving a 7 ft 5 in (2·26 m) diameter pylon-mounted shrouded propeller, located above the sidestructure, and outside the cargo deck area to provide free access and uninterrupted air flow. Each propeller pylon rotates to provide both propulsion and directional control.

HULL: Constructed in marine aluminium with maximum use of corrugated structures to minimise total craft weight. The main hull is formed by a buoyancy raft with port and starboard side structures. Each side-structure contains three Avco Lycoming gas-turbines with associated air intakes, exhausts, shrouded propellers, lift fans, transmissions and auxiliary power systems.

The bottom and deck structures of the hull are separated by longitudinal and transverse bulkheads to form a number of watertight flotation compartments. The cargo deck area is 2,280 sq ft (211·82 m²); the bow ramp opening width is 21 ft 6 in (6·55 m) and the aft ramp width is 27 ft 4 in (8·33 m).

SKIRT: 5 ft (1·52 m) deep "Pericell" loop and cell type.

ACCOMMODATION: Two air-conditioned and sound-insulated compartments, each seating three crew members or observers. Access to each compartment is via the cargo deck.

DIMENSIONS:

Length overall, on cushion
96 ft 1 in (29·30 m)
on landing pads   92 ft 0 in (28·04 m)
Beam overall, on cushion
48 ft 0 in (14·63 m)
on landing pads   44 ft 0 in (13·41 m)
Height overall, on cushion
23 ft 1 in (7·03 m)
on landing pads   18 ft 9 in (5·71 m)
Bow ramp opening width
21 ft 6 in (6·55 m)
Stern ramp opening width
27 ft 4 in (8·33 m)
Cargo deck area   2,280 sq ft (211·82 m²)

WEIGHTS:

Gross weight   334,000 lb (154,221 kg)
Empty weight   180,000 lb (81,697 kg)
Fuel   40,000 lb (18,144 kg)
Design payload   120,000 lb (54,431 kg)
Design overload   150,000 lb (68,038 kg)

PERFORMANCE:

Max speed with design payload   50 knots
Range   200 nm

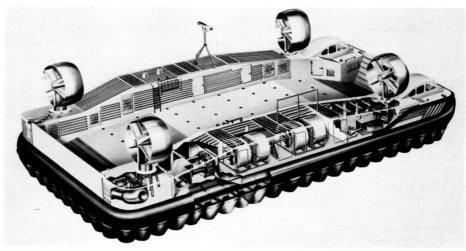

Above and below: The Aerojet-General Jeff (A) amphibious assault landing craft under construction for the US Navy. Designed primarily to meet the US Marine Corp's requirements in the 1980s it will carry tanks, trucks, half tracks and other equipment from LPD, LSD, or LHA support ships to the shore at a speed of 50 knots

Max gradient, standing start   11½%
Nominal obstacle clearance
4 ft 0 in (1·21 m)

AIRCUSHION BOAT COMPANY INC

HEAD OFFICE:
401 Alexander Avenue, Building 391, Tacoma, Washington 98421

TELEPHONE:
(206) 272 3600

EXECUTIVES:
W. W. Buckley, President
F. C. Gunter, Vice-President

The Aircushion Boat Company is responsible for the development of the Airboat—a concept described by the company as an air-cushion-assisted catamaran. Vessels of this series of sidewall craft are based on conventional fibreglass hulls and employ water propeller or waterjet propulsion. Lift is supplied by an independent engine/fan system and flexible skirts are fitted fore and aft to contain the air cushion.

The company states that the cushion supports 75% of the loaded weight of the Airboats, and that as a result of the reduced drag the prototype uses 20% less fuel per mile. Another advantage is that when travelling at high speed, the air cushion softens the ride by preventing heavy slamming. Vessels of this type are being marketed by the company for a variety of applica-

Airboat III during trials on Puget Sound

tions including fast crew boats, water taxis, patrol boats, survey and sports fishing craft.

AIRBOAT III

Airboat III is employed as a development craft and began trials in Puget Sound in January 1974.

It has performed in short 4 ft (1·21 m)

waves at speeds up to 35 knots without undue discomfort to the crew due to slamming. Another characteristic is that it generates very little wash when executing full speed runs on smooth water in protected waterways.

LIFT AND PROPULSION: Two 330 Chrysler petrol engines driving twin water screws propel the craft. A third engine powers a centrifugal fan for cushion lift.

HULL: Fine retardant foam and fibreglass sandwich construction.

DIMENSIONS:

Length	38 ft (11·58 m)
Beam	13 ft 6 in (4·11 m)

WEIGHTS:

All-up weight	16,000 lb (7,257 kg)
Normal payload	3,000 lb (1,360 kg)

PERFORMANCE:

Cruising speed	35 knots
Maximum speed	40 knots plus

42 FT AIRBOAT

The 42 ft (12·8 m) long Airboat is a high speed passenger ferry/freighter capable of operating in 4·5 ft waves. In passenger configuration seating is provided for 21 plus a crew of two.

A feature of the design is the extension of the bow well ahead of the air cushion. When rough water forces the bow down at speed the broad area forward of the cushion planes and raises the bow without slamming.

With the lift fan system off, the craft operates as a conventional displacement catamaran and has a top speed of 15 knots. With the lift system on, acceleration to the cruising speed of 30 knots is easily attained in ten boat lengths. In 8-10 ft (2·4-3·04 m) following seas a stable, near horizontal attitude is maintained while contouring swells and no tendency to broach or lose directional control is experienced.

LIFT AND PROPULSION: Motive power is supplied by three diesels, one for lift and two for propulsion. The lift engine drives a large low rpm centrifugal fan contained in a reinforced box which is an integral part of the hull structure. Power is transmitted via a clutch and Spicer shaft to a heavy duty, lightweight right-angle gearbox. Power delivered to the fan at cruise condition pressure and airflow is 180 hp. Each of the propulsion engines is turbocharged and drives a waterjet. The standard fuel tank capacity is 300 gallons, providing a cruising range of more than 250 miles at 30 knots.

Marine propellers can be fitted to the vessel instead of waterjets if required. The powerplant remains the same, but the propulsion engines supply power through reversing gearboxes to shafts and marine propellers. Hydraulically operated twin rudders are mounted on the transom of each of the hulls. The propeller-driven version is capable of the same top speed, with slightly improved fuel economy.

HULL: Robust, fire-retardant foam and fibreglass sandwich structure, with unitised beam tying the catamaran hulls. High freeboard, wide buoyant hull and low profile for seaworthiness in rough seas and gale force winds.

ACCOMMODATION: In passenger/crew boat configuration, accommodation is provided for 21 seat passengers and a crew of 2. The passenger saloon is completely enclosed with 6 ft 6 in (1·98 m) high headroom throughout. The cabin contains a galley, head and large storage area. The bridge is elevated for 360° view and is located slightly aft of the bow. A sliding hard top provides upward visibility if required.

DIMENSIONS:

Length	42 ft (12·80 m)
Beam	17 ft (5·18 m)

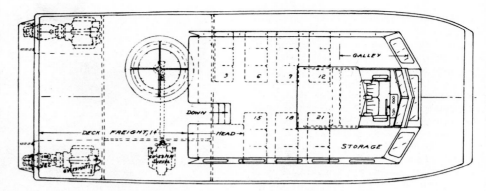

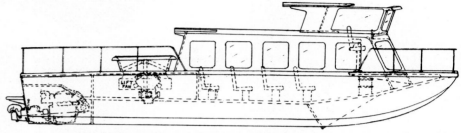

General arrangement of the waterjet-propelled 42 ft Airboat

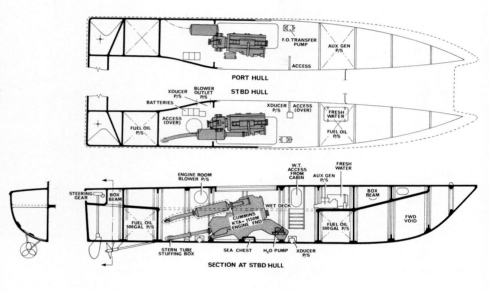

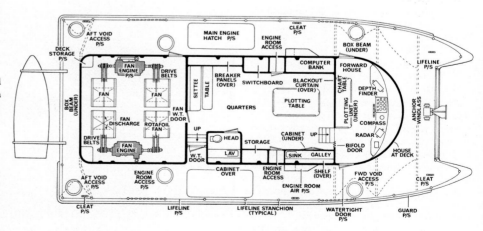

Inboard profile and deck plans of the Airboat IV

PERFORMANCE:

Service speed	30 knots
Maximum speed	in excess of 33 knots
Max speed, displacement condition 15 knots	
Fuel consumption at 30 knots	
	34 gph (154·56 l/ph)
Cruising range at 30 knots	
	over 250 miles (402 km)

AIRBOAT IV

Work on this new addition to the Airboat range began in the summer of 1976. Like the Airboat III, the new vessel, a 55 ft (16·7 m) survey craft, is based on the concept of an air-cushion assisted catamaran hull on which a cabin and pilothouse have been built to suit customer requirements.

In the case of the Airboat IV, the cabin can be adapted to seat up to 40 passengers.

Maximum speed of the new craft, which will be propelled by water screws driven by two 550 hp Cummins KTA 1150 diesels, will be about 35 knots.

LIFT AND PROPULSION: Cushion lift is provided by two 275 hp Volvo Penta TAM D70CS, each driving twin 2 ft (0·60 m) diameter double-entry, centrifugal fans. Fan air is discharged directly through the wet deck, between the catamaran hulls, into the cushion. Motive power for the propulsion system is provided by either two 550 hp Cummins KTA 1150 diesels or twin 800 hp MTU 8V331 diesels. Each engine drives a 2 ft 2 in (0·660 m) diameter Michigan bronze propeller via a reversing gearbox and an inclined shaft. Waterjets can be fitted to the vessel instead of marine propellers if required. Fuel is carried in four 500 gal (2,272 l) capacity integral fibre glass tanks, two in each hull. Refuelling points are located on the weatherdeck, two on each hull. Recommended fuel is grade 2 diesel.

CONTROLS: Hydraulically-operated twin rudders control craft heading on the propeller-driven variants. On models equipped with waterjets, craft direction is controlled by jet flow deflection.

HULL: Fabricated in Airex core, fibre glass sandwich laminate. Decks and top of pilothouse in balsa cored fibre glass. Bow shell plate designed to withstand slamming loads of up to 20 psi.

SKIRT: Patented inflated double-cylinder bags at bow and stern.

ACCOMMODATION: Operating crew comprising captain, navigator and deckhand are accommodated in a raised pilothouse forward. Up to 40 passengers can be accommodated in the main cabin, which is heated and ventilated. Air conditioning is optional. Passenger seats are of lightweight aircraft-type, with a central aisle between the seat rows. Entry doors are at the side of the deckhouse, one port, one starboard.

SYSTEMS; ELECTRICAL: 110 v AC from diesel auxiliary generator. Shore power adaptor, plus 24 v DC supply for engine starting, and 12 v DC for navigation lights, etc.

APU: Onan diesel.

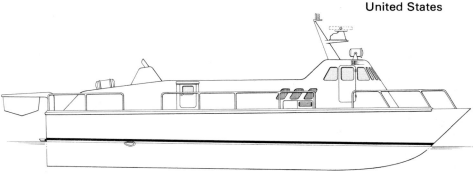

Outboard profile of the Airboat IV

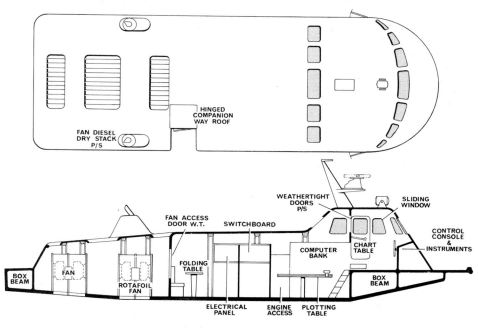

Deck plan of the Airboat IV

DIMENSIONS; EXTERNAL:

Length overall, power off	
	55 ft 0 in (25·90 m)
Length overall, on cushion	
	55 ft 0 in (25·90 m)
Beam overall, power off	
	25 ft 0 in (7·62 m)
Beam overall, on cushion	
	25 ft 0 in (7·62 m)
Height overall, displacement condition	
excluding mast	12 ft 0 in (3·65 m)
Height overall, on cushion	
	13 ft-14 ft (3·9-4·2 m)
Draft afloat, propellers	6 ft 0 in (1·82 m)
Draft afloat, waterjets	3 ft 6 in (1·06 m)

DIMENSIONS; INTERNAL:

Passenger Cabin

Length	40 ft 0 in (12·19 m)
Maximum width	15 ft 0 in (4·57 m)
Maximum height	6 ft 6 in (1·98 m)
Floor area	600 sq ft (55·74 m²)

Baggage holds: In cabin, plus weatherdeck storage locker.

WEIGHTS:

Normal empty weight	
	47,800 lb (21,681·70 kg)
Normal all-up weight	
	65,000 lb (29,483·48 kg)
Normal payload weight	
	4,800 lb (2,177·2 kg)
Maximum payload	9,000 lb (4,082 kg)

PERFORMANCE:

Maximum speed, calm water	35 knots
Maximum speed, calm water, maximum	
continuous power	30 knots
Cruising speed, calm water	30 knots
Turning circle diameter at 30 knots	
	3 boat lengths
Water speed in 4 ft waves and 15 knot	
headwind	30 knots
Maximum wave capability on scheduled	
runs	6 ft 0 in (1·82 m)
Maximum survival sea state	5
Still air range and endurance at cruising	
speed	650 nm

PRICE AND TERMS:

Approx cost of craft, fob Tacoma USA— US $575,000. Base engines extra, depending on choice.

TERMS:

Partial payment on signing contract, plus progress instalments.

BELL AEROSPACE TEXTRON
Division of Textron Inc.

New Orleans Operations
  PO Box 29307, New Orleans, Louisiana
    70189

TELEPHONE:
  504 255 3311

John J. Kelly, Vice-President and General Manager

Donald F. Bonhardt, Director of Product Assurance

Joseph A. Cannon, Director of Marketing

John B. Chaplin, Director of Engineering

Roland Decrevel, 2KSES Project Manager

Hugh F. Farabaugh, Director of Employee Relations and Services

Clarence L. Forrest, Director, Full-Scale Test and Project Manager, SES-100B

Donald E. Kenney, Director of Administration

Clifford F. Lennon, Director of Manufacturing

Robert S. Postle, LC JEFF(B) Project Manager

Murray Shabsis, Director of Materiel

Albert W. Spindler, Director of Public Relations

Bell Aerospace began its air cushion vehicle development programme in 1958. Craft built by the company range in size from the

18 ft XHS3 to the SES-100B, 105-ton surface effect ship test craft which is undergoing sea trials.

The company has rights to manufacture and sell in the United States, machines employing the hovercraft principle through a licencing arrangement with the British Hovercraft Corporation and Hovercraft Development Ltd.

In addition to importing seven BHC SR.N5s, three of which were employed by the US Navy and later by the US Coast Guard for use and evaluation, Bell built three SK-5 Model 7255s—the company's first production ACVs—to a US Army specification. The craft were airlifted to Vietnam, where they performed a variety of missions, including high speed troop/cargo transportation and patrol. One SK-5 Model 7255 is employed in a research programme being conducted by the US Army's Weapons Command, St Louis Missouri.

In January 1969, the US Surface Effect Ships Project Office awarded Bell a contract for the detailed design of a 100-ton surface effect ship test craft. Construction began in September 1969 and the preperation of the craft for trials began early in 1971. An extensive test and evaluation programme began in February 1972 on Lake Pontchartrain, Louisiana.

In May 1973, the SES-100B was transferred to the Naval Coastal Systems Laboratory at Panama City, Florida, for deep water and high sea state testing in the Gulf of Mexico. In January 1974 the company announced that the SES-100B had successfully completed the testing necessary to confirm and expand the technology necessary for the design of a 2,000-ton ocean-going surface effect ship.

In March 1971 the company was awarded a Phase II contract by the US Navy authorising it to start work on a programme covering the detail design, construction and test of an experimental 160-ton AALC (amphibious assault landing craft), designated L. C. JEFF(B).

This work is being undertaken at the company's New Orleans Division, where all its SEV programmes have been consolidated. Construction of the prototype began in 1972.

In March 1972 the Advanced Research Projects Agency of the US Department of Defense awarded Bell a contract under which the company will produce studies of nine different aspects of the ARPA's projected 1,000 ton, 120-knot arctic-based logistics vehicle.

In November 1972, it was announced that Bell has been awarded a $2·9 million contract by US Naval Ship Systems Command to conduct a preliminary design study for a 2,000 ton operational prototype surface effect ship. This study, completed in mid-1973, resulted in preliminary plans for an all-aluminium vessel, designed for speeds in excess of 80 knots.

In July 1974, Bell was awarded a $36 million contract to conduct an advanced development programme for a 2,000-ton, high-speed ocean-going, operational warship —the 2KSES. The 18-month contract awarded by the Naval Material Command covers the design, development and testing of full-scale sub-systems and components including transmission, waterjet systems, lift fans and skirts, as well as a method of controlling the vessel's ride characteristics in a variety of sea states.

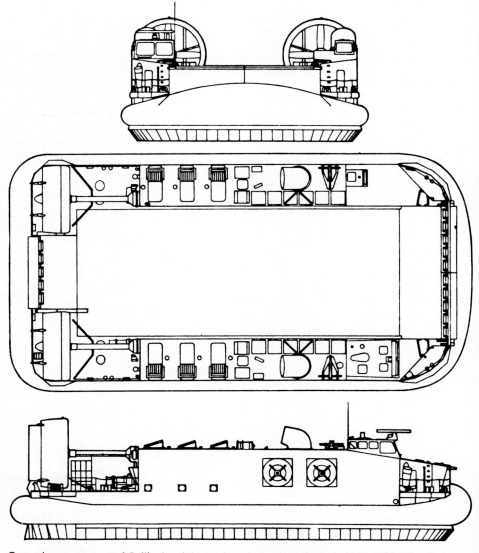

General arrangement of Bell's Amphibious Assault Landing Craft (AALC) JEFF (B). Power is supplied by six 2,800 hp Avco Lycoming gas turbines driving four centrifugal impellers for lift and two 4-bladed ducted propellers for thrust

Bell Aerospace Canada (see Canadian section) has built two prototypes of the Bell Model 7380 Voyageur heavy haul ACV, the second of which has been purchased by the Canadian Ministry of Transport for use by the Canadian Coast Guard. Production of additional Voyageurs is in hand. Two Voyageurs, designated 001 and 003, were transferred to the ACV/SES Test and Training Center, Panama City, in late 1975 for use in a training programme for US Army personnel. The company is also testing the prototype of a new craft, the 15-ton Viking, which has been designed to meet the need for a smaller but similar multipurpose vehicle capable of handling a 5-ton payload. The prototype, equipped for inshore search-and-rescue duties, was completed early in 1974 and is operating with the Canadian Coast Guard.

The company also initiated a programme for the USAF that covers the design, development, installation and test of an air cushion landing system aboard a De Havilland XC-8A Buffalo transport aircraft. The first ACLS landing took place at Wright-Patterson AFB, Dayton, Ohio on April 11th, 1975 and additional tests are being planned.

SK-5 Model 7255

Details of the SK-5 Model 7255 and its predecessor, the Model 7232, will be found in JSS 1972-73 and earlier editions.

AALC JEFF(B)

In March 1971, US Naval Ship Systems Command awarded Bell's New Orleans Operations a contract for the detail design, construction and testing of an experimental 160-ton, 50-knot air cushion assault landing craft.

Two companies are developing ACV test craft to the 150,000 lb (68,038 kg) payload. 50 knot specification—Bell and Aerojet-General. The Bell project is designated L.C. Jeff(B). Both craft will operate from the well-decks of landing ships and also alongside cargo ships.

The Bell contract involves mathematical and scale model investigations, interface and support system design, subsystem and component testing and design and systems analysis.

The 165-ton Amphibious Assault Landing Craft LC JEFF(B) is in the final stages of assembly at Bell's New Orleans Operations. Completion of the craft and initiation of builder's tests is scheduled for the autumn of 1976.

The detailed engineering design of the craft was completed in October 1975. Fabrication of the prototype began in 1972 at New Orleans with the assembly of the main hull plating and bulkheads. At the time of going to press it was in the final stages of construction with systems being installed. On completion the company will conduct a programme of technical trials and contractor's engineering tests. The craft will then be delivered to the US Navy, which will conduct a series of tests and trials with an emphasis on operational use.

A $\frac{1}{6}$th dynamic scale model was constructed for an extensive series of engineering tests on Lake Pontchartrain in 1972. The model, which allows "free-flight" testing with radio control of all major craft functions, was used to confirm the final detailed design. A description of the craft, designated B-23, appears later in this entry.

L.C. JEFF(B) is designed to operate at a nominal speed of 50 knots in Sea State 2, and accommodate up to 75 tons in palletised supplies and/or equipment, up to the size of the 60-ton US Army main battle tank.

To ensure adequate world-wide operational capability, the specification calls for operation in temperatures from 0°-100°F and requires that the performance criteria can be met with a 25 knot headwind on a 100°F day.

LIFT AND PROPULSION: Motive power is supplied by six 2,800 hp Avco Lycoming gas-turbines, driving four 5 ft 0 in (1·52 m) diameter double-entry centrifugal impellers for lift, and two 4-bladed 11 ft 9 in (3·58 m) diameter, Hamilton-Standard variable pitch, ducted propellers, for thrust. Fuel capacity is 6,400 gallons (29,094 litres).

CONTROLS: Deflection of two aerodynamic rudders hinged at the rear of the propeller duct exits, differential propeller pitch, and the deflection of bow thrusters atop the side structures provide steering control. All controls are located in a raised bridge located well forward on the starboard superstructure. The helmsman's platform is raised to provide 360° vision for the two helmsmen, who have within easy reach all the necessary controls, navigation equipment and instruments. A third seat is provided at this level for another crew member or wave commander. On a lower level in the bridge is an engineer's station with monitoring instrumentation and a radar operator/navigator station. The crew will normally comprise four operating personnel and two deck supervisors.

HULL: Overall structural dimensions of the craft (80 ft length, 43 ft beam and 19 ft height) have been dictated by the well deck dimensions of the US Navy's LSDs (Landing Ships Dock), LPDs (Amphibious Transport Dock).

The main hull is formed by a 4 ft 6 in (1·37 m) deep buoyancy raft with port and starboard side structures. The main deck between the side structures forms the cargo deck, which is 66 ft long by 26 ft 4 in wide (20·11 m by 8·02 m), and provides an unobstructed cargo area of 1,738 sq ft (161·46 m²). A full width ramp is provided at the bow and a narrower ramp, capable of taking the main battle tank, at the stern.

The bottom and deck structures of the hull are separated by longitudinal and transverse bulkheads to form a buoyancy raft with a number of watertight flotation compartments. The craft fuel tanks and bilge system are contained within these compartments.

Plating at the bottom and side of the hull is stiffened by aluminium extrusions, and the main cargo deck is in mechanically fastened hollow truss-type core extrusions. The transverse bulkheads consist of sheet webs of aluminium alloy integrally-stiffened extrusions, with upper and lower bulkhead caps,

Top: Stern view of JEFF (B) showing port and starboard propeller ducts. The craft is due to undertake initial builder's trials during the autumn of 1976, followed by delivery to the US Navy for operational testing at Panama City, Florida

Centre: Designed to fit within the dry well decks of the US Navy's LSD and LPD assault ships, JEFF (B) has fore and aft loading ramps for rapid on and off loading of troops, equipment and vehicles such as the 60-ton main battle tank. A typical LSD well deck can accommodate four JEFF (B)s and an LPD can take two

Bottom: Impression of a JEFF (B) coming ashore through surf with skirt inflated and bow and stern ramps raised

also of aluminium extrusions.

The basic framing of the side-structures is aluminium back-to-back channels, which coincide with the transverse bulkheads and are spaced apart to straddle the hull bulkheads.

Each sidestructure contains three Avco Lycoming gas-turbines, and their associated air intakes, exhausts, lift fans, transmissions and auxiliary power system.

SKIRT SYSTEM: Peripheral bag and finger type, with a 5 ft (1·52 m) high cushion compartmented by longitudinal and transverse keels. The upper seal bag attachment hinge line is raised high over the bow ramp area and the vertical diaphragm contains non-return valves similar to those fitted to the SR.N4.

DIMENSIONS:

Length overall	86 ft 9 in	(26·43 m)
stowed	80 ft 0 in	(24·38 m)
Beam overall	47 ft 0 in	(14·32 m)
stowed	43 ft 0 in	(13·10 m)
Height	23 ft 6 in	(7·16 m)
Cargo area	1,738 sq ft	(160·71 m²)
Bow ramp width	28 ft 0 in	(5·34 m)
Stern ramp width	14 ft 6 in	(4·41 m)

WEIGHTS:

Normal gross weight	330,000 lb	(149,688 kg)
Normal payload	120,000 lb	(54,431 kg)
Overload payload	150,000 lb	(68,038 kg)

PERFORMANCE:

Speed	50 knots in sea state 2
Range	200 n. miles
Max gradient continuous	13%

BELL MODEL B-23

This is a one-sixth scale dynamic model of the Bell AALC JEFF(B). Powered by two petrol engines, it is designed for 'free flight' testing under radio control. Data on safety, stability, manoeuvrability and performance is acquired by a lightweight instrumentation system and tape recorder installed aboard the craft.

With cushion inflated, the model is 14 ft 3 in (4·34 m) long, has a beam of 8 ft (2·43 m) and a height of 4 ft (1·21 m). Air cushion depth is 10 in (254·0 mm). The basic weight is 800 lb (362·85 kg), provision being made for the retention of lead ballast to increase the weight to a scale overload condition of 1,750 lb (793·75 kg). This will allow the model to be tested over the entire range of full-scale operating weights. The ballast can be located to allow any desired c.g. or inertia to be obtained.

HULL: The primary structure of the model is fabricated from aluminium honeycomb panels, with secondary structure incorporating fibreglass, styrofoam, and aircraft plywood. The seal system is fabricated in a coated nylon fabric of scale weight and bending stiffness. The model is painted in a bright red and yellow colour scheme. This was selected to provide maximum visibility for the operator and also to obtain the best cine camera coverage for engineering analysis.

LIFT AND PROPULSION: Motive power is provided by two 30 hp JLO two-cylinder, two-cycle petrol engines, one housed in each sidestructure. Each engine drives a scale propeller and a scale fan system through a transmission utilising a centrifugal clutch, tooth belts, and spiral bevel gearboxes. The engines are started electrically, and sufficient fuel is carried for two hours continuous operation.

Powered by two 30 hp JLO 2-cylinder petrol engines, the Bell Model B-23 is a one-sixth scale dynamic model of the JEFF (B) amphibious assault landing craft. Designed for "free-flight" testing, it is radio-controlled and provides data on safety, stability, manoeuvrability and performance

The SES-100B set up a new world record speed of more than 89 knots (103 mph) on June 30th, 1976, with Secretary of the US Navy, J.William Middendorf II aboard. A US Navy crew operated the craft on its record breaking run which was made across an instrumentad test range in St. Andrew Bay, Florida. Its speed was recorded by tracking radar operated by US Navy personnel

CONTROLS: The remote control system provides simultaneous proportional control of the primary flight controls and switching of the instrumentation recorder. The ducted propellers are of controllable-pitch, the bow thruster direction and operating mode (forward/reverse) are controlled, the rudders and engine throttles are also included. In all cases, scale travel and scale rate have been maintained. The control system utilises two modified model aeroplane systems with a transmitter layout especially designed for ease of operation. A fail-safe system is arranged to cut the ignition of both engines if radio control is lost for any reason.

The instrumentation and recording system measures the behaviour of the model and the following characteristics: Model air speed (anemometer), cushion pressure in the fore and aft compartments, seal bag pressure, bow vertical acceleration, longitudinal acceleration, c.g. vertical acceleration, rate gyros for pitch, roll, and yaw, bow thruster position, rudder position, starboard propeller pitch, port propeller pitch, starboard side transmission rpm, port side transmission rpm.

The magnetic tape recorder is an environmentally-sealed, lightweight unit, designed originally for torpedo development. It conforms to IRIG standards and data reduction to oscillograph records will be performed at the Slidell Computer Centre.

PERFORMANCE: The model is capable of exploring the entire operational envelope over water, over land, and in surf. A model speed of approximately 20 knots will represent the full-scale design speed of 50 knots. In favourable conditions it is anticipated that model speeds greater than 30 knots will be obtained.

SES-100B TEST CRAFT

The SES-100B is the official designation for the 100-ton class sidehull surface effect ship (SES) test craft which has been built for the US Navy by Bell Aerospace at New Orleans.

It is part of a long-range programme by the US Navy to develop multi-thousand ton, ocean-going ships with speeds of 80 knots or higher.

This programme stems from research undertaken by the US Office of Naval Research in 1960, the US Navy Bureau of Ships (now the Naval Ship System Command) and the US Maritime Administration, which in 1961 sponsored the first programme for the development of a 100-ton SES, known as the Columbia.

In 1966, based on the results of these early programmes, a joint office of the US Navy and Department of Commerce was formed, known as the Joint Surface Effect Ship Programme Office (JSESPO), with the express purpose of determining the feasibility of building and operating large, fast, surface effect ships of 4,000-5,000 tons and capable of 80 knots or higher speed. Design studies conducted by industry for JSESPO (now SESPO, the US Navy having taken over the complete programme in 1971) over the period 1965-69 covered all aspects of SES design and operation—economic factors, performance characteristics, structural and material parameter and subsystem characteristics—and culminated in the award of two design and construction contracts. Bell Aerospace was awarded a contract to design, build and test a water propeller-driven 100-ton class surface effect ship test craft in January 1969. A similar contract was awarded to Aerojet-General Corporation for a waterjet-propelled test craft.

Construction of the Bell SES began in August 1970. The vessel was launched on July 22nd 1971 for hovering trials, and builder's trials, with the craft underway, began on February 4th, 1972. A test and evaluation programme encompassing performance trials, stability and seakeeping characteristics, structural load investigations, habitability and operational data, and other pertinent data necessary for the development of high speed surface effect ships, was conducted in the New Orleans area and in the Gulf of Mexico where a variety of sea conditions were experienced.

In January 1974, Bell Aerospace announced that the SES-100B had successfully completed the testing necessary to confirm and expand the technology necessary for the design of a 2,000-ton ocean-going SES. Tests are continuing in the Gulf of Mexico, off Panama City, Florida, in support of the 2KSES development programme. The current programme embraces the evaluation of acoustics, structural loads in higher sea states and higher speeds, seal (skirt) loads and ride control.

In April 1974, the SES-100B achieved a speed in excess of 80 knots, which was improved upon in a subsequent high-speed run in November of that year. In May 1975 the test craft achieved a speed of 82·3 knots, while being operated by a US Navy crew, and the speed was recorded by tracking radar at the Naval Coastal Systems Laboratory, Panama City. One June 30th, 1976, the craft set a new ACV world speed record when, with Secretary of the Navy J. William Middendorf II aboard, it attained 103 mph (165 km/h/89 knots) during a crossing of St. Andrew Bay, near Panama City.

Navy Lieutenants Thomas Breitinger, ship commander, and Wayne Huss, first officer, were at the controls of the SES-100B. Others on board included Captain Carl J. Boyd, the Navy's Surface Effect Ships project manager; Commander Richard Castrucci, commanding officer of the Navy's Surface Effect Ships Test Facility, Patuxent River, Maryland, members of Mr. Middendorf's staff and press representatives.

Prior to participating in the record-setting run, Mr. Middendorf operated the SES-100B at speeds of 45 to 50 knots in the choppy waters of the Gulf of Mexico. Craft performance and manoeuvering capabilities also were demonstrated in 3 ft (1·0 m) waves.

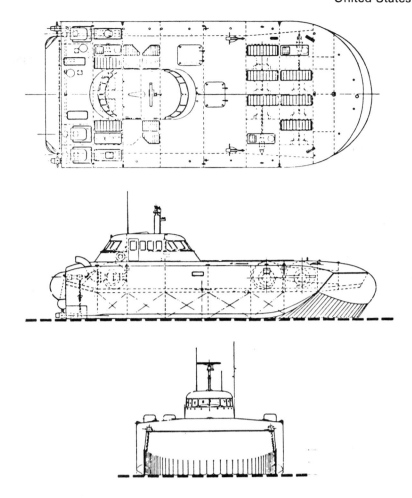

General arrangement of the Bell SES-100B 105-ton test craft

An SM-1 medium-range guided missile was successfully launched from the SES-100B while travelling at a speed of 60 knots across the Gulf of Mexico on April 8th, 1976. Twenty seconds later the SM-1 hit its target, a surplus vessel positioned 10 miles off the Florida coast, on the test range of the Armament Development and Test Centre, Eglin Air Force Base

The craft has operated at sustained speeds of more than 50 knots in Sea State III in the Gulf of Mexico, and has repeatedly demonstrated performance, stability, and habitability exceeding expectations.

It successfully launched an SM-1 (General Dynamics RIM 66B Standard MR) medium-range guided missile on April 8, 1976, while travelling at a speed of 70 mph (60 × knots) across the Gulf of Mexico.

After ensuring that all range safety requirements had been fulfilled, the SES-100B was headed on a westward course toward the YSD (Surplus Yard Salvage Dock) target at a speed of 60 knots. When the predetermined launch point was reached, the SM-1 missile was launched from its canister mounted aft of the SES-100B deckhouse. The solid rocket motor propelled the 16·5 ft missile straight upwards, it then pitched over in a westerly direction toward the target five nautical miles away. The missile's sensing device located the target and guided it to a hit.

Captain Carl J. Boyd, programme manager of the Navy's Surface Effect Ships Project Office (PMS-304) said the achievement marked a major milestone for the US Navy. It was the first vertical launch of an SM-1 missile from any Navy ship.

A Navy crew from the Surface Effect Ship Test Facility, Panama City, supported by Bell Aerospace Textron and General Dynamics personnel, operated the SES-100B on a Gulf of Mexico test range of the Armament Development and Test Center, Eglin Air Force Base, for the test firing of the missile which was unarmed.

Development of SES systems will result in the production of very high speed, multi-thousand ton ships for a variety of missions. Such development would make it possible for the US Navy to have a smaller but more effective fleet which would revolutionise naval warfare.

HULL: The SES-100B is a single, all-welded continuous structure, incorporating two catamaran-style sidehulls and is constructed from high-strength, corrosion-resistant marine aluminium alloy sheet and plate. The hull carries an integral deckhouse welded to the after portion of the weather deck. The deckhouse is so positioned to optimise the ride quality and habitability of the ship's complement of personnel while retaining good visibility from the command station.

The sidehulls, which virtually skim the surface of the water, provide basic stability to the craft and also seal the air cushion and prevent leakage along the port and starboard sides of the ship. The sealing of the air cushion is completed at the bow and stern by flexible fabric seals. The bow seal is of pressurised bag type with convoluted fingers not unlike the proven design previously used on the Bell skimmers. The stern seal is of Bell design and capable of providing the necessary trim to the craft.

The hull was constructed to BAC design under contract by Levington Shipbuilding.

LIFT AND PROPULSION: Power is supplied to the lift system by three United Aircraft of Canada (UACL) ST6J-70 marine gas turbines. The engine/fan systems provide pressurised air to seals and cushion in both normal modes of operation and in the event of system failure. An important feature of the design has been to ensure the safety of ship and crew since the craft is designed to investigate the boundaries of ship operation at high speed in rough seas. The fans, constructed from marine aluminium, are of centrifugal design for ruggedness and stability of operation.

Power is supplied to the two marine propellers by three Pratt & Whitney FT 12A-6 marine gas turbines.

Auxiliary power for engine starting and emergency use is provided by a Solar T-62T-27 high speed turbine producing 100 shp at 8,000 RPM.

All engines are housed in engine rooms beneath the weather deck and take in air through appropriately placed demister screens to minimise sea water and spray ingestion.

Centre: The SES-100B, 105-ton surface effect ship testcraft seen at speed in Sea State 3 in the Gulf of Mexico, off Panama City
Bottom: The deckhouse is at the aft end of the weatherdeck and accommodates a four-man crew and up to six observers. The engines—three FT12A-6s for propulsion and three ST6-J70s for lift—are located beneath the weatherdeck. Air is drawn through demister screens to minimise seawater and spray ingestion

The fuel system, which also serves as a ballast system, is integral with the sidehulls.

ACCOMMODATION: The deckhouse houses all controls necessary for the operation of the craft and accommodation for four test crew and six observers. It is capable of sustaining the crew and observers for greater than 24 hour missions in life support functions. Navigation and communication equipment for all-weather operation is included in the crew subsystem and housed in the deckhouse.

SYSTEMS, EMERGENCY: Safety equipment in the form of fire detection and extinguishing equipment, life rafts, warning lights, etc, meet the requirements of the U.S. Coast Guard Rules of the Road, both International and Inland.

The characteristics of the SES-100B are as follows:

DIMENSIONS:

Length overall	77 ft 8½ in
Beam	35 ft 0 in
Height (top of radar)	26 ft 11 in

WEIGHTS:

Normal gross weight	105 tons
Normal payload	10 tons

POWER PLANTS:
Propulsion
    Three (3) P&W FT 12A-6 marine gas turbines

Lift:
    Three (3) UACL ST6J-70 marine gas turbines

PERFORMANCE:
    Speed greater than 80 knots on calm water

PERSONNEL:

Crew (Test Mission)	Four
Observers	Six

MATERIALS:

Hull and Appendages	Marine aluminium and titanium
Seals	Nylon supported elastainer

BELL MODEL B-26

This is a radio-controlled ⅛th scale free-flight model with sidehulls and seals hydrodynamically representative of the Bell SES-100B. Two contra-rotating air propellers are used for propulsion. A 14-channel tape recorder is installed to record engine speeds, rudder position, cushion and seal pressures, sideslip, pitch, yaw and roll rates, model air speed and accelerations.

The model is 7 ft 3 in (2·20 m) long with a 4 ft 3 in (1·29 m) beam. The basic weight is 480 lb (217·71 kg), with provision for up to 320 lb (145·14 kg) of lead ballast, permitting tests over a wide range of weight and trim conditions. Separate bow, stern and sidehull modules permit variations of seal and sidehull configurations.

HULL: Built into the centre module are four centrifugal lift fans, which are connected through gear belts to an 80 cc, single-cylinder, two-cycle petrol engine. The main structural elements are fabricated in aluminium and edge-grain balsa sandwiched with the bulk of the remaining elements which are built in aircraft plywood, wood and epoxy. All unassigned areas are filled with cast, rigid foam. Bow and stern modules are made of aircraft plywood and wood, and incorporates seal feed air passages. The sidehulls are designed as separate structures. Provision is made for the installation of strain gauges on the attachment linkages, permitting the measurement of hydrodynamic drag.

The seal system is in a coated nylon fabric of scale weight. The patterns were photo-reductions of the Bell SES-100B seals.

PROPULSION: Power is provided by a 40 hp, two-cylinder, two-cycle JLO petrol engine, driving two propellers through a system of gear belts. The engine is started electrically from a battery aboard a chase boat. The model is released from the chase boat when started and recovered upon shutdown

CONTROLS: An adapted six-channel model aircraft radio-control unit provides proportional control of the lift and propulsion engine throttles and scale rate control of the rudders, with on/off control of the recorder, event marker and shutdown. A fail-safe shutdown is incorporated to ground the ignition systems of both engines upon command or loss of radio signal.

PERFORMANCE: The model has explored the operational envelope of the SES-100B, at scale speeds, in excess of 70 knots. It has also been used in the investigation of proposed designed for the Bell LSES, the modular construction permitting replacement of the hydrodynamic elements with new seal and planing surface configurations.

BELL LSES

In November 1972 it was announced that Bell Aerospace had been awarded a US$2·9 million contract by US Naval Ship Systems Command to conduct a preliminary design

Impression of an advanced operational version of an SES prototype. A wide beam, coupled with an active air cushion control system, would keep pitching and rolling to a minimum. The craft would provide a stable platform for military operations in conditions up to Sea State 6

study and define a total programme plan for a 2,000-ton operational prototype surface effect ship. In July 1974, Bell was awarded a $36 million contract to conduct an advanced development programme for the SKSES.

The development of the SES propulsion system, including the transmission and waterjet inlet and pump, the aircushion containment system of lift fans and large flexible seals, and a system to provide control of the ship's ride characteristics in various sea states was accomplished in the programme.

The ship would have a complete combat system, including surface-to-air and surface-to-surface missiles, and anti-submarine sensors and weapons. The accompanying three-view shows the initial configuration under consideration—a vessel 250 ft (76·20 m) long, with a beam of 106 ft (32·30 m). More than

200 engineers and designers at Bell New Orleans Operations are involved in the LSES advanced development programme. Major subcontractors are: The Autonetics Division, Rockwell International, for a role in combat systems integration; Gibbs & Cox Inc, naval architecture, crew support and auxiliary systems; Hydronautics Inc, hydrodynamic design and studies of propeller propulsion and waterjet inlets, the Aerojet Liquid Rocket Co., for waterjet propulsion, Avondale Shipyards Inc. for outfitting and fabrication, installation and furnishing of the deckhouse and British Hovercraft Corporation for support in flexible seal design and other engineering tasks.

Power would be supplied by six 22,500 shp General Electric LM-2500 marinised gas-turbines, two for lift and four for driving the vessel's waterjet propulsion system.

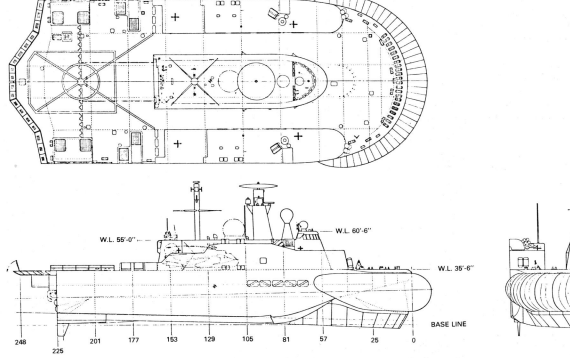
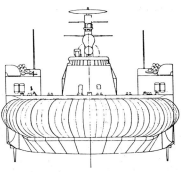

Bell Aerospace Textron's preliminary design for a prototype 3,000-ton ASW SES for the US Navy

A major milestone was reached in December 1975 with the successful accomplishment of seventeen advanced development phase goals. The subsystem development programme has reduced the technical risks (identified by the Navy as the seals, waterjet pumps, waterjet inlets, ride control system and lift fans) to a low level. A parallel design programme has led to significant improvements in the ship design.

Data from extensive testing of ship models and system components has been correlated with results from operations of the SES-100B, SES-100A, XR-1D, test craft and the SR.N4.

Three 1/30 scale ship models have been used in the course of this programme. The first model, SM-2, was used for stability control and seakeeping tests, the second model, SM-5, was tested in high and low Reynolds number wind tunnels, and a flexible PVC model, SM-8, was used to investigate loads.

In order to investigate the effects of model scale, particularly in the area of seal behaviour, a 1/10 scale model, SM-12, was tested in the Navy NSRDC Langley, Va., tow tank. This model, shown in the accompanying photograph, is of modular construction to facilitate configuration changes. The model is 22 ft 6 in (6·85 m) long and has been tested at weights from 3,500 to 4,900 lb (1,588 to 2,222 kg). The model size was selected so that seal material stiffness could be correctly scaled.

Key propulsion systems tests include 1/6 scale waterjet pump endurance and performance tests and a 1/6 scale waterjet inlet tow tank test, which included the automatic control of the inlet area.

Many seal system tests were conducted to verify the configuration, and to develop high-strength materials and attachments. Laboratory tests and environmental tests on the SES-100B and SR.N4 have demonstrated that materials of sufficient strength and endurance are available. Loads for the seals have been predicted, based upon extensive load measurements on models and test craft and the use of advanced load analyses computer programmes. These have been verified using a 1/6 scale bow seal rig shown in the accompanying photograph. The tests simulate the effect of pitch and heave of the ship and wave impact on the bag. Bow seal geometry and loads were measured and compared with the theoretical values in normal and overpressure conditions. The strain and pressure gauge outputs are channelled to a mini-computer and printer to give a direct printout of loads and pressures in engineering units.

The testing and analyses associated with the subsystem development programme have confirmed that all of the US Navy requirements for the LSES can be met.

Three models of the 2KSES are seen in this photograph, taken in the new 22,000 sq ft Engineering and Model Test Facility at Bell's New Orleans Operations. The $\frac{1}{30}$th scale SM-5 wind tunnel model is seen in the left foreground; the $\frac{1}{6}$th scale model bow seal is seen in its rig at the right, and the $\frac{1}{10}$ scale model SM-12 is in the centre background

Predictions of the loads on LSES seals have been based on load measurements and computer analysis programmes to demonstrate that materials of sufficient strength and endurance are available. This $\frac{1}{6}$ scale bow seal rig has been employed by Bell at New Orleans to verify the predicted loads by simulating the effect of pitch and heave and wave impact on the bag

The 22 ft 6 in (6.85 m) long SM-12, the largest SES towing tank model ever built. The SM-12, a $\frac{1}{10}$ scale model of the Bell LSES underwent seal evaluation in the 2,900 ft towing tank at the Naval Ship Research and Development Centre

LANDING VEHICLE ASSAULT

Bell Aerospace has received a US $278,000 contract to participate in designing and model-testing high speed US Marine Corps combat vehciles to be known as the Landing Vehicles Assault (LVAs).

The project is being sponsored by the US Naval Sea Systems Command under a programme to examine vehicles to succeed the current LTVP-7, which is slow in water operations.

The LTVP-7 carries an assault force of 25 Marines at 8 mph overwater toward the beach from the parent ship, then operates at 40 mph overland.

In contrast, the LVA will move at 35 to 70 mph overwater and 40 to 55 mph overland, with greatly improved rough ground performance.

The difference is that the proposed Bell version has an air suspension system, which in combination with a hydropneumatic track suspension gear, will lift the LVA high in the water so it can skim the surface at high speed.

Several companies are participating with Bell in the project. General Motors Corp's Detroit Diesel Allison Division will design the transmission; National Water Lift Co will design land running gear and the primary weapons system; Carborundum Corp, parasitic armour; Alcoa, aluminium armour. Rosenblatt & Sons, New York, will act as hydrodynamic consultants.

The initial 12-month phase of the programme involves building and testing a scale model of the LVA design. Preliminary model tests have already been conducted at Bell's Air Cushion Vehicle Laboratory.

The Bell LVA air suspension system is based on Bell's extensive background in air cushion vehicle technology. The system offers high overwater performance but yet does not degrade the land combat capabilities of the vehicle.

Above and below: Bell's projected landing vehicle assault (LVA) will operate at 35-70 mph over water and 40-55 mph over land. An air suspension system, resembling an inflated rubber ring, lifts the LVA high off the water enabling it to skim the surface at high speed

BERTELSEN MANUFACTURING COMPANY INC

HEAD OFFICE:
9999 Roosevelt Road, Westchester, Illinois 60153
WORKS:
113 Commercial Street, Neponste, Illinois 61345
and
4819 Cortland Street, Chicago, Illinois 60639
TELEPHONE:
312-681-5606, 309-594-2041
OFFICERS:
William R. Bertelsen, Chairman of the Board, Vice-President and Director of Research
William C. Stein, President and Treasurer
Charles A. Brady, Secretary

Dr William R. Bertelsen, a general practitioner and talented engineer, was one of the first to build and drive an air cushion vehicle.

His interest was largely inspired by the difficulties he faced when trying to visit patients by car over icy roads. Having discovered that a helicopter would be too expensive to be a practical solution, he set to work to develop a vehicle that could be lifted free of the ground by air pumped beneath its base. Dr Bertelsen designed his first Aeromobile air cushion vehicle in 1950, and has since built and tested fourteen full-scale vehicles, ranging from simple plenum craft to ram-wings. One, the 18 ft long Aeromobile 200-2, was a star exhibit at the US Government's Trade Fairs in Tokyo, Turin, Zagreb and New Delhi in 1961. First design to be marketed by the company is the Aeromobile 13, a 4 passenger amphibious communications and light utility ACV. The prototype was built in 1968 and trials are complete. A description of this model will be found in JSS 1972-73 and earlier editions. An Aeromobile system of

rapid transit, based on the Aeromobile 13, is described in the section devoted to Tracked Skimmers in this edition.

AEROMOBILE 14

Aeromobile 14 is a lightweight amphibious two or three-seater employing a single gimbal mounted lift fan/propulsion unit of similar design and construction to that introduced by Bertelsen on the Aeromobile 13.

The prototype was completed early in 1969 and trials ended in 1970.

LIFT PROPULSION AND CONTROLS: A single duct-mounted 55 hp (740 cc) JLO twin-cylinder engine driving a 36 in (914 mm) diameter eight-bladed axial-flow fan supplies lift, propulsion and control. The duct is spherical and gimbal-mounted at its centre so that it can be tilted and rotated as required in any direction. The discharge end of the duct faces a fitted aperture in the deck, from which air is fed into the cushion. When the fan shaft is vertical (no tilt), all the discharged air is fed into the cushion. By tilting the gimbal, the operator allows air from the fan to escape across the deck to provide thrust for propulsion and control.

Apart from the propulsion slipstream, there is no loss of lift air since the spherical duct fits closely into the deck aperture, and rotation of the sphere does not increase the air gap. Cushion pressure is 14 lb ft².

A simple mechanical linkage connected to handlebars enables the operator to tilt the fan duct fore-aft, right and left and make integrated movements. The only other controls are a throttle and a choke. Fuel is carried in a single 12 gallon (US) tank located in the deck structure at the CG, with a fuelling point in the centre deck. Recommended fuel is regular automotive gasoline mixed with two-cycle oil.

HULL: Moulded fibreglass with foam filling. Design load 1,100 lb gross weight.

SKIRT: Urethane nylon with conical exterior configuration. Depth 1 ft 0 in (304 mm).

ACCOMMODATION: Tandem seating for three, with operator forward with control handlebars.

SYSTEMS: Electrical: 12 volt alternator on engine for starting.

NAVIGATION: Magnetic compass.

DIMENSIONS:
Length overall, power off 13 ft 0 in (3·96 m)
Length overall, skirt inflated
    13 ft 0 in (3·96 m)
Beam overall, power off 7 ft 0 in (2·13 m)
Beam overall, skirt inflated 7 ft 0 in (2·13 m)
Height overall on landing pads, power off
    3 ft 0 in (0·914 m)
Height overall, skirt inflated
    4 ft 0 in (1·21 m)

Draft afloat   4 in (101 mm)
Draft hovering   3 in (76 mm)
Cushion area   60 sq ft (5·57 m²)
Skirt depth   12 in (304 mm)

WEIGHTS:
Normal empty weight   700 lb (317 kg)
Normal all-up weight   1,100 lb (499 kg)
Normal gross weight   1,100 lb (499 kg)
Normal payload   400 lb (181 kg)
Max payload   500 lb (226 kg)

PERFORMANCE:
Max speed over calm water
    50 mph (80·46 km/h)
Cruising speed, calm water
    40 mph (64·37 km/h)
Turning circle diameter at 30 knots
    100 ft (30·4 m)
Max wave capability   3 ft (0·914 m)
Max survival sea state 5 ft waves (1·52 m)
Still air range and endurance at cruising
  speed   2½ hours
Max gradient, static conditions   10%
Vertical obstacle clearance 1 ft (304 mm)
Price: On request.

AEROMOBILE 15

Employing the same lift, propulsion and control system as the Aeromobile 14, the Aeromobile 15 is a light amphibious four-seater powered by a single 125 hp Mercury outboard engine and capable of a speed of 60 knots over calm water.

The prototype is complete and development is continuing.

LIFT AND PROPULSION: A single duct-mounted 125 hp Mercury outboard engine driving a 36 in (914 mm) diameter, sixteen-

Aeromobile 14 research platform employed by Bertelsen Manufacturing Co for the development of designs using single gimbal-mounted lift/fan/propulsion units.

Aeromobile 15, a 60-knot four-seater powered by a modified 125 hp Mercury outboard. The vehicle is at present being employed as a test-bed for the gimbal-mounted lift/propulsion system. The photographs show the gimbal duct in neutral and in high forward tilt

bladed adjustable-pitch aluminium alloy fan, supplies lift, propulsion and control. The duct is spherical and gimbal-mounted at its centre so that it can be tilted and rotated in any direction. When the fan shaft is vertical, the total airflow is discharged into the cushion. By tilting the gimbal the operator allows air from the fan to escape across the stern to provide thrust for propulsion and control. At the maximum tilt angle of 90² for maximum thrust only 30% of the fan air is delivered to the cushion.

Propulsion and/or control forces, including braking thrust, can be applied throughout 360° from the stern by tilting the duct in the required direction.

The fan duct is controlled from the driver's position by servo system. The driver has a wheel on a control column. Turning the wheel tilts the duct sideways to produce

yaw force, and fore-and-aft movement of the column tilts the duct fore-and-aft to produce forward propulsion or braking. Fuel is carried in one 18-gallon tank located on the cabin floor beneath the rear seat at the C of G. The fuelling point is located on the left deck outside the cabin. Fuel is automotive gasoline with two-cycle oil.

HULL: Moulded fibreglass.

SKIRT: Urethane nylon fabric, 1 ft 6 in (45·7 mm) deep.

ACCOMMODATION: Entry to the cabin is through a sliding canopy which moves from the windshield rearwards. Two bench type seats are fitted, one forward for the driver and one passenger, and one aft for two passengers. The cabin may be heated or air-conditioned if required. In emergencies the sliding canopy, windows and windshield may be kicked out.

SYSTEMS: ELECTRICAL: 12 volt alternator and 12 volt storage battery.

COMMUNICATIONS AND NAVIGATION: A magnetic compass is standard. Radio, radar and other navigation aids optional.

DIMENSIONS, EXTERNAL:

Length overall, power off	18 ft 0 in (5·48 m)
Length overall, skirt inflated	18 ft 8 in (5·68 m)
Beam overall, power off	8 ft 0 in (2·43 m)
Beam overall, skirt inflated	9 ft 10 in (2·99 m
Height overall, on pads, power off	4 ft 4 in (1·32 m)
Height overall, skirt inflated	5 ft 9 in (1·75 m)
Draft afloat	5½ in (139 mm)
Draft hovering	4 in (101 mm)
Cushion area	90 ft² (8·36 m²)
Skirt depth	1 ft 6 in (457 mm)

DIMENSIONS, INTERNAL:

Cabin:

Length	10 ft 6 in (3·2 m)
Max width	4 ft 2 in (1·27 m)
Max height	4 ft 0 in (1·21 m)
Floor area	40 ft² (3·71 m²)

The sliding canopy opens 3 ft (·914 m) rearward from windshield.

WEIGHTS:

Normal empty weight	1,300 lb (589·64 kg)
Normal all-up weight	2,100 lb (952·50 kg)
Normal gross weight	2,100 lb (952·50 kg)

Normal payload	700 lb (317·50 kg)
Max payload	1,000 lb (453·57 kg)

PERFORMANCE (at normal operating weight, estimated):

Max speed over calm water, max power	60 knots
Max continuous power	50 knots
Cruising speed, calm water	50 knots
Turning circle at 30 knots	500 ft (152·4 m)
Max wave capability	3 ft (914 mm)
Max survival sea state	5 ft (1·52 m) waves
Still air range and endurance at cruising speed	3 hours
Max gradient, static conditions	10%
Vertical obstacle clearance	1 ft 3 in (381 mm)

AEROMOBILE 16

Interest in this new vehicle, the biggest to be constructed by Bertelsen so far, is being shown by potential purchasers throughout North America. It employs a lift, propulsion and control system similar to that of the earlier Aeromobile 15.

Power is supplied by two duct-mounted, 155 hp, 2-cycle Mercury outboard engines, each driving a 36 in (914 mm) axial fan. Each duct is spherical and gimbal-mounted at its centre so that it can be tilted and rotated in any direction. When the fan shaft is vertical, the total airflow is discharged into the cushion. By tilting the gimbal the operator allows air from the fan to escape across the stern to provide thrust for propulsion.

The thrust force is instantly available throughout 360 deg and, metered finely by degree of tilt, provides propulsion, braking or yaw torque. The maximum available force is equal to 100% of the propulsion force.

Fuel is carried in two 24 gal tanks.

SYSTEMS, ELECTRICAL: Two 12 v alternators and two 12 v batteries.

DIMENSIONS:

Length overall, power off	24 ft 2 in
Length overall, skirt inflated	24 ft 8 in
Beam overall, power off	14 ft 3 in
Beam overall, skirt inflated	15 ft 4 in
Beam, power off, folded	7 ft 6 in
Height to top of cabin, on landing pads	5 ft 0 in
skirt inflated	6 ft 6 in
Height to top of engine, on landing pads	5 ft 8 in
Cushion height to base of hardstructure	1 ft 6 in
Cargo bay	6 ft wide by 11 ft long

WEIGHTS:

Empty weight	3,000 lb
Gross weight	4,500 lb
Useful load	1,500 lb

PERFORMANCE:

Not available at the time of going to press.

DEPARTMENT OF THE NAVY, NAVAL SEA SYSTEMS COMMAND (NAVSEA)

HEADQUARTERS:
Washington, DC 20360
PROGRAMME MANAGER, HOVERCRAFT AND HYDROFOILS:
James L. Schuler
OFFICE:
US Naval Sea Systems Command, Advanced Technology Systems Division, Code 032, National Center 3, Room 10E54, Washington, DC 20362

The US Naval Sea System Command (NAVSEA), formerly known as the Bureau of Ships, has the responsibility for the research, design construction and logistic support of all US Navy Ships. The Research Directorate of NAVSEA has been the primary technical sponsor of all US Navy hovercraft and hydrofoil programmes since 1960.

The Programme Manager responsible for the development of both types of vessel is Mr. James L. Schuler. Technical Managers have been appointed for each of the several research and development programmes managed and directed by NAVSEA. Technical Manager of the Amphibious Assault Landing Craft Programme is Mr. Melvin Brown of the David W. Taylor Naval Ship Research and Development Centre, Carderock, Maryland. This programme includes construction of the JEFF craft which is an ACV landing craft based on the designs prepared by Bell Aerospace and Aerojet-General Corporation. Details will be found under the respective entries for the two companies.

Technical manager for the Advanced Hydrofoil Systems Programme is Mr. Robert Johnston of the NSRDC at Carderock. This programme includes operation and trials of the PCH-1 and AGEH-1, as well as testing the PGH-1. Current emphasis is on the development of larger and faster hydrofoils.

DOBSON PRODUCTS CO.

HEAD OFFICE:
2241 South Ritchey, Santa Ana, California 92705
TELEPHONE:
(714) 557-2987
WORKS:
Santa Ana, California
DIRECTOR:
Franklin A. Dobson

Dobson Products Co. was formed by Franklin A. Dobson in 1963 to develop and market small ACVs either in complete, factory built form, or as kits for private use. His first model, the Dobson Air Dart, won the first ACV race in Canberra in 1964. The company's Model F two-seater, has been described and illustrated in JSS 1973-74 and earlier editions.

The first Dobson craft designed for quantity production is the Model H. A new craft, the Model R, designed primarily for amateurs who wish to experiment with racing ACVs, is in the early stages of testing. A simplified 3-view and preliminary details are included in this entry.

Dobson Air Car Model H

DOBSON AIR CAR, MODEL H

This is a simplified and slightly larger machine than the original Model H. It has more efficient lift and thrust systems together with simplified controls and a slightly lower structural weight. Minor changes to lower the c.g. and reduce drag were underway as this edition went to press.

LIFT AND PROPULSION: A single engine is used for both lift and propulsion. The engine powers a 4-bladed fan forward and a 2-bladed, variable-pitch propeller aft on the same shaft.

CONTROLS: Lateral motion of a control stick operates a rudder, while fore-and-aft motion controls the propeller pitch, forward for thrust, aft for braking. The control stick also incorporates a motorcycle type twist-grip throttle.

HULL AND SKIRT: Hinged floats are used for buoyancy and these also support a flexible skirt which gives about an 8 in (203 mm) obstacle clearance. With the floats hinged upwards or removed. the overall width is less than 4 ft (1·21 cm).

DIMENSIONS:

Length	11 ft 0 in (3·35 m)
Width	7 ft 6 in (2·28 m)
Height	4 ft 3 in (1·29 m)
Folded width	3 ft 8 in (1·14 m)
Obstacle clearance	8 in (203 mm)
Cushion area	55 sq ft (5·11 sq m)

WEIGHTS:

Empty weight	230 lb (104·32 kg)
Tools and miscell	10 lb (4·52 kg)
Fuel (6¾ U.S. gal)	40 lb (18·14 kg)
Pilot	160 lb (72·57 kg)
Passenger	160 lb (72·57 kg)
Maximum gross weight	600 lb (272·14 kg)

PERFORMANCE: (at gross weight, 80% power), sea level

Cushion pressure	10·9 p.s.f.
Daylight clearance	1·5 in (457 mm)
Obstacle clearance	8 in (203 mm)
Static thrust	75 lb (34·01 kg)
Maximum gradient	1:8
Maximum speed	35-45 mpg (56-72 km/h)
Noise level	95 Db
Endurance at 80% power	2·5 hours
Range	100 miles (160·93 km)
Miles per gallon (U.S.)	15 (24·14 km)

DOBSON AIR CAR, MODEL R

This new single-seater is designed primarily for racing. The driver sits in a reclining position within a streamlined enclosure. It is planned to market the design in kit form.

LIFT AND PROPULSION: Integrated system with motive power supplied by a single McCulloch MC 101 135 cc single-cylinder two-stroke petrol engine. The engine, which is on a shock mounting, drives two 2 ft 0 in (0·609 m) diameter axial-flow fans via a centrifugal clutch and two vee-belts. The fans are specially designed to reduce bending loads.

DIMENSIONS:

Length overall	9 ft 2 in (2·79 m)
Beam overall	8 ft 10 in (2·43 m)
Height overall	2 ft 9 in (0·838 m)

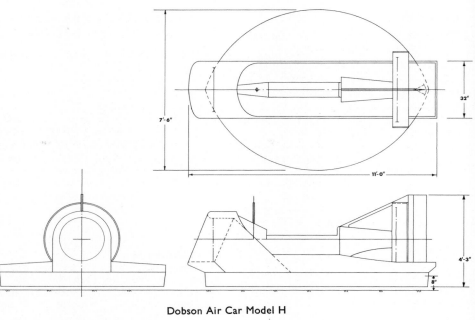

Dobson Air Car Model H

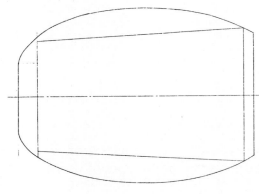

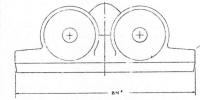

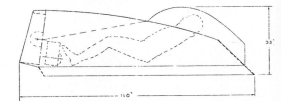

Dobson Air Car Model R

E.M.G. ENGINEERING CO.

HEAD OFFICE:
18518 South Broadway, Gardena, California 90248, USA

OFFICER:
Eugene M. Gluhareff, General Manager

Eugene Gluhareff is a former helicopter designer and project engineer at Sikorsky Aircraft Co. Gluhareff Helicopters was formed in 1952 to build and market small one-man helicopters equipped with G8-2 liquid propane pressure-jet engines. In recent years the company has designed two single-seat ACVs, the MEG-1H Yellow Jacket, powered by two go-cart engines and the MEG-2H Yellow Streak, a similar but larger craft propelled by Gluhareff pressure-jets.

MEG-1H YELLOW JACKET

This single-seat, recreational ACV has a maximum speed of 60 mph (96·50 km/h) over land and 20 mph (32·18 km/h) over water. More than 3,000 sets of plans have been sold since 1971 when the company began marketing plans and component parts.

LIFT AND PROPULSION: Integrated system. Motive power supplied by two 10 hp Chrysler 820 go-kart engines located side-by-side aft of the open cockpit. Each drives a 2 ft 10 in (0·863 mm) diameter, six-bladed, solid spruce fan at 3,600 rpm. Fan blades are cambered. Fuel is carried in a cylindrical ¼ gal (US) go-kart tank mounted above the hull between the two engines. Propulsion air is expelled through twin thrust ports aft.

CONTROLS: At low speeds craft heading is governed by the differential movement of two pedal-operated thrust ports aft or kinesthetic control. By leaning in the required direction the craft can be made to spin, move backwards, forwards or sideways. Stick-operated aerodynamic rudders become effective at about 20-25 mph (32-40·2 km/h).

HULL: Triangular planform, designed to generate aerodynamic lift at speed. Welded structure, mainly in ⅞ in (22·22 mm) diameter 4130 thinwall steel tubing. Thin aluminium skin sections in 2924-T4.20 gauge are pop-riveted into place. Intake ducts and nose sections are in glass fibre. Cockpit box is in riveted aluminium. A tricycle undercarriage is fitted to assist ground handling.

SKIRT: Fabricated in canvas, with 4130 steel reinforcing tubes at hem.

DIMENSIONS:

Length overall	10 ft 7 in (3·22 m)
Max beam	7 ft (2·13 m)
Skirt depth	6 in (152 mm)

WEIGHTS:

Normal empty weight	165 lb (74·83 kg)
Normal gross weight	331 lb (150·13 kg)

PERFORMANCE:

Max speed, calm water	15·20 mph (24·1-32·8 km/h)
Max speed over land	60 mph (96·56 km/h)
Vertical obstacle clearance	6 in (152 mm)

PRICE:

Construction plans US $15·00 per set. Ready-made components available.

MEG-2H YELLOW STREAK

Similar in basic design to the Yellow Jacket, this developed model employs two fin-mounted G8-2-15 pressure-jet engines, each developing 18 lb st for propulsive thrust.

The Gluhareff MEG-1H Yellow Jacket single-seat recreational ACV, powered by two 10 bhp Chrysler 820 go-kart engines. Each drives a six-bladed solid spruce fan. Propulsion air is expelled through twin thrust ports aft

EGLEN HOVERCRAFT INC

HEAD OFFICE:

801 Poplar Street, Terre Haute, Indiana, 47807

Telephone: 812-234 4307

DIRECTORS:

Jan Eglen, President
Alfred Brames, Secretary
O. Keith Owen, Jr, Treasurer
Lewis R. Poole, Comptroller
Woodrow S. Nasser, Director and Attorney
Paul Ferreira, Director, Research
George Kassis, Director
Jerry Chitwood, Director
Clarence Fauber, Director

EXECUTIVES:

Jan Eglen, General Manager
Lewis R. Poole, Works Manager
Lionel Saunders, Director of Production and Research
Terry Moore, Assistant Production Manager

MIDDLE EAST REPRESENTATIVE:

Al-Rodhan Trading & Contracting Est., PO Box 5020,
Kuwait, Arabian Gulf

Eglen Hovercraft Inc. was chartered in August 1969, to design and manufacture recreational hovercraft and other air cushion devices. The company is at present concentrating on the production of the Hoverbug, an amphibious two-seater with a moulded plastic hull. The company is also producing the new Mk 2 model and four- and six-seat ACVs which incorporate a number of design improvements, including the employment of shock-mountings for both the lift and thrust engines. A new product, the Terrehover hoverplatform, is described in the section devoted to ACV Trailers and Heavy Load Carriers.

HOVERBUG Mk 2

A two-seat recreational ACV, the Hoverbug is powered by two Rockwell JLO engines and has a maximum speed of 30 mph (48·28 km/h) over water and 35 mph (56 km/h) overland. The standard version has an open cockpit, but a cabin top to form an enclosed cockpit is available as an optional extra.

The craft is available in either fully assembled or kit form.

Above and below: Eglen Hovercraft Hoverbug, a plastic-hulled two-seater powered by two Rockwell-JLO engines. Speeds of up to 60 mph (96.56 km/h) have been attained by this craft over water with one person aboard. In the lower photograph a Hoverbug is on a trailer prior to being used for spraying pesticides in a fumigation operation

LIFT AND PROPULSION: A 22 hp Rockwell JLO-295 two-cycle engine, mounted immediately aft of the cockpit, drives a 2ft 0 in (609 mm) diameter, 10-bladed Multiwing fan for lift. Thrust is supplied by a 25 hp Rockwell JLO 395 driving a 3 ft 0 in (914 mm) diameter, Banks-Maxwell 2-bladed propeller. Both lift and thrust engines on the Mk 2 model have shock-absorbing mountings, reducing the vibration transmitted to the hull by about 90%. Similar mountings are also employed to attach the thrust duct to the thrust engine frame, resulting in a longer life expectancy for the duct and the rudders, which are now mounted directly onto the duct. The propeller is of laminated hardwood, tipped in stainless steel. The company is currently investigating the use of a 4-bladed propeller in order to reduce noise generation. Fuel capacity is 5 gallons (22·73 litres), representing about 2 hours running. Quick-release fittings to the fuel system facilitate maintenance.

CONTROLS: Directional control is provided by twin aerodynamic rudders hinged at the rear of the propeller duct and operating in the slipstream. Rudder installation on the Mk 2 has been modified to improve rate of turn. Additional pulleys have been introduced into the steering system for smoother steering. Cockpit controls comprise a steering wheel, two ignition switches, two throttles, two chokes, two emergency "kill" switches and a navigational lights switch.

HULL: High gloss, high impact plastic hull, formed by a thermovacuum moulding process developed by Hoosier Fibreglass Industries, Terre Haute, Indiana. Material used is Cycolacbrand ABS, supplied by the Marbon Division of Borg Warner Corporation. Hull side loading racks can be supplied as an optional extra. Two 6 in (152 mm) deep buoyancy chambers in the base of the hull are filled with foam plastic to provide 150% reserve buoyancy. Removable skids are fitted beneath.

SKIRT: Bag type, 1 ft 0 in (304 mm) deep, fabricated in neoprene-coated nylon. Skirt attachment system facilitates rapid removal and refitting.

ACCOMMODATION: Driver and passenger sit side-by-side in an open cockpit on a 4ft 0 in (1·21 m) wide bench-type seat. Optional extras include a cabin enclosure, windshield wipers and a custom upholstered seat.

SYSTEMS: Electrical : 12 volt, 75 watt system for engine starting instruments and navigation lights.

DIMENSIONS:

Length overall, power on	10 ft 0 in (3·04 m)
Beam overall, power on	6 ft 6 in (1·98 m)
Draft afloat	6 in (152 mm)
Skirt depth	1 ft 0 in (304 mm)
Cabin width	4 ft 0 in (1·21 m)

WEIGHTS:

Normal empty weight	400 lb
Payload	400 lb

PERFORMANCE:

Max recommended speed:

over water	30 mph (48·28 km/h)
over land	35 mph (56·32 km/h)
over ice	40 mph (64·37 km/h)

Wave capability (max)
1 ft 6 in - 2 ft 0 in (457·609 mm)

Max gradient at all up weight   1 : 6

PRICE:

Cost of complete craft, FOB Terre Haute:
US$2,495·00

Cost of standard kit   US$1,800·00

New four -seater, developed from the Eglen Hoverbug, during trials

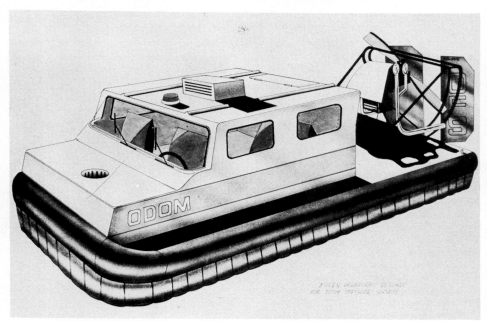

Impression of the new Eglen Hovercraft six-seat offshore survey and utility vehicle

OFFSHORE SURVEY SIX-SEATER

This new Eglen utility hovercraft is designed for a variety of duties including off-shore surveys. Of mixed wood and fibreglass construction, it carries a payload of 1,625 lb (737 kg) and cruises at 35 knots. Construction time is 4-6 months depending on optional equipment or special features required.

LIFT AND PROPULSION: Lift air is provided by a 90 hp Continental PC-60 aero-engine driving a 24 in (609 mm) diameter Rotafoil fan. Cushion pressure is 17-19 psf. Thrust is supplied by a 100 hp Lycoming air cooled piston engine driving a two-bladed Dobson reversible-pitch propeller.

CONTROLS: Craft heading is controlled by twin aerodynamic rudders hinged to the tubular metal guard aft of the propeller. Reversible and variable-pitch propeller provides braking and reverse thrust.

HULL: Wooden frame covered with fibreglass skin and finished with epoxy marine exterior paint. Cabin superstructure is in moulded fibreglass with 30 oz Durasonic ¼ in foam-backed sound proofing. Windows are of the "push out" type, in tinted plastic. Total fuel capacity is 55 gallons.

SKIRT: 14 in (355 mm) deep HDL type.

ACCOMMODATION: Seats provided for driver and five passengers. Optional items include seat belts, heating and air-conditioning and intercom system.

SYSTEMS, ELECTRICAL: 12 volt dc, with auxiliary outlets. Batteries: 2-12 volt, 72 amp hour capacity.

DIMENSIONS:

Length	24 ft (7·31 m)
Beam	10 ft (on cushion) (3·04 m)
Skirt depth	1 ft 2 in (355 mm)
Hover gap	¾ in (19 mm)

WEIGHTS:

Empty weight	2,500 lb (1,179·98 kg)
Payload (incl 400 lb fuel)	1,625 lb
Overload capacity	500 lb (226·79 kg)
Total weight in overload condition	4,625 lb (2,097·85 kg)

TERMS: On request. Domestic orders 50% payment with order, balance upon delivery. Overseas orders. Irrevocable letter of credit for full price placed with American Fletcher National Bank in Indianapolis, Indiana.

GULF OVERSEAS ENGINEERING CORP.

HEAD OFFICE:

PO Box 204, New Iberia, Louisiana 70560, USA

EXECUTIVES:

T. E. Sladek, Vice President and General Manager

Gulf Overseas Engineering Corporation has acquired the exclusive US design and manufacturing rights for the Secat surface effect catamaran from Teledyne Inc. The Secat was developed by Sewart Seacraft, a Teledyne company. With the acquisition of the design, Gulf also obtained the 40 ft (12·19 m) long prototype Secat built by Sewart.

In February 1976 Gulf announced that it had designed a 115 ft (35·05 m) version of the Secat, the Secat 115. This is an all weather air-cushion supported catamaran designed specifically to meet the transportation needs of the offshore oil industry.

Secat 115

In general layout, this craft represents a "scale-up" of the configuration tested with the 40 ft (12·19 m) Secat built by Sewart Seacraft. Secat 115 is designed for a service speed of 29 knots in the open sea and to be capable of operating at full power in 12 ft (3·65 m) seas.

The afterdeck, which is 60 ft long by 40 ft wide, can accommodate a Bell 206B Jet Ranger helicopter.

Propulsion is by two marine propellers, powered by two 1,200 hp marine diesels.

The lift system will be powered by a single 600 hp diesel engine.

The company states that at high speeds the manoeuvrability of the Secat will be comparable to that of a "well-performing crewboat". At low speeds the craft will be able to turn through 360 degrees in its own length.

DIMENSIONS:

Length overall	115 ft 0 in (35·05 m)
Beam overall	42 ft 0 in (12·80 m)

WEIGHTS:

Weight, empty	90 tons
Full load displacement	140 tons

PERFORMANCE:

Cruising speed	29 knots

J-TEC ASSOCIATES, INC.

HEAD OFFICE:

317 7th Ave. S.E., Cedar Rapids, Iowa 52401

TELEPHONE: (319) 366-7511

SALES OFFICE:

Cedar Rapids, Iowa

Europe: Technitron, Inc

625 Madison Ave., New York, New York.

Telephone: (212) 758-2790

STAFF PERSONNEL:

Theodore A. Johnson, President

Robert D. Joy, Vice President

Jerry P. Maland, Vice President, Marketing

J-TEC was founded in 1968 to undertake research, development and production in the field of oceanography. It supported the Lippisch Research Corporation from that time until Dr. Lippisch's death in February 1976. Principal effort was the production of the first two development models of the Aero-Skimmer, a high speed, water propelled boat using the Aeroboat design principals.

In 1975 J-TEC was awarded a Navy contract to prepare a study of the state-of-the-art of the Wing-in-Ground effect machine (WIG). Following the submission of that report J-TEC was awarded a contract to prepare a preliminary hydro and aerodynamic design of a large-size WIG. A tow tank model of the configuration will be delivered to the Navy in 1976 for test and evaluation. Assisting the J-TEC team are Russel Colton, who formerly worked with Dr. Lippisch at Collins and J-TEC; and Henry Borst Associates of Wayne, Pa., including Henry Borst and Ernest Tursich of Northfield, Minn.

Dr Lippisch was renowned as "father" of the delta-wing. His designs included the first delta wing glider, built in 1928 and the first operational rocket-propelled fighter, the Mo 163 of World War II.

The need for more reliable and efficient surface transportation for relatively underdeveloped areas of the world, most of which are either water-bound or water-traced, led Dr Lippisch to investigate air cushion concepts.

He determined that air cushion vehicles employing the dynamic ground effect principle offered greater speed, higher power efficiency, controllability, and flexibility in terms of the kinds of terrain which could be crossed, than aerostatic types. The primary problem, theoretically, lay in the pitch instability of conventional wings when flown at various distances from the surface; i.e., the centre of pressure travels rearward as the surface is

The "winged hull" ground effect vehicle concept originated by Dr Alexander M. Lippisch has received extensive model wind tunnel and prototype testing. The X-112, *upper left*, the earliest flying prototype, confirmed stability characteristics in and out of ground effect. Tests of the X-113 Am *upper right*, in the North Sea, more than verified wind tunnel data on efficiency (50% less power required in ground effect). Projected configurations include a two-seat sports and utility craft, *lower left*, and a 6-ton river bus, *lower right*

approached, causing the nose of a craft to pitch downward.

Dr Lippisch discovered that a low aspect ratio wing, properly designed, would solve this instability problem. The result of his studies was the "winged hull" concept.

The major research work has been performed under contract with or in cooperation with Rhein-Flugzeugbau GmbH and Dornier Gmbh

DESIGN: The "winged hull" combines the waterborne stability of the catamaran with the airborne stability of a unique, reversed delta wing with negative dihedral along the leading edge. The wing tips, or catamaran-type floats, and the wing's trailing edge are on the same plane. This special shape creates stable ground effect, enabling the craft to maintain a selected height from the surface automatically. Moreover, it solves the stability problem. The centre of pressure for the wing remains fixed whether the craft is in or out of ground effect.

The small-span, low aspect ratio wing design of the hull lends itself to simple, rugged construction which will withstand strong impacts without sacrificing loaded weight.

POWER PLANT: Conventional aircraft propulsion is employed.

CONTROLS AND PERFORMANCE: Control of the "winged hull" has proved in flight tests to be remarkably simple and safe. Conventional aircraft controls are used.

At low speeds, the craft operates as a planing boat. During take-off from the water, no control pressures are applied: gradual increase in speed develops the required lift and ground effect automatically. The craft is operated at a height above the surface of up to one-half the hull beam (wing span) for optimum performance.

Flight testing has shown craft of this type to be extremely manoeuvrable. They can travel at speed along a river and negotiate turns of only a few hundred feet in radius.

Because of its inherent stability, the "winged hull" is not restricted to flying in ground effect. It can leave ground effect to fly above obstacles such as bridges, for example, or to operate above a fog bank. Prototype vehicles have converted from ground effect to altitude and back again with no difficulty.

It manoeuvres at altitude in much the same way as a slow-flying aircraft: however, it is least efficient when operated out of ground effect during the brief periods it might be required to do so.

Whilst resembling an aircraft in form and control, the "winged hull" is designed, of course, for highest efficiency in ground effect. Flight tests, including a series performed over rough water in the North Sea near Bremerhaven, have established that 50% less power is required in ground effect, enabling operations in excess of 50 ton-miles per gallon of fuel at speeds in the 90-180 knot range.

APPLICATIONS: "Winged hull" designs ranging from small, two-seat sports and utility craft propelled by Volkswagen engines to river buses. Coastal transports of several tons have been initiated. A retractable

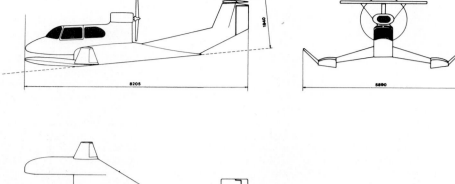

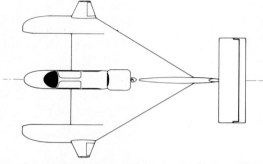

General arrangement of the Lippisch X-113B, a projected two-seat version of the X-113 Am

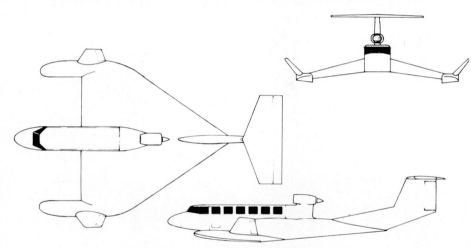

General arrangement of the projected 6-ton river bus

Aero-Skimmer under test. Employing the same basic principles as that of the Aerofoil Boat, but employing water-screw propulsion, craft of this type have reached a speed of 150 knots

wheeled undercarriage would permit amphibious operations in areas poorly suited for dock facilities.

No special depth of water is required when the craft is in ground effect; it will operate equally well over sand banks, beaches, deserts and arctic regions.

Military applications include fast river patrol boats, anti-submarine warfare (ASW) craft, as well as personnel and supply transports.

AERO-SKIMMER

In addition to the aerofoil boat, J. Tech

Associates Inc is in the process of developing a sea-going vehicle designed for operation in the surface effect region.

Its unique configuration overcomes the speed barriers created by supercavitations induced drag on both ship hulls and hydrofoils. At higher speed, only the propeller blades contact the water. The hull itself lifts clear, being supported entirely by aerodynamic surface effect. The present manned research vehicle is designed for specialised naval purposes and reaches over-water speeds in excess of 150 knots.

NEOTERIC—USA—INCORPORATED

HEAD OFFICES:
  Fort Harrison Industrial Park, Terre
    Haute, Indiana, 47804, USA
TELEPHONE:
  (812) 466-2303
EXECUTIVES:
  Chris Fitzgerald, President
  Rob Wilson, Technical Director
  Dave Atkins, Design and Planning
  Barbara L. Harrison, Secretary

Neoteric—USA Incorporated was formed in 1975 by three of the founders of Neoteric Engineering Affiliates Pty Ltd, of Melbourne, Australia (see separate entry). The Neova range of single and two-seat ACVs, which is now being built and marketed by Neoteric USA, was first introduced by the Australian associate. The Neova, which is fully amphibious, is available in kit or ready-built form. A three-seat model, the Neova 3 is nearing production.

NEOVA 2

A highly-manoeuvrable light ACV, the Neova is an amphibious two-seater, intended primarily for recreational use. Neova II is supplied in kit form in four individual modules—base, machinery, ducts and controls and skirt. Individual components can also be supplied, enabling the home builder to assemble any part of the complete vehicle. The purchaser can therefore buy what is needed and make the rest himself to keep costs as low as possible.

The overall dimensions of the machine—7 ft by 14 ft (2·13 × 4·27 m) —allow it to be transported by road on a flat trailer.

LIFT AND PROPULSION: Integrated system powered by a single 46 hp Volkswagen engine driving via a simple chain drive transmission two axial fans. Airflow is ducted into the plenum for lift and two outlets aft for thrust. The power module, comprising engine, transmission and axial-flow fans is mounted on a rubber-seated platform, secured to the main hull by three bolts. It is totally enclosed and when operating is impossible to touch. A large hatch provides ready access to the engine and all components.

CONTROLS: Back and forward movement of a dual stick control column operates two thrust buckets which vary the power and the direction of the thrust. The column is pulled back for reverse thrust and moved ahead for forward thrust. Differential use of the two columns, with one stick forward and the other back, is used for changing craft direction. The aerodynamic rudders at the rear of the propulsion ducts are normally used only for small corrections in heading at cruising speed.

HULL: Home-built models are of ply construction, with steel attachments at lifting and towing points. A two-seat fibre glass body assembly is available as an optional item. Skid pads on the underside protect the structure from damage by abrasion. An inflatable fender is attached to the periphery to prevent structural damage when travelling at low speeds. An integral siphon system prevents the collection of excessive water within the hull. Buoyancy is 150%. The skirt module is removable as a single unit.

ACCOMMODATION: Side-by-side seating for two. Safety features include a cockpit roll bar which is stressed to withstand three times the vehicle's weight. Family models will be equipped with a detachable canopy.

Top: Cruising speed of Neova II is 35 mph (56 km/h).
Centre: The complete power module, comprising engine, transmission and axial-flow fans, is secured to the main hull by three bolts.
Bottom: The roll-bar, aft of the cockpit, is stressed to withstand three times the vehicle's weight

DIMENSIONS:
Length overall	14 ft 0 in (4·27 m)
Beam overall	7 ft 0 in (2·13 m)
Height overall, skirt inflated	5 ft 0 in (1·54 m)

WEIGHTS:
Normal all-up weight	1,000 lb (454 kg)
Payload, maximum	430 lb (196 kg)

PERFORMANCE:
Cruising speed (at 75% power setting)	35 mph (56 km/h)
Max gradient from standing start	1 : 10

Vertical obstacle clearance	8 in (203 mm)
Endurance on full power	1½ hours

PRICES: Neova II

Information Pack US $5.

Deluxe Plan Pack US $ 50.00.

(free with complete kit purchase)

Complete kit $2,953.00.

Module kits $282.00. Individual components and material sets available.

NEOVA SUPER SPORTS

This sophisticated new three-seater is powered by a 130 hp engine. It was designed for large scale production in grp and at present is only being hand made to order.

DIMENSIONS:
Length	15 ft 0 in (4·57 m)
Beam	7 ft 6 in (2·29 m)

WEIGHTS:
All-up weight	1,600 lb (727 kg)
Payload	600 lb (270 kg)

PERFORMANCE:
Cruising speed	55 mph (90 km/h)

PRICE: Approximately $25,000.

LOCKHEED-GEORGIA

HEAD OFFICE:

Hartford, Conn., USA

EXECUTIVES:

R. H. Lange, Manager of Transport Design

Lockheed Georgia's 1·2 million lb Spanloader cargo flying-wing is one of several new projects which, in certain roles will fly in ground effect. The Spanloader, which will have a span of 252 ft (76·81 m) and a length of 208 ft (63·39 m), will be powered by six turbofans, each delivering 52,500 lb thrust.

The standard model is designed to carry a 550,000 lb payload, most of which will be packed in standard 8 × 8 ft × 20 ft (2·4 × 2·4 × 6·09 m) containers, over a distance of 5,000 n. miles. The wing has a thickness of 11 ft (3·35 m) and can accommodate two rows of containers, side-by-side in a cargo compartment which is 300 ft (91·44 m) long. There is an additional 92 ft (28·04 m) long cargo compartment in the fuselage, providing

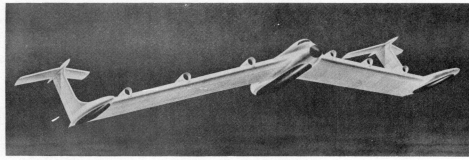

Lockheed-Georgia Spanloader

sufficient space for a total of 38 containers.

A feature of the craft is the use of an air cushion landing system, instead of a conventional landing gear. Two cushions will be located in streamlined containers beneath the wings, and a third will be located beneath the fuselage.

The company states that the low footprint pressure of 2·08 psi will allow the craft to operate from grass or water.

Among possible military applications will be that of long range A & W patrol. By operating in ground effect, it is estimated that the Spanloader would have an endurance of 56 hours, during which time it could cover 11,500 nautical miles at a cruising speed of 200 knots. In this configuration, payload capacity would be 110,000 lb.

MARITIME DYNAMICS

HEAD OFFICE:

1502 54th Ave East, Tacoma, Washington 98401

TELEPHONES:

206 759-1709

206 922-5233

EXECUTIVES:

William C. House, President

Maritime Dynamics is at present undertaking SEV data reduction, performance analysis and model testing for the US Navy. It is also developing a number of new ACV concepts.

POWER BREEZE

HEAD OFFICE:

8139 Matilija, Panorama City, California 91402

TELEPHONE:

(213) 785-0197

EXECUTIVES:

Dan W. Henderson Jr, President/Designer

Power Breeze Air Cushion Vehicle Systems was founded originally to stimulate public interest in ACVs, and is currently selling plans to home builders for a small, easily assembled amphibious single-seater.

A set of plans costs $5·00 and a ready made skirt costs $35·00.

Total cost of construction in the USA, including ply for the hull, skirt material, metal tubing, propeller and engine is about $400. Weight of the craft is 250 lb (113 kg) and the maximum speed is approximately 25 mph (40·23 km/h). The latest model of this circular platform single-seater folds to a width of 4 ft 0 in (1·21 m) to simplify storage and to permit it to be carried by a light truck or pick-up van.

A number of craft have been built to this design in the United States and Australia.

In addition to selling plans, the company is now engaged in the sales of second-hand ACVs, and specialises in finding craft to meet the individual needs of its clients.

Power Breeze are marketing plans for this light, easily assembled amphibious single-seater

ROHR INDUSTRIES, INC.

CORPORATE HEADQUARTERS:
Foot of H Street, PO Box 878
Chula Vista, California 92012
TELEPHONE:
714 575-4111
EXECUTIVES:
Frederick W. Garry, President, Chief
Executive Officer and Chairman of the
Board
Jerome J. Filiciotto, Senior Vice President
Aerospace and Marine Systems
SURFACE EFFECT SYSTEMS DIVISION:
PO Box 23000, San Diego, California 92123
TELEPHONE:
714 560-8008
TELEX:
910-322-1870
EXECUTIVES:
Wilfred J. Eggington, Vice President and
General Manager
G. Douglas McGhee, Vice President,
Programs Director, LSES
W. A. Pulver, Director, Operations
Lynd J. Esch, Manager, Advanced Pro-
grams
George G. Halvorson, Group Manager, Test
and Evaluation
Howard L. Kubel, Manager, Division
Planning
Darren L. Reed, Group Manager, Program
Planning and Control
Jimmie R. Sober, Program Manager,
Testcraft
Glenn F. Guerin, Group Manager, Pro-
curement
Dario E. DaPra, Director, Engineering
F. Patrick Burke, Deputy Program
Director
Charles M. Lee, Group Manager, Ship
Design
Robert S. Cramb, Group Manager, Analysis
Thomas O. Gurley, Group Manager,
Quality Assurance

One of the world's leading producers of aircraft power packages and structures for three decades, Rohr Industries today is a growing and diversified designer and builder of ground transportation systems, industrial products and marine systems as well as aerospace systems.

Founded in 1940 and based in Chula Vista, California, Rohr's main plant comprises 130 acres of land with more than 2 million square feet of covered accommodation. The Chula Vista facility houses over 3,000 pieces of major production equipment representing a $31 million investment. Rohr currently has about 11,000 employees.

Manufacturing facilities include machines, tooling and precision welding equipment that have been utilised extensively in the production of welded aluminium marine structures including boat hulls and offshore mooring systems for fuel transfer.

Rohr's SES Division joined with Litton Industries in 1972 to begin work on preliminary design studies of a US Navy 2000-ton SES with ocean-going capabilities. While working on the design studies, Rohr continued its R & D programme (begun in 1970) on the XR-1, a Navy research testcraft weighing approximately 20 tons.

On completing preliminary design studies, a contract for advanced development of the 2000-ton concept was awarded to Rohr by the US Navy in July 1974. Current work covers bow and stern seals; materials for seals and structures; lift fans; ride control

Rohr's preliminary design for a prototype 3,000-ton ASW SES for the US Navy. At the rear of the deckhouse is a hangar for an ASW helicopter. Power is supplied by six General Electric LM2500 gas-turbines, two for lift and four for propulsion

devices to minimise vertical ship motions; waterjet pumps and reduction gearing. Testing of proposed features is undertaken aboard the XR-1 and the SES-100A, one of two testcraft built by the Navy to support the 2000-ton study programme. Following this development programme, the ship system design will be finalised and the Navy will begin construction and test of a prototype.

Rohr Industries was one of the two successful competitors for the 2000-ton surface effect ship development programme under the direction of the US Navy Surface Effect Ship Project Office.

Work completed in 1976 included extensive scale model testing. Test objectives include the measurement of stability, drag, motions and accelerations. Seal materials and other subsystems components were tested under operational conditions using a specially constructed environmental test rig to verify adequate seal life in an ocean environment. Model tests were conducted to check hull structural components, bow and stern planing seals, variable geometry lift fans, ride control systems and variable area flush inlets.

Extensive subsystem testing was completed on Navy testcraft—the XR-1, a 20-ton vessel and the 100-ton SES-100A.

LSES (3,000-Ton Surface Effect Ship)

The objectives of the Navy's LSES programme are to demonstrate the feasibility of a large, ocean-going SES and to evaluate its utility as a weapon system. At the present, the programme is concentrated on the development and testing of the ship's major subsystems together and parallel ship design.

LIFT AND PROPULSION: Power for the lift system is provided by two General Electric LM 2500 gas-turbines. Lift fans are the centrifugal type, approximately 15 ft (3 m) in diameter. Six fans are installed, three on each side of the ship.

Propulsive power is provided by four General Electric LM 2500 gas-turbines driving four waterjet pumps through reduction gearing.

CUSHION AIR CONTAINMENT: Cushion air is contained by long rigid side walls with flexible seal installations forward and aft. The forward and aft seals are inflated by the cushion air supply and employ a planing surface at the lower extremities to eliminate flagellation damage and minimise hydrodynamic drag. The seals are fully retractable to facilitate craft operation off-cushion.

Propulsive power for Rohr's 3,000 ton SES design is provided by four General Electric LM2500 gas-turbines driving four waterjet pumps through reduction gearing

CONTROLS: Craft direction is controlled by differential and vectored thrust. Motion control includes a cushion pressure relief system and variable geometry inlet control on the lift fans.

HULL: Longitudinally-framed, aluminium alloy structure, welded throughout. Plating in marine-grade aluminium alloy with extruded stiffeners. Design criteria ensures structural integrity in sea state 9.

ACCOMMODATION: Provided for a complement of 125 men. Accommodation standards are to US Navy requirements and include berthing, commissary, recreation and laundry spaces. All living and working spaces are air-conditioned.

SYSTEMS: Electrical system comprises three Solar Saturn gas turbine generators of 720 kw capacity each.

COMMUNICATIONS AND NAVIGATION: Communication and navigation system includes a US Navy Junior Participating Tactical Data System and an anti-collision radar system.

ARMAMENT: Based on latest available Navy equipment for the selected mission demonstrations.

DIMENSIONS:

Length overall	238 ft 6 in (72·69 m)
Beam overall	108 ft 0 in (32·91 m)
Cushion height	18 ft 0 in (5·48 m)
Cushion area	17,000 sq ft (1,579 m²)

WEIGHTS:

Normal all up weight	3,000 tons

PERFORMANCE:

Maximum speed	approximately 80 knots

SES-100A

Rohr Industries, under US Navy contract, provides craft maintenance, logistics and engineering services, test planning and data handling support for the Navy's SES-100A test programme.

The SES-100A, one of two major testcraft supporting the 2,200-ton SES development, was developed by the Aerojet General Corporation under the sponsorship of the US Navy Surface Effect Ship Project Office.

Following completion of over two years of extensive contractor trials, the custody of the craft was transferred to the US Navy in July 1974. The waterjet propulsion system was modified to incorporate variable-geometry flush inlets, in lieu of the original pod-type ram inlets. This major conversion was accomplished, under Navy direction, by Hydronautics Inc. and the Tacoma Boat Company. Subsequently the craft was moved from the Seattle, Washington area to the Navy's Surface Effect Ship Test Facility (SESTF) at the Naval Air Station, Patuxent River, Maryland, where tests have continued under Navy direction.

Primary technical objectives of the test programme over the past two years have been the thorough evaluation of the propulsion system, following installation of the variable area flush inlets, and measurement of the craft's ride quality characteristics with its "heave attenuation" system.

LIFT AND PROPULSION: Motive power for the integrated lift/propulsion system is supplied by four 3,500 shp Avco Lycoming gas-turbines. The transmission system couples the gas-turbines to two Aerojet General two-stage axial/centrifugal waterjet pumps and three axial-flow lift fans through reduction gears. Powerplant airflow is supplied through demisters from inlets located on the topside. The two waterjet pumps

The SES-100A surface effect ship.   Test planning, engineering services and data handling are among the services provided by Rohr under US Navy contract in support of the SES-100A test programme

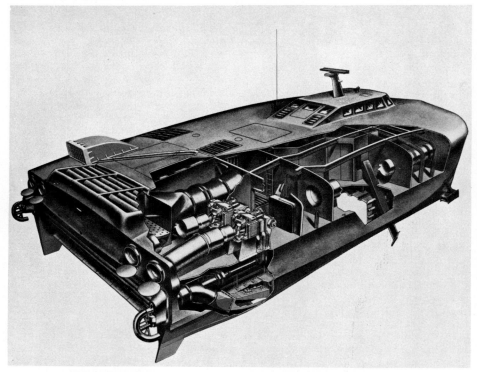

Cutaway drawing of the SE5-100A showing one of the two flush-mounted waterjet inlets and the new stabilising fins which replace the original pod-type inlet and fin assembly

(port and starboard units) are installed on rail mounts that permit them to be removed through a port in the transom. The three axial-flow fans are located in compartments between the port and starboard engines. The four gas turbines can be employed in any combination to drive the lift/propulsion system.

The variable geometry waterjet inlets are illustrated in the accompanying sketch. To provide cavitation-free operation over a wide range of speeds, the throat area of the inlet diffuser is varied by means of a hydraulically actuated linkage connected to the flexible diffuser roof. At low speeds, and while the craft is passing through the "hump" speed, the diffuser throat is in the open position, and is progressively closed to maintain the correct water flow rate as the speed increases.

CONTROLS: At low speeds, directional control is provided by waterjet thrust vector and at high speed by movable skegs, port and starboard. The fuel and fuel-trim subsystem comprises four fuel storage tanks—two in each sidewall; a service tank and bow and stern trim tanks. Trim is adjusted by transferring fuel from tank to tank by means of the fuel transfer pumps.

HULL: The hull, constructed by the Tacoma Boatbuilding Co., Tacoma, Washington, is a welded aluminium skin. It is divided into compartments by transverse and longitudinal bulkheads. The weatherdeck, cargo deck and bridge are glass-reinforced plastic.

ACCOMMODATION: The bridge, which is air-conditioned and sound-insulated, is located on the centreline forward. It accommodates four crew members and six observers.

SYSTEMS: Electrical: Power generation and distribution system supplies electrical and electronic operational equipment and the data acquisition subsystem (DAS). The primary purpose of the DAS is to measure selected testcraft performance parameters and record the resulting data on magnetic tape. The secondary purpose is to provide instantaneous data display.

COMMUNICATIONS AND NAVIGATION: Standard marine radio is carried and radar is included for collision avoidance. A gyro compass is fitted.

HYDRAULIC SYSTEM: 3,000 psig pressure and 100 psig return pressure.

COMPRESSED AIR: Engine bleed air is used for stern seal spring pressurization. Stored compressed air is used for turbine starting and braking.

DIMENSIONS:

Length overall	81 ft 11 in (24·9 m)
Beam overall	41 ft 11 in (12·7 m)
Length-to-beam ratio	1:95
Cushion area	2,467 ft² (230 m²)
Height on cushion	23 ft 0 in (7·01 m)
Draft displacement Condition	10 ft 7½ in (3·22 m)
Freeboard (design load waterline)	8 ft 7½ in (2·62 m)

WEIGHTS:

Light displacement	72·8 short tons
Loaded displacement design	100 short tons

PERFORMANCE: Designed max speed 80 knots.

XR-1 TESTCRAFT

Rohr Industries has operated the XR-1 SES research testcraft under US Navy contract. Originally built by the Naval Air Engineering Facility in 1963, the XR-1 was the first USN craft to demonstrate the captured air bubble principle. Early tests of this craft contributed to the formulation of the Navy's SES development programme and to the decision in 1966 to establish the SES Project Office.

In 1970, the XR-1 was equipped with waterjets and assigned to Rohr for further development and evaluation. Since then, the craft has undergone a series of modifications to evaluate new concepts in cushion seals, waterjet inlet systems, lift air distribution, craft structures, and associated developments in instrumentation. It was the first craft of its type to demonstrate flush and variable geometry waterjet inlets, and to provide operational data on the performance of these concepts under sea state conditions where inlet broachng is induced.

In 1973, further modifications of the craft were undertaken, including the replacement of the earlier rigid, articulated seals with flexible, rubberised-fabric seals and the installation of redesigned lift system to permit investigation of the effects of variations in lift air distribution. In addition, a structural test programme was undertaken, involving rebuilding the bow structure and incorporating instrumentation to permit measurement of structural loads due to slamming in heavy seas.

Although much smaller and less sophisticated than the SES-100A or SES-100B, the XR-1 has proved to be a versatile and relatively inexpensive research vehicle for investigating new SES concepts, and for verifying scaling techniques for application in the design of larger craft.

In October 1974, Rohr began a major reconfiguration of the XR-1 to demonstrate several subsystem innovations being developed under the 2KSES programme. These included: (1) a refined waterjet inlet system with a variable geometry feature similar to

The XR-1, seen in D configuration, has refined waterjet propulsion system with a variable-geometry water inlet similar to that on the SES-100A

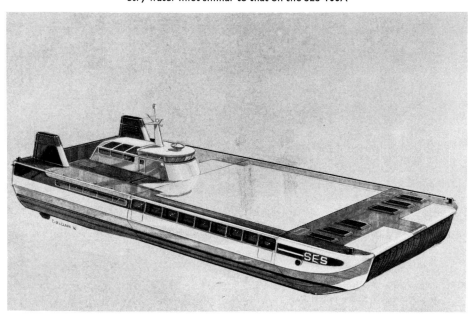

Passenger ferry version of the multi-purpose SES concept

that in the SES-100A; (2) flexible, planing-type bow and stern seals designed for high durability, (3) variable-flow lift fans as an alternate to the use of cushion venting for attenuating craft motion in a seaway, (4) cushion vent valves for comparison with the variable flow lift fans, and (5) a ride control electronic system to sense craft motion and control the lift fans and vent valves. Basic elements of the propulsion system and craft structure were retained in the new configuration which was designated XR-1D.

In April 1976, the XR-1D was shipped to the Surface Effect Ship Test Facility at Patuxent River, Maryland, to be placed under the direction and operational control of the US Navy. Test results over the past twelve months have confirmed the value of the new concepts and the data obtained is currently in use to support the development of the LSES.

PROPULSION: Two T53-L-7A Avco-Lycoming gas turbines; two Pratt and Whitney Seajet 6-1A pumpjets.

LIFT SYSTEM: Three Aerojet Liquid Rocket Company variable output centrifugal fans; two pairs of heave attenuation valves. Cushion pressure, 35,000 cfm at 60 psf.

DIMENSIONS:

Length overall	50 ft (15·0 m)
Beam overall	19 ft (5·79 m)

WEIGHTS:

Operating displacement	43,000 lbs

PERFORMANCE:

Maximum speed, calm water	43 knots

ADVANCED PROGRAMMES

A recent outgrowth of Rohr's SES programme is a concept for a multi-purpose SES platform which has applications as a crewboat to support offshore oil operations, a passenger ferry for commercial operations and a patrol craft for military missions.

LIFT AND PROPULSION: Lift is supplied by two 1,400 shp Avco Lycoming TF14C gas-turbines driving four centrifugal, variable-output lift fans, plus two auxiliaries. Propulsive thrust is provided by two 3,780 shp Avco Lycoming TF-40 gas-turbines driving two Powerjet 20 waterjet pumps.

DIMENSIONS:

Length overall	126 ft 0 in (38·40 m)
Beam	42 ft 0 in (12·80 m)
Draft hullborne	12 ft 6 in (3·81 m)

WEIGHTS:

Displacement, fully loaded	180 tons
Light displacement	92 tons

PERFORMANCE:

Cruising speed, sea state 2	60 knots
Range	750 nm

SURFACE EFFECT SHIPS PROJECT OFFICE

OFFICE:
  PO Box 34401, Bethesda, Maryland 20084
CABLE ADDRESS:
  SESPO, c/o Naval Ship Research and Development Center, Bethesda, Maryland
EXECUTIVES:
  Captain C. J. Boyd, USN, Project Manager

The Surface Effect Ships Project Office, originally sponsored by both the Navy and Commerce Departments, became a wholly Navy sponsored operation on July 1, 1971. In early December 1971, Captain Carl J. Boyd, formerly Commanding Officer, USS Springfield, Sixth Fleet Flagship, was assigned to duties as Deputy Project Manager. Captain Boyd became Project Manager in February 1972.

With the change in sponsorship of the project, there was also a change in programme direction. This change is best described by the following quote from remarks made by Admiral Elmo R. Zumwalt, Jr., former Chief of Naval Operations: "It is my personal conviction that the development of a large SES has the potential for affecting other aspects of naval warfare as profoundly as nuclear power has affected submarine warfare".

The surface effect ship represents a major breakthrough in naval and maritime technology. The U.S. Navy believes the SES principle can be applied in open ocean ships of 2,000 to 10,000 tons. Such ships, capable of sustained speeds of 80-100 knots, would, in the opinion of the Navy, have revolutionary applications in the Navy's missions to control the seas and to project military strength abroad.

The Surface Effect Ship (SES) is a variation of the air cushion vehicle. ACVs employ a cushion of air contained by a flexible skirt around the hull and are normally propelled by air propellers driven by gas-turbine engines. Craft of this type are under development by the U.S. Navy for use as advanced amphibious landing craft. The SES principle employs rigid sidewalls, integral to the hull structure, with flexible seals fore and aft to contain the air cushion. The rigid sidewalls permit the use of water propulsion, either waterjets or propellers, which is more efficient than airscrews at SES operational speeds. They also provide added stability. The U.S. Navy's SES programme has been orientated to this approach since it is believed that it will be superior to the more conventional air cushion vehicle for ships of ocean-going size.

The SES development programme is aimed at expanding the technology to ships of ocean-going size. Phase I of the programme, 1966 to 1973, was focussed on the design, development, construction, and tests of two 100-ton testcraft embodying different approaches to the critical technological areas of propulsion, sidewalls and seals, lift sytems,

Two 100-ton SES's being employed by the US Navy to provide design data for the LSES. The SES-100A, *above*, is propelled by waterjets with flush inlets and has attained speeds in excess of 75 knots while the SES100B, *below*, is propelled by partially submerged supercavitating propellers and has attained speeds in excess of 80 knots. These craft have helped to verify the ability of the SES to operate at predicted speeds, thereby paving the way for the 100-knot Navy

Proposals for a 3,000 ton SES by Bell, *left*, and Rohr, *above*. The vessel will be a weaponised test ship, used to demonstrate the all-round capabilities and open ocean performance of surface effect ships in various fleet roles including ASW, surface and anti-air warfare

and systems of stability and control. The two 100-ton testcraft were completed in 1972 and have since been undergoing extensive testing. Tests to date have demonstrated the validity of the SES concept, and provided verification of the design data base needed for proceeding to larger size ships. Phase II, based on Phase I accomplishments and a major Navy mission analysis, focusses on the design, development, construction and test of one RDT & E funded test ship of about 2-3,000 tons. Construction of this large SES (LSES) will take approximately 3 years and is expected to be completed by mid-1981. At-sea tests of the LSES will entail approximately one year of Navy testing, which will include evaluation of the ship's ability to perform in an operational environment. Since the ultimate objective of the SES programme is to introduce this technology on a broader scale in the future, the development programme plan also includes planning and preliminary design studies for a class of SES escort ships of approximately 3,000 ton size as well as for further development of the SES technology to support design and construction of larger vessels. Plans for both the SES escort and the larger SES will be technology-paced and synchronised with the development and test of the LSES prototype.

Project Events Background

Conducted tests of XR-1, XR-3 and XR-5 manned model testcraft; converted XR-1 from air propulsion to waterjet propulsion utilising both ram and flush inlets and conducted successful tests to 42 knots, top speed for XR-1: initiated key subsystem development in seal design and materials, partially submerged supercavitating propellers and waterjet propulsion, lift fans, structural design and materials and aerodynamic/hydrodynamic response: designed, constructed and tested two 100-ton testcraft (SES 100A has waterjet propulsion: SES 100B has semi-submerged supercavitating propellers). Both 100-ton testcraft have conducted evaluations throughout the operating envelope, which helped to verify the SES principle. Data was obtained on drag, lift, stability, propulsive efficiency, air cushion/seal performance and riding qualities. Test data obtained conformed to design predictions for the essential characteristics necessary to the design of larger SES. Conducted Surface Effect Ship Mission Analysis to examine the more important missions for SES: completed sizing which determined the 2,000-ton SES to be the smallest practical size for evaluation of an ocean-going ship, and that such a ship could be developed with acceptable technical risk.

As a result of Defense Systems Acquisition Review Council (DSARC) review in October 1972, SECDEF authorised Navy to award contracts for preliminary design of a 2,000-ton SES, using four competing contractors. A DSARC review in December 1973 led to a decision by SECDEF authorising the Navy to develop and test SES unique subsystem for two 2,000-ton prototypes and to carry out the necessary concurrent ship design effort for updating the two preliminary designs.

Recent Developments

SES Test Facility—The Surface Effect Ship Test Facility (SESTF) was completed in April 1973 for the U.S. Navy as a test facility for the SES-100A and B and other testcraft as assigned. Other surface effect ships,

XR-1 seen in D configuration, weighs 20 tons. Though smaller than the 100-ton test craft, it has proved to be a versatile research vessel for investigating new SES concepts and for verifying scaling techniques which will be applied to larger SES's

XR-3, a two-man testcraft operated for SESPO by the Naval Post Graduate School, Monterey, California, is used for preliminary evaluation of performance and control. It also provides junior naval officers with the opportunity to operate an SES

XR-5, a 46 ft, 7,500 lb, free-running, manned craft was designed and built for SESPO in 1973. This craft is used to verify the operating characteristics of the high length-to-beam concept. Power performance, dynamic structural response, seakeeping and dynamic stability characteristics can be evaluated almost simultaneously in varying sea states and heading. It has attained 20 knots in 10 in waves which scaled up to 60 knots in 7 ft seas for an SES of 4,000 tons

including the XR-2, XR-5, and the British Wellington class BH-7, have operated from the SESTF.

The Facility, located at the Naval Air Station, Patuxent River, Maryland, consists of a 195-ton capacity syncrolift, a transfer yard with two transfer cars, and a boathouse with support facilities. The boathouse consists of two bays occupying 24,000 square feet. This area can be closed against the weather and is heated and lit, providing an all-weather maintenance and support capability. A warehouse (8,000 square feet), a machine shop (3,000 square feet), and office space (5,000 square feet) complete the Facility. The Facility has access to the telemetering and real-time data reduction facilities of NAS, Patuxent River, allowing it to monitor and to correct test missions, as needed.

The SES-100A is based there and has been undergoing a complete Test and Evaluation programme since March 1975 validating 2,000-ton and larger surface effect ship designs.

SESPO's surface effect ship test facility with the SES-100A in the background. When the 100A docks, the 195-ton sycnrolift raises the craft, together with the transfer car on which it rests, to the deck level. The transfer car and craft are then moved into the boathouse via a rail system

Surface Effect Ships attain high speeds:

Both the waterjet-propelled SES-100A and its sister ship the SES-100B, which is driven by partially submerged supercavitating propellers, have established new speed records for naval surface vehicles. The SES-100A exceeded 75 knots while the SES-100B exceeded 80 knots. These accomplishments help to verify the ability of SES craft to operate at predicted speeds thereby paving the way for the "100 Knit Navy".

Flush Waterjet Inlet Retrofit:

Flush waterjet inlets were designed, built and retrofitted on the SES-100A, a 100-ton waterjet propelled experimental surface effect craft. This craft is currently conducting tests with the new inlets. Flush inlets provide lower drag and are less susceptible to debris ingestion and damage than pod-mounted inlets. The lower drag results in higher craft speed and range.

LSES contracts awarded:

In July 1974, two contracts, amounting to about $72 million, were awarded to Bell Aerospace Textron and Rohr Industries to develop SES-critical sub-sytems and to conduct parallel ship design effort. The data generated from these contracts will minimise the risk in the design and construction of a large open ocean SES prototype. In late 1974, R & D constraints led to a decision for the development of one LSES prototype. By June 1976, when the current sub-system and parallel ship design contracts are due for completion, one contractor is expected to have been selected to design and construct the large SES prototype. However, the decision for the contract design, detail design and construction of the prototype awaits a future DSARC (scheduled for mid-1976).

SKIMMERS INCORPORATED

HEAD OFFICE:
PO Box 855, Severna Park, Maryland, 21146

TELEPHONE:
301-647-0526

DIRECTORS:
M. W. Beardsley. President and General Manager
H. L. Beardsley
W. D. Preston

OVERSEAS REPRESENTATIVE:
United Kingdom: Airhover Ltd, St. Osyth, Essex

Skimmers Inc was formed in April 1966 to produce plans and components for use by homebuilders in constructing the Fan-Jet Skimmer sport ACV. It is affiliated with the Beardsley Air Car Co.

FAN-JET SKIMMER

Fan-Jet Skimmer is one of the world's first practical solo sport ACVs. It was designed by Col. Melville Beardsley, a former USAF technical officer, and one of the pioneers in ACV development in the United States.

The Fan-Jet Skimmer was designed to be the simplest and cheapest one-man ACV that could be devised. More than forty craft of this type have been built to date. The company is now developing a two-seat sports ACV.

HULL: The main structural component is a tractor inner tube, giving 700 lb of buoyancy, around which is an aluminium framework of square tube, and L girders. The topside bow profile is in plywood. The structure is decked in vinyl-coated nylon fabric, which is also used for the self-extending skirt system.

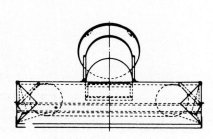

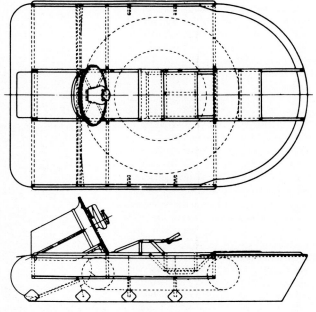

The Fan-Jet Skimmer, designed by Melville Beardsley

LIFT AND PROPULSION: Power for the integrated lift/propulsion system is provided by a Chrysler 2-cycle 6 hp engine, driving an 18 in axial flow fan. The fan has a marine plywood hub with 9 sheet metal formed blades. The primary air flow, used for direct thrust, is ejected through a propulsive slot control flap located aft of the fan duct. The area of the slot can be varied by a hinged flap controlled by a lever. This and the throttle lever and ignition switch are the only controls. The secondary air flow, for cushion lift, passes into a rearward plenum chamber.

CONTROL: The craft is steered by kinesthetic control (body movement) which the designer feels is the ideal method of control for a craft of this size.

DIMENSIONS:

Length overall	9 ft 8 in (2·9 m)
Beam overall	6 ft 2 in (1·8 m)
Height overall on landing pads	36 in (0·9 m)
Skirt depth	9 in (0·2 m)
Draft afloat	5 in (0·12 m)
Cushion area	44 sq ft (4·0 m²)

WEIGHTS:

Normal all-up weight	250 lb (113 kg)
Normal payload (operating)	150 lb (68 kg)
Maximum payload	180 lb (397 kg) approx

PERFORMANCE:

Max speed, calm water	18 mph (29 km/h)
Cruising speed, calm water	18 mph (29 km/h)
Max wave capability	6 in approx (153 mm)
Still air range	35 miles approx (56 km)
Max gradient, static conditions	5° approx

Vertical obstacle clearance 5 in (127 mm)

For full over-the-hump performance with an operator weighing more than 175 lb the installation of two power plants is recommended each identical with the standard single power unit. With an operator weighing up to 225 lb the speed of the twin is approx 20% greater than the standard single engine.

With the overall length of the twin-engine model increased to 11 ft 2 in, it will carry a useful load of 350 lb at maximum speeds of approximately 35 mph over smooth land and 22 mph over calm water.

Price: USA, f.o.b. Severna Park, Maryland:

$1,200·00 for complete vehicle
$595 for kit
Terms of payment 50% down

UNITED STATES HOVERCRAFT MANU-FACTURING CO

HEAD OFFICE:
PO Box 1191, Lynnwood, Washington 98036

TELEPHONE:
(206) 743-3669

OFFICERS:
Gerald W. Crisman, President

A. J. Doug Nunally, Vice President
Edward J. Birney
Michael S. Curtis, Secretary
William D. Crisman, Financial Adviser

Gemco Inc has designed and built a number of light and ultra-light craft, including the first to cross the Mississippi (in 1959).

The company is now concentrating on the development of a new two-seat sports vehicle. the 4/5 seat Eagle, the prototype of which is under construction; two passenger ferries, one for 10-11 passengers the other for thirty, and the Alaskan, a utility vehicle with a payload capacity of 10-12 tons.

UNIVERSAL HOVERCRAFT

HEAD OFFICE:
1204 3rd Street, Box 281, Cordova, Ill. 61242

TELEPHONE:
1-309-654-2588

DIRECTOR:
R. J. Windt

Formed in 1969, this company has designed and built twenty-five different sports and utility ACV prototypes, ranging from an ultra-light single-seater to a seven-seater powered by a 100 hp automotive engine. Plans for some of these designs are available to home builders. This company is currently developing three new single-engined amphibious craft—a 12 ft (3·65 m) two-seater, a 13 ft (3·96 m) four-seater and an 18 ft (5·48 m) six-seater.

Work has also been undertaken on ACVs powered by waterscrews, waterjets and sails.

The company is currently developing three different single-engine amphibious craft—an 11 ft two-seater, a 13 ft four-seater and a 16 ft six-seater. Work has also been undertaken on air cushion vehicles propelled by waterjets, outboard motors and sails.

UH-10

This single-seat amphibious runabout was one of the company's earliest designs. Construction of the prototype was completed in November 1969. The vehicle, which is of wooden construction, attains 27 mph (43·45 km/h) over land and 22 mph (35·40 km/h) over water.

LIFT AND PROPULSION: Integrated system employing a single McCulloch 101 2-cycle 116 cc engine, which drives a 1 ft 9 in (0·53 m) diameter, 12-bladed centrifugal fan mounted vertically on a shaft inside a transverse duct Air is drawn by the fan from each end of the duct. Propulsion air is expelled through an outlet nozzle aft and lift air is ducted into a plenum below. Maximum thrust is 32 lb (14·51 kg).

HULL: Frame is built from fir ribs and stringers and covered with ⅛ in ply.

ACCOMMODATION: Open cockpit with seat for driver. Craft will carry one person

UH-10, an amphibious single-seater powered by single McCulloch 101 2-cycle 116 cc engine

or a load of up to 170 lb (79·35 kg) over water, and up to 225 lb (102·05 kg) over land.

CONTROLS: Multiple rudders in the thrust air outlet provide directional control.

DIMENSIONS:

Length	10 ft 4 in (3·14 m)
Beam	6 ft 0 in (1·82 m)
Height, off cushion	2 ft 6 in (0·76 m)

WEIGHTS:

Weight empty	135 lb (61·23 kg)
Normal loaded weight	310 lb (140·14 kg)
Max loaded weight	360 lb (163·28 kg)

PERFORMANCE:

Max speed:

Over land	27 mph (43·45 km/h)
Over water	22 mph (35·40 km/h)
Max gradient	10%

PRICE: Complete set of plans for home-building, US$6·00.

UH-11

An ultra-light runabout of wooden construction, the UH-11 seats two and has a

top speed of 35 mph (56·32 km/h).

LIFT AND PROPULSION: Integrated system employing a single JLO 2-cycle, 230 cc engine, which drives a 2 ft 0 in (0·61 m) diameter, 4-bladed fan for lift and a 4 ft 0 in (1·21 m) 2-bladed fan for propulsion. Power is transmitted to the lift fan direct and to the propulsion fan through a reduction ratio belt drive.

HULL: Structure built with fir ribs and stringers and covered in ⅛ in (3·17 mm) ply.

ACCOMMODATION: Enclosed cabin with tandem seating for driver and passenger.

CONTROLS: Large single rudder hinged to the rear of the propeller guard, provides directional control.

DIMENSIONS:

Length	11·5 ft (3·48 m)
Width	5·5 ft (1·65 m)
Height (off cushion)	4·5 ft (1·37 m)

WEIGHTS:

Weight empty	175 lb (79 kg)

Normal payload   225 lb (102 kg)
Max payload   325 lb (147 kg)

PERFORMANCE:
Max speed:
over land   35 mph (56·32 km/h)
over water   30 mph (48·28 km/h)
Max gradient   16%

PRICE: Complete plans US$10.00.

UH-12S

This lightweight two-seater is capable of carrying two adults and their camping or fishing equipment at up to 35 mph (56·32 km/h) over water.

LIFT AND PROPULSION: A single JLO 340 or 440 engine drives the lift fan and the thrust propeller via a v-belt system. The 2 ft 2 in (0·66 m) diameter fan turns at a maximum of 3,500 rpm, while the 4 ft (1·21 m) diameter thrust propeller turns at 220 rpm at full throttle.

HULL: Construction is of fir ribs and stringers and ⅛ in plywood covering. Fibreglass applied to all joints and edges.

ACCOMMODATION: Tandem arrangement with passenger seated behind driver on a sliding seat.

CONTROLS: Single aerodynamic rudder behind the propeller provides directional control.

DIMENSIONS:
Length   12·8 ft (3·91 m)
Width   6·0 ft (1·82 m)
Height   5·0 ft (1·52 m)

WEIGHTS:
Empty   275 lb (124·73 kg)
Normal payload   350 lb (150·75 kg)
Max payload   450 lb (204·10 kg)

PERFORMANCE:
Max speed:
over land   45 mph (72·42 km/h)
over water   35 mph (56·32 km/h)
Gradient at 450 lb gross weight   23%

PRICE AND TERMS: US$14.00

UH-12T

This amphibious two-seater is based on the company's original prototype which was built early in 1969. The new hull is easier to build and provides automatic pitch control. As thrust is increased, the aerofoil-shaped hull generates more lift, offsetting the pitching moment caused by thrust. The height of the centre of thrust has also been reduced.

LIFT AND PROPULSION: Motive power for the lift system is provided by 133 cc Chrysler 2-cycle petrol engine which drives a 2 ft 2 in diameter (0·66 m) 4-bladed fan at 4,500 rpm. About 5% of the cushion air is employed to inflate the bag-type skirt. Thrust is provided by a 25 hp JLO 395 2-cycle engine driving a 3 ft 0 in (0·914 m) diameter 2-bladed propeller.

HULL: Mixed wood and fibreglass construction. Structure comprises fir ribs and stringers covered with ⅛in plywood. Cockpit floor and other highly stressed areas strengthened with fibreglass.

CONTROLS: Directional control is provided by a single aerodynamic rudder.

ACCOMMODATION: Single bench seat for driver and one passenger. Cockpit canopy can be fitted for use in cold weather.

DIMENSIONS:
Length overall   12 ft 6 in (3·81 m)
Beam overall   6 ft 0 in (1·82 m)

WEIGHTS:
Empty weight   275 lb (124·73 kg)
All-up weight   600 lb (272·14 kg)

PERFORMANCE:
Max speed:
over land   45 mph (72·5 km/h)
over water   40 mph (64·37 km/h)

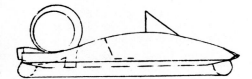
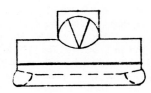
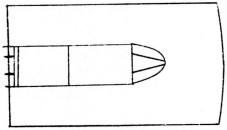

General arrangement of the UH-10 light ACV runabout.

UH-11, a two-seater powered by a single 230 cc JLO 2-cycle engine

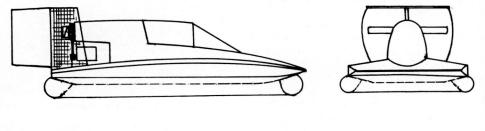
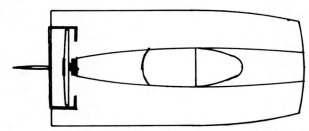

UH-12S a lightweight two-seater for two adults and their camping or fishing equipment

Max gradient   26%
PRICE AND TERMS: Plans US$15·00 per set.

UH-13S

The prototype of this craft was built in 1974 from 1 in (25 mm) thick urethane foam fibreglass laminate. This type of construction proved too difficult for the home builder and so the craft was redesigned for wooden construction. An integrated lift/propulsion system is employed. Once engine speed is above idling the correct amount of lift is automatically maintained throughout the entire engine speed range by a patented system.

LIFT AND PROPULSION: Motive power is provided by a single JLO 440 driving a 2 ft 1 in (0·63 m) diameter four-bladed lift fan and a 4 ft (1·21 m) diameter propeller via a v-belt reduction drive.

HULL: Construction is similar to that of UH-12T.

ACCOMMODATION: Two adults and two children can be carried in two bench-type seats.

CONTROLS: Craft heading is controlled by twin rudders behind the propeller.

DIMENSIONS:

Length	13·9 ft (4·21 m)
Width	6·5 ft (1·98 m)

WEIGHTS:

Empty	350 lb (158·75 kg)
Normal payload	400 lb (181·42 kg)
Max payload	600 lb (272·14 kg)

PERFORMANCE:

Max speed:	
over land, snow, ice	55 mph (88·51 km/h)
over water	45 mph (72·42 km/h)
Max Gradient	26%

PRICE AND TERMS: Complete plans, US$17.00

UH-14B

An amphibious 4-seater, the UH-14B has a maximum payload capacity of over 800 lbs (362·85 kg). Employment of a large slow-turning propeller for thrust permits high-speed cruising while generating very little noise.

LIFT AND PROPULSION: A JLO 230 2-cycle engine turns a four-bladed fan for lift. Thrust is supplied by a JLO 440 2-cycle engine driving a 4 ft (1·21 m) diameter propeller through a v-belt speed reduction system.

HULL: Construction is of fir or pine ribs and stringers, which are covered with ⅛ in plywood.

CONTROLS: Heading is controlled by a large aerodynamic rudder aft of the propeller.

DIMENSIONS:

Length	14·5 ft (4·41 m)
Width	7·0 ft (2·13 m)
Height off cushion	5 ft (1·52 m)

WEIGHTS:

Empty	450 lb (204 kg)
Normal payload	500 lb (226·78 kg)
Max payload	800 lb (362·85 kg)

PERFORMANCE:

Max speed:	
over land, snow, ice	55 mph (88·51 km/h)
over water	50 mph (80·46 km/h)
max gradient at 650 lb gross weight	28%

PRICE AND TERMS: Complete plans US$21.00

UH-14T

The UH-14T is a utility two-seater with a cargo hold aft of its bench-type seat. This space may also be used for a rearward facing seat. Total payload capacity is 700 lb (317·50 kg).

LIFT AND PROPULSION: Lift air is supied by a McCulloch 101 123 cc or a JLO 230 cc engine driving a four-bladed 2 ft 2 in (0·660 m) diameter fan. A JLO 440 engine driving a 3 ft 0 in (0·914 m) diameter two-bladed propeller provides thrust.

HULL: Construction is similar to that of the UH-12T.

CONTROLS: Large aerodynamic rudder at rear of propellers controls craft heading.

DIMENSIONS:

Length	14·0 ft (4·26 m)
Width	6·5 ft (1·98 m)
Height off cushion	4·0 ft (1·22 m)

WEIGHTS:

Empty	400 lb (181·42 kg)
Normal payload	500 lb (226·78 kg)
Max payload	700 lb (317·50 kg)

PERFORMANCE:

Max Speed:	
over land, snow, ice	55 mph (88·51 km/h)

UH-13S, a derivative of the UH-12, originally designed for construction in urethane foam/fibreglass sandwich. Top speed over land is 55 mph (88.51 km/h)

UH-12T, a 45 mph (72.5 km/h) amphibious two-seater, powered by a single 133 cc Chrysler 2-cycle petrol engine

UH-14B, a 4-seater with a maximum payload capacity of 800 lbs (362·85 kg)

over water   45 mph (72·42 km/h)
max gradient at 600 lb (272·14 kg) gross
weight   22%
PRICE AND TERMS: Complete plans,
US$20.00

UH-17S

Construction of the prototype UH-17S,
which has an integrated lift/propulsion system powered by either a Volkswagen or
Corvair engine of 50-140 hp, was completed
in May 1970. The craft, which seats a driver
and up to three passengers, is said to be
extremely quiet and control is precise. It
is capable of towing water or snow skier,
sleds or ski boards.

LIFT AND PROPULSION: A single 75 hp
Corvair automobile engine drives a 3 ft 6 in
(1·06 m) diameter centrifugal fan mounted
vertically on a shaft inside a transverse duct.
Air is drawn by the fan from each end of the
duct. Propulsion air is expelled through
outlets at the stern and lift air is ducted into
a plenum below. The fan feeds air into the
cushion at 240 cfs and provides 150 lb thrust.

ACCOMMODATION: Enclosed cabin seating
driver and up to three passengers on two
bench-type seats.

DIMENSIONS:
Length   17 ft 10 in (5·43 m)
Beam   7 ft 11 in (2·41 m)
WEIGHTS:
Empty weight   950 lb (430·89 kg)
Normal loaded weight 1,600 lb (725·71 kg)
Max loaded weight   1,900 lb (861·78 kg)
PERFORMANCE:
Max speed:
over land   42 mph (67·59 km/h)
over water   35-40 mph (65·64 km/h)
Continuous gradient at 1,200 lb   12%

No plans available.

UH-18S

This craft accommodates up to nine persons
on three bench-type seats. Normal payload
is 1,200 lbs. An automatic lift system
similar to that used on the UH-13S is employed to simplify driving, improve reliability
and decrease maintenance costs.

LIFT AND PROPULSION: Motive power is
supplied by a single Corvair automotive
engine, rated at 85 hp at 3,600 rpm, driving
a 3 ft 0 in (0·914 m) diameter four-bladed
fan for lift via the automatic lift system, and
a 6 ft 2 in (1·87 m) diameter two-bladed
propeller through a v-belt speed reduction
system. The lift fan turns at a constant
2,400 rpm while the propeller turns 1,700
rpm at full throttle.

HULL: Construction is similar to that of
the UH-18T.

CONTROLS: Heading is controlled by triple
aerodynamic rudders located behind the
propeller.

DIMENSIONS:
Length   18·8 ft (5·74 m)
Width   8·0 ft (2·43 m)
Height   6·0 ft (1·82 m)
WEIGHTS:
Empty   1,100 lb (498·92 kg)
Normal payload   1,200 lb (544·28 kg)
Max payload   1,400 lb (635·00 kg)
PERFORMANCE:
Max Speed:
over land, snow, ice 60 mph (96·56 km/h)
over water   55 mph (88·51 km/h)
PRICES AND TERMS: Complete plans,
US$26.00

UH-14T utility two-seater with a total payload capacity of 700 lb (317·50 kg)

A feature of the UH-17S is the integrated lift/propulsion system powered by a 75 hp automobile engine

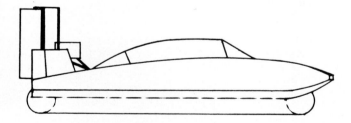

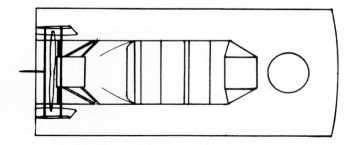
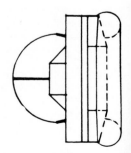

Universal Hovercraft UH-18T, a six seater of mixed wood and grp construction. Propulsive
thrust is supplied by an 85 hp Corvair engine driving a 5 ft 0 in (1·52 m) diameter 2-bladed propeller

Top left and right and bottom left: Universal Hovercraft UH-18S showing its paces off Redondo Beach, California. A nine-seater powered by a single 85 hp Corvair automotive engine, it can tow two water skiers at a time and is capable of operating in the surf zone. *Bottom right:* The UH-18T light utility hovercraft

UH-18T

The prototype of this amphibious six-seater was built in 1971 and has accumulated over 400 operating hours, mainly on open seas.

It was the first hovercraft to visit Catalina island, 26 miles (41·84 km) off the coast of California and the first to complete the journey from Los Angeles to San Diego 105 miles (168·98 km) across open seas. It has also been employed extensively for water and snow skiing.

The aerofoil shaped hull is similar to that of the UH-12T and UH-14T.

LIFT AND PROPULSION: Lift is provided by a 25 hp JLO 395 2-cycle engine driving a 2 ft 6 in diameter 4-bladed fan at 3,200 rpm. About 5% of the air is employed to inflate the bag skirt. Propulsive thrust is supplied by an 85 hp Corvair automobile engine driving

a 5 ft 0 in (1·52 m) diameter 2-bladed propeller at up to 2,800 rpm.

SKIRT: 1 ft 6 in (0·46 m) diameter bag skirt, providing 1 ft 0 in (0·304 m) vertical clearance.

HULL: Mixed wood and grp construction. Hull frame is built from fir ribs and stringers and covered with ¼ in ply. Highly stressed areas covered with glass fibre.

ACCOMMODATION: Driver and up to five passengers seated on two 3-place bench seats. Cabin can be enclosed by canopy in cold weather.

CONTROLS: Craft heading is controlled by a single rudder operating in the propeller slipstream and two auxiliary rudders hinged to the rear of twin fins, one each side of the propeller guard. All three rudders are

operated by a steering wheel. Separate throttle provided for lift and thrust engines.

DIMENSIONS:

Length	18 ft 3 in (5·56 m)
Beam	8 ft 0 in (2·43 m)
Height, off cushion	6 ft 0 in (1·82 m)
on cushion	7 ft 0 in (2·13 m)

WEIGHTS:

Empty weight	1,000 lb (453·57 kg)
Normal loaded	2,000 lb (907·14 kg)
Max loaded	2,400 lb (1,088 kg)

PERFORMANCE:

Max speed:	
over land	70 mph (112·65 km/h)
over water	60 mph (96·56 km/h)
Max gradient	31%

PRICE:

Complete set of plans for homebuilding, US $25·00.

WATER RESEARCH COMPANY

HEAD OFFICE:
3003 North Central Avenue, Suite 600 Phoenix, Arizona 85012

TELEPHONE:
602 265-7722

EXECUTIVES:
Richard R. Greer, President
Dr. John H. McMasters, Chief Engineer
(Members of American Society of Naval Engineers)

The Water Research Company was formed in 1972 to consolidate activities surrounding the patents held or applied for by Richard R. Greer relating to various aspects of water-borne vehicles. The company has subsequently prepared conceptual studies on a class of winged surface effect vessels (WSEV) intended to fill a variety of US Navy and commercial freight applications. The conclusions of this study were published in Naval Engineer's Journal, April 1974, and

further comprehensive conclusions also setting forth energy savings and use of alternate fuels were published in the Jane's Surface Skimmers 1975-76 edition. The company is able to undertake analytical studies on hydrofoil, SES and WIG systems, and can provide contract co-ordination services for such systems. Present efforts are directed to providing assistance in related research activities and further research studies.

THE UNION OF SOVIET SOCIALIST REPUBLICS

CENTRAL LABORATORY OF LIFESAVING TECHNOLOGY

HEAD OFFICE: Moscow

EXECUTIVES:
Yury Makarov, Chief Engineer
A. V. Gremyatskiy, Designer
Yevgeniy P. Grunin, Designer
N. L. Ivanov, Designer
S. Chernyavskiy
Y. Gorbenko

CONSULTANT:
V. Shavrov

DIRECTOR OF FLIGHT TRIALS:
A. Baluyev

The Central Laboratory of Rescue Techniques, a division of OSVOD—the Rescue Organisation for Inland Waters—has designed a small aerodynamic ram-wing machine, capable of 75 mph (120 km/h), which will be used to answer distress calls on the Soviet lakes, rivers and canals. The vehicle, which is available in several versions, is the Eska—an abbreviation of Ekranolyetny Spasatyelny Kater-Amphibya (Surface-effect Amphibious Lifeboat). It has also been referred to as the Ekranolet and the Nizkolet (skimmer).

Apart from meeting emergency situations on waterways, the craft, which is amphibious, is capable of operating in deserts, tundra, arctic icefields and steppeland. Derivatives are to be employed as support vehicles for geologists, communications engineers and construction groups.

In Russian publications emphasis has been given to the potential value of such craft in opening up the mineral wealth of Siberia, the Soviet Far East, Far North and other virgin territories.

As with the X 113 Am and other machines of this type, the vehicle operates on the principle that by flying in close proximity to the ground, the so-called image flow reduces drag by about 70%. Whereas an average aircraft at normal flight altitude carries about 9 lb (4 kg) per hp of engine output, the wing-in-ground effect machine, on its dynamic air-cushion carries up to 44 lb (20 kg), an improvement of more than 400%. Weight efficiency of the craft (ratio of useful load to all-up weight), is 48·9%.

At angles of attack of 2-8 degrees near the ground, its lift is 40·45% greater than when flying out of ground effect. In addition the supporting surface hinders the vortex flow from the lower wing surface to the upper surface which decreases induction drag.

Control of the Eska is said to be easy and pilots require no special training. Within ground effect it is no more complicated to control than a car.

The design, which has been strongly influenced by the Lippisch "aerofoil boat" concept, employs an almost identical short span, low aspect ratio reversed delta wing with anhedral on the leading edge, dihedral tips and wing floats. Preliminary details are given below.

ESKA-1

Designed initially as an amphibious high-speed rescue craft for use on Russia's inland waterways, the Eska has been developed into a general utility vehicle with a wide range of applications in underdeveloped areas.

Eska-1 completed its first flight on August 29th 1973, over the Klyazminskoye reservoir, carrying a pilot, passenger and an additional load. It took off at 74·5 mph (120 km/h)

Eska variant employed as a research craft by the Soviet Ministry of Inland Waterways. The replacement of wingtip floats by spring skids and the low-set tailplane suggest that the craft has a wheel undercarriage and is land based

Above: The Eska-1 has been strongly influenced by the Lippisch "Aerofoil boat" concept, and employs an anhedral, reversed delta wing, dihedral tips and wing floats.
Below: Maximum effective flying height in ground effect is 1 ft-5 ft (0·3-1·5 m). The vehicle, a two-seat aerodynamic ram-wing, is employed as an experimental, high-speed rescue and liaison craft on Russian inland waterways.

after a run of 87-100 yards (80-100 m) and flew for several minutes at between 60-90 ft (20-30 m), before descending to make a low level pass across sandy spits and banks and forcing its way through the thickets and reeds of an islet. After climbing to avoid a launch coming to meet it, it landed and taxied out of the water onto a gently sloping bank.

The youthful design group responsible for the Eska-1 took two years to study world experience of ramwing and aerodynamic ram-wing construction, after which a series of small-scale models were built, followed by the construction and test of five different full-size craft.

Three prototypes similar to Eska-1 had been built by mid-February 1974. Two other models, one with fabric-covered flying surfaces and rear hull, the other a four seater, were reported under construction in March 1974. Variants with greater seating capacity and more powerful engines are being developed, also land-based non-amphibious models.

POWER PLANT: Single 30 hp M-63 motorcycle engine, on tripod dorsal mounting aft of cockpit, drives via shafting a two-bladed fixed-pitch propeller.

CONSTRUCTION: Forward hull design based on that of two-seat sports boat. Corrosion resistant aluminium alloy construction employed for first three craft. Heavy fabric covering employed on wings inboard of tips and hull aft of crew compartment on one later model.

CONTROLS: Single aircraft-type control stick, incorporating engine throttle, located in the centre of the cockpit. Conventional foot-operated bar to control rudder.

ACCOMMODATION: Enclosed cabin for two, seated side-by-side. Access is via hinged hood. Initial arrangement is for rescuer/pilot, with one seat available for the person being rescued. Three and four seat models are under development.

DIMENSIONS:
Wing span overall	22 ft 5⅜ in (6·9 m)
Length	24 ft 7 in (7·55 m)
Height	8 ft 2½ in (2·5 m)
Wing area	148·13 sq ft (13·85 m²)
Tail area	32·4 sq ft (3 m²)

WEIGHTS:
All-up weight	992 lb (450 kg)
Empty weight	507 lb (230 kg)
Useful load	485 lb (220 kg)
Weight efficiency	48·9%

PERFORMANCE:
Max speed with full load in ground effect	75·80 mph (122 km/h)
Cruising speed	68·35 mph (110 km/h)
Take-off speed	34·17 mph (55 km/h)
Landing speed	31·34 mph (50·55 km/h)
Take-off run from water	87-109 yards (80-100 m)
Take-off run from snow	54-65 yards (50-60 m)
Landing run on water (without braking parachute)	43·74 yards (40 m)
Most effective flying height in surface effect	1 ft -4 ft 11 in (0·3-1·5 m)
Max altitude, with 50% load, for obstacle clearance	up to 164 ft (50 m)
Range with full fuel supply	186-217 miles (300-350 km)
Wing loading	(32·5 kg/m²)
Power loading	33 lb/hp (15 kg/hp)

Limiting weather conditions—can operate in force 5 winds

PARAWING EKRANOPLANS

The originator of the idea of applying Rogallo-type flexible delta wings to light ekranoplans is Yevgeniy Grunin, one of the designers of the Eska-1. The parawing is well known for its outstanding aerodynamic qualities and stability and is convenient for transport and storage. Grunin, assisted by S. Chernyavskiy and N. Ivanov, fitted a flexible wing to the fuselage of the Czechoslovakian Let L-13J Blanik, a powered version of the well known two-seat, all-metal sailplane. Power is supplied by a 42 hp Jawa M-150 piston-engine driving a 3 ft 7¼ in (1·10 m) diameter Avia V210 propeller on a tripod mounted aft of the cockpit, an

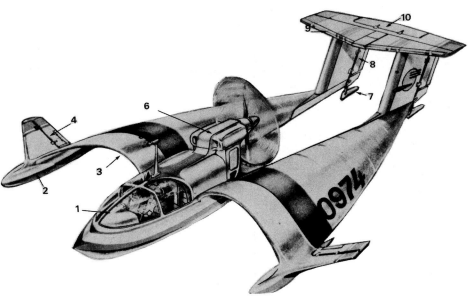

Twin-boom parawing ekranoplan concept. 1. cabin; 2. float; 3. split parawing; 4. aileron; 5. pressure head; 6. powerplant; 7. hydrodynamic rudder; 8. aerodynamic rudder; 10. elevator

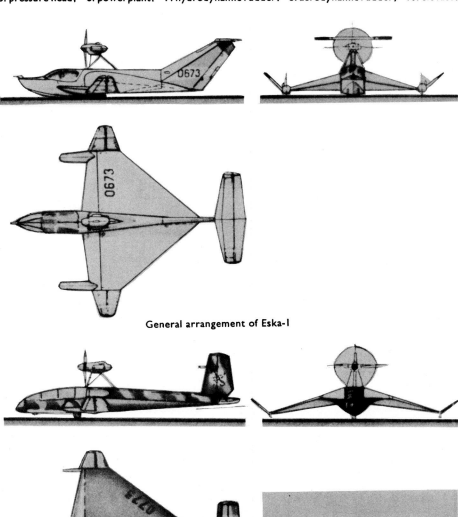

General arrangement of Eska-1

General arrangement of the Shmel, a modified Let L-13J Blanik powered glider fitted with a parawing

arrangement almost identical to that employed on Eska-1. Profiting from the encouraging results of the flight trials, the team has designed a number of small ekranoplan projects incorporating flexible wings, including a modified version of the An-2V, the floatplane version of the Antanov An-2, single-engine general-purpose biplane, still widely employed throughout the Soviet Union. The nature of the modifications can be seen in the accompanying sketch. Realisation of the project would give the 27-year-old design a completely new lease of life and provide a substantial aid to communications in underdeveloped areas for a relatively low investment.

Parawing derivative of the Eska-1

Project for adapting the Antonov An-2V
to a parawing ekranoplan configuration

KHARKOV AVIATION INSTITUTE
ADDRESS: Kharkov

In August 1973, it was reported in Pravda that the Institute of Aviation, Kharkov, had built two amphibious ACVs. At the same time, it was mentioned that ACV research and development was being undertaken at forty national enterprises, in Moscow, Tomsk, Gorki, Gorlovka, Ufa and Volgograd.

KRASNOYE SORMOVO
ADDRESS:
Gorky

This shipyard began work in the ACV field by building a five-passenger air cushion river craft known as the Raduga in 1960-61. Since then it has built the Sormovich, a 30-ton peripheral jet ACV for 50 passengers, the Neva, a plenum-chambered type craft seating 38 and the Gorkovchanin, a 48-seat sidewall craft for shallow, winding rivers.

The latter is now in service on a number of rivers, together with a derivative, the Zarnitsa.

The design of an 80-seat rigid sidewall ferry, the Orion, was approved by the Soviet Ministry of Inland Waterways in 1970. Construction of the prototype began in 1972 and a trial operation began in 1975. The craft, bearing the serial number 01, operated a service connecting Kalinin with towns and villages on the shores of the river Soz.

Preliminary details of an off-shore sidewall vessel, the Rassvet (Dawn) have been announced. Rassvet is similar in general design to the Zarnitsa, but is designed to transport up to 80 passengers along local sea routes.

Like the Zarnitsa, the vessel will be able to run bow-on to flat, sloping beaches and does not require piers or specially prepared moorings.

A third new passenger ferry ACV is the Chayka, which is destined for series production at Sosnovska and will operate between resorts in the Crimea and Caucasus.

In 1969, prototypes of two new fully skirted hovercraft made their debut, the Breeze, a light utility craft, and the Skate, a 50-seat passenger ferry with an all-up weight of 27 tons and a cruising speed of 57·5 mph. Military versions of the Skate, known in the West as Gus, are now in production in addition to the passenger ferry model. Development of the Skate and its naval and army counterparts is believed to have been undertaken in conjunction with the Leningrad Institute of Marine Engineers, also thought to be responsible for the design and construction of the Soviet Union's biggest skirted hovercraft, known in the West as Aist, which is generally similar in shape, size and performance to the SR.N4. The vessel, which is in service with the Soviet Navy as an assault landing craft, is illustrated in this section.

A smaller but similar AALC, capable of carrying supplies and equipment up to the size of a battle tank, is also believed to be in service.

The Sormovo yard is likely to have been responsible for building of the world's largest air cushion vehicle—a wing-in-ground effect machine capable of carrying 800-900 troops at speeds up to 300 knots. In April 1972 it was announced that plans were in hand to build wing-in-ground effect machines capable of navigating rivers at a speed of about 155 mph (250 km/h). A number of these craft are understood to be in experimental service.

220-TON NAVAL ACV
NATO Code Name: "AIST"

"Aist" the first large Soviet amphibious hovercraft, is entering service in small numbers with the Soviet Navy. Built in Leningrad, it is similar in appearance to the SR.N4 Mk. II Mountbatten though probably heavier by some 20 tons and 20 ft (6·09 m) longer (150 ft compared with 130 ft).

Since delivery to the Soviet Navy, the vessels of this type have been employed mainly as a medium-short range, heavy logistic craft, delivering mechanised infantry and tanks to simulated beach heads. In a TV film commemorating the 30th Anniversary of the ending of the 'Great Patriotic War' (World War II) a number of new weapons and forms of transportation in use by the Soviet armed forces were presented, among them an Aist and two Gus air-cushion assault landing craft.

While the latter unloaded part of an assault wave of Soviet marine infantry. Aist lowered its bow loading door/ramp to land a T-62 main battle tank. Alternative military uses for amphibious craft of the Aist type would be mine countermeasures, ASW and missile craft and open sea fast patrol.

LIFT AND PROPULSION: Motive power is thought to be supplied by six gas-turbines driving four centrifugal lift fans and four identical, pylon-mounted propeller units, arranged in facing pairs, with one pusher propeller and one puller propeller port and starboard. The pylons are in the form of an 'A' with the vertical drive shaft from the propulsion engine to the bevel drive gearbox above located in the centre. Each propeller has variable and reversible pitch, negative pitch being applied for braking and reversing.

Intakes for the four 11 ft 6 in (3·5 m) centrifugal lift fans are located in the top of the superstructure, two port and two starboard, forward of the propeller units.

CONTROLS: Craft direction is controlled by twin aerodynamic rudders and differential propeller pitch. Negative pitch is applied for braking and reversing.

HULL: Built mainly in marine corrosion resistant aluminium alloys. Structure appears to follow standard practice for large amphibious ACVs. The main hull is formed by a buoyancy raft based on a grid of longitudianl and transverse frames which form a number of flotation compartments. Two main longitudinal vertically stiffened bulkheads run the length of the craft, separating the central load deck from the outer or sidestructures, which contain the gas-turbines and their associated air intakes, exhausts, lift fans, transmissions and auxiliary power system.

A full-width ramp is provided at the bow and a second at the stern providing through loading facilities.

The angled temporary structure above the longitudinal centreline appears to have been provided to accommodate battlefield missiles on their heavy duty transporters. Unlike tanks, which require less headroom, the missile transporters would have to back out through the rear.

A large wheelhouse is located well forward, above the superstructure, with a twin 30 mm naval mounting above.

SKIRT: Fingered bag type with extremely high hinge line at the bow.

DIMENSIONS:
Length overall	150 ft 0 in (45·72 m)
Beam overall	60 ft 0 in (18·28 m)

WEIGHTS:
All-up weight	220 tons

PERFORMANCE:
Max speed	About 70 knots

AALC

A new air-cushion assault landing craft is believed to be undergoing evaluation. The vehicle is smaller but similar in overall

Above and below: Aist, a 220-ton amphibious assault landing craft operated by the Soviet Navy. Note the high skirt line to protect the bow door against wave impact and the pusher-puller arrangement of the pylon-mounted propellers. Above the control cabin is a twin 30 mm fully-automatic AA mounting

configuration to Aist. Like Aist, it is capable of carrying a T62 or T70 main battle tank.

BREEZE

This interesting light amphibious ACV has external features which are reminiscent of the Vickers VA-2 and VA-3.

It was developed by a design group led by German Koronatov, a graduate of the Leningrad Shipbuilding Institute and was completed in 1968. The craft was built to enable the problems of operating a lightweight hovercraft to be understood more clearly

and to help assess its economic viability.

The design incorporates the cabin and propulsion system of the Kamov KA-30 Aerosled. Its basic dimensions were dictated partly by the requirement that it should be transportable by rail and trailer.

Trials began during the first half of 1969, during which speed and manoeuvrability tests were conducted over water, snow and ice. Instrumentation was installed in the passenger saloon. In calm water, against a 1-2 metre per second wind, the measured speed was 43·5 mph (70 km/h). In similar conditions across ice, the speed was 57 mph (82 km/h). During winter trials the craft operated over snow 1 ft 8 in (50 cm) deep and shrubs 3 ft 3 in (1 m) high. On the river Neva, when the ice was moving, Briz travelled at 37 mph (60 km/h) across the icefloes.

In August 1973, extensive trials were undertaken on the rivers and lakes of the Carolia Isthmus and on the basin's of the Neva and Ladoga. Briz was transported on a trailer to the Burna estuary and made its way to the source. It also negotiated the Lozevsk rapids and continued on up the river Vuoks until it reached the famous waterfall. It negotiated this, also, then returned to the Burna estuary according to plan. During this endurance test, the craft successfully navigated blocked rivers, stony banks, rapids and raging torrents.

The next series of trials took place in a very busy shipping area, across Lake Lagoda to the Neva and thence back to Leningrad During this phase, the Briz completed a distance of 1,000 km (621 miles.) According to the Soviet authorities, the experience gained with Briz confirmed that craft of this type may well have great economic potential.

LIFT AND PROPULSION: Thrust is provided by a 220 hp AI-14RS radial piston engine, driving an AV-59 three-bladed metal, controllable and reversible-pitch propeller. Lift is supplied by two 33 hp Moskvich MZMA-407 automobile engines mounted aft on the sidestructures, one port and one starboard, each driving a set of four (400 mm) diameter axial fans mounted on a cardan shaft. The fans are of welded light alloy construction. Cushion pressure is 150 kg/m².

The thrust engine drives a 1·5 kw, 27 volt dc generator, type GSK-1500. The lift engines drive a 0·2 kw, 12 volt generator each. The circuitry enables the GSK-1500 to work in parallel with two GST 54 batteries connected in series.

CONTROLS: Directional control over most of the speed range is provided by twin aerodynamic rudders operating in the slipstream. Low speed control is assisted by thrust ports fore and aft. Braking and reversing is achieved by reversed propeller pitch.

HULL: Riveted, pontoon-type structure in corrosion resistant V84-4 light alloy. Engine mountings, strengthening members in the hull base and landing pads are in welded AlMg-5 alloy. Hull is divided by four transverse and two longitudinal bulkheads into eight watertight compartments for buoyancy.

SKIRT: Fingered bag type in rubberised fabric. Longitudinal keel and awthwartship stability bags for pitch and roll stiffness. Skirt and fingers easily replaceable.

ACCOMMODATION: Fully enclosed cabin, seating operator and six passengers. If required, seating in the passenger saloon can be removed for transporting cargo.

General arrangement of the Aist 220-ton—amphibious ACV

Aist, with its bow loading door/ramp lowered, lands a T62 main battle tank. Height of the tank, which is 2.40 m lends scale to the size of the bow door

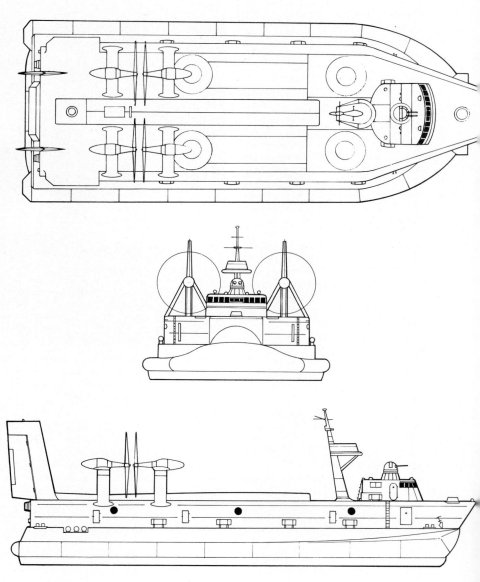

DIMENSIONS:
Length overall, cushionborne.

	27 ft 6 in (8·4¾ m)
Hull length	25 ft 7 in (7·8⅛ m)
Beam overall	13 ft 5 in (4·1 m)
Height overall, cushionborne	
	9 ft 10⅛ in (3·0 m)
Draft, displacement condition	
	11¾ in (0·3 m)
Skirt depth	1 ft 3¾ in (0·4 m)

WEIGHTS:
All-up weight   6,835 lbs (3,100 kg)

PERFORMANCE:
Max speed over land and water
                        62 mph (100 km/h)

CHAYKA-1

News of the existence of the 80-seat Chayka-1 ACV passenger ferry was given in Moscow for the first time on December 13th, 1974. The vehicle is the first of a series of thirty air cushion vehicles of this type being built at the Sosnovskiy shipbuilding yard in Kirovskaya Oblast for the Black Sea Shipping Line.

It was reported in January 1976 that the vessel was the first seagoing passenger ferry ACV to be built in the Soviet Union and that trials of the prototype had been completed.

The Chayka-1 will operate between resorts in the Crimea and Caucasus.

GORKOVCHANIN

The Gorkovchanin is a waterjet-propelled, 48-seat, rigid sidewall ACV, designed for water-bus services on secondary rivers with a guaranteed depth of 1 ft 8 in (0·5 m). In view of the winding nature of these rivers, the craft operates at the relatively low speed of 19-22 mph (30-35 km/h). No marked reduction of speed is necessary in water up to 1 ft 8 in (50 cm) deep.

The craft has been developed from a ten seat scale model built at the experimental yard of the Institute of Water Transport Engineers at Gorky in 1963, and the pre-production prototype was completed in September 1968. Design was undertaken by a team at the Volgobaltsudoproekt special design office.

Preliminary trials were conducted in September and October 1968, and official trials were completed on the Sura river in May and June 1969. During speed tests over a measured mile with a full complement of passengers aboard, 22·75 mph (36·6 km/h) was attained. The main engine developed 265 hp of which approximately 30 hp was used to drive the centrifugal fan.

The craft has covered the journey from Gorky to Moscow (622 miles (1,016 km)) and back in 31 and 27 running hours respectively at an average speed of approximately 22 mph (35 km/h) and has good manoeuvrability when running both ahead and astern. The craft is in production and large numbers are in service. The type is now being superseded by an improved model, the Zarnitsa.

LIFT AND PROPULSION: Integrated system powered by a 3D6H diesel engine rated at 250 hp continuous. The engine is mounted aft and drives a 3 ft 1¾ in (960 mm) diameter six-bladed centrifugal fan for lift, and a 1 ft 4½ in (410 mm) diameter single stage water-jet rotor for propulsion. Fan air is taken directly from the engine compartment. Skirts of rubberised fabric are fitted fore and aft. The bow skirt of production craft is of segmented type. Cushion pressure is 180 kg/cm².

Top: The Breeze light amphibious ACV for ten-passengers. Thrust is supplied by a radial aircraft engine driving a 3-bladed airscrew, and lift by twin Moskvich 407 automotive engines, each driving a set of four centrifugal fans mounted in series on a common shaft. Fan air is drawn through fixed louvres

Bottom: Passengers boarding the Breeze. To facilitate access to the cabin a panel is removed from the lift fan cowl ahead of the engine and a handrail and steps are slotted into position.

The waterjet intake duct is located 4 in (100 mm) below the displacement water level to prevent air entry, with a consequent reduction in the navigable draught.

CONTROLS: Vanes located in the waterjet stream provide directional control. Thrust reversal is achieved by the use of waterflow deflectors.

HULL: Similar in appearance to that of the Zarya, the hull is in riveted D16 corrosion resistant aluminium alloy. The hull bottom and sides have transverse frames and the side-walls and superstructure top longitudinal frames. Thickness of plating on sides and bottom is 1/16 in (1·5 mm) (3/32 in, (2·5 mm) in the bow section); and on the sidewalls

3/64 in (1 mm) (up to 13/64 in (5 mm) in the bow section).

Deck plates are 3/32 in (1 mm) thick and the top of the superstructure is in 1/32 in (0·8 mm) plating.

Acoustic and thermal insulation includes use of 4 in (100 mm) thick foam polystyrene sheeting.

ACCOMMODATION: Seats are provided for a crew of 2, who are accommodated in a raised wheelhouse, and 28 passengers. Access to the passenger saloon, which is equipped with airliner-type seats, is through a single door located at the bow in the centre of the wheelhouse. The craft runs bow-on to flat sloping banks to embark and disembark passengers.

SYSTEMS: Electrical: One 1·2 kW, 24 volt dc, engine-operated generator and batteries.
COMMUNICATIONS: Car radio in wheelhouse and speakers in passenger saloon.
DIMENSIONS:

Length overall	73 ft 2 in (22·30 m)
Beam overall	13 ft 3½ in (4·05 m)
Hull beam	12 ft 7⅝ in (3·85 m)
Height of hull to top of wheelhouse	10 ft 9⅞ in (3·3 m)
Height of sidewalls	1 ft 5¾ in (0·45 m)
Draught afloat	2 ft 1⅝ in (0·45 m)
Draught cushion borne	1 ft 4⅞ in (0·65 m)

WEIGHTS:
All-up weight with 48 passengers, crew and fuel   14·30 tons
PERFORMANCE:
Normal service speed
19·22 mph (30-35 km/h)

Distance and time from full ahead to full astern 65·6 yards (60 m) and 14 seconds

NAVAL RESEARCH HOVERCRAFT

A 15-ton experimental ACV has been employed by the Soviet Navy since 1967 to assess the potential of hovercraft for naval applications and investigate controlability and manoeuvrability. Lift is provided by a single 350 hp radial aircraft engine driving a centrifugal fan and propulsion by two pylon-mounted radials of the same type driving controllable-pitch airscrews.

DIMENSIONS:

Length	70 ft 0 in (21·33 m)
Beam	30 ft 0 in (9·14 m)

WEIGHTS:
Displacement.   15 tons
PERFORMANCE:
Max speed   50 knots

LOGISTIC SUPPORT ACV
NATO Code Name: "GUS"

It is thought that thirty or more of these 27-ton vehicles are in service.

The craft is a variant of the Skate, which was designed as a 50-seat amphibious passenger ferry, but which does not appear to have been put into production.
LIFT AND PROPULSION: Motive power is provided by three 780 hp TVD 10 marine gas-turbines mounted aft. Two drive three bladed variable and reversible-pitch propellers for thrust and the third drives an axial lift fan. Cushion air is drawn through a raised intake aft of the cabin superstructure.
CONTROLS: Craft direction is controlled by differential propeller pitch, twin aerodynamic rudders and forward and aft puff ports. Elevators provide pitch trim at cruising speed.
HULL: Hull and superstructure are in conventional corrosion-resistant marine light alloy. Basic structure comprises a central load-carrying platform which incorporates buoyancy tanks and outer sections to support the side ducts and skirt. The cabin, fuel tanks, lift fan bay engines and tail unit are mounted on the platform.
ACCOMMODATION: Up to fifty troops are accommodated in an air-conditioned cabin. Commander and navigator are seated in a raised wheelhouse.
DIMENSIONS, EXTERNAL:
Length overall, power on
69 ft 11½ in (21·33 m)
Beam overall, power on 23 ft 11½ in (7·3 m)
Height to top of fin   21 ft 8 in (6·60 m)
WEIGHTS:
Normal operating weight   27 tons

The Gorkovchanin rigid sidewall waterbus

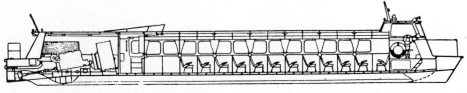

Inboard profile of the Gorkovchanin sidewall craft, powered by a single 265 hp 2DI2AL diesel

An unidentified Soviet research ACV during trials on the Volga

This 15-ton research craft has been employed by the Soviet Navy to assess the potential of the skirted air cushion vehicle for naval applications

PERFORMANCE:
Cruising speed   57·5 mph (92·5 km/h)
Normal cruising range   230 miles (370 km)

ORION-01

Design of the Orion, a rigid sidewall ACV with seats for 80 passengers, was approved in Moscow in the autumn of 1970. The prototype, built in Leningrad, began her trials in October 1973, and arrived at her port of registry, Kalinin, in late 1974, bearing the serial number 01.

The craft is intended for passenger ferry services along shallow rivers, tributaries and reservoirs, and is capable of landing and taking on passengers, bow-on from any flat sloping bank. Cruising speed of the vessel, which is propelled by waterjets, is 32·3 mph (53 km/h). It belongs to the R class of the Soviet River Register.

Experimental operation of the Orion-01 was organised by the Port of Kalinin, Moscow River Transport, the initial run being Kalinin—1st May Factory, a distance of 61·5 miles (99 km), of which 28 miles (45 km) is on the Volga, 26 miles (42 km) on the Ivanov reservoir and 7·5 miles (12 km) on the shallow waters of the Soz. The experience of the first weeks of operation was that there was an insufficient flow of passengers on this particular route.

The vessel was then employed on public holidays only for carrying holiday makers and day trippers on such runs as Kalinin—Putlivo 19 miles (31 km), Kalinin—Kokoshky 12 miles (19 km) and Kalinin—Tarbasa 17·3 miles (28 km), and subsequently on a regular schedule to Putlivo. Finally, Orion-01 was used on the Kalinin—Kimry run, a distance of 85·7 miles (138 km), of which 43·4 miles (70 km) passes through the Ivanov reservoir and 42 miles (68 km) on the Volga.

In all, in 1975, the vessel spent 168 days undergoing trials, of these, it was fully operational on 90 days, and 49 days were spent on repairs or modifications or awaiting work to be undertaken. Time spent underway amounted to 493 hours, during which 7,800 passengers were carried.

Particular attention was paid to assessing the reliability of the skirt. The side sections of the lower part of the bow skirt were badly chafed and split due to contact with the skegs when coming onto the shore. Upper parts of the skirt were not damaged. Problems were also experienced with the aft skirt made from a balloon type fabric. Layers of rubber in the aft part of the segments peeled off; chafing was caused by securing washers and splitting was experienced in the vicinity of the fastenings.

In order to reduce the time spent on repairs, sections of the stern skirt were attached to removable frames. Later a new stern skirt was introduced, based on panels made from a ·47 in (12 mm) thick conveyor belt. This enabled the stern draft, on cushion, to be reduced by $3\frac{7}{8}$ in (10 cm) and the speed to be increased by $\frac{7}{8}$ mph (1·5 km/h). It also improved the reliability of the craft. During the 200 hours underway from the time the skirt was fitted until the end of the vessel's trials, there was no damage.

It was considered that, in the main, the Orion met the requirements of the Soviet operators for the rapid transport of passengers on R Class rivers and reservoirs. The elimination of the defects revealed during the experimental operation will make it possible to improve the vessel's operational characteristics and increase its reliability.

Series production of vessels of this type is being undertaken at the Sosnovska Shipbuilding Yard in Kixovskaya Oblast.

LIFT AND PROPULSION: Integrated system powered by two 520 hp 3D12N-520 diesels mounted in an engine room aft. Each engine drives a Type Ts 39—13 centrifugal fan for lift, and via a cardan shaft, a semi-submerged single-stage waterjet rotor for propulsion. Fan air is fed via ducts to the bow skirt, a transverse stability slot and to the fingered bag skirt aft. Casing of the waterjet system which is removable, forms the stern section of the vessel. In order to reduce vibration the waterjets are mounted on shock absorbers.

Above and below: Gus assault landing craft of the Soviet marine infantry during a beach landing exercise. Note the large bellmouth intake for the lift fan amidship

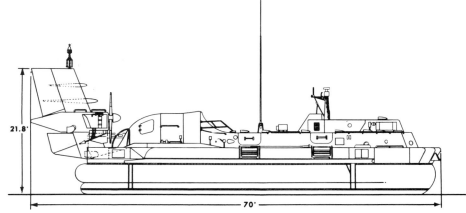

Outboard profile of the Soviet navy version of the 27-ton Gus-class multiduty ACV

HULL: Similar in overall appearance to Zarya and Zarnitsa types. All-welded structure in AIMg-61 aluminium-magnesium alloy.

Lateral framing employed throughout hull with the exception of the bow and stern decks, where longitudinal frames have been

"GUS" IN SERVICE WITH THE SOVIET MARINES

"Gus", the Soviet Union's 27-ton amphibious assault landing craft, is entering service in growing numbers with the Soviet Marine Infantry The photographs on this page have been selected from a series recently released to the Soviet military press. They leave little doubt as to the degree of sophistication attained in Soviet hovercraft design over the past ten years

"Gus" is powered by three 780 hp marinised gas-turbines and cruises at 58 mph. The operating crew appears to comprise a Commander, First Officer, Flight Engineer and Navigator

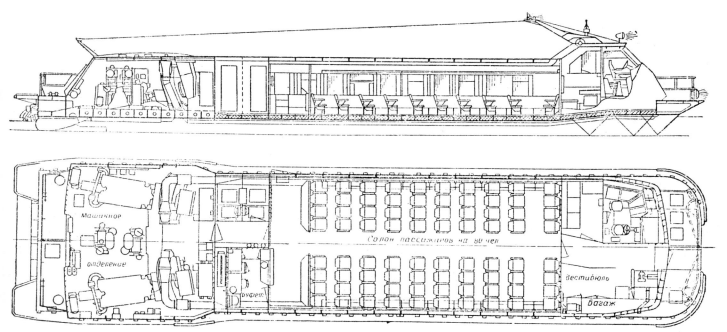

General arrangements of the Orion, 80-seat sidewall ACV passenger ferry. Power is supplied by two 520 hp 3D12N-520 marine diesels, each driving a centrifugal fan and a semi-submerged single-stage waterjet rotor

fitted. Superstructure and wheelhouse are of welded and riveted duralumin construction on longitudinal framing.

ACCOMMODATION: Seats are provided for the operating crew of 2, who are accommodated in a raised wheelhouse, a barman, two seamen and 80 passengers. At the aft end of the passenger saloon are two WC/washbasin units and a bar. There is also an off-duty cabin for the crew. Access to the passenger saloon is via a single door at the bow, in the centre of the wheelhouse. A ram-air intake provides ventilation while the craft is underway. Stale air is drawn out by the lift fans aft.

CONTROLS: Rudders located aft of the waterjet inlets and two waterjet deflectors control craft direction. Rudder and flap movement is effected by cables.

SYSTEMS: Two G-73Z engine-driven generators, linked with two sets of STK-18M batteries, provide 28 volts, 1,200 watts. One battery set is employed for engine starting, the other for supplying current for the ship's systems.

COMMUNICATIONS: Standard equipment comprises an R-809MZ radiotelephone, a Kama-3 UHF radio and an Unja cabin announcement system.

DIMENSIONS:

Length overall	84 ft 7¾ in (25·8 m)
Beam overall	21 ft 4 in (6·5 m)
Height overall to mast top	17 ft 3½ in (5·27 m)
Height to top of wheelhouse	13 ft 0¼ in (3·97 m)

WEIGHTS:

Loaded displacement	28 tonnes
Light displacement	20·7 tonnes
Draught, displacement condition, fully loaded	2 ft 9⅛ in (0·84 m)
Draught, displacement condition, empty	2 ft 5⅞ in (0·76 m)
Draught, cushionborne bows	4 in (0·1 m)
stern	1 ft 8 in (0·5 m)

PERFORMANCE:

Max speed	37·25 mph (60 km/h)

ORION—Stopping and Starting Characteristics:	Shallow water	Deep water
Distance run by vessel from Full Ahead to stop		
Metres	136	120
Time in seconds	67	40
Distance run by vessel from Full Ahead to Full Astern: Metres	84	65
Time in seconds	23	20
Distance necessary for attainment of full speed from stop: Metres	250	330
Time in seconds	60	80

Cruising speed, full load	33 mph (53 km/h)
Max wave height on scheduled runs	1 ft 8 in (0·5 m)
Diameter of turn to port	597 ft (182 m)
Time to complete turn with rudders at 33 deg	187 secs
Time taken from start of berthing procedure to completion	1 min app.
Time taken to attain cruising speed from leaving berth	2 min app.

EKRANOPLAN EXPERIMENTAL

A giant Soviet experimental wing-in-ground-effect machine, with a span of 131 ft 3 in (40 m) and a length of nearly 400 ft (122 m), is undergoing tests on the Caspian sea. Trials began in 1965 and are continuing in the company of proportionally smaller models.

The machine, which operates at heights of 23-43 ft (7-14 m) above the water, has a speed of about 300 knots. Power is supplied by eight marinised gas-turbines mounted above a stub wing forward, and two 'booster' turbines installed at the base of the dihedral tailplane aft. All ten engines are employed at take-off, when thrust has to be 2·5-35 times greater than that required to maintain cruising conditions in flight.

At take-off the thrust from the eight forward engines is deflected downwards to create additional cushion pressure beneath the wing. After take-off the jet exhaust is directed above the upper surface of the wing to create additional lift.

Western WIG specialists, commenting on the design have stated that it does not facilitate pitch stability during its transition from ground-effect to free flight and back again. Thus the machine is probably intended to fly only in close proximity to the surface. This means it may not be able to operate safely either in extremely turbulent weather conditions or in areas where it would encounter projections higher than 50 ft (15·24 m) above the surface.

Soviet experts maintain that craft of this type should be able to negotiate sand spits, shallows, marshes, ice, snow, relatively even and gently sloping banks and low obstacles. Low bridges have been mentioned. They are also stated to be sufficiently seaworthy to operate in rough seas. Wide employment of this type of vessel is foreseen, particularly in the Soviet Navy, which has suggested that they will be invaluable in amphibious operations.

Large numbers of troops could be carried to the selected landing zones with little regard to the condition of the sea, tidal currents, underwater obstacles and minefields, none of which would constitute a hazard.

Advantages in the battle zone will include high speed manoeuvring, and a considerable reduction in the time taken to undertake a mission compared with conventional landing craft.

The capacity of the WIG craft, Ekranoplan machines as they are known in the Soviet Union, will enable them to carry the biggest items of military equipment. Another application for this type of vehicle, according to its designers, is ASW patrol, where its considerable range and endurance will prove an advantage.

References have been made in Soviet technical publications to vehicles with chords of 30-40 m (98 ft 6 in—131 ft 2 in) and speeds of 400 knots being under consideration. This suggests that research is being aimed at a number of alternative configurations including flying wings and delta wings.

EKRANOPLAN RIVER BUSES

The Ministry of the River Fleet announced in April 1972 that it planned to build craft of the Ekranoplan (WIG) type "which will travel within several metres of a river surface at speeds of some 155 mph (250 km/h)".

It seems probable that in order to avoid navigation problems in busy river port areas these craft will be of smaller overall dimensions than the 131 ft 3 in (40 m) span machine described earlier. Low aspect ratio wings are likely to be employed and it is possible that these early production craft are of 5-6 tons displacement. A number of these machines were reported to be in experimental service in 1973.

On Moscow television in July, 1973, a programme commemorating Soviet Navy Day traced the progress of high speed water transportation and confirmed that Ekranoplanes are being developed in the Soviet Union. The craft were described by the commentator as "ground gliders", capable of operating over land, water, snow and ice. A small machine built in Odessa in the early 1960s was shown to viewers, together with a completely new research craft of much larger size.

The craft is of catamaran configuration and carries up to forty passengers in each of the two hulls. The crew and operating controls are accommodated in a central pod carried on the forward wing.

Thrust is provided by six marinised gas-turbines mounted in pairs on the triple fins aft. Length of the craft is about 100 ft.

RADUGA

This experimental amphibious ACV was completed at the Krasnoye Sormovo shipyard

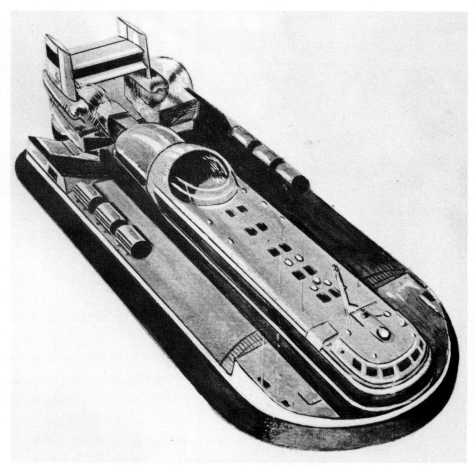

Impression of the Skate 50-seat amphibious hoverferry

Impression of a new catamaran-hulled Ekranoplan research craft now under development in the Soviet Union. Designed for high speed long distance passenger services along the main Soviet rivers, it rides on a dynamic air cushion formed between its wings and the supporting surface below. Seats are provided for forty passengers in each of the twin hulls. Top speed is likely to be between 150-200 knots

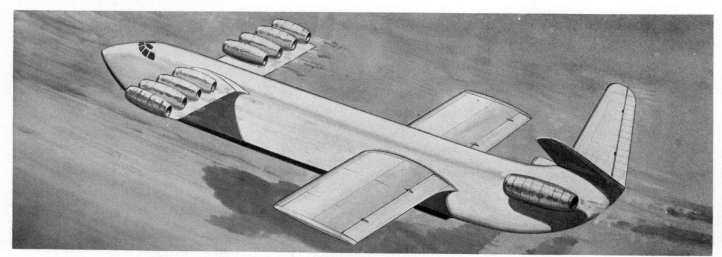

The giant Soviet ten-jet experimental Ekranoplan which is currently undergoing tests on the Caspian Sea

in the summer of 1962 and is reported to have attained a speed of 100 km/h (62 mph) during trials.

Built originally as a peripheral jet type, it is now being used to develop control techniques, and provide amphibious experience and data on skirt design.
LIFT AND PROPULSION: The craft is powered by two 220 hp air-cooled radial engines. One, mounted amidships, drives a 5 ft 11 in (1·8 m) 12-bladed lift fan; the second, mounted on a pylon at the stern, drives a two-bladed propeller for propulsion. The fan delivers air to the cushion via a continuous peripheral skirt, the bow and side sections of which are of the fingered bag type.
HULL: Riveted aluminium construction.
ACCOMMODATION: The cabin seats five.
CONTROLS: Directional control is provided by an aerodynamic rudder operating on the propeller slipstream.
DIMENSIONS:

Length	30 ft 10 in (9·40 m)
Beam	13 ft 6 in (4·12 m)

WEIGHTS:

Operating weight	3 tons

PERFORMANCE:

Maximum speed	75 mph (120 km/h)
Endurance	3 hours

RASSVET (DAWN)

The Rassvet is designed for local sea routes and is an offshore counterpart to the Orion sidewall ACV which is intended for river services. Plans call for the Rassvet to serve resort routes in the Crimea, the Caucasus, on the Caspian and in the Baltic, as well as on large lakes and reservoirs. Like the Orion and the Zarnitsa, its two predecessors, it can run bow-on to flat, sloping beaches to embark and disembark passengers.

Features include shallow draft, good manoeuvrability and seagoing qualities and simple construction.
LIFT AND PROPULSION: Total output of engines driving the lift fans is 150 hp. Propulsive thrust is supplied by twin 520 hp diesel engines, driving two waterjets.
ACCOMMODATION: Up to eighty passengers are accommodated in an air-conditioned cab in airliner-type seats. Captain and engineer are accommodated in an elevated wheelhouse, forward.
DIMENSIONS:

Length overall	86 ft 11·7 in (26·51 m)
Beam overall	23 ft 3¼ in (7·10 m)
Height	29 ft 8·6 in (9·06 m)
Draft on cushion	2 ft 3·6 in (0·7 m)

WEIGHTS:

Displacement fully loaded	44 tons (44·7 tonnes)

PERFORMANCE:

Cruising speed	25 knots
Range	200 nm

SORMOVICH

Launched in October 1965, the Sormovich is a 50-passenger ACV designed by Mr Valeri Schoenberg, Chief Constructor of the Krasnoye Sormovo Shipyard, with the assistance of the N. E. Zhukovski Central Institute of Aerodynamics.

In general layout, the craft represents a "scale-up" of the configuration tested with the Raduga.

In 1970 the craft was equipped with a 4 ft deep flexible skirt. Several experimental services have been operated with the craft. It is not yet in production, although orders are expected from the Ministry of the River Fleet.

The Raduga experimental air cushion vehicle

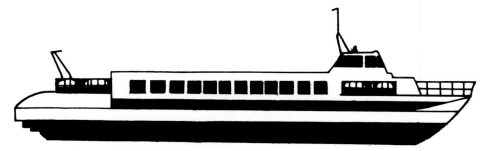

Rassvet (Dawn), a new 80-seat sidewall-type ferry for short sea routes

TESTS: Rigorous acceptance trials included a special programme of runs between Gorky and Gorodets, Gorky and Lyskovo, Gorky and Vasilsursk, and also on the Gorky Reservoir.

These trials confirmed the craft's ability to operate across shoals, sandy spits and dykes, and run on to dry land for cargo handling and repairs.

In the air-cushion mode, her ability to maintain course up- and downwind is satisfactory, and controlled entirely by the rudders. In sidewinds, control is by combined rudder movement and differential propeller pitch. Steering during turns by rudders alone is unsatisfactory, the turning-circle diameter being 2,734-3,280 yds (2,500-3,000 m) with substantial drift. Turning is improved if the manoeuvre is accomplished by varying propeller pitch. The distance from the inception of the manoeuvre to securing a 180 deg. course then drops to 765-1,093 yards (700-1,000 m) and the diameter of the subsequent turning circle falls to 164 yards (150 m.)

Collision avoidance manoeuvres with a floating object employing rudder deflection, showed that avoidance is feasible at a distance of not under 546 yards (500 m). This distance can be reduced, however, if the manoeuvre is accomplished with variable propeller pitch. Successful undertaking of this manoeuvre depends largely on the skill of the operator.

In the air-cushion mode, while accelerating to 37-43 mph (60-70 km/h) and turning through 180 deg in both directions, stability is adequate in any of the load conditions investigated, and passengers may move about freely.

In addition to the basic flight-trial programme, tests were made to check vehicle response to sudden splash-down in case of the emergency shutdown of the main engine while underway. The splash-down tests were conducted at various speeds and drift angles, and showed that the loads imposed are not excessive and that the passengers were not alarmed. In 4 ft (1·2 m) waves the craft operates at reduced speed, but steering control and satisfactory passenger comfort

are maintained.

Since late 1970, Sormovich has been in experimental service with the Volga United Steamship Company.

While operating on the Gorky-Cheboksary run in light conditions and with passengers aboard during the 1971 season, various problem areas were identified. In particular, it was found necessary to improve the reliability of the airscrew and fan drive transmission; improve the design of flexible-skirt and select a stronger material from which it can be manufactured; find ways of reducing engine noise and improve its operation and maintenance; render more effective the devices employed to reduce craft drift during high-speed turns; and raise the overall economic efficiency of the craft.

After modification, the vehicle returned to experimental service on the Gorky-Cheboksary-Gorky passenger run in 1972, with flights scheduled for daylight hours only, in winds not over 32-39 f/sec (10-12 m/sec) and at speeds not above 50 mph (80 km/h). The route selected was generally beyond that negotiable by a conventional vessel, with depths not less than 1 ft 8 in (0·5 m).

Two crew training flights and 42 passenger flights were undertaken during this particular service. Some 5,655 people were carried a total of 15,534 miles (25,000 km).

However, experimental operation of the craft during the 1972 season was a financial loss. The economic viability of Sormovich, as in the previous season, was impaired by the craft being withdrawn from service to eliminate main transmission reduction gear defects and attend to various other repair and maintenance jobs.

A passenger survey indicated that noise levels in the rear of the saloon are acceptable, but high exterior noise levels are a nuisance to shore personnel and members of the public in the vicinity.

Experimental operation of the Sormovich has indicated the possibility of its being used on inland waterways.

During the 1972/73 off-season period, measures were being taken to eliminate the shortcomings revealed, replace the reduction gear, improve flexible-skirt nozzle elements,

and undertake various other modifications
found necessary. There are grounds for
believing that these measures will make
Sormovich into a viable economic proposition.

LIFT AND PROPULSION: All machinery
is located aft behind a sound-proof bulkhead
to keep down the noise level in the passenger
compartments. A single 2,300 hp Ivchenko
AI-20K shaft-turbine, at the extreme stern,
drives the integrated lift/propulsion system.
Its output shaft passes first to a differential
gearbox from which shafts extend sideways
to the two four-blade ducted variable pitch
propellers. A further shaft runs forward
from the differential to a bevel gearbox from
which a drive-shaft runs vertically upward to
the 12-blade variable pitch lift-fan mounted
under the intake on the rear of the roof of
the vehicle. The gas-turbine operates on
diesel fuel. Cushion area is 220 m².

CONTROLS: Each propeller duct contains
two hydraulically-actuated rudders, working
in the slipstream.

HULL: Light alloy buoyancy type, with air
feeding to the cushion through a peripheral
slot. There is a fore and aft stability slot on
each side parallel to and about 5 ft (1·50 m)
inboard of the peripheral slot.

ACCOMMODATION: The crew compartment, forward, contains two seats and is
separated from the main cabin by a partition
containing a door. The front two rows of
seats in the cabin are only four-abreast to
facilitate entry through the forward door on
each side. The remaining 42 seats are six-
abreast, in three-chair units with centre aisle.
Aft of the cabin is a wardrobe on the port
side, with a buffet opposite on the starboard
side. Then comes the main entry lobby,
with a passenger door on the port side and
service door opposite, followed by a toilet
(port) and baggage hold (starboard).

An unusual feature of the Sormovich is that
it is fitted with retractable wheels which can
be lowered to avoid d mage to the hull when
the craft operates over uneven ice or rough
country. The wheels are carried on lightly-
sprung legs, enabling them to ride easily over
obstructions.

The craft is equipped for navigation at
night.

DIMENSIONS:
Length   96 ft 0 in (29·2 m)
Beam   32 ft 9½ in (10·00 m)
Height to top of hull, on cushion (7 m)
WEIGHTS:
Normal loaded weight   36·5 m tons
PERFORMANCE:
Max cruising speed 74·56 mph (120 km/h)

ZARNITSA

Evolved from Gorkovchanin, the Zarnitsa
is a 48-50 seat waterjet-propelled rigid sidewall ferry designed to operate on shallow
rivers, some less than 2 ft 3 in (0·70 m) deep.
Series production is underway, and large
numbers have been delivered.

The prototype was put into trial service
on the Vyatka river, in the Kirov region, in
the summer of 1972, and the first production
models began operating on shallow, secondary
rivers later in the year. During 1973-74,
Zarnitsas entered service on tributaries of
the Kama, Lena and Volga. In March
1974, Zarnitsa-7 was reported to have been
delivered to the Kama River Shipping Line

Above and below: The Sormovich ACV passenger ferry, powered by a single 2,300 hp Ivchenko
AI-20K gas turbine

which will employ the vessel on the upper
shallow reaches of the Vishera and Chusovaya
rivers.

LIFT AND PROPULSION, CONTROLS,
HULL: Arrangements almost identical to
those of the Gorkovchanin.

ACCOMODATION: Seats are provided for
two crew members, who are accommodated

in the raised wheelhouse, forward, and 48-
50 passengers. Access to the passenger
saloon is via a single door located at the bow
in the centre of the wheelhouse. The craft
runs bow-on to flat sloping banks to embark
and disembark passengers.

DIMENSIONS:
Length   72 ft 3 in (22·3 m)

The Zarnitsa 48-50 seat waterjet-propelled rigid sidewall ferry for shallow rivers.

Passenger saloon in the Zarnitsa, looking aft

| Beam | 12 ft 8 in (3·85 m) |
| Skeg depth | 1 ft 6 in (0·45 m) |

WEIGHTS:

| Light displacement | 9 metric tons |
| All-up weight, with 48 passengers, crew and hull | 15 m tons |

PERFORMANCE:

| Service speed | 20-22 mph (33-35 km/h) |

ZARYA (DAWN)

Experiments with high speed "aeroglisseur" (literally air skimmer) water buses, capable of negotiating the many shallow waterways

in the Soviet Union, began in 1961.

The object was to develop a vessel for services on shallow waters, with depths of only 20 in (0·5 m), at speeds of at least 21·5 knots. The prototype Zarya, called the Opytnye-1 (experimental), was put into

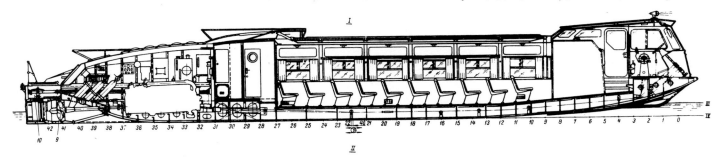

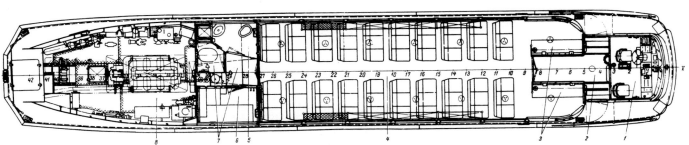

Zarya. I. Inboard profile; II. deck layout; III. design waterline; IV. base line; V. centreline; 1. wheelhouse; 2. bow passageway; 3. luggage enclosure; 4. passenger cabin 5. WC; 6. crew room; 7. stern passageway; 8. engine room; 9. waterjet impeller; 10. steering system

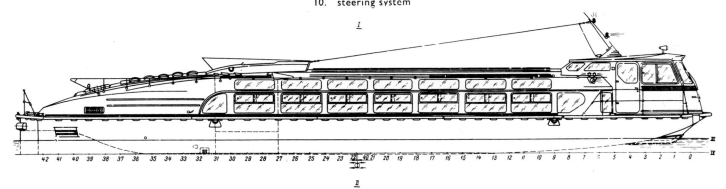

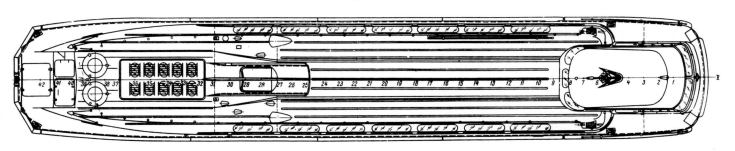

experimental operations on the river Msta in
1963. During trials the craft attained a
speed of 26 mph (42 km/h) and proved to
have a turning radius of 44·76 yards (40-70
m). The craft runs bow-on to any flat,
sloping bank to embark passengers.

Built with a strong aluminium alloy hull
and equipped with a well protected waterjet,
the craft is unharmed by floating logs, even
when they are encountered at full speed.

Variants include models with a flat load
deck in place of the passenger cabin superstructure amidships, and used as light freight
vessels.

Zarya was designed by a team at the
Central Design Office of the Ministry of the
River Fleet Gorky, working in conjunction
with the Leningrad Water Transport Institute. Series production is under way at the
Moscow Shipbuilding and Ship Repair Yard
of the Ministry of the River Fleet.

The latest model is distinguished by its
trimaran bow configuration, which gives
improved performance in waves and enables
the craft to be routed on major waterways.
LIFT AND PROPULSION: Power is provided by a single M-400 watercooled, supercharged, 12-cylinder V-type diesel with a
normal service output of 830 hp at 1,650 rpm
and a maximum output of 1,100 hp at 1,800
rpm. It has a variable-speed governor and
reversing clutch and drives a single 2 ft 2½ in
(0·7 m) diameter waterjet impeller.

The waterjet is of single-stage type, with a
semi-submerged jet discharge. The impeller
sucks in water through an intake duct which
is covered by a protective grille. The
discharge water flows around two steering
vanes which provide directional control.
Waterjet reversal deflectors are employed to
reverse the craft or to reduce the waterjet
thrust when variations in speed are necessary.

A localised ram-air cushion, introduced by
an upswept nose and contained on either side
by shallow skegs, lifts the bow clear of the
water as the craft picks up speed. The
airflow also provides air/foam lubrication for
the remainder of the flat-bottomed hull.
HULL: Hull and superstructure are of all-
welded aluminium alloy plate construction,
the constituent parts being joined by argon-
shielded arc welding. Framing is of mixed
type, with transverse framing at the sides
and the main longitudinal elements within
the hull bottom. The outside shell and
bottom plating is $\frac{13}{64}$ in (5 mm) thick, except
for the base at the bow where it is $\frac{15}{64}$ in
(6 mm) thick. The wheelhouse is in moulded
glass-reinforced plastic.
ACCOMMODATION: Three transverse bulkheads divide the hull into four compartments.
Behind the forepeak and wheelhouse is the
passenger cabin, and aft of this is a compartment housing the crew room, WC and diesel
fuel tank. Aft of this is the engine and
steering compartment. The raised wheelhouse, located at the bow, gives 360 deg.
visibility. Installed in the passenger cabin
in the 60-seat version, are twenty rows of
seats, three abreast, ten rows each side of a
centre aisle. Five additional seats are
installed in short range models and 15 standing passengers can be accommodated. Life
jackets for passengers are stowed in lockers
in the baggage compartment and under
seats at the rear of the cabin.

The crew off-duty room contains a sofa,
table, wall-mounted cupboard, folding stool
and a mirror. The WC contains a wash
basin, a bowel, mirror and soap tray.

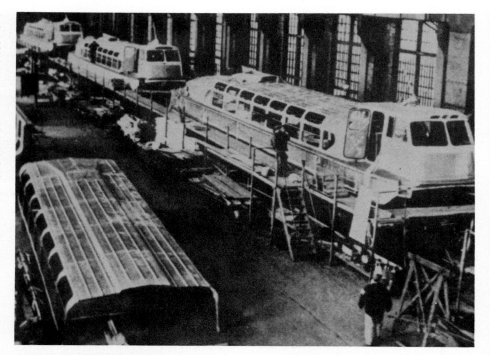

Top: Zaryas in series production at the Moscow Shipbuilding and Ship Repair Yard. Zarya-157
was delivered by rail to Khabarovsk in the autumn of 1974. It will operate on a 200 km route in
the Amur basin. Centre: Stern view of a Zarya in service on one of the shallow tributaries of
the Volga. The vessel is powered by an 830 hp M-400 12-cylinder diesel driving a single-stage
waterjet. Cruising speed is 27·96 mph (45 km/h). Bottom: Compared with earlier variants, this
new model of the Zarya is distinguished by its trimaran bow, introduced for improved seakeeping.
The new bow design allows the vessel to be routed into major waterways

The wheelhouse has rotating seats for the
captain and engineer, two sun visors and
there are two windscreen wipers.

Both the passenger cabin and wheelhouse
are heated by warm air produced by hot water
from the closed circuit main engine cooling

system. Warm air is admitted into the passenger cabin and wheelhouse through a perforated chamber at the bulkhead. The engine room is heated by two 1·2 kW electric heaters and the crew room by a 0·6 kW electric heater. Windows of the wheelhouse and the wheelhouse itself are heated by a 330 kW electric heater.

CONTROLS: Irrespective of load, the radius of turn is between 98-164 ft (30-50 m) with the rudder put hard over at an angle of 30 degrees. This can be decreased if necessary by either throttling down the engine or closing the valves of the reversing system. At slow speed the craft is capable of pinwheeling. The time required to stop the vessel is 8-10 seconds, the coasting distance being between 164-196 ft (50-60 m). Manoeuvrability of the craft is such that it is able to navigate small winding rivers with waterways of 39-49 ft (12-15 m) wide with the radii of windings varying between 131-229 ft (40-70 m) without slowing down.

The vessel can easily pull into shore without landing facilities, providing the river bed slope is no steeper than 3 degrees. The time required for pulling in, embarking passengers, then leaving, averages 1·5 minutes. Steps to facilitate access are located at the bow, port and starboard, and lowered by a control in the wheelhouse.

SYSTEMS, ELECTRICAL: Main engine driven 1 kW generator, rated at 27·5 V, charges the storage batteries and meets the demands of 24 V circuits while the vessel is underway. Four lead-acid batteries to supply 24 V for monitoring and alarm circuitry and starting the main engine. Equipment supplied for charging the storage batteries from a shore-based 220 V cource.

FIRE-FIGHTING: Two tanks containing fire-extinguishing compound and hoses for fighting an outbreak in the engine room. System can be brought into operation either from the engine room or from the wheelhouse. Engine room is also provided with two portable carbon dioxide fire extinguishers. Another of the same type is provided in the wheelhouse and two foam fire extinguishers are standard equipment in the main cabin.

FUEL: Craft is refuelled through a filling hose and a neck on the port side of the superstructure. Fuel is fed to the main engine from a service tank with a capacity of 4·13 m³, sufficient to enable a vessel to cruise for 8 hours without refuelling. In addition, there is a 400 l storage tank which contains a 2 hour reserve to be used in an emergency. The same tank supplies fuel to a water heater.

COMPRESSED AIR: Starting system for main engines comprising three 45 ll air-cylinders, valves (safety, shut-off, pressure reducing and starting) and piping. Pressure 150-75 kgf/cm². Two cylinders in operation, one standby.

The Zarnitsa, a derivative of the Gorkovchanin, is now in series production

The Skat on display in Moscow

DIMENSIONS:

Length	72 ft 3¼ in (22·1 m)
Beam	12 ft 10¾ in (3·93 m)
Moulded depth	3 ft 11½ in (1·2 m)
Draft	1 ft 5¾ in (0·45 m)

WEIGHTS:

Weight empty	16·68 tonnes
Weight with 60 passengers, and stores for 8'hour trip	24·78 tonnes

PERFORMANCE:
Speed (in channel of 0·8 m depth) 27·96 mph (45 km/h)
Range—suitable for service distances of 93 miles (150 km) and above
Endurance at cruising speed 8 hours

UFA AVIATION INSTITUTE

An experimental circular planform ACV, the Skat, has been designed and built by students of the UFA Aviation Institute. The vehicle was displayed in 1970 in Moscow at the USSR National Economy Achievements Exhibition.

OIIMF (ODESSA ENGINEERING INSTITUTE OF THE MERCHANT FLEET) OIIMF-2

This is one of a number of experimental wing-in-ground-effect machines built at the institute by a group of students under the direction of Y. Budnitskiy.

The craft is a single-seater with an all-up weight of 926-992 lb (420-450 kg) and a payload of 176-220 lb (80-100 kg). The wings, floats and hull are of semimonocoque construction and built in duralumin.

Power is supplied by two 18 hp aircooled motorcycle engines driving two 3 ft 11 in (1·2 m) diameter two-bladed airscrews.

Special flaps have been designed to improve the starting characteristics of the craft by creating a static air cushion through the utilisation of the airscrew slipstream. The flaps are located between the wings and are secured by special shock absorption cables in the operating position at the moment of starting the craft. As speed increases so the flaps hinge upwards automatically.

Tests indicate that the flaps noticeably decrease the leakage of air from the high pressure area under the aft wing, thus increasing wing lift and unloading the floats.

A vertical tail assembly and flap are provided for steering and stabilisation. The flap on the aft wing is designed to balance the craft during starting and control it in pitch. The leading wing barely generates any lift at low speeds, therefore a pitching moment, obtained by deflecting the flap upwards, must be created during the initial period of its run in order to balance the craft. As speed increases and the

forward wing comes into operation, the centre of pressure shifts forward, which requires a diving moment (deflection of the flap downward) in order to balance the craft.

Static stability in pitch is provided by constant contact of the aft section of the floats with the water surface and the corresponding stabilising effect of the forward wing.

The vehicle has good manoeuvrability, and the turning diameter, at a speed of 20 mph is approximately 32 ft.

The OIIMF-2 single-seat wing-in-ground effect research craft

DIMENSIONS:

Length overall	16 ft 5 in (5·0 m)		
Hull beam	10 ft 6 in (3·2 m)		
Wing span	9 ft 2¼ in (2·8 m)		
Chord, forward lower wing	3 ft 4 in (1 m)	Chord, upper wing	9 ft 10 in (3 m)

ACV OPERATORS

THE AMERICAS
NORTH AMERICA AND CANADA

CANADA

CANADIAN COAST GUARD HOVERCRAFT UNITS

HEADQUARTERS:
Transport Canada, Canadian Coast Guard Fleet Systems Branch, Tower A, Place de Ville, Ottawa, Ontario, K1A 0N5

UNIT ADDRESSES:
Canadian Coast Guard Hovercraft Unit, PO Box 68, Vancouver, AMF, BC, Canada.

TELEPHONE:
(604) 273 2383
Canadian Coast Guard Development and Evaluation Unit, Department of Transport, 990, Nun's Island Boulevard, Nun's Island, Montreal, Quebec. Canada H3E 1H2

TELEPHONE:
(514) 283 5841

ADMINISTRATION:
Vancouver Unit
Mr H. Buchanan, Regional Director, Canadian Coast Guard, Department of Transport, PO Box 10060, Pacific Centre, 700 West Georgia Street, Vancouver, BC V7Y 1EI
Montreal Unit
Mr W. J. H. Stuart, Director, Fleet Systems, Canadian Coast Guard, Department of Transport, Tower 'A', Place de Ville, Ottawa, Ontario, K1A 0N7

The Canadian Coast Guard Hovercraft Unit in Vancouver was formed on August 5th 1968, to evaluate the use of hovercraft in search and rescue and other Coast Guard duties.

OPERATIONS:
The normal area of patrol is the Straits of Georgia and Gulf Islands—an area of approximately 500 square miles. The unit is often called upon outside this area on search and rescue missions.

The average patrol distance is 80 n miles.

Since April 1st, 1969, the unit has carried out well over 1,000 SAR missions, directly involving some 1,200 persons. These included marine, aircraft distress and mercy missions.

Other operations included the checking, servicing and repairing of marine navigational aids within the patrol area; aircraft accident inspection; water pollution investigation; carriage of Steamship Inspectors for spot safety checks of tugs; working with police departments; excercises with the Canadian Armed Forces vessels; training and familiarisation of selected Government personnel, and experimental work with other Government agencies.

In January 1974, the CCG took delivery of a refurbished Voyageur 002. This forms the equipment of her Development and Evaluation Unit, whose current task is to evaluate the vehicle in various CCG roles. In order to carry out this evaluation the Unit may operate in different areas of Canada; for the past two years, it has been based in Montreal.

Of particular significance has been the development of icebreaking techniques using this vehicle, and as a result of the past two winters evaluation, the CCG Voyageur is now accepted as an operational unit for icebreaking in the Montreal area. Ice up to 30 ins (76 cm) thick can be broken at the rate of 1 square mile (2·25 km²) per hour, in any water depth, and many rivers have been cleared of ice jams to relieve serious flood, threats. In these cases, the jams have been up to 16 ft (4·75 m) thick.

EQUIPMENT: One SR.N5. registration CH-CCG, modified to Coast Guard requirements. Equipment includes navigation and communications equipment such as radar, Loran, Direction Finder and HF/MF, VHF/FM and VHF/AM radiotelephone, 2 × 25 man inflatable liferafts 2 × 100 gallon auxiliary fuel tanks (extending endurance to 7 hours at max power), stretchers, first aid kit, fire fighting equipment, towing gear and other SAR equipment.

One Bell Aerospace Voyageur, registration CH-CGA, also equipped with all the navigation and communications equipment required for safe operation in her area of work. This craft also carries a portable crew module which enables her crew to stay onboard overnight.

NORTHERN TRANSPORTATION COMPANY LIMITED

OPERATIONS OFFICE:
9945-108 Street; Edmonton, Alberta T5K 2G9

TELEPHONE:
(403) 423-9201

TELEX:
037-2480

DIRECTORS:
S. D. Cameron, Chairman of the Board
L. R. Montpetit, President
W. B. Hunter, Vice President Operations
P. L. P. Macdonnell
John H. Parker
Arthur Kroeger
Julien Béliveau
Murray Watts
A. B. Caywood
Director of Air Cushion Vehicle Operations, Bert W. Mead

Northern Transportation Company Limited (NTCL) is a wholly-owned subsidiary of Eldorado Nuclear Limited and was formed in 1931. It is Canada's largest Western Arctic marine transportation operator— and serves approximately 4,800 miles of water routes throughout the Mackenzie River Basin and the Western Arctic. The fleet includes three ocean-going ships, 28 diesel tugs, 163 all steel dual purpose barges with varied capacities up to 1,500 tons, 4 thruster barges and the fleet has a reported capability of some 750,000 tons of cargo in any one season.

To supplement its Marine, Trucking and Aviation Divisions, NTCL operates two BHC SR.N6 vehicles in the McKenzie Delta

CH-NTB-030, a flat-deck version of the SR.N6, employed by the Northern Transportation Company in the Mackenzie Delta and Beaufort Sea areas in support of oil industry activities

CH-NTA Servo 031, a standard passenger version of the SR.N6 with reinforced extended side decks, carrying two container type mobile workshops

and Beaufort Sea area in support of oil industry activities.

One craft, CH-NTA-031 is a standard passenger version and at the end of the 1975 season had completed in excess of 50,000 miles, all within the Arctic circle. The second machine, CH-NTB, has been modified to enable rapid conversion from passenger to flat-deck configuration.

In flat-deck configuration, a standard payload is approximately 12,000 pounds, plus four passengers. Its passenger capacity when not converted is 26. Both machines have VHF, AM, VHF FM, HFSSB, emergency locators, radio compass and radio telephone. A wide variety of support equipment necessitated by the extreme cold is fitted, including dual cabin heating systems.

CH-NTA Servo 031

ALYESKA PIPELINE SERVICE CO

Operates two 160-ton payload hover transporters, "Yukon Princess 1" and "Yukon Princess 2" across the River Yukon.

These hover-transporters carry a substantial number of heavy vehicles as well as equipment and supplies across the river, 20 hours a day, throughout the year. The transporters are winched across the Yukon and can be unloaded and re-loaded in thirty minutes employing the roll-on, roll-off system.

UNITED STATES

BELL AEROSPACE TEXTRON

In 1975-6, Bell Aerospace Textron continued operational trials of its 100-ton surface effect ship test craft in the Gulf of Mexico and St. Andrew Bay at Panama City, Florida. The craft, designed and constructed for the US Navy's Surface Effect Ship Project Office, underwent initial testing on Louisiana's Lake Pontchartrain, near New Orleans, until June of 1973. Bell established an ACV/SES Test and Training Center at the Naval Coastal Systems Laboratory, Panama City, in 1973, where the SES-100B will continue to be utilised extensively to provide technical information to support advanced development efforts for a large surface effect ship. In addition, two Voyageur Heavy-Haul air cushion vehicles, designated 001 and 003, were transferred to Panama City in late 1975 for use in a training program for US Army personnel.

HOVERTRANSPORT INC

HEAD OFFICE:
Bridgeport, Connecticut, USA.
EXECUTIVES:
Robert Weldon, President

This newly formed operator has a US-built HM.2 sidewall hovercraft named "Excalibur". An experimental operation with the craft began on June 26, 1976.

Eventually it is planned to operate a number of HM.2 craft on routes from Huntingdon, Long Island to various other locations in Long Island South.

UNITED STATES ARMY

In 1972, a Bell SK-5 Model 7255 of the US Army's Cold Region Research Laboratory Houghton, Michigan, was operated in Alaska for extended tests over varying arctic terrain and waterways. In early 1973, the SK-5 was shipped to the US Army's Weapons Command, St. Louis, Missouri, for continued operations. In July 1976, the Bell LACV-30-001 was undergoing builders trials at Ft. Story, Virginia, and -002 was under test at Aberdeen Proving Ground, Maryland.

The Bell Viking underwent tests by the US Army Cold Regions Research and Engineering Labs at Toronto Island Airport in the autumn of 1975.

SOUTH AMERICA

BOLIVIA
HOVERMARINE TRANSPORT TITIKAKA LTD

HEAD OFFICE:
La Paz

This company operates a specially furnished 30 seater version of the sidewall HM.2 Mk III hovercraft on Lake Titicaca, between Tiquina Huatajata in Bolivia and Puno, Peru. Lake Titicaca is at an altitude of over 12,500 ft above sea level. Craft operated: HM.2-324.

BRAZIL
COMPANHIA DE NAVAGACAO BAHIANA

ADDRESS:
PO Box 1406, Ave., Franca, Salvador, Bahia.

A Hovermarine HM.2 sidewall hovercraft operates out of Salvador (Bahia) to the site of a large oil refinery on the opposite side of the bay. During off-peak hours the craft operates sightseeing tours.

Craft operated; HM.2 Mk 111 306 "Hovermarine One"
Route(s): Commuter service out of Salvador and routes in Todos on Santos Bay.

SERVICOS DE TRANSPORTES DA BAIA DA GUANABARA (STBG)

This company operates three HM2 Mk III sidewall hovercraft on a 3 n mile route between communities and business areas in the Bay of Guanabara, Rio de Janeiro.

CRAFT OPERATED:
HM2 321 "Gavea"
HM2 322 "Gragoata"
HM2 323 "Guarativa"

VENEZUALA
TURISMO MARGARITA CA

This operator has a fleet of three HM.2 hovercraft which are used on services between the Isla de Margarita and Puerto la Cruz on the Venezualan mainland. The HM.2 takes two hours for the 55 mile long journey.

CRAFT OPERATED:
HM2 325 "Kenndy"
HM2 330 "Kenna"
HM2 331 "Kelly"

AFRICA

ZAIRE
SOCIETE MINIERE DE BAKWANGA
Mbujimayi
R. C. Lulubourg 10,424

CRAFT OPERATED:
CC.7 002

NIGERIA
PIPELINE CONTRACTORS INCORPORATED
CRAFT OPERATED:
Sealand SH.2 007 (The operator of this craft is an oil exploration company and the craft assists in this activity).

ASIA

BRUNEI
GOVERNMENT OF BRUNEI
CRAFT OPERATED:
SR.N5 019 (AMBD 110)
  Reports suggest that this craft may not be in an operational state.

HONG KONG
HONG KONG AND YAUMATI FERRY CO.
  This company, which is believed to be the biggest passenger ferry operator in the world, operates a fleet of four HM.2 Mk III and one HM.2 Mk IV sidewall hovercraft on routes within the Crown Colony of Hong Kong, including the Central/Tsui Wan routes.
CRAFT OPERATED:
HM.2-326 (HYF-101)
       327 (HYF-102)
       328 (HYF-103)
       329 (HYF-104)
HM.2-335 (Mk IV)

INDIA
CITY AND INDUSTRIAL DEVELOPMENT CORP OF MAHARASHTRA LTD.
HEAD OFFICE:
  Nirmal
  2nd Floor
  Nariman Point
  Bombay 40001

TELEPHONE:
  294515 (9 lines)
TELEGRAMS:
  CITWIN
EXECUTIVE:
  M. N. Palwankar, Manager, Town Services
CRAFT OPERATED:
HM.2 Mk III 214 "Jalapriya"
Route(s): Between Greater Bombay and New Bombay, linking Appollo Bunder and Ferry Wharf with Uran and Elephanta.

PAKISTAN
  The Pakistan Coast Guard authority has purchased two SH-2 five or six seat craft for patrol and interception duties.
CRAFT EMPLOYED:
SH.2 009, SH.2 010

PHILIPPINES
BATAAN-MANILA FERRY SERVICES CO.
MANILA
  This company, which also owns a Raketa hydrofoil, has ordered four HM.2 Mk III sidewall hovercraft for passenger ferry service between central Manila and the Island of

Coiregidor. Services to other parts of Manila Bay are also offered. Two HM.2s had been delivered at the time of going to press and a further two were due to be delivered in late 1976.
CRAFT:
HM.2-320
     332
     333
     334

THAILAND
THAI CUSTOMS AUTHORITY
  Klong Toly
  Bangkok
CRAFT OPERATED:
MV-PP1 001 "Customs Hovercraft 1"

TOUR ROYALE
  Bangkok, Thailand
  This company intends operating a fleet of at least three HM.2 hovercraft on routes in Bangkok and other locations.

AUSTRALASIA

AUSTRALIA
MUNDOO PASTORAL COMPANY
ADDRESS:
  Mundoo Island, South Australia
  A Hovergem G-6 agricultural ACV is employed by this company for carrying personnel, cattle and equipment to various islands in the Mundoo group.

THE NATIONAL PARKS COMMISSION
ADDRESS:
  Flinders House,
  17 Flinders Street,
  Adelaide, S. Australia 5000
  The Commission employs a Taylorcraft

Skimmaire for patrol and supervisory work in the Coorong National Park. The Coorong is a large shallow lake within the park. It is about 90 miles long by ½-1 mile wide and connects with the Murray River and the sea. Illegal poaching of water fowl is a problem and the Skimmaire is employed to overcome this. Patrols are undertaken about twice a week and total about 7-8 operating hours. The craft operates at up to 70 miles from base.
SULLIVANS COVE FERRY CO.
  Hobart
  Tasmania
  Sydney

This company operates a single HM2 Mk III craft on regular commuter and tourist services between Hobart and Bellerive across the Derwent Rover.
CRAFT OPERATED:
  HM.2-319 "Michael Howe"

NEW ZEALAND
DEPARTMENT OF CIVIL AVIATION
  The New Zealand Department of Civil Aviation is operating one SR.N6 Winchester for crash rescue services at Mangere Airport, Auckland.
CRAFT OPERATED:
  SR.N6 014 "Whakatopa"

EUROPE & MEDITERRANEAN

BELGIUM
MINISTRY OF WORKS
  Antwerp
CRAFT OPERATED:
HM.2 Mk III 315 "Kallo" (Employed as River Scheldt survey craft).

CHANNEL ISLANDS
HOVERCROSS LTD
  St. Helier, Jersey, C.I.
  Hovercross Ltd operates between Gorey, Jersey and Carteret, France, with HM.2 sidewall hovercraft 303 on charter from International Hoverservices Ltd, of Southampton.

The first service with HM.2 began in July 1975 and it is hoped that services will be maintained until September each year. In 1976 services were operated with HM.2-305. Other C.I. services are also undertaken.

FRANCE
FRENCH NAVY
  Toulon
CRAFT OPERATED:
  2 × N.102
FRENCH RAILWAYS (SNCF)
  In conjunction with British Rail Hovercraft Ltd, Track Railways intend to begin cross-channel hovercraft ferrying services between

Boulogne and Dover in June 1977. The service will be operated under the "Seaspeed" banner and the hovercraft used will be French-built SEDAM N.500s, manned by French personnel.
CRAFT OPERATED:
  N.500-01
  N.500-02
LANGUEDOC-ROUSILLON REGIONAL DEVELOPMENT BOARD
  Montpellier & Perpignan
CRAFT OPERATED:
  2 × N.102 Craft

GREECE
HELLENIC HOVERCRAFT LINES ("HOVERLINES")
Piraeus
EXECUTIVE:
Mr. A. N. Vomvoyiannis, Managing Director
CRAFT OPERATED:
HM.2 Mk III 304 "Natouro 2"
HM.2 Mk III 307 "Natouro 1"
Route(s):
Piraues-Hydra-Spetsai-Porto Heli

ISRAEL
ISRAELI NAVY
The Israeli Navy has two SH.2 Mk 5 nine-seater hovercraft for use as support craft.

ITALY
ITAL HOVER SpA
Zaltere 66
Venice
CRAFT OPERATED:
HM.2 Mk III 302 "Mare 3"
Route(s):
Venice-Sattomarina-Grado
ITALIAN INTERFORCE UNIT
Ancona
CRAFT OPERATED:
SR.N6 036 (HC 9801)

PORTUGAL
SOCIEDADE TURISTICA PONTA DO ADOXE SARL
Avenida Casal Ribeiro 46-6
Lisbon
CRAFT OPERATED:
HM.2 Mk III 301 "Torralta"
HM.2 Mk III 308 "Soltroia"
HM.2 Mk III 316 "Troiamar"
HM.2 Mk III 318 "Troiano"
Route(s):
Setubal-Troia/Sesimbra

NORWAY
DE BLA OMNIBUSSER A/S
Stromsveien 196
Oslo 6
DIRECTOR:
Mr Dahlseide
CRAFT OPERATED:
HM.2 Mk III 317 "Fjordbuss 1"
Route(s):
Oslo-Horten, with calls at Drobak, Filtvet and Tofte

SOVIET UNION
MINISTRY OF THE RIVER FLEET
The 50 seat Sormovich ACV has been operating experimental services on the Volga and Oka rivers and a derivative is expected to go into production. The most widely used commercial ACV at present is the 48-50 seat Zarnitsa sidewall craft. This is being followed into production by the enlarged, 80-seat Orion and the Rassvet (Dawn). The former is intended for services on inland waterways, the latter for local sea routes. Another new ACV passenger ferry is the Chaika, thirty of which are to be built at Sosnovska for the Black Sea Shipping Line.

Well over one hundred Zarya air-lubricated hull craft have been completed and many of these are in service on shallow rivers in the eastern areas of the Soviet Union. Wing-in-ground effect machines are being developed for high-speed ferry services along the main rivers. These are described as being capable of travelling within several metres of river surface at speeds of some 155 mph (250 km/h).

SOVIET ARMY
A military version of the Skate 50-seat fast ferry is in service with the Soviet Army.

SOVIET NAVY
Several experimental ACVs are being evaluated by the Soviet Navy, and a military version of the Skate is entering service in growing numbers with the Soviet naval infantry as an assault landing craft. Largest craft in service is the 220-ton "Aist", similar in many respects to the SR.N4 Mountbatten and employed to carry tanks and mechanised infantry. A smaller, but similar vessel, designed to carry tanks only, is reported to be undergoing trials.

UNITED KINGDOM

BRITISH RAIL HOVERCRAFT LIMITED
(Seaspeed Hovercraft)
HEAD OFFICE:
Royal London House, 22/25 Finsbury Square, London EC2P 2BQ
TELEPHONE:
01-628-3050
TELEX:
883339
REPRESENTATION OVERSEAS:
SNCF, Armament Naval, 3 Rue Ambroise, Paré 75001, Paris, France.
DOVER ROUTE HEADQUARTERS
Seaspeed Hoverport, Eastern Docks, Dover
TELEPHONE:
Dover (0304) 203574
TELEX:
965079
RESERVATIONS:
7 Cambridge Terrace, Dover
TELEPHONE:
01-606 3681
TELEX:
96158
DIRECTORS:
J. M. Bosworth, CBE, Chairman
J. M. Lefeaux, Managing Director
Lord Black of Barrow-in-Furness
D. D. Kirby
SENIOR EXECUTIVES:
A. J. Tame, Commercial and Planning Manager
P. A. Yerbury, Chief Engineer
F. J. Leese, Finance Manager
A. H. Thorne, Route Manager, Dover Strait

British Rail Hovercraft Ltd, a wholly-owned subsidiary of British Railways Board, was formed in March 1966 and launched its first commercial service in July, 1966, between Southampton and Cowes. The cross-channel service for passengers and cars between specially constructed hovercraft

The Princess Margaret, one of two SR.N4 hovercraft operated by British Rail Hovercraft Ltd on its Seaspeed cross-channel routes, Dover-Boulogne and Dover-Calais.

Princess Anne, sister craft to Princess Margaret, arriving in front of the Seaspeed terminal building at Boulogne. In the foreground is one of the fast Autorails which enable the company to operate a through London/Paris service taking 6 hours

terminals at Dover and Boulogne began in August, 1968 using an SR.N4 'The Princess Margaret'. A year later the service was augmented by the introduction of a sister craft 'The Princess Anne' and in October 1970 a service was initiated between Dover and Calais.

In association with British Rail and French Railways the company operates a through London/Paris service taking about 6 hours, using special trains operating from a platform alongside the Boulogne hovercraft terminal. At Calais a coach connection with Lille and Brussels is provided, enabling the through London/Brussels service to be performed by rail/hovercraft/coach in 7 hours.

Government approval was given in March 1976 for the stretching of the two existing SR.N4 Mk 1s and the construction of a new terminal complex at Dover Western Docks.

The stretched craft is designated SR.N4 Mk III and involves lengthening the craft to 185 ft. This modification will increase the vehicle capacity to a maximum of 55 cars and 420 passengers. The four marine Proteus gas-turbines are to be uprated to 3,800 shp each and each will drive a propeller/fan unit with a 21 ft (6·40 m) diameter propeller. The additional power will ensure that the performance of the current craft will be maintained.

Craft motion will be considerably less than that experienced on the standard SR.N4 and for similar comfort levels the larger craft will be capable of operating in waves up to 2 ft (0·61 m) higher than the present craft. Craft capacity will be increased by approximately 70% while costs will increase by some 15%.

The new Dover Terminal will be a purpose built complex situated on 15 acres of reclaimed land lying between the Prince of Wales Pier and the North Pier, in the inner harbour of Western Docks, Dover. Its proximity to Dover Marine Station will enable a rail link to be constructed giving a potential inter-city time between London-Paris of 5¼ hours.

Early summer of 1977 will see the introduction of two Sedam N500 Hovercraft operated under the name of Seaspeed by SNCF (French National Railways). Motive power is supplied by five 3,200 hp Avco Lycoming TF40 marinised gas turbines, two for lift and three propulsion. Maximum speed is 57/62 knots. and cruising speed 44/50 knots. Each craft is able to carry 400 passengers and 45 cars.

By 1978, four of the largest commercial hovercraft in the world, two SR.N4 Mark IIIs and two Sedam N.500s will be operating under the Seaspeed banner, providing an annual total capacity for 550,000 vehicles and 4 million passengers.

DEPARTMENT OF TRADE AND INDUSTRY (DTI)

CRAFT OPERATED: HM.2 Mk III 310 (XW555)

Operated by the National Maritime Institute as a support craft for an offshore research structure in Christchurch Bay. The HM.2 is based on the Lymington River. HM.2 Mk III 310 (XW555)
HD.2 001—Held by The Naval Hovercraft Trials Unit.

HOVERLLOYD LIMITED

ADDRESS:

International Hoverport, Sandwich Road, Ramsgate, Kent

Hoverlloyd's three SR N4's, operating on the Pegwell Bay (Ramsgate)/Calais route carried 933,000 passengers and 153,000 vehicles across the English Channel in 1975. The craft above converted from a standard SR.N4, carries 280 passengers and 37 vehicles, compared with 254 passengers and 30 vehicles on the standard craft. This increase in capacity was achieved by removing the two inner passenger cabins to increase the car deck area and by widening the outer passenger cabins

TELEPHONE:
Thanet (0843) 54881/54761 499-9481
TELEX:
96323
LONDON OFFICE:
Board of Chief Executive, Sales Administration, 49 Charles Street, London W1X 8AE
TELEPHONE:
01-493 5525
TELEX:
262374
DIRECTORS:
Ingemar Blennow (Swedish) Chairman
James A. Hodgson, Deputy Chairman and Managing Director
Folke Kristensen (Swedish)
Hans Pihlo (Swedish)
ASSOCIATE DIRECTORS:
Howard V. Archdeacon

Robert H. Harvey
Emrys Jones
Andrew Ramsay
David Wise

Hoverlloyd was formed by two shipping companies, Swedish Lloyd and Swedish American Line (now both members of the Brostrom group) to operate a cross-Channel car and passenger ferry service between Ramsgate and Calais. The company operates three BHC SR.N4 Mk. II widened Mountbattens. A fourth craft is scheduled to go into service in June 1977. It will be of the same type but with minor modifications.

The crossing between Ramsgate and Calais takes 40 minutes and there are up to twenty return trips a day in summer and a minimum of four a day in winter. On May 1st, 1969, the company opened coach/hovercraft/coach services between London and Paris. This service takes eight hours and a single fare costs from £9.00. There are up to five daily departures during summer and two during winter.

On April 1st 1974, Hoverlloyd opened coach/hovercraft/coach services between London/Kortrijk and Brussels. The service takes seven hours to Brussels and a single fare to either destination costs from £7.60. There are two daily services in the summer peak and a daily departure is maintained year-round.

Passengers are able to buy tickets from travel agents, or by making a booking direct from Hoverlloyd or at the Hoverport. Those travelling with a car pay only for their car, according to its length. The car charge covers the driver and up to four passengers. For vehicles there are three tariffs; 'A', 'B' and 'C'. 'A' tariff is more expensive and is applied in peak hours during summer, in either direction, according to a detailed traffic analysis, 'B' tariff is cheaper and accounts for the balance of the departures listed for the summer. The 'C' tariff applies throughout the year on selected flights and this represents reductions of up to 30% on peak time fares.

The tariffs have been designed to encourage a balance in the origin of cross-channel traffic, and to spread the daily peaks of traffic.

The company's hoverport covers 12½ acres below the cliffs at the north end of Pegwell Bay, Ramsgate. The site is raised 8 ft above the level of the beach, so that operations are not affected by tides. It consists of a group of long low buildings running parallel to the cliffs. Between the buildings and the cliffs is a car park and the car reception area which is joined to the main Ramsgate-Sandwich road by an access road built up the cliff face.

In front of the building is a large square concrete apron with a semi-circular ramp extending at one end. The SR.N4 makes the most convenient approach, parks on the apron in front of the building while it loads and unloads, then departs from the most suitable point.

These buildings contain the main passenger and car terminal area which includes the inspection halls for customs and immigration, duty free shops, cafe, bar, restaurant, banks and other passenger facilities. Next to this area are the administrative offices.

CRAFT OPERATED:
"Swift" (SR.N4 002) registration GH 2004
"Sure" (SR.N4 003) registration GH 2005
"Sir Christopher" (SR.N4 005) registration GH 2008
For delivery in June 1977
SR.N4 006

HOVERWORK LIMITED

(Wholly owned subsidiary of Hovertravel Limited)
HEAD OFFICE:
12 Lind Street, Ryde, Isle of Wight
TELEPHONE;
Ryde 65181 (STD0983)
TELEX:
86513
CABLE:
Hoverwork Ryde
DIRECTORS:
D. R. Robertson (Chairman)
C. D. J. Bland (Managing Director)
E. W. H. Gifford
A. C. Smith
R. G. Clarke

SOME TYPICAL HOVERWORK OPERATIONS

Year	Location	Type of Operation	Type of Terrain
1969	Holland— the Waddenzee	Seismic Survey	Shallow water, tidal area with large expanses of sand banks at low water
1969/70	Abu Dhabi	Seismic Survey	Very shallow water combined with coral reefs
1970	Bahrain	Gravity Survey	Shallow water and operations over coral reefs
1970	Holland— the Waddenzee	Seismic Survey	Shallow water, tidal area with large expanses of sand banks at low water
1970	Tunisia— Sfax	Seismic Survey	Very shallow water.
1970	Algiers	Passengers	Transport from Airport to Fair site including half a mile down a specially prepared road
1971	Bahrain	Seismic Survey	Shallow water and operations over coral reefs
1971	Saudi Arabia —Red Sea	Seismic Survey	Very shallow water combined with coral reefs
1971	Holland— the Waddanzee	Seismic Survey	Shallow water, tidal area with large expanses of sand banks at low water
1971	Holland— Dollard Bay	Service drilling rig	Shallow water, tidal area. 3 miles of sand to cross at low water
1971	Arctic Circle	Logistics	In leads of pack ice over shallow water including plateau of rock with depths from 0·5 to 6 feet
1971	England— North Sea Haisbro & Leman Banks	Seismic Survey	Very shallow water in places, moving sand banks with various tidal streams. Total area strewn with wrecks rendering it unsafe and impractical to use boats.
1972	Tunisia— Sfax	Seismic Surveys	Very shallow water and shoreline land work
1972	North West Territories Canada	Seismic Survey	Shallow water, ice
1972	UK—The Wash	Logistics	Mud, shallow water
1973	UK— Maplin Sands	Geological Survey for London's third airport	Tidal sands, shallow water
1974 through '75 to '76	Saudi Arabia	Seismic Survey	Shallow water, reefs, unchartered areas
1975	Australia— Thursday Island	Casualty evacuation and general transport	Shallow water and reefs. No conventional docking facilities
1975	UK—The Wash	Transportation of men and materials.	Tidal areas half mud half water
1976	UK	Seismic Survey	Tidal area of Liverpool Bay and Blackpool

Hoverwork Limited is a subsidiary of Hovertravel Limited and was formed in 1966. The company provides crew training and charter facilities for all available types of ACVs, thus bridging the gap between the operators and manufacturers.

The company has trained over 45 hovercraft captains and has received some 40 charter contracts, including film sequences and the operation of the SR.N6 craft for mineral surveys all over the world. The company operated the hovercraft passenger service during Expo' 67 at Montreal and a service at the 1970 Algiers Exposition.

Hoverwork is the largest international operator of hovercraft, having access to Hovertravel's 38 seater SR.N6. Hoverwork has undertaken operations in areas from the Arctic to the equator. These have included logistics operations in the northern part of Svalbard and in equatorial parts of South America. To date Hoverwork has operated in the following countries: Canada, South America, Mexico, Brunei, Holland, Bahrain, Kuwait, The Trucial States, Saudi Arabia, Algeria, Tunisia, English North Sea, Spitsbergen and Australia.

During 1976, the company conducted operations in Saudi Arabia, United Kingdom, Australia and Algeria.

HOVERTRAVEL LIMITED
HEAD OFFICE:
12 Lind Street, Ryde, Isle of Wight
TELEPHONE:
Ryde 65181 (STD 0983)
TELEX:
86513-Hoverwork
CABLE:
Hovertravel, Ryde
TERMINAL OFFICES:
Quay Road, Ryde, Isle of Wight (Tel: 65 241)
Clarence Pier, Southsea (Tel. 29988)
DIRECTORS:
D. E. Webb, Chairman
D. R. Robertson
C. D. J. Bland (Chief Executive and Managing Director)
E. W. H. Gifford
SENIOR EXECUTIVES:
G. Palin (Company Secretary)
R. G. Clarke (General Manager)
Hovertravel Limited, formed in 1965, is a

£120,000 company whose main activity has been the operation of two SR.N6 Winchester class hovercraft in the Solent, primarily between Ryde and Southsea. The distance is just over four miles and the frequency varies between one return trip per hour in the winter and five return trips per hour in the summer.

Approximately 420,000 passengers are carried per year, together with fifty tons of freight. The service has gained in popularity and the total number of passengers carried by September 1976 was well over 4 million. The maximum number of passengers carried in one day (using both hovercraft) was over 4,000.

Another craft which had been built at Bembridge, where Hovertravel has extensive workshop facilities, came into service on August 8th 1974. This was the SR.N6 055 GH2035—a 58-seat SR.N6 1S.

The combined fleet operated by Hovertravel, Hoverwork and Solent Seaspeed which during 1976 completed an estimated 8,000 hours of operation, includes :-
3 SR.N6 Mk 1 S, GH2035, GH2014 and GH2015 3 SR.N6s, GH2010, 2012, 2013 1 SR.N6 Flat Deck GH2011

INTERNATIONAL HOVERSERVICES LIMITED

HEAD OFFICE:
138 Rownhams Lane, North Baddesley, Southampton SO5 9LT
TELEPHONE:
0421 23 2588
Telephones: 0703 35378
Also 0703 732588
(from January 1977)
Cables: Highfleet, Southampton
DIRECTORS:
Captain A. S. Hands MRIN, Chairmr and Joint Managing Director
Lieut. Comdr. M. D. Dawson, RN MNI, Secretary and Joint Managing Director
L. R. Colquhoun, DFC, GM, DFM
Mrs E. Hands, Secretary (Alternate Director)
International Hoverservices Limited was formed in January 1969 to operate hovercraft and the first service between Bournemouth and Swanage was opened in July 1970. Since then the company has operated various scheduled and charter services in the Solent and Poole Bay areas, among which is a daily industrial commuter service for Vosper Thornycroft Limited between Cowes, Isle of Wight and their shipyard in Southampton.

The Company provides staff for overseas operations and provides a consultancy and training service for both prospective existing operators.
CRAFT OPERATED:
HM.2 Mark III Nos. 303 ,305, 312

NAVAL HOVERCRAFT TRIALS UNIT

HEAD OFFICE:
HMS Daedalus, Lee-on-the-Solent, Hampshire, PO13 9NY
TELEPHONE:
Lee-on-the-Solent 550143 (STD 0705)
COMMANDING OFFICER:
Commander F. Hefford, DFC, AFC, AFRAeS, RN

The Interservice Hovercraft Unit wound up in December 1974, and in January 1975 the Naval Hovercraft Trials Unit (NHTU) was formed at Lee-on-the-Solent in the presence of Sir Christopher Cockerell and Mr Frank Judd MP (Navy Minister). The Flag Officer Naval Air Command, Vice Admiral P. M. Austin, commissioned the new unit at Lee-on-the-Solent.

Since then, the majority of the trials carried out have been aimed at evaluating the hovercraft in the Mine Countermeasures role, this included a six-month charter of the Vosper Thornycroft VT 2 and a trials period with Hoverlloyd's SR.N4, "Sir Christopher". The BH.7 has been modified to incorporate a sweep deck on the port side. Reports suggest that the Royal Navy eventually intends to order a fleet of MCM hovercraft for minesweeping in coastal regions around Britain.
CRAFT OPERATED:
SR.N6 027 (XV 859) Fitted with dual controls and radar for training.
SR.N6 035 (XV 617)
SR.N6 033 (XV 615)
BH7 001 (XW 255) Modified to MK IV version, embodying bow door.

SOLENT SEASPEED
(A division of Hovertravel Ltd)

TERMINAL OFFICES:
Medina Road, Cowes, Isle of Wight
TELEPHONE:
2337
Crosshouse Street, Southampton
TELEPHONE:
21249

Solent Seaspeed operates the passenger hovercraft route formerly operated by British Rail Hovercraft Limited between Cowes and Southampton.

The distance is just over twelve miles and the frequency of service is approximately hourly and similar to that run by the previous operator.

TRANSHORE INTERNATIONAL LTD

HEAD OFFICE:
133-139 Page Street,
London NW7 2ER, England
TELEPHONE:
01-959 3636
TELEX:
263271

The 60 knot SR.N6 operated by the Naval Hovercraft Trials Unit, HMS Daedalus, Lee-on-Solent

The 50-ton BH7 which has been modified to incorporate a sweep deck on the port side

EXECUTIVE:
D. S. Elbourne, Managing Director

OVERSEAS REPRESENTATIVE:
Transhore International,
c/o PO Box 356,
Alkhobar,
Saudi Arabia

TELEPHONE:
Dauman 24846

TELEX:
67019 Olayan SJ
R. D. Holland, Director

Transhore International is the owner of the world's largest hoverbarge, the Sea Pearl, which is capable of carrying indivisible loads of up to 250 tonnes. The company offers transhipment of general cargoes from ship to shore, and also a specialist service in the transport from ship-to-shore of heavy equipment for major projects.

The NHTU hardstanding with *left*, SR.N6s. At the top left is the VT 2 and in the centre is the BH.7

MIDDLE EAST

EGYPT
EGYPTIAN NAVY
Alexandria

In 1975 the Egyptian Navy purchased three re-furbished SR.N6 hovercraft for coastal defence patrols along the Egyptian coastline. Negotiations are in progress with the Egyptians for the supply of further BHC hovercraft for similar duties.

CRAFT OPERATED:
SR.N6-016
SR.N6-032
SR.N6-034

IRAN
IMPERIAL IRANIAN NAVY
Hovercraft base: Khosrowabad

Eight BHC Winchesters are being operated by the Imperial Iranian Navy on logistics

CRAFT OPERATED:
SR.N6 040(IIN 01) Mark 4
SR.N6 041 (IIN 02) Mark 4
SR.N6 042(IIN 03) Mark 3
SR.N6 043(IIN 04) Mark 3
SR.N6 044(IIN 05) Mark 4
SR.N6 045(IIN 06) Mark 4
SR.N6 046(IIN 07) Mark 4
SR.N6 047(IIN 08) Mark 4
BH.7 002(IIN 101) Mk 4
BH.7 003(IIN 102) Mk 4
BH.7 004(IIN 103) Mk 5
BH.7 005(IIN 104) Mk 5
BH.7 006(IIN 105) Mk 5
BH.7 007(IIN 106) Mk 5

duties and coastal patrol.

Also in service with the IIN are six BH.7 hovercraft. The first two craft, BH.7 Mk 4s, are operated in the logistic support role.

The remaining four are Mk 5s. The Mk 5 is a multi-role craft and is designed to carry surface-surface, surface-air missiles on its side decks.

BH.7 Wellington Mk 5 of the Imperial Iranian Navy

SAUDI ARABIA
Saudi Arabian Coastal and Frontier Guard
Ministry of the Interior, Airport Road, Riyadh

The Saudi Arabian Coastal and Frontier Guard operates a number of SR.N6 Win-

chesters on patrol, contraband control, search and rescue and liaison duties. The craft are attached to bases at Jeddah and Aziziyah on the east and west coasts.

CRAFT OPERATED:
SR.N6 038
SR.N6 048

SR.N6 049
SR.N6 050
SR.N6 051
SR.N6 052
SR.N6 053
SR.N6 054

JAPAN
Airport Hovercraft Service Co Ltd
Started in July 1972, using MV-PP5 09, "Angel No. 1", on a service linking Kajiki and Ibusuki in the Kagoshima Bay. The route currently takes over two hours to accomplish by car but with the hovercraft the 60 km route is achieved in less than an hour. A second craft, MV-PP5 1— "Angel No. 2"— was added to the service in 1973, "Angel No. 3" was delivered in the summer of 1974 and "Angel No. 5" in June 1975.

Japanese National Railways
Kokutetsu Building, 625 Marunouchi 1-chome, Chiyoda-ku, Tokyo

A service between Uno in Okayama Perfecture and Takamatsu in Kagaw Prefecture was inaugerated in November 1972, using MV-PP5 007, named "Kamome" (Sea Gull).

Meitetsu Kaijo Kankosen K. K.
99-1, Shin-myiazaka-cho, Atsuta-ku, Nagoya City

Began regular services across the Mikawa and Ise Bays between Gamagori and Toba in September 1969 with an intermediate stop at Nishin. The craft employed is MV-PP 5 02 which has been named "Haku-cho".

Nippon Hoverline Co Ltd
Sakal Building Edo-cho 1, Ikutaku, Kobe City, Hyogo Pref.

Began its first service in December 1974, with MV-PP5-11 and 12, named Akatombo (Red Dragonfly) Nos 51 and 52, linking the two cities of Osaka and Tokushima, in Western Japan. The route distance of 98 km is covered in 1 hour 25 mins. Each craft carries 48 passengers as opposed to the standard 52-seat configuration on the PP5.

Oita Hoverferry Co Ltd
1309 Nishi-shinchi, Imatsura, Oita City

Operating three MV-PP5 craft, numbers 04, 05 and 06, named "Hobby 1, 2 and 3" on a service between Oita Airport, Oita and Beppu cities. Service began in 1971.

Ryuku Kaiun Co Ltd
1-1 Nishihoi—Machi, Naha
Manager: Ryosei Kuwae

Operates MV-PP15s—01, 02 and 03—on route between Naha and Expo '75 Port at Okinawa. This service began on July 20th, 1975 and the three PP15s each take about 40 minutes to complete the 36-mile route.

Yaeyama Kanko Ferry K.K.
No 1 Aza-ohkawa, Ishigaki City, Okinawa

Delivered to her owners in the spring of 1972, MV-PP5 08—"Koryu"—operates a service linking Ishigaki and Iriomote Island, a distance of about 30 km, taking about 20 minutes, compared with the 2 hours taken by the ships used previously. Yaeyama Kanko Ferry Co Ltd is a joint investment of Taketomi City, Ryuku Kaiun and several other local shipping concerns.

ACV TRAILERS

AND

HEAVY LIFT SYSTEMS

AUSTRALIA

TAYLORCRAFT TRANSPORT (DEVELOPMENT) PTY LTD

HEAD OFFICE:

Parafield Airport, South Australia 5106

TELEPHONE:

(08) 258 4944

DIRECTORS:

R. V. Taylor

J. Taylor

Taylorcraft has recently introduced its Liftaire skirt system for lifting and moving bulky loads and the Trailaire range of ACV trailers with load capacities from 1¼ to 10 tons.

LIFTAIRE SYSTEM

Cushion pressures of up to 130 lbs per square foot of base area can be accommodated by this system which requires minimal fixing to its load. It is thus ideal for moving tanks and other vessels, transportable buildings, damaged aircraft and other bulky or fragile loads.

Once the load is lifted it may be winched or towed over almost any reasonable level surface. Movement on slopes is feasible but requires special precautions as do movements involving loads with a high centre of gravity or asymmetric weight distribution. Very low pulling forces are required on the level and there is complete control for positioning.

The skirt system is easily attached to and detached from most loads, making it ideal for situations where a number of loads are to be moved and for use where space is restricted.

Quotations are given for any task and are usually made in four parts:

1. Skirt system. This may be purchased outright or leased for an operation.
2. Air system. A blower unit and its controls are mounted on a trailer and designed to match the load. This may be leased, if a suitable unit is available, or designed and built for a specific task.
3. Setting up. (First operation only). This involves attendance at the site and return fares from Adelaide, together with freight costs involved.
4. Local Assistance. A compressor or air line, winch(es), towing vehicle and/or tackle and unskilled labour will be required at the site.

TRAILAIRE I

This air cushion assisted trailer is intended for use in situations where the ground is too soft or wet to allow the use of normal trailers. One or more may be towed by a tractor or single units may be man-handled as required. The skirt and lift unit are removable allowing operation as a normal trailer in good conditions. Lift engine is a Kawasaki KT 300.

Towbar and tow ball are interchangeable to simplify handling in confined spaces.

Operation as conventional trailer:

DIMENSIONS:

Length overall (including towbar)

18 ft 0 in (5·49 m)

Width 6 ft 0 in (1·83 m)

Load Space 6 ft × 12 ft (1·83 m × 3·66 m) (Wheel arches at centre)

Loading Height 2 ft (0·61 m)

TYRES: 6·40 × 13

WEIGHTS:

Tare 330 lb (150 kg)

Payload (Max) 30 cwt (1,524 kg)

TRACK: 5 ft (1·52 m) centres

Operation as air cushion assisted trailer:

DIMENSIONS:

Length overall 18 ft 6 in (5·54 m)

Width 8 ft (2·24 m)

Load space

2 each of 6 ft × 4 ft (1·83 m × 1·22 m)

Loading height 2 ft (0·61 m)

WEIGHTS:

Tare 580 lb (263 kg)

Payload (Max) 24 cwt (1,219 kg)

Cushion pressure (Max) 45 lb/sq ft

FUEL:

25 : 1 petrol oil 2·1 gals (10 litres)

TRAILAIRE II

The basic unit is an 8 ft × 16 ft (2·43 m × 4·87 m) platform capable of lifting 2 tons on its 8 ft × 12 ft (2·43 m × 3·65 m) deck.

Diagram showing a typical application of the Liftaire industrial skirt system

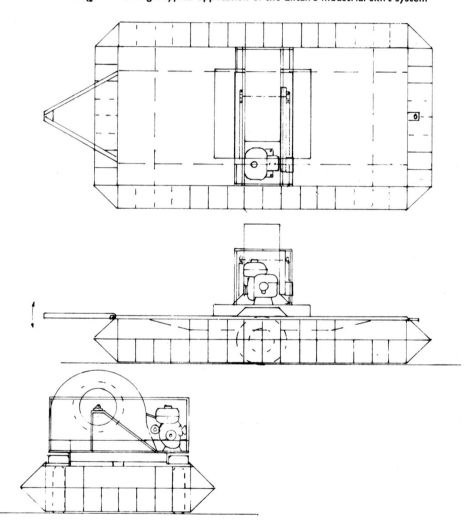

Trailaire I air-cushion assisted trailer

Units may be coupled together to give load platforms of 24 ft × 8 ft; 16 × 12 (4 tons payload) or 16 × 24 ft (8 tons) or spaced to carry long loads, such as pipes. They can be towed by light vehicles or winched over land. Over water an outboard motor or a pump unit may be used for propulsion.

Space alongside the lift engine allows an operator to ride on the platform clear of the load space. Sockets around the platform edge are provided to accept posts to fence-in the load area.

Ground clearance of the standard unit is 10 in but greater clearance can be provided if required. For amphibious operation buoyancy tanks can be fitted, though the standard unit can be operated over water as long as lift power is maintained.

POWERPLANT: GM 308 with 12 v generator, electric starter and 44A battery.

FAN: Double intake 33 in (0·83 m) centrfugal driven through reduction gears, via torque converter.

DIMENSIONS: (SINGLE UNIT)

Length overall cushion-borne
17 ft 8 in (5·38 m)
Width, overall cushion-borne
9 ft 8 in (2·94 m)
Height of deck, hard structure
10 in (254 mm)
Height overall, cushion-borne
20 in (508 mm)
Height of lift unit on pads
4 ft 0 in (1·21 m)
 cushion-borne   4 ft 10 in (1·47 m)
Load Space
12 ft 4 in × 8 ft (3·75 × 2·43 m)
Fence Height (Posts)   3 ft (0·914 m)

WEIGHTS:
Tare weight   1,390 lb (630·46 kg)
Gross weight   6,000 lb (2,721·55 kg)

TRAILAIRE IV

This is a general purpose load-carrying platform for amphibious operation. Over water payload 2·5 tons.

Power is supplied by a single GMH 350 cu in V8 automotive engine driving two DWDI 2 ft 3 in (0·68 m) centrifugal fans at 2,300 rpm via a clutch and 1·5 : 1 reduction. Electric battery for starting. Flashproof exhaust fan for engine compartment operates automatically before engine can be started. Close cooling system with automotive type radiator. 12 v pump for ballast system. 20 gal (90 l) fuel tank.

DIMENSIONS:
Length (hard structure) 24 ft 0 in (7·31 m)
Width (hard structure) 12 ft 0 in (3·65 m)
Height off cushion, load deck, 14 in
Hard structure clearance   12 in (304 m)
Load space 12 ft × 16 ft (7·31 × 4·87 m)

WEIGHTS:
Tare: 8,000 lb (3,628 kg)
Gross: 14,000 lb (6,350 kg)
Overwater payload   2½ tons

BALLAST: 2,000 lb (907 kg) maximum in forward tanks.

BUOYANCY: 15,000 lb (6,803 kg) without raised sides.

PERFORMANCE:
Wave height   4 ft max (1·21 m)
Step   12 in (304 mm)
Endurance   2-3 hours

TRAILAIRE VI

Trailaire VI is designed for heavy duty applications and has a payload capacity of 10 tons. Two versions are available, a fully amphibious verson and a non-buoyant version which can cross water only with the power on.

Power is supplied by a 200 hp Ford V8 automotive engine driving two 2 ft 3 in (0·68 m) centrifugal fans mounted in twin intakes aft.

Drawbar pull at the gross weight of 17 tons is 800 lb (362·85 kg).

DIMENSIONS:
Length (excluding drawbar)
36 ft 6 in (11·125 m)
Beam, hard structure   12 ft 0 in (3·65 m)
 amphibious version
13 ft 0 in (3·96 m)
 sidebodies version 8 ft 0 in (2·43 m)
Hard structure clearance 1 ft 0 in (304 mm)
Loading height   14 in (355 mm)

WEIGHTS:
Gross   17 tons

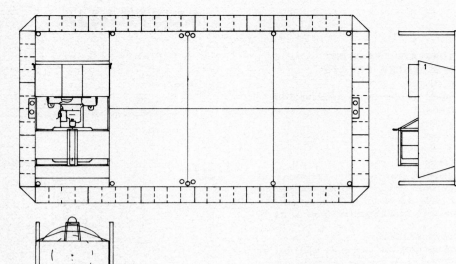

Trailaire II 2-ton capacity air cushion trailer

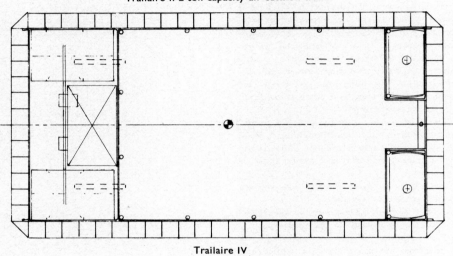

Trailaire IV

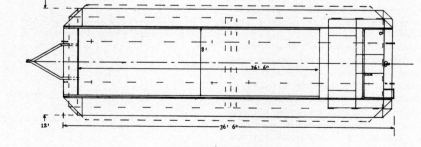

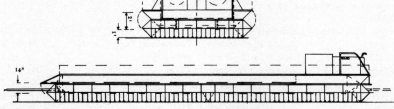

Trailaire VI, 10-ton capacity air-cushion trailer, available in fully amphibious and non-buoyant versions.

Tare   7 tons

PERFORMANCE:
Endurance   4 hours

CANADA

HOVERLIFT SYSTEMS LTD

HEAD OFFICE:

1201, 603 7th Avenue SW, Calgary, Alberta, T2P 2T5 Canada

TELEPHONE:

403 263 3983

DIRECTORS:

R. D. Hunt, P.Eng., President

D. M. Simmons, P.Eng., Executive Vice-President

K. W. Crowshaw, Vice-President

V. H. Redekop, Treasurer

Hoverlift Systems Ltd is a member of the Simmons Group of Companies. The group's main interest is the exploitation of mineral resources, and its entry into the field of industrial air cushion vehicles was through a requirement to mount oil drilling equipment onto an air cushion vehicle to extend its potential mobility during the summer. Initially the company will be concentrating on two product lines: amphibious load-carrying pontoons, and the development of the air cushion assist principle for road vehicles.

RUBBER DUCK

A prototype amphibious platform was produced during the latter part of 1975 and this was used on river crossings throughout the winter of 1975-76 including both the freeze-up period in the autumn and the thaw in the spring—to establish the feasibility of an all-season air cushion ferry, Further work was undertaken during 1976 to establish methods of self-propulsion for general overland and over water applications.

It is intended to produce special purpose variations of the general pontoon concept for use in the following broad situations:

Ferry use on rivers and estuaries.

General transportation over terrain unsuitable for wheeled or tracked vehicles.

Ship-to-shore lightering.

LOAD ASSIST

During 1976 the company began a programme of basic research to develop a technique of air cushion load assist applicable to Canadian environmental requirements. The objective is to provide a load assist package which can be readily attached to existing commercial road vehicles to allow them to continue operation during the periods of restriction or load limitation, and to increase the capacity of existing vehicles under normal operating conditions. This work is being undertaken in conjunction with Alberta Transportation, the Provincial Government Transport Authority.

CONSULTANCY

In addition to the product range mentioned above, Hoverlift Systems Ltd can offer an all Canadian Consultancy Service on all aspects of the industrial application of the air cushion principle by personnel having twelve years practical experience of design and operation.

HOVERLIFT HL-101 RUBBER DUCK

Rubber Duck is a fully amphibious air cushion ferry or ship-to-shore lighter designed and built by oilfield personnel for operation in the Canadian North. The hull is an exceptionally rugged all-metal structure of welded steel construction.

Payload capacity is 20,000 lb (9 t) with 30% reserve buoyancy over water and 30,000 lb (13·5 t) over land at a maximum of 0·85 psi (58 mb) ground pressure.

For ease of transportation the vehicle's side decks fold to permit loading on one live-roll oilfield trailer without crane. It can also be loaded on the C-130 Hercules, one of the transport aircraft engaged in regular supply operations in the Canadian North and other remote regions.

LIFT: Motive power is supplied by a single 197 hp Caterpillar 3208, or equivalent Detroit diesel engine, driving a Joy Industrial steel fan, or equivalent, through a direct coupling.

PROPULSION: Cable and on-board winch or towed by tractor.

HULL: Welded steel structure.

SKIRT: 9 in (229 mm) pitch segmented skirt in hot-bonded natural rubber/nylon material. Spray skirt in neoprene nylon material. Skirt segments capable of routine operation across newly broken ice ledges; may be replaced individually from deck if necessary.

DIMENSIONS:

Length overall	39 ft 4 in (12 m)
Width overall	18 ft 10 in (5·7 m)
Load deck length	
Centre deck	28 ft 0 in (8·5 m)
Side decks	36 ft 0 in (11·0 m)
Load deck width	18 ft 2 in (5·5 m)

PERFORMANCE:

Speeds and gradients within winch or tractor capability.

Capable of crossing ice ridges and ledges 2 ft 6 in (0·76 m) high.

Hoverlift HL-101 Rubber Duck air-cushion ferry or ship-to-shore lighter. Overwater payload capacity is 20,000 lb (9 ton) with 30% buoyancy

DENMARK

A/S SEIGA HARVESTER CO., LTD.

HEAD OFFICE:

15 Sct. Thomas Alle, DK-1824 Copenhagen V, Denmark

TELEPHONE:

Copenhagen 243015

TELEX:

6815

CABLES:

Seigaharv

UK REPRESENTATIVE:

Robert Trillo Limited Broadlands, Brockenhurst, Hampshire SO4 7SX, England. Telephone: Brockenhurst (05902) 2220

SEIGA TORTOISE

Amphibious tug and support vehicle, type 080, for air-cushion platforms

Originally developed as a transporter for reed harvesting operations, the Tortoise is being used increasingly in other fields of operation. More than 300 are now in use for anti-pollution work, seismic survey, general

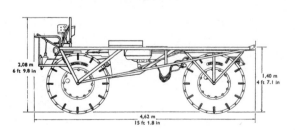

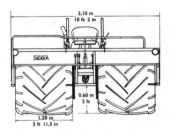

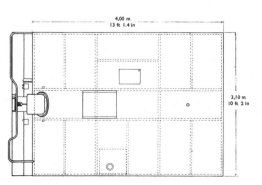

General arrangement of the Seiga Tortoise.

Seiga Tortoise multi-terrain vehicle, powered by one Volkswagen 127 petrol engine or one Lombardini Type LDA 673 diesel

transport, as well as reed harvesting, etc., in over a dozen countries. The Tortoise has a two bar pull of up to 2,500 kg (5,500 lb) and can operate in widely differing conditions from coastal sea, liquid mud of varying consistencies, ice and snow, to shingle, sand and swamp. Buoyancy is provided by the low-pressure Seiga tyres which also propel the vehicle. Additional propulsion may be provided in clear water by an outboard propulsion unit.

Ground pressure, which is very low, is 40 g/cm² (0·6 lb/in²) unloaded an 100 g/cm² (1·5 lb/in²) with a 2-ton load.

Vehicle transmission is by Volvo hydraulic motors, one for each wheel, and steering is obtained from the rear wheels which are mounted on a hydraulically actuated turn-table.

A clear rectangular deck space of 125 ft² (11·63 m²) is provided, with a central driving seat forward of this area.

Engine:
Volkswagen Type 127 (petrol), or
Lombardini Type LDA 673 (diesel).

Transmission and drive:
Two Volvo hydraulic pumps, one for each side of vehicle (separate). Four Volvo hydraulic motors, one for each wheel. Third central hydraulic pump for services. Controls: Hand throttle and foot-actuated band brakes.

Steering:
Rear wheels mounted on turntable hydraulically operated by two rams.

DIMENSIONS:

Length overall	15 ft 2 in (4·62 m)
Width overall	10 ft 2 in (3·10 m)
Height overall	6 ft 10 in (2·08 m)
Deck height	4 ft 7 in (1·40 m)
Deck length	13 ft 1½ in (4·00 m)
Deck width	10 ft 2 in (3·10 m)
Wheel diameter	4 ft 3 in (1·30 m)
Wheel width	3 ft 11 in (1·20 m)
Wheel base	9 ft 4 in (2·85 m)

WEIGHTS:
Empty, Volkswagen 127 3,300 lb (1,500 kg)
Empty, Lombardini 673 3,630 lb (3,630 kg)

PERFORMANCE:
Speed over water, wheel propulsion only
  2-3 mph (3-6 km/h)
Gradient 30-40

FRANCE

SEDAM

HEAD OFFICE:
80 Avenue de la Grande Armée, 75 Paris 17 eme

TELEPHONE:
380-17-69

TELEX:
29-124 Paris

Sedam is developing a range of amphibious barges to offload cargo ships in ports which, because of the vast growth of sea transport, have become almost permanently congested.

This congestion is forcing large numbers of vessels to queue up to be unloaded, and sometimes necessitates a wait of 30-100 days. Such delays, because of the high cost of demurrage and insurance, frequently lead to an increase of 50% to 100% in freighting charges.

Sedam is proposing the use of its Amphi-barges to unload the vessels and carry their cargo to warehouses close to the port, but clear of the main areas of congestion.

Their amphibious capability would enable them to make the transition from water to land and carry their loads up to the ware-houses where conventional fork lift trucks, mobile cranes and other freight handling equipment would be employed for offloading.

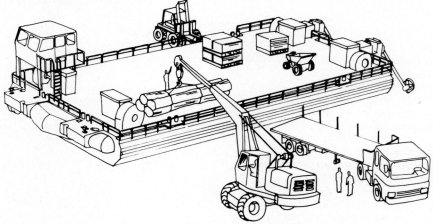

Impression of a 100 ton capacity Amphibarge

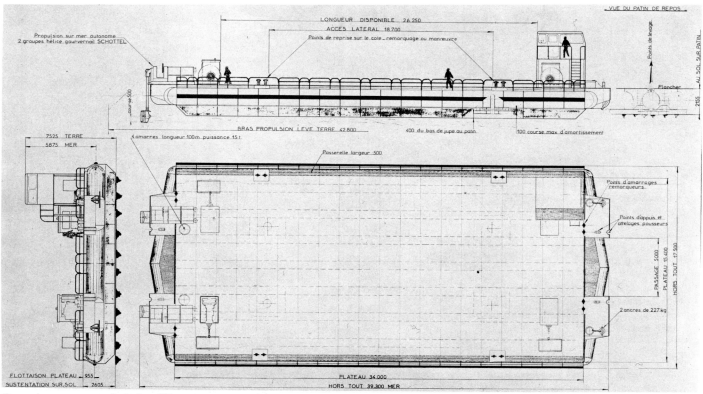

General arrangement of a Sedam 100 ton capacity Amphibarge.   Power for the lift fans could be supplied by four 500 hp marinised diesels.   Two 100 hp diesels driving water-propellers through Schottel drives give a water speed of 5 knots.   The outboard propellers are raised at the point where the land towing system takes over

The manufacture of components for the Amphibarges could take place in the countries in which they are to be used. This would not only permit the customer to make considerable savings in transport costs. it would also create a source of local employment.

Features of the proposed Amphibarges would include the following:

HULL: Modular craft structure comprising a number of cylindrical buoyancy tanks laid side-by-side longitudinally. Surmounting the buoyancy tanks are supports for the deck and below it are fastenings for the multiple skirt system and landing pads. At the bow and stern half-cylinders are employed as strengtheners against impacts incurred during towing or pushing. Surface of the deck is in diamond head plating. In the loading area the deck is strengthened by longitudinal and transverse girders. Railings are optional.

CONTROLS: The operator's position and all necessary controls are located in a raised bridge above the engine compartment on the starboard side. Crew would normally comprise an operator, engineer and seaman.

LIFT: Four marinised diesel-engines, mounted one each side of the load deck, forward and aft, each drive a single centrifugal fan to feed air to the multiple skirt system. The skirts made in a terylene based material, are secured in position by quick-fasteners to facilitate repair and replacement. Skirt life is about 1,000 hours.

PROPULSION OVER WATER: Among alternative methods of water propulsion are tugs and outboard motors. Points for the installation of two outboard engines are provided aft. Speed with outboard engines of suitable output will be about 5 knots.

PROPULSION OVER LAND: Drag overland is approximately 1 % of the total weight when operating over a flat surface with no wind. Towing can be undertaken by a wheeled vehicle or a tractor with caterpillar tracks. Alternatively, one or more winches can be installed aboard, enabling the craft to pull itself overland to a fixed point by employing a cable.

CARGO HANDLING: Optional roller track can be fitted for handling heavy vehicles. Express rollers are available for loading and positioning containers. Removable tank can be provided for the handling of bulk goods.

OPERATING PROCEDURE:

1. Cargo is offloaded directly into the amphibarge by the ship's derricks (20 to 60 t/h according to cargo);
2. the self-propelled amphibarge reaches the shore;
3. the amphibarge is lifted and pulled to the warehouse by minimal towing force (winch or tractor);
4. goods are unloaded by local means (cranes, forklifts, etc.)

Particulars of the A50, A100 and A200 Amphibarges, with payloads capacities of 50, 100 and 200 tonnes, respectively, are given below:

DIMENSIONS:	A50	A100	A200
Length	22 m	35 m	35 m
Width	12 m	18 m	19 m
Loading deck area	220 sqm	500 sqm	500 sqm
Height on rest	2 m	2 m	2·5 m
Max load	1·8 t/sqm	1·8 t/sqm	1·8 t/sqm
Floatability volume	220 m²	500 m²	735 m²
Weight when empty	55 t	130 t	155 t
POWER			
Lift	4 × 300 hp	4 × 500 hp	4 × 500 hp
Propulsion	2 × 100 hp	2 × 200 hp	2 × 300 hp
Generator	20 KVA	20 KVA	20 KVA
PERFORMANCES:			
Payload	50 t	100 t	200 t
Tolerable overload	10 t	20 t	none
Max waveheight	1 m	1 m	1 m
Speed (calm water)	5 knots	5 knots	5 knots
Recommended max gradient	3 %	3 %	3 %
Land speed	5 km/h	5 km/h	5 km/h
FUEL CONSUMPTION			
Lift	250 kg/h	401 kg/h	442 kg/h
Propulsion	35 kg/h	61 kg/h	102 kg/h

JAPAN

MITSUI SHIPBUILDING & ENGINEERING CO LTD

HEAD OFFICE:

6-4 Tsukiji 5-chome, Chuo-ku, Tokyo, Japan

Mitsui has designed a 310-ton hoverbarge, designed for use in either deep or shallow waters. A feature of the craft, designated SEP-1, is the provision of jack-up legs, similar to those employed on some offshore oil rigs. This facility enables the craft to be located above test or survey sites in shallow waters or in areas of marsh or tundra.

NETHERLANDS

NETHERLANDS
J. J. de Bakker

ENGINEERING WORKS:
  Post Office Box 18,
  Hulst
  Netherlands
TELEPHONE:
  (01140) 2212
EXECUTIVES:
  J. J. de Bakker, Managing Director

UK REPRESENTATIVE:
  Cdr Th. Pellinkhof
  139C Gloucester Terrace, Bayswater,
  London W2 6DX
TELEPHONE:
  (01) 262 8159
TELEX:
  Nedham Ldn 23211 att Pellinkhof

J. J. de Bakker builds the unique Amfirol multiterrain vehicle which has been specially designed to traverse silt, mud banks, quicksands, gullies and other marginal terrain impassable to conventional wheeled vehicles.

The Amfirol is propelled by means of the revolving screw principle. Two rotating, torpedo-shaped drums, each fitted with a helical band profile, enable the vehicle to drag itself across almost any type of terrain and also provide it with buoyancy.

POWER PLANT: Motive power is furnished by a Sundstrand hydraulic pump driven by a 135 hp (SAE) NSU rotary engine. Power is transferred to the drums via two separate hydraulic systems and two 2-speed gearboxes.

CONTROLS: In mud, silt and other soft terrain, the drums, which are separately driven, rotate in opposite directions. The speed attained with the drums in contra-rotation is from 8-12 km/h (4·9-7·4 mph). On solid ground, with this form of rotation in use, the vehicle would travel sideways. However, by reversing the rotation of one of the drums so that they both move in the same direction, the vehicle can reach 20-30 km/h (12-18 mph) over a firm surface.

Craft heading over land and water is controlled by rotating one drum faster than the other.

To transport the Amfirol over long distances, planks are placed against the deck of a flat-deck trailer of suitable size and the vehicle will roll up the planks, onto the deck, sideways.

ROTATING DRUMS: Both drums are made in durable manganese steel, while the hull is in stainless steel. The drums are divided by metal partitions into a number of watertight compartments to limit flooding in the event of damage.

DIMENSIONS:

Length overall	18 ft 4½ in (5·60 m)
Width overall	9 ft 10 in (3·00 m)
Height overall	6 ft 6¾ in (2·0 m)
Free deck space	108 ft² (10 m²)

WEIGHTS:

Empty	7,716 lb (3,500 kg)

Payload capacity
  5,512 lb (2,500 kg) afloat and up to 11,025 lb (5,000 kg) on solid ground

TRACTIVE POWER:
  2,205 lb (1,000 kg) in water and up to 11,025 lb (5,000 kg) on solid ground

PERFORMANCE:
  Speeds of up to 18 mph (30 km/h) depending on type of terrain and condition

Top: Amfirol towing a UBM Hover-Systems hoverplatform across marshland. *Centre:* Climbing a steep river bank. *Bottom:* Negotiating a 45 degree slope

UNITED KINGDOM

ACE (1976) LTD

HEAD OFFICE:

35 Randolph Street, Shirley, Southampton

TELEPHONE:

0703 776468

TELEX:

477537

CABLES:

HOVERACE SOTON

DIRECTORS:

F. B. Hake, Chairman

A. Latham, Marketing Manager

R. Gilbert, Chief Designer

R. Henvest, Works Manager

Air Cushion Equipment was formed in April 1968. The company was originally conceived to give a design, consultancy and manufacturing service to industry for the application of the air cushion principle to the movement of heavy loads.

The technology and skirt types developed by the company are based on the original work carried out by Hovercraft Development Ltd and were utilised as a basis for the foundation of Mackley ACE Ltd and UBM hover systems, as well as the world-wide service provided by ACE Ltd via its licensed contractors for oil storage tank movement.

Over the last four years, technical and market research has been carried out into the very heavy and dense load movement field and has involved the introduction of several new skirt types and the study of skirt systems at cushion pressures of up to 11 psi for systems having hover heights of up to 18 inches, and 225 psi for systems for heavy load moving systems using water as the cushion fluid. The most recent product innovation is the ACE "Water Skate" load-carrying pallet range which has established water as the most viable cushion fluid for dense load movement.

ACE has studied the application of skirt

systems to many unusual devices and is capable of the project management for total contracts, whether it be a normal or special application of either the air or water cushion principle.

The company accepts contracts for all work associated with the design and manufacture of flexible structures, as well as the design and/or manufacture of cushion systems.

LOW PRESSURE AIR SYSTEMS

Design services are offered in the application of the hover principle utilising low-pressure air (2 psi and below) for the movement of heavy and awkward loads over unprepared ground. This embraces air cushion systems engineering and the design and manufacture of skirts.

Out of this design development capability emerged the hovertrailer concept, aircraft recovery equipment, amphibious platforms and barges. The two most significant products using ACE design and manufactur-

Twenty-one Type AA Water Skate load-carrying modules were employed to launch this 1,800 tonne capacity deck cargo barge. The launching ramps comprised five 150 ft temporary tracks of compacted limestone overlaid with steel sheet

ing skills are those of Arctic Engineers and Constructors ACT-100 264 ton auw transporter and the Mackley Ace Sea Pearl 750 ton auw transporter.

HIGH PRESSURE AIR SYSTEMS

High pressure air systems have been investigated up to 11 psi statically and 7·5 psi dynamically culminating in the lifting and movement of an 820 tonne concrete caisson. This development programme has led to a greater understanding of air cushion systems in general for large skirted areas and has led to an improvement of design and manufacturing techniques throughout the pressure range up to 11 psi. For operating on roads and bridges the company has developed for CEGB a segmented skirt system which can be clamped beneath a road trailer and will operate at cushion pressures up to 5·5 psi. This system can be adapted to fit most trailers used by the heavy haulage contractors and give a more uniform load distribution over the length of the vehicle, thus relieving stress or concentrated loads from weak ground or bridge structures.

THE "WATER SKATE" LOAD-CARRYING PALLET AND HIGH PRESSURE WATER SYSTEMS

Market and technical research has shown that to lift and move large and dense loads is technically difficult and expensive. For the past three years the company has been investigating new methods of adapting skirt systems for the dense load movement sector of the market, all the time reducing both the capital and operating costs. The latest product to emerge is known as the ACE "Water Skate" load-carrying pallet.

The "Water Skate" load-carrying pallet uses water as the cushion fluid and has been tested up to 225 psi. Modular in application the total system can be used in multiples of the required number from two sizes of pallet with 35 tonnes capacity and 100 tonnes capacity respectively. The equipment uses normal contractors' pumps to give water at the required pressure and flow. One pump can feed several modules via a control manifold and console. The manifold can be used to vary the pressures to each module thus eliminating the necessity to present equipment symmetrically about the centre of gravity. The pressure gauges can be calibrated in weight giving the operator the ability to weigh a bulky structure and to identify the centre of gravity to verify practical readings against calculation.

The areas of use for this product are diverse but include the movement of oil rig jacket structures and deck modules, concrete caissons, transformers, ship sections and hulls, plant and machinery, bridge sections and the launching of structures, ships and boats.

Note: *the word "Water Skate" is a trade mark of ACE Ltd.*

TANK MOVING

Tank moving, using an air cushion for support, has now become a well established procedure. The method offers many advantages over the older conventional forms of movement such as water flotation, mechanical skidding, cranes or bogies. Route preparation is kept to a minimum and it is seldom necessary to reinforce the tank. A tank move can usually be completed in about seven to ten days, depending on the size of

An ACE segmented skirt developed for the Central Electricity Board. By distributing the gross weight beneath the entire underside of a transporter the bending movements and sheer forces imposed on bridges is reduced so that heavy transformers can be carried across without risk

This 700-ton oil storage tank is the largest ever moved by Air Cushion Equipment's hover flotation method.   The operation was undertaken at Pauillac for Shell France.   While the tank was being moved, the roof was floated on a second cushion of air to reduce both the possibility of damage to the roof and the pressure differential developed across the bottom of the tank

An ACE high pressure skirt system in use to lift an 820 tonne concrete caisson

the tank and the distance to be moved. Once the skirt has been assembled on the tank and the tank has been lifted from its foundation, the distance that it can be moved is infinite and only requires the provision of an appropriate means of propulsion and a clearway of adequate width. With all other methods movement is normally limited to comparatively short distances, or the time for the move becomes very extended.

As air is ducted from the fan to the cushion area it percolates through the tank foundation until sufficient pressure is built up to lift the tank. No jacking is required. Once on cushion the tank can be towed or winched

to its new location. The air cushion system allows omnidirectional mobility, hence to change direction or rotate the tank about its vertical axis only requires the application of towing forces in the appropriate direction. Location to dimensional tolerances of ± 2 in can easily be obtained. The towing force required is usually in the order of one per cent of the weight of the tank.

Tanks of all types can be moved on air including those with floating, fixed and column supported roofs and welded or rivetted construction. The illustration shows a 700 tonne floating roof tank being moved in Pauillac for Shell France. This is the largest tank moved on air to date and on this occasion an added innovation was used, floating the roof on a second cushion of air during the move. This not only reduces the possibility of damage to the roof but

also reduces the pressure differential developed across the bottom of the tank.

Tank moving on air cushion is undertaken by licenced contractors as follows:
UK, Western Europe and Arabian Gulf

(part)—Mears Construction Ltd.
Canada and USA—Hover Systems Inc.
Southern Africa—National Process Industries Pty
Japan—Nippon Kensan Co.

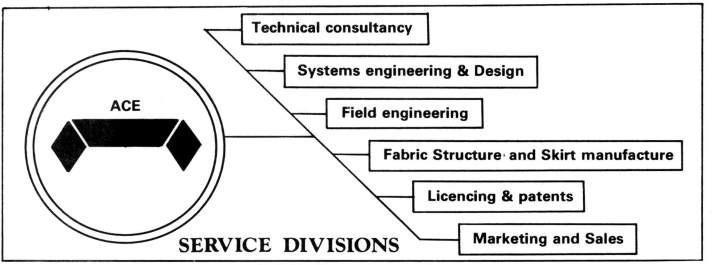

Air Cushion Equipment's operating divisions

BRITISH HOVERCRAFT CORPORATION

HEAD OFFICE:
Osborne, East Cowes, Isle of Wight
DIRECTORS:
See ACV Section

AIR CUSHION HEAVY LOAD TRANSPORTER (AIR CUSHION EQUIPMENT SERIES I)

The development of this equipment was prompted initially by the Central Electricity Generating Board, which is constantly faced with route-planning problems caused by the high weights of laden transporters.

Transformer units now going into service weigh between 155 and 250 tons and 400 ton units are in prospect. On occasion the CEGB has been involved in the heavy expense of strengthening and even rebuilding bridges to accept these loads when no alternative route has been available.

The use of air-cushion equipment, however, provides a practical and economic alternative. By providing an air-cushion under the centre section of an existing transporter it is possible to support a high proportion of its gross weight. Distributing the gross load over the whole length of the transporter reduces the bending moments and sheer force imposed on bridges so that these heavy transformers can be transported without risk over existing bridges.

The investigation into and development of this air-cushion transporter has been supported by the CEGB with the co-operation of the Ministry of Transport and the road haulage companies that operate the transporters.

The transporter illustrated has a length of 90 ft (27·4 m) and a maximum width of 16 ft 10 in (5·13 m). The payload is normally supported between two bogies each of which may have up to 48 wheels.

The skirt containing the air cushion is an easily handled unit which is fitted under the load and side beams of the trailer. Any spaces between the load and trailer frame are 'timbered-in' to take the upward thrust.

This type of skirt system can be built to suit any size of transporter and the one illustrated measures 32 ft (9·57 m) × 14 ft (4·26 m). It is constructed largely of nylon/neoprene sheet extending across the underside of the load platform and formed into a bellows around its periphery. To the bottom

A CEGB heavy load transporter for transformer units. More than 870 bridges have been crossed by this method to date with savings in bridge strengthening costs estimated to be well in excess of £2 million

of the bellows is attached a series of plates, each about 1 ft (0·30 m) long, which make contact with the road surface. Thus, the only escape route for air from the cushion is through the small gap formed between the plates and the ground by the roughness of the surface.

Any general unevenness of the surface, such as the camber of a road or the hump of a bridge, causes the bellows of the 'skirt' to flex so that the plates can remain in contact with the road.

The cushion was designed for a 155-ton lift, when the cushion pressure reaches 5·4 pounds per square inch. At this pressure, when moving over the roughest road surfaces, the volume of air escaping from underneath the shoes is approximately 13,200 cu ft/min (373·5 m³/min) (free air volume flow).

The power to maintain the air cushion is provided by four Rolls-Royce B81SV petrol engines delivering 235 hp (gross) at 4,000 rpm. Each engine drives, through a gearbox, its own centrifugal compressor, with engine,

gearbox and compressor mounted together on a steel underbed as a complete working unit. The four units supplying the power are built onto a road vehicle chassis. This vehicle, which also contains stowage space for the folded cushion container, is attached to the rear of the transporter train whenever it is required for a bridge crossing. It is connected to the air cushion through four, 1 ft diameter air ducts, each connected to a power unit. The ducts are connected by sections of flexible hose to allow for relative movement between the vehicles.

The first commercial load carried by the transporter was a 155-ton transformer for delivery to the Central Electricity Board's sub-station at Legacy, near Wrexham, from the A.E.I. Transformer Division Works at Wythenshawe, Manchester. The route involved crossing the Felin Puleston Bridge which, under normal circumstances, was incapable of withstanding the combined weight of the transporter and the transformer. By using the air cushion to relieve the load on the transporter's wheels the stress on the bridge was reduced by about 70 tons.

Had a conventional transporter been used the bridge would have had to be strengthened at a cost equal to about half the cost of developing and equipping the transporter.

Optimum relief is obtained by taking up about one-third of the gross load in the skirt and transferring this proportion from the bogies to a position under the piece being carried. Current requirements are for re-distribution of between 85 tons and 125 tons of the gross load in this manner and to date over 870 bridges have been crossed using the-air cushion with savings in bridge strengthening costs estimated to be well in excess of £2 million.

Future movements of larger plants are likely to call for relief up to 200 tons. Recognising this potential requirement and also the fact that the existing equipment has already had a considerable part of its operating life the Board decided in 1973, to order a second set of equipment, designated Series II, which would cover all present and anticipated future requirements whilst allowing the Series I equipment to be held for back up and stand by duties. The latter has become particularly important in view of the substantial increase in air cushion assisted movements during the last 18 months.

Series II equipment incorporates new features and design improvements made in the light of operating experience with the original system; main differences being centred around the air supply units.

Air is supplied by four 200 hp gas turbines running on diesel fuel and each directly coupled to an axial compressor to give an output potential up to 7·3 psi with a 20% increase in air capability. The gas-turbines, supplied by Noel Penny Turbines Ltd. are mounted together on a module on the swan necks of the heavy load trailer. The swan necks also carry the control cabin, fuel tanks, batteries, and battery charger so that no separate air supply vehicle is required. The trailer can now operate as a single unit when the air cushion is in situ. The need for flexible air duct sections is avoided, also the loss of time in connecting or disconnecting flexible sections and replacing the rear tractor by the blower vehicle as is required for Series I equipment.

The Series II equipment has had its initial commissioning trials and is expected to be in full commercial service by the end of 1975. A line diagram, accompanying this entry, indicates the differences in layout between the Series I and Series II equipment.

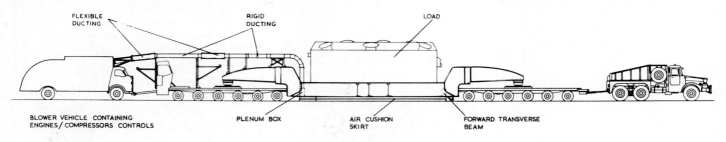

SERIES I ARRANGEMENT

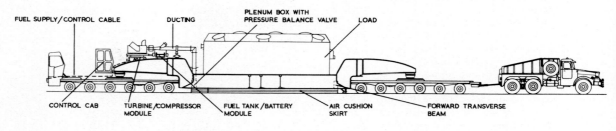

SERIES II ARRANGEMENT

UBM HOVER-SYSTEMS

HEAD OFFICE:
  Lower William Street, Northam, South ampton SO9 2DN
TELEPHONE:
  Southampton 34366
TELEX:
  47106 Hovetrail Soton
DIRECTORS:
  M. J. Phillips, Chairman
  C. S. Richards, Deputy Chairman
  A. Haikney, Managing Director
  L. Beavis, Director
  I. R. Bristow, Director

UBM Hover-Systems (formerly Hover Trailers International) is a division of UBM Engineering Limited, a subsidiary of the UBM Group. It was founded to specialise in the development, construction and marketing of two ranges of hover equipment—aircraft recovery systems and non-self-propelled industrial hoverplatforms of of various types.

AIRCRAFT RECOVERY SYSTEMS

The hover method of aircraft recovery is designed to overcome the enormous difficulties involved in recovering wide-bodied aircraft. It is capable of the recovery of aircraft up to the size and weight of the Boeing 747, and is constructed in modular form so that it can be transported in a standard Boeing 707 air freighter. The advantages of the system are

Bristol Britannia airliner being hovered across a ditch at Gatwick Airport.

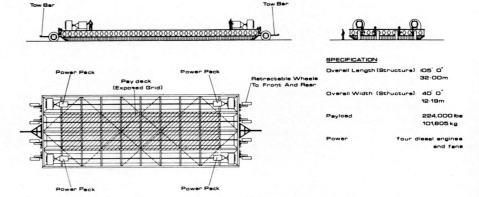

SPECIFICATION	
Overall Length (Structure)	105' 0" 32·00m
Overall Width (Structure)	40' 0" 12·19m
Payload	224,000 lbs 101,605 kg
Power	four diesel engines and fans

A standard 100-ton capacity hover platform

that recovery can be achieved very quickly regardless of the condition of the ground surface, and that secondary damage to the aircraft is reduced to a minimum.

The system was demonstrated at London Heathrow Airport when a DC-4 was hovered over a variety of ground surfaces. During the demonstration it was manoeuvred and hovered across soft ground at speeds of up to 16 km/h (10 mph). Additionally, the equipment has been used under airport operating conditions at Gatwick Airport for the movement of a Britannia. The aircraft was hovered over soft ground for nearly a mile, and at one point was hauled across a 20 ft (6·09 m) wide drainage ditch on a bridge constructed of light steel beams and plywood sheets.

A second method of recovery on hover has recently been developed which dispenses with the pneumatic elevators normally used to support the aircraft. It is designed primarily for small military aircraft of up to 25 tons, and permits the clearance of disabled machines from a runway or the surrounding area quicker and easier than by cranes.

INDUSTRIAL HOVER-PLATFORMS

These non-self-propelled platforms are designed to transport a wide variety of heavy loads over terrain which is impassable for conventional wheeled or tracked vehicles under load. They may be used in widely varying application fields from civil engineering, pipe or cable laying, forestry work, geological and mineral surveying, to agricultural, conservation or drainage schemes.

The basic structure is a rigid steel platform with a strong welded subframe to which a hover skirt is attached. The lift power is supplied by a centrifugal fan driven by a petrol or diesel engine mounted on the

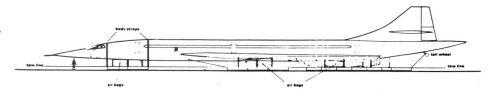

Drawing showing how hover platforms and air bags would be positioned to recover a Concorde airliner

A hover platform loaded with six 12·19 m (40 ft) by 0·68 m (3 ft) diameter pipes crossing soft sand

platform. Special wheels fitted to swinging arms at the rear of the platform give directional control on side slopes and when reversing. Hover height of the platforms varies according to design and size. Individual units of up to 100 tons capacity are available, and awkward loads with high centres of gravity may be transported by linking together two platforms of the same type. Platforms of this type have been sold

in the United Kingdom, Europe, Africa, Asia, North and South America and Australia.

Both the aircraft recovery systems and industrial platforms may be either towed or winched. The ground bearing pressure of the air cushion system is usually less than 1 psi, and the towing force required is very low. For operation in extremely marshy conditions, fully-tracked low ground pressure tractors are the most suitable towing vehicles.

MACKLEY-ACE LIMITED

HEAD OFFICE:
421/427 Millbrook Road, Southampton SO1 3HY
TELEPHONE:
0703 781844
TELEX:
477434 Mackace Soton
DIRECTORS:
D. G. W. Turner (Managing)
J. R. Mackley (Chairman)
F. R. Mackley, CEng, FICE
A. Truslar (Secretary)
M. Fripp

Mackley Ace Limited, a wholly owned subsidiary of J. T. Mackley and Company

Limited, have specialised in the design and construction of cushion supported platform for use in many facets of Industry. They helped to build the world's first hover dredger, have built a range of modular platforms, built the world's largest hover transporter, with a 250-ton capacity in the Middle East and have built two 160-ton hover transporters to cross the River Yukon in Alaska. They are now studying greater payload capacities.

They have recently developed a simple self-propulsion system for their hover platforms. The company has also announced a completely new system for laying submarine cables which simplifies the un-reeling of the

cable.

250 TON ACT

Sea Pearl, the world's largest hover transporter, was launched during 1974 and now operates between Abu Dhabi and Das Island in the Arabian Gulf.

It carries pre-fabricated sections of a liquid natural gas plant for a distance of about 110 miles. Sea Pearl is towed by crawler tractors on land and by a work boat at sea. The use of an amphibious hovercraft allows components to be transported from the fabrication site across rocks and sand, to the sea and then across the sea and directly onto site without having to change the mode of

Two 160-ton payload hoverplatforms employed as chain ferries to carry vehicles and equipment across the Yukon river.

A Mackace 15 ton payload modular platform.

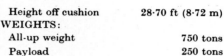

Sea Pearl, the world's biggest hover transporter, in operation in the Arabian Gulf.

A new Mackace self-propelled hover platform

transport for each sector of the journey.

LIFT SYSTEM: Cushion lift is supplied by two 890 hp MWM TBD 602 V12 diesels, each driving a 4 ft 7 in (1·39 m) diameter Alldays Peacock 1,400 BA DIDW centrifugal fan. Each fan delivers 135,000 cu ft (3,823 cu m) of air per minute, giving a cushion pressure of 1 lb sq in (0·7 kg m²).

SKIRT: 4 ft (1·21 m) deep, open segment type, with double segments aft and an anti-spray flap.

BALLAST: A seawater ballast system is fitted to permit the craft to be employed as ship-to-shore transporters.

DECK EQUIPMENT: Two 10 ton hydraulic winches are fitted at the bow for loading plant components, which will either be mounted on rollers or hoverpallets. Twin hydraulic capstans are located amidships for use during mooring, manoeuvring and anchoring.

ACCOMMODATION: Elevated bridge and quarters for a five-man crew.

PERFORMANCE, FULLY LOADED:
Calm water, towing force of 15 tons 7 knots
In 9 ft (2·74 m) high by 250 ft (76·20 m) long waves   3 knots
DIMENSIONS:
Length overall	180 ft 0 in (58·46 m)
Beam overall	80 ft 0 in (24·38 m)
Length, load deck	158 ft 0 in (48·16 m)
Beam, load deck	52 ft 0 in (15·85 m)
Height on cushion	32·70 ft (9·94 m)

Height off cushion	28·70 ft (8·72 m)

WEIGHTS:
All-up weight	750 tons
Payload	250 tons

160 TON AIR CUSHION FERRY

Following experiments conducted in November 1974, Mackace was awarded contracts to build two of these cable-drawn hover ferries, which are now operating across the River Yukon in Alaska. Named the Yukon Princess I and Yukon Princess II, the platforms are used to carry vehicles and equipment across the River Yukon whether frozen solid, breaking up, liquid or just covered with thin ice. The hover platforms are based on a modular float raft with special Mackley Ace skirt frames attached to the periphery. The cushion system gives a hover height of 48 inches when fully laden. In mid-June, 1975 the two craft were carrying up to 2,000 tons of cargo across the Yukon daily.

LIFT SYSTEM: Two 700 hp GM Detroit diesel engines, designed to operate in temperatures of minus 60°F. The engines each drive an Alldays Peacock 1,100 BA DIDW centrifugal fan. Each fan delivers 92,000 cu ft (2,605 cu metres) of air per minute, giving a cushion pressure of 1 lb per square inch (0·7 kg per sq metre).

SKIRT: 5 ft deep, segmented skirt with spray skirt.

WINCHING SYSTEM: Two winches are used to tow the craft backwards and forwards across the 5,000 ft (1,500 metres) crossing.

ACCOMMODATION: There is a heated cabin for the crew and an elevated bridge.

DIMENSIONS (Yukon Princess I):
Length overall	127 ft (38·7 m)
Beam overall	84·5 ft (25·7 m)
Length of load deck	98·3 ft (29·9 m)
Beam of load deck	56 ft (17 m)
Height on cushion	25 ft (7·62 m)
Height off cushion	20 ft (6·1 m)

WEIGHTS (Yukon Princess I):
All-up weight	370 t (375·9 tonne)
Payload	160 t (162·6 tonne)

DIMENSIONS (Yukon Princess II):
Length overall	126·5 ft (38·5 m)
Beam overall	81·5 ft (24·8 m)
Length of load deck	97·8 ft (29·8 m)
Beam of load deck	53 ft (16·1 m)
Height on cushion	25 ft (7·62 m)
Height off cushion	20 ft (6·1 m)

WEIGHTS (Yukon Princess II):
All-up weight	412 t (418·6 tonne)
Payload	160 t (162·6 tonne)

HOVERPLATFORMS

Mackley Ace modular hoverplatform designs have ranged in payload capacity from 15 to 95 tons.

Based on the standard Uniflote pontoon,

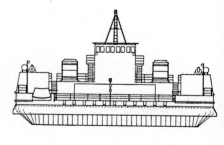

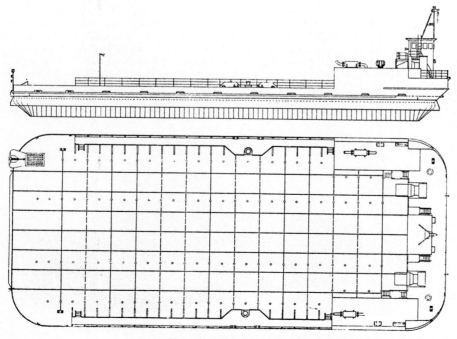

General arrangement of the 250-ton payload capacity Mackley-Ace hover transporter

each platform can be expanded or contracted to suit particular requirements.

Specially fabricated skirt frames are cantilevered off the side of the Uniflote pontoons. The neoprene-coated nylon weave is attached beneath these frames to protect it against accidental damage.

Each frame has its own skirt section attached and is quickly replaced if damaged. The self-contained power packs to power the lift system are also mounted on the skirt frames, leaving the deck area clear. Contract labour can handle and assemble the platforms on site. The platforms are normally winched or towed, although it is possible to propel them with suitable outboard motors such as Harbor-masters.

SPIN TANK

This was developed in response to a request for a simplified cable laying system. The Mackley Ace Spin Tank system of cable laying employs a cushion of low pressure water and simple skirt to support a cable drum on a vertical axis, thus eliminating problems with cable snatch, reel sagging and over-feed. The system has been tested at Mackley Ace's test facilities.

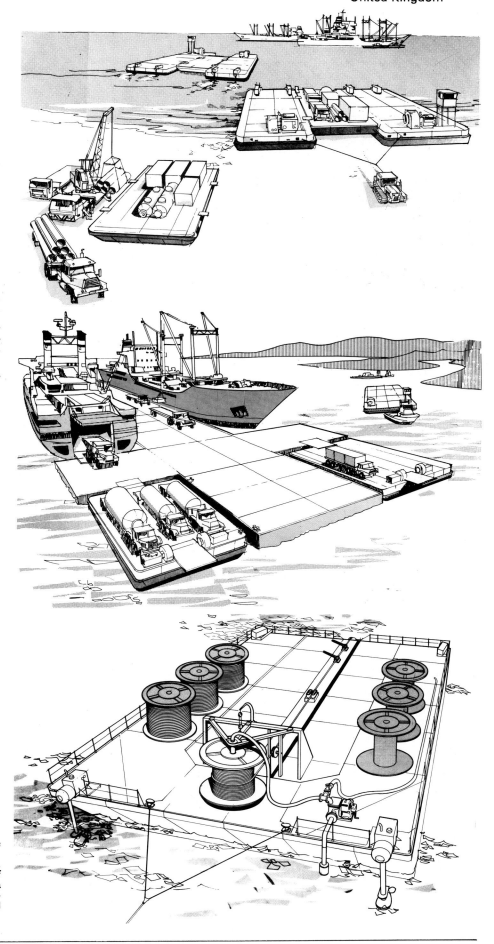

Top and centre: Two proposed ship-to-shore systems employing Mackace transporters. *Below:* The spin tank system of cable laying, developed by Macklay Ace, employs a cushion of low pressure water and a skirt to support a cable driven on a vertical axis, thereby eliminating problems of overfeed, reel sagging and cable snatch

MEARS CONSTRUCTION LIMITED

HEAD OFFICE:
154/158 Sydenham Road, London SE 26 5LA
TELEPHONE:
01-778 7851
TELEX:
947157

EXECUTIVES:
R. W. Bale, BSc. CEng. FICE. Managing Director
D. R. Eales, Director in Charge, Air Cushion Division
P. F. Morgan, Manager, Air Cushion Division
Mears Construction Limited holds the

franchise for Air Cushion Equipment Ltd's system of tank moving throughout the UK Western Europe and parts of the Middle East.

Tanks moved by the company range in size between 48 m diameter, 700 tonnes weight; 68 m diameter 530 tonnes weight and 6 m diameter, 7 tonnes weight. A 700

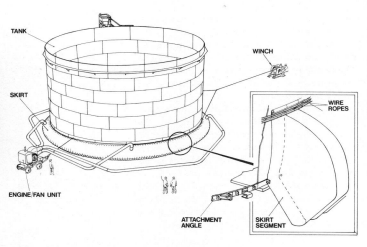

A 68 m diameter tank, weighing 530 tonnes relocated for Stanic at the company's refinery in Livorno, Italy. The technique employed by Mears Construction Limited is shown in the accompanying diagram

tonne tank was relocated by Mears Construction Ltd. for Shell Francaise at their refinery near Bordeaux.

The equipment consists of a segmented skirt system, diesel driven air supply fans and interconnecting ducting, all of which can be readily shipped to any location in the above areas.

Site surveys are undertaken by a Mears Engineer in conjunction with an appointed associate company, in countries outside the UK, which provide non-specialist plant and equipment for the move. Mears provide the lift equipment.

PINDAIR LIMITED
HEAD OFFICE:
Quay Lane, Hardway, Gosport PO12 4LJ
TELEPHONE:
Gosport (070 17) 87830
DIRECTORS:
M. A. Pinder, B.Sc., CEng., MIMechE. (Managing)
A. M. Pinder
John Holland FCA
EXECUTIVES:
N. Horn, Design and Development
M. Pinder, Marketing

B. M. Oakley, Production
R. Bagley, Demonstrations
D. McClunan, Testing and Servicing
V. A. Wells, Administration and Accounts
CONSULTANTS:
D. R. Robertson
E. W. H. Gifford
See ACV Section for company background

Pindair is currently engaged in design studies for several customers requiring rigid and folding hovertrailers of up to 10 tonne capacity. The company welcomes inquiries for specific applications.

RIGID HOVERTRAILERS
Designed for manufacture by Pindair or the customer. Features include low cost, light weight and robust construction.

INFLATABLE HOVERTRAILERS
Designed for manufacture by Pindair. Fully transportable. A 2 tonne version will carry a Land Rover yet is designed to be carried inside a Land Rover. Particularly suitable for military, relief and rescue applications.

VOSPER THORNYCROFT LTD
HEAD OFFICE:
Vosper House, Southampton Road, Paulsgrove, Portsmouth, England
TELEPHONE:
Cosham 79481
TELEX:
86115
DIRECTORS:
See main entry in ACV Section

Vosper Thornycroft released preliminary details of its hoverbarge in May 1976.

The Vosper Thornycroft hoverbarge is designed to carry cargo between ship and shore where there are no conventional port facilities. Hoverbarges can operate over land and water, carrying goods between a ship anchored off any shelving beach and a simple warehouse nearby where they can be unloaded by mobile cranes or fork-lift trucks and transferred to an existing road or railway. When a particular loading or unloading operation has been completed in one place, a hoverbarge operation can be transferred almost in its entirety to another location if desired.

The hoverbarge will have its own fans to maintain an air cushion, with outboard propeller units for propulsion over water. In shallow water it would be connected to an endless cable system to haul it up through the surf and on to a hard area of beach from which it would be towed by a tractor to the unloading point. Vosper Thornycroft hoverbarges would be comparatively slow and simple craft, with relatively modest power units.

Impression of a Vosper Thornycroft hoverbarge facility in operation

THE UNITED STATES OF AMERICA

ARCTIC ENGINEERS AND CONSTRUCTORS

HEAD OFFICE:
  1770 St. James Place, Suite 512, Houston,
    Texas 77027
TELEPHONE: 713 626-9773
CABLES: ARENCO
TELEX: 762587
EXECUTIVES:
  R. G. Longaker, General Manger
  M. R. Bade, Director of Administration
ASSOCIATED COMPANIES:
  Arctic Systems, Calgary, Alberta, Canada

Arctic Engineers and Constructors, a wholly owned subsidiary of Global Marine Inc. of Los Angeles, was formed to create a company with the capability and experience to offer a complete construction and drilling service to the petroleum industry in the Arctic.

Prior to the formation of Arctic E&C, engineers of the parent company had conducted an extensive environment, design, equipment and engineering study of the problems involved in the search for and production of petroleum in the arctic. The study's objective was to analyse and define the operational problems encountered both onshore and offshore. It included analyses of climate, ice properties and distribution, land and air transport vehicles, drilling and construction, transportable arctic housing, and past and present arctic drilling operations.

It was concluded that air cushion transporters, used on a year-round basis, would offer substantial economic and technical advantages in arctic drilling, construction, and transportation.

The company's air cushion transporters are designed to transport heavy equipment and as a foundation support for drilling and construction equipment. The transporters are non-self-propelled and of simple robust construction for ease of operation and maintenance. The company designs air cushion transporters to suit specific operations. It owns and operates the transporters under contract to its clients.

Apart from its activities in the development and exploitation of air cushion transporters, the company has also developed a unique ice breaking attachment for conventional ships. By linking a VIBAC craft (Vehicle, Ice-Breaking, Air Cushion) to the bow of a conventional ship, the ship's ice passage ability is greatly enhanced.

A further development is the company's Pneumatically Induced Pitching System (PIPS) which significantly improves a vessels icebreaking ability by inducing large amplitude pitching at the natural frequency of a given hull.

The company is licensed by Hovercraft Development Ltd.

ACT-100

Construction of the prototype ACT-100 was completed in April 1971. The craft is essentially an ACV barge designed to transport 100-ton payloads throughout the year across Arctic tundra, muskeg and marsh without unduly disturbing the soil and vegetation. It will also traverse offshore ice and open water.

Five months of testing under arctic winter conditions on the Great Slave Lake at Yellowknife during 1971-72 demonstrated that the craft is able to operate in temperatures of —50 deg F without difficulty. It proved extremely stable and manoeuvrable

The ACT-100 air cushion transporter

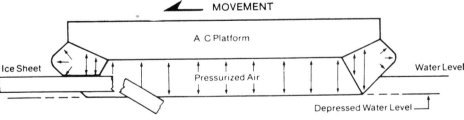

Action of the air cushion platform when an ice sheet is encountered. On contact, the skirt rises above the ice, continuing to act as an air seal. The ice sheet then loses its flotation support from below as the water beneath it is depressed by the cushion of pressurised air within the skirt zone. The ice sheet then becomes a cantilevered ledge and on reaching its critical length breaks, and the overhang section falls off into the displaced water below. The arrows in the drawing above show the force vectors within the skirt

when travelling over level terrain, slopes, water, and over varying thicknesses of ice. It also showed unusual ice-breaking ability in thicknesses up to 660 mm (26 in) and had no difficulty in traversing broken ice.

The Canadian Ministry of Transport employed the ACT-100 under contract to investigate the feasibility of operating air cushion ferries in the Mackenzie River highway system. Initial trials were conducted at Tuktoyaktuk, NWT, in November 1972. The craft was towed 322 km (200

miles) up the Mackenzie for final ferry trials at Arctic Red River in June 1973.

In December 1973 the ACT-100 was employed by Imperial Oil Ltd to transport drill rig supplies and equipment from Langley Island to Adgo Island. Adgo is an expendable artificial island constructed by Imperial in the Beaufort Sea to support an exploratory drilling operation. The ACT-100 carried loads of up to 99·8 tons over ice, broken ice, and water.

LIFT: Cushion air is supplied by two 640 hp

Caterpillar D-348 diesel engines driving two
4 ft 6¼ in (1·37 m) diameter Joy 5425 N.O.L.
steel centrifugal fans. Air is fed directly
into the cushion without ducting. Cushion
pressure is 144 psf. Diesel is contained in a
single 500 US gal integral tank in the main
hull amidships.

CONTROLS: Towing cables to pull vehicle
and wheels beneath center of hull. A liquid
ballast is provided for trim.

HULL: Box-type hull in A537 low temperature alloy steel. Hull is designed to support
a 100-ton payload.

SKIRT: 1·52 m (5 ft) deep fully segmented
skirt in rubber-coated nylon.

CREW: Control cabin accommodates one
operator and assistant. A third member of
the operating crew is the towing vehicle
operator.

ACCOMMODATION: A "habitat" unit, with
complete camp facilities for 35-40 men and
storage facilities, can be mounted on the hull.

SYSTEMS: 110/220 volt, 60 cycle 30 kW
generator for lighting, control and pumping.

COMMUNICATIONS: None permanently
installed.

DIMENSIONS:
Length overall:	
power off	23·71 m (75 ft 3¾ in)
skirt inflated	24·15 m (79 ft 3 in)
Beam overall:	
power off	13·74 m (57 ft 0¾ in)
skirt inflated	18·59 m (61 ft 0 in)
Height overall:	
power off	1·98 m (6 ft 6 in)
skirt inflated	3·20 m (10 ft 6 in)
Draft afloat	1·04 m (3 ft 5 in)
Cushion area	308·068 m² (3,316 sq ft)
Skirt depth	1·52 m (5 ft 0 in)
CONTROL CABIN:	
Length	2·43 m (8 ft 0 in)
Max width	2·74 m (9 ft 0 in)
Max height	2·43 m (8 ft 0 in)
Floor area	6·89 m² (72 sq ft)

FREIGHT HOLDS: Open deck, with tankage available beneath.

WEIGHTS:
Normal empty weight	150 US tons
Normal all-up weight	250 US tons
Normal payload	100 US tons
Max payload	130 US tons

PERFORMANCE (at normal operating
weight):

Speed (dependent on tow vehicle)
6 mph (9·65 km/h) plus
Still air range and endurance at cruising
speed: 12 hours at average speed of
9·65 km/h (6 mph) = 115·87 km (72 miles)
Vertical obstacle clearance
1·21 m (4 ft 0 in)

ADS

The company's latest vehicle—the ADS
(Arctic Drilling System) combines a large air
cushion barge with modern offshore drilling
equipment and an ice-melting positioning
system. It is designed for arctic offshore use.

The system offers two important advantages: (1) the complete drilling system can move
between locations at any time during the
summer or winter, and (2) the unit can remain
over the well bore in ice moving at moderate
speeds.

The three basic components of the ADS are:

(1) a large 70·4 by 43·7 by 4·5 m (231 by
143·5 by 15 ft) self-contained, shallow-draft
aluminium drilling hull.

(2) an air-cushion system capable of lifting
the hull—complete with drilling, crew, and
drilling expendables—2·59 m (8·5 ft) above
the surface.

Impression of the 3,840-ton ADS, designed to carry a complete offshore drilling system

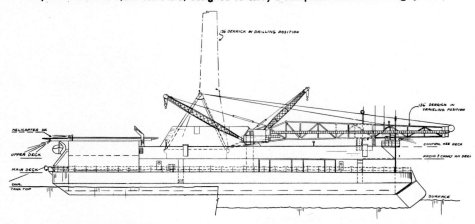

Above: Profile of the 231 ft (70·4 m) long, 3,840-ton air-cushion arctic offshore drilling system
(ADS), showing the derrick in traveling and drilling position, the control house and helipad.
Below: A smaller version of the ADS with a length of 154 ft (46·93 m). Height of the derrick
in drilling position, would be 136 ft (41·45m) measured above the upper deck

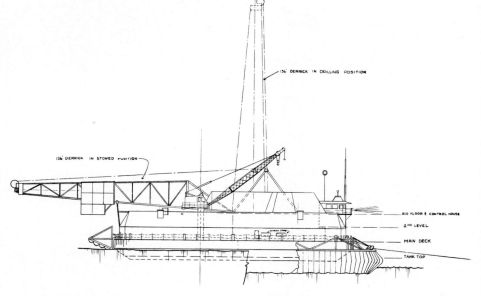

(3) an external hull heating system capable
of melting a ledge of ice moving from any
direction at a rate of 4·57 m (15 ft) per day,
using waste heat from three 1,300 hp Caterpillar D-399 diesel engines.

LIFT AND PROPULSION: A 4,000 kW
common-bus ac power generating system,
with silicon-controlled rectifiers, supplies
power to the drilling equipment and lift fan
drive motors. The system comprises five
800 kw, 1,200 rpm ac generators, driven by
five Caterpillar D-399, series B diesel engines,

each delivering 1,300 hp at 1,200 rpm.
Because the unit will not hover while drilling,
the power system will serve a dual purpose.
It will be used to drive the drilling equipment
when located above a well bore, and the lift
fans when moving to a new location.

The fans deliver a maximum pressure of
1·78 psig. For normal rig moves the maximum cushion pressure will be used only in
an emergency.

SKIRT: 8 ft 6 in (2·59 m) deep, fully-seg-
mented HDL-type skirt in nylon rubber.

PROPULSION: Moving the ADS during the winter season will be accomplished by on-board mooring winches and logistic support vehicles. The support vehicles will pull out approximately 3,000 ft (914·40 m) of 1¾ in (44·45 mm) wire line for each of two modified National 4204-E winches mounted on the bow of the drilling hull. The support vehicles will act as dead men while the winches are taking up the line and pulling the ADS forward.

The support vehicles will have special design features to lock onto the ice sheet and resist the estimated 150,000 lb (68,038·86 kg) maximum lifting force. Winches on-board, powered by GE 752 dc motors, will provide a winching speed of 4 mph (6·43 km/h). An overall average moving velocity of 1 to 2 mph (1·60-3·21 km/h), providing a 24-48-mile (38·62-77·24 km) rig move in one day is anticipated.

It is expected that icebreaker workboats will permit the ADS to be towed through moderately thick ice during the winter season.

LOGISTIC SUPPORT: Candidate vehicles include ice-breaking workboats; self-propelled, 25-ton Voyageur hovercraft; large payload air-cushion barges; conventional barges frozen-in near the drilling locations; fixed-wing aircraft; tracked vehicles and large rubber-tyred vehicles. The selection will be determined by specific condition, economics, availability and other operator requirements.

HULL HEATING SYSTEM: An external heating system on the hull will permit the vessel to remain over the well bore in ice moving at moderate speed.

A four-point mooring system, with ice anchors attached to the ice sheet, allows tension to be pulled on appropriate anchor lines opposing the direction of motion of the ice sheet. This action forces the hot side of the hull to bear against the encroaching ice face. Sufficient heat transfer to the ice sheet melts the ice at a rate equal to the ice sheet motion.

It is anticipated that motion of land-fast ice will be random, and with anchor placement 1,000 ft or more away from the drilling unit, resetting of the anchor spread should not be necessary. However, the ice anchors can be reset.

It is only necessary to melt a ledge of ice equivalent to the draft of the hull and the side or sides exposed to ice motion. If the ice thickness exceeds the hull draft, an auxiliary ice removal system is used below the centre well so that the total projected area of the centre well is open through the ice sheet. Deployment of this system is necessary for riser and guidelines protection and for BOP retrieval when necessary.

This drilling well provides communication between the water below the ice sheet and the "lake" in which the ADS is floating while drilling. This makes the unit buoyant without its weight being transferred to the ice sheet below the barge hull.

The primary hull-heating system uses waste heat recovered from three of the five available D-399 Caterpillar engines during normal drilling operations. Sufficient BTUs are available from this source to melt a volume of sea ice moving toward a corner of the hull at 15 ft per day and exposing the drilling draft area of one side and one end of the hull to ice motion.

A considerable amount of research and development was committed to the ice-melting system. Both model and full scale studies were conducted to learn the mechan-

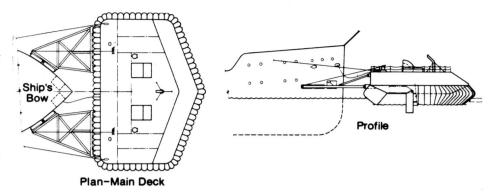

Plan-Main Deck

Profile

Top: An early VIBAC air-cushion ice-breaker, concept designed for attachment to conventional ships travelling through Arctic waters. The unit was an outcome of experience with the ACT-100 on the Great Slave Lake, where it continuously broke ice as thick as 27 in (0·685 mm)
Centre: The Canadian Coast Guard ice-breaker, *Alexander Henry*, pushing a bow-mounted air cushion platform through 17 in (432 mm) thick ice in the Thunder Bay area of Lake Superior at a speed of 9 knots
Bottom: With the ice-breaker platform attached, the cleared track is straighter and wider than that created by conventional ice-breaking techniques and the ship is more manoeuvrable

ism of heat transfer and fluid flow between the hull and ice sheet and to establish heat input requirements for different velocities. These studies confirmed the mathematical model and proved the validity of the concept.

CONTROLS AND SYSTEMS: A central drilling control room is provided for the well-control personnel. Instrumentation will be installed to provide data on mud weight, mud pump pressure and flow rates, casing pressure, pit level, bit weight, rotary torque, rate of penetration and other critical drilling details. All remote BOP and choke line controls will be housed in the centre.

The design also features a large bulk mud,

cement storage and handling system. The bulk storage system will accommodate 6,060 cu ft of mud and 3,140 cu ft of cement. A pneumatic bulk-handling system permits rapid material transfer.

ACCOMMODATION: A totally enclosed and heated working environment will help maintain maximum crew efficiency, even during the coldest Arctic weather. Modern crew quarters for 70 men and a large helipad are included.

A preliminary specification for the 3,840-ton ADS is given below.

DIMENSIONS:
Length overall   231 ft 0 in (70·4 m)

Beam overall	143·5 ft (43·7 m)
Depth of hull	15 ft 0 in (4·5 m)

WEIGHTS AND CAPACITIES:

Gross weight	3,840 long tons
Casing	360 long tons
5 in drilling pipe	12,000 ft
Reserve mud	2,357 bbl
Active mud	746 bbl
Bulk mud	6,060 cu ft
Bulk cement	3,140 cu ft
Stacked materials	17,556 cu ft
Drill water	10,695 bbl
Fresh water	746 bbl
Portable water	746 bbl
Fuel oil	3,731 bbl
Lubricating oil	1,500 gal
Total complement	70 persons

Design of the ADS is 95% complete. The unit, with a gross weight of 3,840 long tons, is designed to operate in land-fast ice in water depths from 0-183 m (0 to 600 ft) during the 7-8 month arctic winter season and in water depths of 9·14-183 m (30 to 600 ft) during the open-water summer season. The ADS is designed to operate in nearshore conditions in the Beaufort Sea at the Mackenzie Delta, the Alaskan North Slope, and the inter-island areas of the Canadian Arctic Islands. It could be used in any arctic land-fast ice areas including the continental shelves of Greenland and Siberia.

VEHICLE, ICE-BREAKING, AIR-CUSHION (VIBAC)

The icebreaking characteristics of the ACT-100 has led to the development of a new vehicle designed specifically to aid the passage of a conventional ship through ice-bound waters.

The craft, known as the VIBAC system, is attached to the bow of the ship as soon as it enters an ice-field. Close visual observation and films have revealed what happens when air cushion platform approaches an ice sheet, and how the air cushion ice-breaking phenomenon takes place.

On making contact with the ice sheet the skirt rises up over the ice while continuing to maintain its air seal. The ice-sheet then penetrates the zone of pressurised air beneath the craft, where the water level with the skirt area is depressed to a lower level than the bottom of the ice layer. The ice has now become a cantilevered ledge without water support beneath. When the cantilevered section reaches its critical length, failure occurs and the overhanging section breaks off and falls in to the depressed water below.

A plough-like deflector attached to the VIBAC unit will thrust the ice aside as the vessel progresses through the ice sheet.

Prospects for improving winter navigation on the Great Lakes have been greatly enhanced by this development in ice-breaking technology. A small Canadian Coast Guard ice-breaker, the Alexander Henry, pushing a bow-mounted air cushion platform in the Thunder Bay area of Lake Superior, has demonstrated it can clear a path through ice up to 17 inches thick while travelling continuously at a speed of nine knots.

Trials conducted during the winter of 1975-76 by the Canadian Coast Guard and Transport Canada have confirmed the capability of this new technology for effectively and efficiently breaking ice under the conditions prevalent on the Great Lakes.

During the trials, the 3,550 hp Alexander Henry rammed the same icefield at full speed without the air cushion platform and crunched to a stop in less than two ship lengths. With the platform attached, not only was the ice-breaker able to maintain forward momentum, but the cleared track was straighter and wide than would have been the case with conventional ice-breaking methods. The ship was also much more manoeuvrable.

Later, the combined VIBAC and ship successfully broke 30 in of ice in a continuous mode as well as a 46 in thick ice ridge.

The Canadian Coast Guard is planning to fit the platform to the bow of an ordinary cargo ship and undertake further trials on the Great Lakes next winter. The unit was moved from Inuvik, N.W.T., for trials, and was modified at the Port Arthur Shipyard in Thunder Bay under the direction of Arctic Systems personnel.

Future experiments with the new technology will investigate its effectiveness in dealing with ridging and rafting of ice such as is encountered on the St. Lawrence River. Studies also will be undertaken on the use of this technology on ice conditions in the Arctic.

EGLEN HOVERCRAFT INC

HEAD OFFICE:

801 Poplar Street, Terre Haute, Indiana 47807

TELEPHONE:

(812) 234 4307

TERREHOVER

Eglen Hovercraft Inc has designed and built a variety of hover platforms, in order to investigate possible agricultural applications. Particular attention is being given to its use for transporting heavy loads, including fertiliser tanks, over wet and muddy fields which cannot be negotiated by conventional farm equipment.

During the past twelve months the company has been developing a tomato bin-carrying harvester platform and a cranberry sprayer. It has also built a hovertractor.

The prototype Terrehover is built in wood and measures 16 ft (4·87 m) long by 8 ft (2·43 m) wide. Air is put under pressure by two 2 ft (0·60 m) diameter axial-flow fans, driven by two JLO Rockwell L395 two-cycle engines. An H.D.L. type segmented skirt is used and the hoverheight is 9 in (228 mm).

Although designed originally to lift 2,000 lb (907·18 kg) the platform has successfully

The prototype Eglen Terrehover, a 16 ft (4·87 m) long hover platform, designed for carrying agricultural equipment over wet and muddy terrain. Production models will be self-propelled, with the operator seated in an enclosed cabin

lifted 4,000 lb (1,814·37 kg), and has applied fertilizer in conditions normally considered too severe for conventional fertilizing equipment. The prototype is towed by another vehicle with low pressure tyres, but the production version will be self-propelled with the operator housed in a cab mounted on the platform. Two centrifugal fans, powered by a small diesel engine, will be used and the engine will also drive an hydraulic pump which will power a hydrostatic motor for propulsion.

The vehicle will be capable of highway operation, riding on wheels which will be retracted while in the hovering mode.

A joint development programme is being undertaken with an internationally-known agricultural equipment company.

TIGER MACKACE HOVER SYSTEMS

HEAD OFFICE:

222S Riverside Plaza, Chicago Illinois 60606

TELEPHONE:

(312) 648 4100

TELEX:

253546

CABLES:

Tigerequip

DIRECTORS:

Thomas V. Murphy

J. T. Mackley

D. G. W. Turner

Michael J. Gray

SENIOR EXECUTIVES:

Thomas V. Murphy

Michael J. Gray

Judith Jordan, Director of Marketing

D. G. W. Turner

Max Fripp

TM 160 HOVER TRANSPORTER

The Trans Alaska Pipeline, the world's costliest construction project ever undertaken by private industry, necessitated crossing the Yukon River throughout the year.

Crossings had to be undertaken in temperatures varying from 90 deg above zero with a river current in excess of 6 mph, to temperatures of 65 deg below zero with winds in excess of 50 mph.

Due to the nature of this project Tiger Equipment & Services Ltd suggested a company who are designers and contractors of numerous hover transporters. Mackley Ace Alyeska Pipeline Service Co accepted the possibility of modifying Mackley Ace transporters to the Yukon River requirements. A contract was negotiated with

Tiger Equipment & Services Ltd who then, in a joint venture with Mackace Hover Systems, undertook the design and construction of the first two air cushion transporter ferry systems.

The initial problem of establishing crossing points was resolved by selecting sites located the minimum distance from the projected pipeline route. The south debarkation area is located on the tip of Carlos Island while the north site is located within five miles of the main artery which supplies the northern sector of the pipeline.

The system had to be capable of operating when the "ice bridge" consisting of reinforced layers of ice capable of supporting traffic crossing the river during winter months, was no longer operable. The time allowed to complete the system was fourteen weeks.

Criteria based on the quantity of supplies necessary to support the work schedule called for two ACTs capable of delivering a payload of 160 tons every 30 minutes. The design of the ACTs had to be sufficiently flexible to permit operation in arctic winters and mild summers, while adjusting to the conditions brought about by the unpredictable Yukon River. The design of the skirt system was especially demanding since the ACT's would be required to hover over solid irregular ice, land, water and any combination of these. The system would also be subjected to floating ice, dislodged trees, and other types of debris during the spring thaw.

Crew of the TM 160 normally comprises one engineer and one deckhand.

LIFT AND PROPULSION: Motive power for the lift system is provided by two Detroit Diesel Model 16V 71T diesels, each developing 700 hp at 2,100 rpm at 85°F. Each engine transmits power to a single squirrel cage, industrial ventilator type centrifugal fan which operates at 1,780 rpm. Volume flow is 133,000 cfm and static pressure 28 in swg. Fuel is carried in two tanks each with a capacity of 500 US gal, located in the engine/fan mountings.

Propulsion is by cable. Two double drum winches are located on the north bank of the Yukon and a tail pulley system is located on the south bank. Cable guides are fitted on both craft and stationary guides are mounted

The two Tiger Mackace hover transporters ferrying trucks across the Yukon

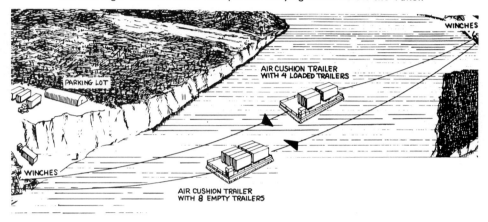

Schematic showing the operation of the two Tiger Mackace TM 160 hover transporters across the Yukon

ahead of the winches. Total length of cable strung across the Yukon is 42,800 ft.

To adjust to the rise and fall of the waterline, mobile loading ramps have been constructed. The ramps have the capacity to handle single-bearing loads in excess of 160 tons.

DIMENSIONS:
Length	129 ft 6 in
Beam	84 ft 6 in
Hull depth	4 ft 0 in
Deck loading space	97 ft by 52 ft

WEIGHTS:
Gross operating weight	865,000 lb

PERFORMANCE:
Max operating speed	8 knots
Max wave capability	6 ft
Max gradient, static conditions	8 deg
Vertical obstacle clearance	4 ft

PRICE: US$ 1·8 million. Lease or cash sale

UNION OF SOVIET SOCIALIST REPUBLICS

ALL-UNION OIL MACHINERY RESEARCH INSTITUTE, WEST SIBERIA
(VNII neftmash)

HEAD OFFICE: Tyumen
DIRECTOR:
A. V. Vladimirskii
EXECUTIVE:
V. A. Shibanov, Head of Air Cushion Vehicle Department

Air cushion platforms with load capacities of up to 200 tons have been under development in the West Siberian lowlands since 1965. Some 80% of the gas and petroleum sites in this area are located amidst almost impassable swamps, salt marshes, taiga and stretches of water.

In the Tyumensk area, where deep wells are being drilled, more than 200 tons of support equipment are required at each site in addition to between 130-180 tons of drilling gear. In 1965, a group of ACV engineers and designers headed by V. A.

PVP-40 air cushion trailer undergoing field tests. The trailer, which has a load capacity of 40-tons, is designed for carrying heavy, single-piece cargoes and machines, drilling and oil-production equipment in the difficult and marshy terrain of Russia's Northern regions

Shibanov left the Urals for Tyumen to apply their efforts to the design of a hoverplatform capable of carrying a complete oil rig across tundra and taiga, and also to the design and construction of an all-terrain vehicle capable of towing the drilling rig, on hover, to the drilling sites.

Small scale models were employed by the group during the development stages, and several attempts were made before a completely satisfactory design was conceived.

The most successful arrangement—the BU-75-VP—is illustrated. It comprises a rectangular, all-metal buoyancy raft (the load carrying member), with side structures to carry a bag-type skirt. A derrick, derived from a standard BU-75 drilling rig, was mounted on the central raft, and the drilling pump, generally delivered to sites separately, was also installed on board. Apart from specialist items of oil drilling gear, the platform is equipped with lift fans and drilling engines which serve a dual purpose by driving the lift fans when the platform is changing location.

Two tractors are normally required to tow the platform in a fully loaded condition.

Transport and routing problems are now greatly simplified as the need to detour virtually impassable lakes, marshes, and snow or water-filled ravines no longer arises. The rig has been employed in oilfields at Shaimskoye, Urai and Samotlor.

Two more multi-ton cargo-carrying ACV platforms have been completed at the Tyumen Ship Repair yard. One new platform, which was put into service in 1974, has a load capacity of 200 tons.

A more recent design has been undergoing tests at the Strezhevoye workings at Alexandrov field in the Tomsk region. Large ACV rigs with a capacity of several thousand tons are under development.

BU-75-VP

DIMENSIONS:

Length	98·43 ft (30 m)
Width	65·62 ft (20 m)

WEIGHTS:

All-up weight	170 tonnes

PERFORMANCE:

Speed (depending on towing vehicle)	About 6 mph (9·65 km/h)

The BU-75-VP oil rig, the first in the world to be mounted on an air-cushion platform

ACV TRAILERS

Three ACV trailers are being developed by the organisation—a six-ton platform; the PVP-40 with a cargo capacity of 40 tonnes and a larger derivative with a capacity of 6-ton counterpart is powered by a single gas-turbine driving twin axial-flow fans. Discs or wheels fitted to swinging arms at the rear provide directional control when reversing and operating on slopes. "Trains" of

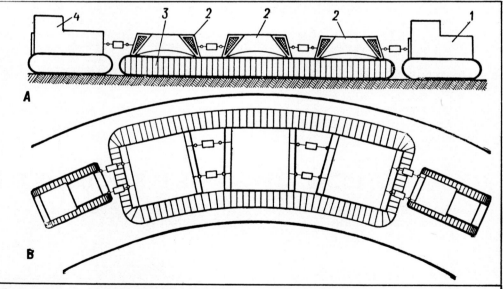

Articulated ACV trailer.

A, Operating arrangement.
B. How turns are negotiated
1, tractor;
2, cargo areas;
3, flexible skirt;
4, second tractor to stabilise trailer motion.

A

B

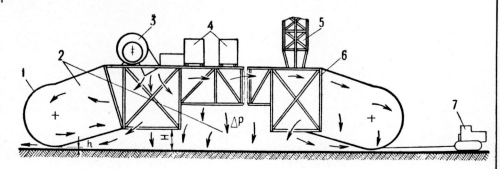

Diagram of a typical Soviet-designed ACV oil rig platform.

1, flexible bag skirt;
2, air cushion;
3, fan;
4, drilling rig engines (employed to drive fans during moves);
5, derrick;
6, drilling rig base;
7, tractor.
h—air gap;
H—hard structure clearance;

ACV trailers can be employed to carry 60 tonnes. The PVP-40 has been undergoing state acceptance trials in Surgut and the Soviet Far North and if put into production will be employed in the construction of oil installations, pipelines, by geological surveys and on drainage and irrigation schemes.

The PVP-40 is powered by a single diesel engine driving two centrifugal fans. Its 60-ton counterpart is powered by a single gas-turbine driving twin axial-flow fans. Discs or wheels fitted to swinging arms at the rear provide directional control when reversing. "Trains" of ACV trailers can be employed to carry heavy loads and a further development is an articulated trailer, several times the length of platforms like the PVP-40, with one tractor forward and another at the rear.

ACV TRACTORS

Towing requirements for the rigs and ACV Trailers built in Tyumen were met at first by conventional GTT amphibious crawler tractors. Since these were unable to cope with very soft terrain, development of a true multi-terrain tractor was undertaken, and this led to the construction of the Tyumen I. This was the first of a completely new ACV type and combined crawler propulsion with air cushion lift. The first model, now relegated to Tyumen's ACV museum, carried a 2-tonne load at speeds up to 25 mph (40 km/h) in off-road conditions. It is described as a broad, squat vehicle on long narrow caterpillar tracks, with a flexible skirt between its crawlers. The second was the MVP-2 which was upgraded soon afterwards to the MVP-3 5-tonne capacity model. The MVP-3 uses extremely narrow crawler tracks for propulsion, steering and support on hard surfaces. As with the Bertin Terraplane series of wheel assisted ACVs, the weight transference to the crawler track is variable according to the nature of the terrain being crossed and the gradient. It is said to be capable of 50 mph (80·46 km/h) over swamps

Rear view of the PVP-40 air-cushion trailer showing the unusual arrangement of varied length segments on the bag skirt

A 6-ton capacity air cushion trailer towed by a five-ton capacity MVP-3 combined ACV/crawler tractor. Both vehicles have been developed by the West Siberian Branch of the All-Union Oil Machinery Research Institute

with 40 in (1·01 m) high hummocks and cruises at 30 mph (48·28 km/h). At the time of its first demonstration to the Soviet press in July 1974, it had completed 60 miles (96·56 km/h) over Siberian swamps.

Operation of the vehicle appears to be relatively simple. Main controls are an accelerator for the single engine, which has an automatic clutch, and two standard tracked vehicle steering levers which skid-steer through the differential use of the tracks.

The policy at Tyumen is to standardise on composite crawler ACV systems rather than air propeller or endless-screw type propulsion.

AIR CUSHION LANDING SYSTEMS

FRANCE

BERTIN & CIE
OFFICE AND WORKS:
  BP 3, 78370 Plaisir, France
TELEPHONE:
  462.25.00
TELEX:
  26 619 AVIATOM PLAIS
DIRECTORS:
  Fernand Channon, President Director
    General
  M. Michel Perineau, Director General
  Georges Mordchelles-Regnier, Director
    General

Bertin & Cie is now developing air cushion landing systems based upon the company's technique of separately-fed multiple plenum chambers.

ATTERROGLISSEUR

The Atterroglisseur is an air cushion drop platform for damping both vertically and horizontally the landing of heavy loads dropped by parachute. The system comprises a platform carrying the load and an air cushion system which includes inflatable balloons fitted on the underside of the platform, a light tray at the base of the balloons, and flexible skirts beneath the tray connected to the balloons.

While in the aircraft, the complete air cushion system is tightly packed beneath the platform and secured in position by a plate. When the platform is dropped, the securing plate detaches itself automatically and both the flexible skirts and the balloons inflate.

On landing the balloons deflate first, thus feeding the skirts continuously. It is only when the balloons are empty that the skirts slowly collapse to bring the platform to a standstill.

AIRCRAFT LANDING SYSTEM

The same basic system but incorporating air generators is being developed as an air cushion landing system for heavy cargo aircraft and wing-in-ground-effect machines, providing them with multi-terrain landing and take-off capability.

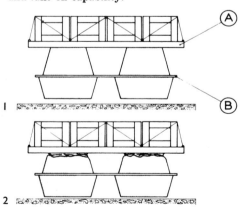

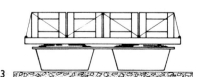

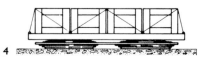

Bertin Atteroglisseur in action. The system is designed to prevent loads dropped by parachute from turning over on hitting the ground. As the loaded platform lands, balloons beneath it cushion the impact as they deflate. Air from the balloons is then fed below into a series of multiple skirts, inflating them and creating an air cushion. This allows the platform to skim the terrain in the dropping zone while the parachutes settle, thus reducing the possibility of the platform and load overturning. When the balloons are finally deflated, the skirts collapse and friction brings the platform to a standstill

Bertin air cushion landing system employed on a giant cargo carrying wing-in-ground-effect machine, providing multi-terrain landing and take-off capability

Four phases during an air drop employing an Atteroglisseur skirted platform: 1. During descent, balloons above the multi-skirt cells are fully inflated; 2. On hitting the ground the balloons are gradually crushed and eject air below to inflate the skirts; 3. Balloons are deflated and collapse; 4. Skirts are flattened and increased friction through surface contact brings the platform to a halt. The platform comprises: A. The load platform with balloons fitted below and B. a light tray, to which the lower ends of the balloons are secured. The multi-cell skirts are hung beneath the tray

THE UNITED STATES OF AMERICA

BELL AEROSPACE TEXTRON
Division of Textron Inc.
HEAD OFFICE:
   Buffalo, New York 14240
TELEPHONE:
   716 297 1000
OFFICERS:
   See ACV Section

The air cushion landing system is designed by Bell to replace wheels, skis, or floats on any size or type of aircraft, with a single system combining the functional capabilities of them all.

This application of the air cushion principle is an outgrowth of work in the field of air cushion vehicles. The system minimises airstrip requirements and enables aircraft to take-off and land on unprepared surfaces, in open fields, on open water, ice, snow, marsh, sand or dirt. Factors contributing to this feasibility are the very low pressure in the bag supporting the aircraft, the elimination of friction because of the air jets, and the increased area of contact during braking.

It has proved to be an ideal gear for crosswind take-off and landing.

The first aircraft to be fitted with ACLS was a Lake LA-4 light amphibian. In November 1970 Bell was awarded a USAF contract to install this equipment on a de Havilland CC-115 Buffalo.

The aircraft, so modified, was redesignated XC-8A and delivered to the USAF in November 1973.

ACLS-EQUIPPED LA-4
Preliminary tests were undertaken with the aid of a specially equipped LA-4 amphibian which performed its first take-off and landing on August 4th, 1967.

The LA-4 ACLS consists primarily of a doughnut-shaped trunk inflated to a thickness of approximately 2 ft (·60 m) by an axial fan. The fan, powered by a separate engine, forces air down into the bag. This flow of air escapes through thousands of small jet nozzles on the underside of the trunk, providing a cushion of air upon which the aircraft floats. The trunk is fabricated from multiple layers of stretch nylon cloth for strength, natural rubber for elasticity and coated with neoprene for environmental stability. When deflated during flight its elasticity ensures that it retracts tighly against the underside of the hull.

At touchdown, six brake skids on the underside of the trunk are brought into contact with the landing surface by pneumatic pillows. When fully inflated for maximum braking, these pillows are each slightly larger than a basketball. For parking on land or water a lightweight internal bladder seals the air jets, thus supporting the aircraft at rest or providing buoyancy to keep it afloat indefinitely.

DIMENSIONS:
AIRCRAFT
Wing span	38 ft 0 in (11·58 m)
Overall length	24 ft 11 in (7·59 m²)
Gross wing area	170 sq ft (15·79 m²)

AIR CUSHION
Length	16 ft 0 in (4·87 m²)
Width	3 ft 10 in (1·16 m²)
Area	45 sq ft (4·18 m²)

LOADINGS:
Wing loading	15 lb per sq ft
Air cushion pressure	55 lb per sq ft

Above: The De Havilland XC-8A landing on grass at the Wright-Patterson Air Force Base
Below: Equipped with an air cushion landing system, the XC-8A can operate from a range of surfaces including rough ground, marshland ice, snow, water and grass. Floats are mounted beneath each wing for operation from water. Fibreglass spring skids beneath the floats prevent the machine from rolling excessively while taxiing

WEIGHTS:
   Gross operating weight
                 2,500 lb (1,113·92 kg)
   Air cushion system weight   258 lb (117 kg)
POWER PLANTS:
   Propulsion engine rating:
      Lycoming Model 0 360 01A   180 bhp
   Air Cushion Engine rating:
      Modified McCulloch Model 4318F (driving
      2-stage axial fan)   90 bhp
PERFORMANCE:
Cruising speed	125 mph (201 km/h)
Stalling speed	54 mph (86·9 km/h)
Take-off run	650 ft (198·12 m)
Landing run	475 ft (144·78 m)

ACLS-EQUIPPED XC-8A BUFFALO
Current activities are being conducted under a joint United States/Canadian programme to adapt the ACLS for military transport aircraft. This would allow such aircraft to operate from a variety of surfaces, including rough fields, soft soils, swamps, water, ice and snow. A contract for the first phase, covering programme definition and air cushion trunk fabrication, was awarded to Bell by the USAF Flight Dynamics Laboratory in November 1970.

It was decided to use a de Havilland Canada

XC-8A Buffalo STOL military transport aircraft, loaned by the Canadian Department of National Defence, as the testbed aircraft for this programme.

United Aircraft of Canada Ltd was made responsible for development and flight qualification of the auxiliary power system, and de Havilland Aircraft of Canada Ltd modified the XC-8A testbed aircraft to take the ACLS installation. The Canadian government funded the work of these two companies.

Taxi tests and an initial take-off on the ACLS were completed in March 1975. The first ACLS landing of the XC-8A took place at Wright-Patterson, Air Force Base, Dayton, Ohio, on Friday April 11th, 1975.

ACLS employs a layer of air instead of wheels as the ground contracting medium. The system's trunk, a large inner-tube like arrangement, encircles the underside of the fuselage, and, on inflation, provides an air duct and seal for the air cushion.

The underside of the rubberised trunk is perforated with hundreds of vent holes through which air is allowed to escape to form the air cushion.

The two ST6F-70 gas-turbine engines that

drive the two-stage fan system to supply air to the ACLS trunk were developed by United Aircraft of Canada, Ltd.

Because the ACLS distributes the weight of an aircraft over a considerably larger area than conventional wheeled systems, and itself exerts a ground pressure of less than 0·20 kg/cm² (3 lb/sq in) it permits operations on surfaces with very low bearing strength.

Hamilton Standard Division of United Aircraft Corp. has modified the standard Buffalo propellers to give the pilot direct control of the blade angle By changing the blade settings differentially, he has more positive directional control while taxiing.

Six skids on the bottom operate when the pilot applies the aircraft brakes. The braking action pushes the skids, of tyre tread-type material, against the ground and stops the aircraft. Stopping distance is comparable to that of conventional wheel and brake landing systems.

The Buffalo will be able to operate from a range of surfaces including grass, unprepared rough ground, snow and water as well as paved surfaces. To date the test programme has included takeoffs and landings on concrete runways, grass and snow, with taxi tests over craters and operations in temperatures down to —20F degrees.

Balancer floats have been mounted on struts beneath each wing for operation on and from water. Beneath the floats are fibreglass spring skids to prevent excessive roll and protect the propellers while taxiing over land. Water operations are planned in the current test programme.

XC-8A BUFFALO
DIMENSIONS:
AIRCRAFT:

Wing span	96 ft 0 in (29·26 m)
Overall length	77 ft 4 in (23·57 m)
Gross wing area	945 sq ft (22·63 m²)

AIR CUSHION:

Length	32 ft 2 in (10·25 m)
Width	14 ft 0 in (4·26 m)
Area	228 sq ft (21·18 m²)

LOADINGS:

Wing loading	14·8 lb per sq ft
Air cushion pressure	170 lb per sq ft

WEIGHTS:

Gross operating weight	41,000 lb (18,597 kg)
Air Cushion system weight	2,220 lb (1,006·92 kg)

POWER PLANT:
Propulsion engines:
Two General Electric Model CT64-820-1, rated at 3,055 eshp
Air cushion engines:
Two United Aircraft of Canada ST6F-70, rated at 800 bhp

PERFORMANCE:

Cruising speed at 10,000 ft	230 knots TAS
Stalling speed, 40 degree flap	
at 39,000 lb	66 knots
Take-off run on level surface	1,130 ft
to 50 feet from level surface	1,640 ft
Landing run	
from 50 feet on level surface	1,130 ft
on level surface	650 ft

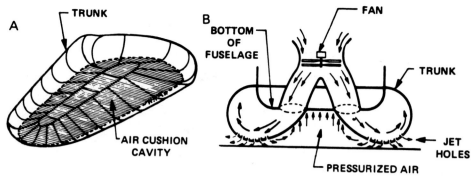

ACLS PRINCIPLE
A. Function of the inflated trunk, left, is to contain the pressurised air in the air cushion cavity. This cushion of air supports the weight of the craft.
B. Air continuously forced through the jet holes pressurises the air cushion cavity, and also provides air bearing lubrication between the trunk and its supporting surface.

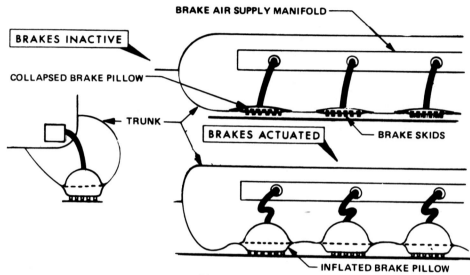

BRAKE SYSTEM
Inflation of the brake pillow of the ACLS-equipped plane brings multiple brake skids into ground contact, drawing the aircraft to a halt

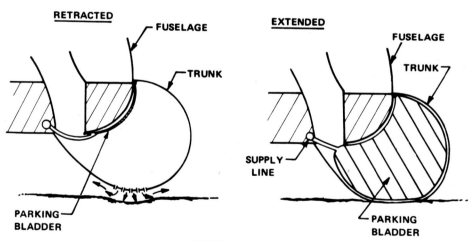

PARKING SYSTEM
A separate bladder within the rubberised air cushion trunk is inflated to support the weight of the aircraft when parked

ACLS APPLICATION CONTRACTS

Bell has also studied the feasibility of using an ACLS on Space Shuttle vehicles and an Advanced Technology Transport under NASA contract, a high-performance fighter under US Navy contract, and has designed an ACLS for a Remotely Piloted Vehicle— the Australian Jindivik—under a USAF contract.

UNION OF SOVIET SOCIALIST REPUBLICS

BARTINI

Robert Oros di Bartini, a Soviet aircraft designer of Italian birth, has indicated that air cushion landing systems are under development in the Soviet Union, and will possibly replace conventional wheeled undercarriages on aircraft by the end of the century.

His Stal-6, of 1933, was the first in the Soviet Union with a completely retractable undercarriage.

Bartini is former head of the group of designers at the Scientific Research Institute

of the Civil Air Fleet.   His Stal-7 was shown
at the 15th Paris Aviation Salon and achieved
a world speed record in 1939.   He worked
with Lavochkin and Myasishchev on fighter
development and his later designs include
the ER-2 long-range night bomber. In
recent years he has participated in the
development of VTOL aircraft.

During the summer of 1970-71 an initial
test programme employing a towed ACLS
test rig was undertaken at Molodezhnaya
Station, Antarctica, during the Sixteenth
Soviet Antarctic Expedition. The air cushion
test rig, which was towed behind a GAZ-47
oversnow truck, took the form of a small
air cushion trailer.

Tests included runs over a series of courses,
including slopes, and surfaces with natural
irregularities.   Performance over a variety
of surfaces was studied, including powdered
snow, ice and compacted ice.

It was later stated that the rig was operated successfully over terrain from which
ski-equipped aircraft could neither take-off
nor land.   Another advantage was that the
skirt did not freeze to the surface, a not
infrequent problem with conventional, ski-
equipped aircraft.

Stage two of the tests involved mounting
sensors employed on the ACLS rig on one of

Soviet ACLS test rig undergoing trial runs during the sixteenth Soviet Antarctic Expedition

the expeditions IL-14's equipped with skis.

Take-offs, landings and taxiing were
performed, mainly under extreme conditions
of wind, temperatures and surface skates, and
the data recorded for comparison with the
rig results.

Instrumentation was provided on the test
rig to record vertical and angular accelerations plus pressures in the air-cushion
plenum.

TRACKED SKIMMERS

BRAZIL

FEI
FACULTY OF INDUSTRIAL ENGINEERING

ADDRESS:

Research Vehicle Department (DEPV),
Faculty of Industrial Engineering, São
Bernado do Campo, Avenido Oreste
Romano 112, São Paulo

TELEPHONE:

443 1155

SENIOR EXECUTIVES:

Baj. Rigoberto Soler Gisbert, Director of
Vehicle Research

The Vehicle Research Department of the
FEI, founded in 1968, has designed a number
of small air cushion vehicles, one of which
is about to be put into production.

The Department's first and most ambitious
project to date has been the design and
construction of the TALAV tracked air
cushion vehicle, development of which is
being supported by the Ministry for Industry
and Commerce through FUNAT—a government fund for sponsoring new technological
developments.

The prototype, an all-metal vehicle propelled by twin Marbore VIs, and seating 20
passengers, displays several novel features,
including the siting of the main passenger
access door at the front. The whole of the
front section moves forward telescopically to
provide space for entry and exit. This
arrangement facilitates the loading of freight
when necessary, and should an emergency
stop occur when carrying passengers on a
narrow elevated guideway, walking out
through the front will be far safer than
through the sides, say the designers.

It is also stated that passenger handling
will be simplified at termini, where the
vehicles can be drawn up side-by-side without
the need to devote valuable space for platforms.

The main application foreseen for vehicles
of this type is that of city centre to suburbs
or city centre to airport links.

To enable construction to be undertaken
without difficulty in developing areas where
manpower is available, the structure is based
on easily-handled sub-assemblies and standard panels of aluminium honeycomb.

The design team is at present concentrating
on the development of an efficient yet
economical approach to the construction
of guideways.

LIFT AND PROPULSION: Cushion air is
delivered by fans powered by a 70 hp engine.

Above and below: Prototype of the FEI, 20-seat TALAV tracked air cushion vehicle. Designed to cruise at 200 mph (321·86 km/h), the vehicle is powered by twin Turbomeca Marbore VI gas-turbines

Cushion pressure, 40 lb ft², cushion area
3,250 ft². Two 900 lb st Turbomeca Marbore
VI gas-turbines supply propulsive thrust.

DIMENSIONS, EXTERNAL:

Length	51 ft (15·54 m)
Width	7·4 ft (2·26 m)
Height	9 ft 5 in (2·87 m)

DIMENSIONS, INTERNAL:

Internal height, passenger saloon
7 ft 0 in (2·13 m)

WEIGHTS:

Empty weight	6,500 lb (2,948·35 kg)
Loaded weight	13,000 lb (5,896·70 kg)

PERFORMANCE:

Cruising speed   200 mph (321·86 km/h)

FRANCE

SOCIÉTÉ DE L'AEROTRAIN

HEAD OFFICE:

Tour Anjou, 33, quai National, 92806
Puteaux

TELEPHONE:

776 43 34

TELEX:

610385 Bertrin Putau

DIRECTOR GENERAL:

Benjamin Salmon

Originally named "Société d'Etudes de
l'Aerotrain", this company was formed on
April 15, 1965 to develop a high speed
transportation system based on air cushion
support and guidance principles conceived by
Bertin & Cie.

The Aerotrain has completed its experimental phase as far as the air cushion
technique is concerned. The 01 half-scale
prototype, after nearly three years of test
runs at speeds up to 215 mph (346 km/h),
has successfully attained its phased design
requirements, namely the verification of
dynamic behaviour, the development of
integrated suspension systems, and the
accumulation of data for the design and
costing of full-scale operational vehicles.

The 02 half-scale prototype has undergone
similar tests in order to produce data for
vehicles operating at speeds above 200 mph
(322 km/h). A speed of 263 mph (322 km/h)
was attained by the vehicle in January 1969.

There are three families of Aerotrain
systems, Interurban, with a speed of 225 mph
(360 km/h); Suburban, with a speed of 113
mph (180 km/h) and the new Tridim system,
designed for speeds of up to 50 mph (80 km/h)
as the distance between stations generally
ranges between several hundred yards and
one or two miles. The speeds selected will
be based on economic considerations. Suburban systems will cover a variety of routes
from city centres to airports and city centres
to satellite towns and suburban areas. The
size, speed and control system of each
vehicle will be decided according to the
route.

Current studies are aimed primarily at
developing associated techniques including
propulsion modes for the various speeds and
environments, controls, signals and stations.

A mathematical model has been developed in order to computerise the various parameters for both families of applications. This will enable operating costs to be obtained, in an optimised form, for given traffic requirements.

Two full-scale vehicles, the 80-seat Orleans inter-city Aerotrain and the 40-44 seat suburban Aerotrain have undergone extensive trials. During trials between 1969 and 1971, the 80-seat 1-80 "Orleans" Aerotrain has completed more than 700 hours of operation on its 18 km (11·2 mile) track north of Orleans, carrying more than 10,000 people at a speed of 160 mph (260 km/h). In January 1973, the vehicle was taken to the UTA maintenance facility at Le Bourget airport where it was equipped with a 15,000 lb st JT8D-11 turbofan, permitting its speed to be studied in the 220-250 mph (360-400 km/h) range.

In November 1973, a speed of 250 mph (400 km/h) was attained and by May 1974, 150 hours of operation had been logged in this configuration, during which 2,000 professionally interested passengers had been carried.

All these programmes, completed or under way, represent a financial development effort of roughly $22 million. The French Government extended its support at every stage by means of various loans, subsidies and orders.

In November 1969, the company formed a US subsidiary, Aerotrain Systems Inc, to build and market Aerotrains in the United States and Mexico. The company is jointly held by Rohr Industries Inc, Bertin et Cie and Société de l'Aerotrain. Rohr's interest is 80%. The company's first prototype was completed in December 1972 and was tested in 1974 on an experimental line built at the US Department of Transport centre at Pueblo, California.

In 1971, another subsidiary was formed, Aerotrain Scandinavia AB, in which the Salen Group has a 50% interest. A third company, formed in Brazil with the support of four French banks, is Aerotrain Systems de Transporte.

In December 1973 an agreement was signed between Bertin & Cie, Aerotrain, Spie-Batignolles, Jeumont-Schneider, SGTE MTE and Francorail-MTE, who will co-operate in the promotion and operation of Aerotrain systems and various aspects of production.

The Aerotrain 01, a research vehicle built for tests up to and above 250 mph on the No. 1 track at Gometz

Turntables are installed at each end of the present Aerotrain test track, but they will not be used normally on operational lines. In service Aerotrains will be able to manoeuvre independently on the flat floor surfaces of stations

The Aerotrain 02, a research vehicle built for tests up to and above 250 mph on the No. 1 track at Gometz

EXPERIMENTAL AEROTRAIN
AEROTRAIN 01

An experimental, half-scale prototype, this vehicle was operated along a test track 4·2 miles (6·7 km) long. The track has an inverted T cross section, the vertical portion being 1 ft 10 in (55 cm) high and the horizontal base 5 ft 11 in (1·80 m) wide. A turn-table is fitted at each end.

The vehicle is of light alloy construction. The slender body has seats at the front for six people, and an engine compartment at the rear. Lift and guidance are provided by two centrifugal fans, driven by two 50 hp Renault Gordini motor car engines, linked by a shaft. The fans supply air to the guidance and lift cushions at a pressure of about 0·35 lb/sq in (25 gr/cm²), the maximum airflow being 350 cu ft/sec (10 m³/sec). Propulsion is provided by a 260 hp Continental aero-engine, mounted at the top of a 3 ft 11 in (1·20 m) tail pylon and driving a reversible-pitch propeller, which is also used for normal braking. There are brake pads at

the rear of the vehicle which grip the vertical track section like a disc brake.

The first test run on the track was made on December 29, 1965. The prototype was intended to evaluate and demonstrate the Aerotrain principle on a small scale, and was developed with the active support of the French Government and French Railways.

Although the vehicle was designed for a maximum speed of 125 mph (200 km/h) tests have been undertaken at higher speeds with the help of booster rockets to supplement the propulsive airscrew. In December 1967, the vehicle reached the top speed of 215 mph (345 km/h) several times with a jet engine assisted by two booster rockets.

DIMENSIONS:

Length overall	32 ft 10 in (10·00 m)
Width overall	6 ft 7 in (2·00 m)
Height overall	12 ft 2 in (3·70 m)
Height to top of body	5 ft 3 in (1·60 m)

WEIGHTS:

Basic weight	5,500 lb (2,500 kg)

PERFORMANCE:

Cruising speed	125 mph (200 km/h)
Top speed	188 mph (303 km/h)

EXPERIMENTAL AEROTRAIN 02

Aerotrain 02 is an experimental half-scale prototype designed for high speed tests on the track at Gometz used by the first prototype.

Due to the track's relatively short length, a more powerful thrust engine, a Pratt & Whitney JT 12, is installed in order to maintain high speeds over a distance of 1·3 miles (2 km) for performance measurements.

During its first series of test runs, the Aerotrain 02 attained 235 mph (378 km/h). A booster rocket was then added, and a series of tests followed, culminating in a record speed of 263 mph (422 km/h) being attained. The average speed recorded over the 2/3 mile track was 255 mph (411 km/h).

The air cushions for lift and guidance are provided by fans driven by a Turbomeca Palouste gas-turbine. At high speed, the dynamic pressure is sufficient to feed the air cushions.

The internal space has been devoted in the main to test instrumentation. Seats are provided only for the pilot and a test engineer.

Aerotrains 01 and 02 were both equipped with propulsion engines which were readily available from the aviation market and capable of giving high speed on a short test track. Operational vehicles use quieter power arrangements.

FULL-SCALE AEROTRAIN I-80 ORLEANS INTERCITY PROJECT

This medium range inter-city vehicle (the Orleans-Paris line will be 70 miles (113 km) long) was designed originally with airscrew propulsion for speeds up to 186·41 mph (300 km/h), but has now been equipped with a silenced turbofan engine which has increased its speed to 250 mph (400 km/h). The vehicle carries 80 passengers in airline comfort in an air-conditioned and sound-proofed cabin.

The lift and guidance air cushions are fed by two axial fans driven by a 400 hp Turbomeca Astazou gas turbine. At high speeds, they will be fed by dynamic intake pressure.

On the original model thrust was supplied by a shrouded propeller, driven independently by two 1,300 hp Turmo 111 gas-turbines.

In January 1973, the vehicle was taken to the UTA maintenance facility at Le Bourget, where it has been fitted with a 15,000 lb thrust Pratt & Whitney JT8D-11 turbofan, which will permit the systematic study of the 1-80 and its components at speeds in the 220-250 mph (354-426 km/h) range.

Hydraulically retractable tyred wheels are incorporated to help to achieve silent operation near and in stations, and also to assist in manoeuvring and switching the vehicle on station floors. The vertical rail of the inverted T track is unnecessary at low speeds.

A very low empty-weight-to-payload ratio has been possible because of the lack of concentrated loads inherent in the vehicle. This permits the use of lightweight supporting structures—tracks and stations.

Vehicles will not be coupled, so that very high frequency services can be maintained throughout the day. With headways as low as one minute, simple or articulated vehicles offer a range of capacities which largely cope with the peaks of traffic expected in known intercity lines.

Two articulated cars with seats for up to 160 passengers and luxury models with a wider aisle and reduced seating capacity are being considered in feasibility studies being undertaken for several projected routes.

DIMENSIONS:
Length overall   101 ft 8 in (30·50 m)
Length at track level   92 ft 6 in (27·75 m)

The I-80HV Aerotrain with its turbofan thrust unit

Height at fan jet air intake
                        17 ft 0 in (5·10 m)
Width   10 ft 8 in (3·20 m)
WEIGHTS:
Gross weight   24 metric tons
PERFORMANCE:
Test speed range
                        220-250 mph (354-426 km/h)

THE GUIDEWAY

The first leg of the future Orleans to Paris line—a track 11·5 miles (18·5 km) long— was completed in July 1969. It includes turntables at both ends and a central platform for manoeuvring and switching.

In mid-1973 the French Government confirmed that the line is to be completed in due course, but did not announce details.

The track has been designed for a service speed of 250 mph (402 km/h). It is mounted on pylons along the entire route. The prefabricated concrete beams, of 67 ft (20 m) span, have a minimum ground clearance of 16 ft (4·90 m). This allows the track to be constructed across roads and cultivated land.

Due to the low stresses produced by the Aerotrain vehicles it has been possible to design a lightweight elevated track structure, which is less expensive than an equivalent ground track. Local ground subsidence, which may occur during the first years after erection, will be countered by adjusting the pylon heads. This will be limited to a simple jacking operation using built-in devices in the pylon structure.

The radii of curves and gradient angles will depend upon the accelerations admissible without causing discomfort to passengers. Banking can be provided if necessary. Banking of 7% is in fact incorporated in three curves in the Orleans track. The radius requirements are therefore the same as for other guided systems of transport for similar speeds. The advantage of the Aerotrain track is that there are no gradient limitations and it can therefore be constructed with a much smaller number of curves.

Aerotrain guideway track beams can be adjusted at the pylon heads in the event of ground subsidence

TESTS

Speed, acceleration and braking characteristics have confirmed expectations, and the riding comfort has proven to be highly satisfactory. Under all operating conditions, including propeller reverse braking, negotiating curves and in cross winds of 31 mph (50 km/h), the average accelerations were less than 0·6 m/s² at all times, with values of 0·3 to 0·5 m/s² during normal cruising conditions.

Since the interior noise level in the passenger compartment is between 75 and 78 dBA, it is possible to converse in normal tones. A level 70-72 dBA will be reached on series production vehicles.

External noise, 90-95 dBA at 65 yards (60 m) compares favourably to that of a modern electric train, with a much shorter duration.

During the 850 hours of operation there was no breakdown which caused the vehicle to stop on the guideway, with the exception of a single incident involving hydraulic circuits to the propeller, which were repaired in less than an hour. Only three items, other than the air cushions, have necessitated

The prefabricated concrete beams of the Orleans track have a minimum ground clearance of 16 ft (4·87 m). This allows the track to be constructed across roads and agricultural land without causing obstruction
Photo: P. M. Lambermont

SIDE VIEW

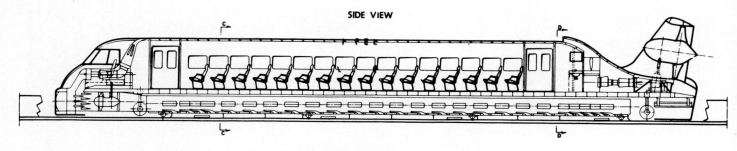

PLAN VIEW

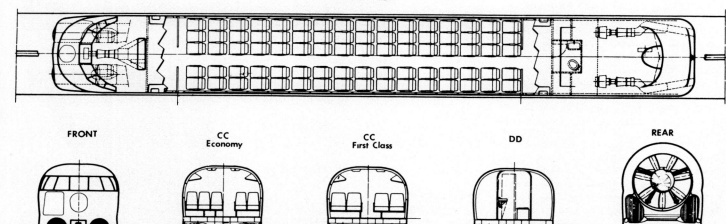

FRONT | CC Economy | CC First Class | DD | REAR

The Aerotrain I-80—a typical Aerotrain configuration for medium-range inter-city traffic, carrying 80 passengers at a cruising speed of 180 mph and a top speed of 190 mph

a major repair since the vehicle was put on the guideway. The air cushions have been completely trouble-free.

The third phase of the test programme consisted of an endurance, or accelerated service test involving 200 hours of running time. Thirty-six operating days were utilised and during the average six hours of continuous operation were completed. The cruising speed established was 154·33 mph (250 km/h). Since this involved acceleration and deceleration between 0 and 154·33 mph (250 km/h) every six minutes, a commercial operation of 1,000-2,000 hours or 200,000-400,000 km in terms of wear on the vehicle was simulated. The rate of air cushion lip wear experienced indicates a useful lip life of 40,000 to 50,000 km and a practically negligible cost factor of ·001 to ·002 francs per passenger/kilometer.

It is to be noted that cultivation has been resumed around and underneath the guideway which, in sharp contrast with the high permanent way maintenance costs experienced by the railways, has required no maintenance whatsoever since it was built.

HIGH SPEED 1-80 HV "ORLEANS" AEROTRAIN

In November 1973, the 1-80 "Orleans" Aerotrain began a series of tests with a new propulsion system. The two Turmo III gas-turbines, which powered a shrouded propeller, were replaced by a 15,000 lb thrust Pratt & Whitney JT8D-II turbofan, fitted with a sound supressor system designed by Bertin & Cie. The ride characteristics remained outstanding at speeds up to 250 mph (426 km/h) in spite of the size of the new propulsion unit which resulted in the vehicle being 4 tons over weight.

The compressors and air feeders remained unchanged.

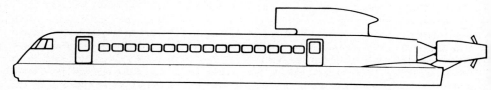

Side view showing the revised configuration of the I-80HV Aerotrain with its new turbofan thrust unit

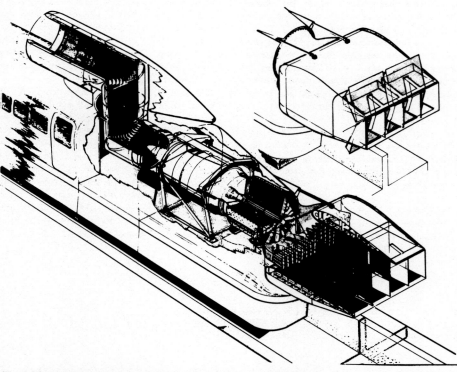

The I-80HV Orleans Aerotrain after being fitted with a 15,000 lb thrust Pratt & Whitney JT8D-II turbofan, which has permitted the behaviour of the vehicle's systems to be studied at speeds of 220-250 mph (354-426 km/h). Considerable attention has been given to sound attenuation. As seen in the cutaway drawing, the air intake has been designed for the maximum effectiveness, and a special high dilution ejection system suppresses the noise of the exhaust gases

Prototype of the 40-44 seat suburban Aerotrain seen on its 1.9 miles (3 km) test track at Gometz

On March 5th, 1974, the vehicle attained 270 mph (430 km/h), with an average speed (in each direction) of 263 mph (418 km/h) over a distance of 1·86 miles. The sound insulation has been extremely effective, resulting in a noise level 21b lower than the original propulsion system.

In 1976, the Orleans vehicle was still in use for demonstrations. By May 1976 it had completed 925 hours of operation including 212 hours with its JT8D-11 turbofan. During this time it has carried 13,500 passengers, 3,280 of whom have been carried at speeds in excess of 250 mph (402·32 km/h).

SUBURBAN AEROTRAIN
AEROTRAIN S-44

The prototype 40-44 passenger suburban vehicle is equipped with a linear induction motor. The vehicle underwent trials at Gometz between 1969 and 1972, where its 2 mile (3 km) test track runs parallel to that used by the Aerotrain 01 and 02 experimental vehicles. During its test programme the vehicle was operated at speeds up to 105 mph (170 km/h). The S-44 is currently undergoing modification as part of the company's development programme for the new 15 mile (24 km) La Défense—Cergy line.

The power for the two axial lift fans is provided by a 525 hp GM Chevrolet V-8 car engine. Practically silent operation is achieved since there is no noise of rolling wheels. No vibration is communicated to the track structure which can therefore be erected in urban areas without fear of any noise disturbing local communities, even if steel is used for the longer spans of the guideway.

This vehicle is equipped with an electrical linear motor developed by the Société Le Moteur Linéaire (Merlin & Gerin Group). It provides a thrust of 18,000 N at 85 mph (137 km/h) and has been currently operated at speeds above 100 mph (160·93 km/h).

Electric current is collected from the three-phase 1,000 V power line set alongside the track.

Braking performance is particularly efficient. During normal operation braking is obtained either by dephasing the linear motor supply (or in the case of failure of this supply by feeding it with DC current from the battery), or by a hydraulic braking system equipped with friction pads which grip the vertical

portion of the track.

The passenger cabin is divided into four ten-seat compartments, each provided with two doors. An additional half-compartment forward can accommodate four passengers seated on folding seats.

Automatic doors are provided on both sides of each passenger compartment which will help to reduce stopping time. The coupling of several of these vehicles will be possible, but this should only be necessary at peak hours for heavy commuter traffic.

The seating arrangement is optional; each of the various layouts is optimised to provide the maximum possible space for passengers.

DIMENSIONS:

Length	47 ft 0 in	(14·4 m)
Beam	9 ft 4 in	(2·75 m)
Height	10 ft 2 in	(3·10 m)

WEIGHTS:

Loaded weight:		
linear motor weight	25,000 lb	(11,500 kg)
automotive version	22,000 lb	(10.000 kg)

PERFORMANCE:

Cruising speed	113 mpn (180 km/h)

A lower speed system is being designed for urban lines with stations only ½ mile apart.

THE GUIDEWAY

In this programme the track is at ground level. The horizontal support is an asphalt carpet and the upright is an aluminium beam which is used for both guiding the vehicle and as an induction rail for the linear motor. A 1·9 mile (3 km) long track has been constructed at the company's base at Gometz.

Operational suburban lines will generally be supported on pylons in order to leave the ground free. The use of an elevated track will reduce the construction time and avoid costly tunnelling on many sections of urban/suburban projects.

PROJECT STUDIES

Société de l'Aérotrain has conducted detailed studies of a dozen projects. The technical and operational characteristics of the vehicles may substantially differ from those of the two prototypes, particularly as regards capacity and cruising speed.

The mathematical model, which has enabled the company to examine technico-economical optimisation procedures, an approach to operations, station design, and baggage handling has produced data based on a number of projected situations. The two major fields which are being investigated are inter-city services and suburban links, mainly between city centres and airports.

Suburban links require, in some cases, a higher capacity than the one provided by the Gometz-type vehicle. Capacity can be increased by widening the vehicles, or coupling them, to provide an hourly capacity of around 10,000 passengers each way.

Projects of an almost urban nature are also being investigated with the Tridim version.

CERGY-PONTOISE—LA DEFENSE
SUBURBAN AEROTRAIN

A decision was taken by the French

Artist's impression of the Cergy-Défense suburban Aerotrain

government in July 1971 to build an Aerotrain rapid transit line from the new business centre of La Défense, just outside Paris, to the new town of Cergy-Pontoise. The line was due to be opened early in 1979. Although the contract for its construction was signed on June 21st 1974, it was cancelled the following month by a new French government which introduced sweeping cutbacks in public expenditure to counter inflation.

The travel time between Cergy-Pontoise and La Dèfense with this system would have been less than 10 minutes. The line was intended to connect with the new express metro linking La Défense with Etoile, and the Opéra, the journey times being 4 and 7 minutes respectively.

Cergy-Pontoise had a population of 200,000 in 1975 and will have between 350,000 and 400,000 by the year 2000. A satellite town of the capital, it is about 30 km west of Paris. TRACK: The length of the route is 15 miles (24 km).

The track will be elevated for most of the distance, providing a clearance of 16 ft (5 m) above ground. Supporting pylons will be 66 to 83 ft (20-25 m) apart. The track itself will be 17 ft 8 in (5·30 m) and will be double. Each side will have an aluminium alloy vertical centre rail providing both guidance for the vehicles and the secondary, or induction element, for the linear motor. Electric power is supplied by wayside rails carrying 1,500 vdc.

The horizontal radii of curves are kept above 1,200 m to allow a high cruising speed. The steepest slope is 6% and occurs when climbing a cliff after a crossing of the Seine.

The Aerotrain vehicle to be used on this service will be supported and guided by air cushions, and propelled by a linear induction motor.

The vehicles will each comprise two units. and on the Cergy-Defense line a train will consist of two coupled vehicles.

SUPPORT AND GUIDANCE: Each unit has its own air cushion guidance and support systems, air for which is put under pressure by electrically driven fans.

PROPULSION: Each unit will be equipped with a linear induction motor of variable voltage and frequency which will be regulated by on-board power-control equipment

BRAKING: Two systems will be employed.

Another line for the first commercial operation is being selected. One possibility is in the Marseilles area, with a section linking the suburbs of the city with Marignane airport and Aix-en-Provence, and extensions to the industrial complexes and new cities under construction around Etang de Berre.

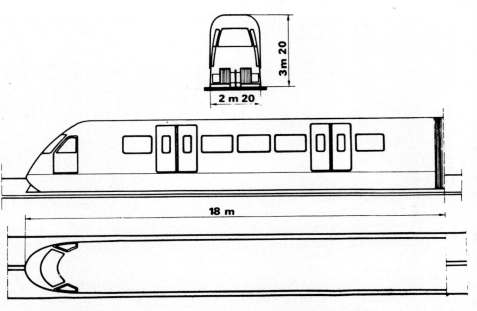

A three-phase powerline alongside the track at ground level provides electric current for the linear motor

TRIDIM URBAN TRANSPORTATION SYSTEM

The Tridim system has been designed to solve the transportation problem in urban areas or suburbs where the distance between stations ranges from a few kilometres down

A unit of the suburban Aerotrain. Two of these 80-seat units are coupled to form a vehicle, and on the Cergy-Défense line, two vehicles will be coupled to form each train—providing a total seating capacity per train of 320 passengers

Above and below: The Rohr-built Aerotrain, constructed under a US Department of Transportation contract. The vehicle, which is 94 ft long, will carry 60 passengers at speeds up to 150 mph. On May 9th 1975, the vehicle became the first all-electric TACV to attain 100 mph.

to several hundred metres.

It is believed that the solution to this problem lies in an overhead transportation system adapted to passenger flows ranging from a few thousand to 10-15,000 per hour and offering appreciable comfort, speed and frequency. To transport 6,000 passengers per hour, trains of 3 vehicles of 50 seats each every 90 seconds will be sufficient. If a larger module is adopted, 20,000 passengers can be carried hourly.

The Tridim system is designed to meet these requirements through the use of an air cushion for suspension and a flexible rack-and-pinion system, rubber-tyred traction-wheels, or linear induction motor for propulsion.

It consists of small-size self-powered air cushion vehicles moving on a lightweight overhead track.

The capacity of each vehicle can be between 4 and 100 seats according to customer requirements. The required capacity can be obtained by varying the width and the length of the vehicles or grouping any number of vehicles to form a train. Since June 1973, a 4-6 seat prototype vehicle has been under test at a research centre of the French National Electricity Company (E.D.F.) located at Les Renardières, near Fontainebleau, on a 1,000 ft (305 m) track which includes a straight section, grades, curves and points.

Characteristics of this vehicle are as follows:

Loaded weight	1·2 tons
Nominal propulsion power	15 kW
Lifting power	4 kW
Max speed	50 km/h
Max slope	20%

Power supply   cc 160V
Number of air cushions   8
Air pressure   900 kg/m²

The Tridim vehicle is built on a modular basis, with additional modules being added as required to provide the desired capacity.

In the case of the type VM 1 (designed for a specific client), the passengers are transported in modules measuring approximately 10 ft by 6 ft and equipped with 9 seats placed along the longitudinal walls. There is also room for a minimum of 4 standing passengers, which brings the rush-hour capacity to 13 passengers for each module, i.e. 52 per vehicle, 36 of whom are seated (the vehicle consists of 4 modules).

Propulsion and lift are obtained from electric energy collected from a "third" rail (direct-current power supply).

The vehicle is guided by a low metal rail fixed on the track in line with the vehicle axis. This is the inverted-T track fundamental to the Aerotrain technique. Besides its guidance function, this rail carries the propulsion rack and keeps the vehicle retained on the track, which makes overturning impossible in the event of incident or abnormal operating conditions.

LIFT: The basic advantages of employing the air-cushion principle are:

suspension of concentrated loads and shocks, hence possibility of a lightweight vehicle structure on the one hand, and of the overhead track on the other; the absence of rolling noise and vibration; vehicle maintenance drastically reduced, and virtually non-existent for the track; and finally low total cost of the transportation system due to the simplicity and the lightweight of the track.

The air cushion system requires a power supply of only 4 to 5 hp per supported metric ton. This is expected to be reduced to the order of 2 hp per metric ton. The air cushion supply is operated by sound-insulated electric fans.

PROPULSION: In the case of the VM 1 the vehicle is propelled by a patented rack-and-pinion system. But alternative methods include rubber-tyred traction wheels acting on the centre guidance rail or linear induction motor, according to requirements. The former consists of a dual rack fixed on the guiding rail and two pinions carried by the vehicles and driven by electric propulsion motors. It allows operation on tracks with steep slopes and maintain acceleration and braking performance in any weather including conditions of snow and ice.

The ability to climb steep slopes enables the stations to be built at street level or at the level of another transportation system for ease of transfer.

OVERHEAD TRACK: The system is intended primarily for an overhead track but it can also be used at ground level or as an underground system. In the case of an overhead track, the viaduct can be made of metal or of reinforced concrete, the choice

A 4-seat Tridim urban transport vehicle on its "switchback" test track

Aerotrain Tridim urban transport vehicle

between the two materials being dictated mainly by the line layout.

This consists of pylons supporting beams of 66 ft to 100 ft span carrying the guideway which has a width of about 7 ft 4 in for single track or 15 ft 6 in for dual track in the case of the VM 1 system. The track itself consists mainly of the guiding rail with its rack.

The absence of concentrated loads, either static or dynamic, allows the use of a light viaduct, which leads to less cost.

As an example, with metal construction, a dual track viaduct weighs approximately 1,300 lbs per metre (VM 1).

VM 1 SPECIFICATION:
The system can be adapted to client specification.

Capacity of the VM 1 is 52 passengers, 36 of whom are seated.

DIMENSIONS:

Length	53 ft 4 in
Width	6 ft 4 in
Height	8 ft 6 in

WEIGHTS:

Empty weight	13,000 lb
Loaded weight	21,800 lb

PERFORMANCE:

Nominal speed	40/50 mph
Maximum speed	50/65 mph
Average acceleration between 0 and 40 mph	0·12 g
Emergency deceleration	0·2 g
Allowable slope at 40 mph	3%
Maximum allowable slope at reduced speed	15% to 25%
Minimum turning radius	80 ft approx.

MOTOR POWER:

for propulsion	150 kW approx.
for cushion	35 kW

OVERHEAD TRACK:

Span	66 ft to 100 ft for normal span
Height above ground	16 ft on the average

Width of track:

single track	7 ft 4 in
dual track	15 ft 4 in

Electrical power supply by conductor rail

URBA

Compagnie d'Energetique Lineaire mb
HEAD OFFICE:
5 Rue Monge, 92 Vanves, France
OFFICERS:
M. E. Barthalon, ScMMIT, Ecole Polytechnique, President Director General

UK REPRESENTATIVE:
mBm Powercels Ltd,
   25 Bedford Row, London WC1
P. Watson, BA MIMarE, Managing Director

The URBA mass transport system, invented in 1966 by M. Maurice Barthalon, aims at providing a means of urban transport which

combines absence of noise, vibration and atmospheric pollution with low capital and maintenance costs and a high degree of flexibility of installation and operation. The vehicle, which may operate singly or in trains, is suspended from its track by an air lift system in which the pressure is sub-atmospheric, and propulsion is by electric linear induction motors. The cabin of the vehicle is suspended from a number of Dynavac air bogies which run within an elevated track the section of which is like a flattened, inverted U, with inward facing flanges on the bottom edges of the sides, on which the air bogies sit when at rest. The Dynavac air bogies house the lift fans which draw air from the space between the track and the top of the bogie, so producing a pressure difference which causes the air bogie to lift off the track flanges.

Special sealing arrangements provide a controlled leak into the lift chamber which decreases as the weight of the vehicle increases, so increasing the pressure difference. The air bogies therefore remain in a stable, floating condition without being in contact with the track.

Lateral guidance is provided by similar but smaller Dynavac cushions between the sides of the bogie and the sides of the track. The air bogies also house the linear induction motors which react with a reactor rail projecting downwards from the centre of the track. This effectively divides the lift chamber into two independent halves, thus providing a degree of roll control. The suspension between the cabin and the air bogie acts as a secondary suspension system (the air cushion being the primary) and provides for articulation of the air bogies so that the vehicle can take curves of small radius.

In order to carry the development of URBA from a vehicle to a fully integrated public transport system, the Société d'Etudes de l'URBA (SETURBA) has been formed by the Caisse des Dépôts et Consignation, the Enterprise Bouygues and the Gazocéan-Technigaz Group.

The registered office of the Society is at 4 Place Raoul Dautry, Paris 15.

SETURBA has accelerated the application of URBA by confirming, technically and economically, the best means of applying this new method of transport and has prepared the constitution of a new company charged with the industrial and commercial development of the URBA system.

A technical and financial appraisal of URBA, undertaken by the SETURBA study group, proved favourable, and this has led to the establishment of Société de l'URBA (S.U.), supported by former associates of SETURBA, finance companies, banks and investors. Capital investment will be between F10-15 million. SETURBA has also launched a marketing programme to communities in France where likely applications are foreseen.

The company states that public funds are being made available in the form of research and development grants, and that the next phase of URBA's development programme is budgeted at F 30 million.

URBA has been specially designed to satisfy the transport needs of medium-size towns of 200,000 to 1,000,000 inhabitants, and the suburbs of large cities.

The prototype URBA 4, and later two URBA 8s coupled together, were demonstrated at Lyon during 1968. The prototype has been in daily use for almost four years at the Ecole Centrale of Lyon, where research and development has been supported by D.G.R.S.T., D.A.T.A.R., A.N.V.A.R. and the Ministry of Transport. To date it has carried 30,000 visitors. The computer analysis of its dynamic behaviour has confirmed

The URBA 4 prototype seats 6/12 passengers and has a cruising speed of 50 mph (80 km/h)

Impression of a single-track URBA 30 line, with supporting columns located in the centre of a highway

its stability, its comfort and its ability to take small radius curves.

Several recent international assessments, including a searching study by Eurofinance, consider URBA as one of the most promising of the new means of transport for the years 1970 to 1990. A certain number of towns in France and abroad, including Rouen, Bordeaux and Montpellier, are already at the stage of serious preliminary studies. Three different lines located in the outskirts of Paris have been studied. A special study has also been undertaken for the new business centre of La Defénse, on the western side of Paris. These bring out the favourable capital and operating costs which should place the price per passenger per kilométre of URBA at a level comparable with that of the bus today.

URBA 8

A prototype urban and suburban monorail URBA 8 is an improved version of the URBA 4, with three linear motors instead of two, and seats for eight passengers. Two URBA

8s were demonstrated at Lyon on December 4th, 1968, on an 87 yard (79 m) track. They operated singly and coupled, with acceleration and deceleration in the range 0·25 to 0·35 g (with 0·5 g deceleration in an emergency) and at speeds up 4o 30 mph (48·28 km/h). It consists of a rectangular-framed cabin seating up to eight passengers and suspended from three Dynavac air bogies running in an experimental 260 ft (80 m) track.

PROPULSION: Propulsion and normal braking is by three Merlin Gerin linear motors of 25 kW, weighing 176 lb (80 kg) and providing a thrust of 220 lb (100 kg) at starting 66 lb (30 kg) at normal service speed. Supply is from 380 volt, 3-phase, 50 cycle mains. The motor is the first to be designed as an industrial unit for vehicle propulsion. An aluminium conductor fin runs down the centre of the track and a set of coils is mounted in each bogie. Conductor rails for current supply to the linear motor and lift fans are in the base of the fin.

CABIN: The cabin is rectangular and

measures 14 ft 10 in (4·5 m) long, 5 ft 3 in (1·6 m) wide and 4 ft (1·2 m) high. It is built from 4 cm square section tube and diecast corners of a type normally used for the framework of holiday bungalows.

The floor is of light alloy and the sides are perspex. Suspension between the cabin and the three air bogies is by rubber cord springs and hydraulic automobile shock absorbers.

Tests have demonstrated that the air bogie concept is suitable for sharp curves, can climb steep slopes and provides good acceleration and braking. It cannot be derailed.

URBA 20

An enlarged version of the URBA 4, this model will seat 20 passengers in a cylindrical cabin and have a top speed of 45 mph (72 km/h). More efficient lift fans will be employed on this model which will require a total of 12 kW for lift power. All-up weight will be 10,470 lb (4,750 kg).

URBA 30

This is the first model designed to go into

URBA 20, a light urban transport vehicle with a service speed of 45 mph (72 km/h) and seating 20 passengers

service as a public transport system and will seat 30 passengers in rows, three abreast. The initial design will have 5 special, light-weight automatic doors on one side. Overall dimensions of the cabin will be: length 29 ft 6 in (9 m), width 6 ft 3 in (1·9 m), height 6 ft 7 in (2 m) overall, loaded weight 5·3 tons. Propulsion will be by linear motors.

Cost of the double overhead track for the

URBA 30 will be in the region of £200,000 per mile excluding wayleaves.

FIRST COMMERCIAL LINE

Bids have been submitted by the Société de l'URBA for two projects, the most promising being a line between the centre of a new town to the south of Paris, and the nearby railway station. The line will be about 3·21 km (2 miles) in length and will have gradients of 10%.

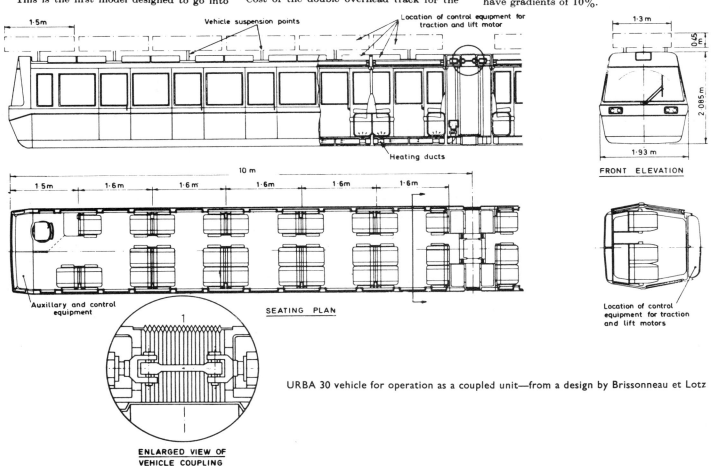

URBA 30 vehicle for operation as a coupled unit—from a design by Brissonneau et Lotz

---

FEDERAL REPUBLIC OF GERMANY (FRG)

TRANSRAPID-EMS
Gesellschaft fur elektromagnetische Schnell-verkehrssysteme (Joint Venture Group Krauss-Maffei and MBB)

HEAD OFFICE:
D-8000 Munich, Steinsdorfstr. 13
TELEPHONE:
(089) 226694/22 73 40
TELEX:
529463 trmue

In April 1974 it was announced that Krauss-Maffei (KM) and Messerschmitt-Bolkow-Blohm (MBB) are to develop jointly a high-speed transportation system.

As agreed with the Federal Minister of Research and Technology, the corporate managements of both companies have decided to conduct their future development activities for a track-guided high-speed transportation system—started in the late sixties—on a joint basis.

In 1971 both companies presented to the public the world's first large-scale test vehicles supported, guided, and driven by magnetic fields. In the meantime extensive testing performed on test rigs and test tracks at Munchen-Allach and Ottobrunn has demonstrated that contact-free magnetic suspension using controlled electromagnets can be achieved and is practical for high-speed ground transportation systems.

Both companies, using different approaches,

arrived at very similar research results.

The chief objective of the joint venture group is to develop a uniform high-speed transportation system for Europe for economic long-haul passenger and freight transportation. To achieve this aim, international links, such as co-operation with DAF Netherlands began in 1973, and plans for the formation of an international management corporation for high-speed transportation are under way.

Research work is being financed by the Federal Minister of Research and Technology as well as by funds from the two companies.

On February 19th, 1976, 401·3 km/h (249 mph) was attained by the Komet research vehicle, a world record for Maglev vehicles.

TRACK

The track for a rapid transit system based on the principle of magnetic suspension and guidance would consist of the supporting concrete pylons and beams, the ferromagnetic support and guidance rails, the secondary part of the linear motor, and the power rails.

In order to ensure the safe operation of a rapid transit system on the one hand, and not to endanger the environment by its operation on the other, the track will be supported on pylons spaced approximately 52 ft 6 in (16 m) apart with the elevation (clearance) of the track being at least 14 ft 9 in (4·50 m). This eliminates to a large extent, the need for special structures at intersections with roads, rail tracks, etc.

A fast and reliable switching system for traffic diverging from and merging with the main line is necessary for smooth and safe operation of a rapid transit system.

Experiments with an electromagnetic switch with no moving parts revealed that special devices were needed on board which added weight and increased aerodynamic drag. Currently, a mechanical switch is being developed.

PRINCIPLE OF MAGNETIC LEVITATION

In the selected principle of magnetic attraction, the vehicles are supported and guided by controlled electromagnets along armature rails fastened to the guideway. Sensors continuously measure the air gap between the vehicle magnets and the armature rails (10-20 mm). The data measured is transmitted to the control unit which controls the attractive forces of the magnets and thus keeps the vehicle in a hovering condition.

In addition to the development of the magnetic levitation and guidance system, vehicle development also includes other components, such as linear motor propulsion energy transfer, vehicle frame, braking, emergency gliding and safety systems. The design of cost-saving, elevated guideways and planning of the necessary stationary facilities, such as stations, power supply, etc. are of equal significance for the overall system.

Knowledge and experience gained and substantiated through extensive testing on various test stands formed the basis for the construction of experimental vehicles and test tracks in Ottobrunn, München-Allach and Manching.

TEST STANDS

Static, dynamic and rotating magnet test stands were built for the purpose of defining and optimising magnets for the levitation and guidance system and various control techniques. Support force losses and braking forces on magnets as a result of eddy current effects at high speeds can be measured and power transmission methods tested on rotation test stands. Switching tests with magnetically levitated vehicles are performed on switch test stands. Linear motor test stands are used to determine thrust and lateral forces on single- and double-sided linear motors and to measure temperature, current and voltage.

BASIC VEHICLE

MBB began work on the vehicle and the test track began in July of 1970. On February 4, 1971, the first suspension tests of the experimental vehicle took place in the test laboratory. On April 2, 1971, the first test runs were made on MBB's special test track.

On the rotary test rig small magnets of about 1 ft length interact with a steel-rimmed aluminium wheel of 1 m diameter. At peripheral speeds reaching 140 m/s, the lift and drag forces on one magnet can be measured as functions of current and gap

Above and below: First full-scale test vehicle to employ magnetic suspension guidance and propulsion, was MBB's basic experimental craft. Weighing 5·6 metric tons and 23 ft (7 m) in length, it has reached 62 mph (100 km/h) on a 766 yard (700 m) track

On May 5, 1971, the experimental vehicle was presented to the public for the first time in the presence of the Federal Minister for Educational Science and the Federal Minister for Transportation.

It demonstrated the feasibility of magnetic suspension and guidance with linear motor propulsion, and it provided information on those parameters not covered during simulation of the system and development of the components.

Weighing 5·6 metric tons and with a length of 23 ft, it has an asynchronous linear motor with 200 kW nominal power which is capable of accelerating the vehicle on the 766 yard (700 m) test track to a speed of 62 mph (100 km/h).

Four controlled suspension magnets and two guidance magnets on each side of the vehicle lift it and guide it during operation with a nominal air gap of ½ in (14 mm) between the magnets and the rails.

TRANSRAPID 02 RESEARCH VEHICLE

In October 1971 Krauss-Maffei started operating an experimental 39 ft 4 in (12 m) long vehicle on a 930 m (1,017 yards) test track. It reached a maximum speed of 164 km/h (101·9 mph). A novel power pick-up system ensures troublefree transmission of electric energy at high speeds. A secondary suspension system with pneumatic shock absorbers and vibration dampers constitutes the link between the vehicle superstructure and the hovering chassis.

Guideway and vehicle concepts provide realistic test data. The test results obtained so far have revealed that the system requirements can be fulfilled without difficulty.

TRACK:
Length	1,017 yards (930 km)
Radius of curvature	875 yards (800 m)

EXPERIMENTAL VEHICLE:
Length	38 ft 4½ in (11·70 m)
Width	9 ft 6 in (2·90 m)
Height above track surface	6 ft 8¾ in (2·05 m)
Number of seats	1 × 7/9
Weight	appr 11 Mp
Payload	appr 2 Mp
Design speed of vehicle	appr 220 mph (350 km/h)

PROPULSION BY LINEAR INDUCTION MOTOR:
Thrust (transient)	appr 3·2 Mp
Present vehicle speed (due to short track length)	appr 100 mph (160 km/h)
Synchronous speed LIM at 50 cps	appr 112 mph (180 km/h)

SERVICE BRAKES:
Brake retardation by LIM	appr 2·5 m/sec²
by jaw brake	appr 8·5 m/sec²
by friction brake	appr 8·0 m/sec²

ELECTROMAGNETIC SUPPORT AND GUIDANCE SYSTEM:

Specific carrying capacity appr 800 kp/m magnet length (25 mm air gap)

Air gap	½ in 1 in (10·25 mm)

POWER SUPPLY:

Support and guidance system:
Voltage 380 V three-phase current, 50 cp	
Output	32 kW

TRANSRAPID 03 RESEARCH VEHICLE

In October 1971, the company started operating a dual-purpose test facility which allows a comprehensive system comparison between magnetic cushion and air cushion techniques using same vehicles on the same track with completely identical operating conditions. Vehicles and track have been designed for a maximum speed of approximately 86·99 mph (140 km/h). The track length is 1,017 yards (930 km) allowing the attainment of a speed of about 100 mph (160·93 km/h), which has already been reached with the magnetic cushion vehicle. This experimental system provides realistic information since it subjects the support, guidance and propulsion system to extreme loads both during straight runs and cornering.

Transrapid 03 is the basic Transrapid 8-ton research vehicle adapted for tests as a tracked air cushion vehicle. The payload of two tons

Krauss-Maffei's Transrapid research vehicle in 02 configuration, with magnetic support, guidance and propulsion systems

Transrapid's 03 research craft permitted a full systems comparison between magnetic and air cushion techniques, using the same vehicle on the same track under completely identical operating conditions

and overall dimensions are identical to those of the vehicle in its earlier configuration. The programme, which is supported by the Federal Ministry of Research and Technology, is enabling the TACV and Maglev concepts to be compared under identical conditions for the first time.

Tests with air cushion support began at the end of 1972 and finished in 1973.

As a TACV, the vehicle is supported and guided by a total of 14 air cushion pads. Six, each with a cushion area of 3 m², support the vehicle on its elevated concrete guideway, and eight, mounted in pairs, each of about 1 m² cushion area, provide lateral guidance along the LIM reaction rail. The air cushion lift system is of plenum type and each pad has a rubber skirt. Cushion air is supplied by a two-stage compressor.

The vehicle is propelled by a French-made LIM system, which accelerates the vehicle to 90 mph (145 km/h) on its 1,093 yard (1,000 m) guideway.

Comparisons covered the following areas: vehicle dynamics; weight; load tolerances; vertical air gap tolerances; specific power requirements for support and guidance; effects on the environment (noise level); reliability; life; reaction to weather influences; maximum speed; aerodynamic drag; investment, operating and maintenance costs.

Results of the comparison: Magnetic levitation technology is superior.

TRACK:
Length	1,017 yards (930 m)
Radius of curvature	875 yards (800 m)

EXPERIMENTAL VEHICLE:
Length	38 ft 4½ in (11·7 m)
Width	9 ft 6 in (2·9 m)
Height above track surface	6 ft 8½ in (2·05 m)
Number of seats	10
Weight	21,170 lb (9,600 kg)
Design speed of vehicle	appr. 86·99 mph (140 km/h)

PROPULSION BY LINEAR INDUCTION MOTOR:
Thrust (transient)	appr. 3·2 Mp
Present vehicle speed (due to short track length)	appr. 100 mph (160 km/h)
Synchronous speed LIM at 50 cps	appr. 112 mph (180 km/h)

SERVICE BRAKES:
Brake retardation by LIM	appr. 2·3 m/sec²
by jaw brake	appr. 8·5 m/sec²
by friction brake	appr. 8·0 m/sec²

ELECTROMAGNETIC SUPPORT AND GUIDANCE SYSTEM:

Specific carrying capacity appr. 800 kp/m magnet length (25 mm air gap)

Air gap	½ in 1 in (10·25 mm)

POWER SUPPLY:

Support and guidance system:

Voltage 380 V three-phase current, 50 cp
Output   32 kW
LIM:
Voltage 2·6 KV three-phase current, 50 cps
Output   5 MVA

MAGNET TEST VEHICLE

Operation of the magnet test vehicle started on the Ottobrunn test track in 1972. This test vehicle consists of a platform supported and guided by wheels and accelerated by a hot water rocket.

The magnet test vehicle was used to test magnets as well as the air gap between magnet and rail and acceleration sensors at different speed levels up to 225 km/h. The components were tested in conjunction with an instrumented test rail mounted in the guideway.

DIMENSIONS:
Vehicle:
Length   11 ft 9¾ in (3·6 m)
Width   8 ft 2¾ in (2·5 m)
Starting weight 2,866 lb (1,300 kg)
Max speed   139 mph (225 km/h)
Propulsion:
Type   hot water rocket
Guideway:
Length   722 yards (660 m)

COMPONENT TEST VEHICLE KOMET

The Komet is an unmanned, magnetically levitated and guided vehicle with a mounting rack for components to be tested. This mounting rack allows the installation of magnets, linear motors and power pick-ups of various designs, which can be tested in combination with equally easily replaceable instrumented rails at speeds up to 400 km/h. The test data are transmitted to a fixed receiving station via a telemetry system. The Komet is accelerated by means of a thrust sled equipped with up to six hot-water rockets in order to achieve the desired high speeds on only 1,300 meters length of test track.

TECHNICAL DATA:
Component Test Vehicle:
Length   8·5 m
Width   2·5 m
Height   1·7 m
Weight (without instrumented components) 8,800 kg
Max speed   400 km/h
Thrust sled:
Length   5·0 m
Width   2·5 m
Height   1·5 m
Starting weight 7,500 kg
Guideway
Track gauge   2·2 m
Length   1,300 m
incl. acceleration section 300 m
Test section   300 m
Deceleration and safety section 700 m

TRANSRAPID 04

The Transrapid 04 is the largest passenger-carrying magnetically levitated and LIM-propelled experimental vehicle in existence to date.

The elevated guideway, with curves of different radii, represents a further development on the way to future applications. Different design principles and materials, such as concrete and steel, were used in order to test various alternatives. For the first time, a LIM reaction rail was mounted horizontally on the guideway beam.

The 2,400 m test track allows the testing of different system components under realistic

The MBB hot-water rocket-driven test carrier on its track at Ottobrunn

The Komet, an unmanned magnetically-guided and levitated component-test vehicle established a world record for maglev vehicles on February 19, 1976 when it attained 401.3 km/h on its 1,300 m guideway

Transrapid 04, the world's largest passenger vehicle employing magnetic levitation and a linear induction motor for propulsion

conditions and at higher speeds. The results of the test programme will be the basis for the definition of future test vehicles and large-scale test facilities.

TECHNICAL DATA:
Vehicle:
Length   15·0 m
Width   3·4 m
Height   2·8 m
Weight   16,500 kg
Max speed   v250 km/h
Propulsion   asynchronous
Type   linear motor
Max thrust   50,000 N
Guideway:
Track gauge   3·2 m
Length   2,400 m
Radii of curvature 800-3,100 m
Span   17-20 m
Max guideway inclination ±11°

PRE-PROTOTYPE TRAIN

Based on the R&D results gained at Krauss-Maffei and MBB, Transrapid-E.M.S, in collaboration with the research and design departments of the parent companies, is

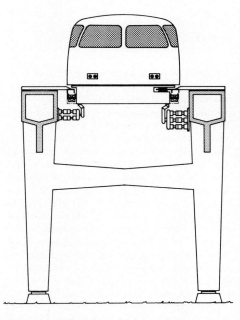
Elevated track employed for the Transrapid 04

currently designing a pre-prototype train. This is to be used for large-scale tests at the "Test Centre for Transportation Technology" planned by the Ministry of Transport and Ministry of Research and Technology in the Donauried Area (Bavaria). This test phase is to ensure the technical serviceability of components and vehicles prior to their final operation in realistic long-duration tests and to provide information on their reliability, safety, maintainability, riding comfort, cost-effectiveness and environmental compatibility

TECHNICAL DATA:

Train (two sections):

Length	64·0 m
Width	4·20 m
Height	4·0 m
Capacity	240 passengers
Payload	24 t
Weight of train	170 t
Max speed	400 km/h
Propulsion	asynchronous
Type	linear motor

TEST SITE

The Federal Ministry of Research and Technology has agreed to a new configuration for the test site for transport technology at Donauried. Changes have been made in the original concept to accommodate wishes of local communities.

The main alteration is a reduction in size so as not to disturb areas of natural beauty and ornithological interest. This has necessitated a compromise solution involving abandonment of certain peripheral facilities.

Total length of track available for wheel-rail or magnetic levitation vehicles has been

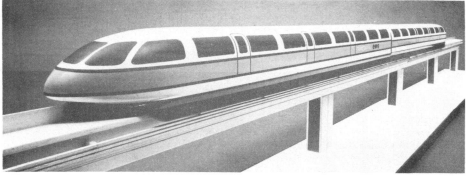

Transrapid concept for a 400 km/h prototype train for 240 passengers. The first section of the train will be tested at the government opersted test facility for transport technology near Augsburg from 1980 onwards. Vehicles of similar design will first be applied to less densely populated areas or to connect them with major airports

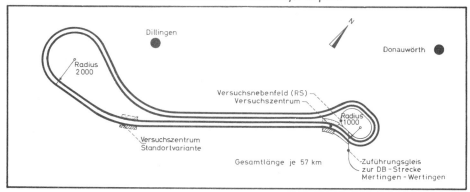

reduced from 75 km to 57 km, while curve radii have been considerably tightened from 2,500 m to 2,000 m and 3,000 m to 1,000 m. Measurement times at maximum speeds of 500 km/h for Maglev and 400 km/h for conventional vehicles have been reduced by 60 s and 26 s respectively.

Both tracks will now run parallel for their entire length, so that tests on vehicles passing in opposite directions will only be possible on the conventional technology inner track. Abandonment of flyovers also means that the test site will be visually more acceptable.

AEG-BBC-SIEMENS

HEAD OFFICE:
D-852 Erlangen, Froebelstr. 19-25
TELEPHONE:
09131-72457
CABLE/TELEX:
6 29 871
DIRECTOR:
Dipl.-Ing. A. Lichtenberg

The Federal German government has funded a joint programme by AEG-Siemens and Brown-Boveri for the design and construction of a repulsive magnetic levitation system which aims at being efficient, economical to operate, comfortable, clean and silent. Self-stabilising lift and guidance forces produced by superconducting magnets provide levitation heights of between 10 and 20 cm. The magnetically suspended vehicles are driven by linear induction motors which can be controlled over their entire speed

A prototype vehicle designed jointly by AEG BBC and Siemans

range with low losses. Tests have recently begun on a special test track at the Siemens Research Centre in Erlangen. The track is laid out in a circle 306 yards (280 m) in diameter to enable individual components of the system to be subjected to endurance tests, using telemetric equipment, in both the rolling and suspended positions. The power supply equipment, the asynchronomous linear motor and the magnet bearers, are currently being subjected to detailed tests in the rolling position.

Testing will later be transferred to a large test track at Donauried, financed by Federal funds.

ITALY

PALERMO UNIVERSITY

HEAD OFFICE:
  Aeronautical Institute, University of Palermo, Viale delle Scienze 90128, Palermo
TELEPHONE:
  422748-427172-227439

DIRECTOR:
  Prof. Ennio Mattioli
  The Aeronautical Institute has designed and built a half-scale TACV prototype, the IAP3, which began its trials in May 1972, along a U-shaped concrete guideway.

Tests have been temporarily discontinued. The Institute is now engaged in research in the field of magnetic levitation, the application of studies undertaken in conventional railway transportation and the development of a new type of marine air cushion vehicle.

THE UNITED STATES OF AMERICA

BERTELSEN INC

HEAD OFFICE:
  9999 Roosevelt Road,
  Westchester,
  Illinois 60153
TELEPHONE:
  312-681-5606
WORKS:
  113 Commercial Street,
  Neponset,
  Illinois 61345

Dr. William R. Bertelsen, Director of Research, Bertelsen Inc, has proposed the use of a vehicle based on the twin-gimbal Aeromobile 13 for a tracked skimmer system. It is described in US Patent No. 3,845,716 issued on November 5th 1974.

Dr. Bertelsen suggests that the system, based on the use of ACVs in simple, graded earth grooves, would be ideal for mass transportation in developing countries where no large investments have been made in

Impression of a tracked air cushion vehicle, based on the Bertelsen Aeromobile 13, in its guideway System

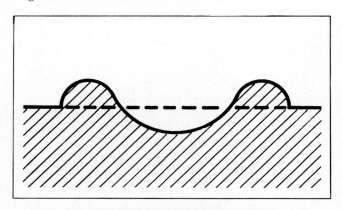

CROSS SECTION OF GRADED GROOVE WITH MINIMAL SURFACE PREPARATION

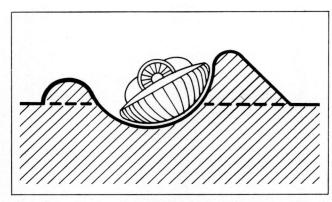

AEROMOBILE SHOWN IN GRADED GROOVE AT SPEED IN LEFT CURVE

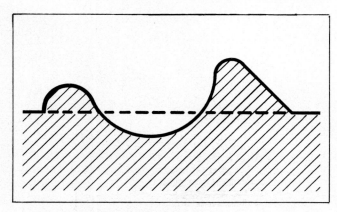

CROSS SECTION OF GRADED GROOVE AT LEFT CURVE

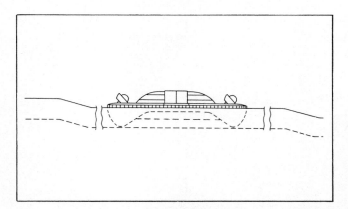

SIDE VIEW, STEPPED AERODUCT FOR GRADE CLIMB AND DESCENT

roads, railways or airlines. The fuel can be petroleum in oil-rich areas or hydrogen in the depleted or polluted areas. Whereas in densely populated countries new rights of way will inevitably be elevated or underground, there should be little difficulty in obtaining rights for the guideways in developing countries. In large countries with relatively empty interiors, the low-cost surface groove will be ideal.

Current or abandoned railway rights-of-way can be used for the Bertelsen Aeromobile-Aeroduct system, since rail gradients are acceptable to the Aeromobile. Hills can be climbed by the use of steps on which the vehicle is on the level or slightly inclined uphill most of the time. It climbs simply by lifting its mass in ground effect up each step, each of which would be slightly lower than its skirt height. Relatively low propulsive power is necessary to climb a hill in this manner and no increase in lift power is necessary.

The Aeromobile vehicles employed for the system would be fully automated. Journey data would be fed into an onboard mini-computer and the vehicles would follow the route through signals emitted at junction points. A tape could guide the car across

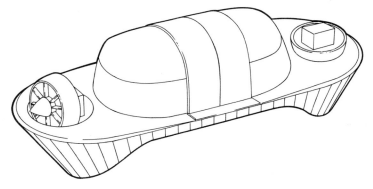

Impression of a tracked air cushion vehicle based on the Bertlesen Aeromobile 13

the country with a sleeping or reading driver. Dr. Bertelsen states that the car would move from low-to-high speed lanes automatically and remain in high-speed lanes until the signals at junctions told it to move down into a slower lane before turning off. This process would be repeated automatically until the car left the automatic guideway system.

In more developed countries, the bottom of the guideway could be protected by

concrete. Tunnels would be built in steel or concrete. Bridges across rivers or canyons would probably take the form of a suspended aluminium tube.

The system is designed to be all-inclusive, providing every type of transport need, from personal transit, "mass" transit, taxis, police, fire and emergency service, mail, freight, parcel, grocery and milk delivery to refuse pickup.

GRUMMAN AEROSPACE CORPORATION

HEAD OFFICE AND WORKS:
South Oyster Bay Road, Bethpage, Long Island, New York 11714
CHAIRMAN OF THE BOARD AND PRESIDENT:
G. M. Skurla
EXECUTIVE VICE PRESIDENT:
R. H. Tripp
SENIOR VICE PRESIDENT—
PROGRAMME MANAGEMENT:
R. S. Mickey
DIRECTOR—TLRV PROGRAMMES:
R. V. Benito

Grumman has completed the detail design and fabrication of a 300 mph (483 km/h) tracked levitated research vehicle TLRV under contract to the US Department of Transportation.

In 1975 the Department was forced to curtail the programme due to financial constraints. The Grumman Tracked Levitated Research Vehicle is being used by the Department for further development of the AiResearch-designed linear motor propulsion system (LIMPS). During the period April 1975 to April 1976, testing was limited to low speed tests of the Airesearch linear motor propulsion system. Due to finding limitations imposed at present, the programme was due to terminate on June 18, 1976, the vehicle itself being put into a preservation status for two years.

GRUMMAN TLRV

The Grumman TLRV is a 51 ft (15·54 m) long air cushion research vehicle designed to ride in a U-shaped track at speeds up to 300 mph (483 km/h). The maximum use is made of developed aerospace hardware and the materials and processes used in the construction of the vehicle are conventional.

The craft was designed to investigate aerodynamic performance and stability, dynamic response of both vehicle and guideway members, secondary suspension requirements, air cushion design and the wearability of flexible skirt material.

Grumman's 51 ft (14·54 m) research vehicle in its guideway at the Department of Transportation's High Speed Test Centre, Pueblo, Colorado

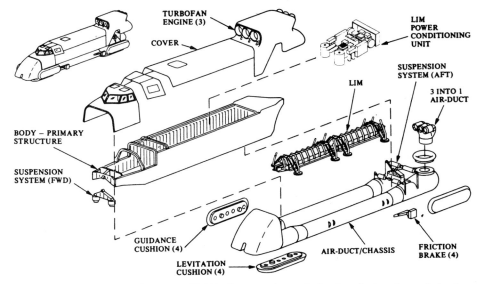

Exploded drawing of the Grumman TLRV, showing the turbofan installation linear induction motor, and body and cover structure

LIFT AND PROPULSION: Three externally mounted JT15D turbofans are employed as compressors for cushion air. Air from the bypass fans is ducted to four lift pads and four guidance pads. During 1973 the vehicle was operated up to 90 mph (144·84 km/h) using only residual thrust from the JT15Ds for propulsion and was expected to reach 125 mph (201·16 km/h) in that mode.

With the linear motor installed, the vehicle is expected to attain speeds in the region of 300 mph (483 km/h).

SECONDARY SUSPENSION SYSTEMS: The body is connected to the chassis by elements which can be operated in an active or passive mode. The entire body can also be banked with respect to the chassis to substantially eliminate lateral acceleration during turns. The levitation and guidance cushions are connected to the chassis by elements which can also be operated actively or passively.

ACCOMMODATION AND SAFETY FEATURES: The vehicle requires only one operator. Three additional seats are provided, however. One seat is for use by a test instrumentation engineer, and the other two will provide observer accommodation. The cabin is surrounded by a strong primary structure and has a 'bird proof' windshield. Both entrance doors are accessible to all crew members. Fire protection includes detection and suppression systems, foam-filled fuel tanks, fire walls and fuel tanks located remotely from the cabin.

BRAKING SYSTEM: Normal braking is applied by aero-brake, reverse thrust and friction pads. Provision for emergency braking includes a form of arresting system built into the guideway, and a 7 ft (2·13 m) diameter drag chute.

DIMENSIONS:

Length overall   51 ft 0 in (15·54 m)

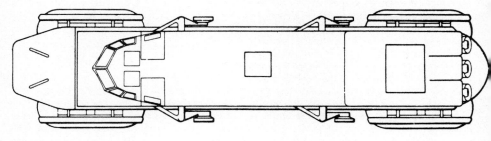

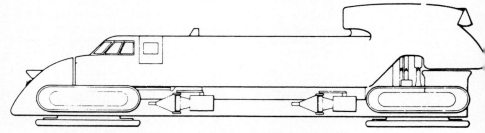

General arrangement of Grumman's TLRV.

Width overall	12 ft 0 in (3·65 m)
Height overall	13 ft 2 in (4·01 m)

OPERATING WEIGHT:

Aero propulsion	34,000 lb (15,422 kg)
Linear induction motor	62,000 lb (28,123 kg)

PERFORMANCE:

Max speed	300 mph (483 km/h)
Min acceleration distance, 0-300 mph (0-483 km/h)	1·9 miles app (3·1 km)
Min braking distance	1·5 miles app (2·4 km)

AIR CUSHION APPLICATORS, CONVEYORS and PALLETS

FRANCE

SOCIÉTÉ BERTIN & CIE

OFFICE AND WORKS:
BP No. 3, 78370 Plaisir, France
TELEPHONE:
462.25.00
TELEX:
26.619
DIRECTORS:
Fernand Chanrion, President Director
General
Michel Perineau, Director General
Georges Mordchelles-Regnier

Air Cushion Handling Division

OFFICER:
M. Croix-Marie
ADDRESS:
Centre d'Essais Aérotrain, Gometz la Ville
91400 Orsay, France
TELEPHONE:
592.03.18
TELEX:
60.090

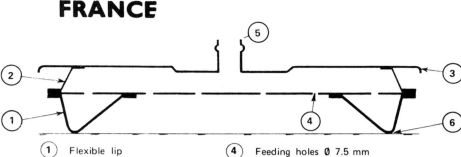

①	Flexible lip	④	Feeding holes Ø 7.5 mm
②	Suspension	⑤	Air supply
③	Frame	⑥	Leakage gap

Basic configuration and components of a Bertin circular cushion

Research on ground effect and air cushion principle applications has been undertaken by Bertin et Cie since 1956. The company developed the original technique of separately fed plenum chambers surrounded by flexible skirts—see entries for SEDAM (ACVs) and Société de l'Aérotrain (Tracked Skimmers). The same basic technology is being applied extensively to industrial materials handling.

In the past, developments in this field have mainly covered special applications. A stage has now been reached where standard equipment can be made available for a large number of handling applications.

Bertin has now made available standard components and, according to the type of problem to be solved, offers clients 'do-it-yourself-kits", plus advice, technological assistance or full design services.

STANDARD DO-IT-YOURSELF KITS

These are available in the following configurations:

1. Circular Cushions

These form the basis of the handling platforms. Their positioning and number is determined by function, the weight and nature of the loads (height, position of centre of gravity etc.).

Three cushions at least must be employed to ensure stability.

The cushions can be fitted on to a chassis with spring fastenings.

The flexible lips will not suffer wear under normal conditions but are interchangeable in cases of accidental damage.

Circular cushions are produced as standard units in three sizes: ϕ 300, ϕ 450, ϕ 600.

General characteristics are given in the accompanying table.

2. Standard Modules

Standard modules, complete with chassis, and based on one of the four types of standard circular cushions available (see table) are available in two models:

—quick assembly modules which can be assembled at will to form platforms in a variety of sizes

—independent pads ready to be inserted beneath loads which have a rigid, flat underside.

Lifting capacity of these modules is comparable to that of the corresponding circular cushion.

Standard Bertin circular cushion

Metal air cushion skids fitted beneath a platform used to feed loads of up to 3,000 kg to a press Off-cushion, beneath the press, the platform withstands pressures of up to 26,000 kg.

3. Honeycomb Cushions

Honeycomb cushions are available in three standard sizes. Fully stable, these cushions allow full use of the load bearing surface for lift. In addition they are very thin but can bear very heavy loads when at rest.

These cushions employ inflatable joints to seal off adjacent square cells which are fed separately through vents from a single plenum. The plenum itself is fed from any suitable compressed air source.

STANDARD UNITS FOR SPECIAL APPLICATIONS

For moving and positioning loads in factories and buildings with low ceiling heights air cushion skids have been designed. These metal pads have no flexible seals, and used over a very even surface, they operate

without surface contact on an air film a few
hundredths of a millimetre deep.

Applications include a 3,000 kg payload
platform—for feeding a press mounted on
seven skids 200 mm in diameter. This unit
can withstand a pressure of 26,000 kg when
at rest beneath the press.

MACHINERY HANDLING IN FACTORIES

Major applications of Bertin air cushions
to solve machinery and material handling
within factories, listed in the past issues
of Jane's Surface Skimmers, include:
Air film cushion sheer tables (1966):
Air cushion platforms to install 40,000 lb
machinery units within factory buildings
(1966):
Air cushion chassis for moving machinery
(1968):
Air cushion conveyors adapted to specific
loads (1969):
Air film conveyors for the transfer of soft
or tacky sheet material (1970):
Loading platform for lorries (1970):
Cast mould press feeding platform on air
cushions (1971):
Transfer of 12 ton spinning mills on air
cushions (1972):
Permanent air cushion platforms for the
transfer of 5 ton diesel engine cooling units
from the assembly line to the dispatching
area (1972):
Air cushion platforms for precise positioning of metal blanks under a magnetic
unstacking unit (1973):
Permanent air cushion platforms fitted
under 30 ton profiling machines facilitating
the use of alternative machines along a
production line (1973):
50-ton capacity platform to introduce loads
within an X-ray control room through
staggered protection walls (1974):
Air-cushion turntable for 50 ton loads of
glassware (1974):
Space-saving air cushion system to rotate
railway trucks along their assembly line
(1975).

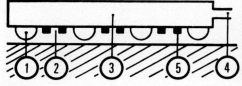

1　*joint*
2　*aperture*　　　　4　*air supply*
3　*chamber*　　　　5　*resting pads*

**Diagram showing the basic structure of
the Bertin honeycomb air cushion pallets**

Circular Cushions

Type	Ø 300	Ø 450	Ø 600	Ø 600R
Overall diameter	0·364 m	0·540 m	0·680 m	0·680 m
Height at rest	0·035 m	0·050 m	0·050 m	0·050 m
Height under pressure	0·045 m	0·070 m	0·075 m	0·075 m
	±5 mm	±5 mm	±5 mm	±5 mm
Weight	5,5 kg	8,5 kg	14 kg	15 kg
Lift area	0·07 m²	0·16 m²	0·28 m²	0·28 m²
Load capacity	500 kg	1,200 kg	2,500 kg	4,000 kg

Honeycomb Cushions

Major characteristics:			
	Type 1	Type 2	Type 3
Length × width (mm)	626 × 329	416 × 768	590 × 590
Height at rest (mm)	22	32	30
Lift area (m²)	0,162	0,250	0,250
Load capacity (kg)	1,000	1,700	3,000

Pushing a loaded case into the workshop.

Left: Loaded platforms in their lowered position.　*Right:* Hull sections supported by three Bertin platforms with pneumatic jacks inactive

AID TO SHIPBUILDING

One of the major European shipyards has adopted Bertin air cushion units to facilitate the positioning of hull sections.

The air cushion platforms are built to carry large sections, weighing 100 tons and measuring 25 m × 15 m (82 ft × 49 ft), and place them in the precise position for assembly. Each platform is fitted with four circular cushions and incorporates one pneumatic jack and four hydraulic jacks, which in turn support a top working surface covered in a film of oil. Once the hull sections have been introduced to the point of assembly, they are raised first by the pneumatic jack, then the hydraulic ones to reach the exact position for fixing. The oil film is used for the final lateral positioning.

Twelve units of this type have been built by Bertin. The employment of circular cushions in conjunction with pneumatic suspension assists operations on the undulating floor surfaces of dry docks.

METAL SHEET HANDLING PLATFORM

A handling platform to facilitate feeding metal sheet to a work post has been produced for CEM at Le Havre, France.

The problem was to bring from an outdoor storage yard cases loaded with 2 × 8 m thick metal sheets to feed cutting units within a workshop.

The cases have been equipped with ten Type 600 Bertin circular cushions and are capable of carrying 20 tonnes of metal sheet in one move.

The cushion air feed has been calculated so as to allow the loads to vary both in weight and centering, so that no special care is required when loading the cases.

TWO-TIER MOBILE LIFTING TABLE

A mobile lifting table for placing sheet materials in a multi-level storage rack has been built for CEM, a company based at Le Havre.

The lower chassis, supported by eight Type 450 circular air cushions, is used to move the loaded table, weighing up to 6 tons, from the loading area to the storage racks. A six-cushion platform, which supports the actual load on the table, enables the material to be placed in position and elevated to the correct level. Once the material is in place, the modular air cushion platform is withdrawn onto the main lift table.

Bertin two-tier lifting table for placing heavy materials in multi-level storage racks

Positioning a case near the cutting units

ETABLISSEMENTS NEU
HEAD OFFICE:
Sac Postal No. 28, 59 Lille, France

Etablissements NEU is a licensee of Jet-

stream Systems Co of Hayward, California. Details of the conveyor system built by the company can be found under the entry for Jetstream Systems Company, USA.

GERMANY

HELMUT FRANK BLECHVERARBEITUNG
HEAD OFFICE:

Laufdorferstrasse, D-6331 Bonbaden, West Germany

This company manufactures Jetstream conveyor systems under licence.

ITALY

DEL MONEGO
HEAD OFFICE:
Piazza della Republica 8, Milan

Del Monego produces Jetstream conveyor systems under licence.

JAPAN

EBARA MANUFACTURING COMPANY
HEAD OFFICE:
11 Haneda Asahicho, Ota-Ku, Tokyo

This company produces Jetstream conveyor systems under licence.

TRINIDAD

COELACANTH GEMCO LTD
HEAD OFFICE:
1 Richardson Street, Point Fortin, Trinidad, West Indies
DIRECTORS:
Nigel Seale
Kelvin Corbie
SECRETARY:
R. Varma

Coelacanth Gemco Ltd., the first company to specialise in the design and construction of air cushion vehicles in the West Indies, has developed a hover conveyor system and a hover pallet.

The pallet, measuring 3 ft × 4 ft, is capable of lifting and moving 1,000 lb, while operated by one man and great potential is seen for the use of these units within Trinidad factories.

The hover-conveyor system is designed in modules of 10 ft and 15 ft, enabling a system of any length to be devised to suit changing production line requirements.

Coelacanth Gemco is also working on a self-contained unit, powered by a 100 hp diesel engine driving a 36 in eight-blade axial fan at 2,500 rpm to produce 30,000 cu ft of air per minute at 6 in w.g. pressure.

This will be used in the movement of oil company tanks between various locations. Multiples of this unit will enable tanks of any size to be moved after attaching the skirt system.

A Coelacanth hoverpallet employed in a workshop to move air-conditioning equipment. This particular model lifts loads up to 1,000 lb (453·592 kg). Other models, operating on factory air supplies of 80 lb sq in, will carry loads of up to 15 tons. The model seen above operates on either 115 or 230 volts ac

UNITED KINGDOM

AIRMATIC ENGINEERING LTD
HEAD OFFICE:
King Street, Sileby, Leicestershire
TELEPHONE:
Sileby 2816 (STD Code 050 981)
EXECUTIVES:
P. Lucas, Marketing Manager

This company is manufacturing and marketing the Pneu-move air bearing system under licence from the National Research Development Corporation of the United Kingdom.

ROTARY AIR TABLES

A range of rotary air tables, of 1-2 tons capacity and 61-84 in (1,550-2,150 mm) in diameter is available for rotating heavy loads. Rotation requires the minimum of physical effort. The equipment is designed for a number of applications, including the following: spray booth, fettling, machine assembly, marking out and inspection.

AIR FLOTATION TABLES

In 1975 the company introduced a range of air flotation tables, based on the principles employed in the Pneu-move air-bearing pad.

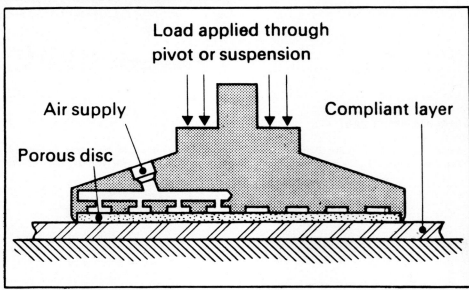

Load applied through pivot or suspension

Air supply

Compliant layer

Porous disc

Sectional view of a Pneu-move air bearing pad. The undersides of the pads have porous stainless steel surfaces which ride on the air flow created between the porous surface and a layer of compliant material below, such as neoprene sheet

Large, heavy sheets can be handled by one man and positioned accurately with the finger tips. Built-in pneumatically-operated breaker bars save time in cutting.

Existing tables of any size can be converted to Air Floatation Tables without difficulty. Alternatively, complete tables can be supplied and installed. Standard types of workshop air compressor are suitable, the output depending on the area of the table surface.

PNEU-MOVE

The Pneu-move system has been developed by the National Engineering Laboratory to enable heavy loads to be moved by hand without necessitating an expensive, high precision, operating surface.

Its low friction, small size, and low power requirement suit it for the movement of heavy machinery, particularly where man-handling in confined spaces may be necessary. It is also suitable for use in the production lines of heavy components where it eliminates the need for powered conveyors, allows accurate positioning because of the low friction, and gives secure parking by switching off the air supply.

Pneu-move air bearing pads enable heavy loads to be moved quickly by hand, without damaging floors

The system consists of an air bearing, mounted on a ball to allow some pivoting, and a track of a compliant material. It can be operated from a normal workshop air supply of 85 psi.

Applications include:

The installation of machines where suitable lifting facilities do not exist in the hosiery, printing, and carton-making industries.

A production flow line, e.g. final assembly of machine tools.

The movement of heavy raw materials, including steel plate.

The handling of components during manufacture, e.g. large fabrications between operations.

Assembly of mining machinery on site.

The movement of heavy loads without damage to floors, in machine tool showrooms and lecture theatres.

PNEU-MOVE AIRMATS

Derived from the company's air bearing pads, the Pneu-move air-mats are designed for the movement of heavy moulds, fixtures and work-pieces across machine tables. Air pressure and flow requirements are low and existing workshop air lines can be used. A range of standard sizes is available but other sizes and special designs can be produced by the company, the standard air supply connector is ¼ in (6·35 mm) BSP.

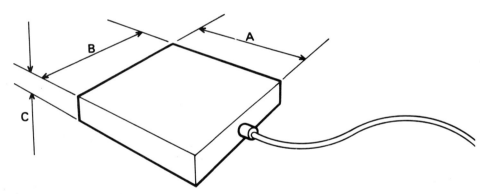

Pneu-Move-Air-Mat. Designed to carry heavy loads over holes and slots on machine tables, the × Air-Mat is suitable for moving components in drilling, tapping, milling, rubber and plastics moulding and many other machine operations

Ref.No.	Dimensions in mm (inches)			Max.load kgf (lbf)		Airflow m^3 / min(scfm)	
	A	B	C				
AM 1	150(6)	150(6)	25(1)	450	(1000)	0.085	(3)
AM 2	150(6)	300(12)	25(1)	900	(2000)	0.170	(6)
AM 3	200(8)	150(6)	30(1¼)	675	(1500)	0.127	(4.5)
AM 4	200(8)	300(12)	30(1¼)	1350	(3000)	0.255	(9)
AM 5	200(8)	600(24)	30(1¼)	2700	(6000)	0.51	(18)
AM 6	300(12)	300(12)	40(1½)	1800	(4000)	0.34	(12)
AM 7	300(12)	450(18)	40(1½)	2700	(6000)	0.51	(18)
AM 8	450(18)	450(18)	50(2)	4500	(10000)	0.85	(30)
AM 9	600(24)	600(24)	45(1¾)	7200	(16000)	1.36	(48)

The above tables give typical performance for a supply of pressure 6kp/cm². (85 psig) of Pneu-Move Air-Mats when used on an average machine tool table with a continuous surface. For loads less than those shown, lower supply pressures may be used, with correspondingly lower airflow rates. Where holes and slots are to be traversed, or if the table is badly worn, some allowance must be made for increased airflow and reduced maximum load.

AIR CUSHION EQUIPMENT (1976) LTD

HEAD OFFICE:
 15-35 Randolph Street, Shirley,
 Southampton
TELEPHONE:
 0703 776468
TELEX:
 477537
CABLES:
 HOVERACE SOTON
WORKS:
 35 Randolph Street, Shirley, Southampton
DIRECTORS:
F. B. Hake, Chairman
A. Latham, Marketing Manager
R. Gilbert, Chief Designer
R. Henvest, Works Manager

ACE "WATER SKATE"* LOAD-CARRYING PALLET

Two sizes of pallet are available:
Module A, with 35 tonne maximum capacity at 6 bar and Module AA, with 100 tonne maximum capacity at 6 bar. Both have a rise height of 75 mm and use water as the cushion fluid.

Due to the modular concept of the system, loads of many thousands of tonnes can be moved by the selection of the numbers of pallets used. A simple flexible skirt system retains water under pressure whilst still allowing sufficient water to escape to lubricate the surface between the skirt and the ground. For movement of heavy loads on sloping surfaces a restraining line is recommended.

Because of the type of flexible seal used in the pallet, it facilitates the movement of a load from one location to another without the use of complex hydraulic jacking systems or heavy cranes. The equipment will operate over any surface from rough concrete to compacted soil with the minimum of ground preparation and the use of supplmentary sheeting.

Water is usually provided via water pumps which can hired from local plant companies, and distributed through normal flexible hoses. Each pallet is controlled by a standard gate valve. When the valve is opened water is supplied to the pallet and the lift of 75 mm is achieved.

The load is normally moved by towing, winching or a combination of both. The drag coefficient, which is very low, especially when using a running sheet, is generally between 2-3% of the total weight.

*trade mark

Type A Water Skate load-carrying pallet

Type AA pallets were used to launch this 300 tonne diving platform

Six type A pallets were employed to move and locate ship sections weighing between 65-110 tonnes in a French dry dock

Close-up of a Water Skate load-carrying pallet in position below a ship section

Module size

'A'

'AA'

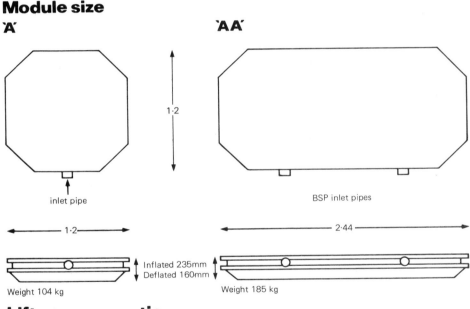

inlet pipe

BSP inlet pipes

1·2

1·2

2·44

Inflated 235mm
Deflated 160mm

Weight 104 kg

Weight 185 kg

Lift pressure ratio

Maximum working pressure 6 Bar (87 psi)

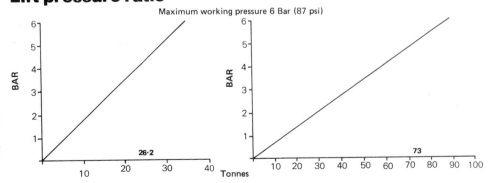

BAR

BAR

26·2

73

10   20   30   40   Tonnes

10 20 30 40 50 60 70 80 90 100

The Skate is a low cost lifting and manoeuvring pad using water under pressure from a standard commercial water pump. The two types shown here have a maximum lift of 35 tonnes and 100 tonnes repectively, and can be employed in a multi-modular system to suit individual requirements

---

BRITISH HOVERCRAFT CORPORATION

HEAD OFFICE:
East Cowes, Isle of Wight
DIRECTORS:
See ACV section

FLOATLOAD (1 Ton)

The 1-ton Floatload hoverpallet consists of a load-carrying, steel and plywood sand-wich platform with four easily removable rubber diaphragm assemblies underneath. Air is supplied through a 1 in BSP connector and control valve.

Designed for moving loads of up to 1 ton on smooth floors, the hoverpallet can also be used in conjunction with standard fork lift trucks, pallets and stillages, which can easily be modified for this purpose. Single man operation of the loaded pallet is easily effected.

Loads may be placed directly on to the platform of the Floataload hoverpallet, but a simple bridge system allowing the units to be slid under the load is more economical. When this is done the centre of pressure should be approximately under the centre of the load.

Operation is by opening the control valve until the load is airborne. The load can then be pushed, pulled or spun with minimum effort, the valve being closed and Floataload withdrawn when the load reaches the required position.

Floataload will operate satisfactorily over any smooth non-porous surface. Sheet metal, linoleum, vinyl, sealed concrete, plywood, smooth asphalt, and similar surfaces are all suitable.

DIMENSIONS:

Max length of pallet   3 ft 10 in (1·16 m)
Width of pallet   2 ft 7 in (0·78 m)

AIR PRESSURE:

Working air pressure for 100 lb (45·3 kg) load   3 lb sq in (0·21 kgf/cm²)
Working air pressure for 1,000 lb (453·5 kg) load   6 lb sq in (0·42 kgf/cm²),
¾ in BSP connection, 1 ton load   8 lb sq in (0·56 kgf/m²)

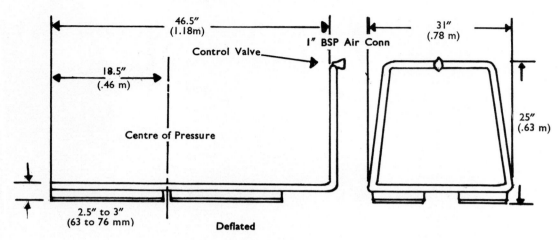

BHC 1 ton Floataload hoverpallet

LIGHT HOVERCRAFT COMPANY

HEAD OFFICE:

Felbridge Hotel & Investment Co Ltd, London Road, East Grinstead, Sussex

TELEPHONE:

0342 24424

EXECUTIVES:

Lindsay H. F. Gatward, Proprietor

This company markets a pedestrian controlled hoverpallet which has a payload capacity of 3 cwt (150 kg).

Lift power is provided by an 8 hp Briggs & Stratton petrol engine which drives a plastic/alloy axial fan mounted beneath a close mesh safety guard. Since the power unit is of the lawn mower type, the general noise level is low.

The pallet which is built in glassfibre can be used over a wide range of unprepared surfaces including snow, ice, mud, water, grass, swamp and sand. Ploughed fields with ridges of up to 6 in (152 mm) can be traversed with a reduced payload. The over-water and swamp applications are restricted by the amount the operator is prepared to become immersed, or the degree by which this ability to control the vehicle is impaired. Machines can be winched across areas of deep water. Working under these conditions, however, applications such as wildfowling, reed collection, slurry control and insect spraying in swamp areas are possible.

Two directional wheels are fitted and these can be adjusted or removed according to the degree of directional control or ground contact pressure required.

A clip-on spraying unit, manufactured by E. Allman & Co Ltd, Birdham Road, Chichester, Sussex, has been developed for use in conjunction with the pallet.

Skirt is of HDC segmented type in nylon-coated polyurethane. Depth is 5 in (127 mm).

Light Hovercraft Co's hoverpallets can be used over a wide variety of unprepared surfaces including agricultural land.   A clip-on attachment can be supplied for crop-spraying

Assembled hoverpallets ready for despatch.   The plastic/alloy axial lift fan is mounted beneath a close mesh safety guard

SPECIFICATIONS:

Length with handle	9 ft 6 in (2·89 m)
Width	4 ft (1·21 m)
Height with handle	3 ft (0·91 m)
Weight (approx)	160 lb (72·57 kg)
Skirt depth	5 in (127 mm)
Fuel capacity	6 pints (3·40 l)
Engine	319 cc (4-cycle)
Endurance (approx)	2 hrs per gallon
Payload	3 cwt (150 kg)
Payload area	28 sq ft (2·6 m²)

One of the applications for which the hover-pallet has proved ideal is that of snow removal. Its payload capacity is 2 cwt (152 kg)

LING SYSTEMS LTD

HEAD OFFICE AND WORKS:
Unit 8,
Station Road,
Gamlingay Sandy,
Bedfordshire, SG19 3HG
TELEPHONE:
Gamlingay 50101
TELEX:
826439

DIRECTORS:
P. J. Long — Joint Managing and
J. R. Arscott, — Sales and Technical Directors

EXECUTIVES:
A. J. Cousins, General Manager, Design & Works

EUROPEAN DISTRIBUTORS:
DENMARK—A.B.C. Hansen Comp A/S, Copenhagen

HOLLAND—Miller Holding MIJ, Amsterdam

Ling Systems Ltd is the exclusive licencee in the UK, Eire, and Holland for Jetstream air cushion conveyor. Equipment is in use to handle a wide range of scrap materials —metal, paper, board and plastic, also many types of unit loads—boxes, both full and empty; plastic bottles; cap closures; can ends and pressed and moulded parts.

ROLAIR SYSTEMS (UK) LTD

HEAD OFFICE & WORKS:
Penta House, Basingstoke Road, Reading RG2 0HS
TELEPHONE:
0734 82551
TELEX:
848122 Garagco Reading
DIRECTORS:
B. H. Wright, RD, BSc, BCom, CEng, MIEE, Chairman and Managing Director
D. L. Campbell, MC.
M. F. Dowding, CBE, MA, CEng, MIMechE.
N. F. Haycock, CEng, MIEE.
R. H. Lacey, CEng, MIMechE.
Lord Macpherson of Drumochter, J.P.
A. A. A. Stammers, MIMechE.

Rolair Systems (UK) Ltd has an exclusive licence from Rolair Systems Inc., of Santa Barbara, California, for the manufacture and sale of air film equipment for the transport of heavy industrial loads. Their range of equipment working off the shop air supply includes ST bearings which may be used in sets of four or more (individual ST bearing capacities range from one ½ ton to 26½ tons); standard steel transporters incorporating four bearings with capacities from 1 ton to 107 tons which may be used separately or in combination for heavier loads. Also available are battery operated steel transporters with in-built air blowers which may be used where no air supply is available or in controlled environments where outside air can not be used. A standard range of air film turntables with capacities up to 62 tons is available.

Existing applications of Rolair equipment

in the UK range from unit loads of less than one ton to over one thousand tons. Applications include generator and transformer movements, ship section transporters, omni-mobile cranes on air bearings and standard transporters for interbay movement, steel ladle transfer cars, turntables incorporated into machine tools or used in paint booths and fettling shops, movements of machine tools, oil rig modules, printing machinery, heavy diesel engines. Rolair transporters can also be used to form a production line for heavy equipment.

UK customers include BP Chemicals, Brush Electricals, CEGB, GEC, Hawker Siddeley Group, IBM, ICI, Kodak, Rolls-Royce, Short Brothers & Harland, Sunderland Shipbuilders and Westland Helicopters.

An unloaded Rolair 24R4 transporter (10¼ ton capacity) and a loaded Rolair 40B6 transporter (18 ton capacity) with an air-drive motor and fixed control handle fitted

A set of four Rolair 16ST bearings with a capacity of 3½ tons, in use to move an item of heavy machinery

UNITED STATES

AERO-GO INC

HEAD OFFICE AND WORKS:
5800 Corson Avenue South, Seattle, Washington 98108
TELEPHONE:
206/763-9380

EXECUTIVES:
Frank M. Cohee, President and General Manager
Kenneth G. Wood, Vice-President, Engineering
William A. Shannon, Vice-President, Sales

EUROPEAN DISTRIBUTORS:
United Kingdom:
Applied Technology Co. Ltd., London (Heathrow) Airport, England
Telephone: SKYport 2811

Scandinavian Representative:
Aero-Go Scandinavia AB, Box 5, S-73050, Skultuna, Sweden
Telephone: 021-70-900

Scandinavian Representative:
Aero-Go Scandinavia AB, Box 5, S-73050, Skultuna, Sweden
Telephone: 021-70-900

Aero-Go was founded in April, 1967 to commercialise air film and air cushion devices developed by the Boeing Company. It holds the exclusive world licence for products and patent rights of Boeing in this field.

The company has developed and is selling the Aero-Caster air film bearing in eight sizes ranging from 12 in to 48 in diameter. These are manufactured in neoprene impregnated nylon material and are thus highly resistant to tearing damage and capable of supporting very large loads. Lifting capacity ranges from 1,000 lb in the 12 in (304 mm) size to 80,000 lb in the 48 in (1·21 m) size. Individual Aero-Casters are employed in combinations to transport heavy loads. Load module systems are available, complete with portable blowers, hose manifolds and air controls.

Aero-Casters are also incorporated in standard pallets designed for a wide range of applications, including loading and unloading trucks, movement of loaded scissorlift tables, wire and cable reel carriers, paper and fabric rolls and production machinery. The Company builds Aero-Trucks and Aero-Turntables to meet customer requirements.

AERO-TURNTABLES

Aero-Turntables are available for use in factory production lines or such applications as paint booths and product shipping/receiving points. Multi-ton capacity air film turntables have been installed for lifting and rotating Boeing 747 jumbo jets during pre-flight testing and compass calibration.

In 1971 Aero-Go installed three air turntables for rotation of rapid transit rail cars for the Bay Area Rapid Transit (BART) system in Northern California. The turntables have been constructed to ride on water film should there be an electrical power failure.

In effect, the Aero-Caster is an open-ended piston with a dynamic end-seal that conserves the volume of air required to lift and float loads. The thin air film under this peripheral seal lubricates the bearing and allows it to float freely only ·005 in above the floor surface. As the caster moves across the surface, the flexible seal automatically contours to provide a constant gap and thus

One of two 70-ton capacity max mobile machine tool bed plate positioning systems built by Aero-Go for Westinghouse Electric Corporation under full load test

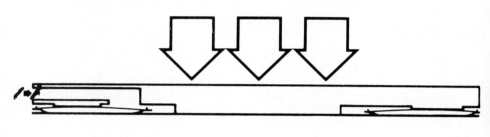

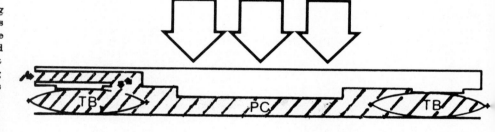

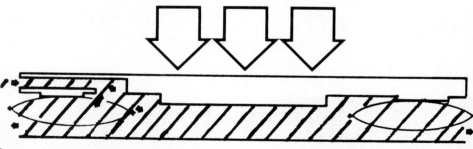

Step one: Aero-Caster "off cushion". The load is solidly supported on the landing pads. Black arrows represent fluid flow. Step two: Fluid enters flexible torus bag (TB) and plenum chamber (PC). Step three: When fluid forced in to the plenum chamber exceeds total load, caster then floats load off the floor

maintain a uniform air flow. When the air is shut off, the captured air bubble within the caster escapes, slowly lowering the load gently and safely to the ground. The casters are self pressure-regulating systems that may be operated without separate line regulators.

MAX MOBILE MACHINE TOOL BED PLATE POSITIONING SYSTEM

The Max mobile bed-plate transport system can instantly "float" pre-fixed workpieces up to a machine tool and precisely align them within a few thousandths of an inch. They arrive ready set-up and are secured at the machine on flush-to-floor docking points.

The Max system combines standard Aero-Caster air film bearings with bed plates and part holding fixtures.

Aero-Casters free the load from the floor to float on a thin layer of nearly-frictionless air. Load movement becomes possible in any direction with 1 lb of force for every 1,000 lb of load weight. The system allows heavy parts to be set-up in a staging area away from the machine. When the machine completes its drilling, boring or milling, the next workpiece is ready to be moved into an exact work position at the tool, which continues to work without waiting for the parts to be set-up.

When floating a total load of 100 tons (machine plus part), the equipment is

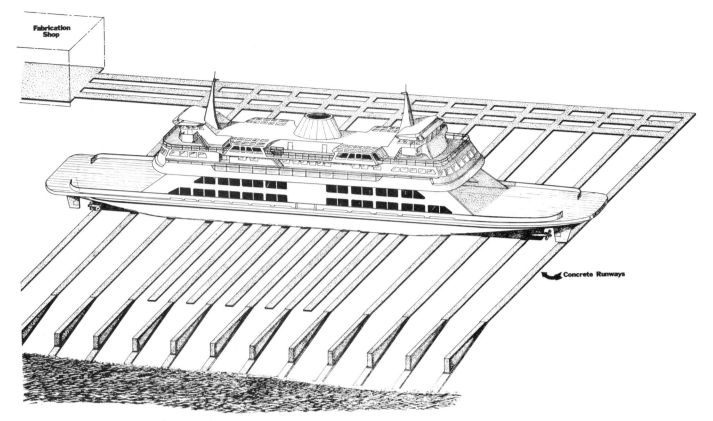

Layout at Vancouver Shipyards, where ship subsections are being lifted and transferred through each assembly stage and finally positioned for side-launching by Aero-Go's water film handling system

powered by a 3 hp electric-hydraulic system. Guidance is positively controlled by cam followers and surface engaging wheels.

Rotation around a central, retractable floor-contacting pivot pin system and forward/reverse directional travel are all remotely controlled by one operator from a portable console. Hydraulically-driven wheels propel the equipped in any direction at speeds from 0-20 fpm as desired.

Final precise positioning at the tool is performed by stopping the Max over load-bearing floor plates which align with landing pads on the unit's underside. Two tapered index pins are then engaged down into floor sockets. The operator deflates the Aero-Casters and the Max settles to the floor and is docked ready for machining to begin.

SHIPYARD FLUID HANDLING SYSTEM

In the spring of 1975, Vancouver Shipyards in British Columbia began lifting and transferring ship subsections. The first completed vessel, weighing 3,400 tons, was moved into launch position totally through the use of Aero-Go fluid bearings.

The basic water bearing building block and runway system allows shipyards to re-evaluate and expand their production potential. They can consider manufacturing oil drilling platforms, barges, or any of a variety of structures fabricated from steel.

The fluid bearing provides the capacity of lifting, rotating, and omni-directional transportation. Sections "floated" together can be accurately raised, lowered, tilted or warped, achieving exact alignment for efficient field welding.

The Vancouver Shipyard system includes 84 model K48NHDW Aero-Caster water film load modules. Each load-carrying module is approximately 2 in deep and 4 ft square, and weighs approximately 170 lb. The module assembly comprises a 48 in diameter, doughnut-shaped water film bearing, constructed of high-strength, flexible nylon-

reinforced materials, joined with a square load-mounting top plate of aluminium extrusion construction.

Each module may receive up to 20 gpm of water, pumped either from a city supply or the sea, to lift a maximum of 40 tons. When inflated, the module raises its load approximately 1½ in. The load is floated on a thin, near frictionless water film between ·005-·007 in thick. On a level plane, the force required to move a 40 ton floating load is 80 lb or only 0·1 % of the weight.

The modules are placed under the vessel's wood cribbing, which is resting on a series of parallel, reinforced concrete runways forming a continuously smooth and non-porous operating surface.

As each ship subsection is prepared to leave the final fabrication ship, the correct quantity of K48NHDW modules are inserted and inflated. Each section is then floated out into the yard under the guidance of small yard tugs or winches. The distance of travel is determined by the overall length of the vessel under construction. Sections are floated together and joined using the omnidirectional capability of the bearings, as well as the vertical alignment control created by varying water pressure inputs to various modules. Sections can be accurately raised, lowered, tilted and warped.

The water film transport system permits the construction of several vessels at one time, positioned side-by-side. Or, different types and sizes of vessels can be built in the same area. Modules may be used in different combinations to handle varying section sizes and load eccentricities.

Matching runways reach down to the water's edge. When ready for side-launch at high tide, the modules float the vessel to the ends of the runways and are then removed. A runway trigger mechanism is released, collapsing the runways to meet matching runways embedded in the sea floor,

and the vessel slips into the water.

Todd Shipyards, Seattle, was the first shipyard anywhere to use the fluid bearing handling system to move ship modules. The shipyard's first use of the water bearing was in February 1974, moving the "Arctic", a 1,200-ton tug and supply vessel to the launch position.

To lift a full vessel, each bearing is inflated with water to pressures ranging up to 50 lb/sq in. In a few seconds, the ship is vertically raised about 1½ in.

The Arctic was one of six tug and supply vessels built by Todd for Allseas of Panama Ltd. Each vessel measures 228 ft by 44 ft by 19 ft and weighed 1,200 tons when completed. The water film handling system gave the company a competitive edge in meeting a required "six ship delivery within eight months" schedule. Since December 1974, Todd has completed four more similar vessels under a 12-ship contract for Theriot Offshore International Ltd. A ship is being delivered each month until the order is completed. These vessels are being chartered in the North Sea in support of offshore oil-drilling and exploration operations.

As each ship section leaves the final fabrication building, it is rolled out on railway bogies onto a railway track which leads to a 12 in deep concrete-surfaced pit outside. Under these rails are a series of eight Aero-Go model K48NHDW Aero-Caster "water film" load modules. Each module is 48 in square and constructed in aluminium extrusions with a 48 in diameter inflatable Aerocaster water film bearing (48NHDW) made of neoprene-reinforced nylon material beneath. At this point, the sections weigh between 150-250 tons. Each section is rotated 90° on the water film turntable to mate with a matching rail system bed.

When the controls are activated, the water film bearings are inflated with pressurised water in a matter of seconds and the turntable's load "floats" on a thin water film. The friction under the load is so reduced that a ½ in cable strap pulled by a small forklift truck is the only drawbar pull needed to turn each section.

The sections are then rolled off the turntable and continue by rail to the Section Joining Area. Here the water film system is employed to position them for joining and

eventually to move the major subassemblies through the final assembly area and eventually to transfer the entire vessel on the side slipways.

The vessel is then moved on a series of up to 29 water film bearing modules which travel over seven, five-foot wide concrete runways. To lift a full vessel each bearing is inflated to approximately 50 psi. In a few seconds, the ship is raised about 1½ inches. This

system consumes a total of 480 gallons per minute of water. The thin water film captured between the flexible bottom face of the bearing and the slipway surface is approximately ·005 to ·007 in thick. A four-man team supervises a ship's movement using two powered winches each controlling one line at each end of the ship. The normal travel speed is approximately three feet a minute.

JETSTREAM SYSTEMS COMPANY

HEAD OFFICE:

3486 Investment Boulevard, Hayward, California 94545

OFFICERS:

Stanley Lenox, President
Warren P. Landon, Vice-President
Eugene S. Batter, Vice-President, Operations
Stanley E. Hurd, Vice-President, Research and Development

Jetstream Systems Company holds the world-wide rights for Jetstream conveyors. The company is currently producing and developing Jetstream conveying and processing equipment and Jetsweep storage and drying systems.

Jetstream uses low-pressure air delivered to a plenum by a fan or fans and introduced to the conveyor surface through various

types of orifices along the full length of the conveyor, to maintain a belt of air flowing close to the conveyor surface. It conveys granular materials, such as sand, iron pellets, grain, etc; paper and metal trim and scrap; cartons; webs or sheets of paper or metal; and practically any other material within reason.

The air can be heated or cooled to condition the product while it is being conveyed. Extremely good results have been attained, especially in the heating, cooling and drying field. Longer or shorter dwell time can be obtained by using different configurations of the conveyor.

Objects are moved by a succession of angularly disposed openings. The system provides constant controlled power around curves and up inclines including vertical faces. Entry points and spurs, inputs and outputs, can be added easily anywhere

along the conveyor.

The objects can be moved upwards along an inclined conveyor and can be discharged into a hopper or other receptacle. The conveyor membrane may be used for moving solid objects by air-jet action and as a support and walkway for workmen while adjusting, operating or maintaining an associated machine.

POWER SUPPLY: Pressure of air necessary: $\frac{1}{10}$ inch water gauge to ½ psi. Air ducting and centrifugal fans are generally fitted as an integral part of the conveyor.

CONVEYOR SYSTEM: Units are designed to suit product. The length can run to 1,000 ft or more and the width from 1 in to 10 ft or more as necessary.

BLOWER H/P: Power requirements for loadings up to 7 lb sq ft (34·17 kgt/m²) $\frac{1}{500}$ hp/sq ft—$\frac{1}{10}$ hp sq ft

ROLAIR SYSTEMS, INC.

ADDRESS:

P.O. Box 3036, Santa Barbara, California

TELEPHONE:

(805) 968 1536

CABLE:

ROLAIRSYS

TELEX:

658-433

WORKS ADDRESS:

As above

SENIOR EXECUTIVES:

R. B. Kieding, President
R. E. Burdick, Vice-President
R. A. Adams, Secretary/Treasurer

DIRECTORS:

C. A. Bunton
R. E. Burdick
H. A. Fritzche
R. W. Kenyon
R. B. Kieding
J. W. Watling Jr

LICENSEES:

Rolair Systems (UK) Ltd:
Compagnie Francaise des Convoyeurs:
Marubeni Corporation

Rolair Systems Inc. manufactures a range of equipment making use of compliant air bearings for moving heavy or large loads. The company was incorporated in 1968 as Transocean Air Systems Corporation. In 1971 its name was changed to Rolair Systems Inc. Key personnel with the company were engaged in the same field with General Motors between 1962-1968.

The company's products include standard catalogue items and unlimited custom-engineered systems.

The basic compliant air bearing device comprises a membrane holding compressed air which conforms to the floor. Controlled escape of this air in a thin layer between membrane and floor forms a frictionless air film which 'floats' the load, enabling it to be

Above and below: Rolair-designed panel line for a major US shipyard. It enables steel plates, weighing up to 100 tons, to be accurately positioned for welding and then transports them down the line to a crane pick-up area. The plates are used in the construction of giant tankers

moved in any horizontal direction by a force only one-thousandth of the weight of the load. Air pressure is self-regulating according to the bearing size and its load. Typically a 2 ft diameter bearing will lift 4,000 lb; four 2 ft bearings will carry a truck.

Several typical applications are described below.

SHIPYARD PANEL LINE

Rolair has constructed and installed a complete air-film panel handling system for a major US shipyard. Comprising several hundred, pylon-mounted upturned air-bearings, it permits the omnidirectional movement of steel plates measuring 3·65 m by 12·19 m (12 ft by 40 ft) for welding. The plates, which can be positioned with great accuracy, are tack-welded five at a time into 100-ton 'blanket' sections, each measuring 12·19 m by 18·28 m (40 ft by 60 ft). Axis positioning is accomplished through the use of low-horsepower, steerable electric drives.

After all five plates have been tacked together, they are driven by linear casters to an overhead welding station, where they are seam welded on both sides, have channels added, and are then driven to the crane pick-up area.

AIR BEARINGS AID SHIP STORAGE

A programme for reverse ship storage and upkeep for the US Navy has resulted in over $1,000,000 savings in both money and manhours.

The Navy's ship repairing facility on Guam operates a reserve craft branch, responsible for the security, maintenance and upkeep of out-of-service-in-reserve Navy vessels. The problem was to store effectively and protect ten 300-ton YFUs, a landing-craft type vessel, against Guam's hostile tropical environmental elements, including typhoons.

In this first-of-its-kind application the problem was solved by utilising four Rolair air film transporters. The 120-ton capacity transporters, each equipped with four air bearings, enabled the craft to be floated on dry land to a "high and dry" area, safe from the problems inherent in water storage.

Experiments had been made previously, using heavy equipment and grease on steel plate, but it took four days and 714 man hours to store one YFU. With air film transporters, two a day can be positioned, requiring 76 man hours each, using very little in the way of equipment.

Manoeuvrability was another problem solved with air film transporters. The air film transporters allowed the manoeuvring of the craft in any direction with little difficulty.

The air film transporters, topped with interfacing keel or bilge blocks, are positioned under the YFU after the craft is lifted to the dock from the water by two floating cranes. A 100 × 400 ft steel-trowelled concrete slab is provided at the dockside for storage. Two lift trucks are used to tow and manoeuvre the craft to their storage position.

After trying both compressed air and water as the fluid for the air bearings, water was determined to be the best fluid for this particular operation. Rolair supplied transporters with both air and water inlets so either could be used.

To remove the air film transporters, a second set of keel or bilge blocks, 6½ feet high was built-up between the concrete slab and the hull. Then, using wedges, the hull was raised a few inches so that the trans-

Above: Rolair air film transporters with keel or bilge blocks being "floated" beneath a crane-supported YFU
Below: A fully "floated" 300-ton YFU landing craft being moved to its storage location on Rolair transporters by two low-horsepower forklift trucks

porters could be simply moved. The 6·5 ft block height was chosen to permit personnel and vehicle access under the hulls for periodic hull inspection.

Securely-anchored, protected bay storage is the normal storage procedure practiced by the Navy for other than small boats. It was recognised that there are a number of economic disadvantages when this storage method is applied. For example, there is the need for cathodic hull protection; periodic dry-docking for barnacle removal; expensive electronic flooding alarm surveillance as well as regular visual waterline checks by each watch. In addition costly anchors ($30,00 each) are lost from time to time during the typhoon season.

It is estimated that the ten YFUs stored at SRF Guam by the "high and dry" method have saved the Navy $100,000 per craft to date, an amount continually increasing due to the reduced inspection necessarc.

OMNI-MOBILE CRANE

Gantry and top-running bridge cranes are available in this line. They can be pushed to the load, lift it and deliver it without the

expense of overhead or ground rails. The company has standard designs available of 5-30 tons and will build units of heavier capacities to meet specific requirements.

The Omni-Mobile Crane solves many of the problems associated with conventional cranes. Its portability allows it to move between bays as well as operating outside the plant, another advantage being that it does not require any changes to the building structure, thus eliminating the need for building permits and civil engineering costs.

The problems associated with compensating for span are also reduced Normally the span of a bay limits the amount of weight that can be carried on an overhead crane. With the Omni-Mobile crane, the span can be one-half or one-third of the bay's span and the crane is still able to reach any load within the bay. Positioning of loads also becomes easier. As it has frictionless movement in any direction, precise positioning is possible.

Unlike wheeled units, no brakes are necessary to hold the crane in position. By turning off the air, the crane base rests solidly on the floor on specially designed support points.

The Omni-Mobile crane's portability and omnidirectional movement is made possible by the four or more Rolair air bearings located underneath the base of the crane.

The Omni-Mobile crane line includes a gantry type with travelling hook and a travelling bridge type. Optional accessories for both include non-powered, retractable guide wheels for positive control; powered drive wheels for movement of the crane structure; rail guides for floor mounted rail guidance; and remote control units for operation of the air system.

They can be operated using standard shop air, or a separate air compressor.

VARIABLE-PLAN SPORTS STADIUM

Rolair air-bearings will be used to vary the seating configurations of a new 28,000-seat stadium under construction in Honolulu.

The stadium comprises four 7,00-seat sections and the air-bearings will be employed to rotate each through a 45 degree arc to provide ideal seating patterns for either football or baseball games.

Located under each of the four stadium sections will be twenty-six Rolair transporters, each incorporating four air-bearings. These will be inflated by three main air compressors, each with a capacity of 1,250 cfm. The sections will be moved by a system of lightweight hydraulic jacks. A rail guideline will prevent the sections drifting when 20-knot Pacific tradewinds are blowing. Each stadium section has a fixed pivot point and it is estimated that only 20 minutes will be required to move each one through its 45 degree arc—a total distance of 53·34 m (173 ft).

In baseball configuration the stadium will have an open double "horseshoe" look. For football the four sideline sections will be moved inward to form straight sidelines. In the football position the spectators on the 50 yard line will be only 12·19 m (40 ft) from the sideline, and only 7·62 m (25 ft) away from the goal line.

Ramps connecting the stadium sections extend and retract on air film with each move.

AUTOMATIC MODULAR HOME PRODUCTION LINE

Rolair has designed and installed a fully-automated air-film walking beam conveyor system which moves factory built home modules simultaneously through eighteen assembly stations several times an hour.

The system can handle modules with lengths of up to 60 ft (18·28 m) and widths up to 14 ft (4·26 m).

ASSEMBLY LINE FOR CRAWLER TRACTORS

One of the most advanced air film systems in operation today is in use at the Caterpillar Tractor plant at Gosselies, Belgium, where an automatic assembly line has been installed by Rolair for Model 225 Excavators.

The first line for these vehicles was installed at the company's plant at Aurora, Illinois. Experience with the Aurora plant has led to certain improvements on the Gosselies plant. For example, air tools are used throughout the line, allowing the air-powered transporters to serve as the air supply for the tools. This enables assemblers to connect their tools at the start of the assembly and leave them connected throughout the line.

The assembly operation begins on a 175-ft-long section of track immediately preceding

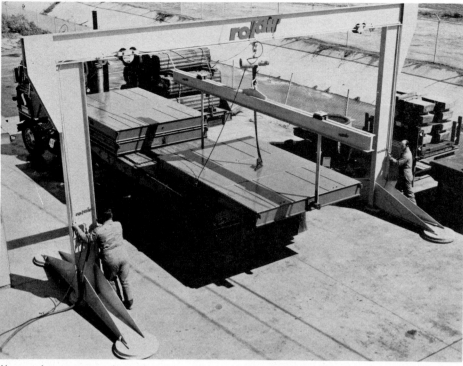

Above: A gantry-type Omni-Mobile crane delivering a 4,000 lb (1814.37 kg) load from the production line onto a flatbed truck
Below: An Omni-Mobile crane of the travelling bridge type. Because of its omnidirectional movement, the crane can be moved around obstacles

the air pallet area. There, drive assemblies are built on manually-propelled transfer carts.

First, the tractor's two planetary gears are aligned on a stationary fixture. A housing is then lifted into position by an overhead crane. After the housing has been connected to the axles, the unit is lifted onto a transfer cart. Small components are then added to the housing as the cart is moved to the end of the track. The sub-assembly and cart now weighs about 18,000-lb and requires two men to push it. At this point the sub-assembly is lifted by the overhead crane and positioned on one of the air pallets. Now one man can easily move the 9-ton load.

Components are brought to the air pallet line on flat-bed trucks and lifted by crane onto the pallets. Workers climb portable step ladders to perform the necessary

welding and bolting operations. The same air source that supplies the pallets is used to power air-articulated assembly tools.

Each transporter has a 45 ft hose mounted on a retractable reel. Air hose connectors are installed below the surface every 25 ft along the assembly line. This allows the transporter 90 ft of travel before changing air connectors.

When air is fed into the system, each bearing diaphragm inflates, traps a shallow bubble of air and lifts the load slightly off the floor. Controlled leakage around the edge of the bearings creates a lubricating layer of air between the transporter and floor. Friction is practically eliminated and the transporter can be moved with a minimum of force.

A master clock controls the complete assembly line. Magnetic sensors are located

Left: Stadium positioned for football, and *right*, for baseball. Rolair air-bearings are employed to rotate each of the four 7,000-seat sections through a 45-degree arc to provide ideal seating patterns for both games

on the bottom of the transporters, and utilising a series of electromagnets embedded every 10 ft along the assembly line floor, the transporter can be directed to move from station to station. The electromagnets are normally energised. When the control clock de-energises a specific electromagnet, the sensor on the transporter opens, providing an air supply to the air bearing, causing the transporter to advance toward the next energised electromagnet. Since each electromagnet is individually controlled, the air transporter can be moved any distance along the line.

At the same time, the air system is activated. Two guide wheels automatically lock onto a V-type floor rail and guide the transporter down the assembly line. As a safety factor, a 25 second delay is provided between air activation and initial machine movement, allowing ample time for assemblers to move from the path of the transporter.

Although the major portion of the line is automatic, some manual movement remains. At the end of the line, where the assembly floor is wide enough for two machines on transporters to operate side-by-side, excavators undergo flushing and computer testing of the hydraulic system. Advancing from the assembly line, the transporter's guide wheels are retracted and two men simply 'float' the 20-ton load into the test area.

In addition to the air film system another innovation for Caterpillar is the use of the team approach. An assembly team matches two assemblers with an inspector, and the three-man team stays with the machine from start to finish. In fact, names of assemblers and inspectors are recorded on metal plates fixed to the finished machine. Better quality has also been achieved through improved methods suggested by the team members, an important benefit of the team-build concept.

With the air film transporter system, Caterpillar feels that the assembly line can be easily altered. It can be lengthened over a weekend simply by laying more concrete. A turn can be added the same way, and if the line has to be shortened, the section no longer required is simply abandoned. A relocation can be effected by simply picking up the whole system and setting it down on a new strip of concrete.

Above: The Omni-Mobile Bed Plate transporters permit workpieces to be set up some distance from machine tools, then floated into place and accurately positioned for drilling, welding and other processes. *Below:* Beneath the transporters are the disc-like air bearings. Precise alignment of each workpiece is assured by machined pads and tapered shot pins on landing struts of the transporter which engage in receptacles in the floor docking points. Positioning within +.001 in is possible

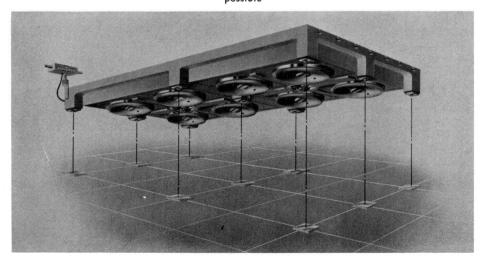

AIRCRAFT GROUND TESTING INSTALLATION

An air flotation system has been installed by Vought to allow quicker positioning of each plane for testing operational equipment. The system uses an air film and replaces hand-operated tripod-type jacks. It has provided not only a saving in time, but a safer environment for testing. Twelve Corsair II light attack aircraft can be closely positioned within a single hangar.

Three air bearings, connected directly to a T-shaped dolly, make up the casters for each of six "sets" of bearings in use in the hangar. Their design is such that they easily handle the 19,000-pound aircraft. On-off air valves for the bearings are operated quickly by a single employee. The bearings have their own stabilising chamber, eliminating any throttling of incoming air. Inlet air pressure is supplied at 75 psig from standard 1-inch plant lines.

Usually three men hand-manoeuvre the dolly for directional accuracy, although one man can easily push the 9 tons of aircraft supported on the air film. In most cases, the flotation system is used in conjunction with a crane for fine positioning of the craft during equipping and testing its gears, wheels and other systems and components.

LOW PROFILE TURNTABLE

In May 1974, Rolair introduced a workshop turntable with load capacities up to 140,000 lb (63,497 kg).

The turntable provides an accurate means of rotating heavy loads in a variety of industrial applications. It has an extremely low profile, projecting only 3-4 in (76-101 mm) above the floor surface, and floats on a thin film of air. Because of its low profile it can be mounted on the surface of existing floors; flush in woodblock floors or in a shallow pit in concrete floors. The necessity for deep pit installation is eliminated.

The system is operated by any standard 90 psi shop air system. The free-floating load deck can be easily removed for installation and inspection.

Turntables are available in sizes up to a 12 ft (3·65 m) diameter table with a 70 ton capacity. Larger capacity tables can be supplied to meet special requirements. A reasonable degree of off-centre loading is possible.

Rotating the Rolair turntable can be done either by hand or by an air-powered drive motor. Hand rotation of even the heaviest loads is possible because of the air film system. One pound (0·45 kg) of force can move a 1,000 lb (453 kg) load.

Optional equipment available for the Rolair turntable includes an air-driven motor which rotates it in either direction at walking speed; an internally-mounted rotational stop that permits a fixed amount of rotation in each direction and a remote control unit.

HEAVY WORKPIECE TOOL BED PLATE

One of the latest additions to Rolair's air film systems is the Omni-Mobile Tool Bed Plate, which combines a system for transporting castings and similar workpieces with flush-to-floor docking points for precise alignment at the machine.

The workpiece is set up apart from the machining operations on a special transporter. After setting up the particular workpiece, or component, is carried by the transporter to the machine and is precisely positioned on the docking points.

In subsequent operations, as a machining step is completed, the transporter can be rotated. For example, it could be rotated 180° for machining on the opposite face of the workpiece. Or, the transporter can be floated to another machine within the machine tool complex. In this situation, a second transporter with a new workpiece from the setup area can be positioned at the first machine within minutes.

The repeatable, precise positioning possible at various machine tools permits a manufacturer to use a series of less expensive single-function machine tools, rather than the high cost machine tools that incorporate multiple machining operations, and require costly setup times.

The Rolair transporter used in the Omni-Mobile Bed Plate system resembles a standard machine tool bed plate. It has standard 1 in T-slots on 12 in centres (keyslots and other spacings available). Mounted in the slots are key-type fixtures which are used to locate and hold the workpiece.

With the system, the setup workpiece is floated from the setup area onto flush-to-floor docking points adjacent to the machine tool. A built-in, directional air-powered drive system provides propulsion.

UNION OF SOVIET SOCIALIST REPUBLICS

LENINGRAD INSTITUTE OF ENGINEERING AND CONSTRUCTION

An air cushion vibrating platform designed to improve the rate of setting and uniformity of concrete has been designed and built by the Leningrad Institute of Engineering and Construction. It oscillates vertically, horizontally and diagonally.

The idea of employing an air cushion in constructing vibrating platforms for the production of prefabricated reinforced concrete was proposed and introduced by technologists in the Byelorussian Ministry of Constructon.

Conventional vibrating platforms require considerable quantities of metal in their construction and costly foundations, the weight of which can be 18-20 times the load capacity of the platform. The concentrated dynamic loads frequently lead to the breakdown of the platform's framework, and during operation the vibration and noise cause severe discomfort to plant personnel.

The operating principle of vibrating platforms using air cushions is as follows. Beneath the vibrating platform, which is a framework with a metal bottom, air is fed by a fan to form an air cushion between the foundation and the bottom of the vibrating platform. As a result, the vibrating platform (along with a form filled with mixed concrete) is lifted into the air. The vibrating system is then switched on and the mixture is allowed to set under the influence of vertical oscillations with an amplitude of 0·3-1 mm. To limit power expenditure, the cushion forms a closed system with an elastic apron. The pressure in the air cushion is 600-800 kg/m² with a lift of 6-10 tons.

These platforms have a load capacity of 2-3 tons. They do not require special concrete foundations and are mounted on a sandy base 100-150 mm thick. The power consumption of existing mass-produced

Students at Novocherkaask Polytechnic with a prototype of their air cushion materials handling platform

platforms with load capacities of 4·6 and 8 tons are 14, 20 and 40 kW, respectively, in contrast to 10, 14 and 28 kW for air cushion vibrating platforms. Use is made of the ability of an air cushion to distribute pressure evenly over the entire reaction surface, and of its outstanding shock absorbing qualities.

NOVOCHERKAASK POLYTECHNIC

The Novocherkaask Polytechnic has developed a series of air pads and platforms capable of supporting loads of up to 12·5 tonnes. The air supply is from a compressor or the factory air supply.

A platform with a load capacity of 40-80

tonnes is in the design stage and a feature is an automatic load relief should the air supply be cut off.

A diagram showing the system evolved at the Polytechnic accompanies this entry. It comprises two or more compressed air pads (1), which are generally rectangular in shape, and two connecting supports for the load or load platform (2). The supports are connected to the air pads by articulated joints (3) and rest on compressed air jacks (4). Air is fed into the pads through a regulator and enters the chamber of the compressed air jack (5). It then passes through the baffle plates (6) which ensure a constant differential in pressure between the cushion air plenums and the compressed air jack chamber. Cushion air enters the plenum (7) and then escapes through the discharge nozzle (8) into the recess (9) between the flexible seals and the supporting surface.

The system has undergone extensive tests and it is thought likely that it will have wide application in Soviet industry, particularly

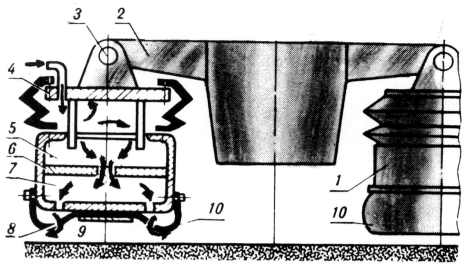

Diagram showing operation of the Novocherkaask Polytechnic air pads and handling platform in the movement of machines and material stocks in warehouses.

HYDROFOILS

CANADA

DE HAVILLAND AIRCRAFT COMPANY OF CANADA, LIMITED

HEAD OFFICE AND WORKS:
Downsview, Ontario, Canada
TELEPHONE:
416 633 7310
TELEGRAMS:
Moth Toronto
DIRECTORS:
J. H. Smith, Chairman
R. Bannock, Managing Director and Chief Executive Officer
D. B. Annan, Vice-President, Operations
T. M. Burns
W. T. Heaslip, Vice-President, Engineering
F. A. Johnson, Vice-President, Contracts and Programmes Administration
D. N. Kendall
S. B. Kerr, Vice-President, Finance
O. G. Stoner
SENIOR EXECUTIVES:
F. H. Buller, Chief Designer
S. Morita, Hydrofoil Project Manager
L. Hemsworth, Vice-President, Personnel & Industrial Relations
J. A. Timmins, Vice-President, Marketing & Sales

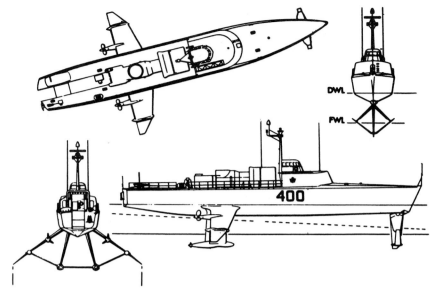

De Havilland FHE-400 ocean-going ASW warship

In early 1961 the Canadian Department of Defense contracted De Havilland Aircraft of Canada Ltd for a feasibility and engineering study based on the NRE ASW hydrofoil report. The company's recommendations were approved in April 1963 and led to the construction of the FHE-400 fast hydrofoil escort warship. The programme had two fundamental objectives: (a) to establish in practice the feasibility of an ocean-going hydrofoil of the proposed size and characteristics (b) to evaluate the prototype as an ASW system.

FHE 400 was commissioned as HMCS Bras d'Or in Halifax and was tested in brief displacement mode trials in September 1968. The foilborne transmission was fitted during the winter of 1968 and the first foilborne trial took place on April 9, 1969. The craft attained a speed of 63 knots during calm water trials in July 1969. Rough water trials during the winter of 1971 culminated in a 2,500 mile "shake down" cruise from Halifax to Bermuda and Norfolk, Va.

Foilborne trials were conducted in 10-15 ft (3·04-4·57 m) waves (sea state 5) at speeds in excess of 40 knots. Hullborne trials were conducted in higher sea states.

While objective (a), to confirm operations feasibility in open ocean conditions, was met, objective (b), ASW system operation, was suspended because of a change in Canadian defence priorities, requiring priority attention to territorial and coastal surveillance. The craft was therefore put into store, although research in this field continued. Reports suggest that the craft is about to be reactivated. In the meantime the company reports that wide interest is being shown in a smaller and similar design—the DHC-MP (Maritime Patrol) 100 which will have the same seakeeping capability. Possible civil applications include oil-rig resupply, coastguard work and fisheres patrol.

FHE-400

FOILS: The foil system is a canard configuration of the surface piercing type and non-retractable. The steerable bow foil is super-cavitating and designed for good response in a seaway. The subcavitating main foil carries 90% of the static weight and is a combination of surface-piercing and submerged foils. The centre high speed foil section is protected from ventilation by the struts and the dihedral foils have full-chord fences to inhibit ventilation. Anhedral foils provide reserve lift at take-off and their tips provide roll restoring forces at foilborne speeds. All foil elements are in welded 18% nickel maraging sheet steel and forgings.

The struts are a compromise to provide the optimum fin effect in yaw in conjunction with the steerable bow foil.

HULL: Hull and superstructure are fabricated from ALCAN D54S, and extensive use is made of large extrusions with integral stringers for the plating.

A crew of twenty is carried, comprising eight officers and twelve men. In order to maintain crew alertness at all times, comfortable crew quarters and good messing facilities were considered essential features. Both were intensively studied by the Institute of Aviation Medicine. The study included the testing of crew bunks on a motion simulator at NCR Ottawa, and the use of a simulator to assess crew efficiency under foilborne conditions.

POWER PLANT: Continuous search for a useful period demands economical operation in any sea state at displacement speeds and the ability to attack at high speeds. For this reason there are two propulsion systems —the foilborne marinised gas-turbine, a 22,000 shp Pratt & Whitney FT4A-2, and a 2,000 bhp Davey-Paxman 16YJCM diesel engine for hullborne power.

The FT4A-2, a marine version of the shaft-turbine engine developed from the JT4 and 5 gas turbine, is enclosed by a protective cowling aft of the bridge.

Shaft power is transmitted to the inboard gearbox directly aft of the engine exhaust elbow and is then transmitted via dual shafts through each of the two inner struts to the outboard gearboxes in the streamlined pods at the intersection of the struts and foils. The dual shafts are combined at the outboard gearboxes into a single drive then taken through an over-running clutch to each of the two 4 ft (1·22 m) diameter fixed-pitch supercavitating propellers.

A governor prevents overspeed if the propellers leave the water in rough seas.

The Paxman Ventura 16YJCM diesel-engine is sited in the engine room, on the ship's centreline. Power is transmitted to the

During sea trials, the FHE 400 reached a foilborne speed of 62 knots. Capable of all-weather operation, the vessel has a maximum take-off displacement of 235 tons

variable pitch hullborne propellers through a dual output gearbox and thence through shafts to gearboxes located in the pods.

The KMW controllable-pitch displacement propellers of 7 ft (2·13 m) diameter are novel, since they are feathered when the craft is foilborne so as to minimise the appendage drag penalty. Slow speed manoeuvring is effected by control of individual propeller pitch settings.

CONTROLS. Diesel power, propeller pitch, main gas turbine speed and individual displacement propeller pitch are all normally controlled by lever from the bridge. Dual wheels are provided to steer the bow foil which acts as the rudder for both foilborne and displacement operation. It is also adjustable to rake enabling the best angle of attack to be selected for foilborne or hull-borne operation. An engineer's console is located in the operation room and starting and stopping of all engines is undertaken from this position. Engine and propeller pitch controls duplicating those on the bridge are provided on the console.

Turns are fully or partially coordinated, depending on speed, by the variable incidence anhedral tips. The tips are also coupled to an auto-pilot and act as stabilisers to supplement the foil system's inherent roll resistance.

SYSTEMS:

AUXILIARY POWER: An auxiliary gas-turbine, a United Aircraft of Canada ST6A-53 rated at 390 hp continuous at 2,100 rpm is used to power electric generators, hydraulic pumps and a salt-water pump. It can also be used to increase the available displacement propulsion power and for emergency propulsion power at reduced speed.

EMERGENCY POWER: The emergency power unit is an AiResearch GTCP-85-291 shaft-coupled turbine rated at 190 hp continuous. In the event of the auxiliary gas turbine becoming unserviceable or being in use for the displacement propulsion, this turbine will power the ship's system. Alternatively bleed air may be drawn from the compressor for main turbine starting.

DIMENSIONS, EXTERNAL:

Length overall, hull	151 ft 0 in (45·9 m)
Length waterline, hull	147 ft 0 in (44 m)
Hull beam	21 ft 6 in (6·5 m)
Width across foils	66 ft 0 in (20 m)
Draft afloat	23 ft 6 in (7·16 m)
Freeboard, forward	11 ft 0 in (3·3 m)

WEIGHTS:

Gross tonnage (normal)	212 tons
Light displacement	165 long tons
Max take-off displacement	235 long tons
Useful load (fuel, crew and military load)	over 70 tons

PERFORMANCE:

Maximum speed, foilborne
50 knots rough water, 60 knots calm water
Cruising speed, hullborne   over 12 knots
Sea state capability
  Sea State 5 significant wave height 10 ft

DHC-MP-100

De Havilland Canada's latest hydrofoil design is the DHC-MP-100, a multi-duty vessel of 104 tons displacement and a maximum speed of 50 knots. Twin gas-turbines power the foilborne propulsion system instead of the single turbine employed in the FHE-400, the foil system has been simplified, and although the craft is smaller than its predecessor the same outstanding sea-keeping performance is maintained.

A worldwide market survey has been

HMCS Bras D'Or during calm water trials

undertaken to determine the needs of potential customers outside Canada and reports indicate that considerable interest is being shown in the craft particularly for the following applications: oil rig re-supply, coastguard patrol, search and rescue, customs and excise, gunboat, missilecraft and ASW patrol.

In general the configuration and construction follows that of the FHE-400.

FOILS: Canard, surface-piercing configuration with approximately 90% of the weight carried by the main foil and 10% by the bow foil. The bow foil is of diamond shape and acts as the rudder for both foilborne and hullborne operations. The main foil, of trapeze configuration combines a fully submerged central section with dihedral surfaces outboard.

POWER PLANT, FOILBORNE: Foilborne propulsion is supplied by two 3,100 shp gas-turbines each driving a fixed-pitch super-cavitating three-bladed propeller. Power is transmitted via dual shafts through each of the two inner foil struts to gearboxes at the intersections of the struts and foils.

Among the engines likely to be specified are the Rolls Royce Marine Proteus, the Marine Tyne and the Avco Lycoming TF 40.

POWER PLANT, HULLBORNE: Hullborne propulsion is supplied by two 400 hp diesels driving two two-bladed propellers through outdrive units.

Data for the basic craft and the main variants are given below.

DHC-MP-100 GENERAL PURPOSE

In this configuration, the craft can be equipped for coastguard, search and rescue, fisheries and environmental patrol, customs and excise duties and oil-rig re-supply.

DIMENSIONS, EXTERNAL:

Length	118 ft 1 in (36 m)
Beam	21 ft 0 in (6·4 m)
Width across main foil	50 ft 9¾ in (15·5 m)
Draft hullborne	17 ft 5⅞ in (5·33 m)
Freeboard, hullborne	8 ft 0 in (2·44 m)

WEIGHTS:

Crew and supplies	2,930 kg
Roll equipment and fuel	26,800 kg
Total payload	29,730 kg
Basic weight	75,740 kg
Displacement	105,470 kg
	(104 tons)

PERFORMANCE:

Maximum speed, est.   50 knots (90 km/h)
Range:
  18,000 kg fuel capacity

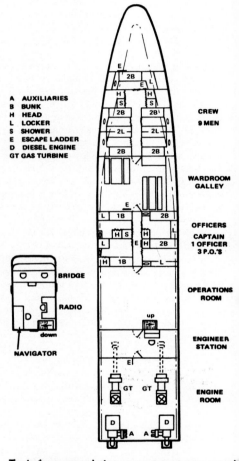

A AUXILIARIES
B BUNK
H HEAD
L LOCKER
S SHOWER
E ESCAPE LADDER
D DIESEL ENGINE
GT GAS TURBINE

CREW
9 MEN

WARDROOM
GALLEY

OFFICERS
CAPTAIN
1 OFFICER
3 P.O.'S

OPERATIONS
ROOM

ENGINEER
STATION

ENGINE
ROOM

BRIDGE
RADIO
NAVIGATOR

Typical accommodation arrangement on a patrol escort version of the MP-100 hydrofoil

at 11·5 km/h (10 knots)
                        3,500 km (1,910 nm)
at 74 km/h (40 knots)   1,180 km (642 nm)
27,000 kg fuel capacity
at 18·5 km/h (10 kt)   5,250 km (2,865 nm)
at 74 km/h (40 kt)   1,770 km (963 mm)

GUNBOAT

For coastal patrol, interdiction or for escorting larger ships or convoys, a 57 mm Bofors gun can be fitted. For self-defence a Vulcan gun is mounted on the afterdeck. Other armament installations can be fitted within weight and c of g limits.

Overload fuel will extend the range in displacement condition to a maximum of 4,600 km (2,500 nm). In the maximum overload condition take-off may be restricted to moderate sea states.

The foil system stabilises the vessel and gives it the seakeeping characteristics of a ship of 1,000/1,500 tons, thus improving accuracy of shot and crew performance for a craft of this size.

DIMENSIONS:

As for basic craft

WEIGHTS:

Crew and supplies	2,930 kg
Bofors gun and ammunition	7,140 kg
Vulcan gun system	1,540 kg
Fuel	18,150 kg
Total payload	29,760 kg
Basic weight	75,740 kg
Displacement	105,500 kg
	(104 tons)

PERFORMANCE:

Range at 18·5 km/h	3,500 km (1,910 nm)
Range at 74 km/h	1,180 km (642 nm)

MISSILECRAFT

To complement the gunboat role, the MP-100 may be fitted with missiles like the Harpoon and Exocet. The fire control system is located in the large operations room.

For self-defence a Vulcan gun system is mounted aft between the missile containers. An alternative arrangement is the mounting of the gun on the foredeck and its detection system above the bridge.

DIMENSIONS:

As for basic craft

WEIGHTS:

Crew and supplies	2,930 kg
Missile system	4,530 kg
Vulcan gun system	1,540 kg
Fuel	20,400 kg
Total payload	29,400 kg
Basic weight	75,740 kg
Displacement	105,140 kg
	(103·5 tons)

PERFORMANCE:

Range at 18·5 km/h	3,960 km (2,150 nm)
Range at 74 km/h	1,340 km (723 nm)

ASW PATROL CRAFT

The craft can cruise at convoy speed on its displacement propulsion units while using variable-depth sonar to search for submarines. On making contact it can attack at high speed.

Lightweight VDS gear is installed. This has a low-drag body and cable and can be towed at over 55 km/h (30 kt). The system is of modular construction and can be quickly installed or removed. Torpedoes can be mounted in multiple tubes. Sonar and fire-control systems and fitted in the operations room. A Vulcan gun can be mounted on the foredeck with sensors above the bridge.

DIMENSIONS:

As for basic craft

WEIGHTS:

Crew and supplies	2,930 kg
VDS gear	5,080 kg
Torpedoes	3,035 kg
Vulcan gun	1,540 kg
Fire control	4,080 kg
Fuel	15,860 kg
Total payload	32,525 kg
Basic ship	75,740 kg
Displacement	108,265 kg
	(106·8 tons)

PERFORMANCE:

Range at 18·5 km/h	
	3,150 km (1,710 n miles)
Range at 74 km/h	1,040 km (565 n miles)

A multi-duty hydrofoil of 104 tons displacement, the DHC-MP-100 is available in a variety of configurations, three of which are depicted above:

Top: Equipped as a fast patrol boat or convoy escort, a 57 mm Bofors automatic gun is mounted on the foredeck and for self-defence, a Vulcan gun package is mounted on the afterdeck.

Centre: Operated as a missile equipped patrol craft, the MP-100 would carry tow launchers aft— Harpoon and Exocet missiles are two choices—and for self-defence, a Vulcan gun pack is mounted aft between the missiles. An alternative arrangement would be to mount the gun on the foredeck and its detection gear above the bridge

Bottom: An ASW version equipped with lightweight VDS gear and torpedos mounted in multiple tubes. Full sonar and fire-control systems are provided in the operations room

WATER SPYDER MARINE LTD

HEAD OFFICE AND WORKS:
157 Richard Clark Drive, Downsview, Ontario, M3M 1V6

TELEPHONE:
244 5404, Area Code 416

DIRECTORS:
J. F. Lstiburek, President
G. A. Leask, Secretary/Treasurer
A. Lstiburek, Vice President

SENIOR EXECUTIVES:
L. Civiera, Sales Manager
J. F. Lstiburek, Designer

Water Spyder Marine Ltd is a wholly-owned Canadian company operating under charter issued by the Government of the Province of Ontario. It produces three fibreglass-hulled sports hydrofoils which are available either ready-built or in kit form.

WATER SPYDER 1-A

The Water Spyder 1-A is a single-seat sports hydrofoil powered by long-shaft outboard of 10-25 hp.

FOILS: The foil system comprises a split W-type surface piercing main foil supporting 98% of the load, and an adjustable outrigged trim tab which supports the remaining 2%.

HULL: Two-piece fibreglass reinforced plastic construction, foam-filled for flotation. Standard fittings and regulation running lights.

ACCOMMODATION: Single fibreglass seat.

POWER PLANT: Any suitable outboard engine of 10-25 hp (Mercury, Evinrude or Chrysler) with long shaft.

CONTROLS: Controls include joy-stick and rudder pedals.

DIMENSIONS:
Length overall, hull   6 ft 0 in (1·828 m)
Beam overall, foils retracted
   4 ft 0 in (1·219 m)
Beam overall, foils extended
   7 ft 0 in (2·133 m)

WEIGHTS:
Weight empty   80 lb (36·24 kg)

PERFORMANCE:
Maximum speed   40 mph (64·37 km/h)
Max permissible wave height in foilborne condition   1 ft 6 in (457·2 mm)
Turning radius at cruising speed app
   10 ft (3·04 m)
Cost of standard craft and terms of payment: US$1,000·00. Terms: cash. Delivery 3 weeks app from date of order, f.o.b. Toronto.

WATER SPYDER 2-B

The Water Spyder 2-B is a two-seat sports hydrofoil powered by a long-shaft outboard of 20-35 hp.

FOILS: The foil system comprises a split W-type surface piercing main foil supporting 98% of the load and an adjustable outrigged trim tab which supports the remaining 2%.

HULL: This is a two-piece (deck and hull) moulded fibreglass construction and incorporates buoyancy chambers. Standard fittings include a curved Perspex windshield and regulation running lights, fore and aft.

ACCOMMODATION: The craft seats two in comfortably upholstered seats. Foils and the trim tab assembly are adjustable from inside the cockpit.

POWER PLANT: Any suitable outboard engine of 20-35 hp (Mercury 200L or 350L Chrysler Evinrude) with long-shaft extension.

CONTROLS: Controls include steering wheel with adjustable friction damper and trim tab control.

DIMENSIONS:
Length overall, hull   12 ft 0 in (3·6 m)
Beam overall, foils retracted
   5 ft 4 in (1·6 m)
Beam overall, foils extended
   7 ft 4 in (2·2 m)

WEIGHTS:
Weight empty   220 lb (99·7 kg)

PERFORMANCE:
Max speed   up to 40 mph (64 km/h)
Max permissible wave height in foilborne mode   1 ft 6 in
Turning radius at cruising speed
   10 ft (3 m) app
Cost of standard craft and terms of payment: US$1,600·00. Terms: cash. Delivery: 3 weeks from date of order, f.o.b. Toronto.

WATER SPYDER 6-A

An enlarged version of the Water Spyder 2. Model 6-A is a six-seat family pleasure hydrofoil boat, with a two-piece moulded fibreglass hull.

The seats, located immediately over the main foil, are arranged in two rows of three abreast, one row facing forward, the other aft.

Power is supplied by a long-shaft outboard motor of 60-115 hp.

DIMENSIONS:
Length overall, hull   19 ft 0 in (5·79 m)
Beam overall, foils retracted
   8 ft 3 in (2·5 m)
Beam overall, foils extended
   13 ft 0 in (3·96 m)
Height overall, foils retracted
   4 ft 6 in (1·37 m)
Floor area   30 sq ft (2·78 m²)

WEIGHTS:
Gross tonnage   1 ton app
Weight empty   980 lb (444 kg)

PERFORMANCE:
Max speed   35-40 mph (56-64 km/h)
Cruising speed   32 mph (51 km/h)
Max permissible wave height in foilborne mode   2 ft 6 in (0·76 m)
Turning radius at cruising speed
   20 ft (6·09 m)
Cost of standard craft and terms of payment: US$3,500·00. Terms: cash. Delivery: Three weeks from date of order f.o.b. Toronto.

Water Spyder 6-A is a six-seat hydrofoil. The main foil, trim-tab support and engine fold upward so the craft can be floated on and off a trailer

CHINA   (People's Republic of)

HUTANG SHIPYARD

HEAD OFFICE AND YARD:
Shanghai

Hydrofoil torpedo boats of the Hu Chwan (White Swan) Class have been under construction at the Hutang Shipyard, since about 1966. Some 60-70 are in service with the navy of the Chinese People's Republic and another thirty have been lent or leased to the Albanian navy, four to Pakistan and one to Romania.

HU CHWAN (WHITE SWAN)

FOILS: The foil system comprises a bow subfoil to facilitate take-off and a main foil of trapeze or shallow vee configuration set back approximately one-third of the hull length from the bow. At high speed in relatively calm conditions the greater part of the hull is raised clear of the water. The main foil and struts retract upwards when the craft is required to cruise in displacement condition.

HULL: High speed V-bottom hull in sea-water resitant light alloy.

POWER PLANT: Thought to be two 1,100 hp M-50 watercooled, supercharged 12-cylinder V-type diesels, each driving its own inclined propeller shaft.

ARMAMENT: Two 21 in torpedo tubes, plus four 12·7 in machine guns in two twin mountings.

DIMENSIONS (approximate):
Length overall   70 ft (21·33 m)

Beam overall	16 ft 6 in (5·02 m)
Hull beam	13 ft (3·96 m)
WEIGHTS:	
Displacement full load	45 tons
PERFORMANCE:	
Max speed foilborne calm conditions	
	55 knots
Range	500 nm approx.

One of four Hu Chwan-class torpedo/fast attack craft built by the Hutang Shipyard, Shanghai, and supplied to the Pakistan Navy in 1973.

FRANCE

SOCIETE NATIONALE INDUSTRIELLE AEROSPATIALE

HEAD OFFICE:

37 Boulevard de Montmorency, 75781 Paris-Cedex 16, France

TELEPHONE:

224-8400

525-5775

CABLE/TELEX ADDRESS:

Aerospatiale-Paris, AISPA 62059F

WORKS:

Marignane, B.P.13, 13722 Marignane

TELEPHONE:

(91) 89.90.22

In 1966 the Direction des Recherches et Moyens d'Essais (Directorate of Research and Test Facilities) initiated a basic hydrofoil design and research programme with the object of building a prototype hydrofoil ferry with a displacement of 55 tons and a speed of 50 knots.

The companies and organisations co-operating in this programme are: Aerospatiale, project leader; STCAN, the hull test centre; several French government laboratories of the DTCN; Alsthom—Technique des Fluides—and Constructions Mecaniques de Normandie.

The main headings of the programme are:

Hydrodynamics (foils, struts and hull)

Foil hydroelasticity data and flutter phenomenon

Automatic pilot

Material technology relative to foils, struts and hull

The design and research programme is nearly complete and the results will be processed and refined using a 4-ton submerged foil test craft, the H. 890, designed by Aerospatiale.

The craft, which was launched on June 16th, 1972 is employed in a comprehensive test programme which is under the control of Aerospatiale and DTCN, a French government agency.

In addition to the SA 800 55-ton hydrofoil ferry, preliminary designs have been completed for a missile-carrying 118-ton hydrofoil combat vessel, the H.851, and a commercial variant, intended for mixed-traffic ferry services. The latest project is a 174 tonne missilecraft with a speed of 54 knots and capable of operating in Force 5 weather at 50 knots. Armament would comprise four Exocet missiles and one rapid-fire automatic cannon.

H.890

This 4·5 seagoing test vehicle is being employed to gather data for foil systems and accelerate the development of autopilot systems for large hydrofoils.

The combination of catamaran hull and

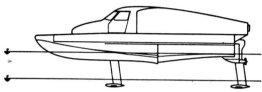
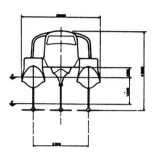
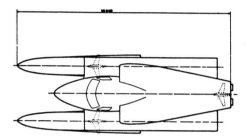

Foil configuration on the H.890 can be changed from canard to conventional (aeroplane) as required

Above and below: The H.890 4-ton submerged foil test vehicle is being employed by Aerospatiale to develop automatic control systems and gather data for the design of larger vessels. It has attained 52 knots during high-speed runs

pure jet propulsion allows the foils to be arranged in either conventional configuration—two foils forward and one aft—or canard configuration, with one foil forward and two aft.

The vessel was developed and built under contract to the French government agency DTCN by Aerospatiale's Helicopter Division in conjunction with Constructions Mecaniques de Normandie and Alsthom—Techniques des Fluides—of Grenoble. It has been undergoing tests on the Etang de Berre since it was launched on June 16th, 1972. A speed of 52 knots has been reached during trials.

FOILS: Fully submerged system with facilities for changing from conventional (aeroplane) to canard configuration as required. In aeroplane configuration about 70% of the weight is supported by the twin bow foils, which are attached to the port and starboard pontoons, and 30% by the single tail foil, mounted on the central hull section aft.

The stern foil rotates for steering and all three struts are fixed (non-retractable). Lift variation of the three foils is achieved by an autopilot system, developed by Aerospatiale and SFENA, which varies the incidence angles of all three foils. During the first series of tests the foils were tested in conventional configuration. During the second series the canard configuration was adopted.

HULL: Catamaran type, constructed in corrosion-resistant light alloys. Central hull, which incorporates control cabin, engine bay and test instrumentation, is flanked by two stepped pontoons.

ACCOMMODATION: Seating is provided for two— pilot and test observer.

POWER PLANT: Twin 480 daN Turbomeca Marbore VIc gas-turbines, mounted in the central hull structure aft of the cabin, power the craft when foilborne. Hullborne propulsion is supplied by a 20 hp Sachs 370 engine driving via a hydraulic transmission a folding-blade Maucour waterscrew located at the top of the aft foil strut. The waterscrew rotates through ±90° for steering.

DIMENSIONS:

Length overall	34·97 ft (10·66 m)
Length waterline	30·51 ft (9·30 m)
Beam overall	12·80 ft (3·90 m)
Draft afloat	5·64 ft (1·72 m)
Draft foilborne	1·21 ft (0·37 m)
Draft foilborne	1·21 ft (0·37 m)

WEIGHTS:

Normal take-off	4·5 m tons

PERFORMANCE:

Cruising speed, foilborne, calm conditions
50 knots
Cruising speed, hullborne, calm conditions
6 knots
Craft is designed to cross waves up to 2·62 ft (0·80 m) high without contouring

H.851

The H.851 is a preliminary design for a missile-equipped combat hydrofoil capable of all-weather operation. Initially it will have a displacement of 118 tons (120 m. tons) and cruise at 45 knots, but later models, with increased power, are expected to attain nearly 60 knots. Development is being

FOILS: Fully submerged canard arrangement with about 80% of the weight supported by the twin aft foils and 20% by the bow foil. The bow foil strut, which rotates for steering, retracts forwards and upwards ahead of the stem, and the two aft struts rotate rearwards and upwards. The strut locking system is designed to dampen shocks resulting from encounters with floating wreckage. Struts and foils have NACA Series 16 profiles.

Lift variation is achieved by an Aerospatiale autopilot system which varies the incidence angles of all three foils. Trailing-edge flaps

Impression of the Aerospatiale H.851 missile-equipped combat hydrofoil, being developed in conjunction with the French Navy

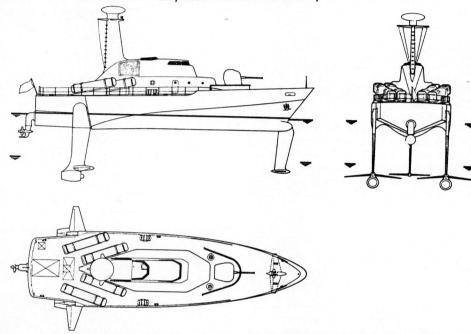

The H.851, 48-knot naval hydrofoil powered by a single SNECMA THS 2,000 gas-turbine driving two SOGREAH water pumps

on the foils augment lift during take-off.

HULL: Constructed in marine corrosion-resistant aluminium alloys.

ACCOMMODATION: Berthing, galley and toilet arrangements for crew of 21.

POWER PLANT: Foilborne propulsion is supplied by a single 5,200 kW SNECMA THS 2000 gas-turbine driving two SOGREAH water pumps, one at the base of each foil strut, via mechanical right-angle drives. Hullborne propulsion is provided by a single 770 kW diesel engine driving a single variable-pitch propeller.

ARMAMENT: Four Exocet MM 38 missiles and one 40 mm Bofors rapid-firing cannon.

DIMENSIONS:

Length overall	114·83 ft (35 m)
Beam overall	49·21 ft (15 m)
Draft hullborne	5·90 ft (1·80 m)
Draft foilborne, foils lowered	27·23 ft (8·30 m)

WEIGHTS:

Displacement, full load
115 tons (117 m. tons)

PERFORMANCE:

Max speed calm conditions	48 knots
Cruising speed, calm conditions	45 knots
Cruising speed, sea state 5	45 knots

Range and endurance:
at 45 knots, calm conditions
1,300 n miles or 29 hrs
at 45 knots, sea state 5
1,165 n miles or 25 hrs
hullborne at 13 knots
2,130 n miles at 163 hrs

SA 800

The SA 800 is a design study for a mixed-traffic hydrofoil powered by two Turmo 111C turbines driving a waterjet propulsion unit. Conventional marine light alloy construction is employed and the craft will have incidence-controlled, fully-submerged foils operated by a sonic/electronic sensing system.

A number of variants of the basic design are being studied for alternative applications, including prospecting, marine research, coastal surveillance and naval patrol. Trials conducted with dynamic models have been successful and are continuing. Preliminary design studies are now complete.

FOILS: The foil system is fully submerged and of "aeroplane" configuration. All three foil struts retract hydraulically completely clear of the water. An SNIAS sonic autopilot system controls the incidence angle of the two bow foils and adjustable control

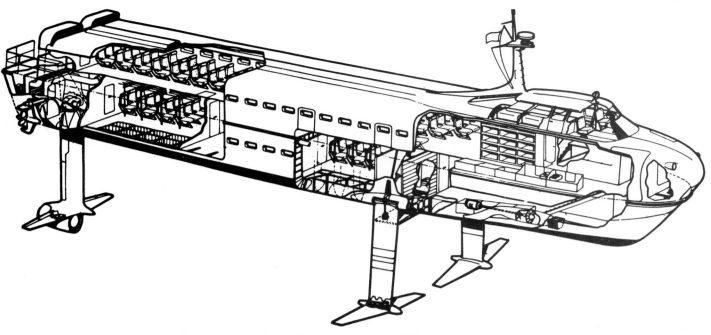

Cutaway showing internal arrangements of the 200-seat passenger ferry

flaps on the rear foils.

HULL: The hull is of conventional marine corrosion-resistant aluminium alloys. Features include a deep vee bow, designed to minimise structural loading due to wave impact, and a flat W section aft for good directional control when hullborne.

POWER PLANT: Foilborne propulsion is supplied by two 1,300 shp Turboméca Turmo 111C gas-turbines driving a SOGREAH waterjet propulsion unit mounted at the base of the aft foil strut.

Output from the transmission shafts of the two turbines, which are mounted end-to-end, intakes outwards, athwart the stern, passes first to a main bevel drive gearbox, then to a drive shaft which extends downwards through the aft foil strut to a waterjet pump gearbox located in a nacelle beneath the aft foil. Air for the turbines is introduced through intakes at the top of the cabin aft. Filters are fitted to the intakes to prevent the ingestion of water or salt spray into the gas-turbine. There is a separate hullborne propulsion system, with a 400 hp diesel driving twin water propellers beneath the transom.

ACCOMMODATION: The elevated wheelhouse forward of the passenger compartment seats the captain and engineer. All instrumentation is located so that it can be easily

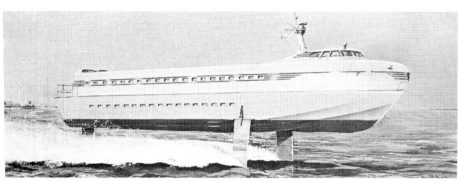

Artist's impression of the SNIA SA-800 waterjet propelled hydrofoil ferry

monitored. Navigation and collision avoidance radar is fitted. Accommodation is on two decks, each arranged with three seats abreast on either side of a central aisle. As a passenger ferry the craft will seat 200—116 on the upper deck and 84 on the lower; and in mixed traffic configuration it will carry 8-10 cars on the upper deck with the lower deck seating capacity remaining at 84. Cars are loaded via rear door/ramps. Baggage holds are provided forward of both upper and lower saloons.

.DIMENSIONS:

Length overall	88 ft 0 in (26·88 m)
Max beam, deck	18 ft 0 in (5·40 m).

WEIGHTS:

Displacement, fully loaded
55 tons (56 m tons)
Payload (200 passengers with luggage or 84 passengers with luggage and 8-10 cars)
40,300 lb (18,300 kg)

PERFORMANCE:

Max speed, calm conditions	55 knots
Cruising speed	50 knots
Cruising speed, Sea State 5	48 knots
Range, at 50 knots, calm sea	250 nm
at 48 knots, Sea State 5	200 nm

Craft is designed to platform over 10 ft (3 m) high waves, crest to trough, and contour 13 ft (4 m) high waves.

ITALY

CANTIERI NAVALI RIUNITI (CNR)—
ALINAVI
(Fincantieri Group)

HEAD OFFICE AND WORKS:
Via Cipro, 11 Genoa
TELEPHONE:
59951
TELEX:
27168 Cant. GE.
DIRECTORS:
Giulio Badaracco, Chairman
Roy Gustafason (Boeing)
Com. te Pietro Notarbartolo (Fincantieri)
MANAGEMENT:
Ing. Francesco Cao, General Manager
Ing. Fabrizio Antonucci, Chief Engineer

This company was formed in 1964 to develop, manufacture and market military advanced marine systems. It is owned jointly by Cantieri Navali Riuniti SpA,

Turning radius of the Swordfish at 40 knots is less than 137 yards (125 m).

(90%), and the Boeing Company (10%).

Under the terms of a Boeing-Alinavi licensing agreement, Alinavi has access to Boeing technology in the field of military fully-submerged foil hydrofoil craft.

In October 1970, the company was awarded a contract by the Italian Navy for the design and construction of the P 420 Sparviero class hydrofoil missilecraft. The craft is an improved version of the Boeing PGH-2 Tucumcari. The first vessel, given the design name Swordfish, was delivered to the Italian navy in July 1974. A further six craft of this type were ordered by the Italian Navy in February 1976.

SWORDFISH

The Swordfish missile-launching hydrofoil gunboat displaces a maximum of 64 metric tons and is designed for both offensive and defensive missions. Its combination of speed, firepower, and all-weather capability is unique in a ship of this class.

The vessel has fully-submerged foils arranged in canard configuration and an automatic control system. A gas-turbine powered waterjet system provides foilborne propulsion and a diesel-driven propeller outdrive provides hullborne propulsion. A typical crew comprises two officers and eight enlisted men.

FOILS: Fully-submerged canard arrangement, with approximately one-third of the dynamic lift provided by the bow foil and two-thirds by the two aft foils. The aft foils retract sideways and the bow hydrofoil retracts forwards into a recess in the bow. Bow doors preserve the hull lines when the forward hydrofoil is either fully extended or retracted. Foils and struts are built in corrosion-resistant stainless steel.

Anhedral is incorporated in the aft foils to enhance the directional stability of the craft at shallow foil depths. In addition, the anhedral assures positive roll control by eliminating tip broaching during rough water manoeuvres.

CONTROLS: Automatic system incorporating two aircraft-type gyros, one to sense pitch and roll and the other to sense yaw, plus three accelerometers to sense vertical movements (heave) of the craft. An ultrasonic height sensor is used to detect and maintain flying height above the water's surface. Information from the sensors is sent to a hermetically-sealed solid-state computer, which calculates movement of the control surfaces necessary to maintain boat stability, and/or pre-selected flying height, and sends appropriate commands to the servo-mechanisms that control flap movement.

Foilborne steering: Helm commanded automatic control system controls hydraulic servo-actuated hydrofoil flaps and steerable forward hydrofoil strut to produce coordinated (banked) turns in design sea conditions.

Hullborne steering: Helm commanded steerable outdrive unit. Helm-driven potentiometer sends signals to a servo-valve controlling steering hydraulic motor. Manual emergency hullborne steering is provided on the aft deck.

HULL: Both hull and superstructure are built entirely in corrosion-resistant aluminium, the hull being welded and the superstructure riveted and welded.

BERTHING: Two fixed berths in the compartment under the bridge, plus eight folding berths in the forward crew space. One toilet and one sink. A folding table with benches in the forward crew space.

Swordfish hullborne with foils retracted.   Continuous speed, hullborne, is 8 knots

First of the Italian Navy's missile equipped hydrofoil gunboats during foilborne firing tests of its 76 mm Oto Melara cannon. Given the design name Swordfish, the craft is the first of the P420 Sparviero Class.

POWERPLANT, FOILBORNE: Power for the waterjet is supplied by one Rolls-Royce Proteus 15M/553 gas-turbine. At the customer's option the craft may be fitted with the "sprint" model of this gas-turbine, which incorporates water injection. The "sprint" model ("wet") develops 5,000 shp maximum versus the 4,500 shp of the normal ("dry") Proteus. Adoption of the "sprint" model permits take-off at higher displacements and therefore, more fuel and/or military payload to be carried. It also provides better craft performance in very high sea states, particularly in conditions of high ambient temperatures. The respective performance characteristics of the Swordfish equipped with 'dry' and 'wet' models of the Proteus are shown in the accompanying performance table.

Engine output is transferred to a single double-volute, double-suction, two impeller centrifugal pump, rated at 28,000 US gpm at 1,560 rpm and absorbing app 4,700 shp (4,766 CV). Water is taken in through inlets on the nose of each aft foil at the foil/strut intersection and passes up through the hollow interiors of the struts to the hull, where it is ducted to the pump. From the pump, the water is discharged through twin, fixed-area nozzles located beneath the hull under the pump.

POWERPLANT, HULLBORNE: A General Motors 6V-53 diesel engine, rated at 160 shp (162 CV) at 2,600 rpm, powers a Schottel-Werft SRP-100 steerable propeller outdrive unit, which is mounted on the centreline of the transom. The unit is retractable and rotates through 360°. Propeller is fixed-pitch. Power is delivered to the outdrive at about 1,700 rpm.

FUEL: Fuel oil is NATO 76, carried in three tanks located amidships and integral with the hull, side keelson and platform deck. Total capacity is about 3,850 gallons (14,550 litres).

Fuel oil system: Two primary 208 volt 400 Hz 7 gpm (26·5 l/min) submerged pumps and two standby 28 volt d.c. 7 gpm (26·5 l/min) external pumps. The d.c. pump is started automatically by a pressure switch in the fuel supply line if a.c. pump power is lost.

Craft may be refuelled through main deck connection at dock or at sea. The fuel tanks are equipped with fuel level indicators and vents.

AUXILIARY SYSTEMS: HYDRAULICS: Two independent systems; foilborne and ship service. Systems pressure, 3,000 psi Systems fluid, MIL-H-5606.

Foilborne system: normal and standby 21·8 gpm pumps serve hydraulic control system.

Ship service system: normal and standby 32·5 gpm pumps serve other uses including hydrofoil retracting and locking, bowdoor, hullborne outdrive retraction and steering, foilborne turbine starting, foilborne turbine exhaust door, cannon loading, and the fixed saltwater fire pump.

ELECTRICAL: Turbine generator sets: At customer's option, either two or three identical sets, one installed in forward machinery space, the other(s) in the aft machinery space.

Each set consists of a Solar T-62 T-32 gas turbine engine capable of developing a maximum output of 150 shp (152 CV) under standard conditions and driving; a General Electric 208 volt 400 Hz 3-phase alternator rated at 75 KVA; a 30 volt d.c. starter-generator with 200 amp generating capacity; and one hydraulic pump for ship service and hullborne steering.

Starting battery sets: One 24 volt, 34 amp-hr capacity starting battery is provided for the hullborne diesel engine and for each solar turbogenerator set.

Emergency battery set: Two additional 24 volt batteries in parallel provide 68 amp-hr capacity to power in emergency conditions, radios, intercommunications system and navigation lights.

Shore power: Craft requires up to 30 KVA of 200 volt 3-phase 4 wire 400 Hz power.

Intercommunication system: The system consists of one station in each space and three external stations, allowing complete craft machinery and weapons coordination.

Every station is a control unit and has a reversible loudspeaker with press-to-talk switch.

Main station is equipped with radio operation access control.

Emergency announcements can be made to all stations simultaneously.

Selective communications are available between any two or more stations.

Navigation horn: One electrically operated horn mounted on forward top of deckhouse.

Signal searchlight: One portable incandescent signal searchlight mounted on the deckhouse canopy.

Depth sounder: Transducer on the hull bottom 6 inches (0.152 metres) above the keel and a recorder at the navigation station measure and record water depth from echo soundings. Recorder may be set for sounding depths of 0-20, 20-45, 40-65, 0-60, 50-110, 100-160 fathoms (0-38.6, 38.6-86.9, 77.2-125.4, 0-115.8, 96.5-212, 193-309 metres). Recorder contains electronic circuits and a two-speed mechanism with a stylus which burns a black mark on moving chart paper. A white line mode of recorder operation eliminates false traces below the true bottom line on the chart and allows detection of small objects close to the bottom and an indication of hard or soft composition of the sea bottom.

Navigation set: The shipboard navigation system (ShipNav) automatically performs, independently of all external aids, precise dead reckoning navigation for both foilborne and hullborne operations. It continuously computes and displays the craft's current position, true heading, true course, and true speed. Actual position is displayed digitally on counters in latitude and longitude coordinates and pictorially on standard charts having local coordinate information. Indicators display true heading, course, and speed.

Speed log: Hull rodmeter, foil rodmeter, rodmeter selector switch and calibration unit, transmitter and remote indicator set measures craft hullborne or foilborne speed, computes the distance travelled and displays both at the navigation station and helm.

PARAMETER	Without water injection		With water injection	
	15°C/59°F	22°C/80°F	15°C/59°F	22°C/80°F
Displacement (metric tons)	62.5	60.0	64	64
Military payload (metric tons)	11.7	11.7	14	14
Fuel (metric tons)	9.4	6.9	9.4	9.4
Max foilborne intermittent speed in calm sea (knots)	50	48	50	48
Max foilborne continuous speed in calm sea (knots)	45	43	45	43
Max foilborne continuous speed in Sea State 4 (knots)	41	39	41	39
Hullborne continuous speed (knots)	8	8	8	8
Foilborne range at max continuous speed (n.m.)	400	300	400	400
Hullborne range (n.m.)	1,050	920	1,150	1,050
Turning radius at 40 knots	less than 125 metres			
Foilborne stability: max vertical acceleration	.25 g (rms) in Sea State 4			
Hullborne stability with foils up*	stable in 50 knot wind			
Hullborne stability with foils down*	stable in 70 knot wind			
Endurance	5 days			

The Swordfish, the first missile-launching hydrofoil vessel to be built for the Italian Navy.

IFF system: The system consists of an IFF/ATC transponder (APX 72) and an IFF interrogator coupled to the radar.

Navigation and search radar: SMA Model 3RM7-250B radar performs navigation and search operations with master indicator, rayplot with variable range marker (VRN) bearing control unit and remote indicator.

Set operates in "X" band and is tunable from 9,345 MHz to 9,405 MHz. Set has two different transmitters and it is possible to select the proper one by a RF switch unit. Peak power output is 7 kW for navigation purposes and 250 kW for search purposes.

Performance includes a minimum range less than 200 yards (182 metres), range discrimination better than 11 yards (10.00 metres), azimuth discrimination less than 1.2 degrees and maximum range of 40 nautical miles.

HF-SSB radio system AN/ARC-102: The AN/ARC-102 uses the Collins 618T/3 HF single-sideband transceiver for long range voice, CW, data or compatible AM communication in the 2,000 through 29,999 MHz frequency range. It is automatically tuned in 28,000 1-kHz channel increments by means of an operator's remote control unit. The operating frequency is indicated directly in

UHF radio system AN/ARC-109: Two identical units are provided. The AN/ARC-109 transceiver has two separate receivers: a main tunable receiver and a guard receiver. Common circuit design is maintained in the two receivers. Each receiver uses carrier-to-noise ratio squelch system. Receiver selectivity is ±22 kHz at —6 db and ±45 kHz at —60 db.

The 20-channel present memory in the frequency control utilises a magnetic core storage system with solid-state drivers and interrogators.

DAMAGE CONTROL: Bilge pumps: Pumps are mounted in the bilge of each water-tight compartment and controlled from engineer's station.

Freon flooding systems: Two 53 pound (24 kg) freon FE1301 (CBR F₃) storage cylinders are provided in the engineer's compartment. One 5 pound (2.27 kg) freon cylinder is piped to Proteus turbine shroud. Systems manually controlled by engineer.

Portable fire extinguishers: A 2 pound (1 kg) dry chemical extinguisher is mounted in each of the seven manned compartments.

VENTILATION AND CONDITIONING: Unit air conditioners (6 units) are distributed throughout the manned spaces to provide heating and cooling.

ARMAMENT: A typical military payload consists of:

One dual purpose 76 mm automatic OTO Melara gun and ammunition

Two fixed missile launchers and two ship-to-ship missiles, e.g. Sea Killers, OTOMAT or Exocet

Gunfire and missile launch control system(s)

Other military electronics, e.g. ECM

A variety of other payloads may be accommodated according to customer needs.

DIMENSIONS:

Length overall	75 ft 4 in (22·95 m)
Length overall, foils retracted	
	80 ft 7 in (24·6 m)
Width across foils	35 ft 4 in (10·8 m)
Deck beam, max	23 ft 0 in (7·0 m)

WEIGHTS:

Max displacement	64·0 metric tons

PERFORMANCE:

Exact craft performance characteristics depend upon the choice of foilborne gas turbine by the customer and operating conditions which, in turn, can affect the quantity of fuel carried. Performance figures shown below, therefore, are representative:

Foilborne intermittent speed in calm water	50 knots
Foilborne continuous speed in calm water	45 knots
Foilborne continuous speed in Sea State 4	38-40 knots
Hullborne continuous speed, foil down	7·6 knots
Foilborne range at maximum continuous speed	up to 400 nm
Hullborne range, up to	1,150 nm
Turning radius at maximum foilborne continuous speed less than 410 ft (125 m)	
Endurance	5 days

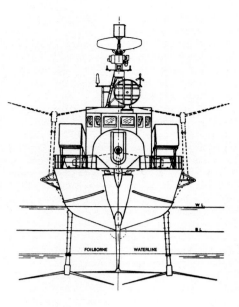

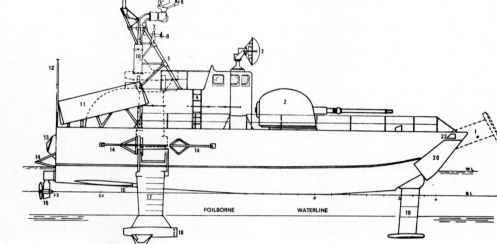

1 Forward hydrofoil retracted
2 OTO Melara 76 mm cannon
3 Fire control radar
4 Vertical ladder
5 Main mast
6 Anemometer
7 Antenna
8 Navigation and search radar
9 Antenna
10 Antenna
11 Surface-to-surface missile launchers (P/S)
12 Ensign staff
13 Turbine exhaust: foilborne propulsion

14 Guards
15 Propeller outdrive: hullborne propulsion
16 Waterjet nozzle (P/S)
17 Aft hydrofoil extended (P/S)
18 Water inlet (P/S): foilborne propulsion
19 Forward hydrofoil extended
20 Bow doors (P/S)
21 Watertight hatches
22 Height sensors: automatic control system (P/S)
23 Optical putter-on
24 Starboard gyrocompass readout
25 Port gyrocompass readout

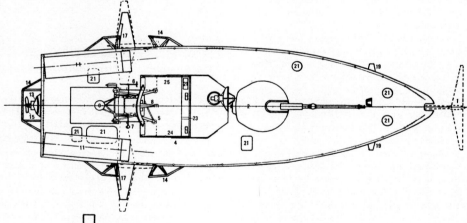

1 Helm/main control console
2 Helm station (starboard)
  Conning station (port)
3 Combat Operations Centre (C.O.C.) door
4 Companionway ladders
5 C.O.C. electric power distribution panel
6 Combat Operations Centre electronics (speed log, radios, etc)
7 Air intake forward machinery room
8 Demister panels for combustion air
9 Aft machinery room
10 Gas turbine engine: foilborne propulsion
11 Forward machinery room
12 Pump drive coupling
13 Waterjet pump
14 Waterjet nozzle (P/S)
15 Main electrical switchboard
16 Main electrical power distribution panel
17 Engineer's console
18 Engineer's station
19 Fuel oil tanks (3)
20 Void
21 Electric hot plate
22 Refrigerator

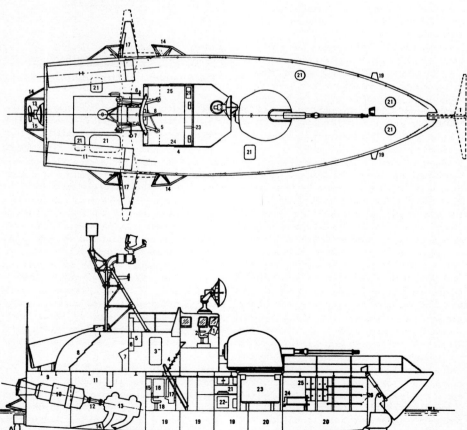

23 Cannon revolving feeding magazine
24 Folding mess table with benches (2)
25 Crew lockers (8)
26 Crew berths (8)
27 Rope locker (P/S)
28 Forward hydrofoil retraction well
29 Watertight doors
30 Galley stores locker
31 Lavatory
32 Sink
33 Officers' stateroom
34 Turbine generator set
35 Diesel engine: hullborne propulsion
36 Search and navigation radar electronics
37 Fire control radar components
38 Fire control radar computer
39 Gyrocompass and Stable element
40 Electronic equipment
41 Automatic control system
42 Electronic equipment bay (unmanned)
43 Water closet

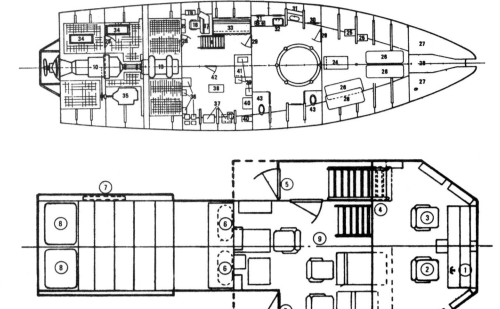

I Helm/main control console
2 Helm station
3 Conning station
4 Companionway ladders
5 Watertight doors (P/S)
6 Air-inlet planums: forward machinery room
    (P/S)
7 Exhaust duct
8 Machinery combustion air inlets
9 Combat operations center

CANTIERE NAVALTECNICA S.P.A.

HEAD OFFICE:
Via S. Raineri, 22 Messina
TELEPHONE:
774862 (PBX)
TELEX:
98030 Rodrikez
OFFICERS AND EXECUTIVES:
Cav Del Lavoro Carlo Rodriquez, President
Dott. Ing. Leopoldo Rodriquez, Executive
    Vice-President and General Manager
SENIOR EXECUTIVES:
Dott. Ing. Giovanni Falzea, Production
    Manager

Cantiere Navaltecnica S.p.A., formerly
known as Leopoldo Rodriquez Shipyard, was
the first in the world to produce hydrofoils in
series, and is now the biggest hydrofoil
builder outside the Soviet Union. On the
initiative of the company's president, Carlo
Rodriquez, the Aliscafi Shipping Company
was established in Sicily to operate the world's
first scheduled seagoing hydrofoil service in
August 1956 between Sicily and the Italian
mainland.

The service was operated by the first
Rodriquez-built Supramar PT 20, Freccia
del Sole. Cutting down the port-to-port
time from Messina to Reggio di Calabria to
one-quarter of that of conventional ferry
boats, and completing 22 daily crossings, the
craft soon proved its commercial viability.
With a seating capacity of 75 passengers the
PT 20 has carried between 800-900 passengers
a day and has conveyed a record number of
some 31,000 in a single month.

The prototype PT 20, a 27-ton craft for 75
passengers, was built by Rodriquez in 1955
and the first PT 50, a 63-ton craft for 140
passengers, was completed by the yard in
1958.

By the end of July 1976, the company will
have built and delivered more than 120
hydrofoils. The new RHS models, the only
craft now built by the company, are fitted
on request with a Hamilton Standard electronic stability augmentation system.

At the time of going to press, the company
had under construction one RHS 70, two
RHS 140s and one RHS 160. Additionally,

Freccia delle Magnolie, a 71-seat Navaltecnica RHS 70 hydrofoil passenger ferry operated by Ministero du Transporti on Lake Maggiore

the company has on order two RHS 70s, one
RHS 140 and one RHS 160. Construction
of the company's first RHS 200 is expected
to be under way by the end of 1976.

Apart from these standard designs, the
company offers a number of variants, including the Mafius 100, Mafius 150 and
Mafius 200 fast patrol craft, the Mafius 300
and 600 fast strike craft and the RHS Hydroil
series of mixed passenger/freight hydrofoils,
based on the RHS 70, 140 and 160, but
adapted for servicing offshore drilling platforms.

RHS 70

This is a 32-ton coastal passenger ferry
with seats for 71 passengers. Power is
supplied by a single 1,350 hp MTU diesel
and the cruising speed is 32·4 knots.

FOILS: Surface-piercing type in partly
hollow welded steel. During operation the
angle of the bow foil can be adjusted within
narrow limits from the steering position by
means of a hydraulic ram operating on a foil

support across the hull.

HULL: V-bottom hull of riveted light metal
alloy construction. Watertight compartments are provided below the passenger
decks and in other parts of the hull.

POWER PLANT: A single MTU MB 12V493
Ty 71 diesel, developing 1,350 hp at 1,500
rpm, drives a 3-bladed bronze aluminium
propeller through a Zahnradfabrik W 800
H 20 gearbox.

ACCOMMODATION: Forty-four passengers
are accommodated in the forward cabin,
nineteen in the rear compartment and eight
aft of the pilot's position, above the engine
room, in the elevated wheelhouse. A W/C
washbasin unit is provided in the aft passenger compartments. Emergency exits are
provided in each passenger compartment.

SYSTEMS, ELECTRICAL: 24 volt generat-
or driven by the main engine; batteries with a
capacity of 350 Ah.

HYDRAULICS: 120 kg/cm² pressure hydraulic system for rudder and bow foil incidence control.

DIMENSIONS:

Length overall	72 ft 2 in (22 m)
Width across foils	24 ft 3 in (7·40 m)
Draft hullborne	8 ft 10 in (2·70 m)
Draft foilborne	3 ft 9 in (1·15 m)

WEIGHTS:

Displacement fully loaded	31·5 tons
Useful load	6 tons

PERFORMANCE:

Cruising speed, half loaded	32·4 knots
Max speed, half loaded	36·5 knots

RHS 110

A 54-ton hydrofoil ferry, the RHS 110 is designed to carry a maximum of 110 passengers over routes of up to 300 miles (485·7 km) at a cruising speed of 37 knots.

FOILS: Surface-piercing type, in partly hollow, welded steel . Hydraulically operated flaps, attached to the trailing edges of the bow and rear foils, are adjusted automatically by a Hamilton Standard stability augmentation system for the damping of heave, pitch and roll-motions. The rear foil is rigidly attached to the transom, its incidence angle being determined during tests.

HULL: Vee-bottom of high-tensile riveted light metal alloy construction, using Peraluman plates and Anticorrodal profiles. The upper deck plates are in 0·137 in (3·5 mm)

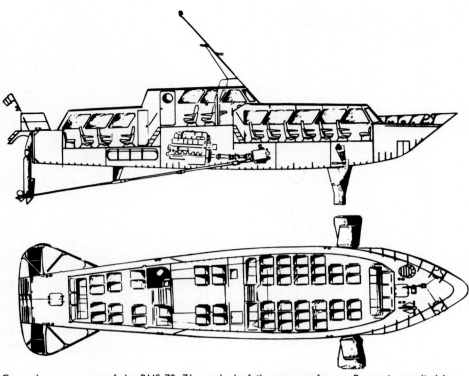

General arrangement of the RHS 70, 71-seat hydrofoil passenger ferry. Power is supplied by a single 1,350 hp MTU MB 12V493 Ty 71 diesel

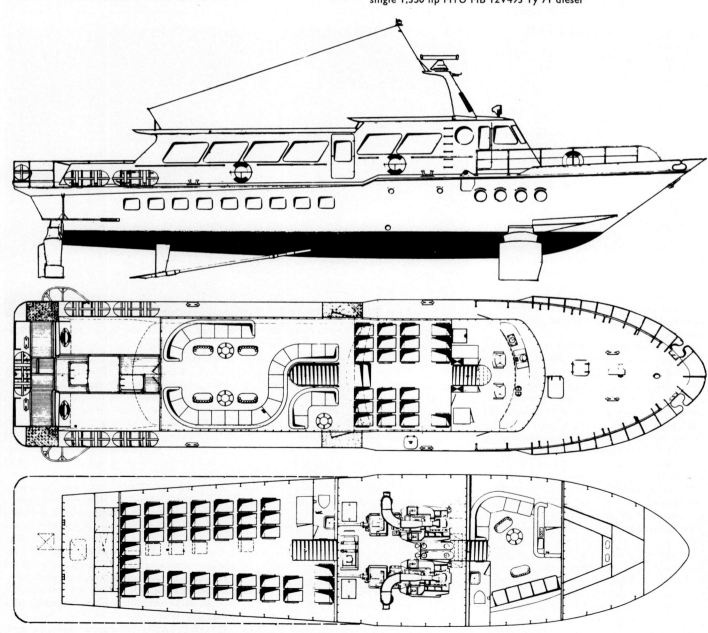

Outboard profile and deck plans of the RHS 110 54-ton hydrofoil passenger ferry

thick Peraluman. Removable deck sections permit the lifting out and replacement of the main engines. The superstructure which has a removable roof is in 0·078 in (2 mm) thick Peraluman plates, with L and C profile sections. Watertight compartments are provided below the passenger decks and other parts of the hull.

POWERPLANT: Power is supplied by two 12-cylinder supercharged MTU MB 12V493 Ty 71 diesels, each with a maximum output of 1,350 hp at 1,500 rpm. Engine output is transferred to two 3-bladed bronze-aluminium propellers through Zahnradfabrik W 800 H20 gearboxes. Each propeller shaft is 3·5 in (90 mm) in diameter and supported at three points by seawater lubricated rubber bearings. Steel fuel tanks with a total capacity of 792 gallons (3,600 litres) are located aft of the engine room.

ACCOMMODATION: The wheelhouse/observation deck saloon seats 58, and the lower aft saloon seats 39. Additional passengers are accommodated in the lower forward saloon, which contains a bar.

In the wheelhouse, the pilot's position is on the port side, together with the radar screen. A second seat is provided for the chief engineer. Passenger seats are of lightweight aircraft type, floors are covered with woollen carpets and the walls and ceilings are clad in vinyl. Two toilets are provided, one in each of the lower saloons.

SYSTEMS:
ELECTRICAL: Engine driven generators supply 220 volts, 50HZ, three-phase ac. Two groups of batteries for 24 volt dc circuit.

HYDRAULICS: Steering, variation of the foil flaps and the anchor windlass operation are all accomplished hydraulically from the wheelhouse. Plant comprises two Bosch pumps installed on the main engines and con-

RHS 110, a 110-seat passenger ferry equipped with a Hamilton Standard stability augmentation system

veying oil from a 13 gallon (60 litre) tank under pressure to the control cylinders of the rudder, foil flaps and anchor windlass.

FIREFIGHTING: Fixed CO_2 plant for the main engine room, portable CO_2 and foam fire extinguishers of 7 lb (3 kg) and 2 gallon (10 litres) capacity in the saloons, and one water fire fighting plant.

DIMENSIONS, EXTERNAL:

Length overall	84 ft 0 in (25·60 m)
Width across foils	30 ft 2¼ in (9·20 m)
Deck beam, max	19 ft 2 in (5·95 m)
Draft afloat	10 ft 9⅞ in (3·30 m)
Draft foilborne	4 ft 1 in (1·25 m)

WEIGHTS:

Displacement, fully loaded	54 tons

PERFORMANCE:

Max speed	40 knots
Cruising speed	37 knots
Range	300 miles (485·7 km)

RHS 140

This 65-ton hydrofoil passenger ferry seats 125-140 passengers and has a cruising speed of 32·5 knots.

FOILS: Surface-piercing V foils of hollow welded steel construction. Lift of the bow foil can be modified by hydraulically-operated trailing edge flaps.

HULL: Riveted light metal alloy design framed on longitudinal and transverse formers.

ACCOMMODATION: 125-140 passengers seated in three saloons. The belvedere saloon, on the main deck above the engine room, can be equipped with a bar, W/C washbasin units can be installed in the forward and aft saloons.

POWER PLANT: Power is provided by two MTU 12V493 Ty 71 12-cylinder supercharged engines, each developing 1,350 hp at 1,500 rpm. Engine output is transmitted to two 3-bladed 700 mm diameter bronze propellers through Zahnradfabrik gearboxes.

SYSTEMS, ELECTRICAL: Two engine-driven generators supply 24 volt d.c. Two

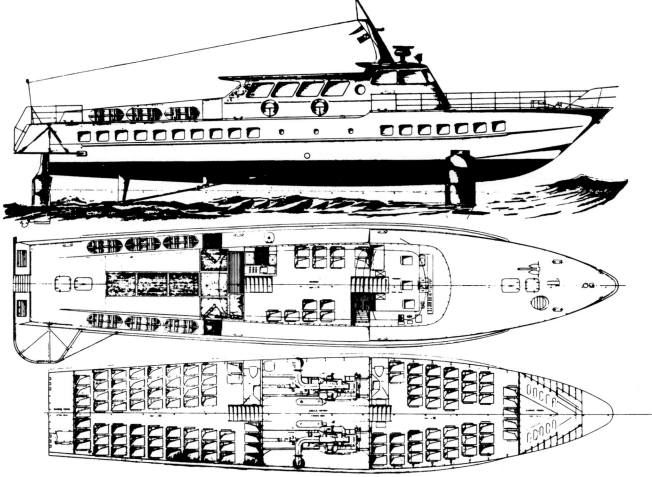

RHS 140, 125-140-seat passenger ferry

battery sets each with 350 Ah capacity.

HYDRAULICS: Steering and variation of foil flap incidence is accomplished hydraulically from the wheelhouse. Plant comprises two Bosch pumps installed on the main engines and conveying oil from a 15·4 gal (70 litre) tank under pressure to the control cylinders of the rudder and foil flaps.

FIREFIGHTING: Fixed CO_2 plant for the engine room; portable CO_2 and foam fire extinguishers in the saloons. Water intake connected to bilge pump for fire hose connection in emergency.

DIMENSIONS:

Length overall	94 ft 1½ in (28·70 m)
Width across foils	35 ft 2¼ in (10·72 m)
Draft hullborne	11 ft 5¾ in (3·50 m)
Draft foilborne	4 ft 11 in (1·50 m)

WEIGHTS:

Displacement, fully loaded	65 tons
Carrying capacity, including 3 tons bunker, and 5 tons fresh water, lubricating oil and hydraulic system oil	12·5 tons

PERFORMANCE:

Max speed, half load	36 knots
Cruising speed	32·5 knots
Range at cruising speed 900 miles (550 kms)	

RHS 160

One of the latest additions to the Navaltecnica range is the RHS 160, an 82-ton passenger ferry with seats for 160-200 passengers and a cruising speed of 36 knots.

FOILS: Surface-piercing W foils of hollow welded steel construction. Craft in this series feature a bow rudder for improved manoeuvrability in congested waters. The bow rudder works simultaneously with the aft rudders. Hydraulically-operated flaps, attached to the trailing edges of the bow and rear foils, are adjusted automatically by a Hamilton Standard electronic stability augmentation system, for the damping of heave, pitch and roll motions in heavy seas.

Condor 4, an RHS 140 operated by Condor Ltd, the Channel Islands hydrofoil ferry company, between Guernsey, Jersey and St Malo

HULL: Riveted light metal alloy longitudinal structure, welded in parts using inert gas. The hull shape of the RHS 160 is similar to the RHS 140 series. In the manufacture of the hull, plates of aluminium and magnesium alloy of 4·4% are used whilst angle bars are of a high-resistant aluminium, magnesium and silicon alloy.

ACCOMMODATION: 160-200 passengers seated in three saloons. Fifty-seven passengers are accommodated in the forward cabin, fifty-seven in the rear compartment and forty-six in the belvedere. Forward and aft saloons and belvedere have a toilet, each provided with W/C washbasin units and the usual toilet accessories.

POWER PLANT: Power is provided by two supercharged MTU MB 12V 652 TB 71 4-stroke diesel engines each with a maximum output of 1,950 hp at 1,460 rpm under normal operating conditions. Engine starting is accomplished by compressed air starters. Engine output is transmitted to two 3-bladed

bronze propellers through two Zahnradfabrik 900 HS 15 gearboxes.

SYSTEMS, ELECTRICAL: Two 35 KVA generating sets, 220 v, 60 cps, 3-phase. Three insulated cables for ventilation, air-conditioning and power. Two insulated cables for lighting, sockets and other appliances, 24 v d.c. for emergency lighting, auxiliary engine starting and servocontrol. A battery for radio telephone supply is installed on the upper deck. Provision for battery recharge from a.c. line foreseen.

HYDRAULICS: Steering is accomplished hydraulically from the wheelhouse. Plant comprises a Bosch pump installed on the main engines and conveying oil from a 10 gallon (45 litre) tank under pressure to the control cylinders of the rudder and anchor windlass, whilst a second hydraulic pump, which is also installed on the main engines, conveys oil under pressure to the flap control cylinders.

FIREFIGHTING: Fixed CO_2 plant of four

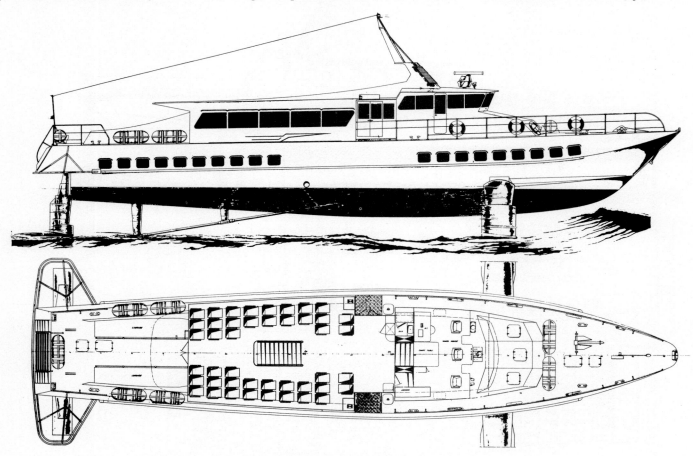

Outboard profile and main deck plan of the RHS 160

CO_2 bottles of about 20 kg each for the engine room and fuel tank space; portable extinguishers in various parts of the craft. Water intake connected to fire pump for fire connection in emergency.

DIMENSIONS:

Length overall	101 ft 6 in (30·95 m)
Width across foils	41 ft 4 in (12·60 m)
Draft afloat	12 ft 6 in (3.70 m)
Draft foilborne	4 ft 6 in (1·35 m)

WEIGHTS:

Displacement, fully loaded	82 tons
Pay load, passengers and luggage	13·5 tons

PERFORMANCE:

Speed, max	39·0 knots
Speed, cruising	36·0 knots
Cruising, range	300 miles

RHS 200

Construction of this 122 ton, 200-262 seat fast ferry is expected to start in 1976. Power will be provided by two supercharged MTU MB 16V 652 TB 71 4-stroke diesel engines. The designed cruising speed is 37·5 knots.

FOILS: Surface-piercing vee foils of hollow welded construction Hydraulically-operated flaps are fitted to the trailing edge of the bow foil to balance out longitudinal load shifting, assist take-off and adjust the flying height. The craft can also be equipped with the Hamilton Standard electronic stability augmentation system, which employs sensors and servomechanisms to automatically position flaps on the bow and stern foils for the damping of heave, pitch and roll motions in heavy seas.

HULL: Vee-bottom hull of high tensile riveted light metal alloy construction, employing Peraluman plates and Anticorrodal frames. The rake of the stem is in galvanised steel.

ACCOMMODATION: Seats can be provided for up to 262 passengers, according to the route served. There are three main passen-

Above and below: The Navaltecnica RHS 160, an 82-ton passenger ferry with seats for 160-180 passengers and a cruising speed of 36 knots

ger saloons and a bar. The standard seating arrangement allows for 60 in the main deck saloon, 75 in the aft lower saloon and 51 in the bow passenger saloon. Seating is normally four abreast in two lines with a central aisle.

The bar, at the forward end of the wheelhouse belvedere superstructure, has either an 8-place sofa or 19 seats.

The wheelhouse, which is raised to provide a 360° view, is reached from the main deck

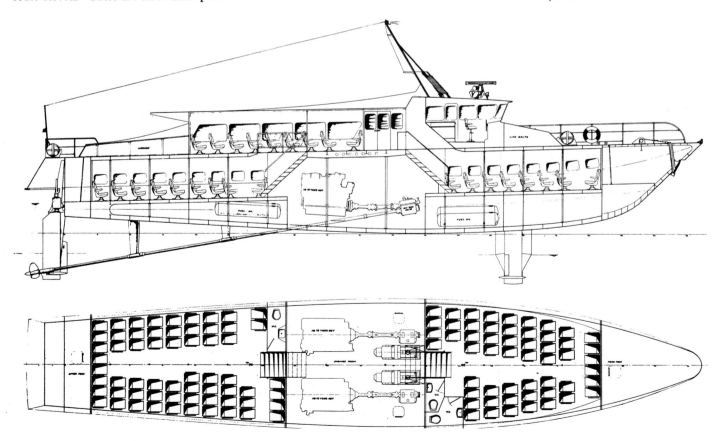

Inboard profile and lower deck plan of the RHS 160

belvedere saloon by a short companionway. Controls and instrumentation are attached to a panel on the forward bulkhead which extends the width of the wheelhouse. In the centre is the steering control and gyro-compass, on the starboard side are controls for the two engines, gearboxes and controllable-pitch propellers, and on the port side is the radar. Seats are provided for the captain, chief engineer and first mate. At the aft of the wheelhouse is a radio-telephone and a chart table.

POWER PLANT: Motive power is supplied by two supercharged MTU MB 16V 652 TB 71 4-stroke diesel engines, each with a maximum output of 2,415 hp at 1,485 rpm under normal operating conditions. Engine output is transferred to two supercavitating, controllable-pitch propellers.

SYSTEMS, ELECTRICAL: Two generating sets. One 220 volt, 3-phase a.c., for all consumer services, the second for charging 24 volt battery sets and operating fire-fighting and hydraulic pumps. Power distribution panel in wheelhouse for navigation light circuits, cabin lighting, radar, RDF, gyro compass and emergency circuits.

FIREFIGHTING: Fixed CO_2 self-contained automatic systems for power plant and fuel tank spaces, plus portable extinguishers for cabins and holds.

DIMENSIONS:

Length overall	116 ft 5⅝ in (35·50 m)
Width across foils	46 ft 6⅞ in (14·20 m)
Draft afloat	14 ft 2⅛ in (4·32 m)
Draft foilborne	5 ft 3¾ in (1·62 m)

WEIGHTS:

Displacement fully loaded	122 tons

PERFORMANCE:

Cruising speed	37·5 knots
Maximum speed	41 knots
Cruising range	275 n. miles

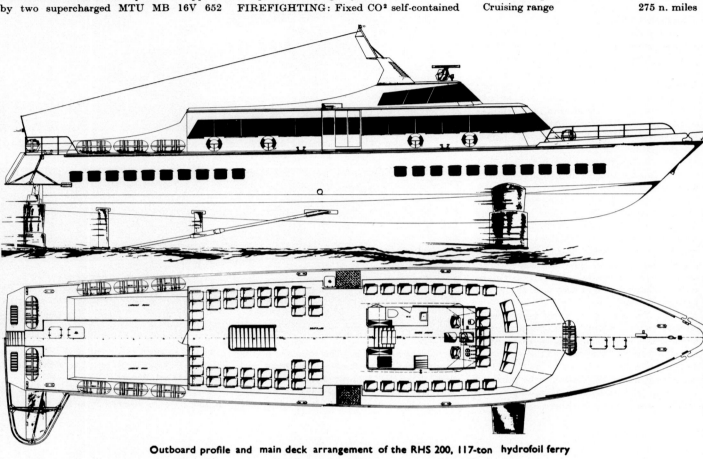

Outboard profile and main deck arrangement of the RHS 200, 117-ton hydrofoil ferry

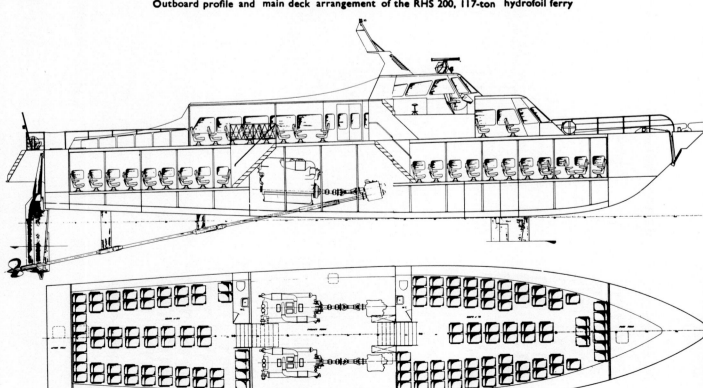

Inboard profile and lower deck arrangement of the RHS 200

RHS ALIYACHT

A luxury hydrofoil yacht of light alloy construction, the RHS Aliyacht is derived from the RHS 110 passenger ferry. It is powered by two 1,350 hp MTU MB 12V493 Ty 71 diesel engines and has a cruising speed of 38 knots.

The craft is equipped with the Hamilton Standard electronic stability augmentation system, which is designed to provide a smoother ride in heavy seas. The system uses sensors and servomechanisms to automatically position foil flaps for the maximum damping of heave, pitch and roll motions.

FOILS: Bow and rear foils are of surface-piercing type, and constructed in partly hollow, welded steel. Two hydraulically-operated flaps, attached to the trailing edges of the bow foil, are adjusted automatically by the stabilisation system for the damping of heave, pitch and roll motions. The rear foil is rigidly attached to the transom, its incidence angle being determined during tests.

HULL: The vee-bottom hull is of high-tensile riveted light metal alloy construction, using Peraluman (aluminium and magnesium alloy) plates and Anticorrodal (aluminium, magnesium and silicon alloy) profiles. The rake of the stem is in 0·137 in (3·5 mm) thick galvanised steel. The superstructure is constructed in 0·078 in (2·0 mm) Peraluman plate, and the roof is detachable to facilitate the removal and replacement of the main engines.

ACCOMMODATION: Main deck accommodation comprises the wheelhouse and radio cabin, a comfortably furnished saloon and a galley. The saloon can be fitted with two four-seat sofas, armchair, tea-table, a meal table with four chairs, and a bar. Below deck, from aft peak forward, is a large cabin for the owner, with its own bathroom and small private drawing room; two double cabins for guests with adjacent WC/wash-basin/shower units, and beyond the engines, a cabin for the captain and engineer, and two single cabins for guests.

The wheelhouse is reached via a companion-way from the saloon and is connected by a door with the upper deck. The pilot's position, controls and instruments are on the port side, together with the radar screen.

POWER PLANT: Power is supplied by two supercharged 12-cylinder MTU MB 12V 439 Ty 71 diesels, each rated at 1,350 hp at 1,500 rpm. Engine output is transferred to two 3-bladed bronze aluminium-propellers through Zahnradfabrik BW 800 H20 gearboxes.

SYSTEMS: Two 10 kW, 220 volt, three-phase ONAN generating sets, coupled to batteries, provide 24 volts dc for engine starting, instrument, lighting, radio, etc.

DIMENSIONS, EXTERNAL:

Length overall	78 ft 9 in (24·50 m)
Beam overall	20 ft 0 in (6·10 m)
Hull beam	19 ft 2¼ in (5·85 m)
Draft afloat	9 ft 8¼ in (2·95 m)
Draft foilborne	4 ft 1¼ in (1·25 m)

WEIGHTS:

Displacement, loaded	52 tons

PERFORMANCE:

Max speed	41 knots
Cruising speed	38 knots
Range	400 miles (644 km)

RHS HYDROILS

These are derivatives of RHS passenger-carrying hydrofoils, and are designed to ferry personnel, materials and equipment between offshore oil rigs and shore bases. Vessels in the series feature an open cargo deck aft of the bridge superstructure instead of an aft passenger saloon. The three main types are the RHS 70, the RHS 140, and the RHS 160 Hydroil.

RHS 70 HYDROIL

The first of the new series of RHS 70 Hydroil offshore drilling platform supply vessels has been built for ENI Oil Corporation, which is employing the craft in the Adriatic. A mixed passenger/cargo version of the RHS 70 passenger ferry, this variant has an open cargo deck aft of the bridge superstructure in place of the Caribe's main passenger cabin. Dimensions of the cargo deck are: length, 24 ft 7 in (7·50 m); width, 11 ft 6 in (3·50 m) and height, 3 ft 5 in (1·05 m).

FOILS: Bow and rear foils are of surface-piercing vee configuration, with about 66% of the weight supported by the bow foil and 34% by the rear foil. Each foil, together with its struts and horizontal supporting tube, forms a rigid framework which facilitates the exchange of the foil structure. The foils are of hollow-ribbed construction and fabricated from medium Asera steel. The forward foil can be tilted within narrow limits by means of a hydraulic ram acting on the foil strut supporting tube. The angle of attack can therefore be adjusted during operation to assist take-off and counteract the effect of large variations in loading.

HULL: The hull is of riveted light metal alloy (Peraluman) and framed on a combination of longitudinal and transverse formers. Watertight compartments are provided in the bow and stern, and a double-bottom runs

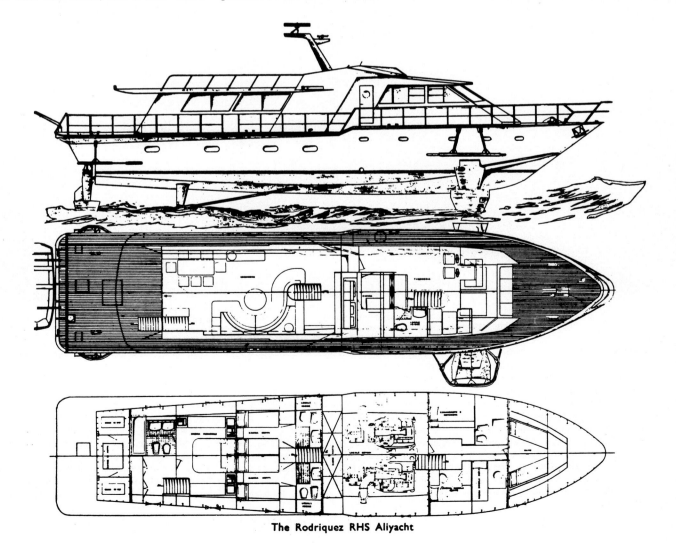

The Rodriquez RHS Aliyacht

The Rodriquez RHS Aliyacht, powered by two MTU diesels each rated at 1,350 hp. Cruising speed is 38 knots and the range 400 miles

Porto Corsini, first of the RHS 70 Hydrofoil 33-ton off-shore drilling platform supply vessels. The craft has been built for ENI, the Italian oil company and is seen operating from one of the company's drilling platforms. Loads of up to 3 tons can be carried on the open cargo deck aft of the bridge structure. Cruising speed with normal payload is 32 knots

from immediately aft of the engine room, beneath the full length of the cargo deck, to the after peak. Contained within the double-bottom are six cylindrical aluminium fuel tanks with a total capacity of 495 gallons (2,250 litres). Access to the fore and aft compartments is via removable deck hatches. The deck is of 0·196 in (5 mm) Peraluman, suitably reinforced to withstand heavily concentrated loads. Two 4·9 in (125 mm) diameter scuppers are provided aft for rapid drainage. Heavy rubber fenders are provided at the bow and stern.

POWER PLANT: Power is supplied by a 12-cylinder supercharged MTU 12V493 Ty 71 with a maximum output of 1,350 hp at 1,500 rpm. Engine output is transferred to a 3-bladed 27·5 in (700 mm) bronze-aluminium propeller through a Zahnradfabrik BW 800 H20 gearbox. The propeller shaft is 3·5 in (90 mm) in diameter, and supported at three points by seawater lubricated rubber bearings. In an emergency, hullborne propulsion is provided by a 105 hp Mercedes OM 352 diesel with a Mercruiser Z-drive. The engine is installed in the aft peak and propels the craft at about 5 knots.

ACCOMMODATION: The craft has a crew of two, and seats up to 12 passengers in a comfortably appointed saloon, immediately aft of the wheelhouse. Passengers have a choice of six armchairs and two three-place settees, one of which converts into a bed for transporting sick or injured personnel. All seats are equipped with safety belts. Aft of the saloon is a fully equipped galley, with refrigerator, a gas cooker with two gas rings, cupboards, plate rack and sink unit. Two folding wooden tables permit up to eight passengers to take meals at one sitting. A toilet/washbasin unit is provided opposite the galley on the port side. The engine room, wheelhouse and passenger saloon are fully heated and ventilated. A full range of safety equipment is carried including inflatable rafts and lifebelts for each passenger and crew member.

SYSTEMS: Electrical: 220 volt 50 Hz three-phase a.c., 24 volt d.c.; provision for 220 volt 50 Hz three phase shore supply. The d.c. supply is from a 24 volt generator driven by the main engine and feeding a 235 Ah battery. AC supply is derived from a 4-stroke Onan diesel generator set, located in the engine room.

HYDRAULICS. One Bosch Hy/ZFR 1/16 AR 101 for steering and bow foil incidence control.

COMMUNICATIONS AND NAVIGATION:
Radio: VHF radio-telephone to customers' requirements.
Radar: Decca, Raytheon etc., to customers' requirements.

DIMENSIONS:

Length overall, hull	68 ft 9 in (20·95 m)
Hull beam	16 ft 7 in (5·06 m)
Width over foils	24 ft 3 in (7·40 m)
Draft afloat	8 ft 10 in (2·70 m)
Draft foilborne	3 ft 9 in (1·14 m)

WEIGHTS:

Max take-off displacement	33·12 tons
Max load on open cargo deck	3 tons

PERFORMANCE (with normal payload)

Cruising speed	32 knots
Range	300 miles (480 km)

RHS 140 HYDROFOIL

The second in the Navaltecnica Hydroil range is a mixed passenger/cargo version of the 65-ton RHS 140. As with the smaller RHS 70 Hydroil, the main passenger saloon is replaced by a large open cargo deck for loads up to 6 tons. The deck is 31 ft 2 in (9·5 m) long, 15 ft 9 in (4·8 m) wide and 6 ft 4 in (1·19 m) high.

The craft will carry a crew of two and up to 14 passengers. Two variants are available, one equipped with seats for 23 passengers and with a cargo capacity of 5 tons and the other with seats for 60 passengers and a cargo capacity of 3 tons. Power will be supplied by two 12-cylinder supercharged MTU 12V493 Ty 71, with a maximum output of 1,350 hp.

DIMENSIONS:

Length overall, hull	93 ft 6 in (28·50 m)
Hull beam	20 ft 0 in (6·10 m)
Width over foils	35 ft 2 in (10·72 m)
Draft hullborne	11ft 6 in (3·50 m)
Draft foilborne	4 ft 11 in (1·50 m)

WEIGHTS:

Normal take-off displacement	64 tons

PERFORMANCE:

Cruising speed	32-34 knots
Range at cruising speed	300 miles (480 km)

RHS 160 HYDROIL

Latest addition to Navaltecnica's range of offshore oil rig support vessels, the RHS 160 features an open cargo deck aft of the bridge superstructure and additional fuel and water tanks in the place of the lower aft passenger saloons. The vessel carries a crew of 5 and forty-two passengers, plus 10 tons of cargo, at a cruising speed of 35 knots.

FOILS: Surface-piercing W foils of hollow, welded steel construction. Craft in this series feature bow and aft rudders, both of which operate simultaneously. Hydraulically-operated flaps, attached to the trailing edges of the bow and rear foils are adjusted automatically by a Hamilton Standard electronic stability augmentation system, for

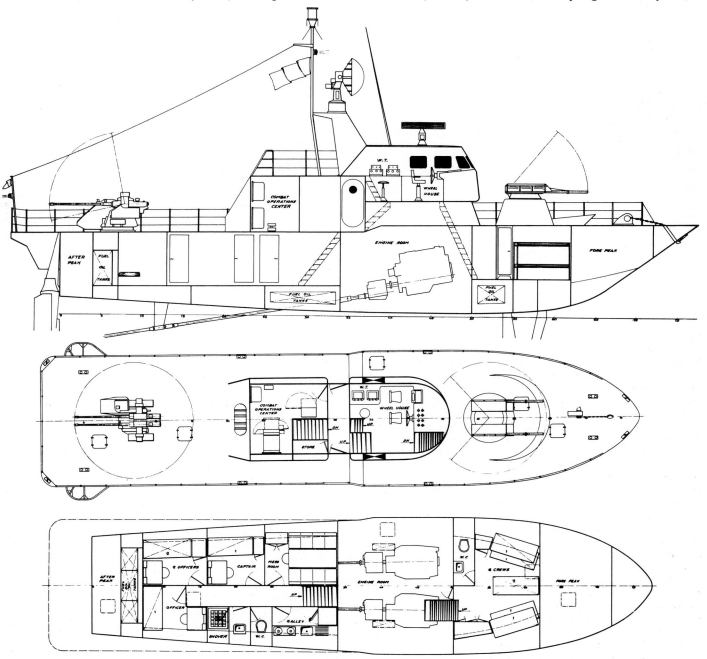

General arrangement of the fast patrol variant of the Mafius 150

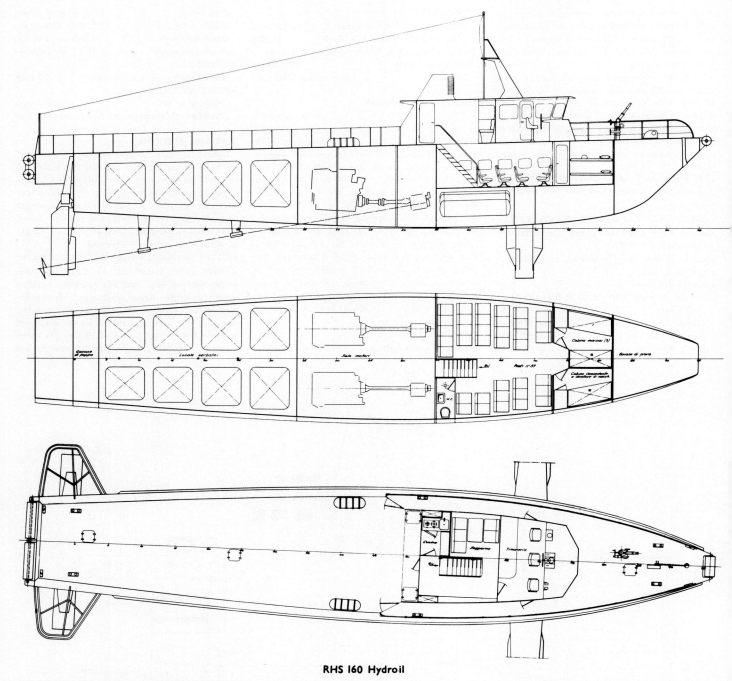

RHS 160 Hydroil

the damping of heave, pitch and roll motions in heavy seas.

HULL: Vee-bottom hull of high tensile riveted light metal alloy construction. In the manufacture of the hull, plates of aluminium and magnesium alloy of 4·4% are used, whilst angle bars are of a high resistant aluminium, magnesium and silicon alloy. Inert gas welding (Argon) is used for strengthening beams, web frames, keelsons and stringers. Steel and rubber fenders are fitted aft and in the sides of the main deck to protect the foils from damage when docking.

ACCOMMODATION: Passengers are accommodated in a forward saloon, seating 37, and the upper belvedere saloon, seating five. The seats, designed for maximum comfort, have arms and each is provided with an ash tray and magazine holder. The toilet, finished in Formica or similar laminate, is provided with a W/C, basin and normal accessories.

Crew members are accommodated in two cabins forward, that on the starboard being provided with two berths and a locker, while the port cabin has three berths and lockers. The wheelhouse is located well forward and has seats for the master in the centre, chief engineer on the starboard side and radar operator on the port side. All steering and other controls are located in the wheelhouse, including a circuit control panel for the navigation lights, craft lighting, radar, gyrocompass and various other electrical consumer and emergency circuits.

POWER PLANT: Power is provided by two supercharged MTU MB 12V TB 71 4-stroke diesel engines, each with a maximum output of 1,950 hp at 1,460 rpm. Engine starting is accomplished by compressed air starters. Output is transmitted to two 3-bladed bronze propellers through two Zahnradfabrik 900 HS 15 gearboxes.

SYSTEMS: ELECTRICAL: Two 35 KVA generating sets, 220 volts, 50 Hz, 3-phase for ventilation and air-conditioning; 220 volts, 50 Hz, single-phase, for lighting and other appliances; 24 volts dc for auxiliary lighting, engine starting and servocontrol.

HYDRAULICS: Steering is accomplished hydraulically from the wheelhouse. Plant comprises a Bosch pump installed on one of the main engines and conveying oil under pressure from a 10 gallon (45 litre) tank to the control cylinders of the rudder and anchor windlass, whilst a second hydraulic pump, which is installed on the other main engine, conveys oil under pressure to the flap control cylinders.

The two systems are interchangeable and equipped with safety valves, manometers and micronic filters.

FIREFIGHTING: Fixed CO_2 plant for engine room and fuel tank space; portable appliances include two 6 kg powder extinguishers and one 5 kg CO_2 extinguisher in the engine room; two 10 litre water extinguishers in the passengers saloons and one 6 kg powder extinguisher in the wheelhouse.

Two water extinguishing systems are provided, one driven by the main engine and the other by a motor driven pump. The system can supply a monitor on the upper deck at the bow and two fire hose water outlets located amidships on the upper deck. A dual-purpose water/foam nozzle can be supplied on request.

DIMENSIONS:

Length overall	103 ft 0 in (31·30 m)
Moulded beam	20 ft 4¼ in (6·20 m)
Width across foils	41 ft 4 in (12·60 m)
Draft hullborne	12 ft 6 in (3·70 m)
Draft foilborne	4 ft 6 in (1·35 m)

WEIGHTS:

Displacement, fully loaded	85 tons

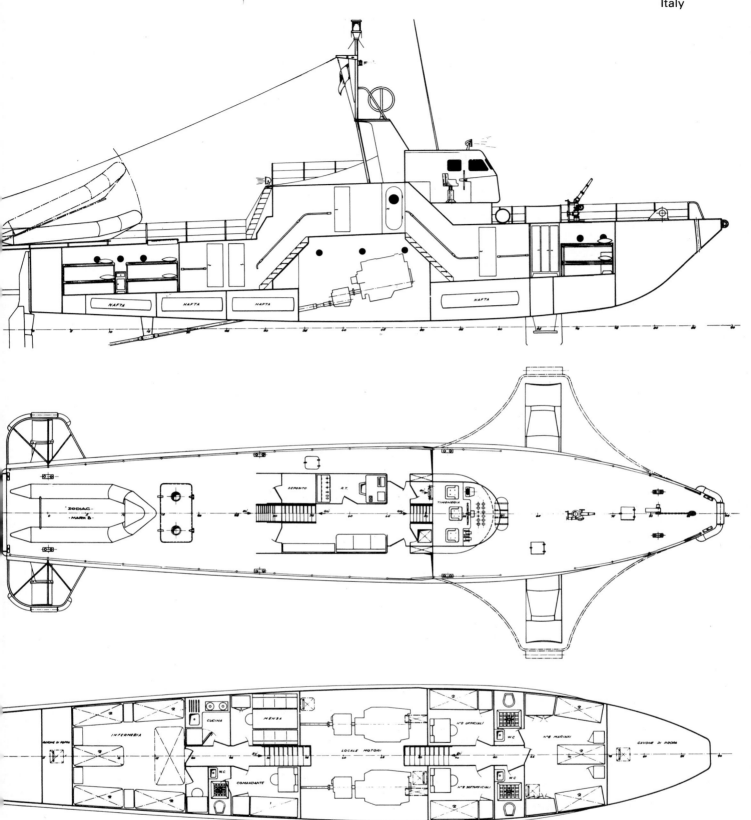

RHS 140 Search and Rescue craft

PERFORMANCE:

Cruising speed	35 knots
Cruising range	200 miles

RHS SEARCH AND RESCUE CRAFT

This new variant of the well-known RHS 140 is a multi-purpose rescue craft equipped for a full range of S & R duties, including fire-fighting and wreck marking. It has a top speed of 36 knots and can operate in heavy seas at a considerable distance from its shore base. A Merryweather dual-purpose water/foam monitor is located on the foredeck and a Zodiac inflatable liferaft is carried on the upper deck aft.

A sick bay is provided and can be fitted out to accommodate 30-40 survivors.

A feature of the design is the filling of the double bottom with expanded polystyrene to provide sufficient buoyancy to make it unsinkable, even with the watertight compartments flooded.

FOILS: Surface-piercing V foils of hollow, welded steel construction. Foil lift is varied by flaps operated by an electronic/hydraulic system developed by Cantiere Navaltecnica in conjunction with Hamilton Standard. Under calm sea conditions, the flaps can be operated manually.

HULL: Riveted light metal alloy design framed on longitudinal and transverse formers. Areas of the attachment points of the bow and rear foils are reinforced with steel. Steel is also used for the rake of the stem, the stern tube for the propeller shaft and the propeller shaft attachment.

ACCOMMODATION: Berths, lockers and living accommodation provided for a crew of eleven, comprising the captain, two officers, two petty officers and six seamen. Seats are provided in the wheelhouse for an operating crew of three. A "flying bridge" with a duplicated set of instruments and controls, provides improved visibility during search operations. A 10-berth sick bay, complete with a small office for the doctor is provided aft. A large roof hatch is provided in the sick bay through which stretcher casualties

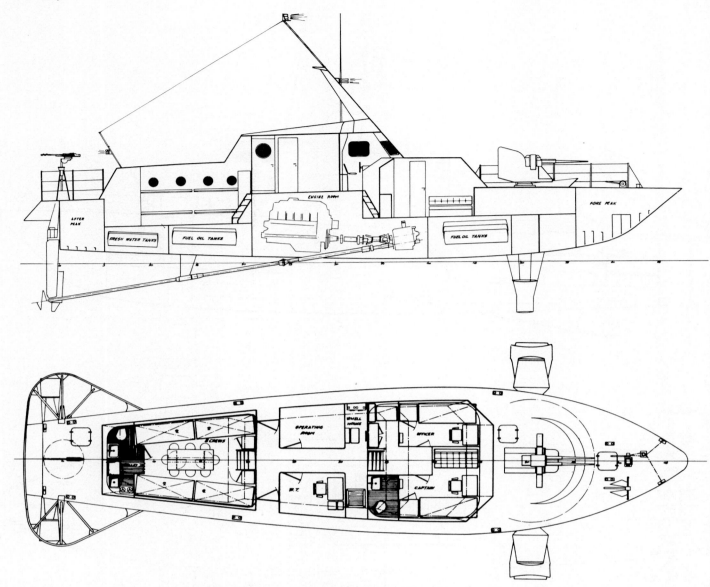

Inboard profile and deck plan of the Mafius 100 fast patrol craft

can be lowered. If required, the sick bay can be fitted out to accommodate 30-40 survivors.

POWER PLANT: Power is provided by two MTU 12V 493 Ty 71 12-cylinder supercharged diesel engines, each developing 1,350 hp at 1,500 rpm. Engine output is transmitted to two 3-bladed, 700 mm diameter bronze propellers through Zahnradfabrik gearboxes.

SYSTEMS, ELECTRICAL: Two engine-driven generators of 24 volts d.c. supply essential services and emergency lights. An a.c. system, powered by a generator set, supplies lighting and all other on board consumers. Two battery sets are provided for starting the main engines and generators.

HYDRAULICS: Steering and variation of foil flap incidence is accomplished hydraulcally from the wheelhouse. Plant comprises two Bosch pumps installed on the main engines and conveying oil from a tank under pressure to the control cylinders of the rudder and foil flaps.

AIR CONDITIONING: Provided on request.

FIREFIGHTING: Fixed CO_2 plant for the engine room and fuel oil bays; portable CO_2 and foam fire extinguishers at various parts of the craft. One Merryweather dual purpose foam/water monitor.

DIMENSIONS:

Length overall	94 ft 1½ in	(28·70 m)
Width across foils	35 ft 2½ in	(10·72 m)
Draft hullborne	11 ft 5¾ in	(3·50 m)
Draft foilborne	4 ft 11 in	(1·50 m)

WEIGHTS:

Displacement, fully loaded
62 tons (63 tonnes)

PERFORMANCE:

Maximum speed	36 knots
Cruising speed	32·5 knots
Endurance at cruising speed	18 hours, 600 miles
Endurance at low speed	50 hours, 600 miles
Cruising range	600 miles (1,110 km)

MAFIUS PATROL CRAFT

Derived from RHS passenger vessels, the Mafius series craft are designed for coast guard and anti-contraband patrol. Suitably armed, they can undertake various naval duties, ranging from patrol to minelaying. The armament shown in the accompanying drawings can be augmented or substituted by sea-to-air and sea-to-sea missiles according to requirements.

MAFIUS 100

The Mafius 100 is similar in design and performance to the two PAT 20 patrol hydrofoils built by Rodriquez for the Philippine Navy.

FOILS: Bow and rear foils are surfacing piercing V configuration and identical to those of the standard RHS 70. About 59% of the total weight is borne by the bow foil and 41% by the rear foil. The foils are of hollow ribbed construction and made from medium Asera steel

Total foil area is 112 sq ft (10·4 m²). The angle of incidence of the forward foil can be varied during flight by means of a hydraulic ram acting on the foil strut supporting tube.

HULL: The hull is of riveted light alloy construction with Peraluman (aluminium and magnesium alloy) plates and Anti-corrodal (aluminium, magnesium and silicon alloy) profiles.

ACCOMMODATION: The crew comprises a captain, two officers and eight NCO's and ratings. The pilot's position is on the left of the wheelhouse, with the principal instrumentation; and the radar operator sits on the right with the auxiliary instrumentation. The pilot is provided with an intercom system connecting him with the officer's cabin, engine room and crew cabin. The internal space has been divided as follows:

(a) The forward or bow room, subdivided into two cabins, one for the captain, the other for two officers, and including a W/C with washstand and a storeroom with a refrigerator.

(b) The stern room, with eight berths for the NCOs and ratings, a W/C with washstand and a galley equipped with a gas stove and an electric refrigerator.

(c) The deck room, aft of the wheelhouse, with tilting sofa and table for R/T equipment.

Air conditioning is installed in the captain's and officer's quarters.

POWER PLANT: Power is supplied by a

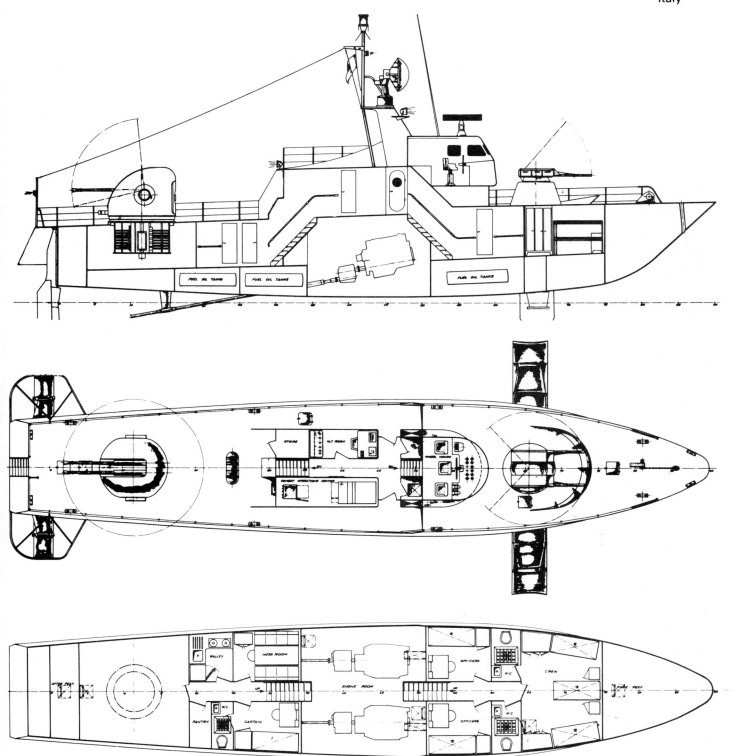

General arrangement of the Mafius 200

supercharged 12-cylinder MTU 12V493 Ty 71 with a max continuous output of 1,350 hp at 1,500 rpm. Engine output is transferred to a 3-bladed bronze aluminium propeller through a Zahnradfabrik BW 800/S reversible gear. Fuel (total capacity 2,800 kg) is carried in ten cylindrical aluminium tanks located in the double bottom beneath the bow room and the stern room. Dynamic and reserve oil tanks in the engine room give a total oil capacity of 120 kg. An auxiliary engine can be fitted in the stern for emergency operation.

ARMAMENT AND SEARCH EQUIPMENT: Single 12·7 machine-gun mounted above well position in bow, and two searchlights or one 8 cm Oerlikon 3Z8DLa rocket launcher.

SYSTEMS:

ELECTRICAL: 220v, 10 kW, diesel generator with batteries. Supplies instruments, radio and radar and external and internal lights, navigation lights and searchlights.

HYDRAULICS: 120 kg/cm² pressure hydraulic system for steering and varying forward foil incidence angle.

APU: Onan engine for air conditioning when requested.

DIMENSIONS:

Length overall, hull	68 ft 6 in (20·89 m)
Hull beam	15 ft 8¾ in (4·79 m)
Beam overall	24 ft 4 in (7·4 m)
Draft afloat	9 ft 1 in (2·76 m)
Draft foilborne	4 ft 0 in (1·20 m)
Height overall:	
hullborne	21 ft 0 in (6·44 m)
foilborne	26 ft 3 in (8·00 m)

WEIGHTS:

Net tonnage	28 tons
Light displacement	26 tons
Max take-off displacement	32·5 tons
Useful load	7·6 tons
Max useful load	8·1 tons

PERFORMANCE:

Max speed foilborne	38 knots
Max speed hullborne	13 knots
Cruising speed foilborne	34 knots
Cruising speed hullborne	12 knots
Max permissible sea state foilborne mode	Force 4
Designed range at cruising speed	540 miles (869 km)
Number of seconds and distances to take-off	20 secs, 328 ft (100 m)
Number of seconds and distances to stop craft	12 secs, 164 ft (50 m)
Fuel consumption at cruising speed	145 kg/h
Fuel consumption at max speed	180 kg/h

MAFIUS 150

This is the fast patrol boat version of the RHS 110 passenger ferry. Modifications include a revised cabin superstructure with

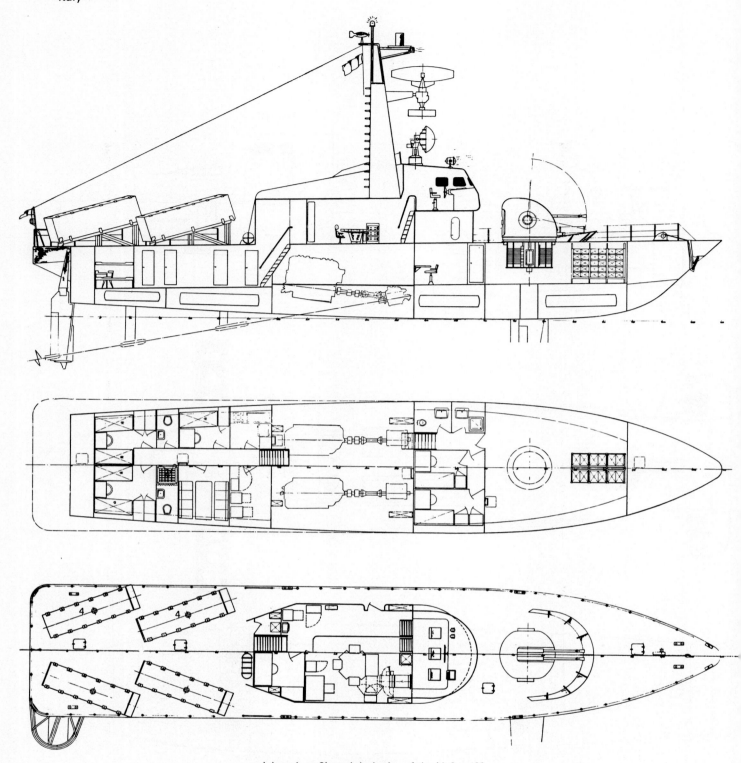

Inboard profile and deck plan of the Mafius 600

an upper bridge; the installation of 8 Sistel Sea Killer medium-range missiles and a 20 mm Hispano-Suiza twin-mounting, and the provision of fuel tanks of additional capacity increasing the operating range to 560 miles (347·96 km).

FOILS, HULL, POWERPLANT: Arrangements similar to those of the RHS 110.

ACCOMMODATION: Berths provided for eight officers and non-commissioned officers and eight ratings.

DIMENSIONS:

Length overall	83 ft 2 in (25·40 m)
Beam overall	27 ft 6¾ in (8·40 m)
Height of hull structure	9 ft 4 in (2·85 m)
Draft foilborne	4 ft 1 in (2·15 m)
Draft hullborne, fully loaded	
	9 ft 10 in (3·00 m)

WEIGHTS:

Displacement, empty	36 tons
Displacement, loaded	50 tons

PERFORMANCE:

Max speed	41 knots
Cruising speed	38 knots
Cruising range	560 miles (896 km)

MAFIUS 200

Derived from the RHS 140 passenger ferry this fast patrol variant is armed with a 40 mm Breda-Bofors twin naval mounting and one 8 cm Oerlikon 3Z8DLa rocket launcher, and has a maximum speed of 37 knots. Above the wheelhouse is an open bridge with duplicate steering, engine controls and instrumentation.

WEIGHTS:

Displacement loaded	64 tons
Displacement empty	50 tons

PERFORMANCE:

Max speed foilborne	37 knots
Cruising speed	34 knots
Minimum foilborne speed	23·3 knots
Range	736 miles (1,127 km)

MAFIUS 300 AND 600 FAST STRIKE CRAFT

The 85-ton Mafius 300 and 118-ton Mafius 600 are two hydrofoil missilecraft designed to augment the existing range of Navaltecnica fast patrol boats.

Though differing in size, the two craft are almost identical in terms of overall design, construction and internal arrangements. Both are equipped with the SAS stability augmentation system, which stabilises the vessels in bad weather, and the Breda-Bofors twin 40 mm/L 70 or similar rapid-fire cannon. In addition the Mafius 300 will carry two Otomat or similar missile launchers and the Mafius 600 will carry four.

Power for the Mafius 300 is provided by two 1,950 hp MTU 12V 652 TB 11 diesels, while the Mafius 600 has two MTU 16V 652 TB 71 diesels each rated at 2,600 hp. Maximum speed of both craft is in excess of 38 knots.

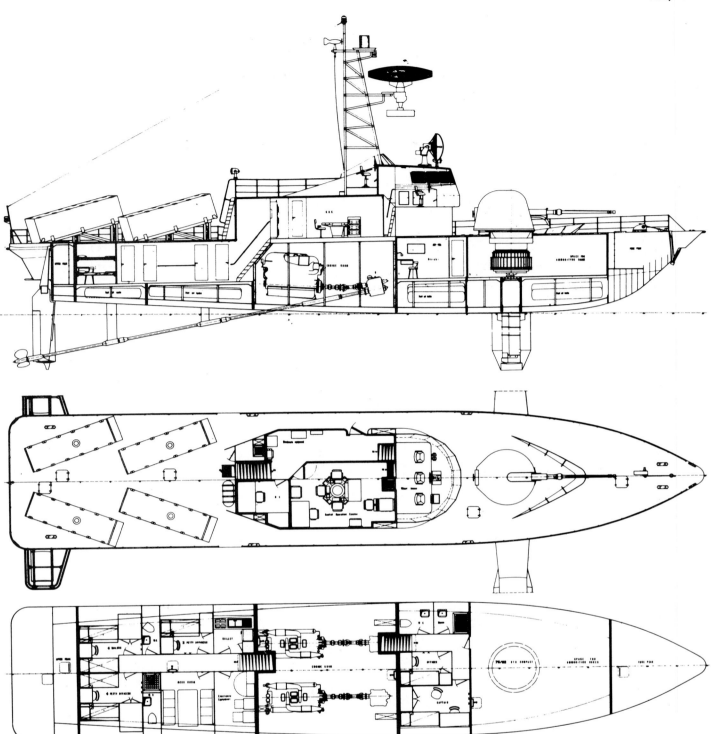

Standard version of the Mafius 600, armed with four missiles and one Oto Melara 76/62 cannon

Dimensions, weights and performance figures are given at the end of the summary. The following characteristics apply to both designs.

HULL AND SUPERSTRUCTURE: Vee-bottom hull of high tensile riveted light metal alloy construction. Argon gas welding employed on strengthened beams, web frames, keelsons and stringers. Basic hull structure is longitudinal; forepeak and after peak are transverse type structures. Steel is employed for the stern, fore and aft foil attachment points, propeller struts and foils. Cadmium plated rivets are used for jointing steel and light alloy components. Side plating ranges in thickness from 3·5 to 5 mm; the upper deck varies from 3 to 4 mm and plating on the stem and stern platforms is 2 mm thick.

The superstructure is built on transverse frames with stanchions and beams every 300 mm.

FOILS: Surface-piercing W foils of hollow welded steel. Craft in this series have a bow rudder for improved manoeuvrability. The bow rudder works simultaneously with the aft rudders to provide fully co-ordinated turns. Hydraulically operated flaps, attached to the trailing edges of the bow and rear foils are adjusted automatically by an SAS electronic stability augmentation system for the damping of heave, pitch and roll motions in heavy seas.

ACCOMMODATION: Berths, living and working accommdoation and full WC/washroom facilities for total complement of twelve, including commissioned and non-commissioned officers and ratings. The wheelhouse, all living spaces and fire control room are air-conditioned. Ventilation system provided for the engine room.

PROPULSION:

Mafius 300

Two MTU 12V 652 TB 71 4-stroke diesels, each delivering 1,950 hp at 1,460 rpm.

Mafius 600

Two MTU 16V 652 TB 71 4-stroke diesels, each delivering 2,600 hp at 1,460 rpm.

On both designs engine output is transferred via a short intermediate shaft, universal joint and Zahnradfabrik 900 HS 15 gearboxes to two hollow, stainless steel propeller shafts operating two, 3-bladed bronze-aluminium propellers. The drive shafts are supported by brackets and on the aft foils by rubber bearings lubricated by the water coolant system.

Stainless steel controllable-pitch propellers are available as an alternative to the fixed-pitch bronze-aluminium type.

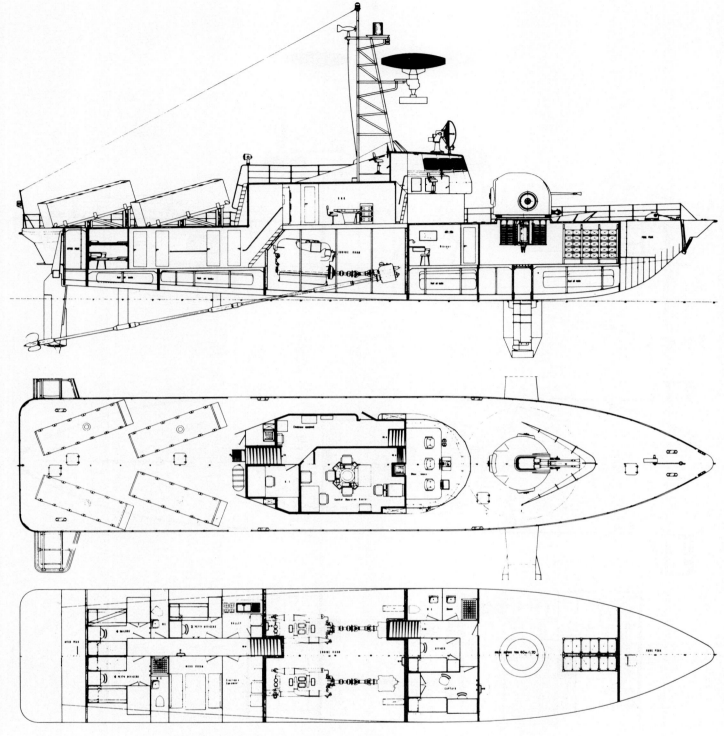

Mafius 600 variant with four missiles and one 40/70 naval twin mount

FUEL OIL: Diesel fuel oil is carried in fibreglass-reinforced, welded aluminium tanks located in the double bottom. All tanks are connected to a service tank from which oil is delivered to the injection pumps. Each engine has two suction and two engine pumps. Before reaching the injection pumps, fuel is fed through two filters in parallel, with replaceable filter elements, and water drain cocks. Injection excess fuel is piped back to the service tank.

Tanks are refuelled through necks on the main deck, each equipped with air vents and fuel level calibrated in kgs and gallons.

SYSTEMS: Two systems are installed, each pressurised by a gear pump installed on one of the main engines. The first is used for the steering system and anchor winch, the second supplies the cylinder operating the lift control flaps and the bow rudder. The two systems are interchangeable and equip-ped with safety valves, manometers and micronic filters. Hydraulic pressure is also used for operating the weapons systems.

DRAINAGE AND FIRE CONTROL: Bilge pumps, operated by the main engines, can empty water from any compartment. Drain valves can be operated from both the engine room or from the deck. One pump can also supply water for fire hoses located on the amidship and aft sections of the vessels, port and starboard.

CO_2 system installed for fuel bays and engine room. Portable dry chemical and foam extinguishers also fitted.

ELECTRICAL: Two systems, dc and ac. 24 volt dc system operates navigation lights, radio and starts auxiliary engines. AC system, for all the other requirements, comprises two diesel generating sets delivering 70 kva, 220 volts, 3-phase 50 Hz. Meters for monitoring voltage, amperage, frequency and power of ac systems are on main switchboard, located in engine room, from which isolated or parallel operation of the two alternators is controlled. Also on board are circuit breaker and switches for the transformer when the craft is connected to shore power, and dis-tributing panels for the power and lighting system.

SAFETY: The presence of smoke, fire and high temperatures in various parts of the craft, as well as the malfunctioning of machinery, auxiliary systems and hydraulics automatically sets off an electric alarm.

NAVIGATION AND COMMUNICATIONS: The craft are equipped with all navigation lights as well as an electrically operated horn and signal lights. Communications and navigation systems (radio, Decca Navigator and Flight Log etc) are fitted to the cus-tomers' requirements and are therefore considered optional equipment.

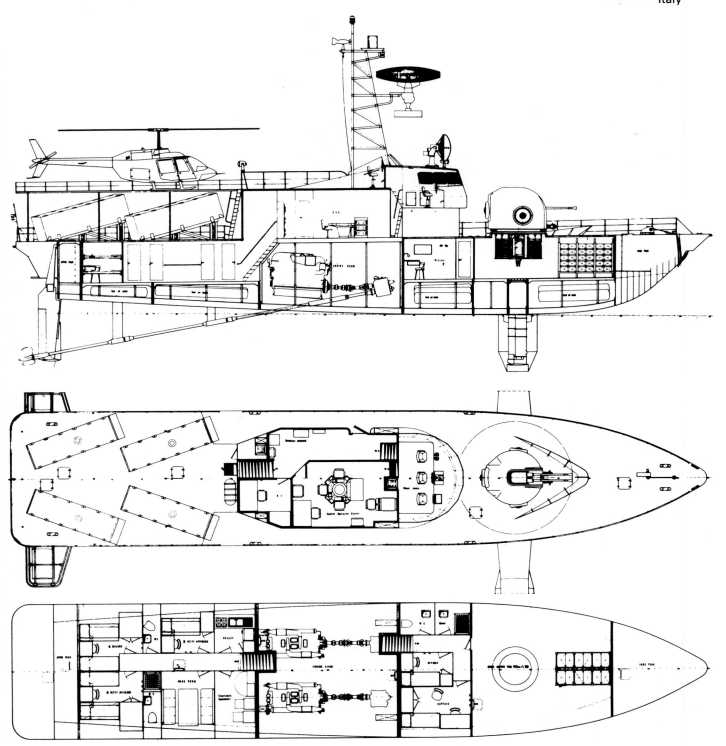

This version of the Mafius 600 has a helicopter landing pad above the missile launchers aft. A
Breda-Bofors twin 40 mm L70 or similar rapid fire cannon is mounted forward

MAIFUS 300:

DIMENSIONS:

Length overall	101·54 ft (30·95 m)
Length, waterline	86·12 ft (26·25 m)
Beam, moulded	20·34 ft (6·20 m)
Beam across foils	41·34 ft (12·50 m)
Draft hullborne	12·14 ft (3·70 m)
Draft foilborne	4·59 ft (1·40 m)

WEIGHTS:

Displacement	83·66 tons (85 tonnes)
Military payload	14·76 tons (15 tonnes)
Liquids, fuel oil and water	11·52 tons (11·7 tonnes)

PERFORMANCE:

Maximum speed	in excess of 37 knots (68·5 km/h)
Cruising speed	36 knots (66·5 km/h)
Cruising range	500 n miles (925 km)

MAFIUS 600:

DIMENSIONS:

Length overall	114·83 ft (35·00 m)
Length, waterline	98·75 ft (30·10 m)
Beam, moulded	22·97 ft (7·00 m)
Beam across foils	47·24 ft (14·40 m)
Draft hullborne	14·93 ft (4·55 m)
Draft foilborne	7·05 ft (2·15 m)

WEIGHTS:

Displacement	116·14 tons (116 tonnes)
Military payload	18·21 tons (18·5 tonnes)
Liquids—oil, fuel, water	16·04 tons (16·3 tonnes)

PERFORMANCE:

Maximum speed	38 knots (70·5 km/h)
Cruising speed	37 knots (68·5 km/h)
Cruising range	500 miles (925 km)

SEAFLIGHT SpA Cantiere Navale

HEAD OFFICE:
Villagio Torrefaro Messina 98019
TELEPHONE:
812.579
DIRECTOR AND SENIOR EXECUTIVES:
Dr Filippo M. Laudini, President and

General Manager
Dott Ing Emanuele Midolo, Technical
Manager
In August 1976 fresh support for Seaflight
was introduced by a new Italian financial
group. Dr Filippo M. Laudini, the new
President and General Manager, has stated

that it is the group's intention to give fresh
impetus to the design and construction
of hydrofoils and to their marketing on a
world-wide basis.

The L90 will be the first production craft
of the re-structured company. The prototype, launched in 1973, has been employed

on the principal routes of the Tirrenian Seas. In the summer of 1973 it operated a service between Italy and Sardinia.

One of the company's latest projects is a 180-seat passenger ferry which will employ a completely new foil system. It is the intention of the new management to put stronger emphasis on the design and construction of hydrofoils for military applications in future.

Construction of the company's yard on the beach at Torre Faro, began in 1962, and the Seaflight P 46 prototype, the C 44, was launched in January 1965. The company has since built eight 30 seat P 46s and seven H 57s, the latter being a larger and more powerful development of the P 46, seating 60 passengers and one L 90.

Descriptions of the P 46 and military variants of this craft and the H 57 appeared in JSS 1972-73 and earlier editions.

SEAFLIGHT L 90

The L 90, latest passenger ferry hydrofoil in the Seaflight series, seats 118-123 passengers and cruises at 35 knots. The prototype, which was launched in 1973, was built under the supervision of Registro Italiano Navale. FOILS: The foil system is of aeroplane configuration with surface-piercing bow and rear foils. Approximately 60% of the load is supported by the bow foil and 40% by the rear foil.

The bow foil, of W type, is attached to a supporting tube inside the hull by a central and two lateral struts. The foil pivots around the axis of the supporting tube between positions of maximum and minimum incidence.

The lift and drag generated by the foil tends to rotate it backwards, particularly during take-off and in rough seas, but

Seaflight's L 90 prototype

this movement is opposed by a spring attached to an arm on the foil assembly shaft. The system is designed to produce the same amount of lift, whether the speed varies or the foil's submerged surface varies in a wave crest or cavity.

Foils, struts and the supporting tube are fabricated in steel. Four shear points are provided, two inside the hull at the attachment points of the support tube arm and the automatic incidence control system, and two externally, at the point of attachment of the two subfoils to the central strut. In the event of damage, the affected foils and their supporting structure can be quickly and easily repaired.

The rear foil combines a horizontal submerged centre section with inclined surface-piercing areas. It is attached to the hull by two struts and the two rudder supports and the angle of incidence is fixed.

HULL: Riveted light alloy construction is employed throughout. The structure is of the transverse type with frames spaced 1 ft 0 in

(300 mm) apart. Full-length longitudinal members reinforce the hull bottom and the decks and run from stem to stern. All plates and sections are specially treated by the company for added protection against corrosion. Braking load of the plates is 30·35 kg/sq mm. The hull is designed for two compartment sub-division and will remain afloat with any two adjacent compartments flooded.

ACCOMMODATION: The standard version accommodates a crew of 3-4 and 118-123 passengers, who are seated in three large saloons. Entry is through one of two side doors, one port, one starboard, in the central saloon, which provides access via a companionway to the aft saloon, the forward saloon and the wheelhouses. There are two WC washbasin units in the aft saloon and one in the forward saloon.

The pilot's position, instruments and controls are on the starboard side of the wheelhouse and there is a crew member's observation position on the port side. Access to the

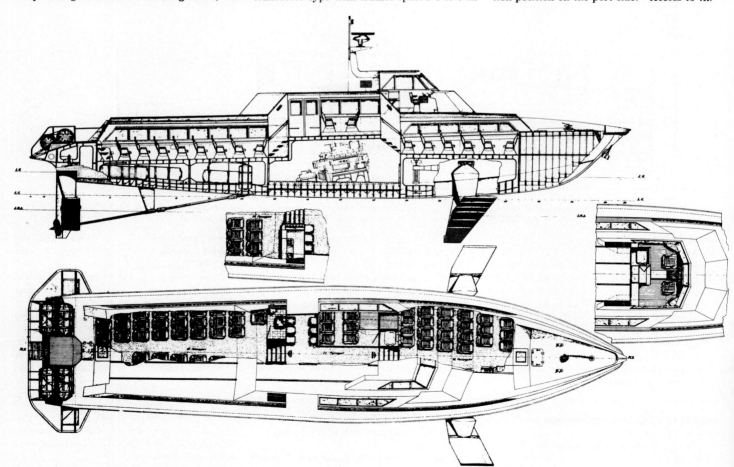
Inboard profile and plan view of the Seaflight L90 passenger ferry hydrofoil. Power is supplied
by two 1,100 hp MB 820 DC diesels

engine room is from the wheelhouse via a watertight hatch.

POWER PLANT: Power is supplied by two supercharged 12 cylinder Mercedes-Maybach MB 820 Dc diesels, each with a maximum continuous output of 1,100 shp at 1,400 rpm. Engine output is transferred to two high tensile bronze propellers through Zahnradfabrik BW 800/s reversible gears.

SYSTEMS:

ELECTRICAL: Two engine driven generators coupled to two battery sets provide 24 volts dc for engine starting, instruments, lighting, radio, etc. Separate diesel ac generating plant can be installed if required.

COMMUNICATIONS AND NAVIGATION: Ship-shore vhf and radar to customer's requirements.

DIMENSIONS, EXTERNAL:

Length overall	89 ft 4 in (27·24 m)
Length waterline, hull	74 ft 6 in (22·70 m)
Draft afloat	10 ft 1 in (3·07 m)
Draft foilborne	4 ft 1¼ in (1·25 m)
Hull beam	19 ft 9¾ in (6·04 m)
Width across foils	32 ft 9¾ in (10·00 m)
Freeboard	5 ft 5 in (1·35 m)
Height overall	26 ft 3 in (8·00 m)

DIMENSIONS: INTERNAL:

Aft passenger saloon compartment, including WC:

Length	28 ft 6½ in (8·70 m)
Max width	15 ft 5 in (4·70 m)
Max height	5 ft 6 in (1·95 m)
Floor area	398 sq ft (37 m²)
Volume	2,472 cu ft (70 m³)
Max take-off displacement	59·5 tons
Deadweight (incl fuel, water, passengers, crew)	14 tons
Payload	10 tons

PERFORMANCE

Cruising speed foilborne 32·4-35 knots

Max wave height in foilborne mode
5 ft 3 in (1·60 m)

Range at cruising speed
270 nautical miles (500 km)

Turning radius at crusing speed
328 yards (300 m)

Take-off distance 218 yards (200 m)

Take-off time	30 seconds
Stopping distance	87 yards (80 m)
Stopping time	10 seconds
Fuel consumption at cruising speed	300 kg/h

Main deck saloon, excluding wheelhouse:

Length	16 ft 8¾ in (5·10 m)
Max width	15 ft 9 in (4·80 m)
Height	6 ft 5 in (195 m)
Turning radius at cruising speed	392 ft (120 m)
Take-off distance	427 ft (130 m)
Max-height	6 ft 5 in (1·95 m)
Floor area	258 cu ft (24 m³)
Volume	1,589 cu ft (45 m³)

Wheelhouse

Length	6 ft 2¾ in (1·90 m)
Width	9 ft 10 in (3·00 m)
Height	6 ft 2¾ in (1·90 m)
Area	64 sq ft (6 m²)
Volume	423 cu ft (12 m³)

WEIGHTS:

Light displacement	45 tons

JAPAN

HITACHI SHIPBUILDING & ENGINEERING CO LTD

HEAD OFFICE:
47 Edobori 1-chome, Nishi-ku, Osaka, Japan

TELEPHONE:
Osaka 443-8051

CABLES:
Shipyard, Osaka

TELEX:
J 63376

WORKS:
Mizue-cho 4-1, Kawasaki-ku, Kawasaki City

TELEPHONE:
Kawasaki 288-1111

DIRECTORS AND EXECUTIVES:
Takao Nagata, President
Nobuo Inoue, Executive, Vice-President, General Manager of Shipbuilding Division (Sales Director)
Giichi Miyashita, Manager of Kanagawa Shipyard

Hitachi, the Supramar licencee in Japan, has been building PT 3, PT 20 and PT 50 hydrofoils since 1961. The majority of these have been built for fast passenger ferry services across the Japanese Inland Sea, cutting across deep bays which road vehicles might take two-to-three hours to drive round, and out to offshore islands. Other PT 20s and 50s have been exported to Hong Kong and Australia for ferry services.

Specifications of the PT 3, PT 20 and PT 50 will be found under Supramar (Switzerland). The Hitachi-built craft are identical apart from minor items.

In the spring of 1974, the company completed the first PT 50 Mk II to be built at its Kawasaki yard. The vessel Hikari 2, is powered by two licence-built MTU MB 820Db diesels, seats 123 passengers and cruises at 33 knots. It was delivered to its owner, Setonaikai Kisen Co. Ltd. of Hiroshima City in March 1975.

By the end of April 1976, Hitachi had built a total of twenty-five PT 50s and fourteen PT 20s.

A special military hydrofoil, based on the

Above: First PT 50 Mk. II to be completed is the Hikari 2, built by Hitachi Shipbuilding & Engineering Co. at its Kawasaki yard for Setonaikai Kisen Co. Ltd. The vessel, which carries 123 passengers and a crew of seven, is employed on the route Hiroshima-Imabari

Below: The second and third Hitachi-built PT 50 Mk. IIs, operated by Arimura Line

Schertel-Sachsenburg foil system, and designated PT 32, has been designed by the company and two are in service with the Philippine Navy.

POLAND

GDANSK SHIP RESEARCH INSTITUTE

ADDRESS:
Technical University, Gdansk
TELEPHONE:
41-47-12
DIRECTORS:
Prof. Dr. Lech Kobylinski

Research on problems connected with hydrofoil design and construction has been conducted by the Department of Theoretical Naval Architecture at Gdansk Technical University since 1956.

Experience with various dynamic test models led to the construction of the K-3 four-seat runabout which, powered by an FSC Lublin converted auto-engine, has a top speed of 27 knots (50 km/h).

In 1961 the Department was invited by the Central Board of Inland Navigation and United Inland Shipping and River Shipyards Gdansk, to design a hydrofoil passenger ferry for service in the Firth of Szczecin. Designated ZRYW-1 the craft seats 76 passengers and cruises at 35 knots. It was completed in 1965. A second craft, the W-2, intended for passenger services in the Baltic, is under development.

During 1966 the Ship Research Institute designed two hydrofoil sports craft, the WS-4 Amor and the WS-6 Eros. The prototypes were completed in 1967 and both types were put into series production during 1972.

In 1971, a catamaran-hulled research hydrofoil, the Badacz II, was built for the Ship Hydrodynamics Division of the Institute. The vessel is employed to tow models of ACVs and hydrofoils in coastal waters and provide data and performance measurements. It is also being employed to test new propulsion systems.

The largest hydrofoil craft to be designed by the Institute is a 300-ton passenger/car ferry.

Details of the ZRYW-1, Amor, Eros and Badacz II can be found in JSS 1974-75 and earlier editions.

SINGAPORE

VOSPER THORNYCROFT PRIVATE LTD, SUPRAMAR—LING HYDROFOIL DIVISION

HEAD OFFICE:
GPO Box 95, Singapore 1
TELEPHONE:
467144
TELEX:
RS 21219
CABLES:
Vosthorny Singapore
WORKS:
200 Tanjong Rhu, Singapore 15
DIRECTORS:
John Rix, Chairman
R. Du Cane, Managing Director
R. G. Bennett
G. E. Maynard

Prof. Yeoh Ghim Seng,
A. A. C. Griffith
S. N. Houghton
EXECUTIVES:
Poul Bakmand, Hydrofoil Sales

Vosper Thornycroft Private Limited, the Singapore subsidiary of the British warship design and construction specialists, is the sole builder in South East Asia of the Supramar range of hydrofoils. The parent company in the UK has an agreement with Supramar AG of Lucerne, Switzerland and the prototype PTS 75 Mk III has been built at the Portchester shipyard for Far East Hydrofoils, Hong Kong. The agreement in Singapore is between Vosper Thornycroft Private Ltd and Supramar-Ling Private Limited, a company established after the signing of a licence agreement between Supramar and Mr Charles Tow Siang Ling, a Singapore businessman.

The Supramar-Ling Division of Vosper Thornycroft Private is building PT 20s and PT 50s and marketing them jointly with Supramar-Ling Private. This is Vosper Thornycroft's first joint venture with a Singapore company and the first time any Singapore shipyard has built hydrofoils.

The vessels under construction are mainly for export. They will be used for high-speed passenger transport, logistic support and patrol duties. Details of the designs are given in this section under Supramar AG, Switzerland.

SWITZERLAND

SUPRAMAR AG

HEAD OFFICE:
Denkmalstrasse 2, 6006 Lucerne,
Switzerland
TELEPHONE:
(041) 36 96 36
TELEX:
78228
MANAGEMENT:
Hussain Najadi, Chairman
Ing. Volker Jost, Technical and Managing Director
Baron Hanns von Schertel, Technical Director
Dipl.-Ing. Ernst Jaksch, Design Manager
DESIGN:
Dipl.-Ing. Ernst Jaksch, Manager Foil Design Division
Dipl.-Ing. Georg Chvojka, Manager Marine Engineering Division
Ing. Vincent Schweizer, Manager Hull Design Division
Dipl.-Ing. Otto Münch, Manager Controls Division
RESEARCH AND DEVELOPMENT:
Baron Hanns von Schertel,
Dipl.-Ing. Eugen Schatté, Hydrodynamics and Propulsion

Supramar was founded in Switzerland in 1952 to develop on a commercial basis the hydrofoil system introduced by the Schertel-Sachsenberg Hydrofoil Syndicate and its licensee, the Gebruder Sachsenberg Shipyard.

The co-operation between the companies started in 1937 and led to the development of the VS6, a 17 ton hydrofoil, which in 1941 attained 47·5 knots, and the VS8 an 80-ton supply hydrofoil completed in 1943 which attained 41 knots. The inherently stable, rigid V-foil system used on these and subsequent Supramar vessels, stems from experimental work undertaken by Baron Hanns von Schertel between 1927-1937.

In May 1953, a Supramar PT 10, 32-passenger hydrofoil began the world's first regular passenger hydrofoil service on Lake Maggiore, between Switzerland and Italy. In August 1956, the first Rodriquez-built Supramar PT 20 opened a service across the Straits of Messina and became the first hydrofoil to be licenced by a marine classification authority for carrying passengers at sea.

Established originally as a research and design office, Supramar has recently been reorganised and will produce hydrofoils of its own design at shipyards independently of the arrangements with its licencees.

The Marketing Department provides, in addition to its normal marketing functions, consultancy service covering financing, leasing and operating.

Supramar employs a staff of over 20, mainly highly qualified scientists and engineers specialising in hydrodynamics, marine engineering, foil design, propulsion and shipyard production. In addition to building its own hydrofoils it licenses other shipyards to produce its hydrofoil designs.

Supramar hydrofoils being built by these companies are referred to elsewhere in this section under the respective company headings.

The latest Supramar design is the PTS 75 Mk III, a development of the PT 50 with increased engine power and full air stabilisation. The prototype was constructed by Vosper Thornycroft at the company's Portchester yard and delivered to Hong Kong in late 1974. The second vessel of this type was completed in early 1976 by Supramar's licensee in Hong Kong. The company has also completed designs for a modernised PT 50 which is available as the PT 50 Mk II. A new version of the PT 150 D, the PTS 150 Mk III, is being introduced with improved air stabilisation and a higher cruising speed. Supramar is now concentrating on the development of second generation hydrofoils with improved performance and greater passenger comfort.

The company is also developing a fully submerged foil system with air stabilisation. First craft to use this system is the Supramar ST 3A, a 4·9 ton experimental boat built under a US Navy contract. During tests in the Mediterranean it demonstrated promising stability and seakeeping qualities and reached a speed of 54·5 knots. Supramar has

completed the design of a patrol boat hydrofoil which meets the tactical requirements of the NATO navies. The vessel, the MT 250G, has an operational displacement of 250 tons and a maximum intermittent speed of 60 knots.

PT 20 Mk 11

The PT 20 Mk 11, a 27-ton boat for 72 passengers, is considered by Supramar to be the smallest size hydrofoil suitable for passenger-carrying coastal services. The first of this very successful series was built by the Rodriquez shipyard at Messina in 1955 and since then nearly 70 PT 20s of various types have been built in Sicily, Japan, Holland and Norway. The design has been approved by almost every classification society. Fast patrol boat variants are also available.

FOILS: Foils are of standard Schertel-Sachsenberg, surface-piercing type, with 58% of the load supported by the bow foil and the remaining 42% by the rear foil. Submerged foil area in foilborne condition is 5·50 m². Together with the struts and a horizontal guide, each foil forms a uniform framework which facilitates the exchange of the foil elements. The medium steel foils are of partly hollow, welded construction. The angle of incidence of the bow foil can be adjusted within narrow limits from the steering stand by means of a hydraulic ram operating on a foil support across the hull. To counteract the effects of large variations in passenger load and to ensure optimum behaviour in sea waves the angle of attack

A Supramar PT 20 built by Hitachi Shipbuilding & Engineering Co Ltd

can be adjusted during operation.

HULL: The hull has a V-bottom with an externally added step riveted into place. Frames, bulkheads, foundations, superstructure and all internal construction is in corrosion-proof light alloy. Platings are of AlMg 5 and the frames, bars and other members are made in AlMgSi. Watertight compartments are provided below the passenger decks and in other parts of the hull.

POWER PLANT: Power is supplied by a supercharged, 12-cylinder MTU 12V 493 TY 70 diesel with an exhaust turbo-compressor. Maximum continuous output is 1,100 hp at 1,400 rpm. A BW 800/HS 20 reversible gear, developed by Zahnradfabrik Friedrichshafen AG, is placed between the engine and the drive shaft.

ACCOMMODATION: The boat is controlled entirely from the bridge which is located above the engine room. Forty-six passengers are accommodated in the forward cabin, twenty in the rear compartment and six aft of the pilot's stand in the elevated wheel-

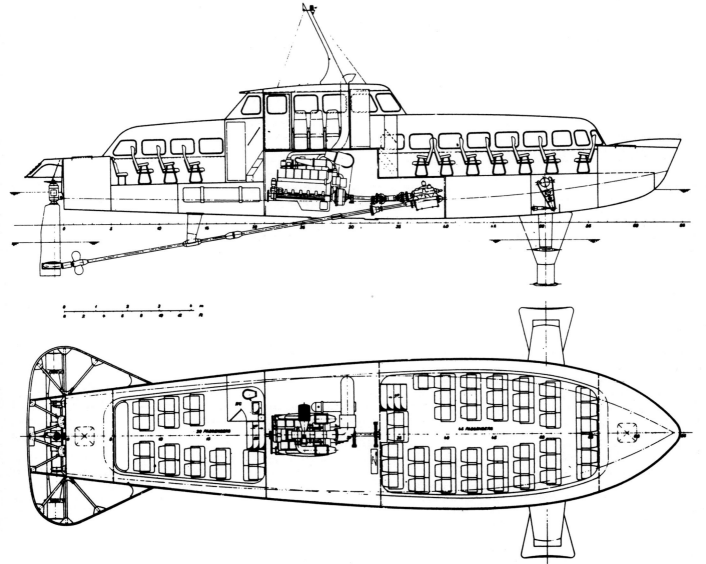

Inboard and outboard profiles and main deck plan of the Supramar PT 20

house. There is an emergency exit in each passenger compartment, and the craft is equipped with an inflatable life raft and life belts for each person. A crew of four is carried.

SYSTEMS:

ELECTRICAL: 24 volt generator driven by the main engine; batteries with a capacity of approx 250 Ah.

HYDRAULICS: 120 kg/cm² pressure hydraulic system for rudder and bow foil incidence control.

COMMUNICATIONS AND NAVIGATION: VHF ship-shore radio is supplied as standard equipment. Radar is optional.

DIMENSIONS, EXTERNAL:

Length overall, hull	68·07 ft (20·75 m)
Length over deck	67·50 ft (19·95 m)
Hull beam, max	16·37 ft (4·99 m)
Width across foils	26·39 ft (8·07 m)
Draft hullborne	10·10 ft (3·08 m)
Draft foilborne	4·59 ft (1·40 m)

DIMENSIONS, INTERNAL:

Aft cabin (inc toilet)	145 sq ft (13·5 m²)
Volume	954 cu ft (27·0 m³)
Forward cabin	280 sq ft (26·0 m²)
Volume	1,766 cu ft (50·0 m³)
Main deck level (inc wheelhouse)	129 sq ft (12·0 m²)
Volume	847 cu ft (24·0 m³)

WEIGHTS:

Gross tonnage	approx 56 tons
Max take-off displacement	32 tons
Light displacement	25 tons
Deadweight (inc fuel, oil, water, passengers, baggage and crew)	7 tons
Payload	5·4 tons

PERFORMANCE (with normal payload):

Cruising speed, foilborne 34 knots (63 km/h)

Max permissible wave height in foilborne mode   4·25 ft (1·29 m)

Designed range at cruising speed
216 nautical miles (400 km)

Turning radius	427 ft approx (130 m)
Take-off distance	493 ft approx (150 m)
Take-off time	25 sec
Stopping distance	230 ft (70 m)

Fuel consumption at cruising speed 150 kg/h

SEA TEST: Prototype tests were undertaken in the Mediterranean in every kind of sea condition, and further tests have taken place off Japan. Acceleration measurements have shown maximum values below 0·5g when accelerometer had been fitted above the bow foil. Maximum lateral acceleration was 0·32g. Measurements were made in wave heights of approx 1·2 to 1·5 m. These are the maximum measurements obtained and subsequent tests have seldom equalled these figures.

PT 20B Mk 11

In this model of the PT 20, the engine room and bridge are arranged in the foreship. This improves the pilot's vision in waters likely to have an influx of driftwood and provides a large main passenger cabin with seats for 55 and an upper deck cabin with seating for 16 passengers.

The layout of this craft has been based on experience gained with the Supramar PT 27 which was designed for servicing the offshore drilling platforms on Lake Maracaibo. This design has been slightly modified to meet the requirements of passenger services.

FOILS: The foil design is similar to that of the PT 20 Mk 11. About 66% of the total weight is borne by the bow foil and 34% by the rear foil. Submerged foil area in foilborne condition is 6·2 m². The forward foil

A Supramar PT 20B

can be tilted within narrow limits by means of a hydraulic ram acting on the foil strut supporting tube. The angle of attack can therefore be adjusted during operation to assist take-off and to counteract the effect of large variations in passenger loads.

HULL: This is of riveted light metal alloy design and framed on a combination of longitudinal and transverse formers. Watertight compartments are provided below the passenger decks and in other parts of the hull, and some are filled with foam-type plastic.

POWER PLANT: Power is supplied by a supercharged 12 cyl MTU 12V 493 TY 70 diesel with a max continuous output of 1,100 hp at 1,400 rpm. Average time between major overhauls is approx 10,000 hours. Engine output is transferred to a 3-bladed 700 mm diameter bronze subcavitating propeller through a BW 800/H 20 reversible gear made by Zahnradfabrik. The propeller shaft is supported at three points by seawater lubricated rubber bearings.

ACCOMMODATION: The PT 20B Mk 11 has a crew of 4 and seats 71 passengers. The main passenger compartment seats 55, and the small cabin behind the pilot's stand seats a further 16. Access to the main compartment is through either of two doors, located port and starboard, to the rear of the wheelhouse. An emergency exit is provided at the rear of the main passenger compartment.

The PT 20B Mk 2 can also be delivered with fully integrated air conditioning equipment. The total passenger capacity will then be reduced to 69.

A full range of safety equipment is carried, including inflatable rafts and lifebelts for each passenger and crew member.

SYSTEMS:

ELECTRICAL: 24 volt generator driven by the main engine, batteries with a capacity of approx 250 Ah.

HYDRAULICS: 120 kg/cm² pressure hydraulic system for operating rudder and bow

foil angle of incidence control.

COMMUNICATIONS AND NAVIGATION: A vhf ship-shore radio is supplied as standard equipment. Radar is an optional extra.

DIMENSIONS, EXTERNAL:

Length overall, hull	68·40 ft (24·16 m)
Length over deck	63·98 ft (19·15 m)
Hull beam, max	16·93 ft (5·16 m)
Width over foils	28·22 ft (8·60 m)
Draft hullborne	9·84 ft (3·00 m)
Draft foilborne	4·27 ft (1·30 m)

DIMENSIONS, INTERNAL:

Main passenger compartment (inc toilet)	
Length	30 ft 7 in (9·3 m)
Width	12 ft 6 in (3·8 m)
Height	6 ft 7 in (2·0 m)
Floor area	237 sq ft (22·1 m²)
Volume	1,553 cu ft (44·0 m³)

WEIGHT:

Gross tonnage	50 tons, app
Max take-off displacement	32·5 tons
Light displacement	25·4 tons
Deadweight (inc fuel, oil, water, passengers, luggage, crew)	7·5 tons
Payload	5·8 tons

PERFORMANCE (with normal payload):

Cruising speed	34 knots (63 km/h)
Max permissible wave height in foilborne mode	4·25 ft (1·29 m)
Turning radius	426 ft (app 130 m)
Take-off distance	492 ft (app 150 m)
Take-off time	app 30 sec
Stopping distance	231 ft (app 70 m)
Stopping time	app 10 sec

Fuel consumption at cruising speed 150 kg/h

PTL 28

The PTL 28 is derived from the PT 27 utility and oil rig supply vessel, three of which have been in service for more than ten years with the Shell Oil Company on Maracaibo Lake, Venezuela.

Features of the new craft include facilities for loading across the bow as well as the stern, twin rudders for improved -man-

A Supramar PTL 28 employed by Shell for servicing offshore oil platforms on Lake Maracaibo, Venezuela

oeuvrability, and a variety of structural and mechanical modifications to simplify and reduce maintenance. The Schottel drive now has only two bevel gears, the hull is of welded construction, and the foil and propeller mounting arrangements have been redesigned to facilitate servicing. All components of a non-essential nature have been omitted.

Normally seats are provided for 54, but the number of passengers can be increased if the range is reduced. The weather deck above the engine room is available for cargo; heavy loads are compensated by a reduction in passenger capacity. A cargo compartment can be made available at the rear of the passenger cabin (up to frame 17), a typical load being 4,023 lb (1,825 kg) of cargo combined with 33 passengers.

FOILS: Schertel-Sachsenburg surface-piercing system similar to that of the PT 20

Mk 11. Bow foil of hollow welded stainless steel. Foil, vertical struts, inclined fins and horizontal supporting tube form a framed structure which can easily be detached when necessary. The complete assembly divides into two to facilitate transport. Once the angle of incidence is adjusted no further alteration is necessary.

The rear foil is similar to the bow foil in type and construction. The complete system is mounted on its bearings at the transom by four bolts.

HULL: Constructed in seawater-resistant light metal alloy, the V-bottomed hull is of hard chine type and framed longitudinally. All joints are welded. Hoist fittings are provided to facilitate maintenance.

POWER PLANT: Power is supplied by a 12-cylinder MTU 12V493 TY70 diesel, rated at 1,000 hp at 1,400 rpm continuous and 1,350 hp at 1,500 rpm maximum.

Engine output is transferred to a 3-bladed bronze propeller through a Zahnradfabrik BW 800 H20 reverse gearbox. Hullborne propulsion is provided by a 150 hp diesel engine directly coupled to a Schottel Z-drive unit which can be rotated through 360°. During take-off and when foilborne, the lower bevel gear and hullborne propeller are retracted hydraulically into a recess in the hull bottom.

ACCOMMODATION: The PTL 28 has a crew of three and seats 54 passengers in a single saloon aft of the engine room. The bridge is located forward and provides a 360° view. The captain's seat, together with the operating controls and instrumentation, is located on the hull centreline.

DIMENSIONS, EXTERNAL:

Length overall, hull	68·07 ft (20·75 m)
Length over deck	67·50 ft (19·95 m)
Hull beam, max	16·37 ft (4·99 m)

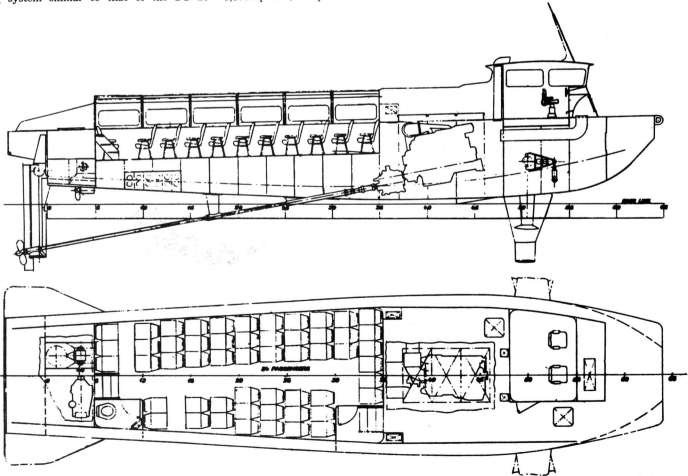

Inboard profile and passenger deck plan of the Supramar PTL 28 utility craft and supply vessel

Width over foils	26·25 ft (8·00 m)
Draft hullborne	9·68 ft (2·95 m)
Draft foilborne	4·92 ft (1·50 m)

WEIGHTS:
Displacement fully loaded

	27·56 tons (28·00 t)
Disposable load	5·51 tons (5·60 t)
Light displacement	22·05 tons (22·40 t)

PERFORMANCE:

Speed max	39·00 knots (72·00 km/h)
Speed cruising	35·00 knots (65·00 km/h)
Range	140 nm approx (260 km)

PT 50 Mk II

The successful and profitable operation of the PT 20 led to the development of the PT 50, a 63-ton hydrofoil passenger ferry designed for offshore and inter-island services. The prototype was completed early in 1958, and more than thirty are now operating regular passenger services in areas ranging from the Baltic and Mediterranean to the Japanese Inland Sea.

The craft has been approved by almost every Classification Society including Registro Italiano Navale, Germanischer Lloyd, Det Norske Veritas, American Bureau of Shipping and the Japanese Ministry of Transport. The requirements of the SOLAS 1960 convention for international traffic can be met by the type if required.

FOILS: Both rear and forward foils are rigidly attached to the hull but the lift of the forward foil can be modified by hydraulically operated flaps, which are fitted to assist take-off and turning, and for making slight course corrections and adjustment of the flying height. The foils are of hollow construction using fine grain and MSt 52·3 steel throughout. Foils in stainless steel construction are optional.

The bow foil comprises the following elements:

Two fins, forming connecting links between the foil and the supporting structure which is riveted to the hull.

The hydrofoil which (according to its foil section characteristics) generates the lift and, with the stern foil, provides transverse stability in foilborne conditions.

Two struts, which transmit the main lift loads to the supporting structure.

The rear foil system comprises the following elements: the hydrofoil, which generates the lift, two side struts, and the single rudder which transmits the lift to the supporting structure.

For improved passenger comfort the PT 50 Mk 11 can be provided with a roll stabiliser on the bow foil. The system, including the motion sensing device, has been developed by Supramar.

HULL: Of hard chine construction, the hull is of partly riveted, partly welded light metal alloy design and framed on longitudinal and transverse formers. Steel is used only for highly stressed parts such as the foil fittings, and the shaft brackets and exits.

ACCOMMODATION: The PT 50 Mk II is available in three interior configurations:

1. For 111 passengers including bar and catering facilities.
2. Standard version, with seats for 122 passengers.
3. Commuter version, seating 136 passengers.

The crew varies from 6-8 members, depending mainly on local regulations.

Passenger seats are of lightweight aircraft type and the centre aisle between the seat

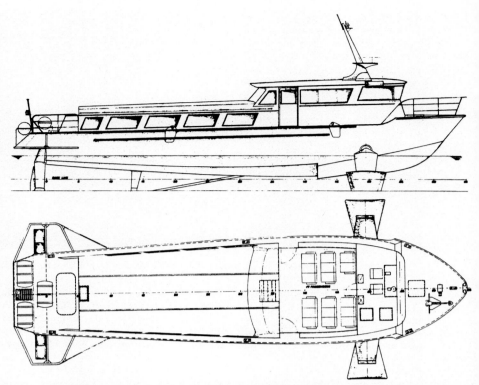

Supramar PT 20B Mk II. *Above:* Outboard profile and plan. *Below:* Inboard profile and passenger deck

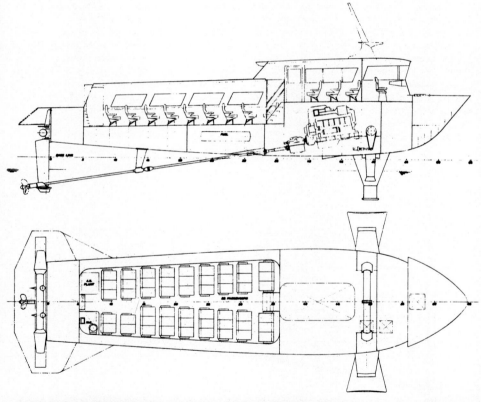

Guia, a Hitachi-built PT 50 which has been in regular service with Far East Hydrofoil Co Ltd, on the 36 km Hong Kong-Macao route for more than 10 years

rows has a clear width of 30 in (0·76 m). Ceilings are covered with lightweight plastic material and the walls, including web frames, are clad in luxury plywood or artificial wood. Toilets are provided in the rear and forward passenger spaces. Floors in the passenger compartments are provided with thick carpets. Each passenger compartment has an emergency exit. Inflatable life rafts and lifebelts are provided for 110% of the passenger and crew capacity.

POWER PLANT: The craft is powered by two MTU 12V 331 TC 71 turbocharged diesels, each developing 1,100 hp at 2,140 rpm continuous. Engine output is transmitted to two 3-bladed 700 mm diameter bronze propellers through two inclined stainless steel propeller shafts, each supported at four points by seawater lubricated runner bearings. Reverse and reduction gear with built-in thrust is manufactured by Zahnradfabrik Friedrichshafen, Germany. The reverse clutches are solenoid-operated from the bridge.

Eight cylindrical fuel tanks with a total capacity of 3,650 litres are located in the aft peak and below the tank deck. Oil capacity is 320 litres.

SYSTEMS, ELECTRICAL: Engine driven generator; 24 volt battery set.

HYDRAULICS: 120 kg/cm² pressure hydraulic system for operating twin rudders and front foil flaps.

AIR CONDITIONING: Air conditioning can be provided as optional equipment.

COMMUNICATIONS AND NAVIGATION: Standard equipment includes UHF and VHF radio telephone. Radar and Decca Navigator is optional.

DIMENSIONS, EXTERNAL:

Length overall	91·00 ft (27·75 m)
Length over deck	86·60 ft (26·40 m)
Hull beam max	19·15 ft (5·84 m)
Beam over deck	17·91 ft (5·46 m)
Width over foils	35·40 ft (10·80 m)
Draft hullborne	11·66 ft (3·55 m)
Draft foilborne	5·08 ft (1·55 m)

DIMENSIONS, INTERNAL:

Aft passenger compartment (inc toilet):

Length	29 ft 7 in (9·0 m)
Width	16 ft 0 in (4·9 m)
Height	6 ft 7 in (2·0 m)
Floor area	474 sq ft (44·1 m²)
Volume	3,108 cu ft (88·0 m³)

Forward passenger compartment (inc toilet):

Length	23 ft 3½ in (7·1 m)
Width	17 ft 9 in (5·4 m)
Height	6 ft 7 in (2·0 m)
Floor area	412 sq ft (37·3 m²)
Volume	2,703 cu ft (67·6 m³)

Main deck foyer:

Length	12 ft 9½ in (3·9 m)
Width	13 ft 1¼ in (4·0 m)
Height	6 ft 7 in (2·0 m)
Floor area	161 sq ft (15·0 m²)
Volume	2,030 cu ft (57·6 m³)

WEIGHTS:

Max take-off displacement	63·3 tons
Light displacement	49·3 tons
Deadweight (inc fuel, oil, water, passengers, baggage and crew)	14·0 tons
Payload	9·5 tons

PERFORMANCE (with normal payload):

Max speed foilborne	36·5 knots (67·5 km/h)
Cruising speed foilborne	34·0 knots (63 km/h)
Range	325 nm (600 km)
Turning radius	1,542 ft (470 m)
Take-off distance	819 ft (250 m)
Take-off time	35 sec

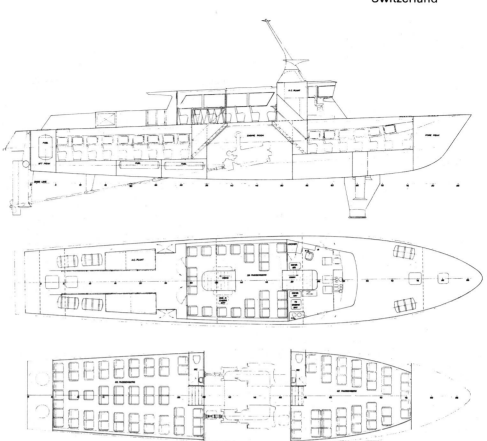

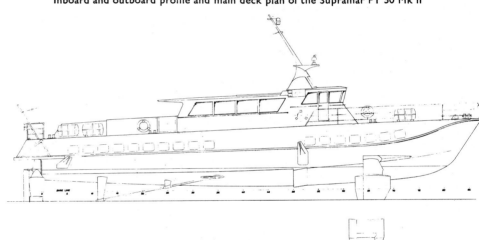

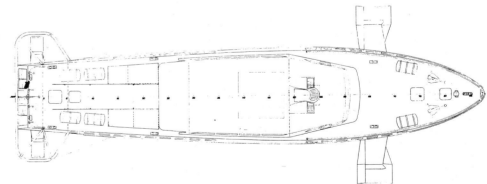

Inboard and outboard profile and main deck plan of the Supramar PT 50 Mk II

Stopping distance	264 ft (80 m)
Time to stop craft	10 sec
Fuel consumption at cruising speed	710 lb/h (300 kg/h)

PTS 75 Mk III

The Supramar PTS 75 Mk III is an advanced derivative of the PT 50. It seats up to 160 passengers and is designed for higher speed, improved seaworthiness and greater riding comfort. By increasing the specific PT 50 engine power of 43 hp/t to 50 hp/t a top speed of about 38 knots is obtained with the vessel fully loaded, and sufficient power is provided for operation in tropical waters.

An improved Schertel-Supramar air stabilisation system is fitted, and this, combined with a new W-foil configuration, considerably reduces rolling, pitching and vertical accelerations. The vessel can operate foilborne in waves up to 6 ft (1·82 m) in height with full power.

The prototype was completed at the Vosper Thornycroft, Paulsgrove, Portsmouth yard in May 1974. The second craft of this type was completed in early 1976 by Supramar's licencee in Hong Kong—Supramar Pacific Shipbuilding Co Ltd.

FOILS: The foil configuration is surface piercing and incorporates the Schertel-Supramar air stabilisation system. The bow foil assembly forms a rigid framework which facilitates the exchange of the foil structure. The foil is of hollow steel construction. It has three supporting struts, one on the centre line and one on either side. These are bolted to welded steel suspension points on the keel and chine respectively. Hydraulically operated flaps are fitted to the trailing edges to assist take-off, facilitate course corrections and provide automatic stabilisation when low frequency disturbances are encountered.

The rear foil is of surface-piercing Schertel-Supramar type and attached to the transom. Method of construction is the same as that employed for the bow foil. The complete assembly—foil, rudder sternpost, rudder, and two inclined struts—forms a rigid frame unit which is attached or detached as necessary. The aftermost propeller bearings are attached to the foil, the propellers being sited aft of the foil.

HULL: Hard chine type, constructed in partly riveted, partly welded corrosion resistant light metal alloy. A longitudinal frame system is employed, with transverse frames 900 mm apart. Steel is used only for highly stressed parts such as the foil fittings and shaft exits. A new hull construction method is being employed for this design. The hull is built in the inverted position and turned upright after the plating is completed.

ACCOMMODATION: Depending on operating requirements, between 130 and 160 passengers can be accommodated in three saloons. In the standard version airliner type seats are provided for 135 passengers, 19 in the upper aft saloon, 61 in the lower aft saloon and 55 in the lower forward saloon.

Ceilings are covered with lightweight plastic material, walls including web frames, are clad in luxury ply or artificial wood, and the floors are provided with thick carpets.

Three toilets are installed on the upper deck, within easy reach of all three saloons.

Passengers board the craft through wide side doors on the upper deck opening to a central foyer from which companionways lead to the lower passenger saloons. A promenade deck is available aft of the upper saloon and can be reached by passengers from the lower saloons via the foyer. Sufficient space for luggage is provided in the foyer. The upper aft saloon can be modified into a small dining room, if required, reducing the passenger capacity by 19.

All passenger saloons have emergency exits. A lifebelt is stowed beneath each seat and most of the inflatable life rafts are stowed aft and on the forward main deck.

POWER PLANT: Power is supplied by two 12 cylinder, MTU MB12 V652 SB70 supercharged diesels, each with a normal continuous output of 1,650 hp at 1,380 rpm, and 1,950 hp at 1,460 rpm maximum. Under tropical conditions normal continuous rating is 1,590 hp at 1,380 rpm and 1,810 hp at 1,460 rpm maximum. Engine output is transferred to two 3 ft 1⅜ in (950 mm) diameter 3-bladed bronze propellers through a Zahnradfabrik BW 900 HS 15 reversible gearbox, which is hydraulically operated and

The second Supramar PTS 75 Mk III to be ordered by Far East Hydrofoil Co. for the Hong Kong-Macao service. The vessel was built in Hong Kong by Supramar Pacific Shipbuilding Co. Ltd.

remotely controlled from the wheelhouse. The propeller shafts are in stainless steel and supported at four points by seawater lubricated rubber bearings. Fuel is carried in integral tanks beneath the lower deck in the bottom compartments.

SYSTEMS, ELECTRICAL: Two 37 KVA water-cooled 60 c/s diesel-driven 380 V generators installed in the engine room. An emergency generator of similar capacity is provided at main deck level.

HYDRAULICS: 120 kg/cm² pressure hydraulic system for operating all hydraulic driven consumers.

AIR CONDITIONING: An air conditioning system is provided. Capacity is sufficient for adequate temperature and humidity conditions in all passenger saloons and on the bridge when operating the craft in tropical conditions.

COMMUNICATIONS AND NAVIGATION: UHF radio, VHF radio-telephone and magnetic compass are standard. Radar, Decca Navigator and gyro compass to customer's requirements.

DIMENSIONS, EXTERNAL:

Length overall, hull	98·5 ft (30·0 m)
Length overall, deck	96·0 ft (29·2 m)
Hull beam max	19·1 ft (5·8 m)
Width across foils	38·1 ft (11·6 m)
Draft afloat	13·1 ft (4·0 m)
Draft foilborne	6·7 ft (1·96 m)

DIMENSIONS, INTERNAL (Standard version)

Aft lower saloon:	
Length	9·0 m
Width	4·6 m
Height	2·15 m
Floor area	42·0 m²
Volume	92·0 m³
Forward lower saloon:	
Length	8·1 m
Width	4·7 m
Height	2·15 m
Floor area	37·0 m²
Volume	82·0 m³
Upper aft saloon:	
Length	4·5 m
Width	4·2 m
Height	2·1 m
Floor area	18·0 m²
Volume	38·0 m³
Foyer	
Length	5·1 m
Width	4·2 m
Height	2·1 m
Floor area	20 m²

Volume	42 m³

WEIGHTS:

Max take-off displacement	85·0 tons
Light displacement	68·5 tons
Disposable load	16·5 tons
(incl fuel, oil, water, passengers luggage and crew)	

PERFORMANCE (with normal payload):

Cruising speed	36·0 knots (66·5 km/h)
Max speed	39·0 knots (72·5 km/h)
Range	180 nm
Turning radius approx	2,350 ft (700 m)
Take-off distance approx	1,600 ft (500 m)
Take-off time approx	50 sec
Stopping distance approx	330 ft (100 m)
Time to stop the craft approx	20 sec
Fuel consumption at cruising speed	approx 600 kg/h

SUPRAMAR PT 100

A variant of the PTS 75 Mk III is the PT 100, designed especially for short-haul commuter routes and accommodating 200 passengers.

Main dimensions and characteristics are identical to those of the PTS 75 Mk III. The layout is shown in the accompanying general arrangement drawing.

SUPRAMAR PTS 150 Mk III

The Supramar PTS 150 Mk III carries 250 passengers and is the world's largest seagoing hydrofoil. The vessels fulfil SOLAS requirements, and have been built under the supervision of Det Norske Veritas, which has granted the class designation IA2-Hydrofoil-K.

FOILS: The foil configuration is a combined surface piercing and submerged system. The bow foil, which provides the necessary static transverse stability, is of the Schertel-Sachsenburg surface-piercing V design and carries 6% of the load. The rear foil, which bears about 40% is of the submerged, Schertel-Subramar air-stabilised type. In foilborne conditions the boat is inherently stable.

Hydraulically-actuated flaps are fitted at the trailing edges of the bow foil to assist take-off and adjust the flying height.

The rear foil is fully submerged.

Air stabilisation is fitted to the rear foil which gives the necessary transverse and longitudinal stability and improves passenger comfort under heavy sea conditions. Separate port and starboard systems are installed

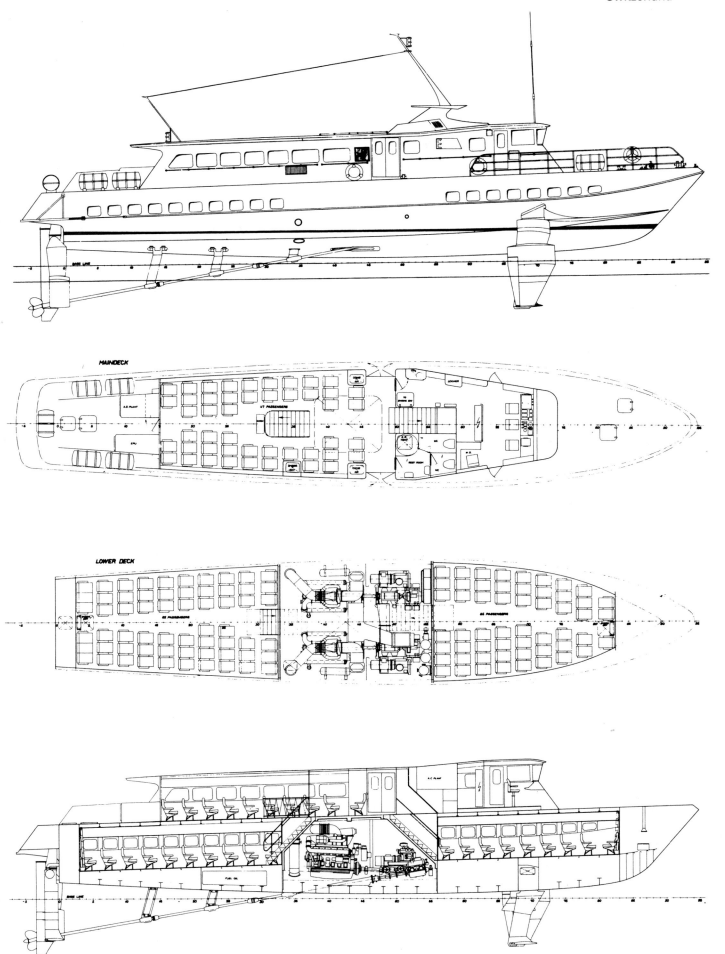

Inboard and outboard profiles and deck views of the Supramar PTS 75 Mk III

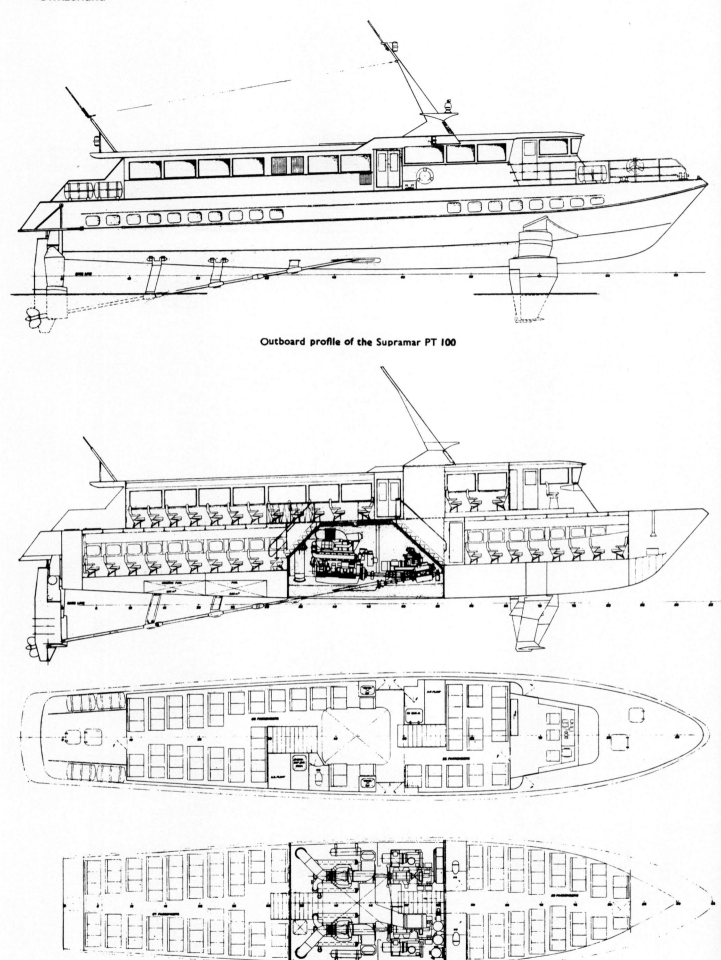

Outboard profile of the Supramar PT 100

Inboard profile and deck plans of the Supramar PT 100, a short-haul commuter
version of the PTS 75 Mk III, accommodating 200 passengers

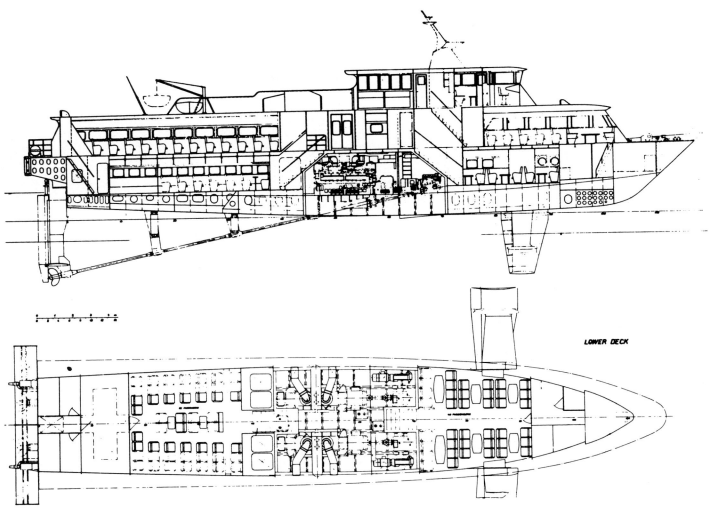

LOWER DECK

Inboard and outboard profiles, main deck and lower deck arrangements of the PT 150 Mk III

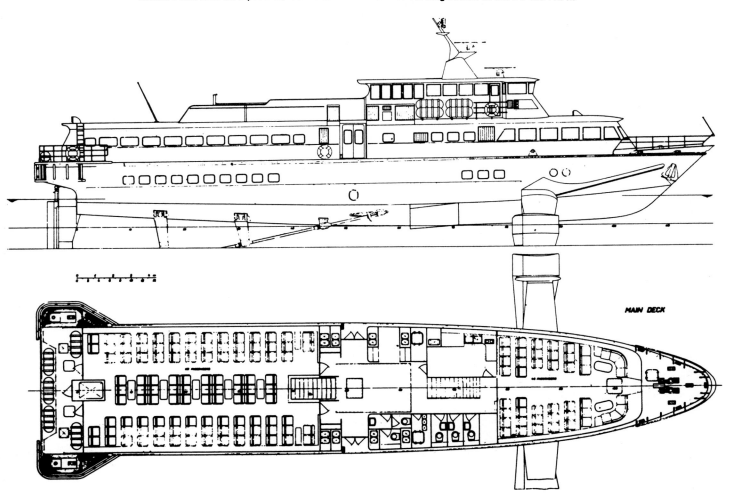

MAIN DECK

to stabilise rolling and pitching.

The system feeds air from the free atmosphere through air exits to the foil upper surface (the low pressure region) decreasing the lift. The amount to lift is varied by the quantity of air admitted, this being controlled by a valve actuated by signals from a damped pendulum and a rate gyro. The stabilising moment is produced by decreasing the available air volume for the more submerged side and increasing that of the less submerged one.

The rear foil includes the lift-generating sections, rudders and the rear suspension structure which serves as a connecting element with the hull. Struts for the aftermost propeller bearings are also attached to the rear foil, the propellers being sited beneath the foil. The complete assembly is a framed structure which can easily be detached from the transom. The angle of attack of the rear foil can be controlled hydraulically both during take-off and when foilborne.

The surface piercing bow foil is provided with air exits on the upper surface (the low pressure region) in order to vary lift and control pitch and heave motions by the quantity of air admitted. This is released by a valve which is actuated by amplified signals taken from a vertical accelerometer and a rate sensor.

Front and rear foil are of hollow construction and by the extensive use of welding, the number of connecting parts requiring screws, bolts or similar means of attachment is reduced to a minimum.

HULL: Partly riveted and partly welded construction and a system of longitudinal and transverse frames has been adopted. It has fairly high deadrise and hard chine sections for performance as a planing hull and for structural impacts in a seaway while foilborne. A step is provided to facilitate take-off. While the main or structure deck is continuous from bow to stern, the lower deck is interrupted by the engine room, sited amidships. The superstructure, which is also longitudinally and transversally framed, is not included in the load bearing structure. Several expansion joints have therefore been provided.

ACCOMMODATION: The PTS 150 Mk III carries 250 passengers in four saloons, two on the main deck and two on the lower deck. The forward compartment main deck, seats 48, and the aft compartment 110. On the lower deck the forward compartment seats 40 and the aft compartment 52.

Passengers board the craft through double doors to the single centralised foyer, from which doors and companion ladders lead to the respective passenger saloons on the upper and lower decks.

Provision is made for all passengers to be served in their seats with cold meals and drinks as in an airliner.

Passenger seats are of lightweight aircraft type. Floors and ceilings are covered with lightweight plastic materials and the walls are clad in luxury plywood. Each passenger saloon has fitted carpets. Each room has an independent ventilation unit. Six toilets are provided.

The bridge, which is on a separate level above the main deck, slightly forward of midships, is reached by a companion ladder at the aft of the forward passenger compartment. All passenger saloons have emergency exits.

The craft carries 12 inflatable RFD liferafts (for 110% of the classified number of

Interior of the PT 150 DC showing the forward saloon on the upper deck and, *below*, the aft saloon on the upper deck seen from the rear

passengers and crew) which are stowed along both sides of the superstructure deck, and on the aft maindeck. Lifebelts are arranged beneath the seats.

POWER PLANT: Power is supplied by two 20-cylinder MTU MD 20V 538 TB8 supercharged and intercooled diesels each rated at 3,400 hp continuous. To improve torque characteristics during take-off two engine-mounted Maybach torque converters are provided.

Reverse and reduction gears are of the lightweight Zahnradfabrik BW 1500HS22 hydraulically-operated type, and incorporate the propeller thrust bearings. They have three shafts and two gear trains, one of which has an idler. The output shafts rotate either in the same direction as the input shaft or the opposite direction, depending upon the gear through which power is directed. Selection is by pneumo-hydraulic double-plate clutches on the input shafts. A mechanical lock-up is provided so that the gear can transmit full torque in the event of clutch slip while in service. This takes the form of a dog clutch which is effective in one direction, and can only be engaged in the "stop" condition. The gearboxes each have integral oil pumps for lubrication and clutch operation.

The angle between the engine crankshaft and the parallel shaft of the gearbox is accommodated by a cardan shaft with universal joints. The converter gear main shaft bearings, as well as those on the reverse

gear primary shaft, are proportioned in such a way as to resist the forces and couples imposed by the cardan shaft universal joints. As a protection against accidents the cardan shaft is installed within a substantial removable tunnel.

SYSTEMS, ELECTRICAL: The total electrical system is supplied by three diesel generators with an output of 65 KVA each, one of them being an emergency generator installed on the upper deck.

In the event of an electrical failure the emergency generator is switched on automatically. The engines are started by fresh air and are fresh-water cooled. The following systems are supplied by the electrical plant. For power and permanently installed heating and cooling equipment: 380 V rotary current, 50 cps. For light, pockets and instrumentation: 220 V ac, 50 cps. For remote control and monitoring 24 V ac.

HYDRAULICS: Steering, variation of the front foil flap angle and the angle of attack of the rear foil are all operated hydraulically. Each system has its own circuit which is monitored by a pressure controlled pilot lamp.

CONTROL: Starting, manoeuvring and operation of the craft is controlled from the bridge, but in cases of emergency the main engines may be controlled from the engine room.

The two main engines are each controlled

by an operating lever designed for single-handed control. Propeller reversal is also by means of these levers, the reverse gear being actuated by pneumatic remote control between bridge and main engines.

To start the boat both operating levers must be put in the "full ahead" position simultaneously. The engine mounted torque converter gear is actuated automatically. Foilborne speed can be regulated by fine adjusting of the operating levers. No other control devices are necessary for the main engines.

Levers for variation of the front foil flap angle and the angle of attack of the rear foil are actuated only before and after starting. During foilborne operation these can be used for trim compensation. All instrumentation and monitoring equipment is installed on the bridge.

AIR CONDITIONING: The vessel is equipped with air conditioning and heating plant which guarantees a room temperature of between 20 and 25°C, dependent upon the relative humidity. Air rate is 25 m³/h, person.

COMMUNICATION AND NAVIGATION: Standard navigation equipment includes a gyro master compass with transformers, rectifiers and one multiple steering repeater positioned ahead of the helmsman, Loran or Decca Navigator and radar.

Communications equipment includes radio telephone equipment for normal and emergency use.

DIMENSIONS, EXTERNAL:

Length overall, hull	124·2 ft (37·9 m)
Length overall, deck	121·8 ft (37·10 m)
Hull beam, max	24·6 ft (7·50 m)
Deck beam, max	24·2 ft (7·40 m)
Width across foils	52·45 ft (16·0 m)
Draft afloat	18 ft (5·5 m)
Draft foilborne	8·5 ft (2·6 m)

WEIGHTS:

Displacement, fully loaded	165 tons
Disposable load (payload plus consumable stores)	23 tons
Passenger capacity	250

PERFORMANCE:

Cruising speed at 6,880 hp	36·5 knots (67·5 km/h)
Range	250 nm (400 km)
Max permissible wave height in foilborne mode at full power (head seas) for passenger acceptability	10 ft (3·0 m)

ST 3A FULLY SUBMERGED FOIL RESEARCH CRAFT

In 1965 the US Navy awarded Supramar a contract for the construction and testing of a 5-ton research craft with fully submerged air stabilised foils. The objectives of the tests were the investigation of the effectiveness and reliability of the Schertel-Supramar air stabilisation system under a variety of wave conditions.

FOIL SYSTEM: The craft was fitted with two fully submerged bow foils and one fully submerged rear foil. The load distribution was 62% on the bow foils and 38% on rear foil. A rudder flap was attached to the end of the rear foil strut.

AIR FEED SYSTEM: Lift variation was achieved without movable foil parts. Each foil has two air ducts with outlets on the suction side. Air was drawn through these apertures from the free atmosphere via the foil suspension tube and the hollow struts. Air valves, controlled by sensors, governed the quantity of air admitted to the respective ducts.

A PT 150D operating in the Baltic

Supramar ST 3A

CONTROLS: The signals of a depth sensor, a rate gyro and damped pendulum were added and amplified. The pneumatic follow-up amplifier drew its propulsion power from the subpressure which was produced at a suction opening at the strut near the foil. The amplifier output was connected with the air valve. The depth sensor probed the submergence depth digitally by means of suction orifices at the front struts. No motor-driven power source was required for the control system which, as well as the air feed system for lift variation of the foils, was designed for simplicity and reliability.

HULL: The hull, of hard chine construction, was basically that of a standard Supramar ST 3, modified to accommodate the new foil system, gas-turbine and test equipment. To facilitate take-off, a step was provided and a ram wedge was fastened to the stern bottom. The hull clearance (tip of step to water surface) of only 1 ft 2½ in (0·36 m) was due to the requirement that an existing ST 3 hull, with an inclined propeller shaft, was to be used for the tests.

POWER PLANT: The craft was powered by a single 1,000 hp GE 7 LM100 PG 102 gas-turbine. Engine output was transferred to 1 ft 3 in (0·38 m) diameter S-C bronze propeller through a reduction gear, a Vee-drive and an inclined stainless steel shaft. A 35 hp Mercury outboard was installed on the port side of the transom to provide auxiliary propulsion. To feed the stabilisation gyros a 6 hp gasoline engine was installed in the forepeak and coupled to a 3-phase ac generator.

DIMENSIONS:

Length overall (hull)	33 ft 10 in (10·32 m)
Breadth over foils	11 ft 10 in (3·6 m)
Breadth over hull	8 ft 10 in (2·7 m)

Draft hullborne	5 ft 1 in (1·55 m)
Draft foilborne (front foil)	1 ft 7½ in (0·50 m)
Hull clearance	1 ft 2½ in (0·36 m)

WEIGHTS:

Displacement	4·9 tons

PERFORMANCE:

Max measured test speed	54·5 knots (101 km/h)
Max speed (design)	56 knots (104 km/h)
Take-off time	14·5 sec.
Stopping distance	50 kt to 5 kt 390 ft (120 m)
Turning radius at 40 kt	750 ft (230 m)

SEA TEST: Sea trials along the Mediterranean coast revealed that the craft, despite a small hull clearance, was capable of taking waves 3-4 ft (0·9-1·2 m) high, and with a minimum length of about 100-120 ft (30·4-36·4 m), at 45 kt in all courses from head to beam seas, partially contouring. In waves over 4 ft (1·2 m) the hull periodically touched wave crests, which was accompanied by a marked speed reduction (very high Froude number) during water contacting. In a following sea, and in all courses up to about 60° to a following sea, foilborne operation was limited to 2½ ft (0·76 m) waves due to the control system, which at that time had no heave sensor. At a wave height of 3 ft (0·91 m) ($\frac{1}{10}$ of boat length), vertical accelerations of only 0·08 g had been measured, which compares very favourably with the sea test results of other craft with fully submerged foils.

SUPRAMAR MT 250

This is a design concept for a 250 t patrol boat hydrofoil which meets the tactical requirements established by the West German and other NATO navies. It conforms to the fast patrol boat standards of the West German Navy and has a max intermittent speed of 60 knots.

Main dimensions of the vessel are similar to those of the Swedish Spica class, Vosper Tenacity, Israeli Sa'ar class and the West German Type 148. It is designed for all-weather operation in the western Baltic, the Skagerrak and other areas with similar operational conditions.

Foilborne propulsion is supplied by gas-turbine powered waterjets. The foil system is of fully-submerged type employing the Schertel-Supramar air stabilisation system.

As a significant part of the total operating time will be in the hullborne mode, a separate hullborne propulsion plant is provided which guarantees adequate speed in the two hull-borne modes: foils retracted and foils extended.

FOILS: Canard system with a single fully submerged bow foil and two fully submerged rear foils. The foils are of welded hollow shell construction in stainless steel. All three are retracted clear of the waterline hydraulically. The design avoids the use of hinged doors or panels to raise the bow foil.

CONTROLS: The stabilisation system is a combined automatic control process employing flaps for damping low frequency motions and air-control for high frequency motions. Roll stabilisation is effected by air control of the outer rear foil and the rear foil struts, also by the operation of flaps on the outer rear foil.

Pitch and heave are controlled by flaps on the bow foil and flaps in the centre section of the aft foil.

The stabilisation system consists of four units: the sensors, a computer (for automatic flight control), a command unit and the transactuators.

HULL: Hull and superstructure is of partly riveted partly welded seawater-resistant light metal alloy. There are seven watertight transverse bulkheads.

INTERNAL LAYOUT/ACCOMMODATION

Accommodation and operations rooms are located almost entirely below deck leaving a relatively large free deck area. Crew would normally comprise twenty one, officers and ratings. Operating and control rooms are all fully air-conditioned. Mine-laying equipment, conforming to NATO standards, can be installed as an alternative to missile launchers. Stand-by-space is available for a substantial number of Mk 55 mines. There are three officer's cabins and two crew rooms, two toilets with wash basins, one pantry, store rooms, operating and control rooms for ship and machinery. The control and operations rooms have direct access to the bridge and the radio room. All facilities are provided for an intended sea endurance of 3-5 days.

POWER PLANT (FOILBORNE): The main propulsion plant consists of a slightly modified version of the Rolls-Royce Marine Olympus TM 3, with the following ratings:

Performance	25,350 ps
Power turbine speed	5,450 rpm
Spec. fuel consumption	0·219 kg/PSh
Ambient air temperature	15°C

This comprises an Olympus gas-generator and a single-stage long-life power unit mounted on a common base. The forward end of the gas-generator mates with the air-intake plenum chamber, which has a cascaded bend to give an undisturbed air-flow to the engine intake. Flexible joints are applied to the faces of the air-intake

The Supramar MT 250 fast patrol boat for all-weather operation. Main powerplant is a Marine Olympus TM3

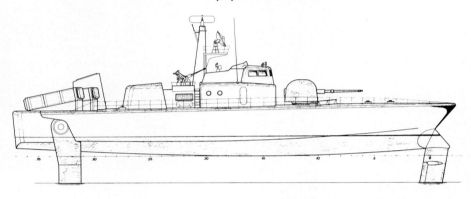

and exhaust system to allow relative movement between the module and the ship's uptakes and downtakes. At the engine ratings given, estimated time between overhaul for the gas generator is 2,000 hours.

A Metastream M 4000 elastic coupling of approximately 1,500 mm length connects the power turbine output shaft with an Allen epicycle gear box. The latter is flanged directly to a Rocketdyne Powerjet 46 pump. The Allen gear box has a reduction ratio of approx 1 : 5·5.

The Rocketdyne Powerjet 46 pump has twin side water intakes and is rigidly mounted to the ship's structure, it transmits thrust via three points.

AUXILIARY PROPULSION PLANT: The auxiliary propulsion plant comprises two 8 cyl MTU 8 V 331 TC 71 diesel engines driving via REINTJES WAV 500 A reverse and reduction gears and inclined propeller shafts two variable-pitch KAMEWA propellers. The propellers are arranged in a duct at the transom.

The MTU 8V 331 TC 71 diesel has the following ratings and characteristics.

Output continuous	750 PS at 2,055 rpm
Output intermittent	815 PS at 2,120 rpm
No of cyl	8 in V-form

ARMAMENT: Optional, but can comprise surface-to-surface missiles of Exocet, Otomat or similar types or OTO Compact gun mount and additional 20 mm anti-aircraft guns. Provision has been made for various types of combat systems including Vega II-53 or Mini-Combat-System WM 28.

DIMENSIONS:

Length overall (foils extended)

	43·70 m	(143·3 ft)
Beam max over deck	9·40 m	(30·8 ft)
Max width over foils	15·80 m	(51·9 ft)
Draft in foilborne mode	3·35 m	(11·0 ft)
Draft in displacement mode,		
with foils extended	6·95 m	(22·8 ft)
with foils retracted	2·20 m	(7·2 ft)

WEIGHTS:

Operational displacement	250 t

PERFORMANCE:

Speed max cont:	
foilborne mode	53 kn
displacement mode, foils retracted	13 kn
displacement mode, foils extended	9·5 kn
Range:	
at max cont speed foilborne	400 nm
at max cont speed hullborne foils extended	1,800 nm
at max cont speed hullborne foils down	1,300 nm

SUPRAMAR MT 80

The MT 80 is designed for operation in coastal waters. A fully submerged retractable foil system enables it to operate under adverse weather conditions. It can be equipped with a variety of weapons and control systems.

The hull and superstructure are of combined riveted and welded light metal alloy construction. The foils are of high tensile structural steel. The main propulsion system consists of one Rolls-Royce Proteus gas turbine driving either a waterjet pump, or a propeller via a double bevel gear arrangement. The armament and weapon control system is optional.

DIMENSIONS:

Length overall	29·00 m
Beam max	5·80 m
Width over foils	8·50 m
Draft hullborne	4·30/1·50 m
Draft foilborne	1·40 m

WEIGHTS:

Displacement	85·00 t

PERFORMANCE:

Speed	classified
Range	classified
Crew	8—12
Sea endurance	3 days

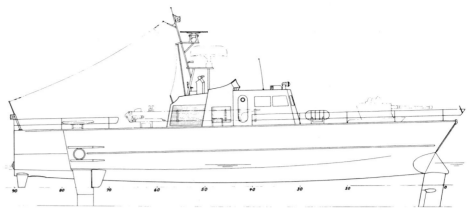

SUPRAMAR 500-SEAT PASSENGER FERRY

In August 1972, Supramar revealed that it is undertaking studies for the design of a 500-seat passenger ferry.

SUPRAMAR CT 70 CATAMARAN HYDRO-FOIL

The Supramar hydrofoil catamaran has been designed expecially for operation in shallow and sheltered waters, where draft limitations preclude the use of conventional hydrofoil craft. Berthing is possible at any existing pontoon or quay facility without adaption, as the foils are well within the hull beam and thereby fully protected against damage while drawing alongside.

One of the major applications foreseen for this new class of hydrofoil is that of fast water bus on urban passenger services. Other likely roles include those of oil-rig support vessel, leisure craft and water sports, especially fishing.

About 80-90% of the lift is produced by

the foils, and the remainder by the partly immersed hull planing surfaces forward, which also provide stability. The arrangement permits the placing of the foils below the water surface at a depth generally free of floating debris.

In the case of partial foil ventilation, the planing surfaces prevent high angles of list and also impede deep immersion in the waves of a following sea. In cases where retractable foils are required a simple method of retraction can be incorporated.

Because of the uncomplicated nature of the concept and the ease of foil retraction, it is felt that it could be successfully applied to outboard craft.

FOILS: System comprises two Supramar type foils arranged in tandem. The bow foil is located at frame 60 and the rear foil at frame 6.

Outboard profile of the Supramar MT 80, 80 t hydrofoil for patrol duties in coastal waters. The foilborne propulsion system comprises a single Rolls-Royce Marine Proteus driving a waterjet pump or a propeller via a double-bevel drive

When foilborne 65% of the weight is supported by the bow foil and the side keels while the remaining 35% is supported by the rear foil. Flying height is adjusted by hydraulically-operated flaps on the bow foil. Foils are in St 52-3 high tensile structural steel.

HULL: The hull, which is of hard chine construction, comprises two side hulls and one central hull. Its design is based on experience gained from the construction of a wide variety of hydrofoil craft.

All members included in the longitudinal strength of the vessel, such as longitudinals, shell and deck plating, are of riveted construction. Transverse members, including web frames and bulkheads, are welded, but the connections with main deck, side and bottom shell, are riveted.

POWERPLANT: Motive power is provided

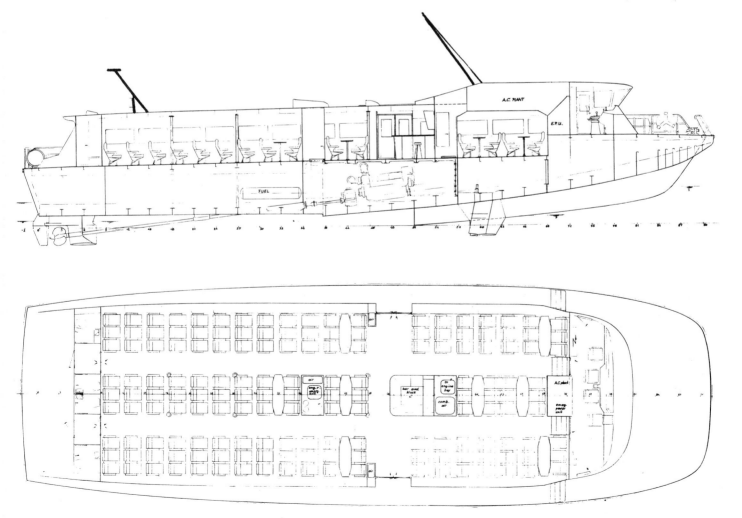

General arrangement of the Supramar CT 70 hydrofoil catamaran

by two MTU 331 type 12-cyl four-stroke diesel engines, each rated at 1,100 PS continuous and 1,300 PS maximum intermittent. Each drives a propeller via an inclined shaft. The engines are rated for 45°C air intake temperature and 32°C seawater temperature.

ACCOMMODATION: Total seating capacity is for 159 to 166 passengers. There is one large saloon only. Major obstructions like staircases, have been avoided. Windows are in safety glass and tinted anti-sun grey. On the standard version passenger seats are each fitted with arm rests, an ashtray and a number plate. Four toilets are located in the aft of the saloon each fully-equipped with WCs, washbasins, mirrors and towels.

On the short-haul model, the passenger seats are more simple and only two toilets are provided. There are three luggage compartments, one adjacent to the embarkation doors leading to the passenger saloon, and two at the aft of the saloon.

DIMENSIONS:

Length overall	28·00 m (91·86 ft)
Beam, max moulded	9·30 m (30·51 ft)
Draft hullborne	1·80 m (5·90 ft)
Draft foilborne	1·00 m (3·28 ft)

WEIGHTS:

Displacement, fully loaded	68·5 t (67·45 tons
Displacement, unloaded	51·7 t (60·90 tons)
Disposable load	15·8 t (15·56 tons)
Payload	13·6 t (13·40 tons)
Driving fuel and crew	3·2 t (3·15 tons)
Number of seated passengers	between 159 and 165

PERFORMANCE:

Max speed, foilborne	about 33 knots (61·5 km/h)
Cruising speed, foilborne	about 31 knots (57·5 km/h)

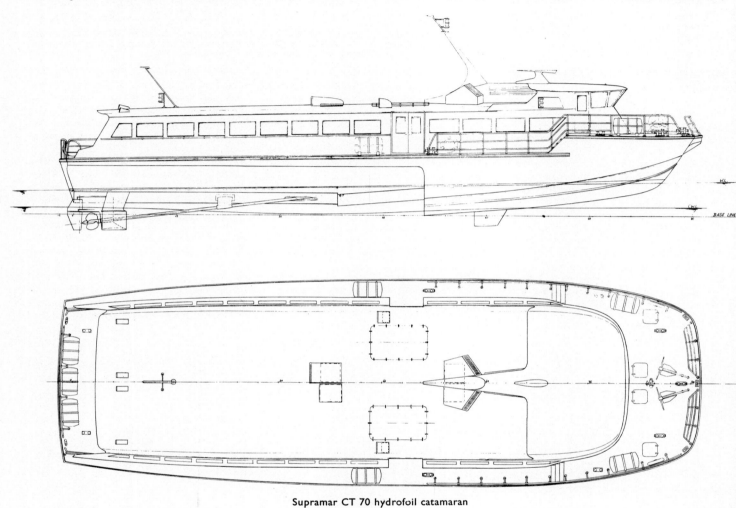

Supramar CT 70 hydrofoil catamaran

UNITED KINGDOM

NEW HYDROFIN LTD

HEAD OFFICE:

Burfield Flat, Bosham Lane, Bosham, Sussex

MANAGING DIRECTOR:

Christopher Hook

Christopher Hook's early Hydrofins demonstrated for the first time the stability and excellent seakeeping qualities of incidence-controlled, submerged foil craft, and marked a turning point in hydrofoil design.

Nearly seventy Hydrofins of various types have been built since 1949 in Norway, the USA, Poland and Israel. The company's latest design is the 22 ft Channel Skipper, a four-seat fibreglass-hulled runabout.

CHANNEL SKIPPER

Developed from the earlier K2 Hydrofin, the K2D Channel Skipper is a four-seat sports hydrofoil fitted with mechanical wave sensors to control the incidence angle of the fully submerged main foils.

FOILS: The fully submerged foil system is of "aeroplane" configuration with 65% of the weight carried on the two main foils and the remainder on the aft foil. All three foils have swept back leading and trailing edges. A high-riding crash preventer plane is mounted ahead of and beneath the bow. The plane is also used as a platform for mounting a lightweight pitch sensor which is hinged to the rear. The sensor rides on the waves and continuously transmits their shape through a connecting linkage to vary the incidence angle of the main foils as necessary to maintain them at the required depth. A filter system ensures that the craft ignores small waves and that the hull is flown over the crests of waves exceeding the height of the keel over the water.

Two additional sensors, trailing from port and starboard beams immediately aft of the main struts, provide roll control. The pilot has overriding control through a control column, operated in the same manner as that of an aircraft.

All three foils and the crash plane arm are retractable. The crash plane arm retracts into a hull slot: the two main foils swing forward above the displacement waterline and the rear foil strut assembly retracts upwards into the hull at the same time raising the propeller and drive shaft.

POWER PLANT: Motive power is provided by a single 80 hp Ford diesel engine, driving a 3-bladed propeller through a Z-drive.

DIMENSIONS:

Length overall	22 ft 0 in (6·71 m)
Length waterline, hull	18 ft 0 in (5·48 m)
Hull beam	6 ft 7 in (2·00 m)
Length overall, foils extended	19 ft 7 in (5·96 m)
Max beam, foils retracted	10 ft 9 in (3·27 m)

Max beam, foils extended 13 ft 5 in (4·09 m)
Draft afloat, foils retracted 1 ft 7 in (0·48 m)
Draft afloat, foils extended 5 ft 3 in (1·60 m)
Freeboard 2 ft 6 in (0·78 m)

WEIGHTS:

Gross tonnage	1·8 tons
Net tonnage	1·2 tons
Light displacement	1·2 tons
Useful load (fuel, water, passengers, baggage and crew)	1,300 lb (598 kg)

PERFORMANCE:

Cruising speed, foilborne 32 knots (51 km/h)
Cruising speed, hullborne
8-12 knots (14-21 km/h)
Sea state capability   Unlimited in seas corresponding to Barnaby's "average rough sea" providing they conform as regards proportions
Turning radius at cruising speed
150 ft (45·7 m) fully banked on turns.

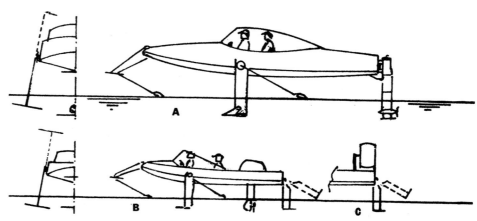

A, New Hydrofin Channel Skipper; B, Hydrofin conversion kit employing a standard long-shaft outboard; C. Hydrofin craft propelled by a ducted fan

UNITED STATES OF AMERICA

BOEING MARINE SYSTEMS
A Division of the Boeing Company

HEAD OFFICE:

PO Box 3999, Seattle, Washington 98124

TELEPHONE:

206 237 1500

EXECUTIVE:

Robert E. Bateman, Vice-President and General Manager, Boeing Marine Systems

Boeing Marine Systems, now a separate operating division of the Boeing company, was formed in 1959 to conduct research, development, design, manufacture and the testing of high performance marine vehicles system. Boeing's entry into the hydrofoil field was announced in June 1960, when the company was awarded a $2 million contract for the construction of the US Navy's 120-ton PCH-1 High Point, a canard design which was the outcome of experiments with a similar arrangement in the US Navy test craft Sea Legs.

Boeing has also built a jet-driven hydroplane, the HTS, for testing foil models at full-scale velocity; the Fresh-1, a manned craft for testing superventilating or supercavitating foils at speeds between 60-100 knots and a water-jet test vehicle, Little Squirt. Descriptions of Fresh-1 and Little Squirt appear in JSS 1970-71 and earlier editions. The company also completed a highly successful waterjet propelled gunboat, the PGH-2 Tucumcari, for the US Navy's Ship Systems Command. Its operational trials included several months of combat evaluation in Vietnam as part of the US Navy's coastal surveillance force. Data provided by the vessel assisted the design and development of the NATO/PHM, which is a 'scaled up' Tucumcari, and the Jetfoil commercial hydrofoil.

Pegasus, first of the Boeing/NATO PHM (Patrol Hydrofoil Missile) class vessels, was due to be delivered to the US Navy during 1976. Main armament comprises eight AGM-84A Harpoon anti-ship missiles and one rapid-fire 76 mm cannon. Top speed is stated to be in excess of 50 knots

High Point was modified by Boeing during 1972 to incorporate a new automatic control system, new struts and foils, a new diesel for hullborne propulsion and a steerable forward strut to provide improved manoeuvrability. The craft was returned to the US Navy in a new configuration, identified as Mod-1, in March 1973. In its revised form it is employed as a testbed for hydrofoil weapons compatability.

On April 4th 1975, the PCH was operated by the US Coast Guard for one month as part of a continuing research and development programme to evaluate high-speed water craft for the US Coast Guard use. Operating in Puget Sound and around San Francisco, the craft was employed on fisheries patrol, marine environmental protection and search and rescue missions.

On January 19th 1973, the keel was laid for the first 110-ton 250-seat Jetfoil passenger ferry. The hull was assembled in a former 727 assembly building at Renton, Washington, and the first craft was launched on March 29th, 1974 on Lake Washington, which is adjacent to the plant. The first five Jetfoils are now in operation and another five are under construction.

The company is at present examining the possibility of exporting the Jetfoil on a modular basis, with the customer purchasing a basic hull, which would contain all the essential systems, and installing his own superstructure.

In April 1973, US Naval Ship Systems Command awarded the company a $42,602,384 contract for the design and development of the 235 metric ton NATO PHM missile-equipped patrol boat, under the terms of which Boeing is to build lead craft for the US Navy for evaluation. The first PHM, Pegasus, was launched on November 9th 1974. Delivery of the first craft to the US Navy was due to take place in late 1976. Participating in the NATO PHM programme with the US Navy are Italy and the Federal Republic of Germany. Early on in the programme participating countries are expected to purchase Boeing-built PHMs for their own navies. The US Navy programme anticipates the procurement of a six-ship squadron initially. Determination of the eventual force level will be made at a later date. Design studies are now being completed on bigger and faster hydrofoil including the 1,300-1,500 ton Destroyer Escort Hydrofoil (DEH), a vessel capable of open ocean missions and of crossing the Atlantic without refuelling.

PCH-1 HIGH POINT

General design of the PCH-1 High Point was specified by the US Navy's Bureau of Ships, with responsibility for detail design and construction assigned to Boeing. The ship was accepted by the US Navy in August 1963 and based at the Puget Sound Naval Shipyard at Bremerton, Washington. Since then it has been undergoing a wide range of tests to evaluate the performance of an inshore hydrofoil ASW system.

High Point had a major modification and overhaul by Boeing in 1972 and was returned to the US Navy in March 1973. The new configuration is identified as Mod-1. In its revised form it is employed as a weapons test-bed to evaluate PHM missile ship equipment and weapons and ASW devices. Two RGM-84A-1 Harpoon blast test vehicles were successfully launched from the deck of the vessel while foilborne at 40 knots off British

Above: The PCH-1 High Point launching a McDonnell Douglas RGM-84A-1 Harpoon anti-ship missile during tests on the Joint US-Canadian Range, Nanoose, Canada, in January 1974. *Below:* PCH-1 bearing the insignia of the US Coast Guard, which operated the vessel during the month of April 1975 as part of a continuing research and development programme to evaluate high-speed water craft for S & R missions, fisheries patrol and marine environmental protection

Columbia on the US-Canadian Nanoose range during December 1973-January 1974.

Both firings were conducted in normal sea conditions and moderate winds, the first being made while foilborne with the vessel straight and level, and the second while turning foilborne at 5 deg/sec. The dynamic stability of the craft was measured throughout the tests and the gas-turbine was monitored to establish any possible harmful effects caused by the blast of the Aerojet-General 300 lb solid-propellant booster employed in the launch. The success of the test confirmed the suitability of the launch canister design for use on the PHM and other hydrofoils.

During April 1975, the PCH-1 was employed by the US Coast Guard in Puget Sound and off San Francisco. It undertook a number of duties, from fisheries patrol to search and rescue missions, as part of a programme to evaluate high-speed water craft for possible use by the US Coast Guard.

FOILS: Submerged fixed incidence canard foil system, with 68 per cent of the foil area located aft, and trailing-edge flaps on all foils for lift control, is a scaled-up version of that employed on Sea Legs. The foil struts retract vertically into the hull. Foils are of built-up construction in HY-80 weldable steel, and struts are in HY-130 steel.

HULL: Hull and superstructure are of all-welded, corrosion resistant 5456 aluminium. Integral plate stiffener extrusions are extensively used for decks and portions of the sides not having excessive curvature.

ACCOMMODATION: A crew of 18 is carried to provide a three-section watch: on duty at any given time are one officer of the deck/helmsman, one lookout on bridge, one radar operator and one navigator required in combat information centre, and two engineers on watch in main control. The wheelhouse seats two operators—OOD on port and the helmsman on the starboard side. In addition there are seats for two observers. Crew accommodation is ventilated and heated only. Entry is via four watertight doors in the deckhouse and two watertight hatches on main deck.

POWER PLANT: Foilborne propulsion is provided by two Proteus Model 1273 gas-turbines, each rated at 4,250 hp max and 3,800 hp continuous. The turbines are located aft and take air through the two towers housing the retracted foil struts. The exhaust is discharged directly aft through the transom. Each gas-turbine is coupled to a pair of contra-rotating, subcavitating five-bladed propellers, 34 in. in diameter, through two right-angle gearboxes one at the top of each aft strut and the others in each of the underwater nacelles.

Hullborne propulsion is supplied by a single GM 12-V-71 (N75) rated at 525 hp for continuous operation. The engine is coupled to a 43 in (1,092 mm) diameter propeller through a retractable outdrive unit, which is steerable through 360 degrees and rotates about the axis of the horizontal shaft for retraction.

CONTROLS: Altitude and foilborne stability are controlled by an automatic control system, the heart of which is a computer. This governs motion of the trailing-edge flaps and the steerable forward strut in response to inputs from ultrasonic height sensors, position and rate gyros, accelerometers, feedback on control surface positions and helm commands. The system is active and all control surfaces are continuously moving in response to computer commands. On the bow foil, which is of single inverted tee (T) configuration, lift is varied by two trailing-edge flaps driven by a single actuator. The aft foil, of shallow M configuration, has two ailerons and two trailing-edge flaps. Each flap and its corresponding aileron are driven by a single hydraulic actuator.

Pitch is controlled by the flaps on the forward and aft foils. The gains in the control system were selected to provide automatic trim. Roll is controlled by differential operation of the flaps on the aft foil system. A roll to steer system causes the vessel to perform banked turns. Hullborne steering is accomplished by rotation of the hullborne propulsion unit about a vertical axis. This unit can also be rotated upward 87° about a longitudinal axis to eliminate its drag during foilborne operation.

The attitude control is entirely automatic except for steering. The take-off procedure on the PCH-1 is simply to set the desired flying height, then advance the throttles. At a gross weight of 117 tons take-off occurs at 24 knots with 3,750 total horsepower delivered to the transmission system, the speed stabilizing at 40 knots at that power setting. Minimum foilborne speed is 24 knots. At a cruising speed of 44 knots 4,400 hp is required, with propellers turning at 1,350 rpm.

SYSTEMS: ELECTRICAL: 100 kw (450 volts, 60 cycles 30).

HYDRAULICS: 3,000 psi ship's service for hullborne steering, strut and foil extension/retraction, engineering auxiliaries, and separate 3,000 psi system for foilborne control surfaces.

ELECTRONICS: Raytheon Pathfinder 1605, radar, UHF and HF radio transceivers.

ARMAMENT: Two fixed twin-tube Mk 32 torpedo tubes mounted on main deck at waist of ship.

DIMENSIONS:

Length overall, hull	115 ft 9 in	(35·28 m)
Length waterline, hull	110 ft 5 in	(33·65 m)
Hull beam	30 ft	(9·14 m)
Beam overall with foilguards		
	38·42 ft	(11·71 m)
Draught afloat	8·58 ft	(2·62 m)
Freeboard	8·75 ft	(2·67 m)

WEIGHTS:

Light displacement	99·6 long tons
Normal take-off displacement	
	127·2 long tons
Useful load (fuel, water, etc)	27·6 tons

PERFORMANCE:

Max speed foilborne	50 knots
Cruising speed foilborne	30-40 knots
Max speed hullborne	25 knots
Cruising speed hullborne	8 knots

PGH-2 TUCUMCARI

A 58-ton waterjet-propelled hydrofoil gunboat, the PGH-2 was ordered from Boeing by the US Navy's Ship Systems Command in 1966, under a $4 million, fixed price PGH

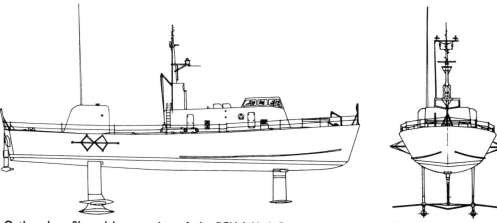

Outboard profile and bow-on view of the PCH-1 High Point in its new Mod-1 configuration. Note the shallow M aft foil, which has two ailerons and two trailing edge flaps. Output of each of the two Proteus 1273 gas-turbines has been uprated to 4,000 shp

(Patrol Gunboat Hydrofoil) programme. The craft was designed, constructed and tested in 23 months and delivered on schedule to the US Navy on March 7, 1968.

The craft operated with both the US Navy Pacific Fleet Amphibious Command, San Diego, and the Atlantic Amphibious Forces, Norfolk, Virginia. Its operational trials included several months of combat evaluation in Vietnam as part of the US Navy's 24-hour coastal surveillance force in Operation Market time.

In 1971 the craft was deployed to Europe for operation with the US Sixth Fleet in the Mediterranean following a series of demonstrations for officials of NATO navies.

In November 1972, Tucumcari ran aground in the Caribbean, seven miles east of Puerto Rico, while conducting nightime operations with amphibious forces. No crewmen were killed or seriously injured. Due to damages sustained while removing the craft from the coral reef, the craft was struck from the list of active US Navy vessels and sent to the US Naval Research and Development Center where it has been employed for structural evaluation and fire containment tests. A full technical description of the vessel appeared in JSS 1974-75 and earlier editions.

BOEING NATO/PHM

The NATO Hydrofoil Fast Patrol Ship Guided Missile (NATO/PHM) originated in mid-1969 when C-IN-C South presented to NATO a requirement for a large number of fast patrol boats to combat the threat posed by missile-armed fast patrol boats in the Mediterranean.

The concept of a common fast patrol boat was studied, and in September 1970 it was decided that the submerged foil craft of 140-tons proposed by the US Navy was the vessel most suited to NATO mission requirements. In October 1971, the United States indicated that it would proceed at its own expense with the design of the vessel and share the results of the studies with those nations wishing to purchase PHMs. It also offered to conduct all aspects of design and development, contracting and management in co-operation with governments entering into project membership. Costs would be reimbursed only by those nations engaged in the project.

Letters of intent, acknowledging design and cost scheduled obligations, were provided by Italy and the Federal Republic of Germany in April and May 1972, respectively. Although only three governments have decided to participate actively, future project membership is not restricted. Interested observers include Canada, Denmark, the Netherlands, France and the United Kingdom. Greece and Turkey have also considered participation.

In November 1971, the US Navy awarded Boeing a $5·6 million contract for the preliminary design of a 230-ton craft and the purchase of mechanical and electronic components for at least two of the vessels. Seventeen months later, Boeing was awarded a $42,607,384 contract for the design and development of the PHM for NATO navies. Under the terms of the contract the first craft, the Pegasus, was built for the US Navy.

Pegasus was launched on November 9th,

PHM-1 Pegasus underway during hullborne trials on Lake Washington with bow and rear foils fully retracted. The twin waterjet pumps of the hullborne propulsion system, powered by two 800 hp Mercedes-Benz diesels, propel the craft during long-range cruising and slow speed manoeuvring

1974, and made its first foilborne flight on February 25th, 1975. Pegasus achieved its classified designed speed, completed the Navy-conducted phase of testing its weapons, and then began operational evaluation in the San Diego area in the autumn of 1975. The outcome of the tests is expected to lead to a US Navy production decision by mid-1976, followed by a number of overseas procurement orders. Delivery of the vessel to the US Navy is scheduled for 1976. The contract calls, tentatively, for five further craft to follow initially, with the eventual force level to be determined at a later date. It is the first US Navy vessel designed and built on the metric system.

On May 3rd 1974, Boeing announced the receipt of a $3,809,235 cost plus fixed fee contract from US Naval Sea Systems Command for the preliminary design of a Patrol Hydrofoil Missile ship for the Federal Republic of Germany. The company stated that the design will be essentially the same as that of the lead vessel.

Co-operative production will be founded upon a production data package, which will be available after the trials and operation of the first vessel. A competitive procurement from a United States shipbuilder will be available to prospective NATO purchasers, in addition to which each participating nation will receive a complete production data package should they wish to build PHM in their own shipyards. However, it is envisaged that lead ship acquisition will be under a United States production contract, on a commercial basis between Boeing and individual NATO shipbuilders or governments.

The PHM has sufficient design flexibility to allow for individual variations by any country. These variations will be primarily in the weapons systems installed, and the participating nations, current and future, can acquire the standard PHM carrying whatever combat equipment is determined necessary to meet national requirements.

The standard PHM is approximately 131·2 ft (40·0 m) long, has a beam of 28·2 ft (8·6 m) and a full load displacement of about 231 tons (235 tonnes). Foilborne range is in excess of 500 nautical miles at speeds in excess of 40 knots in 8-12 ft seas. The hull form and size, the major structural bulkheads and decks, foils and struts, waterjets, pumps, controls and main propulsion machinery are identical. The auxiliary equipment and arrangements, deckhouse and crew accommodation are also of standard design, but variations in the latter are possible to suit the manning requirements of individual countries.

The PHM is designed on similar lines to the 64-ton Tucumcari, a development of which is being built by Advanced Marine Systems—Alinavi SpA for the Italian Navy. The primary peacetime missions of the craft are to patrol straits and exits through restricted waters, support task force operations and shadow potentially hostile forces. Employment will, in general, depend on national defence requirements and each country's responsibility within NATO. The mission of the PHMs employed by the US Navy will be to conduct surveillance, screening and special operations, with the following contingent tasks: patrol and blockade in coastal areas, island waters and inland sea areas; to augment screening of local convoys against surface attack; to provide fast transport for lightly equipped troops, to augment screening ships during arrival and departure of convoys or amphibious task forces.

Top: Pegasus launching a test missile during operational and technical evaluation. The firing, conducted by the US Navy at Port Hueneme, California, was to test the structure of the PHM's Harpoon anti-ship missile system. The evaluation included the testing of the Mk 94 fire control system and the 76 mm Oto Melara dual-purpose rapid-fire cannon
Centre: Pegasus entering into a high speed turn. A Boeing three-axis automatic control system regulates the height of the PHM's hull above the waves. The vessel banks inwardly into all turns. The ACS introduces the correct amount of bank and steering to coordinate the turn in full
Bottom: Close-up of the stern showing the shallow 'M' main foil, the control flaps and one of the two hydraulic actuators employed for retracting and extending the rear foil assembly. Also visible are the foilborne and hullborne waterjet discharge nozzles together, with the reverse gates on the latter

FOILS: Fully-submerged canard arrangement with approximately 32% of the dynamic lift provided by the bow foil and 68% by the aft foil. The aft foil retracts rearwards and the bow foil retracts forward into a recess in the bow. Bow doors preserve the hull lines when the forward foil is either fully extended or retracted. The foils and struts are in 17·4 PH stainless high strength steel. Both forward and aft foils are welded assemblies consisting of spars, ribs, and skin.

Flaps are fitted to the trailing edges to provide control and lift augmentation at take-off and during flight. The bow foil system incorporates a strut that rotates to provide directional control and reliable turning rates in heavy seas.

The shallow 'M' or inverted double pi configuration of the aft foil is designed for improved hydroelastic and turning characteristics. The primary strut structure consists of spars, ribs and skin welded into watertight assemblies. The struts are designed as beam columns, and rigidly attached to the foil support structure at the hull.

The struts are attached to the hull with pivot pins that allow the foils to rotate clear of the water. Hydraulic actuators are used for retraction and extension, mechanical stops and position locks being employed to secure the foils in either position.

CONTROLS, FOILBORNE: The helm, throttle and an automatic control system (ACS) provide continuous dynamic control during take-off, foilborne operation and landing. Once take-off is complete, the ACS requires no attention on the part of the crew. It controls the craft by sensing craft attitude, motion rates and acceleration, then comparing them electronically with desired values. Any deviations are processed by analog control computer which generates electrical commands causing hydraulic actuators to reposition the control surfaces, thus minimising detected errors. The foilborne control surfaces are trailing edge flaps on each of the foils, plus the rotating bow foil strut which acts as the foilborne rudder.

Manual controls and displays for both hullborne and foilborne conditions are concentrated at the helm station and include the wheel, a foil-depth selector, a foil-depth indicator, a ship-heading indicator and a heading holding switch.

CONTROLS, HULLBORNE: Steering control in the hullborne mode is provided by stern rudders which rotate electrohydraulically in response to the wheel. An automatic

heading control, similar to that employed for foilborne operation is incorporated, together with the necessary heading reference provided by the gyrocompass.

POWER PLANT, FOILBORNE: The foilborne propulsion system comprises a single 18,000 shp, two-stage, two-speed waterjet, driven through two sets of reduction gears by a single General Electric LM 2500 marine gas-turbine, developed from the GE TF39, which powers ths USAF's C-5 transport and the DC-10 Trijet.

Both the foilborne and hullborne propulsion systems were designed by Aerojet Liquid Rocket Company, Sacramento, California, under a Boeing contract.

The single foilborne propulsion pump is capable of handling 90,000 gpm and the two hullborne pumps will each operate at approximately 30,000 gpm.

Engine installation and removal for overhaul is accomplished through hatches located in the main deck between the deckhouse and exhaust outlet.

The vessel is capable of operation on JP-5 or diesel fuel.

POWER PLANT, HULLBORNE: Twin waterjet pumps powered by two 800 hp Mercedes-Benz 8V331TC80 diesels propel the vessel when hullborne. The hullborne system provides long-range cruising and slow speed manoeuvring, while the gas turbine is available when required for high-speed foilborne operation.

HULL: Hull and deckhouses are all-welded structures in AL 5465 alloy.

ACCOMMODATION: Crew will average 21 officers and men, but will vary according to the armament carried. Accommodation on the US Navy version is provided for four officers—the CO has a separate cabin—three chief petty officers and fourteen enlisted men. The superstructure accommodates the bridge, which contains steering and engine control consoles and is elevated to provide a 360 degree view. A short ladder from the bridge leads down to the command and surveillance

deckhouse that accommodates the fire control, radar, communications and navigation equipment The size of the deckhouse provides flexibility in accommodating various national equipment requirements. The space aft of the superstructure and forward of the foilborne engine exhaust is used to erect rigging for replenishment and refuelling.

Below the main deck, about one third of the PHM's length is devoted to crew accommodation, the forward third is occupied by the primary gun, automatic loader mechanism, ammunition storage and forward foil, and the after third is occupied by the unmanned machinery spaces.

All manned spaces are equipped with a recirculating air conditioning system to give a maximum air temperature of 27 deg C at 55% relative humidity in summer, and a minimum inside temperature of 18 deg C in winter. The officer staterooms, crew quarters and lounge/messing area are fully air-conditioned, the temperature being controlled by individual thermostats in the spaces concerned.

SYSTEMS, ELECTRICAL: Ship's service electric plant comprises two 200 kw generator sets providing 450 volt 3-phase, 400 Hz AC power. One is capable of handling entire electrical load, the second is provided as a standby. Through the use of static power conversion equipment, limited 3-phase, 60HZ AC power and 28 volt DC is available for equipment requirements. In port, the craft can utilise shore power, or use its own auxiliary power unit for this purpose as well as battery charging and emergency use of navigation and radio equipment.

HYDRAULICS: 3,000 psi to actuate the hullborne and foilborne controls, foil retraction and hullborne engine starting. Dual hydraulic supply is provided to each service with sub-system isolation fore and aft in the event of major damage.

FIRE EXTINGUISHING: Dry chemical equipment throughout craft, and a fixed total flooding-type Freon 1301 system.

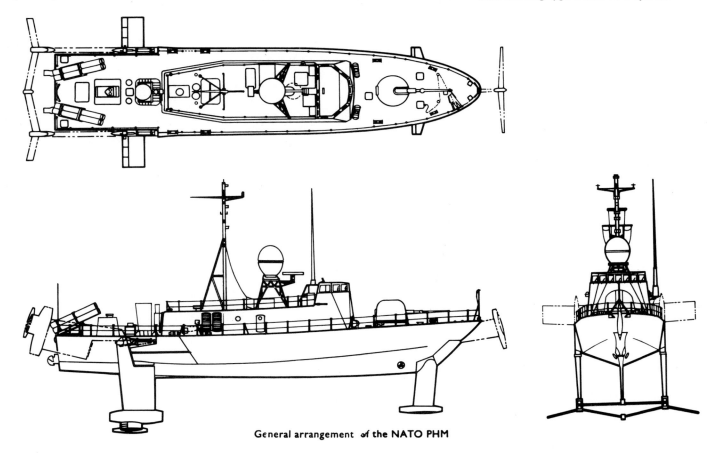

General arrangement of the NATO PHM

WEAPONS/FIRE CONTROL: Either WM-28 radar and weapons control system or American model, the Mk 92. Both systems embody a combined fire control and search antenna system, mounted on a single stabilised platform and enclosed in a fibreglass radome. The Italian Argo system can also be installed.

GUNS: Standard primary gun is the Oto Melara 76 mm gun, which is unmanned and automatically controlled by the fire control system. The craft can also be delivered with secondary guns. If specified two Mk 20 Rh 202 20 mm AA cannon can be provided, one each, port and starboard, adjacent to the fire control antenna structure.

MISSILES: The prototype carries Harpoon missiles with eight launchers, but Exocet, Otomat, Tero or any smaller missile system can be installed. Space is provided aft to accommodate the four launchers, port and starboard, in parallel pairs. The launchers are deck-fixed in elevation and azimuth.

Armament of the standard US Navy version will be eight McDonnell Douglas AGM-84A Harpoon anti-ship missiles in lightweight container launchers; one Mk 75 Mod 1 76 mm cannon and one Mk 92 Mod 1 GFCS.

Western Germany's PHMs will be armed with Aerospatiale Exocet missiles and the Italian vessels, if procured, will carry Oto Melara Otomats.

The following details apply to the model under construction for the US Navy.

DIMENSIONS:
Length overall,
foils extended	131·2 ft (40·0 m)
foils retracted	147 ft 6 in (45 m)
Beam maximum, deck	28·2 ft (8·6 m)
Max width across foils	47 ft 6 in (14·5 m)

Draft:
hullborne, foils retracted	9ft 5 in (2·9 m)
hullborne foils extended	23·2 ft (7·1 m)
foilborne, normal	8·9 ft (2·7 m)

WEIGHTS:
Displacement, full load including margins
235 metric tons

PERFORMANCE:
Max speed foilborne in excess of 50 knots
Cruising speed foilborne,
sea state 0-5	in excess of 40 knots
hullborne	in excess of 10 knots

Sea state:
can negotiate 8·13 ft seas at speeds in excess of 40 knots
Foilborne range	in excess of 600 n miles
hullborne range	in excess of 1,800 n miles

BOEING JETFOIL 929-100

This is a 110-ton waterjet-propelled commercial hydrofoil for services in relatively rough waters. It employs a fully-submerged, automatically-controlled canard foil arrangement and is powered by two 3,710 hp Allison 501-K20A gas-turbines. Normal foilborne cruising speed is 42 knots.

Typical interior arrangements include a commuter configuration with up to 284 seat and a tourist layout for 190 tourists plus baggage.

The company is also evaluating various utility models with open load decks suitable for search and rescue duties, offshore oil-rig support and firefighting. Two utility derivatives for offshore rig crew and priority/ emergency cargo support are showing great potential. They are 50 and 100 seat crew/ supply boat versions with considerable cargo capacity for supporting rigs within 50-250 nautical miles from shore.

Five Jetfoils are currently in service. Two

Top and Centre: Jetfoil 003 Kamehameha, one of three Jetfoils operated between the Hawaiian Islands by Pacific Sea Transportation Ltd, Honolulu. Note the lower aft promenade deck on this tourist version, which carries 190 passengers and their luggage

Bottom: Passenger accommodation is fully air-conditioned and arranged on two decks. This photograph was taken in the upper passenger saloon of Jetfoil 002 Madeira, one of two Jetfoils operated by Far East Hydrofoil Co, Hong Kong, on its Hong Kong-Macao service. Seats are provided on this particular model for 284 passengers. Cruising speed is 45 knots (51·8 mph; 83·3 km/h)

with Far East Hydrofoil Co, Hong Kong and three with Pacific Sea Transportation Ltd, Hawaii.

Keel-laying of the first Jetfoil took place at the company's Renton, Washington, plant on January 19th 1973, and the craft was launched on March 29th, 1974. After testing on Puget Sound and in the Pacific, the craft was delivered to Pacific Sea Transportation Ltd for inter-island services in Hawaii. High speed foilborne test began in Puget Sound in mid-July and it was reported that the vessel attained a speed of 48 knots during its runs.

During a rigorous testing programme to prove the boat's design and construction, Jetfoil One operated for 470 hours, including 237 hours foilborne. The latter phase of testing was conducted in the rough waters of the straits of Juan de Fuca and the Pacific Ocean, where it encountered wave swells as high as 30 ft, winds gusting up to 60 knots and wave chop averaging six feet high. The vessel was refurbished prior to delivery to Hawaii in October, 1975 as the third craft for Pacific Sea Transportation's SeaFlite service.

The first operational Jetfoil service was successfully initiated on April 25th by Far East Hydrofoil Co, of Hong Kong, with Jetfoil 002, Madeira. Prior to this, the Jetfoil received its ABS classification, was certificated by the Hong Kong Marine Department and passed US Coast Guard certification trials, although a USCG certificate was not completed since the craft would not be operating in US waters.

The first US service began in Hawaii on June 15th, with the first of three Jetfoils, 003 Kamehameha, starting inter-island runs. By the end of the summer all five Jetfoils were in service. Boeing has another five Jetfoils under construction with long lead items ordered on boats 11-25. An active world-wide marketing programme is underway to sell these high-speed craft, which are currently priced at $7 million.

FOILS: Fully submerged canard arrangement with a single inverted tee strut/foil forward and a three-strut, full-span foil aft. The forward foil assembly is rotated hydraulically through 7 degrees in either direction for steering. All foils have trailing-edge flaps for controlling pitch, roll and yaw and for take-off and landing. Hydraulically-driven foil flap actuators control the variation in flap positions through linkages between actuators and flap hinge points. Foils and struts retract hydraulically above the waterline, the bow foil forward, and the rear foil aft. All structural components of the foil/strut system are in 15·5 PH corrosion resistant all-welded steel construction.

CONTROL: The craft is controlled by a three-axis automatic system while it is foilborne and during take-off and landing. The system senses the motion and position of the craft by gyros, accelerometers and height sensors, signals from which are combined in the control computer with manual commands from the helm. The resulting computer outputs provide control-surface deflections through electro-hydraulic servo actuators. Lift control is provided by full-span trailing edge flaps on each foil. Forward and aft flaps operate differentially to provide pitch variation and height control. Aft flaps operate differentially to provide roll control for changes of direction.

The vessel banks inwardly into all turns, to ensure maximum passenger comfort. The ACS introduces the correct amount of bank

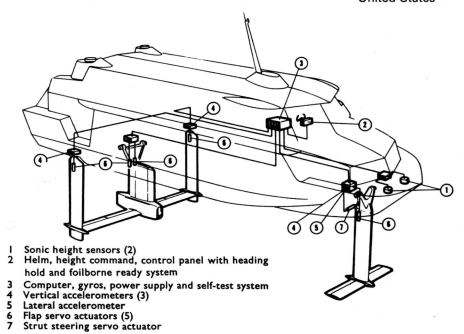

1 Sonic height sensors (2)
2 Helm, height command, control panel with heading hold and foilborne ready system
3 Computer, gyros, power supply and self-test system
4 Vertical accelerometers (3)
5 Lateral accelerometer
6 Flap servo actuators (5)
7 Strut steering servo actuator

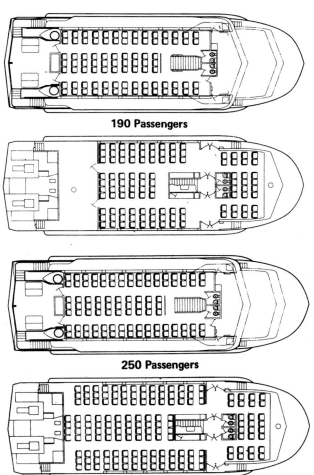

190 Passengers

250 Passengers

Typical interior arrangements on the 929-100 Jetfoil include a commuter configuration with 250 seats, a tourist layout for 190 tourists plus baggage and a mixed-traffic version for 190 passengers plus up to four compact cars. Seats are track mounted to facilitate spacing changes, removal or replacement. Food and beverage service units can be installed

and steering to coordinate the turn in full. Turn rates of up to 6 degrees per second are attained within 5 seconds of providing a heading change command at the helm.

Three basic controls only are required for foilborne operation. The throttle is employed to set the speed, the height command lever to set the required foil depth, and the helm to set the required heading. If a constant course is required, a "heading hold" circuit accomplishes this automatically.

For take-off, the foil depth is set, the two throttles advanced, and the hull clears the water in about 60 seconds. Acceleration continues, until the craft automatically stabilises at the command depth and the speed dictated by the throttle setting. The throttle setting is reduced for landing, the craft settling as the speed drops. The speed normally diminishes from 45 knots (cruising speed) to 15 knots in about 30 seconds. In emergencies more rapid landings can be made by the use of the height command lever to provide hull contact within two seconds.

HULL: Hull and deckhouse in marine aluminium. Aircraft assembly techniques used, including high-speed mechanised welding processes.

POWERPLANT: Power for the waterjet propulsion system is supplied by two Allison 501-K20A free-power gas-turbines, each rated at 3,300 shp at 80 deg F (27 deg C) at sea level. Each is connected to a Rocketdyne Powerjet 20 axial-flow pump through a gearbox drive train. The two turbine/pump systems are located in their own bays, port and starboard, separated by the slot in the hull into which the central water strut retracts for hullborne operation. The system propels the craft in both foilborne and hullborne modes. When foilborne, water enters through the inlet located at the forward lower end of the aft centre foil strut. At the top of the duct, the water is split into two paths and enters into each of the two axial flow pumps. It is then discharged at high pressure through nozzles in the hull bottom.

The water path is the same during hullborne operations with the foils extended. When the foils are retracted, the water enters through a flush inlet located in the keel. Reversing and steering for hullborne operation only are accomplished by reverse-flow buckets located immediately aft of the water exit nozzles. A bow thruster is provided for positive steering control at low forward speeds.

A 4,000 gallon (15,140 litre) integral fuel tank supplies the propulsion turbine and diesel engines. Recommended fuel is Diesel No. 2. The tank is fitted with a 2 in (5 cm) diameter fill pipe and fittings compatible with dockside refuelling equipment. Coalescent-type water separating fuel filters and remote-controlled motor-operated fuel shut-off valves are provided for fire protection.

ACCOMMODATION: Passenger accommo-

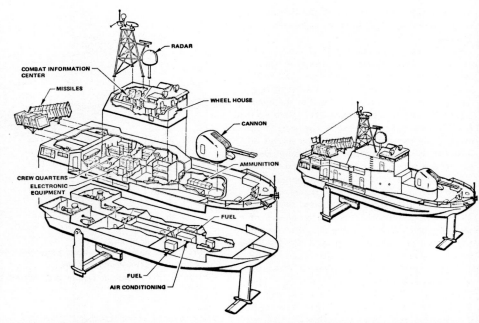

Projected 114-ton fast patrol boat version of the Jetfoil. The company is examining the possibility of exporting the Jetfoil on a modular basis with the customer purchasing a basic hull, which will contain the power plant and all the necessary systems, and installing his own superstructure

dation is fully air-conditioned and arranged on two decks, which are connected by a wide, enclosed stairway. The cabins have 3 ft 0 in (91·4 cm) wide aisles and 6 ft 9 in (2·06 m) headroom. In the commuter configuration 56 cu ft (1·58 cu metres) per passenger is provided and 66 cu ft (1·87 cu meters) in the tourist configuration. Floors are carpeted and 2 ft 0 in (61 cm) seats are provided. Lighting is indirect and adjustable from the wheelhouse. Interior noise is near conversation level (below 68 db SIL). Passengers are entertained and informed by a public announcement system. Each deck level has two WC/washbasin units. Drinking water dispensers are located on each passenger deck.

Quality of the ride in the craft is comparable with that of a Boeing 727 airliner. The vertical acceleration at the c of g is designed to be no more than 0·04 g, with lateral acceleration less than that of the vertical. Angles of pitch and roll will be less than 1 deg RMS. Passenger discomfort in an emergency landing is prevented by a 'structural fuse', which limits deceleration to less than 0·4 g longitudinally and 0·8 g vertically so that a passenger would not be thrown from his seat in the event of the craft striking a major item of floating debris at full speed. The 'structural fuse', when actuated, causes the foil and strut to rotate backwards, protecting the system from sustaining signifi-

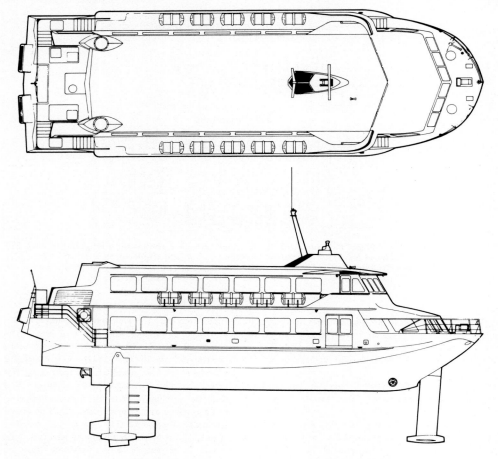

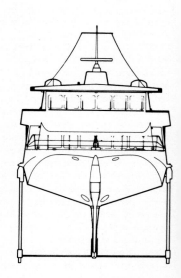

General arrangement of the Boeing Jetfoil

cant damage. The fuses can be reset while under way in some cases, depending on the degree of impact.

Crew comprises a captain and first officer plus cabin attendants.

SYSTEMS: ELECTRICAL: 60-cycle, 440 volt a.c. electrical system, supplied by two diesel-driven generators rated at 62·5 KVA each. Either is capable of supplying all vital electrical power. 90 KVA capacity shore connection facilities provided, and equipment can accept 50-cycle power. Transformer rectifier units for battery charging provide 28 volts dc from the ac system.

HYDRAULICS: 3,000 psi (210·9 kg/cm²) system to actuate control surfaces. Each pump connected to a separate system to provide split system redundancy in the event of a turbine, pump, distribution system or actuator malfunctioning.

EMERGENCY: Craft meets all applicable safety regulations of the US Coast Guard and SOLAS. Hull provides two-compartment sub-division and a high degree of stability. Life rafts and life jackets are provided.

NAVIGATION: Equipment includes radar. A low-light-level television system covering potential collision zone is available as an optional extra.

DIMENSIONS:
Length overall, foils extended
90 ft (27·4 m)
Length overall, foils retracted
99 ft 0 in (30·1 m)
Beam overall, maximum   31 ft (9·5 m)
Draught afloat, foils retracted 4·8 ft (1·5 m)
foils extended   16·3 ft (5·0 m)
WEIGHTS:
Displacement   110 long tons
PERFORMANCE:
Maximum speed   50 knots
Normal service speed   42 knots
Turning radius at 45 knots
less than 1,000 ft (304·80 m)
Normal endurance at cruising speed 4 hours
Maximum endurance   8 hours
Maximum wave height foilborne
12 ft 0 in (3·65 m)

MODULAR JETFOIL

In November 1974 Boeing announced that consideration was being given to the export of Jetfoils on a modular basis. One approach would be to supply operators, both commercial and military, with the basic Jetfoil hull, complete with foils, powerplant and control system, and the operator would arrange to install his own superstructure.

This would give them access to craft embodying the latest developments in hydrofoil technology and permit them to add superstructure tailored to their own particular needs. Variants would range from passenger ferries and utility craft for offshore marine operations, to coastguard patrol vessels and missile gunboats.

The modular concept is expected to appeal in particular to lesser developed countries, since by completing the craft locally, a useful saving in hard currency could be realised. A substantial amount of the superstructure could be riveted together by fairly low-skilled labour. The cost per hull unit,

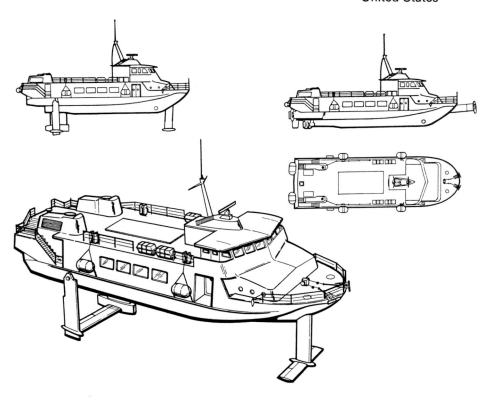

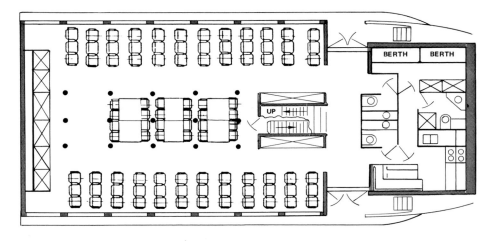

Above and below : Outboard profiles and main deck view of the offshore oil rig support model of the Boeing Jetfoil

once production is established, is expected to be about $6 million.

Maintenance requirements are expected to be reasonably low. The Allison 501-K20A gas-turbines have a life of 18,000 hours, and the Boeing autopilot, the most sensitive part of the system, has a life expectancy of 3-4 years under normal operating conditions, allowing 3,000 hours in service each year.

Allison is willing to negotiate contract rates for servicing the gas-turbines at a fixed-rate per operating hour.

Boeing states that modifications could be made to the design to allow the installation of alternative engines, such as the Rolls Royce Tyne or Proteus, should countries like the United Kingdom prefer them.

Weapons suitable for the military models include the Oto Melara 76 mm rapid-fire

cannon and the Emerson 30 mm cannon, the Argo control system and the Otomat, Exocet, Penguin and Gabriel anti-ship missiles.

Another Boeing concept is the regional final assembly centre, a number of which would be established around the world in order to supply customers with complete vessels made up from imported hulls and superstructures. At the same time the arrangement would meet the growing demand in lesser developed areas for greater participation in industrial programmes.

The centres, which would not be owned or operated by Boeing, would simply be involved with their importation, assembly and marketing. Likely areas for the establishment of these centres include the Caribbean, Greece, Iran, Japan, Taiwan, Indonesia and Scandinavia.

DAK HYDROFOILS
NEW YORK OFFICE:
PO Box 161, Honeoye, New York 14471, USA
HAWAII OFFICE:
PO Box 827, Hanalei, Hawaii 96714

PROPRIETOR AND CHIEF DESIGNER:
David A. Keiper

Dak Hydrofoils is currently designing and developing simple low-cost hydrofoil conversion kits for outboard powerboats. These are based on those available from the com-

pany for existing racing catamarans.

The arrangement employs identical lateral foils, positioned in a similar location, plus a fully-submerged stern foil. Lighter craft will have a simple foil beneath the outboard engine. Heavier craft, of up to 1,500 lb

(680·38 kg) loaded weight, have a retractable 6 in (152 mm) chard foil supported by twin struts.

The propeller is lowered by a combination of engine shaft extension or extensions, and/or lowering the engine by means of parallel bars.

A 12 ft dinghy equipped with DAK hydrofoils for an owner in New Zealand. Power is supplied by a 9.5 hp engine

DEPARTMENT OF THE NAVY, NAVAL SEA SYSTEMS COMMAND (NAVSEA)

HEADQUARTERS:
Washington DC 20362

ADVANCED SHIP DEVELOPMENT MANAGER:
James L. Schuler

OFFICE ADDRESS:
US Naval Sea Systems Command, Advanced Technology Systems Division (Code 0322), National Center Building 3, Room 10E54, Washington DC 20362

The Research and Technology Directorate of the US Naval Sea Systems Command (NAVSEA) is the primary technical sponsor for all US Navy hydrofoil and hovercraft programmes. The programme manager responsible for the development of all types of high performance ship concepts is Mr James L. Schuler (Code 032).

The NATO PHM hydrofoil is being acquired under the direction of Capt. Edw. W. Molzan, USN. The Surface Effect Ship is being developed under the direction of Capt. Carl Boyd, USN.

Technical manager of the US Navy Advanced Hydrofoil Systems Development Programme is Mr Robert Johnston of the David W. Taylor Naval Ship Research and Development Centre. The Amphibious Assault Landing Craft (AALC) Programme

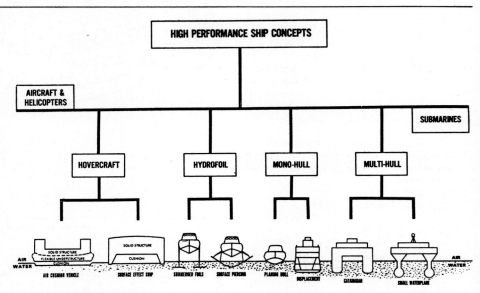

High performance ship concepts under development by US Naval Sea Systems Command

is being managed by Mr J. Benson (NAVSEA 032J). The AALC Programme includes the construction of two air cushion vehicles of about 160 tons design all-up weight. The craft are the JEFF (A) being built by the Aerojet General Corporation and the JEFF (B) being developed by the Bell Aerosystems Corporation.

DYNAFOIL INC.

HEAD OFFICE:
881 West 16th Street, Newport Beach, California 92663

TELEPHONE:
(714) 646-9231

DIRECTORS:
David J. Cline, Chairman
James M. Dale, Secretary/Treasurer
Paul D. Griem, Executive Vice President

Dynafoil, Inc. was formed in December 1971 to develop the Dynafoil sport craft. The development of this vehicle began in late 1970 with the construction of IRMA 1, the foil configuration of which has been the foundation for all subsequent work. Patents for the foil configuration have been applied for in all the main consumer countries, and have been granted in the USA.

DYNAFOIL MARK I

This fibre glass-hulled sports hydrofoil is a marine counterpart to the motorcycle and snowmobile. The bow foil is mounted at the base of a handlebar-equipped steering head and the handling characteristics are similar to those of a motor cycle. Production began in June 1975.

FOILS: Canard configuration with a fully submerged main foil located aft and bearing 60% of the load and small incidence-control-

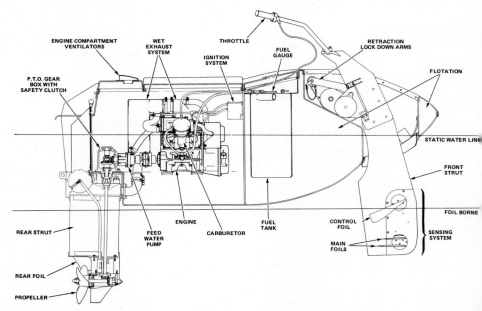

Inboard profile of the Dynafoil Mark I showing the power plant and transmission arrangements

led twin-delta foil forward. The angle of incidence is controlled mechanically by a curved planing control foil to achieve a constant flying height. Both the control foil and the bow foils rotate on pitch axes located forward of their centre of hydrodynamic lift. In normal flight the trailing edge of the control foil skims the water surface, while the twin delta bow foil maintains its designed angle of incidence. If the bow rises too high above the mean water line, the control foil pitches upwards, allowing the foils to operate in a neutral position, in which it generates little or no lift. Conversely, downward pitch at the bow decreases the angle of attack of the control foil, which, through a linkage system causes the bow foils to increase its incidence angle, thus restoring normal flight. The aft foil has anhedral to prevent tip breeching and ventilation and is set above the propeller. The foils are in cast 356-T6 aluminium while the struts are of fibreglass. Both foils retract fully, the bow foil rotating upwards and rearwards, the aft foil rearwards and upwards against the transom.

CONTROLS: Steering is accomplished by turning the front foil strut. All turns enter a fully co-ordinated bank.

HULL: Two-stage deep V hull, comprises two fibreglass mouldings bonded together at the beltline. After bonding, all voids not employed for functional components are filled with 2 lb density polyurethane foam providing 600 lb of buoyancy.

ACCOMMODATION: Open cockpit with a motor cycle pillion-style seat for two.

POWER PLANT: The Mark I is available with a choice of two engines—either a 340 cc, 26 hp, or a high performance 440 cc, 36 hp, 2-cylinder, 2-stroke Xenoah engine. Power is delivered to the outdrive through a 90° gearbox mounted inboard. The overall gear ratio is 1·75:1. Final drive is through a bevel gear at the base of the rear strut. The propeller, made by Michigan Wheel, is of 3-bladed subcavitating design in cast aluminium. A single 5 gallon (US) (18·92 l) fuel tank is located amidships, with a refuelling neck on the outside hull at the bow.

DIMENSIONS:

Length overall, hull	7 ft 0 in (2·13 m)
Length overall,	
foils retracted	8 ft 0 in (2·43 m)
foils extended	7 ft 0 in (2·13 m)
Hull beam	3 ft 6 in (1·06 m)
Beam overall,	
foils retracted	3 ft 6 in (1·06 m)
foils extended	3 ft 6 in (1·06 m)
Draft afloat,	
foils retracted	1 ft 0 in (304 mm)
foils extended	3 ft 0 in (914 mm)
Draft foilborne	1 ft 6 in (457 mm)
Freeboard	1 ft 2 in (355 mm)
Height overall, hullborne	2 ft 0 in (609 mm)
	3 ft 6 in (1·06 m)

WEIGHTS:

Light displacement	350 lbs (158·75 kg)
Normal take-off displacement	
	550 lbs (272·14 kg)
Max take-off displacement	
	800 lbs (362·85 kg)

PERFORMANCE:

Max speed foilborne 40 mph (64·36 km/h)

Above and below: The Dynafoil Mark I two-seat sports hydrofoil. Note the twin delta configuration of the forward foil, the incidence of which is controlled by the curved planing foil located above

Max speed hullborne	5 mph (8·04 km/h)	
Cruising speed,		
foilborne	30 mph (48·28 km/h)	
hullborne	5 mph (8·04 km/h)	
Designed endurance and range at cruising speed, approx	65 miles (104·60 km)	
Turning radius at cruising speed		15 ft (4·57 m)

Fuel consumption at max speed
2-5 gph (9·0-22·7 lph)

SEA TEST: Craft has been tested in 3-4 foot chop and 8-10 foot swells.

PRICE: $1,995·00, plus options.

EDO CORPORATION, GOVERNMENT PRODUCTS DIVISION

HEAD OFFICE:

13-10 111th Street, College Point, New York 11356

EXECUTIVES:

L. M. Swanson, Director, Air MCM Applications

Edo Corporation has developed a foil-equipped catamaran MCM system which speeds the process of magnetic mine clearance and reduces the hazards of mine sweeping operations. The system, the Edo Mark 105, is designed to be towed by the US Navy's RH-53D Sea Stallion and other heavy-lift helicopters of similar size and performance. The first unit formed to operate Mk 105 Airborne Minesweeping Gear was the HM-12 helicopter mine countermeasures Squadron,

which operated off North Vietnam to clear mines from the entrance to the port of Haiphong and undertook the aerial sweeping of the Suez Canal during the spring of 1974. The operation—code named Nimbus Star—was said to have been a complete success.

It has been stated that a mine can be detonated almost immediately beneath the Mk.105 without the craft sustaining major structural damage.

If required the equipment can be towed behind a BHC BH.7 amphibious hovercraft or other suitable ACV. Tests with this arrangement have been undertaken in the UK and USA.

It is reported that ten RH-53D Sea Stallions, together with towed sweeping equipment, have been supplied to the Naval

Air Transport Battallion, Iran.

Advantages claimed for the system include the following: lower acquisition and maintenance costs; fewer operating personnel required; low equipment vulnerability and bigger areas cleared within a given time.

Normally the helicopter/seasled combination is conveyed to the affected area aboard an amphibious assault craft. The helicopter lifts-off with the sled at the end of a line, lowers it into the water, extends its foils, and sets off to sweep the minefield.

The towline, which is 450 ft (137·16 m) long, also serves as an electric cable for carrying control signals to the sled, and as a fuel transfer line in the case of extended operations.

A portable winch in the helicopter is used to handle the craft, the sweep cables and the

The Edo Mark 105, probably the most sophisticated of all mine counterm-easures systems, has been under development for some years. It comprises a helicopter and a towed hydrofoil sea sled, on which is mounted a tur-bogenerator that energises magnetic sweep cables, thus simulating the magnetic field of a ship

towing cable during launching and retrieval. The system can be operated from either ships or shore bases equipped with crane facilities and small boats for handling the sweep cables which stream out behind the seasled.

MARK 105 AIRBORNE MINESWEEPING GEAR

The Mk 105 is a helicopter-towed, magnetic minesweeping system mounted on a 27 ft 6 in (8·38 m) long catamaran seasled. Foils are fitted to permit high speed operation and provide improved seakeeping performance. Aboard the craft is a turbogenerator which provides energy for the magnetic sweep cables and powers a hydraulic pump for foil retraction.

FOILS: Surface-piercing tandem configuration with two inverted V foils forward and two aft, balancing the loading between them. High-riding pitch control subfoils of similar configuration are located ahead of the two bow foils. Bow and stern foils are rotated for retraction and extension by a self-contained hydraulic system.

HULL: Catamaran hull comprising two tubular pontoons of light metal alloy construction, connected by an aerofoil section platform on which is mounted a gas-turbine powered electric generator set and the retrieval rig structure to which handling lines are attached. The two ends of the towing bridle are attached to the inward faces of the twin pontoon hulls forward of the platform. Wheels are attached to the underside of the pontoons to facilitate deck handling. Fuel for the turbogenerator set is carried in two centrally located tanks, one in each pontoon.

TOWING AND OPERATION: The 450 ft (137·16 m) long towing cable terminates in an electrical connector and fuel fitting. As well as providing the towing links between the platform and the helicopter, all electrical commands and supplementary fuel pass through the cable. The cable consists of an electrical core containing nineteen individual conductors, around which is a double layer of steel wire. Surrounding this is a hose, and fuel flows through the annular space between the inner diameter of the hose and the steel wire reinforcement.

The 27 ft 6in long sled is generally carried aboard an Amphibious Assault Ship (LPH) or Amphibious Transport Dock (LPD), which also act as a mobile base for the helicopters. The helicopter lifts the sled off the deck then lowers it into the water to enable the sweepgear streaming operation to be completed.

The tow cable is then picked up and the sled is towed, foilborne, into the sweep area. Once in the area, the sled can be towed at lower speeds, hullborne, to simulate a displacement vessel and its magnetic (or in the case of the Mk 106, combined magnetic and acoustic) signature.

SYSTEMS: A gas turbine generator set, mounted within a nacelle on the platform provides energy for the generation of the magnetic field. The complete power pack comprises a gas turbine driven AC generator, a rectifier, a controller containing the water-borne electronics and batteries to power the electronics system.

MAGNETIC SWEEP CABLE: This is attached to the after end of the sweep boom located on the underside of the port pontoon. It comprises an upper electrode attached to the end of a trailing cable and a lower electrode fitted to the boom fin. The potential between the electrodes, employing the water as a conductor, produces a magnetic field which simulates that of a ship.

CONTROL PROGRAMMER: Located in the helicopter this is the only manned station employed in the system. It contains the airborne electronics and all the controls and instrumentation necessary.

The console contains the fuel transfer control panel, turbine indicators, hydrofoil and sweep boom actuators and the generator controls and indicators.

From the console the operator can start and stop the turbine, raise and lower the foils and control the magnetic influences generated through the conductor cables trailed behind the sled.

DIMENSIONS:

Length overall	27 ft 6 in
Beam, catamaran structure only	11 ft 7 in
across foils	21 ft 0 in
Height, foils extended:	
to top of retrieval rig	17 ft 3 in
to top of nacelle	13 ft 6 in
foils retracted, to base of wheels	11 ft 6 in

WEIGHTS:

Empty weight	5,522 lb
Gross weight	6,432 lb

PERFORMANCE:
Towing speeds and sea state capability not available

Mark 106

An earlier airborne minesweeping system was the Mark 104, which can also be carried, towed and recovered by helicopters. This is used to detonate acoustic mines. It comprises a venturi tube and a water activated turbine which rotates a disc to reproduce a ship's acoustic signature. The latest model in the series combines the duties of the Mk 104 and 105 to provide both acoustic and magnetic influences and is known as the Mk 106.

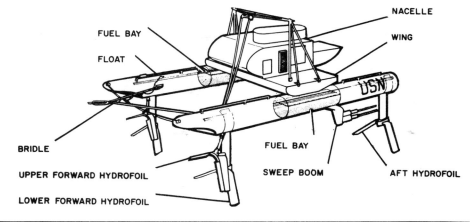

This drawing shows the surface-piercing tandem foil system of the Edo Mark 105 and the high-riding pitch- control-subfoils

GRUMMAN AEROSPACE CORPORATION
HEAD OFFICE:
Bethpage, New York 11714
TELEPHONE:
516-575-2417
CABLE/TELEX:
GRUMAIRBETHPAGENY 961430
DIRECTORS:
G. M. Skurla, Chairman/President
SENIOR EXECUTIVES:
R. H. Tripp, Executive Vice President
D. L. Walsh, Director, Marketing

Grumman entered the hydrofoil field in 1956 when it acquired Dynamic Developments Inc, producer of the experimental XCH-4, built for the Office of Naval Research in 1955. Powered by two aircraft engines with air propellers, this eight-ton vessel established a world's speed record for hydrofoil craft, by exceeding 78 knots (145 km/h). In 1958 Grumman designed and built the XCH-6 Sea Wings, also for the Office of Naval Research. Sea Wings was the first hydrofoil to employ both supercavitating foils and a supercavitating propeller and attained speeds in excess of 60 knots.

In 1960, Grumman was awarded a contract by the Maritime Administration for the design and construction of the HS Denison, an 80-ton open ocean research vessel which was launched in June 1962. This craft (described in the 1967-68 edition) was operated at speeds above 60 knots, demonstrating good foilborne manoeuvrability and seakeeping ability in rough water.

Grumman also completed the guidance design for the 328-ton, 212 ft (64·6 m) AG (EH) Plainview for the US Navy. The foils for this craft were the forerunners of those used on the Dolphin and the more recent PGH-1 Flagstaff.

The primary purpose of the Plainview is to establish the possibility of operating large submerged foil craft in high sea states, and explore many possible mission assignments including ASW, hydrographic data collection, surveillance, search and rescue and escort duties.

In December 1972 it was equipped with a single missile container and launched three NATO-configured Sea Sparrow missiles during rough water trials off the coast of Washington. The craft is currently undergoing overhaul. From early 1975 onwards it will be employed as an analysis tool in support of future large hydrofoil development for the US Navy.

Two Dolphin 1 class hydrofoils were built for Grumman by Blohm & Voss, Hamburg but development of this class has now been discontinued. The company is now concentrating on the development of military hydrofoils for use by the United States and

Grumman's PGH-I Flagstaff hydrofoil patrol gunboat equipped with a 40 mm rapid-firing cannon

PGH-I Flagstaff bearing the insignia of a US Coast Guard cutter during a series of successful evaluation trials held by the USCG between November 1974 and February 1975

foreign navies. Flagstaff is currently in service with the US Navy and between April and June 1971 was employed on 152 mm (6 in) gun-firing trials for the Navy Electronics Laboratory at San Diego, California.

A series of underwater explosion tests have been conducted with the Flagstaff in an experiment aimed at obtaining data on the shock responses of hydrofoil craft. The Flagstaff was the first and so far the only hydrofoil to undergo such tests.

In early 1974, the company announced plans for the design of an 83·5 ton derivative,

the Flagstaff Mk II. Power is supplied by either a Rolls-Royce RM-2B or Allison 501K20 gas-turbine and the maximum foilborne speed is 50 knots.

In March 1975, a second version of the PG(H)-1 was announced—the Flagstaff Mark III. With an overall length of 83 ft (25·30 m), 10 ft (3·04 m) longer than the Mark II, this model is designed primarily for high endurance operations calling for long range and low payloads. In April this was followed by the announcement of another new design—the Dolphin III. An enlarged model of the Dolphin I (see JANE'S SURFACE SKIMMERS 1970-71 and earlier editions) it is intended as a high-speed utility and crew boat for servicing offshore oil rigs.

PG(H)-1 FLAGSTAFF

The 67·5 ton PG(H)-1 Flagstaff hydrofoil gunboat was launched on January 9th, 1968. It underwent preliminary trials in July 1968, and was delivered and placed in service at West Palm Beach in September 1968.

Since then the craft has operated from the US Naval Base, Coronado, California. For five-and-a-half-months it underwent operational trials in South Vietnam. Between 1st September 1969 and 19th February 1970, Flagstaff was employed on various missions in Phase II of "Opeval" and "Market Time", operating from Da Nang.

Between November and December 1970 the craft was modified to mount a 152 mm M551 gun from a Sheridan light tank on its foredeck. The gun fires conventional 6 in shells or Shillelagh missiles and has a laser range-finder giving instant accurate ranging. It is capable of hitting a target at a range of up to 4 miles (6·43 km).

Between November 1974 and February 1975 the vessel underwent evaluation by the US Coast Guard in a number of missions including: enforcement of laws and treaties, fisheries and contraband enforcement, search and rescue, marine environmental protection, servicing aids to navigation and marine science activities.

The craft is currently in use by the US Navy to evaluate fleet equipment and for the study and development of fleet hydrofoil tactics.

FOILS: Fully submerged system of conventional configuration, split forward, and a single foil aft. About 70% of the weight is supported by the twin forward foils and 30% by the aft foil. Foil section is sub cavitating, 16-series. All three foils are incidence-controlled and operated by an Airesearch hydropilot. The stern foil strut rotates ±3° for steering and all three retract completely clear of the water. Foils (by Potvin Kellering) are forged 6061-T652 aluminium and struts (by Blohm & Voss) are in HYSO 4130 and HY80 steel. Foil area is 100 sq ft (9·29 m²).

HULL: The hull structure is of combined welded and riveted corrosion resistant 5456 aluminium. The pilot house roof is of fibreglass sandwich. All frames and bulkheads are welded assemblies and transverse framing is used throughout.

PROPULSION: The main engine is a 3,550 hp Rolls-Royce Tyne Mk 621/10 gas turbine, flat rated to 90°F. Power is transmitted through a mechanical right angle drive to a KaMeWa 45 in (1·14 m) diameter, 3-bladed supercavitating, controllable-pitch propeller. Nominal rpm at cruising speed 1,000. Hullborne power is supplied by two 202 hp GM 6V diesels driving twin Buehler 1 ft 4¼ in (419 mm) diameter waterjets, equipped with ±35° steering and reversing nozzles.

SYSTEMS, ELECTRICAL: Ship's service generator sets: twin GM 4-53N diesels with Delco 120 volt, 50kW, 62·5 kVA, 3-phase Delta, 60-cycle at 1,800 rpm. Emergency power (generators inoperable): 2 sets batteries 200 Ah, 24 volts, for autopilot, gyroscope and navigation lights, all automatically switched.

RADIO: VHF and HF transceivers.

RADAR AND NAVIGATION: Decca TM626 at navigator's station and repeater in commander's station. Bendix ADF-162A automatic direction finder, Raytheon 726

Flagstaff from the forward starboard quarter, showing the test installation of a 152 mm M551 howitzer gun turret

The Flagstaff Mk.II can be equipped for a variety of military roles, including missile craft, ASW, search and rescue and fast transport. In the impression above, the craft is armed with Gabriel ship-to-ship missiles

depth sounder, Arma Mk 26 gyrocompass, Chesapeake EM-log speed log, Bendix prototype DRAI and DRT navigation system.

FIREFIGHTING AND DAMAGE CONTROL: Diesel-driven 50 gpm bilge pump, plus 50 gpm diesel-driven deck service pump, portable electric 250 gpm pumps and hand pump. Deck SW connection for fighting fires in other craft. Walter Kidd. Central CF BR fire extinguishing system in two 251 lb cylinders. Four portable 2½ lb Ansul Foray Combo Pacs.

ARMAMENT. Main battery (until Nov 1970): single 40 mm Mk 3 Mod 0 rapid firing cannon. Machine guns: two twin mounts 50 cal Mk 56 Mod 0. Mortar: One 81 mm Mk 2 Mod 0. Small arms: M16 rifles (11), ·38 Cal pistols, 12 ga shotguns. New main gun battery as from December 1970: 152 mm M551 howitzer, firing conventional 6 in shells or Shillelagh missiles. Laser range finder. Main gun battery has now been removed.

DIMENSIONS:

Length overall hull	73 ft 0 in (22·2 m)
Length overall, foils extended	86 ft 6 in (23·36 m)
Length overall, foils retracted	89 ft 0 in (27·1 m)
Hull beam	21 ft 5 in (6·5 m)
Extreme beam, foils retracted tip-to-tip	37 ft 1 in (11·28 m)
Draft, foils extended, static	13 ft 11 in (4·26 m)
Nominal draft foilborne	5 ft 8 in (1·72 m)

WEIGHTS:

Displacement, fully loaded, as delivered 67·5 long tons
1971, with 152 mm howitzer 72 long tons

PERFORMANCE:

Cruising speed, foilborne
In excess of 40 knots
Cruising speed, hullborne
In excess of 7 knots

FLAGSTAFF MK II

In March 1974, Grumman announced that plans were underway for an improved version of the PG(H)-1, known as the Flagstaff Mk II, Intended primarily for military applications. the new model is designed as a high-speed patrol gunboat or missile craft, but it can be equipped for a number of alternative roles including search and rescue and fast military transport.

The chief differences between this craft and its predecessor lie in the installation of a gas turbine of greater power output—either a 3,800 hp Rolls Royce Tyne RM2B or a 3,950 hp Allison 501-K20A, the introduction of an improved mechanical right-angle drive improved hydropilot system, and the provision of larger foils and longer struts. The fully loaded displacement is increased from 67·5 to 83·5 long tons. Max payload, including fuel, is 65,457 lbs.

FOILS: Fully submerged system of conventional configuration, comprising twin inverted T foils forward and a single inverted T foil aft. Approximately 70% of the load is supported by the two forward foils and 30% by the aft foil. All three foils are incidence controlled and operated by a hydro-pilot system employing electrohydraulic actuators. The stern foil power strut, together with the propeller, rotates ±3° for steering and all three foil/strut units retract completely clear of the water for hullborne manoeuvring. The foils are in 7075-T73 aluminium and the struts are in HY-130 steel. Break joints are incorporated on the two forward struts, so that should either of them strike large items of debris each would break clean at the point of its connection to its yoke. A shear bolt releases the aft strut permitting it to rotate rearwards and upwards above the transom.

HULL: Hull is in welded 5086-H 111 and H 117 marine aluminium. The deckhouse and skin are in 1 ft 11¼ in (587 mm) wide-ribbed and integrally stiffened extrusions, each 25 ft (7·62 m) long.

ACCOMMODATION: Crew will vary according to the nature of the missions for which the craft is employed and the type of armament carried. Minimum crew requirement is three, maximum is fourteen. The forward superstructure accommodates the bridge, which contains steering and engine control consoles and is elevated to give a 360° view. The helmsman and CO are seated on a raised deck and the chief engineer and navigator are accommodated on the main deck. All crew accommodation is air conditioned. Entry to the deckhouse is via two 2 ft 2 in × 5ft 0 in (660 mm × 1·52 m) watertight doors, one port, one starboard. An emergency exit is located aft, behind the pilothouse on the weather deck. Escape hatches are provided in the living spaces.

POWER PLANT, FOILBORNE: Foilborne propulsion is supplied by either a 4,489 hp Rolls-Royce RM 2B Tyne or a 4,250 hp Allison 501-K20A gas-turbine. Power is transmitted to the propeller through a Grumman Z-drive—a horizontal shaft leading to a bevel gear over the stern in the aft foil strut, then via a vertical shaft and a second bevel gear to a horizontal propeller shaft. Reduction is 13:1. A 3 ft 9 in (1·14 m) diameter KaMeWa, 3-bladed controllable-pitch, supercavitating propeller is fitted. Fuel—total capacity is 5,179 US gallons—is carried in four tanks located forward of CG, in vicinity of main foils. Oil capacity is 130 US gallons. Fuelling points are located amidships, on deck aft of deckhouse. Fuel recommended is JP5 or Diesel No. 2.

POWER PLANTS, HULLBORNE: Hullborne propulsion is supplied by two 220 hp GM 6V-53N diesels, driving two Jacuzzi 14YJ marine waterjets, equipped with steering and reversing nozzles.

SYSTEMS:
ELECTRICAL: Diesel generator set. Two GM 4-53N diesel engines driving Delco generators rated for 50 kw 440 volt 3-phase service.
HYDRAULICS: 3,000 psi for foil control and ship service systems.
ELECTRONICS: Decca Model TM 626 radar with display at navigator's station and

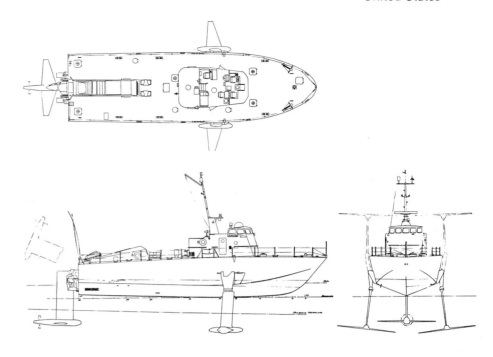

General arrangement of the Grumman Flagstaff Mk.II, 84-ton high-speed patrol gunboat or missile craft

repeater at CO's station.
COMMUNICATIONS: HF system AN/ARC-94 Collins 618T-2B. VHF system: AN/ARC-51A.
ARMAMENT:
MISSILES: Standard, Standard ARM, Harpoon, Sea Killer, Sea Sparrow, Exocet MM 38, Gabriel or Penguin surface-to-surface missiles.
GUNS: Choice of the following systems for surface engagement, shore bombardment, AA defence or missile interception: 76/62 Oto Melara, 35 mm Twin Oerlikon, 30 mm Twin Hispano Suiza, 20 mm Twin Emerson, 20 mm Vulcan, 40 mm Bofors, 30 mm Emerson GE or 20 mm Phalanx.

DIMENSIONS, EXTERNAL:
Length overall, hull	73 ft 0 in (22·25 m)
Length waterline, hull	66 ft 8 in (20·34 m)
Length overall, foils retracted	91 ft 0 in (27·74 m)
Length overall, foils extended	86 ft 10 in (26·45 m)
Hull beam	21 ft 5 in (6·53 m)
Beam overall foils retracted	39 ft 3 in (11·963 m)
Beam overall, foils extended	40 ft 9 in (12·420 m)
Draft afloat, foils retracted	5 ft 1½ in (1·562 m)
Draft afloat, foils extended	16 ft 0 in (4·87 m)
Draft foilborne	7 ft 8 in (2·33 m)
Freeboard, maximum	7 ft 1¼ in (2·18 m)
Height overall to top of mast	38 ft 1½ in (11·62 m)

DIMENSIONS, INTERNAL:
Cabin length	14 ft 4 in (4·36 m)
Max width	12 ft 0 in (3·65 m)
Max height	9 ft 0 in (2·74 m)
Floor area	160 sq ft (14·86 sq m)
Volume	1,280 cu ft (36·24 cu m)

WEIGHTS:
Light displacement	52·28 long tons
Normal take-off displacement	83·5 long tons
Normal payload	29,957 lbs (9,505·916 kg)
Useful load, including fuel	65,457 lbs (29,690·78 kg)

PERFORMANCE:
Max speed, foilborne	52 knots
Most economical cruising speed	42 knots
Max speed, hullborne (gas-turbine power plant)	20 knots
Cruising speed, hullborne (diesel displacement engines)	9 knots
Max. permissible sea state in foilborne mode	4-5
Designed endurance and range at cruising	approx 940 nautical miles
Number of seconds to take-off	approx 25 sec
Number of seconds and distance to stop craft	3 to 4 seconds, 200 ft (60·96 m)
Fuel consumption at cruising speed	1,590 lb/hour (721 kgs/hour)
Fuel consumption at max. speed	1,900 lb/hour (860 kgs/hour)

DETAILS OF SEA TEST (based on PG(H)-1):
Location	West Palm Beach, Florida
Sea states	2,3, 4 and 5
Location of accelerometer, forward and amidships	
Heave 0·2± g in 8 ft (2·43 m) high waves	
Average 0·05± rms g in 4 ft 6 in (1·37 m) high waves	

FLAGSTAFF Mk. III

In March 1975 Grumman announced that plans were underway for a second version of the PG(H)-1—the Flagstaff Mk.III. The new model is intended primarily for high endurance operations, calling for long-range and low payloads. These would include patrol, surveillance and search and rescue duties.

The chief difference between this craft and the Flagstaff Mk II are as follows:

An increase of 10 ft (3·04 m) in the overall length, bringing it to 83 ft 0 in (25·30 m);

Fuel load raised from 15,890 lb (7,207 kg) to 51,390 lb (23,310 kg);

Replacement of the waterjets (for hullborne propulsion) by propellers on retractable outdrives;

Installation of more powerful diesel engines, raising the hullborne speed to 11·5 knots;

Reduction in the useful load of 4,067 lb to 61,390 lb, due to the longer hull structure.

Design range of the vessel at its most economical cruising speed of 42 knots is

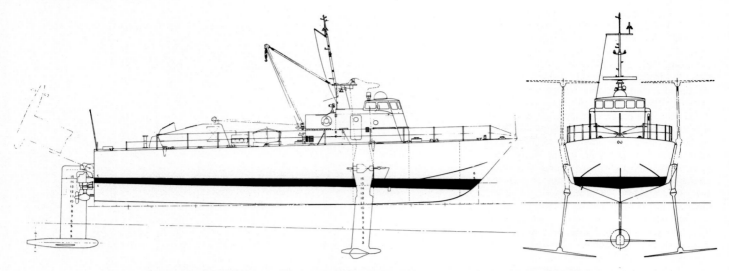

Outboard profile and bow-on view of the 83 ft (25·29 m) long Flagstaff Mark III, a 90-ton military
hydrofoil designed for high endurance operations including search and rescue

1,350 nautical miles.

FOILS: Fully submerged system of conventional configuration, comprising twin inverted T foils forward and a single inverted T foil aft. Approximately 70% of the load is carried by the two forward foils and 30% by the aft foil. All three foils have tapered planform and the total foil area is 160·5 ft² (14·91 m²). Foil loading is 1,223·6 lb sq ft forward and 1,048 lb/sq ft aft. The incidence angle of the forward foils is variable in flight from +9° to —4°, while that of the rear foil is variable from +10° to —2°. Incidence angles of all three foils are controllable and operated by a hydropilot system employing electrohydraulic actuators.

The foils are contour machined in 7075-T73 solid aluminium forgings, and the struts are of welded construction in HY-130 steel. The stern foil power strut, together with the propeller, rotates 3° to port and starboard for steering, and all three foil/strut units are retracted hydraulically completely clear of the water for hullborne manoeuvring. The forward foils retract sideways through an angle of 177°, while the rear foil retracts aft through an angle of 111°. Break joints are incorporated on the two forward struts. In the event of ½g impact or more, shear bolts will separate strut and foil from yoke. Struts and foils are designed to clear the hull after separation to prevent hull damage. A shear bolt releases the aft strut permitting it to rotate rearwards and upwards above the transom. The hydraulic retraction cylinders and transmission shaft disconnect automatically on strut retraction.

HULL: The hull is in welded 5086-H111 and H117 marine aluminium. The deckhouse and skin are in 1 ft 11⅛ in (587 mm) wide ribbed and integrally stiffened extrusions each 25 ft (7·62 m) long.

ACCOMMODATION: Crew will vary according to the nature of the missions for which the craft is employed and the type of equipment and armament carried. Minimum crew requirement is three, maximum is fourteen. The forward superstructure accommodates the bridge, which contains steering and engineering control consoles and is elevated to give a 360° view. The helmsman and commanding officer are seated on a raised deck and the chief engineer and navigator are accommodated on the main deck. All crew accommodation is air-conditioned. Entry to the deckhouse is via two 2 ft 2 in × 5 ft 0 in (0·660 m × 1·52 m)

watertight doors, one port, one starboard. An emergency exit is located aft behind the pilothouse on the weatherdeck. Escape hatches are provided in the living spaces.

POWER PLANT, FOILBORNE: Motive power for the foilborne propulsion system is supplied by either a 4,480 hp Rolls-Royce RM 2B Tyne or a 4,250 hp Allison 50LK20 A gas-turbine. Power is transmitted to the propeller via a Grumman Z-drive with a reduction ratio of 13:1. A 3 ft 9 in (1·14 m) diameter KaMeWa controllable-pitch, supercavitating propeller is fitted. Fuel is carried in six integral tanks located amidships, with a total capacity of 8,770 US gallons. Recommended fuel is JP-5 or Diesel 1 or 2. Refuelling points are located amidships on the weatherdeck, aft of the deckhouse. Oil capacity is 130 US gallons.

POWER PLANT, HULLBORNE: Motive power for the hullborne propulsion system is provided by two Detroit 6-7LN diesels, each developing 257 hp at 2,300 rpm. Power is transmitted via two Model OD-8500 precision V-drive retractable outdrives to two 2 ft 2 in (0·660 m) diameter three-bladed propellers.

SYSTEMS:

AIR-CONDITIONING: 5-ton packaged water chiller.

ELECTRICAL: Diesel generator set. Two GM 4-53N diesel engines driving Delco generators rated for 50 kW, 440 volt, 62·5 KVA, 3-phase, 60Hz at 1,800 rpm.

HYDRAULICS: 3,000 psi pressure for foil strut retraction, incidence control, foilborne steering and miscellaneous hydraulic motors.

ELECTRONICS:

STANDARD: Decca radar Model TM626 with display at navigator's station and repeater at CO's station. OPTIONAL: Radio HF, AN/ARC-94 Collins Model 618T2B. UHF ANARC-51A.

DIMENSIONS:

Length overall, hull	83 ft 0 in (25·30 m)
Length waterline, hull	75 ft 0 in (22·80 m)
Length overall, foils retracted	101 ft 0 in (30·79 m)
Length overall, foils extended	96 ft 10 in (29·54 m)
Hull beam	21 ft 5 in (6·53 m)
Beam overall, foils retracted	39 ft 3 in (11·96 m)
Beam overall, foils extended	40 ft 9 in (12·41 m)

Draft afloat, foils retracted	4 ft 9 in (1·44 m)
Draft afloat, foils extended	16 ft 0 in (4·88 m)
Draft foilborne	3 ft 0 in (0·914 m)
Freeboard	8 ft 0 in (2·43 m)
Height overall, foilborne cruising	45 ft 0 in (13·71 m)
Height overall, hullborne	33 ft 10 in (10·32 m)

DIMENSIONS, INTERNAL:

Cabin length	14 ft 4 in (4·36 m)
Max. width	12 ft 0 in (3·65 m)
Max. height	9 ft 0 in (2·74 m)
Floor area	160 sq ft (14·86 sq. m)
Volume	1,280 cu ft (36·24 cu. m)

WEIGHTS (LONG TONS):

Light displacement	54·09 tons (54·97 t)
Normal take-off displacement	83·5 tons (84·84 t)
Max. take-off displacement	90·0 tons (91·47 t)
Normal deadweight	29·41 tons (29·87 t)
Maximum deadweight	35·91 tons (36·50 t)
Normal payload	4·46 tons (4·53 t)
Maximum payload	25·71 tons (26·13 t)

PERFORMANCE (with normal payload):

Max. speed, foilborne	52 knots
Cruising speed, foilborne	48 knots
Most economical speed foilborne	42 knots
Max. speed, hullborne	11·5 knots
Cruising speed, hullborne	8·0 knots

Max. sea state and wave height in foilborne mode
Sea State 4-5: wave height 16 ft (4·87 m)
Designed range at cruising speed, approx
1,290 n.mi at 48 knots
at most economical speed
1,350 n.mi at 42 knots
Turning radius at cruising speed
750 ft (228 m)
Number of seconds and distance to take-off
30 sec. 1,150 ft (350 m)
Number of seconds and distance to stop craft
3-4 seconds, 200 ft (60·9 m)
Fuel consumption at max. speed
52 knots = 2,200 lb/hr
Fuel consumption at cruising speed
48 knots = 1,910 lb/hr
Fuel consumption at most economical foilborne speed 42 knots = 1,590 lb/hr

DETAILS OF SEA TEST (based on PG(H)-1):
Location: West Palm Beach, Florida
Sea State(s): 2, 3, 4 and 5
Location of accelerometers: forward and

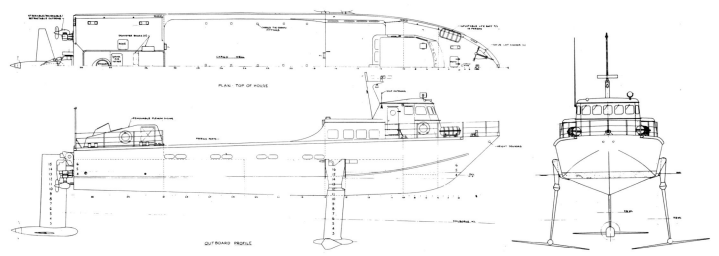

General arrangement of the Grumman Dolphin Mk.III, a 52-knot utility and crew boat for servicing off-shore oil rigs

amidships

Heave: 0·2± RMS G in 8 ft (2·43 m) high waves

0·05± RMS G in 4 ft 6 in (1·37 m) high waves

DOLPHIN MARK III

In April 1975, plans were announced for a second version of the Dolphin I, known as the Dolphin III. The new craft, which has an 18 ft by 28 ft (5·47 × 8·51 m) cargo well aft of the deckhouse, is intended primarily as a high speed utility and crew boat for servicing offshore oil rigs.

Among the main differences between the Dolphin III and its predecessor are the following:

An increase of 24·5 tons in the full load displacement, raising it from 59 long tons to 83·5 tons:

An increase of 10 ft (3·04 m) in the overall length, bringing it to 83 ft (25·30 m):

Provision of improved transmission and hydropilot systems:

Installation of a more powerful gas-turbine for foilborne operation:

The rearrangement of the passenger cabin and deck to carry passengers and cargo.

Designed range of the vessel at its most economical cruising speed of 42 knots is 610 nautical miles.

FOILS: Fully submerged system of conventional configuration, comprising twin inverted T foils forward and a single inverted T foil aft. Approximately 70% of the load is carried by the two forward foils and 30% by the aft foil. All three foils have tapered planform and the total foil area is 160·5 ft² (14·91 m²). Foil loading is 1,223·6 lb/sq ft forward and 1,048·8 lb/sq ft aft. Incidence angle of the forward foils is variable in flight from +9° to —4°, while that of the rear foil is variable from +10° to —2°. Incidence angles of all three foils are controlled and operated by a hydropilot system employing electrohydraulic actuators. The foils are contour-machined in 7075-T73 solid aluminium forgings, and the struts are of welded construction in. HY-130 steel. The stern foil power strut, together with the propeller, rotates 3° to port and starboard for steering, and all three foil/strut units are retracted hydraulically completely clear of the water for hullborne manoeuvring. The forward foils retract sideways through an angle of 177°, while the rear foil retracts aft through an angle of 111°. Break joints are incorporated on the two forward struts.

In the event of ½g impact or more, shear bolts will separate strut and foil from yoke. Struts and foils are also designed to clear the hull after separation to prevent hull damage.

A shear bolt releases the aft strut permitting it to rotate rearwards and upwards above the transom. The hydraulic retraction cylinders and transmission shaft disconnect automatically upon strut retraction.

HULL: The hull is welded 5086-H111 and H117 marine aluminium. The deckhouse and skin are fabricated in 1 ft 11⅛ in (587 mm) wide ribbed and integrally-stiffened extrusions, each 25 ft (7·62 m) long.

ACCOMMODATION: Normal crew requirements are for a captain, engineer, oiler and deckhand. Seating is provided in the wheelhouse for the captain (starboard) engineer (port) and oiler (folding seat). The number of seated passengers accommodated in the cabin aft of the pilothouse can vary from 24 to 48 depending on customer requirements. Air-conditioning is provided in both crew and passenger accommodation. Entry to the pilothouse is via a 2 ft 2 in × 5 ft 0 in (0·660 m × 1·15 m) door. An emergency exit is provided in the passenger cabin, opening onto the cargo well aft. Emergency equipment includes two inflatable 15-person liferafts.

POWER PLANT, FOILBORNE: Motive power for the foilborne propulsion system is provided by either a 4,480 hp Rolls-Royce RM 2B Tyne, or a 4,250 hp Allison 501K20A gas-turbine. Power is transmitted to a 3 ft 9 in (1·14 m) diameter KaMeWa controllable-pitch, supercavitating propeller via a Grumman Z-drive with a reduction ratio of 13:1. Fuel is carried in four integral fuel tanks, with a total capacity of 5,179 US gallons, located in the vicinity of the main foils. Normal fuel load is 3,328 US gal—23,298 lb. Recommended fuel is JP-5 or Diesel 1 or 2. Refuelling points are located on the well deck, aft of the cabin. Oil capacity is 130 US gallons.

POWER PLANT, HULLBORNE: Motive power for the hullborne system is provided by two Detroit 6-71N diesels, each delivering 257 hp at 2,300 rpm. Power is transmitted via two Model OD-8500 precision V-drive retractable outdrives to two 2 ft 2 in diameter, three-bladed propellers.

SYSTEMS:

AIR-CONDITIONING: 5-ton packaged water chiller.

ELECTRICAL: Diesel generator set. Two GM 3-53N diesel engines driving Delco

generators rated for 40 kW, 440 volt, 3-phase 60Hz at 1,800 rpm.

HYDRAULICS: 3,000 psi pressure for foil strut retraction, foil incidence control, foilborne steering and miscellaneous hydraulic motors.

ELECTRONICS:

Standard: Raytheon 4100 series or equivalent Optional: HF radio, AN/ARC 94, Collins 618T2B: UHF radio, AN/ARC-51A

DIMENSIONS, EXTERNAL:

Length overall, hull	83 ft 0 in (25·30 m)
Length waterline, hull	75 ft 0 in (22·86 m)
Length overall, foils retracted	101 ft 0 in (30·79 m)
Length overall, foil extended	96 ft 10 in (29·54 m)
Hull beam	21 ft 5 in (6·53 m)
Beam overall, foils retracted	39 ft 3 in (11·96 m)
Beam overall, foils extended	40 ft 9 in (12·41 m)
Draft afloat, foils retracted	4 ft 9 in (1·44 m)
Draft afloat, foils extended	16 ft 0 in (4·88 m)
Draft foilborne	3 ft 0 in (0·914 m)
Freeboard	8 ft 0 in (2·43 m)
Height overall, foilborne cruising	45 ft 0 in (13·71 m)
Height overall, hullborne	33 ft 10½ in (10·32 m)

DIMENSIONS, INTERNAL:

Cabin length	15 ft 3 in (4·63 m)
Max. width	19 ft 6 in (5·90 m)
Max. height	7 ft 6 in (2·28 m)
Floor area	208 ft² (19·32 sq. m)
Volume	1,855 ft³ (51·94 cu. m)

Freight hold:

Cargo well amidships

18 ft 0 in × 28 ft 0 in (5·47 m × 8·51 m)

WEIGHTS: (long tons)

Light displacement	46·01 tons (46·77 t)
Normal take-off displacement	83·50 tons (84·84 t)
Max. take-off displacement	90·0 tons (91·47 t)
Normal deadweight	37·49 tons (38·07 t)
Max. deadweight	43·99 tons (44·70 t)
Normal payload	26·23 tons (26·66 t)
Max. payload	34·93 tons (35·50 t)

PERFORMANCE:

Max. speed, foilborne	52 knots
Max. speed hullborne	11·5 knot
Cruising speed, foilborne	48 knots
Most economical speed	42 knots
Cruising speed, hullborne	8·0 knots

Max. permissible sea state and wave height

in foilborne mode

Sea states 4-5, wave height 16 ft (4·87 m)

Designed range at cruising speed of 48 knots
585 n. miles

Designed range at most economical cruising
speed of 42 knots   610 n. miles

Turning radius at cruising speed
750 ft (228 m)

Number of seconds and distance to take-off
(theoretical, approx)
30 seconds, 1,150 ft (350 m)

Number of seconds and distance to stop
craft (theoretical, app)
3-4 seconds, 200 ft (60·9 m)

Fuel consumption at max. speed
52 knots — 2,200 lb/hr

Fuel consumption at cruising speed
48 knots — 1,910 lb/hr

at most economical speed
42 knots — 1,590 lb/hr

Details of Sea Test (Based on Dolphin 1)

Locations: Kiel, Hamburg West Germany, to
Las Palmas, Canary Islands
Sea States 2, 3, 4 and 5

Location of accelerometer: forward and
amidships

Heave 0·2 ± RMS G in 8 ft (2·43 m)
high waves

Heave 0·05 ± G in 4 ft 6 in (1·37 m)
high waves.

AG(EH)-1 PLAINVIEW

The 320 ton AG (EH)—the designation means auxiliary general experimental hydrofoil—was built by the Lockheed Shipbuilding & Construction Company, Seattle, Washington. It is being used by the US Navy's Hydrofoil Systems Testing Unit, Bremerton, Washington to investigate the performance of a large seagoing hydrofoil under operational conditions. The guidance design and preparation of contract specifications were undertaken by Grumman under the direction of the Bureau of Ships.

A contract for detailed design and construction was awarded to Lockheed Shipbuilding and Construction Company in June 1963 and the hull was launched in June 1965. The craft successfully completed her maiden flight on March 21st, 1968 at Puget Sound and was officially delivered to the US Navy on March 1st 1969. It was given the US Navy classification "In Service, Special" in March 1969 and US Navy research and development trials are continuing.

FOILS: The foil system is fully submerged and automatically controlled by a Hamilton Standard autopilot system similar to that used in High Point. The foil arrangement is of conventional type with 90% of the weight carried on the two main foils and the remainder on the aft foil. The three foils, which have considerable sweep and taper, are geometrically similar with an aspect ratio of 3. The swept back leading edges help to delay cavitation and facilitate the shedding of seaweed and other neutrally buoyant debris. They also reduce impact loads associated with water entry after foil broaching. The main foils have some dihedral while the tail foil is flat.

Total foil area is 509 sq ft, and foil loaded is 1,460 lb ft² max. Foils are constructed in welded HY80 steel.

The main foils are extended, retracted and locked in each terminal position by means of a hydraulically-operated activating arm, connected to the upper part of the strut. The two foils are synchronised to be raised and lowered together in the transverse plane. The aft foil operates in a similar manner, but can be raised and lowered independently.

AGEH-1 Plainview, 328-ton US Navy ocean-going hydrofoil warship research vessel, moored in Puget Sound with foils retracted. Two 4-bladed propellers at the end of the pods on the main foils struts propel the vessel when foilborne

Maximum foilborne speed of the Plainview, which is powered by two 14,500 hp GE LM1500s, is in excess of 50 knots. It is designed to operate in sea state 5 conditions and has undergone trials in 8-10 ft (2·43-3·04 m) waves off Victoria BC

In the interests of weight economy, the Plainview's hull is built largely from specially extruded aluminium planks, each 40 ft (12·19 m) in length and 2 ft 1 in (0·635 m) in width. Struts and foils are built in HY-80 and HY-100 steel alloys. The bow shape is designed to minimise structural loadings due to wave impact

Foil lift variation is by change in the incidence angle; each can move through +11 deg to —4 deg. The single aft foil controls pitch angle.

The aft foil strut rotates for use as a rudder. Steering can be flat (rudder only) or fully coordinated, using differential main foil angles for banked turns, with the aft strut trailing.

HULL: The hull is almost completely fabricated in 5456 aluminium alloy. All deck, side and bottom plating is made from integrally stiffened, aluminium extruded planks. The hull is predominantly welded construction with the exception of the pilot house and certain longitudinal hull seams that act as crack stoppers.

The hull shape is designed to minimise the structural loadings due to wave impact and the bow shape has been developed for this specific purpose. Bottom deadrise is carried to the transom with the same objective.

ACCOMMODATION: Crew of twenty-five, comprising four officers and twenty-one enlisted men. The pilothouse, CIC compartment, living, messing and berthing spaces are air-conditioned. Sanitary and washroom areas, galley, displacement and main engine room are all mechanically ventilated. In the wheelhouse, the pilot's position is on the left, with the principal instrumentation; the co-pilot is on the right, and the observer between and slightly aft. Entry to the deckhouse is via three standard US Navy quick-acting aluminium doors—one aft port and one forward starboard on the main deck, and one aft on the lower deck. Emergency equipment includes 7-man liferafts, seven life rings, four aircraft markers, one kapok heaving line and emergency scuttles port and starboard.

POWER PLANT: Foilborne propulsion is supplied by two General Electric LM 1500s (marine version of the J-97), each of 14,500 hp continuous rating, connected by shafting and gearing to two 4-bladed, 5 ft 0 in (1·52 m) diameter supercavitating titanium propellers at the end of the propulsion pods on the main foils. The hydrodynamic design of the propellers was undertaken by Hydronautics Inc, and they were built by Hamilton Standard. The blades are bolted to the hubs and each blade is replaceable. The air inlet for the main turbines is introduced at the top of the deckhouse. Because of the need to prevent ingestion of water or saltspray into the gas turbines, there are lowered deflectors over the inlet opening, followed by a bank of sheet metal spray separators. There is a dam for solid water separation and four right angle turns before the air

reaches the engine bellmouths.

The hullborne powerplants are two General Motors V12-71 diesels each rated at 500 hp. Each diesel drives aft through a shaft to a right angle gear drive resembling a large outboard motor, mounted on the side of the hull. Each of these right angle drives is retractable about a horizontal axis and steerable about a vertical axis through 360 deg. rotation. A 4 ft 5 in (1·34 m) diameter five-bladed subcavitating propeller is mounted at the end of each right angle drive.

Auxiliary power is supplied by two GMC V8-71 engines driving two 100 kW generators.

SYSTEMS:

AIR CONDITIONING: The pilothouse, CIC compartment, living, messing and berthing spaces are air-conditioned during the cooling season by a 15 ton capacity Trane type compressor system. Sanitary and washroom areas, galley, displacement engine room, main engine room, windlass room and the engineers control booth are all mechanically ventilated.

HYDRAULICS: 3,000 psi operates foils, steering, extension, retraction and locking of struts and anchor windlass and starts propulsion diesels.

ELECTRONICS: Raytheon Pathfinder radar with AN/SPA-25 repeater, AN/WRC-1B Bendix radio, AN/URC-58 radio RF Comm Inc, two AN/ARC-52X Collins radios.

ARMAMENT: Six Mk 32 torpedo tubes in two tri-mounts, port and starboard, aft of the deckhouse. One Mk 44 torpedo stowed

in each tube. Single missile cannister fitted in late 1972 for demonstration launching of three NATO-configured Sea Sparrow missiles.

DIMENSIONS, EXTERNAL:

Length overall, hull	212 ft 0 in (64·61 m)
Length waterline, hull	205 ft 1¾ in (62·48 m)
Length overall, foils retracted	223 ft 8 in (68·17 m)
Length overall, foils extended	219 ft ½ in (66·75 m)
Hull beam	40 ft 5 in (12·31 m)
Beam overall, foils retracted	82 ft 8 in (25·19 m)
Beam overall, foils extended	70 ft 0 in (21·59 m)
Draft afloat, foils retracted	6 ft 3 in (1·90 m)
Freeboard, fwd	15 ft 6 in (4·72 m)
aft	7 ft 6½ in (2·29 m)
Height to top of mast	54 ft 9½ in (16·69 m)

WEIGHTS:

Light displacement	265 tons
Normal take-off	290 tons
Max take-off	328 tons

PERFORMANCE:

Max speed foilborne	in excess of 50 knots
Cruising speed foilborne	42 knots
Max speed hullborne	13·4 knots
Cruising speed hullborne	12 knots
Max permissible sea state and wave height in foilborne mode	

(Design sea state) Beaufort 5 Sea state 5

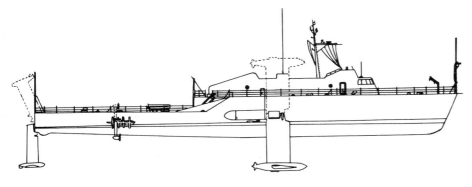 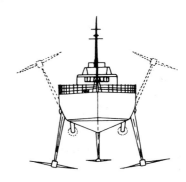

General arrangement of the AGEH-1 Plainview

HYDROFOILS INCORPORATED

HEAD OFFICE:
PO Box 115, Red Bank, N.J. 07701, USA

TELEPHONE:
(201) 842-1260

OFFICERS:
Kenneth E. Cook, President

Hydrofoils Incorporated has designed a fibreglass-hulled two-seater, the Mirage, for powerboat racing. The company, in conjunction with the American Power Boat Association, is examining the possibility of establishing a new racing class which would lead to the inception of a water counterpart to multi-turn Grand Prix road racing.

One of the company's latest projects is a 28 ft (8·53 m) patrol hydrofoil employing foils of similar configuration to those of Mirage.

Performance of the Mirage is said to compare favourably with that of other high performance craft. At the time of going to press, production quantities, top speed and the retail price were in the process of being settled. Preliminary details are given below.

MIRAGE

This novel recreational craft is intended

Note the novel canard arrangement incorporating an inverted vee main foil with a conventional vee foil forward. Wing-shaped stabilisers on the main foils limit the degree of immersion of the main foil thereby maintaining the hull at a negative angle of attack, and preventing the craft from blowing over at high speed

as a water-borne equivalent to a two-seater sports car. One major objective has been to produce a craft capable of tight, high-speed turns, thus permitting boats of this type to race on relatively small courses. The prototype is fitted with a 350 cu in Chevrolet automobile engine, but a wide range of alternative petrol engines can be fitted.

FOILS: Surface piercing canard configuration. About 75% of the load is borne by the inverted vee foil aft and the remainder on the small conventional vee foil at the bow. Wingshaped stabiliser foils are attached to the inverted vee main foil at calm water line level to limit the degree of foil immersion, maintaining the hull at a negative angle of attack to prevent it somersaulting at high speed. Foils are of supercavitating design and fabricated in high strength aluminium. Small rudder surfaces are attached at right angles to main foil. Various sizes available. Rudder design is a compromise between maximum steering capability and optimum fin effect to limit yaw, roll and drift in high-speed turns. The aft foils hinge upwards for towing, reducing the overall beam to conform with state trailer laws.

HULL: Planing type hull. Moulded fibreglass structure with aluminium frames and marine ply stringers.

ACCOMMODATION: Open cockpit with twin upholstered bucket seats for driver and one passenger.

POWER PLANT: Single 350 cu in Chevrolet automobile engine installed aft of the cockpit. Output is transferred via a Casalle vee-drive to a Stellings chrome-plated high-performance 2-bladed propeller. Drive is air, water and oil-cooled and provides forward and neutral quick-change. Ten different gear ratios are available from 1·03:1 to 1·37:1. Total fuel capacity is 15 gallons.

CONTROLS: Craft heading is controlled by twin rudders operated from the cockpit by a steering wheel. There is also a foot-operated throttle and a gear shift lever. The boat is equipped with an automatic bilge pump.

SYSTEMS, ELECTRICAL: 12 volts d.c. starter, alternator and voltage regulator.

DIMENSIONS:

Length overall, hull	16 ft 6 in (5·02 m)
Beam overall	13 ft 0 in (3·96 m)
Beam overall, hull	8 ft 0 in (2·43 m)
Draft, hullborne	3 ft 0 in (0·91 m)
Draft, foilborne	1 ft 6 in (457 mm)

WEIGHTS:

Displacement	1,800 lb (816·42 kg)

PERFORMANCE:
Details not available at time of going to press.

KITS: The Mirage is available both as a complete craft or in kit form. A kit information package is available at $US 7·00.

28 ft PATROL HYDROFOIL

Hydrofoils Incorporated is completing a design study for a 28 ft (8·53 m) patrol hydrofoil, with living and sleeping accommodation for a crew of four. Foil configuration is similar to that of the Mirage. Power will be supplied by either a single or twin engines driving marine propellers through V-drive shafts or retractable outboard drives.

A provisional 3-view drawing accompanies this entry.

DIMENSIONS:

Length overall, hull	28 ft 0 in (8·53 m)
Length overall, foils retracted	30 ft 0 in (9·14 m)
Length overall, foils extended	30 ft 0 in (9·14 m)
Hull beam	11 ft 11 in (3·63 m)
Beam overall, foils extended	19 ft 0 in (5·79 m)
Draft static, foils retracted	2 ft 0 in (0·609 m)
Draft static, foils extended	7 ft 0 in (2·13 m)
Draft foilborne	2 ft 6 in (0·67 m)
Height overall, foilborne	10 ft 0 in (3·04 m)
Height overall, static	6 ft 0 in (1·82 m)

Top: The two-seat Mirage racing hydrofoil during tests
Bottom: Hull of the Mirage is in moulded glassfibre with an aluminium frame

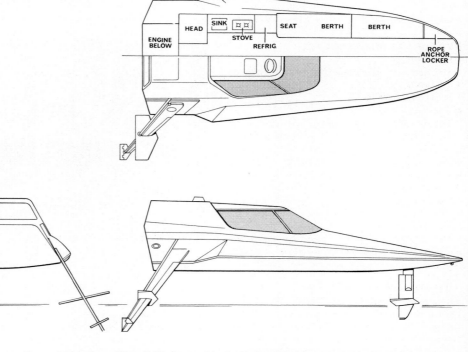

Design study for a 28 ft (8.53m) patrol hydrofoil completed in 1976 by Hydrofoils Inc

UNION OF SOVIET SOCIALIST REPUBLICS

KRASNOYE SORMOVO SHIPYARD

HEAD OFFICE AND WORKS:
  Gorki
OFFICERS:
  M. Yuriev, Shipyard Director
  Dr Rostilav Yergenievich Alexeyev, Head
    of the Central Design Bureau for Hydro-
    foil Vessels
  Ivan Yerlykin, Chief Hydrofoil Designer
EXPORT ENQUIRIES:
  V/O Sudoimport, 5 Ul. Kalyaevskaya,
    Moscow K-6, USSR
TELEPHONE:
  251-60-37, 251-05-05, 251-03-85
TELEX:
  272
UK REPRESENTATIVE:
  Umo Plant Ltd,
  Blackhorse Road, Letchworth,
  Hertfordshire SG6 1HR
TELEPHONE:
  Letchworth 71411/6
TELEGRAMS:
  Umoplant, Letchworth
TELEX:
  825247

Voskhod 2-01 during a test operation on the Gorky-Kineshma route. Features of this 34-knot Raketa replacement are a stern engine room, vee-drive, variable-pitch propeller and embarkation areas fore and aft. The craft can operate foilborne in waves up to 4 ft 7 in (1·4 m) high

Krasnoye Soromovo is one of the oldest established shipyards in the Soviet Union. In addition to building displacement craft of many kinds for the Soviet River Fleet, the yard constructs the world's widest range of passenger hydrofoils, many of which are equipped with the Alexeyev shallow draft submerged foil system. Dr Alexeyev started work at the end of 1945 on the design of his foil system which had to be suitable for operation on smooth, but open and shallow rivers and canals. He succeeded in making use of the immersion depth effect, or surface effect, for stabilising the foil immersion in calm waters by the use of small lift coefficients.

The system comprises two main horizontal lifting surfaces, one forward and one aft, with little or no dihedral, each carrying approximately half the weight of the vessel. A submerged foil loses lift gradually as it approaches the surface from a submergence of about one chord. This effect prevents the submerged foils from rising completely to the surface. Means therefore had to be provided to assist take-off and prevent the vessel from sinking back to the displacement condition. The answer lay in the provision of planing sub-foils of small aspect ratio in the vicinity of the forward struts arranged so that when they are touching the water surface the main foils are submerged approximately to a depth of one chord.

The approach embodies characteristics of the Grunberg principle of inherent angle of attack variation comprising a "wing" and a stabiliser system. When the Alexeyev foils drop below the shallow draught zone, the craft converts momentarily to the Grunberg mode of operation duplicating its configuration. The otherwise inactive sub-foils, coming into contact with the water surface become the Grunberg stabilisers, causing the foils to climb up into the shallow draught zone where they resume normal operation in the Alexeyev mode.

The foils have good riding characteristics on inland waters and in sheltered waters.

The system was first tested on a small launch powered by a 77 bhp converted car engine. Three more small craft were built to prove the idea, then work began on the Yard's first multi-seat passenger craft, the Raketa, the first of which was launched in June 1957.

The yard also co-operates with the Leningrad Water Transport Institute in the development of seagoing craft with fully submerged V-type and trapeze-type surface piercing foils, similar in configuration to those of the Schertel-Sachsenburg system. Craft employing V or trapeze are generally described as being of the Strela-type, Strela being the first operational Soviet design to use V foils. Seating 92-passengers, the vessel is powered by two M-50 diesels and, visually speaking, is a cross between the PT 20 and the PT 50, though smaller than the latter. A military derivative, the Pchela (Bee) is currently employed by the Soviet frontier police for coastal patrol in the Baltic, Black Sea, Caspian and other sea areas.

The first hydrofoil vessels to enter service with the Soviet Navy were the 75-ton P8-class, wooden-hulled torpedo boats which were equipped with bow foils and gas-turbine boost. These have now been retired.

Included in this entry are photographs of a new hydrofoil fast patrol boat, based on the Osa missile-firing FPB hull and given the NATO code name Turya. Like the earlier P8-class and the highly successful Chinese Hu Chwan-class, the new craft has a bow foil only. Powered by three 4,330 hp diesels it has a top speed of about 45 knots under calm conditions. Further military hydrofoil designs are under development.

Amongst new Soviet passenger hydrofoils being prepared for series production in the period 1976-1980 at yards on the Baltic and Black Sea, are the gas-turbine powered, 98-105 seat Typhoon passenger ferry, the first Soviet production craft to have a fully submerged foil system the Voskhod, a 71-seat Raketa replacement and the waterjet-propelled, 250-seat, 45-50 knot, Cyclone. In June 1973, it was announced that a new seagoing hydrofoil mixed-traffic ferry had been designed at Gorky. The craft will carry 200 passengers and 40 vehicles at a speed of 43 mph (70 km/h). The Typhoon, which was built in Leningrad has been undergoing operational trials carrying fare-paying passengers between Leningrad and Telinna, a journey time of 4½ hours. Further development of the seagoing Kometa-M is underway, including the fitting of air stabilisation on the stern foil and struts, increased passenger accommodation and the re-location of the engine room aft to reduce noise in the passenger saloon.

Substantial numbers of Soviet hydrofoils— Kometas, Raketas and Volgas—are being exported. Countries in which they are being operated include Austria, Bulgaria, Czechoslovakia, Finland, Yugoslavia, Italy, Iran, France, East Germany, Morocco, Spain, Western Germany, Poland, Romania, the United Kingdom and the Philippines.

Voskhod-2

Designers of the Voskhod, which is destined to replace craft of the 17-year-old Raketa series, have drawn on engineering experience gained with the Raketa, and also the more sophisticated Meteor and Kometa.

Among the basic requirements were that the Raketa's general characteristics should be preserved: foilborne operation should be possible in 1 m (3 ft 3 in) high waves, with a 3% safety factor; accommodation should be acceptable from health and safety viewpoints; noise levels should be significantly reduced, and that the maximum use should be made of standard mechanical, electrical and other components and fittings proven on the Raketa.

In fact, the end product bears little resemblance to its predecessor. In the visual sense, the Voskhod is more akin to a scaled-down Kometa with its engine room aft, replacing the rear passenger saloon.

Among the many design improvements to attract operators in the Soviet bloc countries and elsewhere are the following:

1. Employment of a vee-drive transmission, giving greater mean calm water clearance height aft, thereby reducing hydrodynamic drag under certain load conditions.

2. Provision of alternative embarkation points to facilitate passenger handling; Bow embarkation platforms are incorporated for loading from low level pontoons, and a stern embarkation area, above the engine room, for loading from high landing stages.

3. Raising the number of seated passengers from 64 to 71 for more profitable operation on medium distance services.

4. Generous additional soundproofing, including cowlings on the engine and reduction gear, and the provision of sound absorbing material in the engine room on the deckhead, sides and forward bulkhead.

5. Provision for the future replacement of the M 401A diesel by a 2,000 shp M 415 diesel.

6. Fitting of a variable-pitch, six-bladed propeller for improved handling and operating characteristics.

In June 1974, Voskhod 2-01 was put into service on the route Gorky-Kineshma, across the vast Gorky reservoir which cannot be navigated by the Raketa because of its limited seaworthiness. It continued in service until the end of the 1974 navigation season. During this time it was demonstrated that its operating and technical performance was significantly superior to that of the Raketa.

Experience accumulated during this experimental service indicated the need for a number of minor modifications which will be incorporated in the first series of production craft.

At the time of its inception, it was announced that the Voskhod would be available in a number of versions to suit a variety of local navigation and traffic requirements Voskhod-3 will be powered by a gas-turbine

The vessel is designed for high-speed passenger ferry services during daylight hours on rivers, reservoirs, lakes and sheltered waters. It meets the requirements of Soviet River Register Class 'O' with the following wave restrictions (3% safety margin): foilborne, 4 ft 7 in (1·4 m): hullborne, 6 ft 7 in (2 m).

The passenger saloons are heated and provided with natural and induced ventilation. Full air-conditioning can be installed in craft required for service in tropical conditions. The crew comprises a captain, engineer, motorman and barman.

FOIL: Fixed foil system, comprising one bow foil, one aft foil, plus an amidship foil to facilitate take-off. Bow and amidship foils appear to be of shallow vee configuration and each has four vertical struts. The fully submerged stern foil has two side struts and is supported in the centre by the end bracket of the propeller shaft. The surface and lower parts of the foil struts and stabiliser are in Cr18Ni9Ti stainless steel, while the upper parts of the struts and stabiliser and also the amidship foil are in AMg-61 plate alloy.

HULL: Similar in shape to that of the

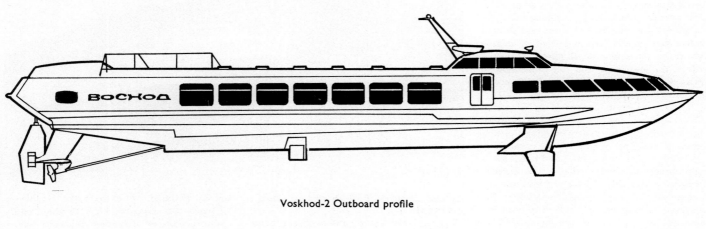

Voskhod-2 Outboard profile

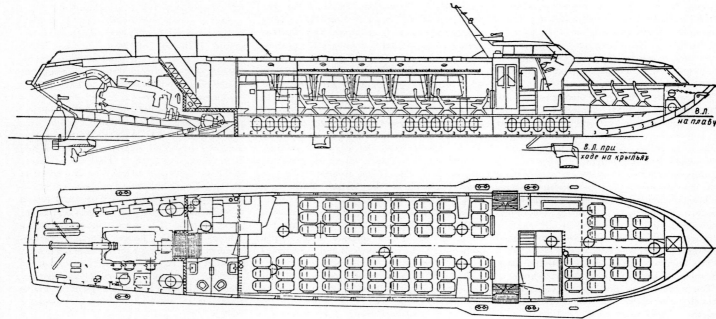

Voskhod-2. Inboard profile and deck plan

Kometa and earlier models of the Sormovo hydrofoils series, with a wedge-shaped bow, raked stem and spoon-shaped stern. A single step is provided to facilitate take-off. In fabricating the basic structure, which is largely in AMg-61 aluminium magnesium alloy, extensive use has been made of arc and spot welding. The hull is framed on longitudinal and transverse formers. Below the deck it is divided into eight watertight compartments by transverse bulkheads. It will remain afloat with any one compartment, or the machinery space flooded. Access to the forepeak, which houses the anchor capstan, is via the forward passenger saloon, and then through a rectangular hatch on the forecastle. Aft of the main passenger saloon is an area split into three compartments by two longitudinal bulkheads. The lower central space contains the reduction gear and vee-drive, the starboard compartment contains the sanitary tank and the port compartment forms part of the double-bottom. Entrance to the engine compartment is via a door on the port side of the main deck. An emergency exit is provided on the starboard aft.

POWER PLANT: Power is supplied by a single M-401A water-cooled, supercharged 12-cylinder V-type diesel, delivering a normal service output of 830 hp at 1,450 rpm and a maximum output of 930 hp at 1,550 rpm. The engine is sited aft, with its shaft inclined at 9°. Output is transferred via a flexible coupling to a single, 6-bladed variable-pitch propeller via an R-21 vee-drive gearbox.

CONTROLS: Single semi-balanced rudder in AMg plate provides directional control. Operation of the engine, rudder, reverse gear and fuel supply is effected hydraulically from the wheelhouse.

ACCOMMODATION: Voskhod-2 carries a four-man operating crew, comprising captain, engineer, motorman and barman. Embarkation platforms sited immediately below the wheelhouse provide access for both passengers and crew.

The captain and engineer are accommodated in a raised wheelhouse located between the forward and main saloon. Main engine controls are located in both the wheelhouse and the engine room.

Passengers are accommodated in two saloons, a forward compartment seating 17 and a main saloon seating 54. The main saloon has three exits, two forward, leading to the embarkation platforms and one aft leading to the stern embarkation area. Between the two saloons, on the starboard side, is a crew rest cabin. The saloons are fitted with upholstered seats, racks for small handluggage and pegs for coats. Spacing between seats is 900 mm and the central aisle is 800 mm wide.

At the rear of the main saloon is a small buffet and bar, and aft of the main saloon, at the foot of the rear embarkation steps are two WC/washbasin units.

SYSTEMS; ELECTRICAL: Power supply is 24-27 volts dc. A 3kW generator is attached to the engine and supplies 27·5 volts while the craft is operating. Four 12 volt storage batteries, each of 180 amp/hr capacity and connected in series-parallel to form a single bank, supply power during short stops. An auxiliary circuit can be connected to shore systems for 220 volt, single-phase, 50·c/s AC supply.

FIREFIGHTING: Four carbon dioxide and four foam fire extinguishers for the passenger

Turya foilborne. This new, 190 ton hydrofoil-assisted fast patrol craft is in production at more than one yard in Western Russia and one in the Soviet Far East

saloons and wheelhouse. Remote-controlled system employing "3·5" compound in the engine room.

HEATING AND VENTILATION: Heating in the saloons is provided by pipes circulating water from the internal cooling circuit of the engine. Ventilation is both natural, using the dynamic pressure of the approaching air flow, and induced, by means of electric fans.

During the spring and autumn, the temperature of the ventilating air can be heated up to a temperature of 21°C.

DRINKING WATER: Hot and cold water supplies. An electric boiler supplies hot water for washbasins and the small kitchen behind the snackbar. Drinking water tank has capacity of 138 l.

BILGE WATER: System designed for bilge water removal by shore-based facilities or service vessels.

ANCHOR: Matrosov system, weighing 77 lb (35 kg), attached to an anchor cable ⅓ in (8·4 mm) in diameter and 262 ft (80 m) long, and operated by hand winch in the forepeak.

DIMENSIONS:

Length overall	86 ft 7½ in (26·4 m)
Hull length	86 ft 3½ in (26·3 m)
Beam overall	18 ft 0½ in (5·5 m)
Hull height (excl. wheelhouse)	10 ft 6 in (3·2 m)
Draft hullborne	6 ft 6¾ in (2 m)
Draft foilborne	3 ft 7¼ in (1·1 m)

DIMENSIONS, INTERNAL:

Deck area	1,130 sq ft (105 m²)
Deck area per passenger	15·35 sq ft (1·48 m²)

WEIGHTS:

Displacement, fully loaded	27·5 tonnes
Passengers per displacement tonne	2·55
Payload, passengers and buffet/bar equipment	5·9 tonnes
Payload/displacement ratio	21·2%

PERFORMANCE:

Max. speed, calm water, wind not in excess of force 3
at 1,550 rpm (930 hp)
39·76 mph (64 km/h)
at 1,450 rpm (830 hp)
37·28 mph (60 km/h)

Turning circle diameter	
hullborne	348 ft (106 m)
foilborne	1,246 ft (380 m)

Range, based on normal fuel supply of 1,400 kg   310·68 miles (500 km)
Max. wave height, with 3% safety margin

hullborne	6 ft 7 in (2 m)
foilborne	4 ft 7 in (1·4 m)

TURYA

Latest hydrofoil to enter service with the Soviet Navy is a diesel-powered torpedo-boat with a displacement of about 165 tons. The vessel, which is based on the well-proven Osa missile-firing FPB hull, is equipped with a fixed, surface-piercing vee or trapeze foil set back approximately one-third of the hull length from the bow. At 20-23 knots in relatively calm conditions, the foil system generates sufficient lift to raise the greater part of the hull clear of the water, providing a "sprint" speed of 40-45 knots.

In addition to improving the maximum speed, the foils reduce the vessel's wave impact response, thus enhancing its performance as a weapon platform.

The installation of a pocket-size, variable-depth sonar on the transom suggests that the primary duty of Turya is anti-submarine patrol. The main armament appears to comprise four 21 in single AS torpedo tubes similar to those mounted on the Shershen class fast attack craft, a forward 25 mm twin mount and a twin 57 mm AA mount aft.

A substantial production programme is under way, involving more than one yard in the West and one in the Soviet Far East.

FOILS: Single main foil of trapeze or vee configuration set back one-third of hull length from bow. Raises greater part of hull bottom clear of the water in calm conditions at speed of about 20 knots depending on sea conditions and loading. Similar system employed earlier on Soviet P.8 class, now retired, and on the highly successful Chinese Hu Chwan class.

HULL: Standard Osa hull, welded steel construction.

POWER PLANT: Believed to be three high-performance diesels, each developing 4,300 hp and driving variable-pitch propellers through inclined shafts.

SYSTEMS, RADAR: Pot Drum and Drum Tilt.

DIMENSIONS:

Length	123 ft 1 in (37·5 m)
Beam	27 ft 10⅝ in (8·5 m)
Draft	5 ft 10⅞ in (1·8 m)

WEIGHTS:

Max. loaded displacement	190 tons
Normal displacement	165 tons

PERFORMANCE:

Max. speed foilborne	40-45 knots

TYPHOON

The Typhoon, a gas-turbine powered fast ferry for 98-105 passengers, is the first production craft with automatically controlled fully-submerged foils to be built in the Soviet Union.

The prototype, constructed in Leningrad, was launched after preliminary fitting out on December 12th, 1969. It is designed to operate at a service speed of 40-42 knots under calm conditions and 38 knots in sea state 4. The craft is at present undergoing trials. Phase 1 of the test programme covered the foil system, the gas-turbine power plant, hull design and mechanical and other systems and during Phase 2, which was undertaken during 1972 and 1973, the vessel was put into passenger service to permit technical assessments to be made under commercial operating conditions.

It is stated that in waves of up to 2 m (6 ft 6 in) high, not more than 10% of the 40-42 knot service speed is lost. Under these conditions, the Typhoon can complete the journey from Leningrad to Tallina, the Estonian capital, in 4½ hours.

Ten new inventions have found application in the design and the prototype has been awarded a certificate by the State Inventions and Discoveries Committee.

Late in 1975, it was announced that the Typhoon was to enter production at a shipyard on the Baltic as part of the shipbuilding programme for the period 1976-1980.

FOILS: Fully submerged system of conventional configuration with 77% of the weight borne by the bow foil and 23% by the stern foil. The bow foil is supported by four vertical struts which are tapered from top to bottom. The two outboard struts are supported by auxiliary fins which provide additional stability during the transition from displacement to foilborne mode. Twin rudders are fitted at the trailing edges of the aft foil struts. The foils are built in OCr17Ni7Al high strength stainless steel. A sonic/ electronic autopilot system controls four flaps on the bow foil and two on the stern foil. The total weight of the autopilot system, including all electronic components, assemblies, drive mechanisms and cables is less than 1,320 lb (600 kg). The system stabilises the craft from take-off to touchdown in heave and all three axes—pitch, roll and yaw. It is programmed to govern the angle of trim, the c of g position in relation to speed and see that the craft makes coordinated banked turns according to speed and sea state. Overriding manual control can be introduced if necessary.

Two independent electro hydraulic-drive systems are installed to actuate the flaps. Each has two pumps, one connected to the reduction gear of the main engine, the other to its turbo-compressor. Fluid reaches the actuating mechanisms under a pressure of 150 kg/cm². Should one of the mains leading to the actuating mechanisms become unserviceable the second is connected. The failure of one bow or one stern flap in conditions up to sea state 4 does not reduce the stability of the vessel.

HULL: Similar in shape to that of the Kometa and earlier models in the Sormovo hydrofoil series, with a wedge-shaped bow, raked stem and spoon-shaped stern. There are two steps beneath the hull to facilitate take-off. The hull is of riveted construction and built in high strength aluminium magnesium alloy V-48TL. Longitudinal and transverse framing is employed with a

'Sprint' speed of the Turya, the primary duty of which appears to be anti-submarine patrol, is about 40-45 knots

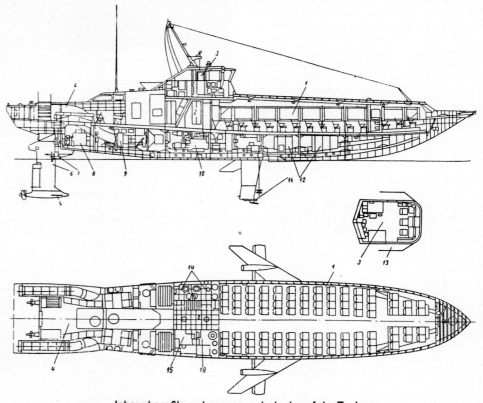

Inboard profile and passenger deck plan of the Typhoon:
1, passenger saloon; 2, vestibule; 3, wheelhouse; 4, promenade deck; 5, stern foil; 6, Z-drive foilborne transmission; 7, Z-drive hullborne transmission; 8, 165 hp diesel, 9, AI-23C-1; gas-turbines 10, diesel generators; 11, bow foil; 12, fuel tanks; 13, bridge; 14, lavatories; 15, bar; 16, baggage compartment

spacing of 19·68 in (500 mm) in the hull and 39·37 in (1,000 mm) in the superstructure. By locating the wheelhouse aft of amidships, it has been possible to reduce the length of the control system cables while preserving good all-round vision.

Beneath the passenger saloon superstructure the hull is divided by transverse bulkheads into nine watertight compartments in which are accommodated the fuel tanks, diesel generators, gas turbines and diesel for hullborne propulsion. A watertight door is installed in the bulkhead separating the diesel generator and gas-turbine compartment. The craft is designed to remain afloat should any two adjacent compartments become flooded.

POWER PLANT: Foilborne power is supplied by two 1,750 hp Ivchenko AI-23C-1 marine gas-turbines, each driving a single 2·23 ft (0·68 m) diameter three-bladed propeller at 2,200 rpm cruising. The gas-turbines are started by starter generators from batteries and exhaust gases are expelled through an extension aft of the transom to prevent the craft from becoming covered with smoke or fumes.

Power from the main engines is transmitted to each propeller via a K-1700 Z-drive column, which is bolted to the transom. The drive shaft of each turbine is connected to the shaft of the upper reduction gear of the Z-drive. Power is transmitted via two sets of bevel gears and two vertical shafts to a nacelle which is divided into three compartments. The central compartment contains the lower reduction gear which transmits power from the two vertical shafts to the propeller shaft.

The stern foil is welded to the casing of the nacelle's bow compartment which contains the stern foil flap actuating mechanism.

Hullborne propulsion is supplied by a 165 hp 6ChSP13/14 low-speed diesel driving two four-bladed propellers through KP-150 right-angle drives, which rotate for steering and retract upwards when the craft is foilborne. The columns are steered either from the central control console in the wheelhouse or from a portable control panel which can be operated from any part of the vessel.

ACCOMMODATION: The vessel carries an operating crew of four—captain, engineer, radio operator/electrician and a seaman.

The Typhoon, first gas-turbine powered passenger craft with fully-submerged foils to be built in the Soviet Union. Designed to operate at 36-45 knots, it seats 98-105 passengers. *Top Left:* The basic similarity of the Typhoon's spoon shaped hull to that of the Kometa-M and other Sormovo designs is apparent. *Top Right:* Typhoon during take off. Glass doors lead from the saloon into the vesitbule and onto the promenade deck visible in this photo. *Bottom Left:* View aft from the air-conditioned passenger saloon which can be equipped with 98-105 airliner-type seats. From the vestibule at the far end there are entrances to the baggage compartment, wheelhouse and W/C washbasin units. *Bottom Right:* Captain B. V. Gromov, centre, at the helm, who has been responsible for handling the Typhoon during her trials programme with his engineer, G. V. Shikhurin.

Passengers are accommodated in an air-conditioned saloon equipped with 98-105 airliner-type seats. Glass doors lead from the saloon into the vestibule and onto the promenade deck. From the vestibule there is an entrance to the baggage compartment, wheelhouse and WC/wash basin units. The panels along the sides of the saloon are covered in non-inflammable laminated plastic and above with Pavinol imitation leather glued onto plywood. The deckhead is covered with Pavinol on a wooden frame. A special vibration-absorbing covering has been applied to the bulkhead facing the turbine compartment.

Rafts type PSN-10 are stored in containers along the sides of the vessel. These can be launched onto the water either by manual or automatic control from the wheelhouse. Lifebelts and lifejackets are carried aboard the vessel.

SYSTEMS: Electrical: Two 22 kW generators and eight batteries type 6STK-180. Main electrical equipment operates on 400HZ.AC current. Shore supply is effected through a transformer.

NAVIGATION. Gyro course indicator, magnetic compass, hydraulic log and anti-collision radar.

COMMUNICATION: Ship-ship, ship-shore transceiver operating on R/T and W/T, also emergency radio.

DIMENSIONS:
Length overall	103 ft 2¼ in (31·4 m)
Width across foils	32 ft 9¾ in (10·0 m)
Hull beam	18 ft 4½ in (5·6 m)
Hull draught, displacement mode	
	4 ft 3⅛ in (1·3 m)

Draft, hullborne, including foils
    13 ft 5¾ in (4·1 m)
Mean draft foilborne
    3 ft 7 in-4 ft 3 in (1·1-1·3 m)
Distance of bow foil below hull base line
    9 ft 2 in (2·8 m)

WEIGHTS:
Normal loaded displacement	65 tons

PERFORMANCE:
Max speed	45 knots
Service speed	40-42 knots
Hullborne speed	5 knots
Max permissable sea state	

Designed to maintain a cruising speed of 38 knots in sea state 4

SEA TESTS

In sea state 4, vertical acceleration measured in the bows was reported to be at all times less than 0·5g in January 1975. At the same time it was stated that angles of pitch and roll are around 0·75 degrees. In sea state 4, one bow flap and one stern flap out of action have not adversely affected stability.

BUREVESTNIK

First Soviet gas-turbine hydrofoil to be designed for series production, the Burevestnik has two 2,700 hp marinised aircraft gas turbines driving two two-stage waterjets The prototype was launched in April 1964 and it was intended to build two models; one for medium-range, non-stop inter-city services, seats 130 passengers, the other, for suburban services, seats 150.

There is a four-man crew, comprising captain, engineer, motorman and a seaman.

After extensive trials and modifications, the prototype Burevestnik began operating on the Gorky-Kuibyshev route (about 435 miles (700 km) on April 26, 1968. At the time of going to press with this edition, it was

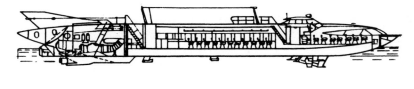
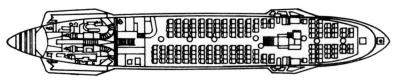

Inboard profile and deck view of the waterjet-propelled Burevestnik, powered by two 2,700 hp Ivchenko Al-20 gas turbines

understood that the vessel is still under development and has not yet entered production.

FOILS: There are two main foils and a midship stabiliser foil, all built in titanium alloy. Each is square-tipped and slightly wedge-shaped in planform. The foils are secured to the hull by struts and brackets. Each foil strut is welded to the upper surface of the foils, then bolted to the brackets. Upper and lower ends of the struts are connected by flanges. As with other craft employing the Alexeyev system, the foil incidence can be adjusted when necessary by the insertion of wedges between the flanges and the foils when the craft is in dock.

HULL: Hull and superstructure are built in aluminium-magnesium alloy. The hull is of all-welded construction and framed on longitudinal and transverse formers.

ACCOMMODATION: The prototype has two air-conditioned saloons with airliner-style seating for a total of 150 passengers. The well glazed forward saloon seats 38, and the aft saloon 112. The saloons are decorated with pastel shade panels and sound-proofed with glass fibre insulation. The engine room is at the stern and separated from the saloon by a sound-proof double bulkhead.

POWER PLANT: Motive power is supplied by two 2,700 shp Ivchenko marinised gas turbines, adapted from those of the IL-18 airliner. These operate on either kerosene or light diesel fuel and have a consumption of 300 gallons per hour. Sufficient fuel can be carried to operate non-stop over a range of 270 nautical miles (500 Km). The shaft of each of the two double suction centrifugal pumps for the waterjets is connected with the shaft of one of the turbines by means of a flexible coupling, via a reduction gear.

Auxiliary power is supplied by two 100 hp turbo-generators, used for starting the main engines and generating the electrical supply when the craft is operating.

CONTROLS: Four rudders adjacent to the waterjet streams provide directional control. Reversing is achieved by applying deflectors to reverse the waterflow. The waterjets themselves are fixed and cannot be rotated.

Operation of the turbines, waterjets, rudders and deflectors is all effected from the wheelhouse by electro-hydraulic control.

SYSTEMS ELECTRICAL: Two 12 kw 28.5 volt generators mounted on each of the main engines supply power when the craft is operating. Two 14 kw 28.5 volt generators driven by the auxiliary turbines supply power when the craft is at rest or when the 12 kw generators are inoperative. Eight acid storage batteries are connected in series to give 24 volts supply power during short stops.

HYDRAULICS: 170 kg/cm² pressure hydraulic system for operating rudders, hydro-reversal unit and anchor.

COMMUNICATIONS: A radio transmitter/receiver with r/t and w/t facilities is installed in the wheelhouse for ship-shore and inter-ship communications on SW and MW bands. A public announcement system is fitted in the passenger saloons and a two-way crew communications system is installed in the wheelhouse, engine room, anchor, gear compartment and mooring stations.

DIMENSIONS:

Overall length	142 ft 0 in (43·3 m)
Hull beam	19 ft 8¼ in (6·0 m)
Width across foils	24 ft 3¼ in (7·4 m)

Burevestnik prototype during trials on the Volga

Draft afloat	6 ft 7 in (2·0 m)
Draft foilborne	1 ft 4 in (0·4 m)
WEIGHTS:	
Light displacement	41 tons
Full load displacement (max)	67 tons
PERFORMANCE:	
Max fuel load	11·5 tons
Cruising speed	50 knots (93 km/h)
Range	310 miles (500 km)
Max wave height at reduced speed	3 ft 3 in-4 ft (1 to 1·2 m)
Max wave height at full speed	2ft (0·6 m)
Speed astern	4-6 mph (6-9 km/h)
Stop to full speed and distance	95-100 seconds, 1,203 yds (1,100 m)
Stopping time from full speed and distance	25 seconds, 394 yds (360 m)

BYELORUS

This craft was developed from the Raketa via the Chaika for fast passenger services on winding rivers less than 3 ft (1 m) deep and too shallow for vessels of the standard type.

In 1965 it was put into series production at the river shipyard at Gomel, in Byelorussia.

FOILS: The shallow draught submerged foil system consists of one bow foil and one rear foil.

HULL: Hull and superstructure are built in aluminium magnesium alloy. The hull is of all-welded construction and the superstructure is both riveted and welded.

ACCOMMODATION: The craft seats 40 passengers in aircraft-type seats, although the prototype seated only 30.

Byelorus, a 30-45 seat hydrofoil for fast ferry services on shallow waters, seen on the Irtysh river. Powered by a 735 hp M-50 diesel driving a waterjet, the craft cruises at 34 knots (60 km/h)

POWER PLANT: Power is supplied by an M-50 F-3 or M-400 diesel rated at 950 hp maximum and with a normal service output of 600 hp. The wheelhouse is fitted with an electro hydraulic remote control system for the engine and fuel supply.

DIMENSIONS:

Length overall	60 ft 6 in (18·55 m)
Hull beam	15 ft 2 in (4·64 m)
Height overall	13 ft 11 in (4·23 m)
Draft foilborne	1 ft 0 in (0·3 m)
Draft hullborne	2 ft 11 in (0·9 m)

WEIGHTS:

Light displacement	9·6 tons
Take-off displacement	14·5 tons

PERFORMANCE:

Cruising speed	34 knots (60 km/h)

CHAIKA

An experimental 30-passenger craft, Chaika is used as a test bed for the development of diesel-operated waterjet systems. It was designed initially as a 30 passenger waterbus for shallow rivers but was found to be unsuitable for negotiating sharp river bends at high speed. However, craft of this type are reported as being in limited service on the Danube.

In June 1971 it was announced that the craft had been employed in the development of superventilated V and trapeze foils for a speed range exceeding 50-80 knots.

HULL: Hull and superstructure are built in aluminium magnesium alloy.

POWER PLANT: An M-50 diesel, developing 1,200 hp drives a two-stage waterjet.

CONTROLS: Rudders adjacent to the water stream govern the flow of the ejected water for directional control.

DIMENSIONS:

Length overall	86 ft 3 in (26·3 m)
Hull beam	12 ft 6 in (3·8 m)
Draught afloat	3 ft 10 in (1·2 m)
Draught foilborne	1 ft 0 in (0·3 m)

WEIGHT:

Displacement loaded	14·3 tons

PERFORMANCE:

Cruising speed, foilborne	
	46·5 knots (86 km/h)

CYCLONE

The Cyclone, a project for a 140-ton, 250-seat hydrofoil ferry, was announced in February 1969. It was reported in November 1975 that the prototype was undergoing sea trials. As this edition went to press it was announced that the vessel is to be put into series production at Poti on the Black Sea.

An enlarged, double-deck derivative of the Kometa, the Cyclone seats 250 passengers

A Raketa, left, and a Byelorus, being overhauled in readiness for the 1976 navigation season

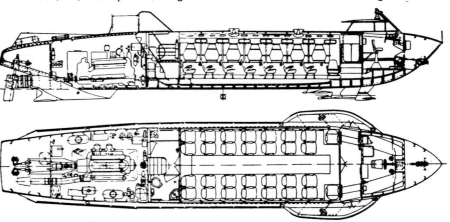

Profile and deck plan of the waterjet-propelled Byelorus, a 40-seat ferry for fast passenger services on winding rivers less than 3 ft 3 in deep

Chaika, an experimental 30-passenger craft powered by a diesel-driven waterjet.

and is powered by an 8,000 hp (5,900 kW) gas-turbine, making it the most powerful Russian commercial hydrofoil to date. The gas-turbine drives a waterjet propulsion system which gives the craft a maximum speed of 45-50 knots and a cruising speed of 42 knots.

Foils are believed to be of surface-piercing, trapeze configuration, similar to those of the Kometa-M. A stability augmentation system is fitted for greater comfort in high sea states. It has been stated that the vessel is the fastest of the Soviet Union's commercial hydrofoils.

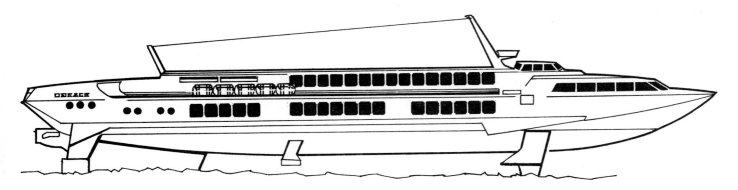

Outboard profile of the 140-ton Cyclone, a waterjet-propelled 250-seat hydrofoil ferry with accommodation on two decks. Design cruising speed is 42 knots

NEW MIXED-TRAFFIC FERRY

In June 1973 it was announced that a new seagoing hydrofoil designed at the Sormovo shipyard will carry 200 passengers and 40 vehicles at a speed of 43·49 mph (70 km/h). It will be able to operate foilborne in waves up to 6 ft 7 in (2 m) high. Although designed primarily for routes on the open sea, the vessel is also likely to be employed on inland waterways.

KOMETA

Derived from the earlier Meteor, the Kometa is the first seagoing hydrofoil to be built in the Soviet Union. The prototype, seating 100 passengers, made its maiden voyage on the Black Sea in the summer of 1961, after which it was employed on various passenger routes on an experimental basis. Operating experience accumulated on these services led to the introduction of various modifications before the craft was put into series production.

Kometas are built mainly at Gorki, but in addition a number are being assembled at Poti, one of the Black Sea yards, from prefabricated sections sent from Gorki.

Kometa operators outside the Soviet Union include Inex-Nautical Touring, Split, Yugoslavia; Empresa Nacional de Cabotage, Cuba; Archille Onorato, Napies, Italy; and Transportes Touristiques Intercontinentaux, Morocco. Other vessels of this type have been supplied to Iran, Romania, Poland, Bulgaria and Eastern Germany.

Export orders have mainly been for the Kometa-M, which was introduced in 1968. Two distinguishing features of this model are the employment of new diesel engines, with increased operating hours between overhauls, and a completely revised surface-piercing foil system, with a trapeze bow foil instead of the former Alexeyev shallow draft submerged type.

A fully tropicalised and air-conditioned version is now in production and this is designated Kometa-MT.

The present standard production Kometa-M seats 113-116. Because of the additional weight of the Kometa-MT's air-conditioning system and other refinements, the seating capacity is reduced in the interest of passenger comfort to 102.

The standard craft has proved to be exceptionally robust and has a good, all-round performance. On one charter, a Kometa-M covered 3,300 miles (5,310 km) by sea and river in 127 hours. It can operate foilborne in waves up to 5 ft 7 in (1·7 m) high and travel hullborne in waves up to 11 ft 10 in (3·6 m).

In June 1974 it was announced that, starting in 1975, production of the Kometa would be significantly increased. One of the features of the latest models is the relocation of the engine room aft to reduce the noise in the passenger saloons and the employment of a vee-drive instead of the existing inclined shaft. The arrangement is expected to be similar to that on the Voskhod-2. The revised deck configuration allows more seats to be fitted.

Employment of a surface-piercing trapeze-type bow foil provides the Kometa-M with improved seakeeping capability in waves. The foil system comprises a bow foil, aft foil, and two auxiliaries, one (termed "stabiliser") located above the bow foil for pitch stability, the other sited amidship near the longitudinal centre of gravity to assist take-off. The foils are connected to the hull by struts and

Top: A Kometa-M operating on the Black Sea. Sponsons are attached to the hull fore and aft to protect the foils while mooring. *Centre:* One of nine Kometa-Ms being operated by Onorato, the Italian shipping line. The stabiliser foil amidships facilitates take-off. *Bottom:* A Kometa-M of Inex, the Yugoslavian operator. The vessel, which has a service speed of 32 knots, operates a coastal service on the Adriatic between Krila, Zadar and Split

brackets. Middle and side struts of the bow foil are of the split type. The lower and upper components of each strut are connected by flanges and bolts. The upper sections are connected to the hull by the same means.

The bow and stern foils are of hollow welded stainless steel construction. The midship and pitch stability foils and the upper components of the foil struts are in aluminium-magnesium alloy.

HULL: Similar in shape to that of the earlier Meteor, the hull has a wedge-shaped bow, raked stem and a spoon-shaped stern. Hull and superstructure are built in AlMg-61 and AIM-6g alloys. Hull and superstructure are of all-welded construction using contact and argon arc welding. The hull is framed on longitudinal and transverse formers, the spacing throughout the length of the hull is 500 mm and in the superstructure 1,000 mm.

Below the freeboard deck, the hull is divided by watertight bulkheads into thirteen compartments, which include the engine room, fuel compartments, and those containing the firefighting system, tiller gear and fuel transfer pump.

ACCOMMODATION: The current production model Kometa MT seats 102 passengers. It carries a four-man operating crew, comprising captain, engineer, motorman and a seaman, plus one barman. Embarkation platforms sited immediately below the wheelhouse provide access for both passengers and crew.

The captain and engineer are accommodated in a raised wheelhouse located between the forward and main saloons, and equipped with two seats, a folding stool, chart table, sun shield and a locker for signal flags. The wheelhouse also contains a radar display and radio communications equipment.

Main engine controls are installed in both the wheelhouse and engine room.

Passengers are accommodated in three compartments, a forward saloon seating 22, and central and aft saloons seating 54 and

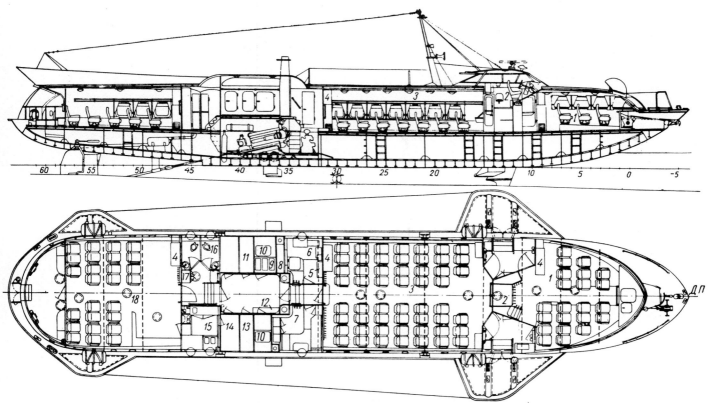

Internal arrangement of the current production Kometa-M, designed for tropical operation. 1, 22-seat forward passenger saloon; 2, wheelhouse; 3, 54-seat main passenger saloon; 6, control position; 7, duty cabin; 8, liquid fire extinguisher bay; 9, battery room; 10, engine room; 11, boiler room; 12, installation point for portable radio; 13, store; 14, provision store; 15, bar; 16, WC/washbasin units; 17, boatswain's store; 18, 26-seat aft passenger saloon

26 respectively. The central saloon has three exits, two forward, leading to the embarkation platforms and one aft, leading to the promenade deck. This is located in the space above the engine room and is partially covered with a removable metallic awning.

To the starboard side is a crew's off-duty cabin, hydraulic system pump room, bar store and bar, and to the port are two toilets, boiler room, battery room and fire extinguishing equipment.

The aft saloon has two exits, one forward leading to the promenade deck, the other aft, leading to the weather deck, which is used for embarking and disembarking when the vessel is moored by the stern.

Floors of the passenger saloons, crew's cabins, bar and wheelhouse are covered in coloured linoleum and the deckhead in the passenger saloons, as well as bulkheads and the sides above the lower edge of the windows, are finished in light coloured pavinol. Panels of the saloons beneath the windows are covered with plastic.

Passenger saloons are fitted with upholstered chairs, racks for small hand luggage and pegs for clothing. The middle and aft saloons have niches for hand luggage and the former is fitted with cradles for babies. The bar is fully equipped with glass washers, an ice safe, an automatic Freon compressor, electric stove, etc.

SAFETY EQUIPMENT: A full range of lifesaving equipment is carried including inflatable life rafts, each for 25 persons, 138 life jackets, and 6 circular life belts, two with life lines and two with luminous buoys. Life rafts are located two on the forward sponsons and two on the aft sponsons. When thrown into the water the life rafts inflate automatically. Life jackets are stowed under the seats in all saloons, and the circular life belts are stowed on the embarkation and promenade platforms. Kometas for export are

provided with life jackets on the basis of 25 persons per raft.

FIRE FIGHTING EQUIPMENT: An independent fluid fire fighting system is provided for the engine room and fuel bay. An automatic light and sound system signals a fire outbreak. The fire fighting system is put into operation manually from the control deck above the engine room door. Boat spaces are equipped with hand-operated foam and CO_2 fire extinguishers, felt cloths and **fire axes.**

POWER PLANT: Power is supplied by two M-401A water-cooled, supercharged 12-cylinder V-type diesels, each with a normal service output of 900 hp at 1,550 rpm and a maximum output of 1,000 hp at 1,600 rpm. Guaranteed service life of each engine before first overhaul is 2,500 hours. Each engine drives via a reverse gear its own inclined shaft and the twin propellers are contra-rotating. The shafts are of steel and are parallel to the craft.

The propellers are of three-bladed design and made of brass.

Main engine controls and gauges are installed in both the wheelhouse and the engine room. A diesel-generator-compressor-pump unit is provided for charging starter air bottles; supplying electric power when at rest; warming the main engines in cold weather and pumping warm air beneath the deck to dry the bilges.

Diesel oil tanks with a total capacity of 6,612 lb (3,000 kg) for the main engines and the auxiliary unit are located in the afterpeak. Two lubricating oil service tanks and one storage tank located at the fore bulkhead of the engine room have a total capacity of 551 lb (250 kg). Diesel and lubricating oil capacity is sufficient to ensure a range of 230 miles (370 km).

CONTROLS: The wheelhouse is equipped with an electro hydraulic remote control system for the engine reverse gear and fuel

supply, fuel monitoring equipment, including electric speed counters, pressure gauges, lubricating and fuel oil gauges. The boat is equipped with a single, solid aluminium magnesium alloy balanced rudder, which is controlled through an hydraulic steering system or a hand-operated hydraulic drive. In an emergency, the rudder may be operated by a hand tiller. Maximum rudder angle is 35 degrees in hullborne conditions and 5·6 degrees foilborne. In the event of the steering gear failing the craft can be manoeuvred by differential use of the main engines, the rudder being locked on the centre line. The vessel can be pinwheeled in hullborne condition by setting one engine slow ahead, the other slow astern and turning the rudder hard over.

SYSTEMS:

ELECTRICAL: Power supply is 24 volts dc. A 1kW dc generator is attached to each of the two engines and these supply power while the craft is operating. A 5·6 kW generator is included in the auxiliary unit and supplies power when the craft is at rest. It can also be used when under way for supplying the heating plant or when the 1·0 kW generators are inoperative. Four 12 volt acid storage batteries, each of 180 amp/hr capacity and connected in series to provide 24 volts, supply power during short stops.

HYDRAULICS: The hydraulic system for controlling the main engines and reverse gear consists of control cylinders located in the wheelhouse, power cylinders located on the engines, a filler tank, pipe lines and fittings.

ANCHORS: The craft is equipped with two Matrosov anchors—a main anchor weighing 165 lb (75 kg) and a spare anchor weighing 110 lb (50 kg). The main anchor is raised by means of an electric winch located in the forepeak. The cable of the spare anchor can be heaved in manually and is wound over a drum fitted with a hand brake.

COMMUNICATIONS: A radio transmitter/receiver with r/t and w/t facilities is installed in the wheelhouse for ship-shore and inter-ship communications on SW and MW bands. A portable emergency radio and automatic distress signal transmitter are also installed in the wheelhouse. A broadcast system is fitted in the passenger saloons and a two-way crew communications system is installed in the wheelhouse, engine room, anchor gear compartment and mooring stations.

NAVIGATION: The following navigation aids are standard: a gyro compass, magnetic compass (reserve) and log.

KOMETA-M

DIMENSIONS:

Length overall	115 ft 2 in (35·1 m)
Beam	31 ft 6 in (9·6 m)
Height, foilborne from waterline to tip of mast	28 ft 7 in (8·7 m)
Draft, hullborne	11 ft 9¾ in (3·6 m)
Draft, foilborne	5 ft 6⅞ in (1·7 m)

POWER PLANT:

Two 1,100 hp water cooled supercharged 12-cylinder diesels

PERFORMANCE:

Cruising speed	34-35 knots (60-63 km/h)
Fuel consumption gr/bhp/hr	180
Oil consumption gr/bhp/hr	5·0

KOMETA-MT

DIMENSIONS:

Length overall	115 ft 2 in (35·1 m)
Beam	36 ft 1 in (11·0 m)
Height, foilborne, waterline to tip of mast	30 ft 2¼ in (9·2 m)
Draft, hullborne	11 ft 9¾ in (3·6 m)
Draft, foilborne	5 ft 6⅞ in (1·7 m)

POWER PLANT:

Two 1,000 hp water-cooled, supercharged 12-cylinder diesels

WEIGHTS:

Light displacement (max.)	46·2 tonnes
Fully loaded displacement (max.)	60·5 tonnes

PERFORMANCE:

Maximum speed	34 knots
Service speed	32 knots (58 km/h)
Fuel consumption, gr/bhp/hr	182
Oil consumption, gr/bhp/hr	58
Range	240 km

Development of the Kometa is continuing. Current research is aimed at the introduction of a stability augmentation system employing either control flaps on the bow foil or air stabilisation on the stern foil and struts; the reduction of labour involved in construction; the introduction of design improvements through the use of grp and sandwich construction; noise reduction in the saloons and the extension of the cruising range.

METEOR

Dr Alexeyev's Meteor made its maiden voyage from Gorki to Moscow in the summer of 1960, bringing high performance and unprecedented comfort to the river boat scene, and setting the pattern for a family of later designs.

The craft is intended for use in daylight hours on local and medium-range routes of up to 373 miles (600 km) in length. It meets the requirements of Class O, experimental type, on the Register of River Shipping in the USSR.

Accommodation is provided for a crew of five and 116 passengers. Cruising speed at the full load displacement of 54·3 tonnes across calm water and in winds of up to Beaufort force 3 is about 35 knots (65 km/h).

FOILS: The foil arrangement comprises a bow foil and a stern foil, with the struts of the bow system carrying two additional planing subfoils. The foils are attached to the struts, which are of split type, by flanges and bolts. The foils are in stainless steel, and the subfoils in aluminium magnesium alloy. The foil incidence can be adjusted when necessary by the insertion of wedges between the flanges and the foils when the vessel is in dock.

HULL: With the exception of the small exposed areas fore and aft, the Meteor's hull and superstructure are built as an integral unit. The hull is framed on longitudinal and transverse formers and both hull and superstructure are of riveted duralumin construction with welded steel members. Below the main deck the hull is sub-divided longitudinally into eight compartments by seven bulkheads. Access to the compartments is via hatches in the main deck. The craft will remain afloat in the event of any two adjacent compartment forward of amidship flooding or any one compartment aft of amidship. Frame spacing in the hull is about 500 mm while that in the superstructure is 1,000 mm.

POWER PLANT: Power is supplied by two M-50 12-cylinder, four-stroke, supercharged, water-cooled diesels with reversing clutches. Each engine has a normal service output of 1,000 hp at 1,700 rpm and a maximum output of 1,100 hp at 1,800 rpm. Specific consumption at rated output g/bhp/hr is not more that 193, and oil, not more than 6. Guaranteed overhaul life is 1,000 hours. Each engine drives its own inclined propeller shaft through a reverse clutch. Propeller shafts are in steel and the propellers, which are 5-bladed, are in brass. The drives are contra-rotating.

Refuelling is effected via filler necks on each side of the hull. Fuel is carried in six tanks located in the engine room. Total fuel capacity is 3,200 kg. Lubricating oil, total capacity 370 litre, is carried in two service tanks and a storage tank located on the forward bulkhead in the engine room. Fuel and lubricating oil is sufficient for a cruising range, foilborne, of not less than 373 miles (600 km).

AUXILIARY UNIT: 12 hp diesel for generating electrical power when the craft is at its moorings, warming the main engines in cold weather and operating drainage pump.

CONTROLS: Control of the engines, reverse gear and fuel supply is effected remotely from the wheelhouse with the aid of a hydraulic system comprising transmitter cylinders in the wheelhouse, and actuators on the engine. The engines can also be controlled from the engine room.

Craft heading is controlled by two balanced rudders, the blades of which are in solid aluminium magnesium alloy. The rudders are operated hydraulically from the wheelhouse, the rudder angle being checked by an electric indicator in the wheelhouse. In an emergency, with the craft in hullborne conditions, the rudder is put over with the aid of a detachable hand filler fitted to the rudder stock.

At low speed the craft is capable of turning in its own length by pinwheeling—employing both engines with equal power in opposite directions—one ahead, the other astern.

Minimum diameter of the turning circle is approx 273 yds (250 m) with the engines running at low speed (700-750 rpm) and with the rudder put through an angle of 35 degrees. Turning circle diameter when operating foilborne with the rudder at an angle of 10 degrees is approximately 820 yds (750 m).

The vessel takes-off for foilborne flight in 120-140 seconds, i.e. within a distance of 25-28 lengths of her hull.

Landing run, with engines reversed, ranges from 1·5 to 2 hull lengths, while the braking distance without reversing the engines is within 3-4 lengths of the hull.

ACCOMMODATION: Passengers are accommodated in three compartments, a forward saloon seating 26, and central and aft saloons

The Meteor is powered by two 12-cylinder M-50 diesels, each with a normal service output of 908 hp. Ahead of the central fin is a removable metallic awning above the promenade deck

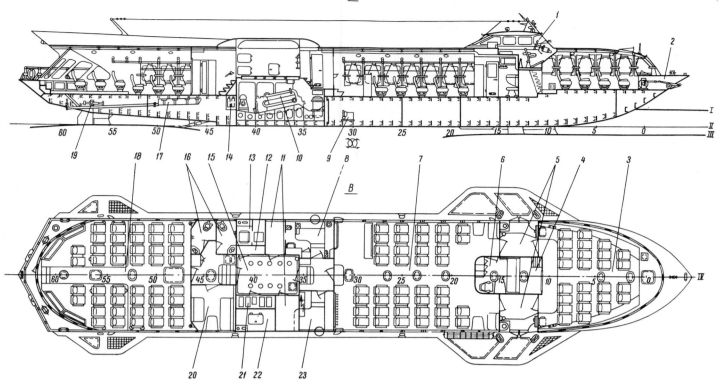

Meteor. General Arrangement.
A. inboard profile; B. main deck plan. I. waterline hullborne; II. hull base line; III. waterline foilborne; IV. longitudinal centreline. I. wheelhouse; 2. anchor compartment; 3 forward passenger saloon, 26 seats; 4. luggage compartment; 5. embarkation companionway; 6. crew duty room; 7. midship passenger saloon, 42 seats; 8. bar; 9. refrigeration unit; 10. engine room; II. pantry; 12. boatswain's store; 13. calorifies; 14. fire fighting equipment; 15. promenade deck; 16. WCs; 17. tank; 18. aft passenger saloon, 44 seats; 19. tiller gear; 20. four-seat passenger cabin;, 21. storage batteries; 22. hydraulic units; 23. main switchboard

seating 42 and 44 passengers respectively. The central saloon has three exits, two forward leading to the embarkation platforms and one aft leading to the promenade deck above the engine room. On the port side of central saloon, aft, is a small buffet/bar. Beneath the wheelhouse is a duty crew room and a luggage compartment which opens into the forward saloon.

The aft saloon has two exits, one leading to the promenade deck above the engine room and one to the weather deck aft. Forward and aft on both sides of the craft are sponsons to protect the foil systems during mooring. The forward pair are used as embarkation and disembarkation platforms.

SYSTEMS, ELECTRICAL: 24-28.5 volts dc from the vessel's power supply or 220 volts ac, 50 cycle, from shore-to-ship supply sources.

RADIO: Ship-to-shore radio telephone operating on any of ten pre-selected fixed frequencies. Also passenger announcement system and crew intercom.

NAVIGATION: Magnetic compass.

COMPRESSED AIR: System comprises two air storage bottles, each of 40 litre capacity, used for starting the main engines, operating emergency stop mechanism, closing feed cocks of the fuel tanks, recharging the hydraulic system accumulator and the ship's siren.

FIREFIGHTING: Remote system for fighting outbreak in engine room, with automatic light and sound indicator operating in wheelhouse. Hand-operated foam and CO_2 extinguishers provided in passenger saloons and wheelhouse.

DIMENSIONS:

Length overall	112 ft 2¼ in (34·5 m)
Beam overall	31 ft 2 in (9·5 m)
Height foilborne above water surface	
Draught afloat	22 ft 3¾ in (6·8 m)
	7 ft 10½ in (2·4 m)
foilborne	3 ft 11¼ in (1·2 m)

WEIGHTS:

Light displacement	37·2 tonnes
Fully loaded	54·3 tonnes

PERFORMANCE:

Cruising speed, calm water	35 knots (65 km/h)
Limiting sea states:	
Foilborne	Beaufort Force 3
Hullborne	Beaufort Force 4

MIR

First Soviet passenger craft to use a surface-piercing foil system was the MIR (Peace), built in the autumn of 1961. Described as the first Soviet seagoing hydrofoil it is in many respects similar to the Supramar PT 50. The hull is of welded aluminium construction and the foils are in high tensile stainless steel. It can undertake voyages in up to State 4 seas and has a maximum speed of 47 knots

(87 km/h). Power is supplied by twin M-50 diesels driving twin screws. The engines are electro hydraulically controlled from the wheelhouse, which has an auto-pilot system for emergencies.

MOLNIA

This popular six-seat hydrofoil sports runabout was derived from Alexeyev's original test craft. Many hundreds are available for hire on Russian lakes and rivers and in slightly modified form the type is now being exported to countries including the United Kingdom and the USA. The craft is navigable in protected off-shore water up to 2 miles from the land and has particular appeal for water-taxi and joy-ride operators.

FOILS: The hydrofoil assembly comprises two forward foils, one aft foil and planing sub-foils.

POWER PLANT: Powered by a 77 bhp CAZ652 Volga car engine, it has a top speed of about 32 knots (60 km/h) and a range of

Molnia, a popular six-seat runabout powered by a 77 bhp CAZ652 Volga car engine. Maximum speed is 32 knots (60 km/h).

about 100 nautical miles (180 km).

HULL: Built in sheet and extruded light alloy, the hull is divided into three compartments by metal bulkheads. The forepeak is used for stores, the midship compartment is the open cockpit, and the compartment houses the engine and gearbox. The cockpit is fitted with a steering wheel, throttle, reverse gear lever and an instrument panel adapted from that of the Volga car. Individual life jackets for each passenger are incorporated into the seat cushions.

DIMENSIONS:

Length overall	27 ft 11 in (8·50 m)
Hull beam	6 ft 5 in (1·95 m)
Draught afloat	2 ft 10 in (0·85 m)
Draught foilborne	1 ft 10 in (0·55 m)

WEIGHTS:

Displacement:	
loaded	1·8 tons
empty	1·25 tons

PERFORMANCE:

Max speed at 1·8 tons displacement	32 knots (60 km/h)
Fuel capacity	17 gall (80 litres)
Range	97 nautical miles (180 km)

NEVKA

This light passenger ferry and sightseeing craft is in series production at a Leningrad shipyard and the first units have been supplied to Yalta for coastal services on the Black Sea. A multi-purpose runabout, it is intended to cope with a variety of duties including, scheduled passenger services, sightseeing, VIP transport and crewboat. The standard version seats a driver and 14 passengers.

An export model was due to be launched in 1976.

The prototype, illustrated in the accompanying photograph, has an aluminium hull, but production models are in glass-fibre reinforced plastics.

The craft, which is designed to operate in waves up to 3 ft (1 m) high, is the first small hydrofoil in the Soviet Union to employ surface-piercing foils, and also the first to employ a diesel engine in conjunction with a Z-drive.

In December a 1971 waterjet-propelled variant made its first cruise along the Crimean coast. The 16-mile trip from Yalta to Alushta was made in half an hour.

FOILS: Bow and stern foils are of fixed V surface-piercing configuration and made of solid aluminium magnesium alloy.

HULL: Glass fibre reinforced plastic structure assembled in four basic sections. The outer hull is assembled with the transom, the deck with the rib of the windscreen, the cabin/cockpit with the engine air intakes and afterpeak, and the inner hull with the companionway at the aft of the cabin.

The lower hull is subdivided by watertight bulkheads into four compartments.

The hull contours are designed to facilitate easy transition from hull to foilborne mode and minimise structural loadings due to wave impact. Two transverse steps are incorporated.

ACCOMMODATION: The craft can be supplied with an open cockpit and folding canopy, as a cabin cruiser with a solid top or as a sightseeing craft with a transparent cabin roof. As a cabin cruiser. the craft is equipped with bunks, a galley and toilet. The driver's stand can be located either at the forward end of the cabin or in a raised position amidships.

Nevka prototype during trials. This light passenger ferry and sightseeing craft is now in series production at a Leningrad shipyard. Power is provided by a 235 hp diesel driving a 3-bladed propeller via a Z-drive

Model of a projected luxury cabin cruiser version of the Nevka

POWER PLANT: Power is supplied by a single 3D20 four-cycle, six-cylinder diesel, developing 235 hp at 2,200 rpm. The engine, located aft, drives a three-bladed propeller via a DK-300 Z-drive.

CONTROLS: Craft heading is controlled by a single balanced rudder in solid aluminium alloy mounted aft of the rear foil main strut and operated by a steering wheel via a mechanical linkage. Other controls include a footpedal to control engine speed, and a reverse lever.

SYSTEMS, ELECTRICAL: Power is 24 volts dc. A 1kW engine-mounted generator supplies power while the craft is operating.

Two 12 volt acid storage batteries, each of 180 amp/hr capacity and connected in series to give 24 volts, supply power during stops.

FIRE FIGHTING: An independent fluid fire fighting system of aircraft type is installed in the engine bay and is operated remotely from the driving seat.

DIMENSIONS:

Length overall	35 ft 11 in (10·9 m)
Hull beam	8 ft 11 in (2·7 m)
Beam overall	13 ft 2 in (4·0 m)
Draft, hullborne	5 ft 3 in (1·7 m)
Draft, foilborne	2 ft 9 in (0·9 m)

WEIGHTS:

Max take-off displacement	5·90 tons

Perspective drawing of the export model of the 15-seat Nevka showing foil details

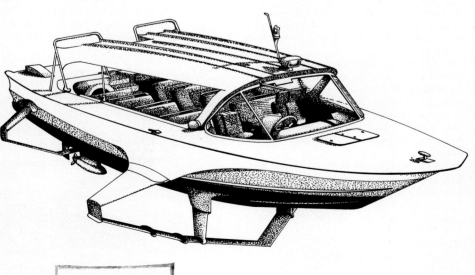

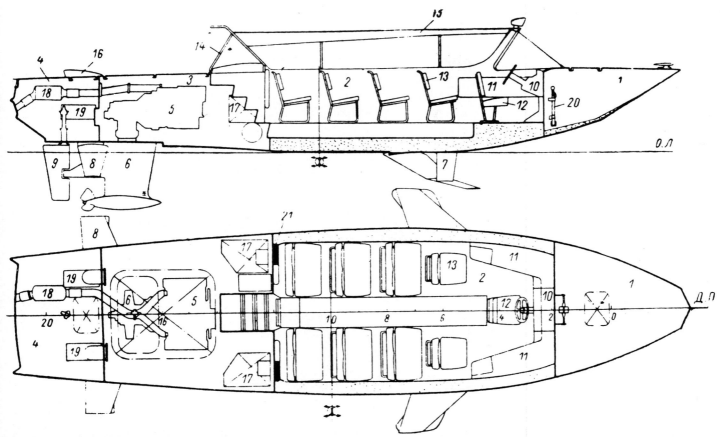

Internal arrangements of the standard Nevka, seating a driver and 14 passengers. (a) Inboard profile; (b) deck plan.   1. forepeak; 2. passenger cabin; 3, engine bay; 4, afterpeak; 5, 235 hp 3D20 four-cycle six-cylinder diesel; 6, DK-300 Z-drive; 7, bow foil; 8, rear foil; 9, rudder; 10, control panel; 11, lockers; 12, driver's seat; 13, passenger seat; 14, guard rail; 15, detachable awning; 16, engine air intakes; 17, fuel tank; 18, silencer; 19, storage batteries; 20, anchor; 21, lifebelt

Displacement unloaded	4·1 tons
Payload	1·05 tons
PERFORMANCE:	
Cruising speed	30 knots
Normal cruising range	160 miles
Diameter of turn at max speed	
	357 ft (109 m)
Take-off time	app 30 secs
Max permissible wave height in foilborne mode	3 ft 3 in (1·0 m)
Fuel and lube oil endurance	6 hours
Fuel consumption per hp at cruising rating, g/hr	178

PCHELA (BEE)

This military derivative of the Strela is in service with the KGB for frontier patrol duties in the Baltic, Black Sea, Caspian and various other sea areas. The craft is equipped with a full range of search and navigation radar and is reported to have a speed of about 35 knots. Twenty-five were built between 1965-1972. The craft carry depth charges and two twin machine gun mounts.

RAKETA

The prototype Raketa was launched in 1957 and was the first multi-seat passenger hydrofoil to employ the Alexeyev shallow draught submerged foil system. Several hundred are now in service on all the major rivers of the USSR.

In January 1973 it was announced that more than three hundred Raketas were being operated on rivers and lakes in the Soviet Union, including sixty-six in service with the Volga United River Shipping Agency.

Variants include the standard non-tropicalised Raketa M seating 64 passengers; the current export model, the 58-seat Raketa T, which is both tropicalised and air-conditioned, and finally the Raketa TA, modified in

Raketa M operated on the Rhine by the Köln-Dusseldorfer Shipping Company between Cologne and Koblenz.

London by Airavia Ltd, and licensed by the UK Department of Trade to carry up to 100 passengers (58 seated) on high density commuter and tourist routes on sheltered waters such as Westminster—Greenwich.

Reports suggest that production of the Raketa has now stopped and that yards previously involved in their fabrication and assembly will be building Voskhod and other designs in future.

The description that follows applies to the Raketa T, the standard export variant, powered by an M-401A diesel and with a cruising speed of about 32 knots (58 km/h).

The vessel is designed for high-speed passenger ferry services during daylight hours on rivers, reservoirs and sheltered waters in tropical climates. It meets the requirements of the Soviet River Register Class 'O' with operation restricted to 2 ft 7 in (0·8 m) waves when foilborne and up to 4 ft 11 in (1·5 m)

when hullborne.

The passenger saloon is provided with natural and induced ventilation and seats 58. The crew comprises a captain, engineer, deckhand and barman.

FOILS: The foil system comprises one bow foil, one aft foil and two dart-like planing sub-foils, the tips of which are attached to the trailing edges of the outer bow foil struts. Foils, sub-foils and struts are in welded stainless steel. The bow foil, which incorporates sweepback, and the straight aft foil, are both supported by three vertical struts.

The base of the centre strut aft provides the end bearing for the propeller which is located beneath the foil.

HULL: The hull is framed on longitudinal and transverse formers and all the main elements—plating, deck, partitions, bulkheads, platforms and wheelhouse—are in riveted duralumin. The stem is fabricated in interwelded steel strips. Below the freeboard deck the hull is divided into six watertight compartments employing web framing.

ACCOMMODATION: The passenger saloon seats 58 in aircraft-type, adjustable seats. At the aft end of the saloon is a bar. The saloon has one exit on each side leading to the promenade deck and one forward, leading to the forecastle. Aft of the saloon is the engine room, promenade deck, with additional seats, two toilets, a storeroom and a companionway leading up to the wheelhouse.

The craft carries a full range of life-saving and fire fighting equipment. There are 62 life jackets stowed in the passenger saloon and four for the crew in the wheelhouse and under the embarkation companionway. Two lifebelts are provided on the embarkation platform and two on the promenade deck. Fire fighting equipment includes four foam and four CO_2 fire extinguishers, two fire axes, two fire buckets and two felt cloths.

POWER PLANT: Power is supplied by a single M-401A water-cooled, supercharged 12-cylinder V-type diesel, with a normal service output of 900 hp. The engine drives via a reverse gear and inclined stainless steel propeller shaft a three-bladed cast bronze propeller. The fuel system comprises two fuel tanks with a total capacity of 1,400 kg, a fuel priming unit, and a hand fuel booster pump. A compressed air system, comprising a propeller shaft-driven air compressor and two 40-litre compressed air bottles is provided for main engine starting, emergency stopping, operating the foghorn and scavenging the water intake.

The diesel generator unit comprises a Perkins P3.152 diesel engine employed in conjunction with a Stamford C20 alternator.

CONTROLS: The wheelhouse is equipped with a hydraulic remote control system for the engine, reverse gear and fuel supply. The balanced rudder, made in aluminium-magnesium alloy, is controlled hydraulically by turning the wheel. A hand tiller is employed in an emergency. Employment of gas exhaust as a side-thruster to assist mooring is permitted at 850 rpm.

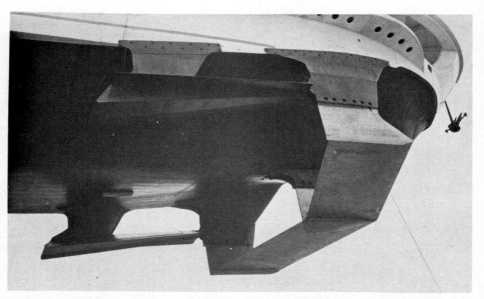

Top: The bow foil and planing stabiliser foils. *Bottom:* Aft foil assembly comprising the foil, three supporting struts and bearing for the inclined propeller shaft

SYSTEMS, Electrical: A 3kW generator, rated at 27·5 V and coupled to the main engine is the main source of power while the vessel is under way. A 50 cycle, 230 V, 1,500 rpm three-phase alternator supplies ac power. Four 12 volt acid storage batteries, each with a 132 ah capacity and connected in series to give 24 volts, supply power during short stops.

HYDRAULICS: The hydraulic system for controlling the main engine, reverse gear and fuel supply, consists of control levers located

Pchela fast patrol boats of the KGB frontier guard. Note the surface-piercing trapeze foils.

in the wheelhouse and on the main engine, power cylinders located on the engine, a filler tank, pipelines and fittings.

HEATING AND VENTILATION: Passenger saloon and wheelhouse are provided with natural ventilation, using ram inflow when the boat is in motion. Norris warming air-conditioning if fitted for use in hot weather. One conditioner is installed in the wheelhouse and eight are installed in the passenger saloon and bar. The cooled air is distributed throughout the saloon by electric fans installed on the ceiling. One is provided in the wheelhouse. A radio-telephone with a range of about 19 miles (30 km) is installed for ship-to-shore and ship-to-ship communication. The vessel also has a public address system and intercom speakers linking the engine room, wheelhouse and forecastle.

DIMENSIONS:

Length overall	88 ft 5 in (26·96 m)
Beam amidships	16 ft 5 in (5·0 m)
Freeboard	2 ft 7½ in (0·8 m)
Height overall (excl mast)	14 ft 8 in (4·46 m)
Draft, hullborne	5 ft 11 in (1·8 m)
foilborne	3 ft 7¼ in (1·1 m)

WEIGHTS:

Displacement, fully loaded	27·09 tonnes
light	20·31 tonnes

PERFORMANCE:

Service speed, about	32 knots (58 km/h)
Max wave height, foilborne	2 ft 8 in (0·8 m)
Max wave height, hullborne	4 ft 11 in (1·5 m)
Turning diameter, hullborne	3-4 boat lengths
Turning diameter, foilborne	15-16 boat lengths

RAKETA FIRE TENDER

The Raketa fire tender has been designed to tackle fires on river ships and vessels in coastal areas.

The adaptation of an existing fast craft for this purpose had the advantages of reducing development time and building costs.

FOILS: Identical arrangement to that of the standard Raketa.

HULL: Riveted D16 duralumin construction. Two monitors are mounted on the weather deck, one at the bow and one amidships. Water for the two monitors is supplied by an 8HDH rotary pump driven by a 590 hp M609 12-cylinder diesel controlled from the wheelhouse.

Outlets and valves are provided on the two monitor stands for the attachment of one 5·9 in (150 mm) fire-fighting hose to each, or two four-way forks, to which four 3·03 in (77 mm) hoses can be joined. Spray hoses are laid along the sides of the weather deck, one port and one starboard, each with four spray nozzles.

The vessel carries a 220 gal (1,000 l) foam tank and mixer for extinguishing highly inflammable and combustible liquids. Foam can be delivered either by the two monitors or fire hoses.

A special waterjet propulsion system is provided to offset the thrust of the hoses and monitors when working and keep the craft stationary. The vessel is equipped with VHF and UHF radio and a ship's broadcast system for control of the 6-man fire fighting crew.

Start-up of the fire fighting systems when empty takes 70 seconds and 10 seconds when full.

SPUTNIK

The 100-ton Sputnik was the first of the Soviet Union's large hydrofoils. On its

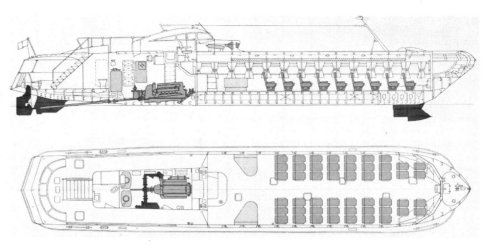

Inboard profile and plan view of the standard 50-seat Raketa. On short-range commuter services, additional passengers are seated around the promenade deck aft, and others are permitted to stand. The high density traffic version accommodates up to 100 passengers

The 100 ton Sputnik, first of the Soviet Union's large hydrofoil passenger ferries

maiden voyage in November 1961, the prototype carried 300 passengers between Gorki and Moscow in 14 hours. Although a heavy autumn storm was encountered en route the craft was able to continue under way at a cruising speed of 40 knots through several large reservoirs with waves running as high as 8 ft.

FOILS: The foil system comprises a bow and rear foil with the outer struts of the bow assembly carrying two additional planing subfoils.

HULL: The hull is welded in AlMg-61 aluminium magnesium alloy. Adoption of an all-welded unit construction facilitated prefabrication of sections at the Sormovo shipyard and elsewhere, the parts being sent to other yards in the USSR for assembly. One yard used for assembling Sputniks is at Batumi, on the Caspian Sea.

POWER PLANT: Power is supplied by four 850 hp M-50 water cooled, supercharged V-type diesels, each driving its own propeller shaft and controlled electro hydraulically from the forward wheelhouse.

ACCOMMODATION: Passengers are accommodated in three saloons, a well-glazed fore compartment seating 68, and central and aft compartments each seating 96. On short, high frequency services, the seating is increased to 108 in the latter compartments by the substitution of padded benches instead of adjustable aircraft-type seats. Two separate off-duty cabins are provided for the 5-man crew. The cabins are attractively finished in pastel shades and fully insulated against heat and sound. Full fire fighting and other emergency provisions are made and in addition to lifebelts for all passengers and members of the crew, two inflatable rubber boats are carried.

DIMENSIONS:

Length overall	157 ft 2 in (47·9 m)
Beam overall	29 ft 6 in (9·0 m)

Draught afloat	4 ft 3 in (1·3 m)
Draught foilborne	2 ft 10 in (0·9 m)
WEIGHTS:	
Displacement full load	110 tons
PERFORMANCE:	
Cruising speed	41 knots (75 km/h)

STRELA

Developed from the Mir and intended for services across the Black Sea, the prototype Strela (Arrow) completed its acceptance trials towards the end of 1961. The craft, which was designed and built in Leningrad, was first put into regular passenger service between Odessa and Batumi, and later between Yalta and Sebastapol. More recently a Strela 3 has been operating a service between Leningrad and Tallinn. It covers the distance in four hours, ninety minutes faster than the express train service connecting the two ports.

Two 970 hp 12-cylinder V-type M-50 F3 diesels driving twin screws give the Strela a cruising speed of 40 knots (75 km/h). The craft has a trapeze type surface piercing bow foils with a horizontal centre section between the main struts, and can operate in State 4 seas.

It carries 82-94 passengers in airliner type seats.

DIMENSIONS:

Length overall	96 ft 1 in (29·3 m)
Beam overall	26 ft 4 in (8·3 m)
Draft afloat	7 ft 7 in (2·25 m)
Draft foilborne	3 ft 11 in (1·2 m)
WEIGHTS:	
Displacement, full load	46 tons
PERFORMANCE:	
Cruising speed	40 knots
Sea state capability	4 ft (1·22 m) waves
Range of operation	740 km

The prototype Strela during trials off the Yalta coast

The Vikhr employs the same hull as the Sputnik and is designed for regular year round services of the Black Sea

Time to reach service speed from stop	130 seconds
Distance from full speed to stop	234 m
Full speed ahead, to full speed astern	117 m

VIKHR (WHIRLWIND)

Seagoing version of the 100-ton Sputnik, Vikhr employs the same hull and is one of the most powerful passenger hydrofoils operating today. Described as a "coastal liner", it is designed to operate during hours of daylight on inshore services on the Black Sea up to 31 miles (50 km) from the coast. The craft was launched in 1962 and is

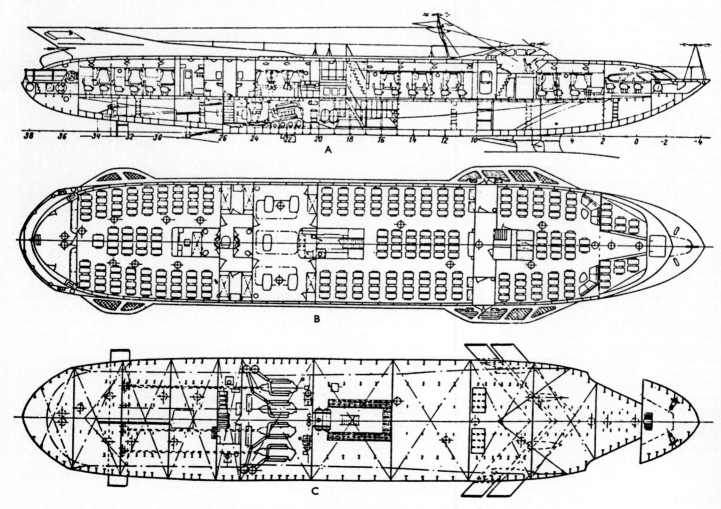

Internal arrangement of the Vikhr. a. profile; b. main deck plan; c. holds

currently in service on the Odessa-Herson route.

FOILS: Compared with the Sputnik, innovations include more sharply swept back foils, a form of stability augmentation, and an amidship foil, in addition to those fore and aft, to increase seaworthiness and stability. The bow and rear foils and their struts are in stainless steel, foil and stabiliser are made in aluminium magnesium alloy.

HULL: Similar to the Sputnik. Two steps are aligned with the flare of the sides. Hull ands superstructure are of welded AIMg-61 aluminium magnesium alloy.

ACCOMMODATION: There are three passenger saloons, seating a total of 268 passengers. The forward saloon seats 78, the central saloon seats 96, and the aft 94. At the rear of the central cabin is a large buffet and bar, beneath which is the engine room. From the bar double doors lead to the off-duty quarters for the seven-man crew.

In high seas, passengers board from the stern, across the promenade deck. In normal conditions, embarkation takes place through a wide passageway across the vessel between the fore and middle saloons. Seats are arranged in rows of four abreast across each cabin with two aisles, each 3 ft 4 in (1 m) wide, between, to ease access to the seats.

POWER PLANT: Power is supplied by four 1,200 hp -M50-F3 diesel engines, with DGKP (diesel generator, compressor pump) auxiliary engines. Each engine drives a 3-bladed propeller via a reverse gear and its own inclined stainless steel shaft. The central shafts are inclined at 12° 20′ and the side shafts at 13° 13′.

An overriding control valve is fitted to the control systems of the main engines, so that the fuel gauges of all four can be controlled

simultaneously. This makes it possible to maintain a uniform load on the engines, immediately the craft becomes foilborne, thus increasing the life of the engines. The craft can operate satisfactorily with one engine out.

CONTROLS: The wheelhouse is equipped with an electro hydraulic remote control system for the engines, reverse gear, fuel supply etc. Twin balanced rudders are hydraulically operated by two separate systems—main and emergency.

SYSTEMS, ELECTRICAL: Power supply is 24 volts dc. A 1kw dc generator is attached to each of the engines and these supply power when operating. Two KG-5·6, 5·6kW generators are included in the auxiliary unit and supply power when at rest. They can also be used when under way for supplying the heating plant or when the 1kW generators are inoperative. Four 12 volt acid storage batteries, each of 180 amp/hr capacity and connected in series to provide 24 volts, supply power during stops.

COMMUNICATIONS: A radio transmitter/receiver is installed in the wheelhouse for ship-shore and inter-ship communication on r/t, also a receiver. A ship's broadcast system is also installed with speakers in the passenger saloons.

NAVIGATION: Equipment includes radar, and a radio direction finding unit, both with displays in the wheelhouse.

DIMENSIONS:
Length overall   156 ft 0 in (47·54 m)
Beam   29 ft 6 in (9·0 m)
Height of hull to awning deck
   18 ft 2 in (5·54 m)
Draft afloat   13 ft 6 in (4·1 m)
Draft foilborne   4 ft 11 in (1·5 m)
WEIGHTS:
Displacements, full load   117·5 tons
PERFORMANCE:

Max speed   43 knots (78 km/h)
Cruising speed   35·8 knots (66 km/h)
Cruising range   240 miles (386 km)
Max wave height in foilborne condition
   4 ft 11 in (1·5 m)
Distance from full speed to full stop
   328 yards (300 m)
Distance from full speed ahead to full speed astern   245 yards (224 m)
Time to reach service speed from stop
   190 seconds

VOLGA 70

First export version of the Molnia sports hydrofoil, the Volga 70 incorporates various design refinements including a completely redesigned bow foil.

Powered by a 90 hp Volvo Penta diesel engine it was introduced at the end of 1972. The cruising speed is four km/h slower than that of the earlier model, but engine maintenance is easier and the acquisition of spares is simplified in many parts of the world. The new model has been purchased by companies and individuals in the USA, West Germany, Sweden, The Netherlands and Singapore.

FOILS: the foil system consists of a bow foil with stabilizing sub-foil and a rear foil assembly. The foils are of stainless steel.

HULL: Built in sheet and extruded light alloy, the hull is divided into three compartments by metal bulkheads. The forepeak is used for stores, the midship compartment is the open cockpit and the aft compartment houses the engine and gearbox.

ACCOMMODATION: Seats are provided for six—a driver and five passengers. The controls, instruments, magnetic compass and radio receiver are grouped on a panel ahead of the driver's seat. A full range of safety equipment is provided, including life jackets for six, life line, fire extinguisher and distress flares. A folding awning can be supplied.

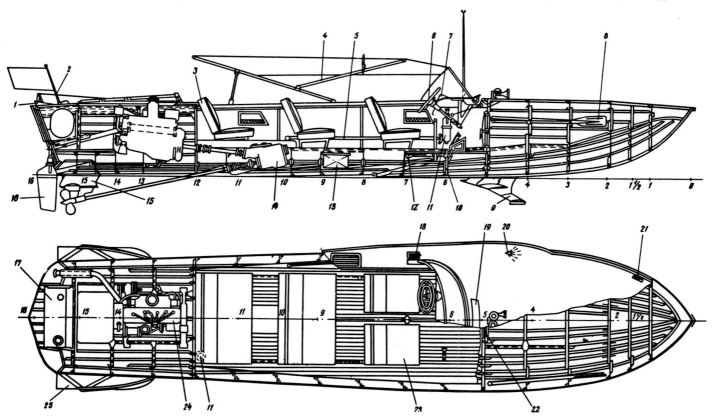

Inboard profile and plan of the Volga

I stern light; 2 flag pole; 3 bench seat; 4 awning; 5 dog hook; 6 steering column; 7 instrument panel; 8 oar; 9 bow foil assembly; 10 anchor line; II fire extinguisher OY-2; 12 anchor; 13 storage battery; 14 reduction and reverse gear; 15 rear foil assembly; 16 steering and rudder gear; 17 fuel tank; 18 cleat; 19 air intake; 20 side running light; 21 fairlead; 22 cover of first bulkhead hatch; 23 seat; 24 M652-Y six-cylinder automotive engine; 25 foilguard

Volga 70 six-seat water taxi and runabout powered by a 106 hp Volvo Penta diesel engine. Cruising speed is 28 knots.

POWER PLANT: Power is supplied by a single Volvo Penta AQD 32A/270TD diesel with a steerable outboard drive delivering 106 hp at 4,000 rpm. Fuel capacity is 26·4 gal (120 l), sufficient for a range of 150 miles.
SYSTEMS
ELECTRICAL: 12 volt dc. Starting, instrument and navigation lights and siren, are provided by an engine-mounted generator and an acid storage battery.

VOLGA-70
DIMENSIONS:

Length overall	28 ft 1 in (8·55 m)
Beam	6 ft 10⅝ in (2·10 m)
Height above water when foilborne	
	3 ft 2⅝ in (0·98 m)
Draft hullborne	3 ft 0 in (0·92 m)
Draft foilborne	1 ft 8½ in (0·52 m)

WEIGHTS:

Loaded displacement	4,255 lb (1,930 kg)
Light displacement	2,977 lb (1,350 kg)

PERFORMANCE:

Max speed	30 knots
Cruising speed	28 knots
Range	150 miles

VOLGA-275
The chief difference between this new, luxury, version of the Volga and the Volga 70

Volga-275, latest version of this popular six-seater, with a semi-enclosed cockpit. Power is supplied by a 106 hp Volvo Penta AQD 32A/270TD diesel engine. Maximum speed is 23 knots

lies in the provision of a semi-enclosed cockpit forward, sheltering the driver, and the passengers sitting immediately behind him, from spray.
FOILS AND HULL: Almost identical to Volga-70.
ACCOMMODATION: Seats are provided for six—a driver and five passengers. The driving position is glazed on three sides. In the cockpit are four soft seats which can be converted into comfortable bunks. There is also an area forward of the engine with a removable mattress. A folding awning is provided.

DIMENSIONS:

Length overall	8·50 m
Beam overall	2·10 m
Draft hullborne	0·90 m
Draft foilborne	0·50 m

PERFORMANCE:

Max speed	28 knots

WEIGHTS:

Displacement, fully loaded	2,050 kg

SAILING SKIMMERS

POLAND

INSTYTUT LOTNICTWA (AVIATION INSTITUTE)

ADDRESS:
02256 Warszawa, Al Krakowska 110/114
TELEPHONE:
46-09-93
TELEX:
81-537

Dr. Jerzy Wolf is employing an ultra-light wing, constructed by the Aviation Institute while undertaking research on agricultural aircraft, as a sail for an experimental "skimmer" sailing craft.

The wing raises the hull above the water surface and also acts as a sail.

The object of Dr. Wolf's experiments is to develop a sailing vessel which offers a higher speed that that attained by current sailing hydrofoils.

The wing, which has inherent directional and lateral stability, is hinged to the mast top, slightly ahead of the centre of pressure, and pulls the craft obliquely in a similar way to a kite of high lift/drag ratio. The angles of attack and roll are controlled by lines or push-pull rods connected to a control cross-bar. Craft heading is controlled by a conventional water rudder.

ZAGLOSLIZG (Sailing Skimmer) Z-70

The Z-70, built in 1970, employs a modified Cadet class sailing dinghy hull equipped with an adapted centreboard and rudder. This particular hull design was selected because of its low weight, high rigidity and low construction cost.

The wing, built originally to aid research into an agricultural aircraft project, has been adapted by the addition of a vertical stabiliser. It is covered in Dacron material and has a sail area of 140 sq ft (13·0 m²). The all-up weight is 33 lb (15 kg) and breaking load 1,188 lb (540 kg).

The complete craft has an empty weight of app. 176 lb (80 kg). According to the designer, over-rigging the craft has proved a great help, since it facilitates the transition from hull-borne to sailborne state. Support is also provided by the centreboard and rudder plate. It is stated that very little trim is required in heel.

ZAGLOSLIZG (Sailing Skimmer) Z-71

Designed in 1971, this is equipped with a specially built lightweight strut-and-cable sail wing, differing slightly from the earlier design. It features a trimming device and simplified control.

The craft can be towed in the air behind a motor boat, like a conventional kite-glider.

DIMENSIONS:

Length overall, hull	10 ft 6 in (3·20 m)
Beam	4 ft 3 in (1·30 m)
Draft, centreboard lowered	3 ft 11 in (1·20 m)
Sail wing span	23 ft 0 in (7·0 m)
Max chord sail wing	11 ft 6 in (3·50 m)
Sail wing area	150 sq ft (14 m²)
Aspect ratio	3·5 : 1
Stabiliser area	22 sq ft (2 m²)
Mast height	9 ft 6 in (2·90 m)

WEIGHTS:

Empty weight	154 lb (70 kg)
Gross weight	330 lb (150 kg)
Sail wing	26 lb (12 kg)

PERFORMANCE:

Lift/drag ratio of sail wing	about 6 : 1
Max angle of wing setting	60 deg
Horizontal lift/drag ratio for 45 deg heel	4·2 : 1
Lift/drag ratio of centreboard and rudder plate	10·2 : 1
Max craft/speed wind velocity ratio	3 : 1
Optimum angle of apparent wind	19 deg
Optimum heading angle	109 deg
Wind velocity for take-off	18 fps (5·5 m/s)
Minimum speed for take-off	24 mph (40 km/h)
Optimum airborne speed	34 mph (55 km/h)

ZAGLOSLIZG (Sailing Skimmer) Z-73

Developed from the Z-70 and Z-71, the Z-73 employs a modified Cadet class dinghy hull, equipped with a high aspect ratio centre-board and rudder.

During 1974, several further modifications were made to the sailwing, including the addition of a bow stabiliser to assess the advantages of a canard configuration, and a horizontal stabiliser surface to assess the value of a conventional configuration.

The mast was moved aft of the cockpit, and foot-operated rudder bar steering was installed.

Based on the test results, a further development model—the Z-75—is being built, the wing of which will also be used as an ultra-light, tailless hang-glider.

The wing, covered in nylon, incorporates a light vertical stabiliser, and has inherent directional and lateral stability.

Altitude control is based on a combination of incidence and heel angle control. Excessive altitude results in increased drift and a loss of speed and lift. This leads to a

Above: Z.73 in primary configuration. *Below:* Z.73 with its mast moved aft of the cockpit and fitted with an improved wing control

restoration of normal trim, with the hull riding at a predetermined height above the water level. The restoring forces are described as being similar to those of a vee-foil sailing hydrofoil.

DIMENSIONS:

Length overall, hull	10 ft 6 in (3·20 m)
Beam	4 ft 3 in (1·30 m)
Draft, centreboard lowered	3 ft 11 in (1·20 m)
Sailwing span	21 ft 4 in (6·5 m)
Aspect ratio	4·7:1
Stabiliser area	13 sq ft (1·2 m²)

WEIGHTS:

Empty weight	150 lbs (68 kg)
Gross weight	330 lb (150 kg)
Sailwing	22 lb (10 kg)

PERFORMANCE: (Design)

Lift/drag ratio, sailwing	app 8:1
Max angle of wing setting	60 deg
Horizontal lift/drag ratio for 45 deg heel	3·5:1
Lift/drag ratio of centre board and rudder	2·1:1
Wind velocity for take-off	21 fps (6·5 m/s)
Minimum speed for take-off	27 mph (45 km/h)
Optimum airborne speed	36 mph (60 km/h)

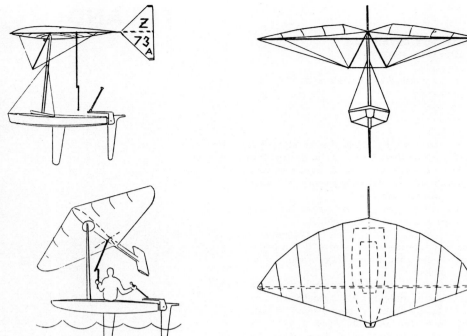

General arrangement of the Z-73A, incorporating a sketch showing the control arrangements

UNITED KINGDOM

NEW HYDROFIN LTD

HEAD OFFICE:

Burfield Flat, Bosham Lane, Bosham, Sussex.

EXECUTIVES:

Christopher Hook, Managing Director

Christopher Hook was responsible for the conception, design and development of the fully-submerged hydrofoil, which he demonstrated in the USA in 1951 with his Red Bug prototype and later with his Miami-built conversion sets. He became a partner of the late Herr G. Sachsenburg, the pioneer hydrofoil builder, and has completed hydrofoil design and consultancy contracts in the US, Israel, Holland, France, Norway and Italy, as well as with Strathclyde University.

He is currently developing a self-tending sail rig for sailing hydrofoil craft comprising sails that tilt to windward and have full furling.

Miss Bosham (Rotasail) retains all the good points of Miss Bosham 1 the first fully-reefing, rotating rig with sail tilting and transverse stability on a very narrow hull by incidence-controlled hydrofoil. Whereas on Miss Bosham 1 roller reefing was used on sails with an aspect ratio of only 1½, the new reefing method of Miss Bosham 3 is much simpler and the AR is 3½. The sails (now 4 in number) are of sleeve form, retained at the leech, but free to slide round the large diameter tube mast to accommodate the change in the two cambers as the wind changes sides. To furl, the leech cable is un-hooked at the bottom end plate and the whole sail treated like a curtain. A special line (not shown) pulls the leech cable forward at the top of the mast. Thus one, two, three or four sails may be set and the rig is greatly simplified.

Another important improvement is the addition of the "seeker", seen as a small rectangular blade directly over the central mast. Its function is to detect small changes in apparent wind direction and apply more air rudder deflection sooner than would

result from a fixed air rudder. Too much mechanical advantage to the seeker will produce hunting but the correct amount results in a perfectly steady sail setting, while any turbulence shed by the sails, and picked up by the air rudder, is at once corrected by advance information from the seeker.

Obviously the seeker cannot be given sole control of the air rudder since the pilot must select his course, which may be ahead or astern. To do this he is provided with a line, called the Aeolus line (see illustration), and the spring-loaded line passes up the centre of the mast to differential levers from which the resultant of pilot and seeker information is transmitted to the air rudder. For instance, if the pilot centres his line, and the seeker is also aligned to the boom, all sails will remain luffed irrespective of the hull attitude to the wind. Whether

the boat moves forwards or backwards depends on which way the pilot moves his control line. Sailing, and even tacking backwards is quite easy as is the hove-to position with the hull broadside to the wind to get maximum drift resistance from leeboard(s) and foil strut.

In a gust, putting the helm down makes no difference to the pressure on the sails and it is the air rudder which must be moved by the control line. Similarly, air rudder setting depends on speed. The sail tilting facility is not useful in light airs or in tracking, but even in these positions it permits the sails to be upright despite some heeling. There is thus never a downward component of wind force tending to increase hull displacement as in a heeling yacht. In strong winds a light boat can obtain quite a large

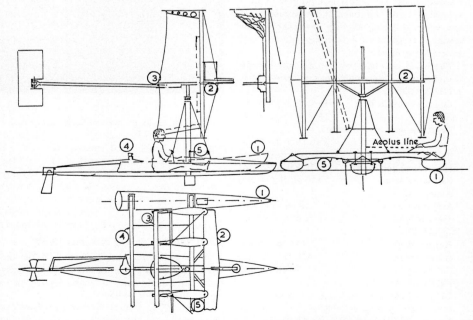

Miss Bosham 3, designed as a trainer for the Rotasail system

air lift from a well tilted sail system. To obtain this effect the masts are attached to the cross-spar (that rotates wth the boom) by forward pointing bolts and the sail cloth must have a "button-hole" in way of these to permit it to slide as described. It will be seen that the mast rigging is a closed frame, ending at the tilting winch in the boom near the central masthead. In small craft this winch is turned by hand but in large craft this will be done by electric winch. Since there is about as much sail area below the bolt axis as there is above, it follows that wind forces are balanced out, thus greatly reducing the need for bracing wires. If we examine the wind forces in each sail we find about half taken by the mast and transmitted to the rigging described, one quarter taken by the spar connecting all the leeches to the boom and one quarter turned into torques at the ends of the masts. Hence the need for a fairly large diameter tube which, aerodynamically, produces a very gentle stall. Transmission of the torque to the bolt is avoided by a smaller inside tube from bolt to leech and the end plates are supported by gussets (not shown). These will, in practice, prevent the concave camber at the ends.

Unlike previous rotating rigs, the roller bearing is at the mast-head thus allowing a fixed mast to be well stayed to the hull.

With increasing sizes the balanced sail will be much easier to engineer than the same area would be in the classical Bermuda form and enormously easier than the proposed square-rigger with unsupported masts. Inertial forces in a heavy sea will need watching. The long air rudder boom is ultra-light but a spring-loaded joint could be inserted at some stage while the cross spar joint to the main boom will require to be progressively thickened. Tapered masts would tend to reduce inertial problems.

Unorthodox high speed sailing has been demonstrated at the expense of considerable added complexity of control and the smallest changes of course speed or wind demand constant and considerable control power

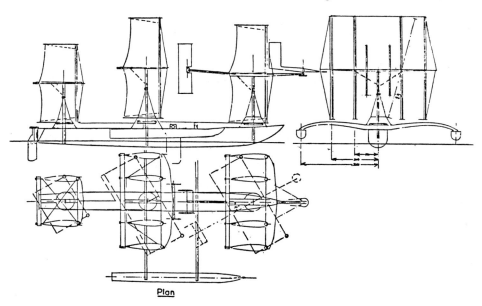

Plan

Impression of the Rotasail applied to a large vessel. On this three-master, the foremast has the air vane and rotates the other two by below-deck chains or stepped belting. Maximum advantage is drawn from the low C of P. For example, with three masts and ten sails, the general C of P is well under half the off-deck height of a Bermuda sail of the same area, and the Rotasail carries more than twice the sail area for the same capsizing moment.

inputs due to an inherently unstable set of forces.

Rotasail may employ one or two hydrofoils for transverse stability depending on whether the danger of lost downwards lift, due to surfacing, is an acceptable risk or not. In a racing craft it will be acceptable since the speed run may be made with a leeward foil. Hydrofoil incidence control must be automatic by sensor. and with some form of damping of which viscous is best. There is also a need for a pilot adjustment between the sensor and the foil. All this is well understood. The foil may be totally retracted as may be the lee-board shown on the drawing.

APPLICATIONS: The uses of such a boat are varied and new ones are being suggested constantly, particularly for the Third World

and in steady wind areas with warm climates. Sport, inter-island transport, sight seeing cruises, medical work, fishing fleet service, oil wells, ocean bed exploration and, later on, ocean cruises are some of the proposals. Where delays due to calms could cost money some auxiliary power can be installed on deck. Fuel for same may be stowed in the side floats. In the main, however, this is purely a wind-powered vessel. Building is starting mainly as Technical College projects and for small craft.

Key parts can be supplied in moulded grp such as: floats (assembled finished or unjoined sides nested for easy transport), grp hydrofoil with carbon fibres, cross spar, boom and extension are available as well as detailed designs of all parts. (Metric). Special sheet for large R/C model or fully flying type. Prices on request.

UNITED STATES OF AMERICA

DAK HYDROFOILS

HEAD OFFICE:
PO Box 181, Honeoye, New York 14471, USA

PACIFIC ADDRESS:
PO Box 827, Hanalei, Hawaii 96714

PROPRIETOR AND CHIEF DESIGNER:
David A. Keiper

Design of the Williwaw, the world's first seagoing sailing hydrofoil, began in 1963. Construction of the craft, which is based on a specially designed trimaran hull, began in May 1966 and tests started in November 1967.

After nearly three years of trials along the California coast, Williwaw, manned by David Keiper and one other crew member, successfully completed a 16-day passage between Sausalito, California and Kahului Harbour, Maui, Hawaii, in September 1970—the first ocean crossing by a hydrofoil sailboat.

Heavy seas and strong winds were encountered on the first two days of the voyage, during which the craft made 200 miles per day. At times the craft attained 25 knots, but light winds in mid-ocean prevented the craft from making the passage in record time.

The craft entered chartered sailing yacht service in March 1971, operating from Hanelei Hawaii and before returning to Sausalito, California, completed about 2,000 miles of inter-island sailing around Hawaii, mainly in open sea conditions.

Williwaw was entered in the Pacific Multihull Association speed trials held in Los Angeles Harbour on May 9th 1975. Average speed was determined over a 250 yard (229 m) course, planned so that the true wind was approximately 10 to 20 degrees aft of the beam. On one run, with a reasonably steady wind of 17 knots, Williwaw averaged 17·5 knots over the course. On another run, with a stronger wind of 24 knots, under gusty and turbulent conditions with 1½ ft very short wave chop, Williwaw averaged 18·5 knots.

The foils stabilised the craft perfectly. The bow kept up high in all runs, while various racing catamarans of 14 to 38 ft experienced serious problems with bow burying. Two catamarans capsized. The three-man crew on Williwaw stood on the windward deck, holding onto the shrouds, while the crews of the catamaran had to lie down and hold on tight to avoid being

thrown overboard.

Various modifications to the craft were undertaken during 1974-75, and in the summer of 1975 a second series of sea trials were undertaken in the South Pacific to test these modifications.

Williwaw sailed to Hawaii again in June 1975. Wind was generally light until deep within the tradewind region. In heavy tradewind squalls with the boat running down steep 15 ft seas, the foils were found to stabilise perfectly and the bow was never submerged.

On a run from Hanelei, Hawaii to Whangaroa, New Zealand, made between November and December 1975, with stopovers in Samoa and Tonga, moderate trade winds were experienced during the first 2,000 miles of the voyage and generally light winds during the last 2,000 miles. During the first twelve days of the voyage, the foils were left set continuously. Over one ten-day period, the craft completed 1,650 miles, including a doldrums crossing. Self-steering was used for most of the way, with the helm tied. Only the working sail area of 380 ft² was used.

The return trip from New Zealand to

Hawaii was made via Rarotonga and Penrhyn in the Cook Islands. When the craft left New Zealand, a disturbed south west air stream was generating 35 knot squalls, day and night. Seas were very irregular and the boat would occasionally slam into walls of water at speeds in excess of 20 knots. About 500 miles from the New Zealand coast one freak wave encountered was 35-40 ft high, and had a slope greater than 45 degrees. The trough was flat-bottomed, with no rounding between the slope and the trough. Descending the slope, the bow was well above the surface. After impact there was no tendency for the stern to lift. The bow remained under for about 2 seconds before it emerged and the boat started moving again. Waves such as this have been known to pitchpole yachts, monohull and multihull, but the hydrofoil trimaran showed no such tendency.

Williwaw has now operated sailing excursions from Hanalei, Hawaii, during the summers of 1971, 1975 and 1976. By the end of August, 1976, it had completed 19,000 miles of sailing.

Dak Hydrofoils is currently developing simple low-cost hydrofoil conversion kits for existing racing catamarans with lengths ranging from 12-20 ft (3·65-6·90 m). These were test marketed between 1972-1974. Economic conditions permitting, Dak Hydrofoils hopes to begin the full-scale marketing of ready-to-install foil sets for a variety of multihulls in 1977 or 1978.

The design of 16, 35 and 40 ft hydrofoil trimarans is continuing, and complete boats will be built to order. A modified conversion kit introduced in 1974 is also suitable for outboard powerboats.

WILLIWAW

A prototype sailing hydrofoil, Williwaw has a specially designed trimaran hull attached to which are four foils—a deep V-foil at the bow, a ladder·foil at the stern, and one laterally outboard of each of the port and starboard pontoons. The stern foil pivots and serves as a rudder when hullborne.

The craft accommodates 2-3 passengers, together with cruising supplies.

It is able to remain fully foilborne for unlimited distances in moderate seas as long as there is adequate wind power.

Various modifications and improvements were made to the craft during 1974-75. These included the addition of streamlined fairings at the four main intersections of the lifting surfaces and struts on the bow foil the installation of a retractable leeboard for improved windward performance in light airs, and the facing of various aluminium foil fittings with stainless steel to prevent wear and tear around the shear/fastening bolts.

FOILS: The bow foil, of surface-piercing V configuration, is mounted between the pontoon bows and that of the main hull. Foils, supporting struts and sub-foil elements, are of welded aluminium, with a protective coating of vinyl. Foil section is NACA 16-510 with 6 in (152·4 mm) chord throughout the system. The foils have fairly high aspect ratio. Foil loading during a normal take-off is: bow foil 40%, stern foil 20% and leeward lateral foil 40%, depending on sail heeling forces. Dihedral of the bow foil is 30-50 degrees.

The lateral foils, which are not as deep as the bow and stern foils, are of 4-rung ladder type, and have 35 degrees dihedral. The stern foil is of 3-rung ladder configuration with zero dihedral at rest, but craft heel

gives it 10-15 degrees dihedral. Under most conditions the rungs are fully submerged. The entire stern foil pivots for steering action. Shear bolts protect bow and stern foils from damage if debris is struck.

Foil retraction arrangements are as follows:

After the removal of shear bolts the bow foil swings forward and upwards through 90 degrees; the lateral foils swing outwards and over, and are laid flat on the deck through a second pivot axis, and the stern foil swings aft and over through 180 degrees. Retraction of the bow and lateral foils is achieved through the use of a simple block and tackle.
CONTROL: A tiller-operated, combined stern foil and rudder, controls direction in foilborne mode; paired struts, also tiller operated, provide rudder control when hullborne.
HULL: Lightweight, but robust trimaran hull with small wing deck to avoid aerodynamic lift. Marine ply structure sheathed with glass fibre. Built-in attachment points for foils. Mast supported by main frame.
ACCOMMODATION: The craft is designed for 2-3 people, with cruising supplies, but has

flown with nine aboard. The deep cockpit accommodates the helmsman and one crew member. The cockpit, which provides adequate shelter from the strong winds developed by high-speed sailing, forms the entrance to main and stern cabins. The main cabin seats four comfortably. There are two berths in the main cabin and one in the stern cabin. The main cabin also includes a galley, shelving and a marine head. There is generous stowage space in the pontoon hulls.
SAIL AND POWERPLANT: Sail power alone on prototype, but a small outboard auxiliary engine can be fitted if required. Total sail area is 380 ft² (35·30 m²).
SYSTEMS: Electronics: Radio direction finder normally carried.
DIMENSIONS:

Length overall, hull	31 ft 4 in (9·54 m)
Length waterline, hull	28 ft 0 in (8·53 m)
Length overall, foils retracted	
	33 ft 0 in (10·05 m)
Length overall, foils extended	
	32 ft 0 in (9·75 m)

Williwaw sailing in San Francisco Bay before her historic trans-ocean voyage to New Zealand

Demonstrating the stability of Williwaw while foiling in gusty conditions

Hull beam:
Main hull at WL   3 ft 0 in (0·91 m)
Hull overall, foils retracted
    16 ft 4 in (4·97 m)
Beam, overall, foils extended
    25 ft 0 in (7·62 m)
Draft afloat, foils retracted
    1 ft 4 in (0·40 m)
Draft afloat, foils extended
    4 ft 0 in (1·21 m)
Draft foilborne
    1 ft 6 in-2 ft 6 in (0·45 m-0·76 m)
Freeboard   2 ft (0·61 m)
Pontoon deck
    1 ft 6 in-3 ft 6 in (457-762 mm)
Main hull deck
    2 ft 6 in-3 ft 6 in (762 mm-1·06 m)
Height overall to masthead
    39 ft 0 in (11·88 m)
DIMENSIONS, INTERNAL:
Cabin (Wheelhouse, galley, toilet included)
Length   28 ft 0 in (8·53 m)
Max width   16 ft 0 in (4·87 m)
Max height   5 ft 4 in (1·62 m)
Volume   480 cu ft (13·78 cu m)
WEIGHTS:
Light displacement   2,200 lb (997·88 kg)
Normal take-off displacement
    3,000 lb (1,360 kg)
Max take-off displacement
    3,600 lb (1,632 kg)
Normal payload   800 lb (362·8 kg)
Max payload   1,400 lb (635 kg)
PERFORMANCE (in steady wind and calm water, with normal payload):
Take-off speed
Normally 12 knots. Craft is able to take-off with a 12-knot beam wind and accelerate to 18-20 knots
Max speed foilborne   30 knots
Cruising speed foilborne   12-25 knots
Max permissible sea state and wave height in foilborne mode:
Sea state almost unlimited at 12 knot average speed with wind aft of beam. Foils well behaved in all conditions met so far. Sails reefed down in heavy conditions to maintain comfort and ease of handling. Craft shows no tendency to pound.
Turning radius at cruising speed
    150 ft (45·72 m)
Number of seconds and distance to take-off
5 secs in strong wind, two boat lengths
Number of seconds to stop craft
    8 seconds, turning dead into wind
SEA TESTS: Craft operated in strong winds and breaking seas including steep 15-20 ft seas in Pacific en route to New Zealand and one freak wave 35-40 ft high with 15-50 degree slope. It has completed a return voyage from the California coast to Hawaii, and a second Pacific voyage from California to New Zealand and back to Hawaii. By the end of August 1976, the craft had covered 19,000 miles.
Speed is significantly more than wind speed in conditions of steady wind and calm water. The craft can match wind speed in moderate seas, but not in heavy seas. In heavy seas, broad reaching or beam, it has averaged 15 knots for hours at a time, winds gusting to Force 5 and 6. Speeds may climb to 30 knots or drop to 5 knots, depending upon local wind and waves. Acceleration and decelerations are gradual and not objectionable. The ride is far smoother than that of displacement multihulls.

PACIFIC EXPRESS 35

Successor to Williwaw, the Pacific Express is a second generation hydrofoil cruising

Williwaw in Auckland harbour, with foils retracted

catamaran. It is designed to be sailed solo when necessary, and avoid many of the problems inherent in conventional trimarans —pounding, broaching, tunnel interference, quick motion, pitchpoling, poor control and poor self-steering in heavy seas.

The craft is wider than its predecessor, has fully buoyant float hulls, is equipped with a more efficient hydrofoil system and has a slightly greater load-carrying capacity.

It is designed to operate in a wide variety of conditions, from heavy storm seas to light airs. In heavy seas, with foils set, it is exceptionally stable and capable of high speeds.

The length, 35 ft (10·66 m), is the shortest in which it is convenient to have full standing headroom as well as a flush deck. Through its proportionately wider hulls, it should be able to exceed true wind speed more substantially than Williwaw and. be able to fly fully foilborne at about 50 degrees from

Outboard profile of the Pacific Express 35

the true wind. The boat should be able to beat to windward with complete comfort for the crew.

In light airs and calms, with foils retracted, the craft makes the most of the available wind.

FOILS: Configuration similar to that of Williwaw. Foils have a 6 in (152 mm) chord and are fabricated in heavily anodized aluminium extrusions. Bolts, washers, etc, are in stainless steel. Bow and lateral foil are fixed while sailing. Tiller-operated combined stern foil and rudder controls craft direction when foilborne. All four foils retract manually after the removal of sheer bolts.

HULL: Main hull bottom and topside, triple diagonal wood strips, remainder in plywood. All wood saturated with epoxy.

SAIL: Sail area as a cutter 650 ft². Sloop working sail area 485 ft².

DIMENSIONS:

Length overall	35 ft 0 in (10·66 m)
Length waterline, static	31 ft 8 in (9·65 m)
Mast height	40 ft 0 in (12·19 m)
Beam, foils retracted	22 ft 0 in (6·70 m)
Draft, foils retracted	1 ft 6 in (457 mm)
Draft (static) foils extended	5 ft 0 in (1·52 m)
Outboard projection of lateral foils	4 ft 0 in (1·21 m)

WEIGHTS:

Normal loaded displacement	4,000 lb

PERFORMANCE:

Top speed, strong wind, flat water	45 knots
Normal foilborne speed range	13-30 knots
Speed to become fully foilborne	13 knots
Speed to become half foilborne	9 knots
Wind required to become fully foilborne	
in flat water	11-12 knots
in average seas	12-15 knots
Average hull clearance at high speed	2 ft 0 in (0·60 m)
Maximum sea state for foilborne operation	unlimited

In heavy seas, sails are reefed in order to obtain a good balance between speed, comfort and safety.

SPEED FREAK

This is a special racing craft which will make the maximum possible ratio of boat speed to true wind speed on one tack,

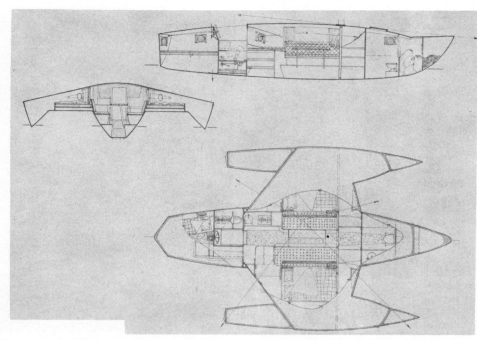

Inboard profile and deck plan of the Pacific Express 35 hydrofoil racing/cruising Trimaran

Hobie-16 Dak-foil conversion with foils retracted

although capable of sailing on both tacks. The design is based on a proa hull, which will incorporate special aerodynamic features. Standard 2 in (50 mm) Dak Hydrofoil foil extrusions will be used. Overall length will be 16-20 ft (4·87-6·09 m).

DONALD NIGG

ADDRESS:
7924 Fontana, Prairie Village, Kansas, 66208

TELEPHONE:
913 642 2002

Development of the Flying Fish began in 1963 at Lake Quivira, an inland lake in Kansas. Donald Nigg believed that if the pitchpole moment and vertical stability problems could be solved, the front-steering three-point suspension system typical of the modern ice-yacht offered several advantages. Previous craft had often used three-point suspension, but all appear to have used rear steering. To develop this new approach, Exocoetus, an experimental platform was built. It was evolved through three distinct versions during 1964-67 and established the basic feasibility.

Interest in the experiments resulted in numerous requests for plans, but although the craft was ideal as a development platform, it was not a design suitable for home construction. In response to these requests the Flying Fish was developed.

Topping 20 knots on a close reach in a light wind

To keep the costs to a minimum, the craft is designed to carry a sail area of 100-150 sq ft. It was anticipated that most of those interested in building a sailing hydrofoil would be small boat sailors, owning a boat carrying a mainsail of this size. The design thus allows the builder to share the sail and rigging with an existing dinghy.

A true development class of sailing hydrofoil has been slow to emerge, but the Flying Fish may mark the beginning of such a class. The Amateur Yacht Research Society, Hermitage, Newbury, Berkshire, United Kingdom, is promoting the design as a development class.

Sets of plans for the Flying Fish have been supplied to potential builders in many countries, including Brazil, Canada, Greece, Australia, the United States and the United Kingdom.

FLYING FISH

First of a development class of sailing hydrofoils, the Flying Fish has been specially developed for home builders. Built mainly in wood and with a length overall of 16 ft 6 in (5·02 m), it has a maximum foilborne speed of more than 30 knots.

The estimated cost of constructing a craft of this type, less sail and rigging (the 125 sq ft mainsail and rigging from a Y-Flyer were used for the prototype illustrated), is US $250,000.

FOILS: The foil configuration is surface piercing and non-retractable with 16% of the weight supported by the vee bow foil and the remaining 84% by the outrigged main foils. The latter are also of the vee type, with cantilevered extensions at the apex. Total foil area is 1·42 m² (15·3 sq ft) and the foil loading is 300 lb sq ft max at 30 knots. The front foil and its supporting strut are built in aluminium and oak, and the main foil is in oak only.

STEERING: A basic feature of the design is the use of front rather than rear steering. Directional control is provided by the movement of the hinged bow foil.

HULL: This is an all-wooden structure built in fir plywood, ¼ in thick and sealed. Torque load is carried by the skin, and bending loads are carried by the skin and the internal beam structure.

The crossbeam provides stability when in dock and in a displacement condition at low speeds. At 2-3 knots the horizontal safety foils at the top of the vee of the rear foils provide interim foil stabilisation up to the take-off speed of 5 knots and prevent dragging an end of the crossbeam in the water. At

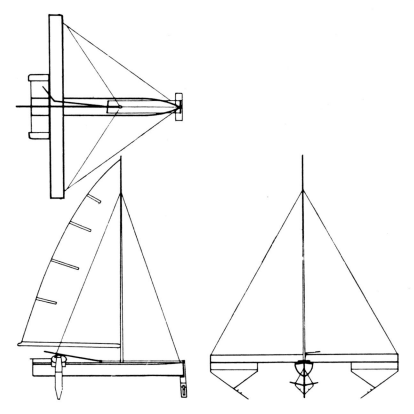

The Nigg Flying Fish

foilborne speeds the safety foils preclude the possibility of an end of the crossbeam being driven into the water by sudden heeling.

RIG: A cat rig of 9·2-13·9 m² (100-150 sq ft) area is recommended.

DIMENSIONS:

Length overall, hull (plus boom overhand at rear, dependent on sail plan)

	5·02 m (16 ft 6 in)
Length waterline, hull	4·87 m (16 ft 0 in)
Beam	6·09 m (20 ft 0 in)
Draft afloat (fixed foils)	1·06 m (3 ft 6 in)
Draft foilborne	
	12-30 in over operating speed range
Height, approx	7·3 m (24 ft 0 in)

PERFORMANCE:

Max speed foilborne

Over 30 knots, design cruise range optimised for 20-30 knots

Max speed hullborne	5 knots
Min wind for take-off	10 knots

Number of seconds and distance to take-off (theor. app)

3 secs with 15·2 m (50 ft) run in favourable wind

Number of seconds and distance to stop craft (theor. app)

Can land from 20 knots in 45·6 m (150 ft) in about 6 seconds

SEA TEST: The craft has been tested in 10-25 knot winds, on both sheltered inland lakes and on ocean bays, with a max chop of about 18 inches. Speeds up to approx 30 knots have been attained.

HYDROFOIL OPERATORS

One of three Boeing Jetfoils operated by Pacific Sea Transportation Ltd. on its Sea Flite services between the Hawaiian islands

HYDROFOIL OPERATORS

NORTH AMERICA
CANADA
BRITISH COLUMBIA STEAMSHIP CO
Type(s): Boeing Jetfoil, 1, 224 passengers.
Route(s): Experimental six-week service from Seattle to Victoria BC, starting September 17th, 1976. Cooperative venture between Boeing and BCS to test market.
USA
DEPARTMENT OF THE NAVY,
NAVAL SEA SYSTEMS COMMAND (NAVSEA)
The Boeing/NATO PHM, Patrol Hydrofoil, Guided Missile, is a NATO project, sponsored jointly by the US Navy, the Federal Republic of Germany and the Italian Navy. It is being developed by NAVSEA PMS 303.
The first craft, the Pegasus, began operational evaluation in the San Diego area in the summer of 1975. The US Navy programme anticipates procurement of a six-ship squadron initially with the determination of the eventual force level at a later date.
Sea World
1720 South Shores Road, Mission Bay, San Diego, California
TELEPHONE: 224-3535
This company operates three 28-seat Atlantic Hydrofoils Inc. Sea Worlds (Sprague Engineering Co) on ten minute sightseeing tours around Mission Bay. The craft were the first built on the West Coast to be licensed for commercial use by the US Coast Guard.
US Navy Pacific Fleet Amphibious Command
Type(s): Flagstaff, PGH-1
Base: San Diego
US Naval Ship Research and Development Center
Type(s): High Point, PCH-1; Plainview AGEH-1
Purpose: US Navy hydrofoil development programme.
SOUTH AMERICA
ARGENTINA
Alimar SA
Type(s): PT 50, 3 (Rodriquez)
Route: Buenos Aires-Colonia-Montevideo
BOLIVIA
Crillon Tours Ltd
ADDRESS: PO Box 4785 Av Comacho 1223 Ed, Krsul, La Paz
Type(s): Albatross, 2 (Honold), modified by Helmut Kock
Route(s): Lake Titicaca

BRASIL
Aerobarcos do Brasil, TRANSTOR
Type(s): PT 20, 3 (Rodriquez),
RHS 110, 1 (Navaltecnica)
CUBA
Type(s): Kometa M, 1 (Sormovo)
Route(s): Batabano—Nueva Gerona
VENEZUELA
Compania Shell
Type(s): PT 20, 3 (Werf Gusto)
Route: Offshore oil drilling operations on Lake Maracaibo
ASIA AND PACIFIC
CHINA
Navy of the Chinese People's Republic
Type(s): Hu Chwan Class, 60 plus (Shanghai)
Operational areas: Coastal waters
HAWAII
Pacific Sea Transportation Ltd.
Seaflite Services
HEAD OFFICE: 233 Keawe Street, Honolulu, Hawaii
Type(s): Jetfoil, 3 (Boeing) Kamehameha, Kalakana and Kuhio.
Route(s): Daily services between Oahu and Maui, Oahu and Kauai and Maui and Kailua-Kona on the Island of Hawaii.
INDONESIA
Sundaharya Corp, Djakarta
Type(s): PT 20 (Rodriquez)
Route(s): Indonesia Coast
JAPAN
Boyo Kisen Co. Ltd.
Type(s): PT 50, 1 (Hitachi)
Route(s): Yanai—Matsuyama
Type(s): PT 20, 1, "Shibuki No 2" (Hitachi)
Route(s): Yanai—Matsuyama
Isizaki Kisen Co. Ltd.
Fukae, Ohaki-cho, Saeki-gun,
Hiroshima-ken, Japan
Type(s): PT 50, "Kosei" (Hitachi)
Route(s): Hiroshima-Kure-Matsuyama
Type(s): PT 50, 1 (Hitachi)
Route(s): Hiroshima-Kure-Matsuyama
Type(s): PT 20 "Kinsei", 1 (Hitachi)

Route(s): Onomichi-Matsuyama
Type(s): PT 20 "Tsobasamaru", 1 (Hitachi)
Route(s): Hiroshima-Kure-Matsuyama
An additional PT 50 was delivered to the company during 1967.

Kansai Steamship Co Ltd..
Soze-che, Kita-ku, Osaka
Type(s): PT 50, 1 "Haya Kaze" (Hitachi)
Route(s): Osaka-Koke-Shodoshima-Takamatsu
Type(s): PT 20, 2, "Hayate" Nos 1 and 2 (Hitachi)
Route(s): "Hayate No 1", Himeji-Syodoshima-Takamatsu "Hayate No 2", Koke-Sumoto

Meitetsu Kaijo Kankosen Co.
99-1 Shin-miyazaka-cho, Atsuta-ku, Nagoya City
Type(s): PT 50, 1 "Osyo" (Hitachi)
Route(s): Nagoya-Toba-Gamagori-Nishiura-Irako
Type(s): PT 20, 2 "Taihomaru" and "Hayabusamaru" (Hitachi)
Route(s): Nagoya-Toba-Irako-Gamagori-Shinojima and Kowa-Shinojima-Irako-Toba-Nishiura

Nichimen Co. Ltd.
(Kinkowan Ferry Co. Ltd.)
Type(s): PT 50, 1 "Otori No 3" (Hitachi)
Route(s): Kajiki-Kagoshima-Ibusuki

Nissho-Iwai Co. Ltd.
(Hankyu Lines Co. Ltd.)
Type(s): PT 50, 2 "Zuiho" and "Houo" (Hitachi)
Route(s): Koke-Tokushima

Hankyu Lines Co. Ltd.
Type(s): PT 20, 2, "Amatsu" and "Kasugano"
Route(s): Kobe-Naruto

Setonaikai Kisen Co. Ltd.
Ujina Kaigani-chome, Hiroshima
Type(s): PT 50, 3 "Wakashio", "Otori No 1" and "Otori No 2" (Hitachi)
Route(s): Onomichi-Setoda-Imabari and Hiroshima-Kure-Matsuyama
Type(s): PT 50, 1, "Kondoru" (Hitachi)
Route(s): Hiroshima-Kure-Matsuyama
Type(s): PT 50, 1. (Hitachi)
Route(s): Onomichi-Setoda-Imbari
Type(s): PT 50, 4 "Hibiki No 1", "No 2" and "No 3" and "Shibuki No 1" (Hitachi)
Route(s): Onomichi-Setoda-Omishima-Imbari and ("Shibuki No 1") Yanai-Matsuyama

HONG KONG
Shun Tak Co
Type(s): PT 20, 1 (Rodriquez)
Route(s): Hong Kong-Macao
Hong Kong Macao Hydrofoil Co
PT 50, 4 (Rodriquez); RHS 140, 5 (Navaltecnica)
Far East Hydrofoil Co. Ltd.
HEAD OFFICE:
36th Floor, Connaught Centre, Connaught Road, Hong Kong
TELEPHONE:
H-243176
TELEX:
74200
CABLES:
Setedam, Hong Kong
DIRECTORS:
Stanley Ho, Managing Director
EXECUTIVES:
K. B. Allport, Group Manager
D. Hay, Technical Manager
Route(s): Hong Kong-Macao, distance 36 nm by the Southern Route, Services half-hourly, sunrise to sunset, i.e. 15,400 trips per annum. Approximate total number of passengers carried per year-1,450,000. Craft: PT 50, 4, Guia, Penha, Taipa, Balsa (Hitachi Zosen): RHS 110, 4, Cerco, Praia, Barca, Cacilhas (Navaltecnica); RHS 160, 1, Lilau: (Navaltecnica): PTS 75 Mk 111, 1, Rosa (Vosper Thornycroft): Jetfoil, 2, Madeira, Santa Maria, (Boeing).

CEYLON
Royal Ceylon Navy
Type(s): Waterman, 1 (International Aquavion)
Communications and patrol

KOREA
Hans Ryeo Developments Co. Ltd.
Type(s): PT 20, 1 (Rodriquez)

PHILIPPINES
Bataan Manila Ferry Services
Manila
Type(s): Raketa TA (Sormovo/Airavia)
Tourist Hotel and Travel Corporation
Type(s): PT 20, 2 (Rodriquez)
Route(s): Manila-Corregidor
Philippine Navy
Type(s): PT 20, 2 (Rodriquez); PT 32, 2 "Bontoc", Baler", (Hitachi)
Coastal Patrol

AUSTRALASIA
AUSTRALASIA
Public Transport Commission of New South Wales
HEAD OFFICE:
No. 2 Jetty, Circular Quay, Sydney,
N.S.W. 2000
TELEPHONE:
27.9251
TELEX:
NSWTC AA25702
TERMINAL OFFICES:
No. 2 Jetty, Circular Quay 27.9251
Manly Wharf, Manly 97.3028
EXECUTIVES:
T. F. Gibson, General Manager
W. Heading, Superintendent Engineer
OPERATIONS: Routes served and frequency. Sydney to Manly, 7 miles, every 20 minutes between 7 a.m. and 7 p.m.
Approximate number of passengers carried during year: One million.
CRAFT IN SERVICE:
PT 20, 1 (Hitachi), 72 passengers, built 1965.
PT 50 (Rodriquez), 140 passengers, built in 1966.
PT 20, 1 (Hitachi) "Manly", 72 passengers, built 1965.
PT 50 (Rodriquez), "Fairlight", 140 passengers, built 1966
PT 50 (Rodriquez), "Dee Why", 140 passengers, built 1968
PT 50 (Rodriquez), "Palm Beach", 140 passengers, built 1969
RHS 140 (Navaltecnica), "Curl Curl" built in 1971.
Tires Pty Ltd TD
HEAD OFFICE:
Corner Junction, Road and Gray Terrace, Rosewater, Outer Harbour, South Australia
Type(s): Aquavion Waterman, 1.
Route(s): Port Adelaide to Outer Harbour. Hourly service. Also educational and scenic tours of Port River, Adelaide.
NEW ZEALAND
Kerridge Odeon Corporation
Type(s): PT 20, 1 (Rodriquez)
Route(s): Auckland-Waiheke Island

EUROPE, MEDITERRANEAN AND NEAR EAST
ALBANIA
Albanian Navy
Type(s): Hu Chwan (White Swan) Class, 30 (Shanghai)
Operating areas: Coastal waters

BULGARIA
Bulgarian Shipping Line
Type(s): Kometa, 4
Route(s): Bourgas-Nesetow-Varna
Bulgarian River Fleet
Type(s): Meteor, 2: Raketa,2
Route(s): Danube, between Rousse and Silistra

CHANNEL ISLANDS
Condor Ltd
Type(s): PT 50, 1 (Rodriquez) RHS 140, 2 (Navaltecnica), RHS 160 (Navaltecnica)
Route(s): Guernsey-Jersey-St. Malo
CYPRUS
Wonder Shipping Ltd
HEAD OFFICE:
c/o Hanseatic Ship management/Jeropoulov & Co., Limassol.
Type(s): PT 50, 1 (Rodriquez)
Route(s): Larnaca-Lebanon-Syria.

DENMARK
Dampskipsselskapet Oresund
Type(s): PT 50, 2 (1 Rodriquez, 1 Westermoen); RHS 140, 1, (Navaltecnica)
Route(s): Copenhagen-Malmo

EGYPT
Ministry of Commerce, Cairo
Type(s): PT 20, 3 (Rodriquez)
Route(s): Abu Simbel-Asswan
Nile Sightseeing Service
FINLAND
Paijanteen Kantosiipi Oy
Type(s): Raketa, 1 (Krasnoye, Sormovo)
Route(s): Lahti-Jyvaskyla, across Lake Paijane
FRANCE
Vedettes Armoricaines
Ier Eperon,
56 rue d'Aiguillon, 29N Brest,
Type(s): Kometa, 1, (Sormovo)
GERMANY
Water Police
Type(s): PT 4, 3 (German Shipyard)
Route(s): Patrol service on the Rhine
Köln Düsseldorfer Shipping Co
Type(s): Raketa, 1 "Rhine Arrow" (Sormovo)
Route(s): Cologne—Koblenz
GREECE
Hellenic Hydrofoil Lines
Type(s): Kometa 2 (Sormovo), plus one Kometa on order
Route(s): Brindisi—Corfu; Otranto—Corfu (Igoumenitsa)
   80 mile run takes 2½ hours.   Fare Drs 600 (£8·80) single
HUNGARY
Hungarian Navigation Company
Type(s): Raketa, 2 Chaika, 2, Meteors, 2 plus (Krasnoye-Sormovo)
Route(s): Budapest-Vienna
IRAN
Type(s): Kometas (Sormovo)
Route(s): Persian Gulf
ITALY
Aliscafi SNAV, SpA
Type(s): PT 20, 7; PT 50, 8 (Rodriquez)
Route(s): Messina-Reggio-Isole-Lipari and Naples-Capri-Ischia.
Onorato
Aliscafi del Tirreno
Naples
Type(s): PT 50, 2 (Westermoen) PT 20, 1 (Rodriquez) Kometa and
   Kometa M, 8 (Sormovo)
Route(s): Naples Bay, Naples-Capri, Naples-Capri-Ischia
SAS, Trapani
Type(s): PT 50, 1: PT 20, 3 (Rodriquez)
Route(s): Trapani-Egadi Islands
Adriatica SpA di Navigazione
Venaezia
Type(s): PT 50, 1 (Rodriquez), RHS 160, 1 (Navaltecnica)
Route(s): Tremoli-Isoledi Tremiti
Ministry of Transport, Milan
Type(s): PT 20, 2 (Rodriquez); RHS 70, 1 (Navaltecnica)
Route(s): Lake Garda
Compagnia di Navigazione
Type(s): PT 20, 2 (Rodriquez); RHS 70, 2 (Navaltecnica)
Route(s): Lake Maggiore
Compagnia di Navigazione
Type(s): PT 20, 2 (Rodriquez); RHS 70, 2 (Navaltecnica)
Route(s): Lake Como
G. & R. Salvatori, Naples
Type(s): PT 50, 2 (Westermoen)
Route(s): Naples-Capri
Sar Nav
(Societa Sarda per Navigazione Veloce)
HEAD OFFICE:
   Via Lombardia 38, Olbai
Type(s): Seaflight L90 "Squalo Bianco", 1
Route(s): Civitavecchia-Olbai
Societe Sirena, Palermo
Type(s): PT 50, 1 (Rodriquez)
Route(s): Palermo-Ustica
Societe Tosco Sarda di Nav Porto Ferraio
Type(s): PT 20, 3, PT 20 Caribe, 1 (Rodriquez)
Route(s): Piombino-R, Matima-P. Azzutto
AGIP, Milan
Type(s): PT 20, 1, PT 50, 1 (Rodriguez)
NORWAY
De bla Omnibusser A/S
Type(s): PT 20, 2 (Westermoen)
Route(s): Oslofjord

Stavangerske Dampskibsselskab
Type(s): PT 50, 1; PT 20, 1, (Rodriquez); RHS 140, 1,
   (Navaltecnica)
Route(s): Stavanger-Haugesund-Bergen
Hardanger Sunnhordelandske Dampskibsselskap
Box 268, 5001, Bergen
Type(s): PT 20, 1 (Westermoen); RHS 140, 1 (Navaltecnica)
Route(s): Bergen-Tittelsness
Fosen Trafikklag A/S
Skaneskaia 6, Trondheim
Type(s): PT 20 Nisen (Westermoen)
Route(s): Trondheim area
Joh. Presthus Rederi
Bergen
Type(s): PT 150, 3 (Westermoen)
Route(s): Copenhagen-Malmo
MOROCCO
Transports Touristiques Intercontinentaux, Tangier
Type(s): Kometa, 2 (Sormovo design)
Route(s): Tangier-Algericas, Tangier-Marbella
POLAND
Central Board of Inland Navigation
Type(s): ZRYW-1
Route(s): Szczecin-Swinoujscie
Type(s): Kometa 3 (Sormovo)
Route(s): unknown
ROMANIA
Romanian Navy
Type(s): Hu Chwan, 1
Operating area: Coastal waters
SWEDEN
Svenska Rederiaktiebolaget Oresund
Type(s): PT 50, 2 (Rodriquez), RHS 140, 1 (Navaltecnica)
Route(s): Copenhagen-Malmo
UNITED KINGDOM
Red Funnel Steamers Ltd
Type(s): Seaflight H 57, 1, RHS 70, 2 (Navaltecnica)
Route(s): Southampton-Cowes
YUGOSLAVIA
INEX-Nauticki Turizam
Obala Lazareta 3, Split
PP/POB 199,
TELEPHONE: 47-651, 45-758
TELEX: 11227
DIRECTOR: B. Tomic
Type(s): Replacement fleet, understood to comprise two Raketa
Ts and three Kometa MTs
Route(s): Adriatic coastal services; tourist and passenger services
between Italy and Yugoslavia
INEX-Nautical Tourism
Kolarceva 8,
Beograd
TELEX: 11 240
Globtours
Obala,
Portoroz.

USSR
Ministry of the River Fleet
   The Soviet Ministry of the River Fleet operates hydrofoil passenger
ferries on practically all the major rivers, lakes, canals and reservoirs
from Central Russia to Siberia and the Far East.
   In 1958, when hydrofoils were first introduced to the rivers of the
USSR, they carried ten thousand passengers.   By 1968 the number
of passengers carried had grown to three million.   During the
1969-70 navigation season there were 80 hydrofoil services on the
Volga alone, operated by vessels of the Raketa, Meteor, Sputnik
and Burevestnik series.   There are now more than 150 hydrofoil
passenger services in the Soviet Union and it was stated that during
1972 the 200 craft operating these services carried about 20 million
passengers.
   In addition to craft on inland waterways employing the Alexeyev
shallow draft submerged foil system, Strela-type craft, with surface-
piercing foils, operate in the Gulf of Finland, and supported by
Kometas and Vikhrs, provide year-round services between ports on
the Black Sea.
   Three new hydrofoil passenger ferry designs are to be put into
production—the Cyclone, a seagoing, waterjet-propelled ferry with
seats for 250 and capable of 40 knots, the Typhoon, a gas-turbine
powered 90-seat vessel with fully submerged, autostabilised foils

and the Voskhod (Sunrise), a Raketa replacement. The Voskhod will provide greater, comfort and improved facilities for passengers and crew and air-conditioning will be installed. As with the Raketa, a family of variants will be available to suit a wide variety of operating and traffic conditions. Fastest of the series is reported to be the Voskhod-3, powered by a gas-turbine and capable of 43 knots.

The Raketa has given excellent service and has extremely low operating costs. The cost of carrying passengers on the craft is stated to be lower than that of either displacement-type passenger ferries or automobiles. Similar low-cost operation is demonstrated by the 260-passenger Sputnik on the Moscow-Astrakhan route. It has been found that the cost of operating a Sputnik on this service is only 8% of that of the latest displacement-type passenger ferry of the United Volga Steamship Line. Time saving is one of the most important considerations. In many cases, hydrofoils take passengers to their destinations faster than trains. For example, a Raketa service covers the 516 miles (800 km) from Gorky to Kazan in 12 hours, while trains take 20 hours for the same journey. Price of the ticket is the same, however, whether the journey is undertaken by hydrofoil or rail.

The Meteor service from Moscow to Sormovov takes 13 hours 40 minutes to cover 559 miles (900 km). A conventional passenger ship requires about three days to cover this distance.

In 1976 it was announced that sea trials had confirmed that the Kometa can operate successfully in Arctic waters. Tests conducted off the Kola Peninsula and Kamchatka, in the Soviet Far East, demonstrated that the craft is capable of navigating through areas with broken ice without sustaining damage.

Soviet Frontier Police

Some twenty-five Pchela patrol hydrofoils, derived from the Strela passenger ferry, are in service with the KGB Frontier Police in the Baltic, Caspian and the Black Sea areas.

Soviet Navy

The first sightings of a new hydrofoil fast patrol boat known by the NATO code name Turya, were made in the Baltic in the Spring of 1973. This new vessel, which is equipped for ASW work, is based on the hull of the Osa missile craft. The design employs a fixed surface-piercing bow foil only. Powered by three 4,330 hp diesels it has a top speed of about 45 knots under calm conditions. Production is in hand at three Soviet naval shipyards.

POWER PLANTS AND PROPULSION SYSTEMS

CANADA

KOHLER OF CANADA LTD

HEAD OFFICE:

6390 Northwest Drive, Malton, Ontario, Canada

TELEPHONE:

416-677-4733

TELEX: 06-968574

EXECUTIVES:

D. W. F. Seston, Director of Marketing and Sales

Several Canadian light air cushion vehicle designs are equipped with Kohler 2 cycle engines.

Model:	K295-2AX	K340-2AX	K340-2AS	K440-2AN K440-2AS	K440-2LC
Bore:	2·264 (in)	2·441 (in)	2·362 (in)	2·766 (in)	2·667 (in)
	57·5 (mm)	62·0 (mm)	62·0 (mm)	68·0 (mm)	68·0 (mm)
Stroke:	2·205 (in)	2·205 (in)	2·362 (in)	2·362 (in)	2·362 (in)
	56·0 (mm)	56·0 (mm)	60·0 (mm)	60·0 (mm)	60·0 (mm)
Displacement:	17·69 (cu in)	20·62 (cu in)	20·69 (cu in)	26·60 (cu in)	26·60 (cu in)
	290 (c cm)	338 (c cm)	339 (c cm)	436 (c cm)	436 (c cm)

PRATT & WHITNEY AIRCRAFT OF CANADA LTD

HEAD OFFICE & WORKS:

P.O. Box 10, Longueuil, Quebec

EXECUTIVES:

T. E. Stephenson, Chairman

D. C. Lowe, President

R. H. Guthrie, Vice-President, Industrial & Marine Division

E. L. Smith, Vice-President, Operations

K. H. Sullivan, Vice-President, Marketing

E. H. Schweitzer, Vice-President, Product Support

V. W. Tryon, Vice-President, Finance and Administration

E. A. Clifford, Engineering Manager, Industrial and Marine Division

P. Henry, PR Manager

In addition to its compact range of low-power aircraft turbines (eg the PT6A turbo-prop, PT6B, PT6T and T400 turboshafts, and JT15D turbofan), P & WC also manufactures a marine derivative of the PT6, the **ST6 series of turboshafts. These engines are rated at 550 shp and upwards, and are installed in a number of ACV and hydrofoil vessels. These include the FHE-400 ASW hydrofoil where ST6 engines drive the generators and hydraulic pumps for the ship's services and foil control, and also provide emergency propulsion power for hullborne operation. The US prototype Surface Effect Ship SES-100B is equipped with three ST6J-70s to power its eight lift fans, and two ST-60 series engines power the Canadian research hydrofoil Proteus. Two ST6T-75 Twin-Pac turbines power the Bell Aerospace Canada Voyageur hovercraft and a single ST6T-75 provides power in that company's Viking craft. A series of larger Voyageurs for the US Army designated LACV-30 are powered by ST6T-76 engines.**

Including aero-engine installations, over 7,000 of this series of gas-turbines have been delivered. Between them they have accumulated running experience in excess of 12 million hours.

ST6 MARINE GAS-TURBINE

ST6 marine gas-turbines are designed and manufactured by Pratt & Whitney Aircraft of Canada Ltd. Details of the engine specifications are given below:

TYPE: A simple cycle free turbine engine with a single spool gas generator and a multi-stage compressor driven by a single stage turbine. Burner section has an annular combustion chamber with downstream injection. The single stage-free turbine is connected to the output shaft via a reduction gearbox.

The ST6T-75 and ST6T-76 Twin Pac TM are dual engines with the two engines

ST6 gas-turbine

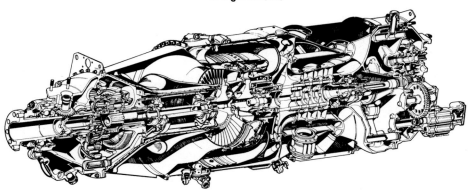

Cutaway of the ST6-70. The model illustrated, the ST6J-70, differs from the ST6K-70 only in the main reduction gearbox

STG-77 seen from above

mounted side-by-side and coupled to a twinning reduction gear.

AIR INTAKE: Annular air intake at rear of engine with intake screen.

COMPRESSOR: Three axial-flow stages, plus single centrifugal stage. Single-sided centrifugal compressor with 26 vanes, made from titanium forging. Axial rotor of disc-drum type with stainless steel stator and rotor blades. Stator vanes are brazed to casing. The rotor blades are dove tailed to discs. Discs through-bolted with centrifugal compressor, to shaft. Fabricated one-piece stainless steel casing and radial diffuser.

COMBUSTION CHAMBER: Annular reverse-flow type of stainless steel construction, with 14 Simplex burners. Two glow or spark plug igniters.

GAS GENERATOR: Single-stage axial. Rotor blades mounted by fir tree roots.

POWER TURBINE: Single or dual-stage axial. Rotor blades mounted by fir tree roots.

BEARINGS: Gas generator and power turbine supported by one ball bearing and one roller bearing each.

SHAFT DRIVE: Single, or two-stage planetary reduction gear or direct drive-depending on engine model. Torque measuring system incorporated with reduction gearing.

FUEL GRADE: Diesel Nos. 1 and 2 and Navy Diesel or aviation turbine fuel.

JET PIPE: Single port exhaust discharging vertically upwards or at 60° port or starboard of vertical. Alternatively twin ports discharging horizontally on some models.

ACCESSORY DRIVES: Mounting pads on accessory case including for starter or starter-generator and tacho-generator. Also tacho-generator drive on power section.

LUBRICATION SYSTEM: One pressure and four scavenge gear type pumps driven by gas generator rotor. Integral oil tank.

OIL SPECIFICATIONS: Type 2 synthetic lube oil PWA-521 MIL-L-23699.

ST6 ENGINE DATA SUMMARY
Sea Level Standard Pressure at 15°C (59°F) Inlet Temperature

IMPERIAL MEASURE

Model	Maximum		Intermediate		Normal		Output RPM (max)	Length (in)	Width (in)	Height (in)	Weight (ins)
	SHP	SFC*	SHP	SFC*	SHP	SFC*					
ST6J-70	620	0·64	580	0·65	510	0·67	2,200	62	19	19	350
ST6K-70	620	0·64	580	0·65	510	0·67	6,230	60	19	19	317
ST6L-77	811	0·589			654	0·62	33,000	52·2	19	19	306
ST6J-77	750	0·608	650	0·631	550	0·66	2,200	62	19	19	379
ST6K-77	690	0·62	620	0·64	550	0·66	6,230	60	19	19	350
ST6L-80	1,065	0·58	955	0·60	840	0·62	30,000	59·4	19	19	360
*ST6T-75	1,700	0·62	1,500	0·63	1,300	0·65	6,600	66·4	44·4	31·6	730
*ST6T-76	1,850	0·615	1,645	0·627	1,440	0·65	6,600	66·4	44·4	31·6	730

METRIC MEASURE

Model	Maximum		Intermediate		Normal		Output RPM (Max)	Length (mm)	Width (mm)	Height (mm)	Weight (kg)
	kW	SFC*	kW	SFC*	kW	SFC*					
ST6J-70	463	·389	433	·395	380	·407	2,200	1,575	483	483	159
ST6K-70	463	·389	433	·395	380	·407	6,230	1,524	483	483	144
ST6L-77	605	·358			488	·377	33,000	1,326	483	483	139
ST6J-77	560	·371	485	·384	410	·401	2,200	1,575	483	483	172
ST6K-77	515	·377	463	·389	410	·401	6,230	1,524	483	483	159
ST6L-80	794	·353	712	·365	627	·377	30,000	1,509	483	483	164
*ST6T-75	1,268	·377	1,119	·383	970	·395	6,600	1,687	1,128	803	332
*ST6T-76	1,380	·374	1,227	·381	1,074	·395	6,600	1,687	1,128	803	332

*SFC = lb/hp/hr (Imperial)
= Kg/kW.h (Metric)

TWIN-PACᴛᴍ

FRANCE

CLUB FRANÇAIS DES AEROGLISSEURS
HEAD OFFICE:
41 and 43 Rue Aristide Briand
95130 Meung sur Loire

Club Francais des Aeroglisseurs is marketing a special propulsion unit for high performance lightweight air cushion vehicles. The unit, given the name "Diagloo", comprises an adapted 600 cc Citroen air-cooled, automotive engine, driving a 4 ft 7⅛ in (1·40 m) diameter, two-bladed Merville propeller via a reduction and reverse gearbox. Engine output is 32·5 bhp (33 cv) at 6,000 rpm.

The unit weighs 220 lb (100 kg) and is supplied complete with an aerodynamically profiled hood. Series production has begun. The price is approximately F 5,000.

The Diagloo propulsion unit for light sports ACVs

SOCIÉTÉ TURBOMÉCA
HEAD OFFICE AND WORKS:
Bordes (Pyrénées Atlantiques)
PARIS OFFICE:fi
1 Rue Beaujon, Paris 8c

PRESIDENT AND DIRECTOR GENERAL:
J. R. Szydolowski

The Société Turboméca was formed in 1938 by MM. Szydlowski and Planiol to develop blowers, compressors and turbines for aeronautical use.

In 1947 the company began development of gas-turbines of low power for driving aircraft auxiliaries and for aircraft propulsion.

Many of Turboméca's production series

aircraft turbines have been adapted to industrial and marine duties including installation in French air cushion vehicles of various types. General descriptions follow of the main Turboméca turbine engines at present in production or under development. Reference is also made to air cushion vehicle and hydrofoil installations.

TURBOMÉCA ARTOUSTE

The Artouste is a single-shaft turboshaft engine which has been manufactured in quantity in two versions, the 400 shp Artouste IIC and the 563 shp Artouste IIIB. The 590 shp Artouste IIID has also been developed. More than 1,500 of the earlier Artouste II were built to power the Sud-Aviation Alouette II helicopter. The Artouste II has a single-stage centrifugal compressor, annular reverse-flow combustor and two-stage axial turbine. In the second generation Artouste III in which the pressure ratio is increased from 3·88 : 1 to 5·2 : 1, a single-axial stage compressor has been added ahead of the centrifugal impeller. The turbine also has an additional stage.

A single Artouste drives the two propulsion airscrews on the Naviplane BC 8.

The following description refers to the Artouste IIIB.

TYPE: Single-shaft axial-plus-centrifugal turboshaft.

COMPRESSOR: Single-stage axial plus single-stage centrifugal compressor. Two diffusers, one radial and the other axial, aft of compressor. Pressure ratio at 33,500 rpm at S/L 5·2 : 1, Air mass flow 9·5 lb/sec (4·3 kg/sec) at 33,500 rpm at S/L.

COMBUSTION CHAMBER: Annular type, with rotary atomiser fuel injection. Torch igniters.

TURBINE: Three-stage axial type. Blades integral with discs. Row of nozzle guide vanes before each stage.

JET PIPE: Fixed type.

STARTING: Automatic with 4,000 watt starter-generator. Two Turboméca igniter plugs.

DIMENSIONS:
Length	71·46 in (1,815 mm)
Height	24·68 in (627 mm)
Width	20·47 in (520 mm)

WEIGHT (Dry):
Equipped	401 lb (182 kg)

PERFORMANCE RATING:
563 shp at 33,500 rpm

FUEL CONSUMPTION:
At T-O and max continuous rating
0·71 lb (322 gr) ehp/rh

TURBOMÉCA TURMO

The Turmo is a free-turbine engine available in both turboshaft and turboprop versions spanning the 1,200 to 2,000 shp power bracket. First generation Turmo IIIC and E series have a single-stage axial plus single-stage centrifugal compressor, annular reverse-flow combustor, two-stage axial compressor-turbine, and mechanically-separate single-, or two-stage power turbine. Second-generation Turmo X engines have an additional axial compressor stage and other refinements. By December 1975 more than 1,700 Turmo engines had been built.

Main versions of the Turmo at present in production or under development include:
Turmo IIIC7: Derived from the Turmo III B, this model (with two-stage power turbine) has a 1,610 shp at max contingency rating and powers early Sud-Aviation SA 321 Super-Frelon three-engined military helicopters. Two will power the projected

Turbomeca Turmo 1,300 shp IIIc free-turbine turboshaft, two of which will power the projected Aerospatiale SA 800 mixed-traffic hydrofoil ferry

Turbomeca Turmo XII free-turbine, developed from the Turmo IIIF installed in the turbotrains of SCNF

The **889** shp Turbomeca Turmastazou XIV free-turbine turboshaft

Aerospatiale 46-ton patrol boat hydrofoil under development for the French navy.

The Turmo IIIF also powers the Turbotrains of SNCF.

Turmo IVC: Based on the Turmo IIIC, this is a special version with a single-stage power turbine and powers the Sud-Aviation SA 330 Puma twin-engined military helicopter. The engine has a maximum contingency rating of 1,555 shp.

Turmo IIIC7 This model (which reverts to the standard two-stage power turbine) is in the same series as the Turmo IIIC and E and has a maximum emergency rating of 1,610 shp. It is installed in Sud Aviation SA 321 F and J Super-Frelon civil three engined helicopters.

Turmo IIIC2: Embodies new materials for the gas generator turbine, and offers

an emergency rating of 1,610 shp.

Turmo IIIE3: Two each rated at 1,282 shp, power the Bertin/Société de l'Aerotrain Orléans 250-80 tracked air-cushion vehicle. Both engines drive a ducted seven-bladed 7 ft 7 in (2·30 m) diameter Ratier-Figeac FH-201 hydraulically operated reversible-pitch propeller for propulsion. The Turmo IIIE is rated at 1,580 shp.

Turmo IIIF: This model has been in production since 1970 to power the production version of the SNCF Turbotrain operating on the Paris-Caen-Cherbourg, Lyon-Nantes, Lyon-Strasbourg, Lyon-Bordeaux and Bordeaux-Toulouse runs.

In the United States it is employed in the AMTRAK locomotives on the Chicago-St Louis run and in Iran it is employed on locomotives on the Teheran—Mashed line.

MARK	PERFORMANCES I.S.A. CONDITIONS								COMPRESSOR CHARACTERISTICS (at take-off rating)					TURBINE		Power off-take/propeller RPM (tr/mn)	OVERALL DIMENSIONS (mm)			Bare engine weight (kg)	Poids moteur équipé (kg)
	Shaft power at max. contingency rating (ch)	Shaft power at take-off (ch)	Shaft power at max. continuous (ch)	Residual thrust (kg)	Total equivalent power (ch) Take-off	Max. contin.	S.F.C. at take-off related to (g/ch.h) Shaft power	Total equiv. power	Number of stages Axial	Centrif.	Débit Air mass flow (kg/s)	Pressure ratio	RPM (tr/mn)	Number of stages Gas generator	Free turbine		Length	Width	Height		
TURBOSHAFT ENGINES																					
ARTOUSTE III D	–	598(1)	550	40	634	586	334	315	1	1	4,3	5,2	33 500	3	–	5.864	1815	522	665	130	178
ASTAZOU II A		530	480	35	562	510	288	261	1	1	2,5	6	43 500	3	–	5.922	1427	516	560	115	142
ASTAZOU III		598	530	30	625	559	281	269	1	1	2,5	6	43 500	3	–	6.179	1433	483	508	115	147
ASTAZOU XIV H		598 (1)	598(1)	57	651	651	284	260	2	1	3,33	7,5	43 000	3	–	6.334	1470	500	565		160
ASTAZOU XVIII A		885 (2)	816				255		2	1	3,35	7,5	43 000	3	–	5.830	1419	523	711		170
ASTAZOU XX A		1018 (4)	916				248		3	1	4,2	9,5	42 000	3	–	5.855	1529	533	721		195
TURMO III C7	1 632	1570	1292				287		1	1	6,2	5,90	33 600	2	2		1975	693	718		325
TURMO IV C	1 580	1517	1280				287		1	1	6,15	5,85	33 450	2	1	22 840	2184	637	719		227
ARRIEL	690	650	600				260		1	1	2,4	8	51 800	2	1	6 000	1217	480	626		128
MAKILA	1 935	1800	1650				214		3	1				2	2		2000	570	570		
TURBOPROP ENGINES																					
ASTAZOU XVI D	–	925	796	64	981	852	249	235	2	1	3,33	8,05	43 089	3	–	1 783	1556	581	581		200(3)
ASTAZOU XVI G	–	978	890	64	1 035	946	248	235	2	1	3,33	8	43 000	3	–	1 970	1556	645	645		228
ASTAZOU XX	–	1400	1234	72	1 464	1296	210	201	3	1			42 000	3	–		1677	580	580		
BASTAN VII	–	1060 (4)	1060	100	1 150	1150	278	256	2	1	5,85	6,8	32 000	3	–	1 517	1911	736	802		370

TYPE	PERFORMANCES I.S.A. CONDITIONS							COMPRESSOR CHARACTERISTICS (at take-off rating)					TURBINE		OVERALL DIMENSIONS (mm)			Bare engine weight (kg)	Equipped engine weight (kg)
	Thrust at take-off (kg)	Thrust at max. continuous (kg)	Ducted fan Dilution	LP compressor pressure ratio	S.F.C. (kg/kg.h) Take-off	Max. continuous		Number of stages Axial	Centrif.	Air mass flow (kg/s)	Pressure ratio	RPM (tr/mn)	Number of stages		Length	Width	Height		
TURBOJET ENGINES																			
ARBIZON III	–	380	330			1,12	1,11	1	1	6	5,5	33 000	1	–	1361	410	410		115
MARBORE II	–	400	400			1,15	1,15		1	8	3,85	22 600	1	–	1566	567	684	140	159
MARBORE VI	–	480	480			1,11	1,11		1	9,6	3,72	21,500	1	–	1416	594	631	140	159
AUBISQUE I A	–	742	625	2	1,5	0,618	0,60	1-1	1	22,2	6,9	33 000	1	–	2288	650	750		292
ADOUR (5)	–	2340 (6)	1746	0,79	2,44			2-5		42,7	10,8		1 - 1	–	2895	795	1137		748
LARZAC 04 (7)	–	1345	1250	1,13		0,703	0,675	2-4		21,7	10,65		1 - 1	–	1343	600	760		290
ASTAFAN III	–	790 (8)	715	7,7	1,32	0,365	0,359	1-2	1	31		43 000	3	–	2030	665	665	210	
ASTAFAN IV	–	1150 (9)	1020	7	1,34	0,31	0,305	1-3	1	39		42 000	3	–	2218	780	780	220	

(1) Up to + 55° C, or 4,000 m	(4) Up to + 40° C, or 2,500 m	(7) In cooperation with SNECMA
(2) Up to + 35° C, or 2,000 m	(5) In cooperation with ROLLS-ROYCE	(8) 850 kg with water injection
(3) Without starter generator	(6) 3,382 kg reheat lit	(9) 1,230 kg with water injection

March 1976

Table of Turbomeca's current range of gas-turbine engines

Turmo IIIN₈: Rated at 1,250 shp, this version powers the twin-engined SEDAM Naviplane N300 marine air-cushion vehicle. The engines are cross-coupled to drive two three-bladed 11 ft 10 in (3·60 m) diameter Ratier-Figeac FH 195-196 hydraulically-operated variable-pitch propellers for propulsion and two eleven-bladed 6 ft 3 in (1·85 m) diameter Ratier-Figeac FD 155 hydraulically-operated variable-pitch axial fans for lift.

Turmo XII: Developed from the Turmo IIIC this second-generation model has a two-stage axial compressor ahead of the centrifugal stage. With a maximum continuous rating of 1,610 shp, the Turmo XII is planned for a new SNCF Turbotrain.

Two Turmo IIIC series engines with a combined installed power of 2,564 shp, are to power the projected Sud-Aviation SA800 second-generation hydrofoil.

The following details apply to the Turmo-IIIC₇:

TYPE: Free-turbine axial-plus-centrifugal turboshaft.
AIR MASS FLOW: 13·7 lb (6·2 kg)/sec.
DIMENSIONS:
Length 77·8 in (1,976 mm)
Width 27·3 in (693 mm)
Height 28·2 in (717 mm)
WEIGHT DRY:
With standard equipment 715 lb (325 kg)

PERFORMANCE RATINGS:
T-O 1,550 shp
Max continuous 1,292 shp
FUEL CONSUMPTION:
At T-O rating 0·60 lb (273 gr)/shp/hr
At max continuous rating 0·64 lb (291 gr)/shp/hr

TURBOMÉCA MARBORE

The Marbore single-shaft turbojet has been built in greater numbers than any other Turboméca engine. By December 1974 over 9,000 880 lb (400 kg) thrust Marbore IIs and 1,058 lb (480 kg) thrust Marbore VIs had been manufactured by Turboméca and its licensees for trainer aircraft and target drone applications. Of this total, 5,229 Marbore engines were manufactured by Turboméca. In both these versions the engine comprises a single-stage centrifugal compressor, annular reverse-flow combustor and single-stage axial turbine.

Two Marbores will power the SA 890 hydrofoil test platform currently under development by Aérospatiale for the French Ministry of National Defence.

A Marbore II powers the lift system of the SEDAM Naviplane BC8 marine ACV. The exhaust gases are ducted along channels designed to entrain additional air to augment the efflux.

The following details relate to the Marbore VI:

DIMENSIONS:
Length with exhaust cone but without tail-
pipe 55·74 in (1,416 mm)
Width 23·35 in (593 mm)
Height 24·82 in (631 mm)
WEIGHT (Dry):
Equipped 309 lb (140 kg)
PERFORMANCE RATINGS:
T-O 1,058 lb (480 kg) st at 21,500 rpm
Cruising 925 lb (420 kg) st at 20,500 rpm
SPECIFIC FUEL CONSUMPTION:
At T-O rating 1·09
At cruising rating 1·07

TURBOMÉCA ASTAZOU

The Astazou is another of the later generation Turboméca engines, incorporating the experience gained with earlier series and making use of new design techniques. It has an extremely small gas-producer section and has been developed both as a turboshaft and as a turboprop driving a variable-pitch propeller.

The compressor consists of one, or two, axial stages followed by a centrifugal stage, with an annular combustion chamber and three-stage turbine. Accessories are mounted on the rear of the main intake casing. Pressure ratio is 6:1 and air mass flow 5·5 lb/sec (2·5 kg/sec) for the two-stage compressor engines, and 8 : 1 and 7·4 lb/sec (3·4 kg/sec) for the three-stage compressor engines respectively. In the turboshaft version, the rpm of the output shaft is 5,922.

Well over 1,900 Astazou engines of various types have been built. The following are the main Astazou variants:

Astazou II. This is a 535 hp turboprop (with two-stage compressor) which powers a version of the Naviplane N 102.

Astazou IIA. A 523 shp turboshaft (two-stage compressor) version powering the Sud-Aviation SA 318C Alouette II Astazou helicopter. A 450 shp Astazou provides power for the integrated lift and propulsion system of the SEDAM Naviplane N 102 marine ACV. The engine drives a 5 ft 7 in (1·70 m) diameter axial lift fan and two three-bladed variable-pitch propellers for propulsion.

Astazou IIIN. Rated at 592 hp, is the definitive (two-stage compressor).

Astazou IV. New version especially designed for industrial duty and in particular to form, associated with a Jeumont-Schneider AC generator, a 300 kW generating set It is installed in the RTG turbotrains made in France, USA and Iran. It is also being tested by the French Navy.

Astazou XIV (alias AZ14). Current major production turboshaft version (with three-stage compressor) rated at 852 shp. The engine is the standard power plant for the Naviplane N 102.

The B version is installed in the Alouette III helicopter and the H version in the SA 342 Gazelle helicopter.

Astazou XVI (alias AZ16). First Turbomeca production engine to embody the company's new air-cooled turbine. Rated at 913 shp for Jetstream aircraft and the FMA IA 58 Pucará counter-insurgency aircraft of the Argentine Air Force.

Astazou XVIII. An uprated version of the Astazou XVI with take-off power of 1,554 ehp and sfc of 0·512 lb (232 gr)/ehp/hr.

A turboshaft version is installed in the SA 360 Dauphin helicopter. Thermodynamic power: 1,032 shp, sfc of 0·57 lb/shp hr.

Astazou XX. This later version has an additional axial compressor stage, and is rated at take-off at 1,445 ehp for an sfc of 0·45 lb (204 gr)/ehp/hr.

Turboshaft version has 1,281 shp thermodynamic power, with sfc of 0·508 lb/shp hr.

The following details refer to the Astazou IIIN:

DIMENSIONS:
Length   40·7 in (1,433 mm)
Basic diameter   18·1 in (460 mm)
WEIGHT, DRY:
Equipped engine   325 lb (147·5 kg)
PERFORMANCE RATINGS:
T-O   592 shp at 43,500 rpm
Max continuous   523 shp at 43,500 rpm
FUEL CONSUMPTION:
At T-O rating   0·627 lb (284 gr)/shp/hr
At max continuous rating   0·644 lb (292 gr)/shp/hr

TURBOMÉCA BASTAN

A compact single-shaft turboprop in the 1,000 to 2,000 shp power bracket, the Bastan has its main application in the Nord 262. The 1,065 ehp Bastan VIC powering the original 262 series aircraft, comprises a single-stage axial compressor plus single-stage centrifugal compressor, annular reverse-flow combustor and three-stage axial turbine, and is equipped with water-methanol injection. The higher rated Bastan VII is capable of maintaining its 1,135 ehp T-O power up to an ambient temperature of 40°C. This version is entering production to power the new 262C and incorporates an additional axial compressor stage.

The following details refer to the Bastan VII:
DIMENSIONS:
Length   75·2 in (1,911 mm)
Height   31·6 in (802 mm)
Width   21·7 in. (550 mm)
WEIGHT, DRY:
Basic engine   639 lb (290 kg)
PERFORMANCE RATINGS:
T-O and max continuous   1,135 ehp
FUEL CONSUMPTION:
At T-O and max continuous ratings   0·572 lb (259 gr)/shp/hr

TURBOMÉCA TURMASTAZOU

This is a new free-turbine direct-drive turboshaft comprising the Astazou XIV single-shaft gas generator section provided with a mechanically-independent power turbine. The Astazou turbine has two stages in place of its normal three, and the power turbine has two stages also. Development is underway of the 889 shp Turmastazou XIV with a view to its use in twin-engined helicopters. The engine has also been proposed for the Bertin/Société de l'Aérotrain Orléans tracked ACV.

Turmastazou XVI. This version introduces the Turboméca air-cooled turbine, and gives a take-off rating of 1,015 shp for an sfc of 0·51 lb (231 gr)/shp/hr.

The following details refer to the Turmastazou XIV:

DIMENSIONS:
Length   54·0 in (1,371 mm)
Height   21·8 in (553 mm)
Width   17·3 in (440 mm)
WEIGHT, DRY:
Equipped engine   approximately 341 lb (155 kg)
PERFORMANCE RATINGS:
T-O   889 shp
Max continuous   792 shp

GERMANY

MTU
Motoren-und Turbinen-Union Friedrichshafen GmbH

HEAD OFFICE:
799 Friedrichshafen, Postfach 289
TELEPHONE:
(07541) 2071
TELEX:
MTUFH 0734-360
TELEGRAMME:
MOTORUNION
DIRECTORS:
Rolf Breuning, Executive President
Hugo B. Saemann, Executive President
Dr. Hans Dinger
Dr. Karl A. Müller
Dr. Ernst Zimmermann

The MTU-group of companies, formed in 1969 by the M.A.N. AG and the Daimler-Benz AG, consists of MTU-München GmbH and MTU-Friedrichshafen GmbH.

MTU-Friedrichshafen comprises the two plants of the previous Maybach Mercedes-Benz Motorenbau GmbH at Friedrichshafen and is owned 84 by MTU-München GmbH.

MTU-München, in turn is owned equally by M.A.N. and Daimler-Benz.

MTU-Friedrichshafen is today the development and production centre for high-performance diesel engines of Maybach, M.A.N. and Mercedes-Benz origin and as such embodies the experience of these companies in diesel engine technology. In

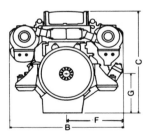
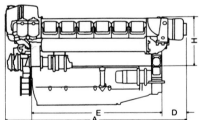

Engine type	A	B	C	D	E	F	G	H
6V331 TC 71-81	1585	1400	1280	218	1023	720	475	717
8V331 TC 71-81	1864	1400	1280	269	1251	720	475	717
12V331 TC 71-81	2429	1400	1352	318	1707	720	442	717

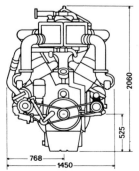
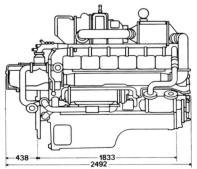

addition to diesel engines, MTU-Friedrich-shafen is responsible for sales and application of industrial and marine gas-turbines.

For application in hydrofoils MTU-Fried-richshafen offers the following engines:

331 engine family

12 V 493

652 engine family

538 engine family

The areas of responsibility of the two MTU companies are as follows:

MTU-München:

Development, production and support of light-weight, advanced-technology gas-turbines mainly for aircraft applications.

MTU Friedrichshafen:

Development, production and application of high-performance diesel engines.

Engine type	A	B	C	D	E	F	G
12V 652 TB 71-81	2450	1747	2230	225	1900	748	550
16V 652 TB 71-81	2950	1791	2265	243	2500	984	625

The following table defines power ranges in connection with application characteristics and reference conditions.

Output characteristics of operational engines usually depend on the special demands of the hydrofoil, from the operating profile to the application, and therefore will be specified for each system.

Engine type	A	B	C	D	E	F	G
12V 538 TB 81	2545	1620	2220	220	1785	810	725
16V 538 TB 81-82	3220	1620	2361	459	2252	810	595
20V 538 TB 81	3600	1620	2340	250	2960	810	657

MTU diesel engines for main propulsion of vessels, application groups 1C and 1D:							
Engine model	Continuous output			Intermittent output			Engine weight (dry)
	rpm	kW	hp	rpm	kW	hp	kg
Application group 1C							
6 V 331 TC 71	2055	470	560	2120	450	610	1580
8 V 331 TC 71	2055	550	750	2120	600	815	1920
12 V 331 TC 71	2055	820	1120	2120	900	1220	2910
12 V 493 TY 70	1400	810	1100	1500	1000	1360	3250*
12 V 652 TB 71	1380	1220	1660	1460	1440	1960	4850*
16 V 652 TB 71	1380	1620	2205	1460	1920	2610	6235*
Application group 1D				1000 hours per year			
6 V 331 TC 81	2260	450	610	2340	500	680	1580
8 V 331 TC 81	2260	600	815	2340	660	900	1920
12 V 331 TC 81	2260	900	1220	2340	1000	1360	2980
12 V 538 TB 81	1710	1440	1960	1760	1570	2135	5400
16 V 538 TB 81	1710	1920	2610	1760	2100	2860	6950
16 V 538 TB 82	1710	2140	2910	1760	2340	3180	6950
20 V 538 TB 81	1710	2400	3265	1760	2620	3565	9200

*Weight of engine with light alloy housing

—Continuous output A DIN 6270
—Intermittent output PÜDIN 6270 (2 hours within 12 operating hours)
Reference conditions:
Intake air temperature 20°C (45°C with 331 TC, 32°C with 538 TB 81)
Seawater temperature 20²C (no influence on 331 TC, 27°C with 538 TB 81)
Altitude   Sea level

MTU projects and delivers as a supplement to their diesel engine programme complete propulsion systems, comprising diesels and marine gas-turbines. This enables selection of either CODEG or CODAG arrangements.

RHEIN-FLUGZEUGBAU GMBH

HEAD OFFICE AND MAIN WORKS:
D-4050 Mönchengladbach 1, Flugplatz,
PB 408
TELEPHONE:
(02161) 66 20 31
TELEX:
08 525 06
EXECUTIVE DIRECTORS:
Dipl.-Volksw. W. Kutscher, commercial
Dipl. Ing. A. Schneider, technical

RFB has developed a fan thrust pod
module for wing-in-ground-effect machines,
gliders, air cushion vehicles and air-propelled
boats.

By combining rotary engines of the Wankel
type with a ducted fan, the company has
produced an extremely compact power unit
which can be mounted on either a fuselage
or a wing in much the same way as gas-
turbine pods. The air cooling system
permits prolonged ground running when
necessary with full throttle.

The system has been fitted to the L13
Blanik glider and also to boats.

SG 85

Length	3 ft 11½ in (1,200 mm)
Height, incl. 200 mm connection	3 ft 3⅜ in (1,000 mm)
Width max	2 ft 5½ in (750 mm)
Weight	58 kg
Inside shroud diameter 2 ft 1⅜ in (650 mm)	
Power	50 hp
Static thrust at 5,400 rpm (with muffler installed)	90 kg
Noise level with full throttle at 1,000 ft altitude	54 dB (A)

Rotor:
3-blades-rotor in fibre-reinforced plastic with
errosive protection.
Shroud: plastic.
Engine cowling: glass-fibre reinforced plastic.
Engine: Rotary engine KM 914/2V-85
("Wankel" system; two coupled engines
25 hp each) with electric starter 12 V.,
generator, exhaust-gas system and complete
assembly sets ready for installation.
Connection: Metal-construction as pylon
having a connection-part.
Fuel: Mixture 1:30
Fuel consumption:
full throttle   5,500 rpm: 3·3 gph (15 l/h)
cruising speed 5,000 rpm: 2·5 ghp (11·5 l/h)

RFB Fan Pod Type SG 85

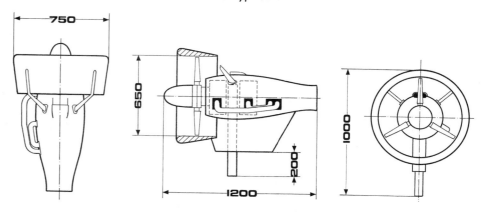

RFB Fan Pod, incorporating a Wankel rotary engine

SG 85 thrust pod mounted on an Espadon Canot 422 inflatable dinghy, built by Etablissements
George Hennebutte

VOLKSWAGEN (GB) LIMITED
(Incorporating Audi NSU (GB) Limited)

REGISTERED OFFICE:
Volkswagen House, Brighton Road, Purley,
Surrey CR2 2UQ
TELEPHONE:
01-668 4100
TELEGRAMS:
Veemoto Croydon
TELEX:
263226

WANKEL ROTARY PISTON ENGINE

Relatively high power from a compact,
vibration-free, lightweight engine are features
which have attracted many lightweight ACV
owners to the Wankel rotary design. The
description below applies to Type KKM 612.

WANKEL KKM 612

TYPE: Twin-rotor rotary piston engine,
water-cooled.
CHAMBER VOLUME: 2 × 497·5 cc
COMPRESSION: 9:1.
OUTPUT: 115 DIN HP/85 KW, 128 SAE
HP.
TORQUE: 16 mkp/157 Nm at 4,000 rpm.
CARBURETTOR: Solex twin choke down-
draught carburettors with automatic choke.
FUEL PUMP: Diaphragm with filter and
electric delivery pump.
PRESSURE-FED CIRCULATORY LUB-
RICATING SYSTEM: One pump with micro
full-flow filter and two gear pairs, one for
lubrication of engine bearings and one for
oil pressure in the torque converter.

TRANSMISSION: Torque converter.
ELECTRICAL EQUIPMENT: Thyristorised
high voltage condenser ignition.

Voltage	12 volt
Starter	12 volt 2 HP
Battery	12 volt 66 Ah
Alternator	14 volt/770 watt (charges even at idling speeds)

TYPE 122

The air-cooled petrol engines powering
over 20 million Volkswagen cars and vehicles
are also produced as industrial power units
in which role they have been proved reliable
and economical in millions of hours running.
There are three versions available, the Type
122 developed from the 1,192 cc Volkswagen
car engine; the 1,584 cc Type 126A developed

from the 1,500 cc van engine; and the 1,795 cc Type 127 developed from the 1,700 car engine.

TYPE: Air-cooled four-cylinder, horizontally-opposed four-stroke petrol engine available with or without governor.

CYLINDERS: Four separate cylinders of special grey cast iron, with integral cooling fins. Cast alumimiun heads, one for each two cylinders, with shrunk-in sintered steel valve seats and bronze valve guides. Bore 3·032 in (77 mm). Stroke 2·520 in (64 mm). Cubic capacity 72·74 cu in (1,192 cc). Compression ratio 7:1.

CRANKCASE: Two-part magnesium pressure casting with enclosed oil sump and flange for mounting the engine on machine or pedestal.
CRANKSHAFT: Forged, with hardened journals, mounted in three aluminium bearings and one three-layer, steel-backed bearing (No. 2).
CONNECTING RODS: Forged steel, I-section shank. Three-layer, steel-backed, lead-bronze big-end bearing shells with white metal running surfaces.
PISTONS: Aluminium with steel inserts, two compression rings and one scraper ring.
CAMSHAFT: Grey cast iron, with three steel-backed, shell-type bearings in crankcase, driven by helical gears.
VALVES: One inlet and one exhaust valve per cylinder. Exhaust valves have special armoured seating surfaces. 'Rotocap' valve rotating devices can be fitted on request.

COOLING: Radial fan, driven by belt from crankshaft. Protective grille on fan intake.
LUBRICATION: Forced feed gear-type pump. Full flow, flat tube oil cooler in fan airstream. Oil capacity 4·4 pints (2·5 litres).

CARBURETTOR: Downdraft Solex 26 VFIS on engine with governor. Downdraft Solex 28 PCI with accelerator pump, on engine without governor. Both have choke for cold starting.

IGNITION: With magneto; high tension, partly-supressed Scintilla-Vertex magneto with built-in automatic short-circuit switch as adjustable speed limiter. With coil ignition: 12 volt and centrifugal spark advance distributor.

PLUGS: Bosch W145 T1.
FUEL: Normal commercial petrol of 86 octane rating minimum.
STARTING: Hand cranking lever or electric starter.
GOVERNOR: Centrifugal type, operating on carburettor throttle, driven by toothed belt.

EXHAUST SYSTEM: Cylindrical muffler located transversely at bottom of engine, with exhaust pipes from cylinders and damper pipe with short tail pipe.
MOUNTING: By four bolts in the crankcase flange.
COUPLING: Engine is connected to driven shaft by a clutch or flexible fixed-coupling.
PEDESTALS AND TRANSMISSIONS: Suitable flange pedestals, with or without couplings or clutches, can be supplied as well as gearboxes with direct drives or drives of various ratios for clockwise or anti-clockwise rotation.

The Wankel KKM 612 115 hp twin-rotor water-cooled piston engine.

Volkswagen Type 127 industrial engine

DIMENSIONS:
Width   29·4 in (748 mm)
Height   26·2 in (665·5 mm)
Length   29·2 in (740·5 mm)
WEIGHT, Dry:
With standard equipment, approx
                                    205 lb (93·5 kg)
PERFORMANCE RATINGS:
Continuous rating
        34 bhp DIN at 3,600 output rpm
FUEL CONSUMPTION:
At 20 bhp at 2,000 output rpm
                0·534 lb (242 gr)/bhp/hr
At 30 bhp at 3,600 output rpm
                0·590 lb (268 gr)/bhp/hr

OIL CONSUMPTION:
Approx 20 to 35 cc/hr at 3,000 output rpm

TYPE 126A

TYPE: Air-cooled four-cylinder, horizontally-opposed four-stroke petrol engine available with or without governor. Construction generally similar to Type 122 with following exceptions:
CYLINDERS: Bore 3·543 in (85·5 mm).

Stroke 2·717 in (69·0 mm). Cubic capacity 96·50 cu in (1,584 cc). Compression ratio 7·7 : 1.

CARBURETTOR: Downdraft Solex 26 or 28 VFIS on engine with governor. Downdraft Solex 32 PCI on engine without governor.

DIMENSIONS:
Width   29·9 in (760·0 mm)
Height   26·5 in (675·5 mm)
Length   28·5 in (723·0 mm)
WEIGHT, Dry:
With standard equipment, approx
                                    220 lb (100 kg)
PERFORMANCE RATINGS:
Continuous rating
        44 bhp DIN at 3,600 output rpm
FUEL: 90 octane minimum

FUEL CONSUMPTION:
At 28 bhp at 2,000 output rpm
                0·496 lb (225 gr)/bhp/hr
At 44 bhp at 3,600 output rpm
                0·562 lb (255 gr)/bhp/hr

OIL CONSUMPTION:
Approx 25 to 40 cc/hr at 3,000 output rpm

TYPE 127

TYPE: Air-cooled, four-cylinder, horizontally-opposed four-stroke petrol engine of low profile design.

CYLINDERS: Bore 3·740 in (93 mm). Stroke 2·165 in (66 mm). Cubic capacity 109·53 cu in (1,795 cc). Compression ratio 7·3 : 1.

COOLING: Radial fan on crankshaft.

CARBURETTOR: Solex 32 PCI downdraft or two Solex 34PDSIT downdraft.

IGNITION: 12 volt battery.

DIMENSIONS:

Width	3·780 in (960 mm)
Height (without air cleaner)	2·189 in (556 mm)
Length	3·264 in (829 mm)

WEIGHT, Dry:
With standard equipment   273 lb (124 kg)

PERFORMANCE RATINGS:

Maximum continuous ratings at 4,000 rpm	
Single carburettor	62 bhp DIN
Twin carburettor	68 bhp DIN

FUEL: 90 octane minimum.

FUEL CONSUMPTION:
At 3,000 output rpm
0·506 lb (230 gr)/bhp/hr
At 4,000 output rpm
0·561 lb (255 gr)/bhp/hr

ITALY

CRM FABRICA MOTORI MARINI

HEAD OFFICE:
20121 Milano, via Manzoni, 12

TELEPHONE:
708. 326/327

CABLES:
Cremme

DIRECTORS:
Ing F. Mariani
Ing. B. Piccoletti
Ing. S. Rastelli
Mr. S. Sussi
Minoja p.i. Vittorio

CRM has specialised in building lightweight diesel engines for more than twenty years. The company's engines are used in large numbers of motor torpedo boats, coastal patrol craft and privately-owned motor yachts. More recently, the engines have also been installed in hydrofoils.

During the 1960s the company undertook the development and manufacture of a family of 18, 12 and 9-cylinder diesel engines of lightweight high-speed design, providing a power coverage of 300 bhp to 1,350 bhp. These comprise the 18-cylinder CRM 18D/2 and 18 D/S-2 of 1,050 to 1,350 bhp with mechanically-driven supercharging and turbo-driven supercharging respectively and its cylinders arranged in an unusual W arrangement of three banks of six cylinders each; the 12-cylinder CRM 12 D/S-2 of 900 bhp with two banks of six cylinders and first in the new series to introduce turbo-charging; and the 715 bhp CRM 9 D/S-2 with a W arrangement of three banks of three cylinders and offering the option of turbo-charging or natural aspiration.

All engines available in a magnetic version, the disturbance of their magnetic field being reduced to insignificant amounts, for special applications.

Details of these engines are given below.

CRM 18

First in CRM's new series of lightweight high-speed diesels, the CRM 18 is an 18-cylinder unit with its cylinders arranged in a W form comprising three banks of six cylinders. Maximum power is 1,050 bhp at 1,900 rpm with mechanically driven supercharging and 1,350 bhp, at 2,075 rpm, with exhaust gas turbo-charging. One 1,050 bhp 18D/2 engine powers the Finnish Tehi 70-passenger Raketa-type hydrofoil.

The following description relates to the mechanically supercharged CRM 18 D/2 and turbo-supercharged CRM 18 D/S.

TYPE: 18-cylinder in-line W type, four-stroke, water-cooled mechanically-supercharged (CRM 18 D/2) or turbo-supercharged (CRM 18 D/S) diesel engine.

CYLINDERS: Bore: 5·91 in (150 mm). Stroke 7·09 in (180 mm). Swept volume 194·166 cu in (3·18 litres) per cylinder.

CRM 18 D/S-2   marine diesel rated at 1,350 bhp at 2,075 rpm

Total swept volume: 3,495 cu in (57·3 litres). Compression ratio: 16·25 : 1. Separate pressed-steel cylinder frame side members are surrounded by gas-welded sheet metal water cooling jacket treated and pressure-coated internally to prevent corrosion. Cylinders are closed at top by a steel plate integral with side wall to complete combustion chamber. Lower half of cylinder is ringed by a drilled flange for bolting to crankcase. Cylinder top also houses a spherical-shaped pre-combustion chamber as well as inlet and exhaust valve seats. Pre-combustion chamber is in high-strength, heat and corrosion resistant steel. A single cast light alloy head, carrying valve guides, pre-combustion chambers and camshaft bearings bridges each bank of cylinders. Head is attached to cylinder bank by multiple studs.

PISTONS: Light alloy forgings with four rings, top ring being chrome-plated and bottom ring acting as oil scarper. Piston crowns shaped to withstand high temperatures especially in vicinity of pre-combustion chamber outlet ports.

CONNECTING RODS: Comprise main and secondary articulated rods, all rods being completely machined I-section steel forgings. Big end of each main rod is bolted to ribbed cap by six studs. Big-end bearings are white metal lined steel shells. Each secondary rod anchored at its lower end to a pivot pin inserted in two lugs protruding from big-end of main connecting rod. Both ends of all secondary rods, and small ends of main rods have bronze bushes.

CRANKSHAFTS: One-piece hollow shaft in nitrided alloy steel, with six throws equi-spaced at 120°. Seven main bearings with

white metal lined steel shells. Twelve balancing counterweights.

CRANKCASE: Cast light alloy crankcase bolted to bed plate by studs and tie bolts. Multiple integral reinforced ribs to provide robust structure. Both sides of each casting braced by seven cross ribs incorporating crankshaft bearing supports. Protruding sides of crankcase ribbed throughout length.

VALVE GEAR: Hollow sodium-cooled valves of each bank of cylinders actuated by twin camshafts and six cams on each shaft. Two inlet and two outlet valves per cylinder and one rocker for each pair of valves. End of stem and facing of exhaust valves fitted with Stellite inserts. Valve cooling water forced through passage formed by specially-shaped plate welded to top of cylinder.

FUEL INJECTION: Pumps fitted with variable speed control and pilot injection nozzle.

PRESSURE CHARGER: Two mechanically-driven centrifugal compressors on CRM 18 D/2, or two exhaust gas turbo-driven compressors on CRM 18/0/S-2.

ACCESSORIES: Standard accessories include oil and fresh water heat exchangers; fresh water tank; oil and fresh water thermostats; oil filters, fresh water, salt water and fuel hand pumps; fresh water and oil temperature gauges; engine, reverse gear and reduction gear oil gauges; pre-lubrication, electric pump and engine rpm counter. Optional accessories include engine oil and water pre-heater, and warning and pressure switches.

COOLING SYSTEM: Fresh water.

FUEL: Fuel oil having specific gravity of 0·830 to 0·840.

LUBRICATION SYSTEM: Pressure type

STARTING: 6 hp starting motor and 600 Watt generator for battery charging.
LUBRICATION: By gear pump.
REVERSE GEAR: Hydraulically operated, with brake on transmission.
REDUCTION GEAR: Standard ratios, 1·5 : 1-2 : 1.
DRY WEIGHT: 4,120 lb (2,200 kg).

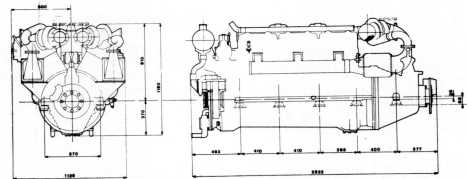

Fiat-Carraro V12SS 700 hp marine diesel. Two of these 12-cylinder water-cooled and super-charged engines power the Seaflight H57 hydrofoil passenger ferry

AIFO/FIAT-Carro V12SS, 700 hp supercharged 12-cylinder marine diesel engines

UNITED KINGDOM

CATERPILLAR TRACTOR
Caterpillar Tractor Co Ltd
55 St. James's Street,
London SW1A 1LA
England
TELEPHONE:
01-493 1882

Caterpillar is the UK subsidiary of the Caterpillar Tractor Co, a leading US manufacturer of diesels who has supplied engines worldwide, equivalent to hundreds of millions of diesel horsepower. Engines are sold for marine, electrical power and industrial applications, and are supported by more than 900 Caterpillar dealer facilities for parts and service: more than 14,000 dealer servicemen provide a 24-hour service to diesel operators. The engines are designed to give a high degree of component interchangeability, equal on V-models to 90 per cent of all parts.

Specific applications include Hovertrailer International standard, pipe, logging and high pressure trailers with lifting capacities up to 100 tons, powered by Caterpillar Model 3145, 3160, 3304, D343, D346 and D348 engines. Mackley Ace offshore hover platforms with lifting capacities of 30 tons and over, are powered by Model D334,

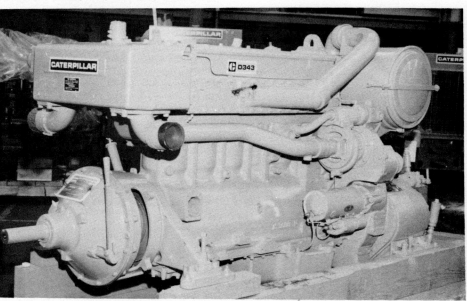

Caterpillar Model D343 marine diesel engine

D346 and D348 engines which are also used in Air Cushion Equipment bulk storage tank removal systems.

MODEL 3304NA, 3304T AND 3306T
TYPE: Six-cylinder in-line four-stroke water-cooled, turbo-supercharged diesel engines.

with gear pump.

OIL: Mineral oil to SAE 40 HD, MIL-L-210GB.

OIL COOLING: By salt water circulating through heat exchanger.

STARTING: 24 volt 15 hp electric motor and 85 amp, 24 volt alternator for battery charge, or compressed air.

MOUNTING: At any transverse or longitudinal angle tilt to 20°.

REVERSE GEAR: Bevel crown gear wheels with hydraulically-controlled hand brake.

REDUCTION GEAR: Optional fitting with spur gears giving reduction ratios of 0·561 : 1, 0·730 : 1 and 0·846 : 1. Overdrive ratio 1·18 : 1.

PROPELLER THRUST BEARING: Incorporated in reduction gear or in overdrive. Axial thrust 6,620 lb (3,003 kg) at 1,176 rpm

DIMENSIONS:

Height	51·33 in (1,304 mm)
Width	53·15 in (1,350 mm)
Length	116·5 in (2,960 mm)

WEIGHTS, Dry:

Engine	3,690 lb (1,665 kg)
Reverse gear, generator and starter	900 lb (410 kg)
Reduction gear or overdrive, with propeller thrust bearing	330 lb (150 kg)
Total	4,920 lb (2,225 kg)

PERFORMANCE RATINGS:

CRM 18 D/S:

Maximum power	1,350 bhp at 2,075 rpm
Intermittent service	1,250 bhp at 2,020 rpm
Continuous service	1,040 bhp at 1,900 rpm

FUEL CONSUMPTION:

CRM 18 D/S-2 at continuous service rating
0·37 lb (0·170 kg)/bhp hr

OIL CONSUMPTION:

CRM 18 D/S-2 at continuous service rating
0·007 lb (0·003 kg)/hr

CRM 12 D/S-2

Second in the new CRM series of lightweight diesels is the 900 bhp 12 D/S-2 with two banks of six cylinders set at 60° to form a V assembly. The bore and stroke are the same as in the CRM 18 series, and many of the components are interchangeable, including the crankshaft, bedplate, cylinders and pistons. The crankcase and connecting rod-assemblies are necessarily of modified design; the secondary rod is anchored at its lower end to a pivot pin inserted on two lugs protruding from the big-end of the main connecting rod. The fuel injection pump is modified to single block housing all 12 pumping elements located between the cylinder banks.

A major innovation first developed on the 12 D/S (and later provided for the other engines in the series) was the introduction of an exhaust gas driven turbo-charger. This involved a complete revision of the combustion system and all components comprising the cylinder heads. Conversion to turbo-charging avoided the mechanical power loss expended in driving the blower, and enabled a greater volume of air to be forced into the cylinders. The effect on

CRM 9 D/S 2 marine diesel rated at 715 bhp at 1,950 rpm

specific fuel consumption was a reduction to around 0·35 lb to 0·37 lb (160 to 170 gr)/bhp/hr in conjunction with exhaust temperatures not exceeding 530°C (986°F) at maximum rpm. Two Holset turbo-chargers are fitted.

TYPE: 12-cylinder in-line V type, four-stroke water-cooled, turbo-supercharged diesel engines.

DIMENSIONS:

Height	47·4 in (1,204 mm)
Width	47·64 in (1,210 mm)
Length	99·60 in (2,530 mm)

WEIGHTS, Dry:

Engine	2,735 lb (1,240 kg)
Reverse gear, generator and starter	900 lb (410 kg)
Reduction gear or overdrive, with propeller thrust bearing	330 lb (150 kg)
Total	3,965 lb (1,800 kg)

PERFORMANCE RATINGS:

Max power	900 bhp at 2,035 rpm
Intermittent service	850 bhp at 2,000 rpm
Continuous service	750 bhp at 1,900 rpm

FUEL CONSUMPTION:

At continuous service rating
0·40 lb (0·18 kg)/bhp/hr

CRM 9 12 D/S-5

Third in development and smallest in the new CRM lightweight series of diesels is the nine-cylinder three-bank engine of similar configuration to the CRM 18 units. Both a naturally-aspirated version, the 415 bhp CRM 9, D/A, and a turbo-supercharged version, the 715 bhp CRM 9 D/S-2, are available.

TYPE: Nine-cylinder in-line W type, four-stroke, water-cooled, naturally-aspirated (CRM 9 D/A) or turbo-supercharged (CRM 9 D/S-2 diesel engine).

WEIGHTS, Dry:

Engine, CRM 9 D/S-2	2,447 lb (1,110 kg)

Reverse and reduction gear, with propeller thrust bearing, generator and starter	1,356 lb (615 kg)
Total	3,803 lb (1,725 kg)

PERFORMANCE RATINGS:

CRM 9 D/S-2, max power
715 bhp at 1,950 rpm

Continuous service	550 bhp at 1,800 rpm
Intermittent service	660 bhp at 1,900 rpm

FUEL CONSUMPTION:

CRM 9 D/S-2 at continuous service rating
0·385 lb (0·176 kg)/bhp/hr

CRM 12D/SS

As a development of 12D/S-2, the 12D/SS is available for applications where a high rating is required, but space is limited.

Dry sump and wet sump versions are available for installation in engine-rooms with limited space available.

TYPE: Twelve cylinder V-60°, four stroke water-cooled, turbo-supercharged and inter-cooled diesel engine.

DIMENSIONS:

Height, dry sump	1,299 mm
Height, wet sump	1,427 mm
Width	1,210 mm
Length	2,642 mm

WEIGHTS, DRY:

Engine	1,340 kg
Reverse gear, generator and electric starter, (compressed air starter option)	410 kg
Reduction gear (optional)	150 kg

PERFORMANCE RATING:

Max. power	1,265 bhp at 2,050 rpm
Intermittent power	1,150 bhp at 1,985 rpm
Continuous power	1,000 bhp at 1,900 rpm

FUEL CONSUMPTION:

At continuous service rating
0·175 kg/bhp/hr

FIAT/AIFO

Applicazioni Industriali Fiat OM

HEAD OFFICE: Via Carducci 29, Milan

TELEPHONE: 877-066/8

AIFO Carraro V12SS, 700 hp 12-cylinder diesel engines are installed in the H 57 60-passenger hydrofoil ferries built by Seaflight, Messina.

CARRARO V12SS

TYPE: Pre-chamber injection, vee-form 12-cylinder, turbocharged and inter-cooled four-stroke diesel engine.

OUTPUT: Basic engine, 700 bhp; maximum shaft output 650 hp at 1,500 rpm.

BORE AND STROKE: 142 × 180 mm.

FUEL INJECTION: Bosch type pumps and

centrifugal governor; fuel feeding pumps; fuel cartridge filters.

ENGINE COOLING: By fresh water into closed circuit with thermostatic control valve.

OIL COOLING: By salt water circulating through a heat exchanger.

Counterclockwise rotation viewed from rear.
CYLINDERS: Bore 4·75 in (121 mm).
Stroke 6·0 in (152 mm). Total swept
volume 3304NA and 3304T 425 cu in
(6·9 litres), and 3306T 638 cu in (10·5 litres).
COMPRESSION RATIO: 17·5 : 1. Molybdenum alloy cast from cylinder liners water-cooled over full length, and specifically designed to give operating life equal to engine. Cylinder head assemblies cast in molybdenum and nickel alloyed grey iron, with intake manifold cast integrally with head to improve air flow and minimise maintenance. Water 'directors' located in the head force coolant against surfaces near combustion heat to eliminate hot spots.

PISTONS: Copper and nickel alloyed aluminium pistons elliptically ground and tapered from base to crown. Integrally cast iron ring band provides long-life wearing surface for top two of three piston rings. Intermediate ring is of twist design to seal efficiently and improve oil control. All rings are thick chrome plated. Gudgeon pins hardened to Rockwell 50C and ground to a 'fit' tolerance of only 0·0003 in (0·00076 cm). Retained by 'C' ring circlips.

CONNECTING RODS: Forged, hardened and shot-peened for high strength. Steel-backed aluminium bearings.

CRANKSHAFT: Steel forging, induction hardened, stress relieved and shot peened. Journals super-finished to within one micron of final smoothness.

CRANKCASE: Five or seven steel-backed aluminium bearings, with heavily ribbed bearing supports cast integrally with high tensile block.

VALVE GEAR: Valve rotators rotate 3° on each lift-off to give better valve seating and longer life. Exhaust valves faced with cobalt and tungsten alloy to retain hardness at operating temperatures. Exhaust seats have nickel based alloy replaceable inserts. Stainless steel intake valve heads and intake inserts contribute to efficient operation.

FUEL INJECTION: Precombustion chamber fuel system mixes fuel and air to atomize fuel for clean burning, and each chamber has an electric glow plug for reliable cold-weather starts. Capsule-type fuel injection valve with single large-diameter self-cleaning orifice. 'No-adjustment' fuel system with automatic fuel-air ratio control. Separate pump for each cylinder located on side of engine. Easily replaced spin-on filters with plastic-impregnated cellulose filter.

TURBO-SUPERCHARGER: Single-stage centrifugal air compressor driven by single-stage centripetal turbine energised by exhaust gases.

ACCESSORIES: Include fuel priming pump, 24-volt alternator, gear-driven jacket and auxiliary water pumps, speed governor, oil cooler, tachometer drive.

COOLING SYSTEM: Jacket water pump minimum flow 63 gal/min (3·98 litre/sec). Normal sea water pump flow 65 gal/min (4·10 litre/sec) (for six cylinders).

LUBRICATION SYSTEM: Fully-pressurised system with gear-type pump and full-flow heavy duty filter system. Continuous oil spray lubricates piston gudgeon pins. Turbo-supercharger and engine bearings receive immediate lubrication on starts through bypass valve.

OIL COOLING: Tube-bundle type jacket water heat exchanger.

STARTING: Air motor mounted on starboard side of engine. Normal starting air pressure 90-100 lb/sq in. Or, 24-volt electric starter.

Caterpillar Model D346 marine diesel engine

GEAR: Reverse and reduction gear hydraulically operated, full power for both clockwise and counter-clockwise propeller rotation. Gear ratio 2 : 1, 2·95 : 1, 3·83 : 1, 4·5 : 1.
DIMENSIONS with gear:
3304NA, 3304T:

Height	41·3 in (1,049 mm)
Width	36·0 in (914 mm)
Length	57·0 in (1,447 mm)

3306T:

Height	47·8 in (1,214 mm)
Width	37·2 in (945 mm)
Length	75·8 in (1,925 mm)

WEIGHTS, Dry with gear:

3304NA, 3304T	2,220 lb (1,007 kg)
3306T	2,675 lb (1,210 kg)

PERFORMANCE RATINGS:
3304NA:

Maximum (flywheel)	115 hp
Continuous (shaft)	82 hp

3304T:

Maximum (flywheel)	200 hp
Continuous (shaft)	121 hp

3306T:

Maximum (flywheel)	300 hp
Continuous (shaft)	184 hp
Normal working range	1,500-2,200 rpm

FUEL CONSUMPTIONS:
At continuous (shaft) rating:

3304NA	5·25 gal/hr (19·9 litre/hr)
3304T	7·80 gal/hr (29·5 litre/hr)
3306T	11·10 gal/hr (41·9 litre/hr)

MODELS D343T AND TA, D346, D348 AND D349

(Basic features of these models are in general similar to the D330 and D333 series, with following main differences).

TYPE: Eight, twelve and sixteen cylinder 60°V in-line (except for six-cylinder straight in-line D343), four-stroke, water-cooled, turbo-supercharger-aftercooled diesel engines. Counterclockwise rotation viewed from rear.

CYLINDERS: Bore 5·4 in (137 mm). Stroke 6·5 in (165 mm). Total swept volume D343 893 cu in (14·6 litre), D346 1,191 cu in (19·5 litre), D348 1,786 cu in (29·3 litre), and D349 2,382 cu in (39·1 litre). Compression ratio, 16·5 : 1, except for D343 16·8 : 1. One-piece nickel-chrome alloyed grey iron cast cylinder block, precision bored and milled. Conventional studs on V models are complemented by extra length studs extending into bearing saddle area.

TURBO-SUPERCHARGER AND AFTER-COOLER: Turbo-charger similar to 3304 and 3306 models with addition of water-cooled aftercooler interposed between compressor air delivery and cylinder manifold. System doubles rate of airflow to engine and lowers exhaust temperatures.

ACCESSORIES: Hydro-mechanical governor gear-driven fuel priming and transfer pumps, gear-driven jacket-water pump.

COOLING SYSTEM: Jacket water pump minimum flow 350 gal/min (22·10 litre/sec) except for D343 160 gal/min (10·10 litre/sec).

GEAR: Ratio, D343 2·1 : 1, 2·5 : 1, 3 : 1, 3·5 : 1, 4·5 : 1 and 6 : 1, D346 2·19 : 1, 3·03 : 1, 4·09 : 1 and 5·17 : 1; D348 2·07 : 1, 2·92 : 1, 3·86 : 1, 5·17 : 1 and 5·?8 : 1, D349 2 : 1, 2·94 : 1, 3·54 : 1, 4·67 : 1 and 5·88 : 1. All ratios at 1,800 engine continuous rpm.

DIMENSIONS with gear:
D343TA:

Height	55·65 in (1,413 mm)
Width	41·46 in (1,053 mm)
Length	84·52 in (2,147 mm)

D346:

Height	73·12 in (1,851 mm)
Width	60·12 in (1,527 mm)
Length	102·99 in (2,616 mm)

D348:

Height	77·20 in (1,960 mm)
Width	60·12 in (1,527 mm)
Length	118·73 in (3,015 mm)

D349:

Height	77·20 in (1,960 mm)

Width   60·12 in (1,527 mm)
Length   156·05 in (3,964 mm)
WEIGHTS, Dry with gear:

D343TA	6,040 lb (2,742 kg)
D346	9,320 lb (4,230 kg)
D348	11,335 lb (5,146 kg)
D349	14,855 lb (6,744 kg)

PERFORMANCE RATINGS (flywheel):
D343T:

| Maximum, at 2,000 rpm | 395 hp |
| Continuous, at 1,800 rpm | 245 hp |

D343TA:

| Maximum, at 2,000 rpm | 550 hp |
| Continuous, at 1,800 rpm | 365 hp |

D346:

| Maximum, at 2,000 rpm | 735 hp |
| Continuous, at 1,800 rpm | 480 hp |

D348:

| Maximum, at 2,000 rpm | 1,100 hp |
| Continuous, at 1,800 rpm | 725 hp |

D349:

| Maximum, at 2,000 rpm | 1,470 hp |
| Continuous, at 1,800 rpm | 970 hp |

FUEL CONSUMPTION:
D343T, D343TA:

19·4 gal/hr (74 litre/hr) at 365 hp

D346:	25·8 gal/hr (95 litre/hr) at 480 hp
D348:	38 gal/hr (144 litre/hr) at 725 hp
D349:	51·6 gal/hr (190 litre/hr) at 970 hp

MODEL 3160

TYPE: Eight cylinder 90°V in-line, four-stroke, water-cooled, normally aspirated diesel engine.

CYLINDERS: Bore 4·5 in (114 mm). Stroke 5·0 in (127 mm). Total swept volume 636 cu in (10·4 litres). Compression ratio 16·5 : 1. Cast heads with integral air inlet manifold in alloyed grey iron. Intake and exhaust valve seats staggered to reduce thermal stress concentrations. Crescent-shaped bevel adjacent to each intake valve seat imparts swirl to incoming air to improve combustion. Bores honed to within 0·00005 in (0·0127 mm) tolerance between top and bottom.

PISTONS: Aluminium alloy pistons tapered and elliptically ground for correct shape under operating load and heat. One compression and one scraper ring with integrally cast nickel-iron insert for compression ring to minimise ring groove wear. Compression ring coated with molybdenum for extra life and less friction, and twisted for seal efficiency and oil control. Fully floating large 1·5 in (38 mm) diameter gudgeon pins, ground to 0·00003 in (0·00762 mm), and hardened on inner and outer surfaces.

CONNECTING RODS: Forged H-section rods, ground to precise balance. Steel-backed aluminium alloy bearings.

CRANKSHAFT: Forged, fixture-quenched, through hardened. 90°V design of engine results in balanced power strokes forces for smooth running.

CRANKCASE: Cast nickel-chrome alloyed grey iron block featuring deep skirt design extending 4 in (101·6 mm) below centre-line of crankshaft for added strength and rigidity. Main bearing caps fit into machined recesses in block rib structure, with securing cap-screws positioned at 30° angles to obviate need for cross-bolting. Five main bearings with large wipe area, supported by ribbed block, recess-fitted bearing blocks. Steel-backed aluminium alloy bearings.

VALVE GEAR: Special heat resistant alloy steel intake and exhaust valves for corrosion resistance. Exhaust valves seat on replaceable hardened steel inserts for long life. Dual valve springs with different resonant frequencies to minimise float and prevent damage if one spring fails.

FUEL INJECTION: Fuel fed from low-pressure diaphragm transfer pump to fuel manifold. Separate pump plunger for each cylinder driven by fuel systems' own camshaft. Four orifices 0·012 in (0·305 mm) wide, spray fuel in cone-shaped pattern against shaped piston crown.

ACCESSORIES: 12-volt charging alternator, hydro-mechanical speed governor, fuel, jacket water and sea or fresh water pumps, 12-volt starter motor.

COOLING SYSTEM: Jacket water pump flow at continuous power rating 60 gal/min (3·79 litre/sec).

LUBRICATION SYSTEM: Gear-driven six-lobe pump passes oil through multi-plate oil cooler, then through two spin-on filters to oil gallery supplying all bearings surfaces with immediate lubrication.

STARTING: 12-volt electric.

GEAR: Reverse and reduction gear, with ratios 1·50 : 1, 1·97 : 1, 2·50 : 1, 2·96 : 1.

DIMENSIONS with gear:

Height	35·75 in (908 mm)
Width	34·3 in (860 mm)
Length	46·3 in (1,590 mm)

WEIGHT, Dry with gear: 1,610 lb (730 kg)

PERFORMANCE RATING (shaft):
Continuous, at 2,400 rpm   146 hp

FUEL CONSUMPTION:
At 75 per cent shaft hp

5·9 gal/hr (22·3 litre/hr)

RUSTON PAXMAN DIESELS LIMITED
(a management company of GEC Diesels Limited)

HEAD OFFICE & WORKS:

Hythe Hill, Colchester, CO1 2HW

Manufactured at the Colchester Works of Ruston Paxman Diesels are three of the world's most advanced diesel designs; the vee-form 'Ventura', built in 6, 8, 12, and 16-cylinder sizes covering 450 to 2,400 bhp, the RP200 built in 8, 12, 16 and 18 cylinder covering 1,000-3,720 bhp, and the Napier 'Deltic'—an 18-cylinder engine of unique triangular configuration—in powers from 1,500 to 4,000 shaft horsepower. These engines, with their compact overall dimensions and low unit weight, are particularly suitable for the propulsion of high-speed craft including hydrofoils and hovercraft.

The 'Ventura' is being incorporated in several current designs for hydrofoils and rigid sidewall ACVs.

VENTURA (YJ) AND VALENTA (RP200) DIESELS

TYPE: YJ engines: Direct injection 60°, vee-form 6, 8, 12 and 16-cylinder, turbo-charged or turbo-charged and after-cooled four stroke diesel engine. RP200 engine: Direct injection, vee-form 8, 12, 16 and 18 cylinder, turbocharged and water-cooled, four-stroke engine.

OUTPUT: YJ engines: 450-2,400 bhp, 1,000-1,600 rev/min. RP200 engines: 1,000-3,720 bhp, 1,000-1,600 rev/min.

BORE AND STROKE: 7·75 × 8·5 in (197 × 216 mm).

Paxman 12-cylinder Valenta marine diesel developing 2,475 bhp at 1,600 rpm

SWEPT VOLUME (per cylinder): 401 cu in (6·57 litres).

HOUSING: Fabricated high quality steel plate.

CRANKSHAFT AND MAIN BEARINGS: Fully nitrated shaft carried in aluminium tin pre-finished steel-backed main bearings. Engine fully balanced against primary and secondary forces.

CONNECTING RODS: Fork and blade type with steel-backed, aluminium tin lined large end (forked rod) and steel-backed, lead bronze lined, lead tin flashed bearings (blade rod).

PISTONS: Conventional aluminium alloy, oil cooled with Alfin bonded insert for top ring. Three compression rings and one oil control ring. (YJ): Three compression rings and one oil control ring (RP200).

CYLINDER HEAD: High grade casting carrying four valve direct injection system.

LINERS: Wet type seamless steel tube, chrome plated bore and water side surface, honeychromed for surface oil retention.

FUEL INJECTION: External Monobloc pumps located below air manifolds. (YJ): single unit pumps (RP 200). Pump plungers and camshaft lubricated from main engine pressure system. Feed and injection pump driven from engine drive and gear train; a fuel reservoir and air bleed system fitted. Injectors of the multi-hole type spray fuel into the toroidal cavity in the top of piston. Injectors retained by clamp and are external to head cover (YJ); sleeved connection inside cover (RP 200).

GOVERNOR: Standard hydraulic 'Regulateurs Europa' unit with self-contained lubricating oil system; mechanical, electrical or pneumatic controls. Alternative makes available.

PRESSURE CHARGING AND INTERCOOLING: Napier water-cooled exhaust-gas-driven turboblowers mounted above engine. Air to water intercooler of Serck manufacture for after-cooled versions (YJ and RP 200).

LUBRICATION: Pressure lubrication to all bearing surfaces; separate pressure and cooling pumps. (YJ): single pump system (RP 200). Oil coolers mounted externally and integral with engine (fresh water cooled (YJ); sea water cooled (RP 200). Full flow single or duplex oil filter can be supplied. Centrifugal filters fitted as standard (YJ).

FRESH WATER COOLING: Single pump at free end, shaft-driven from drive end gear train. Thermostatic control valve mounted above pump, giving quick warm-up and even temperature control of water and oil circuits (YJ); oil thermostat (RP 200).

EXHAUST: Single outlet from turboblower(s). Dry type manifolds (YJ); water-cooled manifolds (RP 200).

STARTING: Air, electric or hydraulic starting.

FUEL: Gas oil to BS.2869/1970 Class A1 and A2 or equivalent, and certain gas turbine fuels. Other classes of fuel subject to specification being made available.

LUBRICATING OIL: Oils certified to MIL-L-2104B (with a TBN of not less than 9).

OPTIONAL EXTRA EQUIPMENT: Gearboxes, starting control systems, and all associated engine ancillary equipment necessary for marine applications.

NAPIER DELTIC DIESEL

TYPE: 18-cylinder, opposed piston, liquid cooled, two stroke, compression ingition. Three banks of six cylinders in triangular configuration.

Deltic charge-air cooled, turbo-charged diesel engine with integral reverse reduction gear, developing 4,000 slip.

OUTPUT: Covers horsepower range of 1,500-4,000 shaft hp. Charge-cooled engine rating up to 3,000 shaft hp continuous at 1,800 rev/min. Half hour sprint rating up to 4,000 shaft hp at 2,100 rev/min. Weight/power ratio 3·94 lb/shp.

BORE AND STROKE: Bore—5·125 in (130·17 mm). Stroke—7·25 in × 2 (opposed piston) (184·15 mm × 2).

SWEPT VOLUME: (total): 5,284 in² (88·3 litres).

COMBUSTION SYSTEM: Direct injection.

PISTONS: Two piece—body and gudgeon pin housing. Gudgeon pin housing with fully floating gudgeon pin shrunk into body and secured with taper seated circlip. Body-skirt and gudgeon pin housing in light alloy, piston crown in 'Hidurel' material. Oil cooled. Three gas, two oil control and one scraper ring.

CONNECTING RODS: Fork and blade type with steel backed, lead bronze, lead flashed, indium infused thin-wall bearings. Manufactured from drop forgings, machined and polished all over.

CRANKSHAFTS: Three crankshafts machined from forgings and fully nitrided. Each shaft fitted with viscous type torsional vibration damper. Each crankpin carries one inlet and one exhaust piston, thus, the loading on all crankpins is identical and reciprocating forces are balanced within the engine.

CRANKCASES AND CYLINDER BLOCKS Three crankcases and three cylinder blocks arranged in the form of an inverted equilateral triangle all of light alloy construction. Crankcases substantially webbed and carrying each crankshaft in seven, thin-wall, steelbacked, lead bronze, lead flashed indium infused main bearings. Cylinder blocks each carry six 'wet' type liners, have integrally cast air inlet manifolds and mount the injection pumps camshaft casings.

CYLINDER LINERS: 18 'wet' type liners

machined from hollow steel forgings, bores chrome plated with honeychrome process applied, finished by lapping. Coolant side flash tin plated. In areas of liquid contact with exhaust coolant-area, flash chrome plated.

TURBOCHARGER: Geared-in type, single stage, axial flow turbine and single-sided centrifugal compressor mounted on common shaft. Light alloy main castings. Charge-cooled engines have charge-air coolers (one for each cylinder block) incorporated within the overall dimensions of the turbocharger unit.

PHASING GEAR: To combine the output from the three crankshafts. A light alloy gear casing containing an output gear train linked to the crankshafts by quill-shafts and passing the torque to a common output gear. All gears hardened and ground and carried in roller bearings. Gear train also provides drives for auxiliary pumps and engine governor.

FUEL SYSTEM: Pressurised system from engine driven circulating pump supplying 18 'jerk' type fuel injection pumps one per cylinder mounted in banks of six on camshaft casings secured to each cylinder block. Each pump supplies a single injector per cylinder.

LUBRICATION: Dry sump system with engine driven pressure and scavenge pumps. Twin pressure oil filters engine mounted.

COOLING: Closed circuit system with engine driven circulating pump. Engine mounted circulating pumps for sea-water system for cooling coolant heat exchanger and oil cooler, also for charge-air coolers.

STARTING: Air starting to six cylinders of one bank.

MOUNTING: Four point by resilient mounting units.

REVERSE GEAR: Marine reverse reduction gearbox incorporating a hydraulic friction clutch can be supplied as an integral unit.

ROLLS-ROYCE (1971) LIMITED (INDUSTRIAL & MARINE DIVISION)

HEAD OFFICE:
PO Box 72, Ansty, Coventry CV7 9JR,
Warwickshire
TELEPHONE:
Coventry 613211 (STD 0203)
TELEGRAMS:
Roycov, Coventry
TELEX:
31637

In April 1967 Rolls-Royce Limited formed a new division merging the former industrial and marine gas-turbine activities of Rolls-Royce and Bristol Siddeley. The new division was known as the Industrial & Marine Gas-Turbine Division of Rolls-Royce.

In May 1971 the present company, Rolls-Royce (1971) Limited, was formed combining all the gas-turbine interests of the former Rolls-Royce company.

It offers a wider range of industrial and marine gas-turbines based on aero-engine gas generators than any other manufacturer in the world. It has available for adaptation a large selection of the gas-turbines being developed and manufactured by the Rolls-Royce Derby Engine Division, the Bristol Engine, and Small Engine Divisions. Marinised gas-turbines at present being produced and developed by the Company include the Gnome, Proteus, Tyne, Olympus and Spey.

Over 1,626 of these marine and industrial engines are in service or have been ordered for operation around the world and the total value of the export orders received up to mid-1974 was approximately £85 million. 22 navies have selected the company's marine gas-turbines to power naval craft, following the initial orders from the Royal Navy in the late 1950s.

HYDROFOILS: The Boeing PCH High Point is powered by two Proteus gas-turbines while single Proteus turbines power the Boeing PGH-2 Tucumcari and CNR-Alinavi Swordfish. A Tyne powers the Grumman designed PG(H)-1 Flagstaff and the Super Flagstaff. Rolls-Royce marine gas-turbines can also be specified as alternative power-plants for the modular version of the Boeing Jetfoil.

HOVERCRAFT: The Gnome powers the BHC SR.N3, SR.N5 and SR.N6. The Proteus powers the SR.N4, the BH.7 and the new Vosper Thornycroft VT 2.

MARINE GNOME

TYPE: Gas-turbine, free-turbine turboshaft.
AIR INTAKE: Annular. 15°C.
COMBUSTION CHAMBER: Annular.
FUEL GRADE:
        D.E.R.D. 2494 Avtur/50 Kerosene.
        D.E.R.D. 2482 Avtur/40 Kerosene.
Diesel fuel BSS 2869 Class A
DEF 1402 or NATO F75
TURBINE: Two-stage axial-flow generator turbine and a single-stage axial-flow free power turbine.
BEARINGS: Compressor rotor has a roller bearing at the front and a ball bearing at the rear. Gas generator turbine is supported at the front by the compressor rear bearings, and at the rear by a roller bearing.

Single stage power turbine is supported by a roller bearing behind the turbine disc and by a ball bearing towards the rear of the turbine shaft.

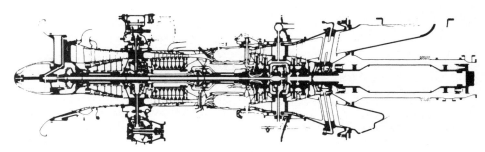

Rolls-Royce Marine Tyne RM2D rated at 5,800 bhp

JET PIPE: Exhaust duct to suit installation.
ACCESSORY DRIVES: Accessory gearbox provides a drive for:—The fuel pump, the hydro-mechanical governor in the flow control unit, the centrifugal fuel filter, the dual tachometer and the engine oil pump.
LUBRICATION SYSTEM: Dry sump.
OIL SPECIFICATION: D.E.R.D. 2487.
MOUNTING: Front: three pads on the front frame casing, one on top, one on each side. Rear without reduction gearbox, mounting point is the rear flange of the exhaust duct centre-body. With reduction gearbox mounting points are provided by two machined faces on the reduction gearbox.
STARTING: Electric.
DIMENSIONS:

Length	72·8 in (1,667 mm)
Width	18·2 in (462 mm)
Height	20·75 in (527 mm)

PERFORMANCE RATINGS:

Max	1,400 bhp
Cont	1,100 bhp

Ratings are at maximum power-turbine speed, 19,500 rpm. A reduction gearbox is available giving an output speed of 6,650 rpm.
SPECIFIC FUEL CONSUMPTION:

Max	·61 lb (276 gr) bhp/hr
Cont	·63 lb (286 gr) bhp/hr

OIL CONSUMPTION:

	1·2 pints (0·67 litre)/hr
Power Turbine	1·5 pints (0·84 litres)/hr

MARINE OLYMPUS

Gas generator and single stage power turbine.
TYPE: Gas-turbine, two-shaft turbojet.
AIR INTAKE: Annular 15°C.
COMBUSTION CHAMBER: Eight.
FUEL GRADE: Diesel fuel B.S.S. 2869 Class A. DEF 2402 or NATO F. 75.
TURBINE (ENGINE): Two stage, each stage driving its own respective compressor—5 stage low pressure or 7 stage high pressure.
TURBINE (POWER): Single stage axial flow.
BEARINGS: Compressor rotor forward end supported by a roller bearing and rear end by a duplex ball bearing.

The power turbine rotor assembly and mainshaft are supported as a cantilever in two white metal bearings housed in a pedestal.
JET PIPE: Exhaust duct to suit installation.
ACCESSORY DRIVES: Power turbine. Accessories are mounted on the main gearbox which is a separate unit transmitting the turbine's power output to the propeller shaft. These include pressure and scavenge oil pumps. Speed signal generator, iso-speedic switch and rev/min indicator are driven by the pedestal-mounted accessory gearbox.

LUBRICATION SYSTEM: The gas generator has its own integral lubrication system which is supplied with oil from a 27 gal tank. Components in the system are:—a pressure pump, main scavenge pump, four auxiliary scavenge pumps and an oil cooler.

Power Turbine: Bearings are lubricated and cooled by a pressure oil system.
OIL SPECIFICATION: Gas generator. D. Eng R. D. 2487. Power turbine. O.E.P. 69.
MOUNTING: The mounting structure depends on the customer's requirements for a particular application.
STARTING: Air or electric.
DIMENSIONS:

Gas Generator:		
Length	11 ft 9 in	(3·6 m)
Width	4 ft 3 in	(1·29 m)
Weight	6,500 lb	(2·94 kg)
Power Turbine:		
Length	12 ft 9 in	(3·9 m)
Width	8 ft 0 in	(2·4 m)
Height	9 ft 9 in	(3 m)
Complete Unit:		
Length	22 ft 3 in	(6·8 m)
Width	8 ft 0 in	(2·4 m)
Height	9 ft 9 in	(3 m)
Weight	21 tons	

PERFORMANCE RATING:
Max
        28,000 bhp at max power-turbine speed of 5,660 rpm.
SPECIFIC FUEL CONSUMPTION:
Max   0.47 lb (226 gr) bhp/hr
OIL CONSUMPTION:

Gas Generator:	
Max	1·5 pints (0·84 litres)/hr
Power turbine	1·5 pints (0·84 litres)/hr

MARINE PROTEUS

TYPE: Gas-turbine, free-turbine turboprop.
AIR INTAKE: Radial between the compressor and turbine sections of the engine. 15°C.
COMBUSTION CHAMBERS: Eight, positioned around the compressor casing.
FUEL GRADE: DEF 2402—Distillate diesel fuel.
TURBINE: Four stages coupled in mechanically independent pairs. The first coupled pair drive the compressor, the second pair form the free power turbine, which drives the output shaft.
BEARINGS: HP end of compressor rotor is carried by roller bearing, the rear end by a duplex ball bearing. Compressor turbine rotor shaft is located by a ball thrust bearing, as is the power turbine rotor.
JET PIPE: Exhaust duct to suit installation.
ACCESSORY DRIVES: All accessories are driven by the compressor or power turbine systems. Compressor driven accessories are: compressor tachometer generator, fuel pump and centrifugal oil separator for the breather. The power turbine tachometer generator and

governor are driven by the power turbine. The main oil pressure pump and also the main and auxiliary scavenge pumps, are driven by both the compressor and power turbines through a differential gear.

LUBRICATION SYSTEM: The engine is lubricated by a single gear type pump connected by a differential drive to both the compressor and power turbine systems.

OIL SPECIFICATION: OEP 71. D.E.R.D. 2479/1 or D.E.R.D. 2487 (OX 38).

MOUNTING: Three attachment points comprise two main trunnions one on each side of the engine close to the diffuser casing and a steady bearing located beneath the engine immediately aft of the air intake. Engines are supplied with integrally-mounted reduction gears giving maximum output shaft speeds of 5,240, 1,500 or 1,000 rpm depending on the gearbox selected.

DIMENSIONS:
Length	113 in (2,870 mm)
Diameter	42 in (1,067 mm)
Weight (dry)	3,118 lb (1,414 kg)

PERFORMANCE RATINGS:
Max	4,500 bhp
95 per cent power	4,250 bhp
80 per cent power	3,600 bhp

SPECIFIC FUEL CONSUMPTION:
At max rating   0·565 lb (253 gr)/bhp/hr

OIL CONSUMPTION:
Average   0·5 pints (0·28 litres)/hr

MARINE TYNE RM2D

Gas generator and two stage power turbine.
TYPE: Gas-turbine, two-shaft turboprop.
AIR INTAKE: Annular. 15°C.

COMBUSTION CHAMBER: Cannular containing ten flame tubes.
FUEL GRADE: Diesel fuel Grade A. DEF 2402B AVCAT.
TURBINE (ENGINE): Two stage, each stage driving its own respective compressor—six stage low pressure and nine stage high pressure.
TURBINE (POWER): Two-stage, axial flow free turbine.
BEARINGS: Compressor rotor forward end supported by a roller bearing and at the rear end by a thrust ball location bearing.

The power turbine front stubshaft is supported on a roller bearing and the rear on a thrust bearing.

JET PIPE: Exhaust duct to suit installation.
ACCESSORY DRIVES: Engine and power turbines accessories are mounted on the external wheelcase of the engine and the primary gearbox accessories gearcase.
LUBRICATION SYSTEM: The gas generator lubricating oil system comprises fuel pump, scavenge pumps, filters, and magnetic plugs. The primary gearbox is also fed from the gas generator lubricating oil system.

OIL SPECIFICATION: DERD 2487

MOUNTING: The forward engine mounting comprises two cantilever frames constructed of tubular members, one each side of the engine. The frames are joined by a diagonal strut across the uppermost members.

The reduction gearbox is supported in a similar way by three tubular steel supports, one either side and one beneath the gearbox. The ends of the engine and gearbox supports are attached to the central main engine support frame by means of spherical bearings. The centre of the unit is supported through a dogged ring into the main central frame.

STARTING: Air or electric.
DIMENSIONS:
Length	158 in (401·3 cm)
Width	50 in (127 mc)
Height	54 in (140 cm)

WEIGHT: 6,800 lb (3,084 kg)
PERFORMANCE RATINGS: RM2D.
Max 5,800 bhp (5,880 cv) at max power turbine speed of 14,500 rev/min (primary gearbox output speed as required).

SPECIFIC FUEL CONSUMPTION:
Max   0·461 lb (209 gr)/bhp/hr

MARINE SPEY

The Marine Spey is based on the TF41 aero engine, largest of the spey family of gas turbines. The TF41 was developed jointly by Rolls-Royce and the Detroit Diesel Allison Division of General Motors Corporation under a joint $200 million contract awarded by USAF Systems Command in August 1966 for an advanced version of the RB168-25 Spey turbofan to power the LTV A-70 Corsair 11 fighter bomber for the USAF.

By May 1974 more than 1,000 TF41s had been delivered and the production of the TF41 for the Corsair 11 fighter bomber was expected to continue into the 1980s.

The Marine Spey has been under development since 1972 under a programme sponsored by the British Ministry of Defence.

DIMENSIONS:
Complete unit (including mounting frame):

BOEING PCH-1 HIGH POINT
GRUMMAN PGH-1 FLAGSTAFF

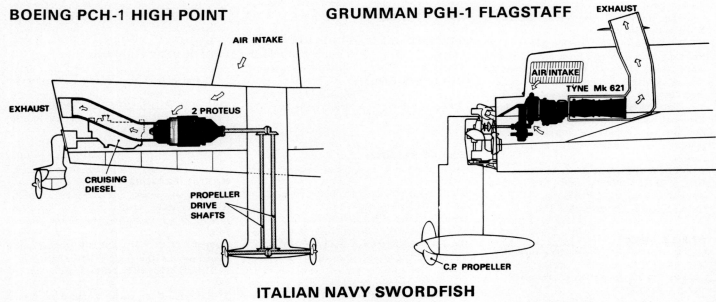

ITALIAN NAVY SWORDFISH

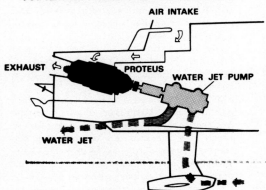

Rolls-Royce marine gas-turbines are employed on the PCH-1 High Point, the PGH-1 Flagstaff and the Swordfish Hydrofoils

Length (air intake flare to drive coupling)
215·8 in (5,481 mm)
Width   100 in (2,540 mm)
Height   98 in (2,089 mm)
Dimensions of gas generator change unit only:
Length   105·0 in (2,677 mm)
Max diameter   35·82 in (910 mm)
WEIGHT:
Estimated weight of complete unit
17,150 lb (7,800 kg)
Estimated dry weight of gas generator change unit   3,250 lb (1,474 kg)

NOMINAL PERFORMANCE:
*Maximum power   16,750 bhp
*Specific fuel consumption
0·395 lb/bhp/hr (0·24 kg/kWh)
*Based on L.C.V. of fuel of 18540 btu/lb (43,125 kJ/kg)
No power off-takes
No intake or exhaust duct losses
Ambient air temperature of 15°C (59°F) and a pressure of 14·7 lbf/in² (101·3 kPa)
TYPE: Marine gas-turbine, incorporating two independently driven compressors, an axial-flow free-power turbine and exhaust volute, all on a lightweight mounting frame.
GAS GENERATOR CHARACTERISTICS
AIR INTAKE: Direct entry, fixed, without

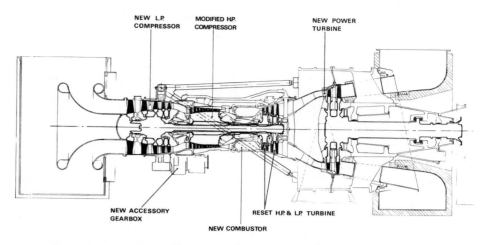

Rolls-Royce Marine Spey SMIA, rated at 16,750 bhp

intake guides.
L.P. COMPRESSOR: 5 axial stages.
H.P. COMPRESSOR: 11 axial stages.
COMBUSTION SYSTEM: Tubo-annular type with ten interconnected straight flow flame tubes.
TURBINES: Impulse reaction, axial-type. Two H.P. and two L.P. stages.
EXHAUST: Fixed volume.

STARTING: Air/gas starter motor.
FUEL SYSTEM: Hydromechanical high pressure system with automatic acceleration and speed control.
FUEL GRADE: Diesel fuel Grade 'A', Def 2402 or NATO F-75.
LUBRICATION SYSTEM: Self-contained gear pump filters and chip detectors.
POWER TURBINE: 2-stage free axial-flow turbine.

THE UNITED STATES OF AMERICA

AIRESEARCH MANUFACTURING COM-PANY, a division of the Garrett Corporation
402 South 36th Street, Phoenix, Arizona 85034
TELEPHONE:
(602) 267-3011
EXECUTIVES:
Jack Teske, Vice-President and Manager
Donald L. Cauble, Assistant Manager
Malcolm E. Craig, Sales Manager

AiResearch Manufacturing Company, Phoenix, Arizona, is the world's largest manufacturer of small gas turbine engines for commercial, military, marine and industrial application, as well as a leading producer of air turbine starters, air motors, pneumatic valves and control systems for aircraft and aerospace applications. The company occupies approximately 1 million sq ft of facilities on 220 acres of land with its main facilities adjoining Phoenix Sky Harbor International

Airport. Its employees number approximately 4,800.

GTP/GTPF990
Currently under development is a fully marinized 5,000 hp advanced gas-turbine scheduled to be available in the late-1970s. The engine is designed in two configurations. a free turbine (GTPF990) for propulsion, pump and compressor drive, and a coupled turbine (GTP990) for applications such as generator sets for primary and secondary power. The engine is being designed specifically for ease of maintenance and long TBO, and is expected to commence service with a TBO of 6,000 hours.
Specification details available are as follows:
TYPE: Simple-cycle, single-shaft (GTPF990) or twin-shaft (GTP990).
COMPRESSOR: Two-stage centrifugal.
COMBUSTION CHAMBER: Single, annular.

TURBINE: Two-stage axial gas generator.
FUEL GRADE: DF-2.
DIMENSIONS:
Length   108 in (274·3 cm)
WEIGHT, Dry:
Fitted with lightweight gearbox
4,000 lb (1,814 kg)
Fitted with heavy-duty gearbox
5,000 lb (2,449 kg)

PERFORMANCE RATING:
Continuous S.L. 100°F: 5,000 shp at 18,000 rpm gas generator speed and 16,400 rpm power turbine speed.
System output speed   3,600 rpm

ME 831-800
A further development by AiResearch is a fully marinized turbomarine power system, having a continuous power rating of 380 shp and an intermittant rating of 610 shp. This unit, designated ME831-800, is under devel-

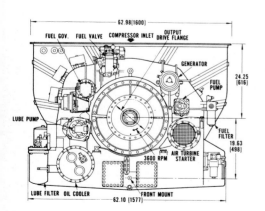

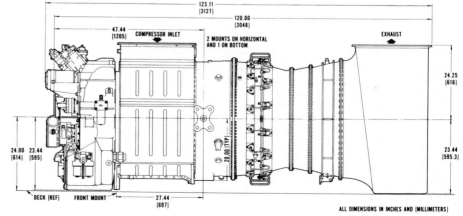

The Garrett GTPF 990, 5,000 shp heavy duty gas-turbine for marine applications

opment for the Boeing NATO PHM hydro-foil secondary power system, which uses two units per ship.

Specification details available are as follows:

TYPE: Simple-cycle, single-shaft.
COMPRESSOR: Two-stage centrifugal.
COMBUSTION CHAMBER: Single, reverse-flow.

TURBINE: Three-stage axial.
FUEL GRADES: DF-1 and DF-2 per ASTM. D975, VV-F-800, MIL-F-16884 and MIL-R-46005, Jet A, A-1 and B per ASTM D1665. JP-4 and JP-5 per MIL-F-5624 and VV-K-211.
DIMENSIONS:

Length	72 in (182·9 cm)
Width	39 in (99·1 cm)

Height	34 in (86·4 cm)
WEIGHT, Dry:	1,500 lb (680·4 kg)

POWER RATING:

Continuous S.L. 100°F	380 shp
Intermittent	610 shp
Rated rotor speed	41,730 rpm (max)

System output speed constant speed, two output pad speeds of 8,000 rpm and two at 3,600 rpm

---

AVCO LYCOMING
Avco Lycoming Division of Avco Corporation

HEAD OFFICE:
550 South Main Street, Stratford, Connecticut 06497
WORKS:
Stratford, Connecticut
PRESIDENT OF AVCO CORPORATION:
George L. Hogeman
VICE-PRESIDENTS—LYCOMING DIVISION:
Joseph S. Bartos (General Manager)
Dr. H. K. Adenstedt (Senior Vice-President)
Seymour L. Rosenberg (Controller)
James F. Shanley (Administration)
E. Louis Wilkinson (Factory Operations)
Michael S. Saboe (Engineering and Development)
Martin J. Leff (Product Support and Marketing)
Dr. Fritz Haber, International Operations
T. B. Lauriat, Chief, Marine Industrial Applications, Avco Lycoming
K. M. Austin, Manager, Avco International Overseas Corporation

The Avco Lycoming Division, Stratford, is the turbine engine manufacturing division of the Avco Corporation.

Avco Lycoming is mainly producing two families of gas-turbine engines. Designated T53 and T55, these are both of the free-turbine type and are available in turboshaft, turbofan and turboprop form. The T53 in particular has been built in large numbers to power US Army helicopters. Industrial and marine versions of the T53 and T55 are designated TF12B and 14C and the new Super TF 25, TF 35 and TF 40 respectively. The TF12 and TF 14 turbines are no longer being offered except for large quantity orders.

TF12A and TF14B

The TF12 and TF14 engines are developments of the T53 aircraft engine. The T53 is a turboshaft with a free power turbine, which was developed under a joint, USAF/US Army contract. It has logged over 22 million hours of operation with the US armed services and operators in 28 other countries.

The TF14B is an uprated version of the TF12B. Redesigned "hot end" and initial stages of compressor section provide substantially increased power for hot day performance. Four turbine stages, compared with two in earlier models, and variable-incidence inlet guide vanes combined with redesigned first two compressor stages, permit greater airflow and lower turbine temperatures. This version has atomising combustor to facilitate operation on a wider range of fuels. Applications include US Navy ATC/CCB and ASPBs (Assault Support Patrol Boats).

TYPE: Free turbine turboshaft engine.
AIR INTAKE: Side inlet castings of aluminium alloy, supporting gearbox and front

Avco Lycoming TF 12 B marine gas turbine engine of 1,150 shp

Avco Lycoming TF 25 C marine gas turbine engine of 2,500 shp

main bearings.
COMPRESSOR: Five axial stages followed by a single centrifugal stage. Four-piece aluminium alloy casing with one row of variable-incidence inlet guide vanes and five rows of steel stator blades, bolted to one-piece steel alloy diffuser casing with tangential outlet to combustion chamber. Rotor comprises one stainless steel and four aluminium alloy discs with stainless steel blades, and one titanium impeller mounted on shaft supported in forward ball thrust and rear roller bearings. Pressure ratio 6·3 : 1.
COMBUSTION CHAMBER: Annular reverse-flow type, with one-piece sheet steel outer shell and annular liner. Twenty-two

atomising fuel injectors.
FUEL CONTROL SYSTEM: Hydro-mechanical controls for gas generator and for power sections. Woodward system with one fuel pump. Pump pressure 600 lb/sq in (42 kg/cm²). Main and emergency flow controls. Separate interstage air-bleed control.
FUEL GRADE: MIL-F-16884F, JP-4. JP-5, CITE, marine diesel.
TURBINE: Four axial-flow turbine stages. Casing fabricated from sheet steel. First two stages, driving compressor, use hollow-air-cooler stator vanes and cored-out cast steel rotor blades, and are mounted on outer co-axial shaft to gas producer. Second stages, driving reduction gearing, have solid

steel blades, and are spline-mounted to shaft.

EXHAUST UNIT: Fixed-area nozzle. Stainless steel outer casing and inner cone, supported by four radial struts.

ACCESSORIES: Electric starter, Bendix-Scintilla TGLN high-energy ignition unit. Four ignitor plugs.

LUBRICATION: Recirculating system with gear pump. Filter. Pump pressure 70 lb/sq in (4·9 kg/cm²).

OIL GRADE: MIL-L 23699.

DIMENSIONS:

Length overall	51·4 in (1·30 m)
Width	30·4 in (0·72 m)
Height	42·6 in (1·08 m)

WEIGHT (Dry):

Less tailpipe	920 lb (417 kg)

POWER RATINGS:

Max intermittent (peak)*	
TF12B (at 59°F)	1,275 shp
TF14C (at 59°F)	1,600 shp
Max continuous (normal)*	
TF12B (at 59°F)	1,150 shp
TF14C (at 59°F)	1,400 shp

*All ratings based on no inlet pressure loss and no exhaust pressure loss.

FUEL CONSUMPTION:

At max continuous rating:

TF12B	·60 sfc 99 US gall/hr
TF14C	118 US gall/hr

OIL CONSUMPTION: 1·0 lb (450 gr)/hr

SUPER TF25 AND SUPER TF35

These engines are developments of the T55 aircraft engine.

Current production and development versions are as follows:

TF25C. High-speed shaft-turbine engine, with output shaft speed equal to power turbine speed. Integral oil tank and cooling system. An earlier TF25 powers the Vosper Thornycroft VT1, the Coastal Patrol Interdiction Craft (CPIC-X) and the Mitsui MV-PP15 155-seat hoverferry.

TF35. Uprated, redesigned version of the TF25. New turbine section with four stages and variable-incidence inlet guide vanes. First two compressor stages transonic. New atomising fuel nozzles. Earlier TF35s power a number of six-engined Patrol Ship Multi-Mission craft (PSMM); a more powerful production model of the 95-ft, high-speed CPIC patrol boat: a number of tri-engine waterjet ferries for the San Francisco Bridge and Highway Authority off the coast of California and the Aerojet-General SES-100A surface effect test craft. This 100-ton vessel employs four TF35 engines, each rated at 3,300 shp (maximum).

AIR INTAKE: Side inlet casting of aluminium alloy supporting optional reduction gearbox and front main bearings. Provision for intake screens.

COMPRESSOR: Seven axial stages followed by a single centrifugal stage. Two-piece aluminium alloy stator casing with one row of inlet guide vanes, fixed on TF25, variable on TF35, and seven rows of steel stator blades, bolted to steel alloy diffuser casing to which combustion chamber casing is attached. Rotor comprises seven stainless steel discs and one titanium impeller mounted on shaft supported in forward thrust ball bearings and rear roller bearing. TF25C pressure ratio 6 : 1 and 6·5 : 1 for TF35C.

COMBUSTION CHAMBER: Annular reverse flow type. Steel outer shell and inner liner. Twenty-eight fuel burners with downstream injection.

Avco Lycoming Super TF 34 direct drive two-stage, free-power marine gas-turbine, rated at 3,500 shp continuous and 4,050 shp boost power

Cutaway of the Avco Lycoming Super TF40 marine gas turbine

FUEL SYSTEM: Woodward fuel control system. Gear-type fuel pump, with gas producer and power shaft governors, flow control and shut-off valve.

FUEL GRADE: MIL: J-5624 grade JP-4, JP-5, MIL-F-46005 or marine diesel standard and wide-cut kerosene.

TURBINE: Two mechanically-independent axial-flow turbines. First turbine with single-stage on TF25 and two-stages of TF35 drives compressor. Has cored-out cast steel blades and is flange-bolted to outer co-axial drive shaft. Hollow stator vanes. Second, two-stage turbine drives output shaft. Has solid steel blades and is mounted on inner co-axial drive shaft.

EXHAUST UNIT: Fixed area nozzle, with inner cone, supported by six radial struts.

ACCESSORIES: Electric, air or hydraulic starter. Bendix-Scintilla TGLN high-energy ignition unit. Four igniter plugs.

LUBRICATION: Recirculating type. Integral oil tank and cooler.

OIL GRADE: MIL-L-17808, MIL-L-23699.

DIMENSIONS:

Length:	
Super TF25	50·1 in (1·27 m)
Super TF35	52·2 in (1·32 m)
Width:	
Super TF25, 35	34·4 in (871 mm)
Height:	
Super TF25, 35	43·8 in (1·11 m)

WEIGHT (Dry):

Super TF25	1,324 lb (600 kg)
Super TF35	1,414 lb (641 kg)

PERFORMANCE RATINGS:

Max intermittent (peak):

Super TF25	3,000 shp
Super TF35	4,050 shp

Max continuous (normal):

Super TF25	2,500 shp
Super TF35	3,500 shp

FUEL CONSUMPTION:

At max continuous rating:

Super TF25	·62 sfc 198 US gall/hr
Super TF35	·56 sfc 223 US gall/hr

SUPER TF40

The TF40 engine is a scaled-up TF35 with higher mass flow. It has a four stage turbine section and variable-incidence inlet guide vanes. The first two compressor stages are transonic, and new atomising fuel nozzles are fitted.

Both the Jeff A (Aerojet General) and Jeff B (Bell Aerospace) AALCs employ TF40s. Jeff A employs six, each developing 3,350 shp continuous four drive individual, steerable ducted propellers, and the remaining two drive separate centrifugal lift fans. In the case of Jeff B, the six engines are arranged in two groups of three, located port and starboard. Each trio drives a single propeller and lift system through integrated gears.

Other craft now powered by TF40s include the SEDAM N.500, which employs two for lift and three, mounted in separate nacelles, for propulsion, and a twin hull waterjet ferry, currently being built in Scandinavia.

AIR INTAKE: Side inlet casting of aluminium alloy housing internal gearing and supporting power producer section and output drive shaft. Integral or separately mounted gears are operational. Provision for intake filters and/or silencers.

COMPRESSOR: Seven axial stages followed by a single centrifugal stage. Two-piece aluminium alloy stator casing, with one row of variable inlet guide vanes, and seven rows of steel stator blades bolted to steel alloy casing diffuser, to which combustion chamber casing is attached. Rotor comprises seven stainless steel discs and one titanium impeller mounted on shaft supported in forward thrust ball bearing and rear roller bearing. TF40 pressure ratio is 7·2 : 1.

COMBUSTION CHAMBER: Annular reverse flow type. Steel outer shell and inner liner. Twenty-eight fuel burners with downstream injection.

FUEL SYSTEM: Woodward fuel control system. Gear-type fuel pump, with gas producer and power shaft governors, flow control and shut-off valve.

FUEL GRADE: MIL-T-5624, JP-4, JP-5; MIL-F-16884 diesel, standard and wide-cut kerosene.

TURBINE: Two mechanically-independent axial-flow turbines. First turbine, with two stages, drives compressor. It has cored-out cast steel blades and is flange-bolted to outer co-axial drive shaft. Hollow stator vanes. Second two-stage turbine drives output shaft. It has solid steel blades and is mounted on inner co-axial drive shaft. (Other features include: integral cast first turbine nozzle, cooled first turbine blades in both first and second stages, second turbine vane cooling, second turbine disc and blade cooling, and a modified third stage nozzle shroud).

EXHAUST UNIT: Fixed area nozzle, with inner cone, supported by six radial struts.

ACCESSORIES: Electric, air or hydraulic starter. Bendix-Scintilla TGLN high-energy ignition unit. Four igniter plugs.

LUBRICATION: Recirculating type. Integral oil tank and cooler.

OIL GRADE: Synthetic base oils.

DIMENSIONS: SUPER TF40

Length	52·2 in (1·32 m)
Width	34·4 in (871 mm)
Height	43·8 in (1·11 m)

PERFORMANCE RATINGS:

Max intermittent (at 59°F sea level)— 4,600 shp

Max continuous (at 59°F —sea level) 4,000 shp

FUEL CONSUMPTION:

At max continuous rating ·54 sfc/255 US gall/hr

OIL CONSUMPTION: 1·0 lb (454 gr/hr)

BRIGGS & STRATTON CORPORATION

HEADQUARTERS AND WORKS:
Milwaukee, Wisconsin 53201
CENTRAL SERVICE DISTRIBUTORS FOR
GREAT BRITAIN AND IRELAND:
Autocar Electrical Equipment Co Ltd.
16 Rippleside Commercial Estate, Ripple Road, Barking, Essex

Briggs & Stratton is a major American supplier of low-power four-stroke gasoline engines an important application of which is in motor lawn mowers of both US and European manufacture. Several installations of Briggs & Stratton in ACVs have been made. These include the American Bartlett M-8 Flying Saucer, a small lightweight craft powered by a single 3 hp Briggs & Stratton engine mounted above a central plenum chamber driving a two-bladed Banks-Maxwell Mod 30-14 30 in diameter pusher propeller; and Coelacanth Gemco's Pluto two-seat test vehicle which has two 7 hp Briggs & Stratton engines each driving 42 in fans, one for lift and a second for propulsion.

CUMMINS ENGINE COMPANY INC

OFFICES:
Cummins Engine Company Inc, 1000 Fifth Street, Columbus, Indiana, 47201.
Cummins Engine Company Ltd, Coombe House, St Georges Square, Maldon Road, New Malden, Surrey

The Cummins Engine Company was formed in 1919 in Columbus, Indiana. It produces a wide range of marine diesel engines which are now manufactured and distributed internationally. In addition to manufacturing plants in the United States, the company also produces diesel engines in Brazil, India, Japan, Mexico and the United Kingdom. All these plants build engines to the same specifications thus ensuring interchangeability of parts and the same quality standards.

Cummins marine diesels power the Seaflight 46 (two VT8N-370-M) hydrofoil, and the Hovermarine HM.2 sidewall hovercraft.

On the latter, two VT8-370-Ms, each derated to 320 bhp, supply propulsive power, and a single V-504-M, derated to 185 bhp, drives the lift fans.

MODEL V-555-M

Horsepower	240
Governed rpm	3,300
Number of cylinders	8
Bore and stroke	4⅛ × 4¼ in
Piston displacement	555 cu in
Operating cycles	4
Crankcase oil capacity	5 gals
Coolant capacity	9·5 gals
Net weight (engine less gear)	1,850 lbs

BEARINGS: Precision type, steel backed inserts.

CAMSHAFT: Single camshaft controls all valve and injector movement. Induction hardened alloy steel with gear drive.

CAMSHAFT FOLLOWERS: Roller type for long cam and follower life.

CONNECTING RODS: Drop forged, 6·72 in centre to centre length. Taper piston pin end reduces unit pressures.

COOLER, LUBRICATING OIL: Tubular type, jacket water cooled.

CRANKSHAFT: High tensile strength steel forging. Bearing journals are induction hardened.

CYLINDER BLOCK: Alloy cast iron with removable, wet liners. Cross bolt support to main bearing cap.

CYLINDER HEADS: Two, one each bank. All fuel lines are drilled passages. Individual intake and exhaust porting for each cylinder. Corrosion resistant inserts on intake and exhaust valve seats.

DAMPER, VIBRATION: Compressed rubber type.

FUEL SYSTEM: Cummins self adjusting system with integral flyball type governer. Camshaft actuated injectors.

GEAR TRAIN: Heavy duty, located rear of cylinder block.

LUBRICATION: Force feed to all bearings. Gear type pump.

PISTONS: Aluminium, cam ground, with two compression and one oil ring.

PISTON PINS: 1½ in diameter, full floating.

THERMOSTAT: Dual, modulating by-pass type.

VALVES: Dual intake and exhaust each cylinder. Each valve 1⅝ in diameter.

STANDARD EQUIPMENT:

CORROSION RESISTOR: Mounted, Cummins spin on type, checks rust and corrosion, controls acidity, and removes impurities from coolant.

DIPSTICK, OIL: Port side when viewing engine from drive end.

ELECTRICAL EQUIPMENT: 12 volt, 58 ampere ac system. Includes starting motor, alternator, regulator, magnetic switch and starting switch.

EXCHANGER, HEAT: Tubular type, mounted.

FILTERS: Cummins. Lubricating oil full flow paper element type, mounted. Fuel, spin on, mounted.

FLYWHEEL: For reverse and reduction gear.

GOVERNOR: Mechanical variable speed type.

HOUSING, FLYWHEEL: S.A.E. No. 3.

INTAKE AIR: Silenced.

MANIFOLD, EXHAUST: Two, fresh water cooled.

PAN, OIL: Aluminium, rear sump type, 5 U.S. gallon capacity.

PUMP, COOLANT: Belt driven, centrifugal type, 80 gpm at 3,300 rpm.

PUMP, EAW WATER: Belt driven rubber impeller type, 48 gpm at 3,300 rpm.

SUPPORT, ENGINE: Marine type, front and rear.

MODEL V-903-M

Horsepower	295
Governed rpm	2,600
Number of cylinders	8
Bore and stroke	$5\frac{1}{2} \times 4\frac{3}{4}$ in
Piston displacement	903 cu in
Operating cycles	4
Oil pan capacity	5 U.S. gals
Engine coolant capacity	12 gals
Net weight with standard accessories	2,800 lbs.

BEARINGS: Precision type, steel backed inserts. 5 main bearings, $3\frac{3}{4}$ in diameter. Connecting rod—$3\frac{1}{8}$ in diameter.

CAMSHAFT: Single camshaft controls all valve and injector movement. Induction hardened alloy steel with gear drive.

CAMSHAFT FOLLOWERS: Roller type for long cam and follower life.

CONNECTING RODS: Drop forged. Taper piston pin end provides superior load distribution and maximum piston crown material.

COOLER, LUBRICATING OIL: Tubular type, jacket water cooled.

CRANKSHAFT: High tensile strength steel forging. Bearing journals are induction hardened. Fully counterweighted.

CYLINDER BLOCK: Alloy cast iron with removable, wet liners.

CYLINDER HEADS: Two, one each bank. All fuel lines are drilled passages. Individual intake and exhaust porting for each cylinder.

DAMPER, VIBRATION: Compressed rubber type.

FUEL SYSTEM: Cummins wear-compensating system with integral, flyball type, mechanical variable speed governor. Camshaft actuated injectors.

LUBRICATION: Force feed to all bearings. Gear type pump.

MAIN BEARING CAPS: Cross bolted for rigidity.

PISTONS: Aluminium, cam ground, with two compression and one oil ring.

PISTON PINS: $1\frac{3}{4}$ in diameter, full floating.

THERMOSTAT: Single unit, modulating by-pass type.

VALVES: Dual intake and exhaust each cylinder. Each valve $1\frac{1}{4}$ in diameter. Heat and corrosion resistant face on all valves.

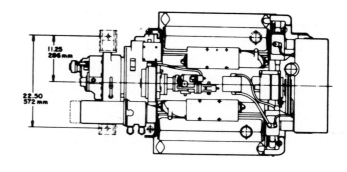

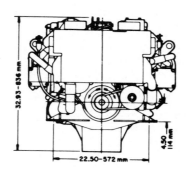

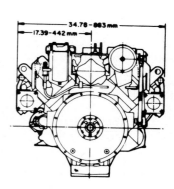

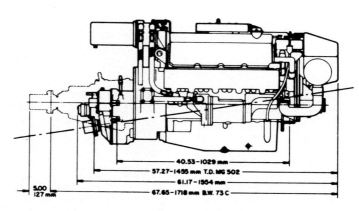

Cummins 8-cylinder V-555-M diesel, rated at 240 hp

STANDARD EQUIPMENT:

CLEANER, AIR: Silencer type.

CORROSION RESISTOR: Cummins, Mounted. Throw-away unit. Checks rust and corrosion, controls acidity, and removes impurities from coolant.

DIPSTICK, OIL: Port side when viewing engine from drive end.

ELECTRICAL EQUIPMENT: 12 volt, 55 ampere a.c. system. Includes starting motor alternator, regulator, and starting switch.

EXCHANGER, HEAT: Tubular type, mounted.

FILTERS: Cummins. Lubricating oil, full flow replaceable paper element type, mounted. Fuel, paper element throw-away type, mounted.

FLYWHEEL: For reverse and reduction gear.

GEAR, MARINE: Capitol 4HE-10200, 2·00:1 reverse and reduction gear with propeller shaft companion flange.

GOVERNOR: Mechanical variable speed type.

HOUSING, FLYWHEEL: S.A.E. No. 2.

MANIFOLD, AIR INTAKE: Two, located on inside of engine Vee.

MANIFOLD, EXHAUST: Two, fresh water cooled, with outlet to rear.

PAN, OIL: Aluminium, front sump type, 5 U.S. gallon capacity.

PUMP: COOLANT: Gear driven, centrifugal type, 78 gpm at 2,600 rpm.

PUMP, RAW WATER: Gear driven, 61 gpm at 2,600 rpm.

SUPPORT, ENGINE: Marine type, $22\frac{1}{2}$ in centres.

MODEL KTA-1150-M

Power rating	520 bhp (388 kW)
Governed rpm	1,950 (1,950)
Power rating	470 bhp (350 kW)
Governed rpm	1,800 (1,800)
Number of cylinders	6
Bore and stroke	$6\frac{1}{4} \times 6\frac{1}{4}$ in (159 × 159 mm)
Piston displacement	1,150 cu in (18·86 litres)
Operating cycles	4
Lube system oil cap	15·5 US gals (59 litres)
Coolant capacity	9 US gals (34·9 litres)
Net weight, dry	3,800 lbs (1,725 kg)

AFTERCOOLER: Two. Jacket water cooled.

BEARINGS: Precision type, steel backed inserts. 7 main bearings, 5½ in (140 mm) diameter. Connecting rod—4 in (102 mm) diameter.

CAMSHAFT: Single camshaft controls all valve and injector movement. Induction hardened alloy steel with gear drive.

CAMSHAFT FOLLOWERS: Roller type for long cam and follower life.

CONNECTING RODS: Drop forged 11·4 in (290 mm) center to center length. Rifle drilled for pressure lubrication of piston pin. Taper piston pin end reduces unit pressures.

CRANKSHAFT: High tensile strength steel forging. Bearing journals are induction hardened. Fully counterweighted.

CYLINDER BLOCK: Alloy cast iron with removable, wet liners.

CYLINDER HEADS: Individual cylinder heads. Drilled fuel supply and return lines. Corrosion resistant inserts on intake and exhaust valve seats.

FUEL SYSTEM: Cummins PTTM self adjusting system with integral flyball type governor. Camshaft actuated injectors.

GEAR TRAIN: Heavy duty, induction hardened, located at front of cylinder block.

LUBRICATION: Force feed to all bearings. gear type pump. All lubrication lines are drilled passages, except pan to pump suction line.

PISTONS: Aluminium, cam ground, with two compression and one oil ring. Oil cooled.

PISTON PINS: 2·4 in (61 mm) diameter, full floating.

TURBOCHARGER: Scroll diffuser, side mounted.

VALVES: Dual intake and exhaust each cylinder. Each valve 2·22 in (56 mm) diameter. Heat and corrosion resistant face on intake and exhaust valves.

AIR CLEANER: Two stage dry type for vertical mounting.

COOLER, LUBRICATING OIL: Plate type, jacket water cooled.

CORROSION RESISTOR: Fleetguard, mounted, dual spin-on type.

DAMPER, VIBRATION: Viscous type.

DIPSTICK, OIL: Mounted on either port or starboard side of engine.

DRIVE, ALTERNATOR: High capacity, poly-v belt arrangement driven from accessory drive pulley.

ELECTRICAL EQUIPMENT: 24 or 32 volt positive engagement starting motor and 24 or 32 volt ignition proof alternators with built-in voltage regulators.

EXHAUST OUTLET CONNECTIONS: Straight or 90° turbo exhaust connection for adapting 5 in (127 mm) piping.

EXCHANGER, HEAT: Copper-nickel tubular type, engine mounted.

FILTERS: Fleetguard. Lubricating oil: spin-on, full flow, paper element type, mounted on either port or starboard side of engine and by-pass type, not mounted. Fuel: dual spin-on, paper element type, mounted.

FLYWHEEL: For 14 or 18 in (356 to 457 mm) over centre clutch, reverse and reduction gear.

GEAR, MARINE: Twin Disc MG-521: 2·19 : 1, 3·03 : 1, 4·09 : 1. Twin Disc MG-527: 3·86 : 1, 5·18 : 1. Capitol HP 6900 : 2·5 : 1. Capitol HP 7700: 3·5 : 1, 4·5 : 1. Capitol HP 28000: 5·16 : 1, 6·0 : 1.

GOVERNOR: Mechanical variable speed.

HOUSING, FLYWHEEL: S.A.E. O with marine mounting pads.

MANIFOLD, EXHAUST: Water cooled.

PAN, OIL: Aluminium, rear sump type, 10·0 US gallon (37·9 litre) capacity.

PANEL, INSTRUMENT: Not mounted. Includes ammeter, tachometer or hour meter, lube oil temperature gauge, oil pressure gauge and engine water temperature gauge.

POWER TAKE-OFF: Front mounted. Twin Disc clutch models SP-114 for up to 150 hp (112 kW) and SL-214 for up to 215 hp (161 kW).

PUMP, COOLANT: Gear driven, centrifugal type, 185 gpm (700 litre/min) at 1,950 rpm.

SHIELD, BELT: For alternator drive.

STARTING AID: Manual ether cold start aid.

SUPPORT, ENGINE: Three point marine type, front cover, and marine gear.

DETROIT DIESEL ALLISON
(Division of General Motors Corporation)
GENERAL OFFICES:

PO Box 894, Indianapolis, Ind.

TELEPHONE:

317-244-1511

DETROIT DIESEL ALLISON
INTERNATIONAL OPERATIONS
(Division of General Motors Corporation)

25200 Telegraph Road, Southfield, Michigan 48075

GENERAL MOTORS POWER PRODUCTS—
EUROPE
(Division of General Motors Corporation)

PO Box 6, London Road, Wellingborough, Northamptonshire, England NN8 2DL

Detroit Diesel Allison has been active in the development of gas-turbines for aircraft, industrial and marine use for many years. Production of the first Allison gas-turbine began in the 1940s, when the company built the power plant for the P-59, the first jet-powered aircraft to fly in the United States.

Later, the Allison T56 turboprop aircraft engine was developed. It demonstrated outstanding reliability and the same basic design has been adapted for industrial and marine applications. In the early 1960s, the first Allison 501-K gas-turbine powered electric powerplant went into service. Today, the 501-K industrial series engines are not only used in electric powerplants but also in industrial and marine applications.

ALLISON 501-K SERIES

The Allison 501-K series industrial gas-turbine incorporates a 14-stage axial-flow compressor, with bleed valves to compensate for compressor surge.

Of modular design, it comprises three main sections: the compressor, combustor and turbine. Each section can be readily separated from the other. Modular design provides ease in handling and servicing of the engine.

Detroit Diesel Allison 501-KF two-shaft marine gas turbine

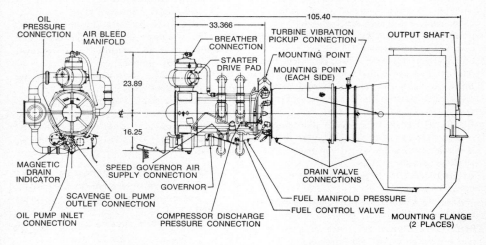

General arrangement of the Allison 501-KF two-shaft marine gas-turbine

The first stage of the four-stage turbine section is air-cooled, permitting the engine to be operated at higher than normal turbine inlet temperatures.

The combustor section of the 501-K consists of six combustion chambers of the through-flow type, assembled within a single annular chamber. This multiple provides even temperature distribution at the turbine inlet, thus eliminating the danger of hot spots.

The 501-K Series engines are available in either single-shaft or free turbine design.

The lightweight, compact size of the 501-K lends itself to multiple engines driving a single shaft through a common gearbox, or as a gas generator driving a customer-furnished power turbine.

The engine can be operated on a wide range of liquid fuels. Designation of the marine model is 501 KF, a brief specification for which follows. Dimensions are shown on the accompanying general arrangement drawing.

Exhaust gas temperature	994°F
Inlet air flow	26,000 cfm
Exhaust air flow	81,000 cfm
Engine jacket heat rejection	6,000 BTU/min
Lube heat rejection (Gasifier)	1,270 BTU/min
Maximum liquid fuel flow	360 ghp
Liquid fuel DF-1, DF-2 per Allison EMS66	
Lubricant	
Synthetic oil per Allison EMS 35 and 53	

Specific fuel consumption: 0·503 lb/hp/hr
Required Auxiliaries:
25 hp starter;
20-29DC volt electrical power;
Power take-off shaft and couplings;
Temperature and speed controls from engine-furnished signals;
Oil cooler;
Auxiliary lube pump;
Compressor inlet sensor;
Gauge panel, meters and associated components;
Engine exhaust diffusing tailpipe.

DOBSON PRODUCTS CO

HEAD OFFICE:
2241 South Ritchey, Santa Ana, California 92705
TELEPHONE:
(714) 557-2987
WORKS:
Santa Ana, California
DIRECTOR:
Franklin A. Dobson

Franklin Dobson has been building and marketing light ACVs in kit and factory-built form since 1963.

His company is now specialising in the design and construction of light ACV components evolved after a more thorough engineering approach. The components include reversible-pitch propellers and fans— the main purpose of which is to provide light craft with adequate braking—and suitable ducts, screens, etc.

Preliminary details of the company's first 3 ft (0·91 m) diameter, variable-pitch two-bladed propeller are given below.

DIMENSIONS:

Diameter	36 in (0·91 m)
Chord	4·25 in (104 mm)

Blades	2
Solidity (at 0·6 rad)	·125
Pitch range	60 deg (nom. +40, —20)
Max shaft dia.	1·25 in (28 mm)
Total weight	5 lb (approx) (0·45 gr)
Design rpm	3,000
Max rpm	3,250
Horsepower req.	7 to 10
Max static thrust (with shroud)	
75 lb (forward or reverse) (34·01 kg)	
Max thrust at 60 mph	50 lb (22·67 kg)

A duct with integral screen, suitable for use with this propeller, is also under development.

GENERAL ELECTRIC COMPANY AIRCRAFT ENGINE GROUP

HEADQUARTERS:
1000 Western Avenue, West Lynn, Massachusetts 01910
VICE PRESIDENT AND GROUP EXECUTIVE:
Gerhard Neumann
COUNSEL:
J. W. Sack

The General Electric Company entered the gas-turbine field in about 1895. Years of pioneering effort by the late Dr Sanford A. Moss produced the aircraft turbosupercharger, successfully tested at height in 1918 and mass-produced in World War II for US fighters and bombers.

The company built its first aircraft gas-turbine in 1941, when it began development of Whittle-type turbojets, under an arrangement between the British and American Governments.

Since that time, General Electric has produced a series of successful designs, from the J47, which powered the Boeing B47 and the North American F 86 series of aircraft, to the big CF6 turbofan powering the new McDonnell Douglas DC-10 wide-body transport.

Three General Electric marinized gas-turbines are in marine service, the LM-100, the LM1500 and the LM2500. The LM100 powers the Bell SK-5 air cushion vehicle and the Avalon high-speed ferry, the LM1500 powers the AGEH-1 Plainview and seventeen US Navy patrol gunboats and the LM2500 powers the Boeing NATO/PHM hydrofoil fast patrol ship.

LM2500

The LM2500 marine gas turbine is a 2-shaft, simple cycle, high efficiency engine. Derived from the GE TF39 CF-6 high-bypass turbofan engines for the US Air Force C-5 transport and DC-10 and A300B commercial jets. The engine incorporates the latest features of compressor, combustor, and turbine design to provide maximum progression in reliability parts life, and time between overhaul. The

GE LM 2500 gas turbine

engine has a fuel rate 25% lower than that of current production marine gas turbines in its power range. This is made possible by high compressor pressure ratio, high turbine inlet temperature and improved cycle efficiency.

The LM2500 marine gas turbine has been specified for the foilborne power of the joint U.S. Navy/NATO Patrol Hydrofoil Missile ship (PHM) being built by the Boeing Company, Seattle, Washington.

This engine is in production for the U.S. Navy's new Spruance class destroyer fleet, the first major warships in the U.S. Navy to employ marine gas turbines for propulsion, and it will also power the U.S. Navy's new class of Patrol Frigates and the new Fast Frigates for the Italian and Peruvian navies.

Two LM2500s power the Gas Turbine Ship (GTS) Admiral William M. Callaghan roll-on/roll-off cargo vessel operated for the U.S. Navy Military Sealift Command by American Export Line. The ship has over 55,000 engine operating hours to date.

TYPE: 2-shaft, axial flow, simple cycle.
AIR INTAKE: Axial, inlet bellmouth on duct can be customised to installation.
COMBUSTION CHAMBER: Annular.
FUEL GRADE: Kerosene, JP4, JP5, Diesel, heavy distillate fuels and natural gas.

TURBINE: 2-stage gas generator, 6-stage power.

JET PIPE: Customised to fit installation.

OIL SPECIFICATION: Synthetic Turbine Oil (MIL-L-23699) or equal.

MOUNTING: At power turbine and compressor front frame.

STARTING: Pneumatic, hydraulic.

DIMENSIONS:

Length	20 ft 6 in (6·24 m)
Width	7 ft 7¼ in (2·3 m)
Height	7 ft 6¼ in (2·6 m)

PERFORMANCE RATINGS:

27,500 shp at 59°F (15°C) at sea level

SPECIFIC FUEL CONSUMPTION:

0·39 lb (0·177 kg)/hp/hr

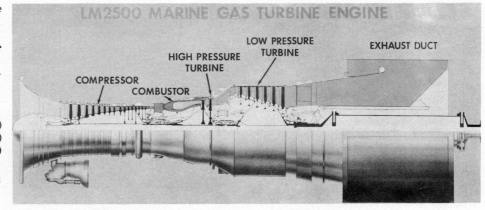

Internal arrangements of the GE LM2500 marine gas-turbine

McCULLOCH CORPORATION

ADMINISTRATION OFFICES:

5400 Alla Rd., Los Angeles, CA 90066

ASSEMBLY PLANT:

6151 W. 98th St., Los Angeles, CA 90045

MAIN MANUFACTURING PLANT:

648 Lake Havasu Dr., Lake Havasu, Ariz. 86403

AFFILIATES:

Malton, Ontario, Canada; Mechelen, Belgium; Singapore; Seven Hills N.S.W., Australia; Sao Paulo, Brazil.

PRESIDENT:

Richard V. Dempster

VICE-PRESIDENTS:

G. E. Maffey, Jr., Engineering

P. F. Masterson, Treasurer-Finance V.P.

M. V. Nodar, Administration

S. E. Page, Secretary-General Counsel

S. J. Stephenson, Marketing

R. D. VanderLeek, International Operations

SALES:

C. L. Hammond, Director, General, Product Sales

McCulloch Corporation produces a variety of small gasoline engines making extensive use of aluminium and magnesium high-pressure die castings. Over the past 25 years it has supplied more than 60,000 engines to the US armed services for use in radio-controlled target aircraft and helicopters.

Amateur builders have made extensive use of McCulloch target drone engines in light aircraft and autogyros, and air cushion vehicles. Current models include improved versions of the MC49E, MC92 and MC101B single-cylinder, two-stroke series and details are given hereunder. New engines planned cover 12 to 34 hp in single or twin-cylinder versions.

McCulloch MC49E, 80·3 cc

DISPLACEMENT: 4·9 cu in (80·3 cc)

BORE: 2·125 in (54 mm)

STROKE: 1·375 in (35 mm)

COMPRESSION RATIO: 6 : 1

WEIGHT: 12 lbs (5·5 kg)

INLET VALVE: Dual petal, high flow reeds, on vee block for full power at all speeds, and sensitivity towards inlet and exhaust tuning.

CARBURETTOR: Racing diaphragm type. Consistent metering in any position. ¾ in (19 mm) adjustable for idle and midrange mixture. Butterfly throttle and choke. Integral fuel pump.

AIR FILTER: Low restriction washable element air filter optional.

PISTON: Heat resistant aluminium alloy. Oversize available. ·010 in, ·020 in, ·030 in.

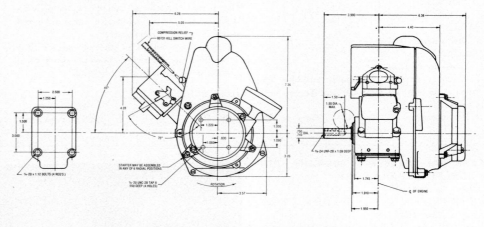

General arrangement of the MC101M/C giving dimensions

PISTON RINGS: Two narrow steel type with wear face for quick sealing, low friction and long life. Super abrasive resistant. Unpinned.

BEARINGS—

CONN ROD: Full complement M-50 tool steel needle rollers, hardened shaft and rod ends.

WRIST PIN: Two needle roller bearings in piston.

MAIN: 1 ball bearing, 1 needle roller.

CRANKSHAFT: Counter-balanced, hot forged steel hardening and ground.

ENGINE: Single cylinder, two-cycle, air-cooled. Loop scavenged.

CYLINDER-CRANKCASE: Die cast aluminium alloy with precision honed cast iron reborable liner. Deep finned integral head.

DIRECTION OF ROTATION: Clockwise (facing power take-off shaft).

IGNITION: Waterproof high tension extra high output magneto. Heat resistant, moistureproof coil bonded to lamination.

SPARK PLUG: Champion J8J.

FUEL OIL MIXTURE: 40:1 with McCulloch oil and automotive regular grade gasoline.

FLYWHEEL: High pressure die cast aluminium alloy with integral magneto magnets, steel hub.

STARTER: McCulloch, six position, automatic rewind starter is standard.

CLUTCH: Conventional types adaptable.

MOUNTING: Four bolt holes provided on the P.T.O. side and four bolt holes on the bottom of crankcase. Engine operates in any position.

List price, USA, $150.00

McCulloch MC92 (99·3 cc)

DISPLACEMENT: 6·05 cu in (99·3 cc).

BORE: 2·165 in (55 mm).

STROKE: 1·635 in (41·5 mm).

COMPRESSION RATIO: 9·4:1.

WEIGHT: 11 lb 9 oz (5·2 kg)

INLET VALVE: Dual petal, high flow reeds on vee block for full power at all speeds, and sensitivity towards inlet and exhaust tuning.

CARBURETTOR: BDC 22 1⅜ in (35 mm) bore with 1⅛ in (29 mm) venturi assures high flow air delivery. Adjustable high and low mixture needles. Optional choke kit for air filter installations. Integral fuel pump and filter screen. Optional twin-stage fuel pump kit, also for previous MAC big bore carbs.

AIR FILTER: Conventional types adaptable.

ENGINE: Single cylinder, two-cycle, air-cooled. Loop scavenged.

CYLINDER-CRANKCASE: Die cast aluminium alloy with precision honed cast iron reborable liner. Deep finned detachable head.

DIRECTION OF ROTATION: Clockwise (facing power take-off-shaft).

DIRECTION OF ROTATION: Clockwise (facing power take off shaft).

IGNITION: Waterproof high tension extra high output magneto. Heat resistant, moistureproof coil bonded to lamination.

SPARK PLUG: Champion L-88.

FUEL OIL MIXTURE: 20:1 with McCulloch oil and automotive regular grade gasoline.

FLYWHEEL: High pressure die cast aluminium alloy with integral magneto magnets, steel hub.

STARTER: McCulloch, six position, automatic rewind starter is standard.

COMPRESSION RELEASE: Button type for easy starting, button locks out when engine starts.

KILL SWITCH WIRE: Standard.

CLUTCH: Conventional types adaptable.

MOUNTING: Four bolt holes provided on the P.T.O. side and four bolt holes on the bottom of crankcase. Engine operates in any position.

List price, USA, $175·00.

McCULLOCH MC 101B (123 cc)

DISPLACEMENT: 7·5 cu in (123 cc).

BORE: 2·280 in (58 mm)

STROKE: 1·835 in (46·6 mm).

COMPRESSION RATIO: 9·4:1.

WEIGHT: 9·4:1.

INLET VALVE: Dual petal, high flow reeds on vee block for full power at all speeds, and sensitivity towards inlet and exhaust tuning.

CARBURETTOR: Optimised bore and venturi dimensions (same as MC92 carburettors), with twin stage integral fuel pump; maximum volume inlet needle, seat and passages. Wide range high and low mixture needles (gasoline, alky and beyond). Choke kit optional for air filter installation. Integral large area fuel filter screen.

AIR FILTER: Conventional types adaptable.

PISTON: Heat resistant aluminium alloy. Oversize available: ·010 in, ·020 in, ·030 in, ·050 in.

PISTON RINGS: Two narrow steel racing type with wear face for quick sealing, low friction and long life. Super abrasive resistant. Pinned.

BEARINGS—

CONN ROD: Full complement M-50 tool steel needle rollers; hardened shaft and rod ends.

WRIST PIN: Two needle roller bearings in piston. Extra length for additional lubrication and cooling.

MAIN: Two full complement high capacity ball bearings.

CRANKSHAFT: Counter-balanced, hot forged steel, carburised, hardened and ground. Counter-balanced, hot forged steel hardened and ground. Extensively shot peened and tungsten counterweights. Super finished throw.

ENGINE: Single cylinder, two-cycle, air-cooled. Loop scavenged.

CYLINDER-CRANKCASE: Die cast aluminium alloy with precision honed cast iron reborable liner. Deep finned detachable head.

DIRECTION OF ROTATION: Clockwise (facing power take-off shaft).

IGNITION: Waterproof high tension extra high output magneto. Heat resistant, moistureproof coil bonded to lamination.

SPARK PLUG: Champion L-78.

FUEL OIL MIXTURE: 20:1 with McCulloch oil and automotive regular grade gasoline.

FLYWHEEL: High pressure die cast aluminium alloy with integral magneto magnets, steel hub.

STARTER: McCulloch, six position, automatic rewind starter is available.

COMPRESSION RELEASE: Button type for easy starting, button locks out when engine starts.

KILL SWITCH WIRE: Standard.

CLUTCH: Conventional types adaptable.

MOUNTING: Four bolt holes provided on the P.T.O. side and four bolt holes on the bottom of crankcase. Engine operates in any position.

List price, USA, $220·00.

Top: MC 101B. Centre: MC 92. Bottom: MC 49E

NORTHROP CORPORATION, VENTURA DIVISION

HEAD OFFICE AND MAIN PLANT:
   1515 Rancho Conejo Boulevard, Newbury Park, California 91320
TELEPHONE:
   (805) 498-3131

In 1972 Northrop Corporation acquired the rights to this engine from McCulloch Corporation. The 4318 series continues to be made and sold by Ventura Division, which uses the engine to power the MQM-36 Shelduck.

Model 4318F

TYPE: Four-cylinder horizontally-opposed air-cooled two-stroke.
CYLINDERS: Bore $3\frac{3}{16}$ in (80·8 mm). Stroke $3\frac{1}{8}$ in (79·4 mm). Displacement 100 cu in (1·6 litres). Compression ratio 7·8 : 1. Heat-treated die-cast aluminium cylinders with integral heads, having hard chrome plated cylinder walls. Self-locking nuts secure cylinders to crankcase studs.
PISTONS: Heat-treated cast aluminium. Two rings above pins. Piston pins of case-hardened steel.
CONNECTING RODS: Forged steel. "Free-roll" silver-plated bearings at big-end. Small-end carries one needle bearing. Lateral position of rod controlled by thrust washers between piston pin bosses and small-end of rod.
CRANKSHAFT: Four-throw one-piece steel forging on four anti-friction bearings, two ball and two needle, one with split race for centre main bearing.
CRANKCASE: One-piece heat-treated perm-anent-mould aluminium casting, closed at rear end with cast aluminium cover which provides mounting for magneto.
VALVE GEAR: Fuel mixture for scavenging and power stroke introduced to cylinders through crankshaft-driven rotary valves and ported cylinders.
INDUCTION: Crankcase pumping type. Diaphragm-type carburettor with adjustable jet.

Northrop Model 4318F 4-cylinder, horizontally opposed 2-stroke

FUEL SPECIFICATION: Grade 100/130 aviation fuel mixed in the ratio 20 parts fuel with one part 40SAE two-cycle outboard motor oil (or 30 parts fuel to one part Super Red oil).
IGNITION: Single magneto and distributor. Directly connected to crankshaft through impulse coupling for easy starting. Radio noise suppressor included. BG type RB 916S, AC type 83P or Champion REM-38R spark plugs. Complete radio shielding.
LUBRICATION: Oil mixed with fuel as in conventional two-stroke engines.
PROPELLER DRIVE: RH tractor. Keyed taper shaft.

STARTING: By separate portable hydraulic starter.
MOUNTING: Three mountings lugs provided with socket for rubber mounting bushings.
DIMENSIONS:
Length	27·0 in (686 mm)
Width	28·0 in (711 mm)
Height	15·0 in (381 mm)

WEIGHT, DRY
   Less propeller hub   77lb (34·9 kg)
POWER RATING:
   Rated output: 84-96 hp at 4,100 rpm
SPECIFIC CONSUMPTION:
   Fuel/oil mixture   0·90 lb (0·408 kg)/hp/hr

ROCKETDYNE DIVISION
ROCKWELL INTERNATIONAL

HEAD OFFICE:
   6633 Canoga Avenue, Canoga Park, California 91304
EXECUTIVES:
   Hal Oquist, Director of Waterjet Propulsion Programmes
John Lauffer, Programme Manager, Powerjet 16, 20, 24 Programme

The technology gained in the design and manufacture of high-performance pumps for the US space programme has enabled Rocketdyne to develop a new family of waterjet propulsion systems, called Powerjet 16, 20 and 24. These propulsion systems employ advanced-design, axial-flow pumping elements to produce a compact, lightweight waterjet propulsor. Simplicity of design minimises the number of components necessary in the units, while allowing accessibility for servicing or replacement of seals and bearings. All system components, which are designed to meet American Bureau of Shipping requirements, have been built in materials selected for their resistance to cavitation damage, and seawater and galvanic corrosion.

Rockwell 20s power the six Boeing Jetfoils currently in service. On each Jetfoil, dual PJ20s, each driven by a Detroit Diesel

Powerjet 20, designed for hydrofoils and high-speed craft with diesels and gas-turbines developing up to 3,700 hp. Pump flow rate is 23,150 gpm

Allison 501-K20 gas-turbine rated at 3,500 horsepower, deliver a 22,000-gallon-per-minute water flow.

Jetfoils operate regularly at a cruising speed of 45 knots in 12-foot seas to transport inter-island commuters in the Hawaiian chain, and passengers between Hong Kong and Macao.

The six vessels in service have carried 560,000 passengers over 26 million passenger miles, during which the Powerjet 20 units have logged in excess of 17,000 pump hours.

Another new vessel to employ Rocketdyne Powerjets is the American Enterprise, the world's first turbine/waterjet-powered fast offshore crew and supply boat, which has achieved speeds in excess of 35 knots during trials. Power is supplied by two Powerjet 16 waterjet pumps driven by Detroit Diesel Allison Model 16V-92T engines, developing 860 shp each, and one Powerjet 24 pump on the centreline driven by a Detroit Diesel Allison Model 501-KF gas-turbine, rated at 5,430 hp maximum output. The aluminium-hulled American Enterprise is designed to carry 60-90 passengers and up to 30 long tons of high priority cargo at speeds not previously associated with conventional planing hull crew/supply boats.

POWERJET 20
TYPE: Single-stage, axial-flow

APPLICATION: Designed for hydrofoils and high-speed craft at 3,500 hp and medium- to high-speed craft at lower horse-power. Two Powerjet 20 propulsion units, each of which is driven by an Allison 501-K20A gas-turbine through a 6·37:1 reduction gearbox, power the Boeing 929 Jetfoil, 106-ton, 45-knot passenger-carrying hydro-foil. In this application, the gearbox is used in conjunction with an over/under con-figuration, which results in a compact installation. Input horsepower to the gear-box is 3,700 at 13,250 rpm.

ACCESSORY DRIVE: For the Boeing Jetfoil, Powerjet 20 is coupled to a gearbox that provides two pads for accessory drive. The first pad supplies power for the boat's hydraulic system, while the second directs power to gearbox, pump, and turbine lubrication and scavenge pump.

PRIME MOVERS: Diesels and gas-turbines up to 3,700 horsepower.

LUBRICATION SYSTEM: External re-circulating supply, with 2·5- to 3·5-gpm flow

Powerjet 16, single-stage axial-flow waterjet pump for diesels and gas turbines developing between 700 and 1,500 hp

at 55 to 70 psi provided by a gerotor-type pump that contains both pressure and scavenge cavities.

LUBE OIL GRADE:
 MIL-L-23699
 MIL-L-2106
 Diesel crankcase oil—API (D Series)
 Automobile differential oil—API (M Series)
SPECIFICATION:

Operating range		
Input horsepower		3,500
Input shaft speed		2,080 rpm
Total inlet head	26 feet at	2,080 rpm
Pump flowrate		23,150 gpm
Propulsion pump weight:		
Dry		1,712 lb
Wet		2,326 lb

*4,300 horsepower also available.

Powerjet 24 designed for inputs of 4,000-5,000 hp. Pump flow rate at 30 knots is 45.000 gph

POWERJET 16

TYPE: Single-stage, axial-flow.

APPLICATION: Designed for high propulsive efficiency at moderate speeds in all types of hull configurations.

PRIME MOVERS: Diesels and gas-turbines developing between 700 and 1,500 hp. Three inducer trims are available for direct coupling to most marine diesels.

LUBRICATION SYSTEM: Integrated recirculating system.

LUBE OIL GRADE:

MIL-L-23699

MIL-L-2105

Diesel crankcase oil—API (D Series)

Automobile differential oil—API (M Series)

SPECIFICATION:

Operating Range:

	Trim Number		
	1	2	3
Maximum horsepower, up to	1,500	1,137	1,010
Input horsepower*	1,025	900	800
Input shaft speed, rpm	2,000	2,100	2,100
Total inlet head, feet, as low as	35	31	28
Pump flowrate (at 30 knots), gpm	17,800	16,200	15,300
Propulsion pump weight:			
Dry			1,950 lb
Wet			2,200 lb
Steering vector			±22 degrees
Reverse thrust	50% of forward gross thrust to a maximum of 1,025 hp		

*Direct drive

POWERJET 24

TYPE: Single-stage, axial-flow.

APPLICATION: Designed for high-propulsive efficiency at moderate speeds.

PRIME MOVERS: Diesels and gas turbines developing up to 5,000 hp.

LUBRICATION SYSTEM: External recirculating supply requiring 3·8 to 4·2 gpm flow at 55 to 70 psi.

Lube oil grade:

MIL-L-23699

MIL-L-2105

Diesel crankcase oil—API (D Series)

Automobile differential oil—API (M Series)

SPECIFICATION:

Operating range:

Input horsepower	4,000*
Input shaft speed	1,640 rpm
Total inlet head	43 feet at 1,640 rpm
Pump flowrate (at 30 knots)	45,000 gpm
Propulsion pump weight	
Dry	3,900 lb
Wet	4,800 lg
Steering vector	±22 degrees
Reverse thrust	50% of forward gross thrust to a maximum of 1,330 hp

* 5,000 hp also available

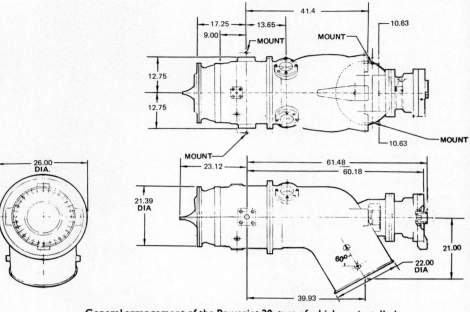

General arrangement of the Powerjet 20, two of which are installed on the Boeing Jetfoil

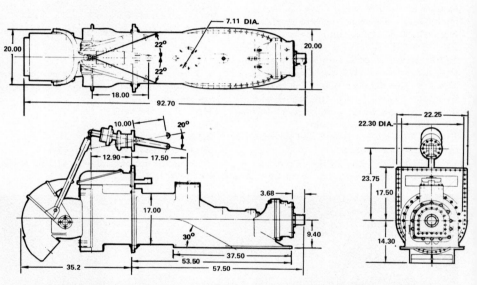

The Powerjet PJ16, for diesels and gas-turbines delivering between 700 and 1,500 shp

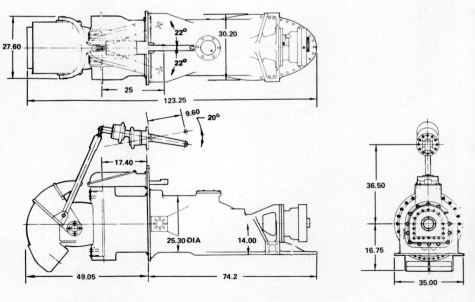

The Powerjet PJ 24 for diesels and gas-turbines developing up to 5,000 shp

SCORPION INC.

HEAD OFFICE:
Crosby, Minnesota 56441
TELEPHONE:
(218) 546-5123
PROJECT ENGINEER: Chuck Srock

Scorpion Inc. has purchased the JLO Division of Rockwell Manufacturing. The Company is now manufacturing and marketing the Cuyuna range of axial-fan cooled twin-cylinder engines, developing 29 hp-40 hp.

The engines are serviced through a network of 2,000 independent service outlets and central distributors throughout the US and Canada.

CUYUNA AXIAL-FAN TWIN-CYLINDER ENGINES

Models 295, 340, 400 and 440

Features of this range include a standard mounting for all models to ease installation; low engine profile with built-in shrouding; lightweight construction to reduce overall vehicle weight and high interchangeability of all parts. Crankshafts, crank cases, blower assemblies, magnetos, recoil starters and hardware items are fully interchangeable, thus reducing spare parts inventory requirements and lowering maintenance costs. Specifications for the four standard productions are given in the accompanying table.

Type	Twin Cylinder Axial-Fan Cooled			
Model	295	340	400	440
Bore	2.185″	2.362″	2.559″	2.658″
Stroke	2.362″	2.362″	2.362″	2.362″
Displacement	290 cc	339 cc	389 cc	428 cc
Compression Ratio	12.5:1			
Maximum Torque	6500 R.P.M.			
Brake HP/rpm	29 HP 6500/7000 rpm	32 HP 6500/7000 rpm	38 HP 6500/7000 rpm	40 HP 6500/7000 rpm
Base Mounting Hole Thread	$\frac{7}{16}$—14 UNC			
Cylinder	Aluminium with Cast Iron Sleeve			
Connecting Rod Bearing Upper	Needle			
Connecting Rod Bearing Lower	Needle			
Connecting Rod Matl.	Forged Steel			
Main Bearing	4 Heavy Duty Ball Bearings (1 Dual Row Bearing, P.T.O.)			
Ignition	Bosch			
Lighting Coil	12 Volt, 150 Watt			
Contact Breaker Gap	.014″ to .018″			
Ignition Setting Before TDC	.102″ to .112″ (Cam Fully Advanced)			
Spark Plug Thread	14 × 1.25 mm $\frac{1}{2}$″ Reach			
Gap	.016″ to .020″			
Type	Bosch W-260-T-2 (or) Champion N-3			
Rotation	Counter-Clockwise Viewed From P.T.O. End			
Fuel-Oil Mixture	40:1 (1 pt to 5 gal)			
Lubrication	Premium Gasoline & Cuyuna 2 Cycle Engine Oil			
Carburettor Type	2 $\frac{15}{16}$″ Center to Center Bolt Dimension			
Starter	Rewind Type, Standard; Electric, Optional			
Rope Material	Nylon			
Weight	62 lbs.			

Horsepower ratings established in accordance with specification SAE-J 607.
Engines will produce no more than 78db when used with Cuyuna approved carburettor/muffler/intake silencer systems, according to SAE-J192 specification.

TURBO POWER AND MARINE SYSTEMS, INC

(Subsidiary of United Technologies Corporation)

HEADQUARTERS:
1690 New Britain Avenue, Farmington, Connecticut USA, 06032
TELEPHONE:
(203) 677-4081
EXECUTIVES:
Rolf Bibow, President, Power Systems Division
T. S. Melvin, Vice President and General Manager, TPM
A. B. Crouchley, Marketing Manager
R. F. Nordin, Manager, Domestic Sales
A. Hart, Director International Sales
D. G. Assard, Manager, Engineering Programmes
K. H. Truesdell, Manager, Systems Installation & Service

Turbo Power and Marine Systems, Inc. (TPM), a wholly owned subsidiary of United Technologies Corporation in its Power Systems Division, designs and builds industrial and marine gas turbine power plants and power plant systems. It also provides a continuing systems support for each of its installations.

Canadian sales of TPM gas turbines are handled by Pratt & Whitney Aircraft of

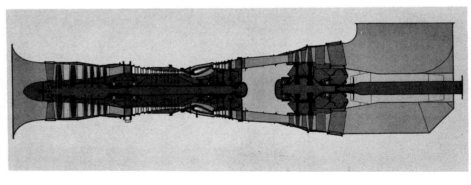

Cross-section of the TPM FT9 marine gas-turbine, rated at 33,000 shp at 100 deg F

Canada Limited, Post Office Box 10, Longueuil, Quebec, Canada, which also manufactures and handles the sales of the PWA of Canada ST6 marine gas turbine.

TPM's efforts have resulted in over 1,100 gas turbines supplied or ordered in the United States and in 20 other countries. The turbines will supply more than 30,000,000 horsepower for electric power generation, gas transmission and industrial drives as well as for marine propulsion.

TPM MARINE GAS TURBINES

Turbo Power and Marine Systems offers the FT4 48,800 shp gas turbines for marine propulsion.

TPM is also developing a new marine gas turbine under a US Navy contract. The design of the new gas turbine is based on the extensive operating experience of the TPM FT4 marine gas turbine and the Pratt & Whitney Aircraft JT9D fan jet engine. Designated the FT9, the new gas turbine will have an initial marine rating of 33,000 shp at 100°F with inlet and exhaust duct losses of 4 and 6 inches of water. Advantages of the new FT9 gas turbine will include modular construction for maintainability and low fuel consumption. Details of the FT9 are shown in the cross section illustration.

MARINE INSTALLATION

TPM FT4 marine gas turbines were first used for boost power in military vessels, including two Royal Danish Navy frigates, twelve US Coast Guard Hamilton Class high endurance cutters and four Canadian Armed Forces DDH-280 Iroquois Class destroyers. Another boost power application of the FT4 is in the Fast Escort and ASW vessel Bras d'Or also built for the Canadian Armed Forces. Another application is for two new 12,000 ton Arctic ice breakers for the US Coast Guard; the first of the new vessels, the Polar Star, has been commissioned and is the most powerful ice breaker in the world. With three TPM FT4 marine gas turbines, these vessels will be capable of maintaining a continuous speed of three knots through ice six feet thick, and will be able to ram through ice 21 feet thick.

TPM marine gas turbines are used for both the main and boost propulsion in the four new Canadian DDH-280 destroyers. These are the first military combatant vessels to be designed for complete reliance on gas turbine power. TPM marine gas turbines are also used in a military surface effect ship programme.

Four 32,000 ton container ships with TPM marine gas turbines are in trans-Atlantic service with Seatrain Lines. These vessels are Euroliner, Eurofreighter, Asialiner and Asiafreighter.

Another commercial vessel where TPM FT4 gas turbines will be used as the main propulsion unit is the FINNJET, a high speed Finnlines passenger liner being built by the Wartsila Shipyard in Helsinki for service in the Baltic Sea.

TPM MARINE POWER PAC

The photograph shows a TPM FT4 marine gas turbine completely packaged as a marine power pac ready for installation, with the minimum of interface connections to be made. Each is built upon a rigid mounting frame and includes a housing and gas turbine mounting system, together with controls, accessory equipment, wiring and piping. A remote control system is also provided. Installation is simple. Since all the equipment is pre-tested at the factory before shipment, time required for checkout after installation is minimised.

The gas generator portion of the gas turbine is easily removed for servicing. With a spare gas generator to replace the one removed for servicing, the ship's power plant can undergo major maintenance without tieing longer than necessary for a normal turn-around at dock.

The FT4 gas turbine comprises the gas generator and one power (free) turbine. The independent power turbine accepts the kinetic energy of the gas generator and converts it to mechanical energy through a shaft which extends through the exhaust duct elbow.

GAS GENERATOR

TYPE: Simple cycle two spool turbine engine. A low pressure compressor is driven by a two stage turbine and a high pressure compressor is driven by a single turbine. The burner section has eight burner cans which are equipped with duplex fuel nozzles.
AIR INTAKE: Fabricated steel casing with 18 radial struts supporting the front compressor bearing and equipped with a hot bleed air anti-icing system.

TPM Marine Power Pac with an FT4 gas turbine

Current production model of the FT4 marine gas-turbine, rated at 48,800 shp maximum intermittent and 39,000 shp normal output

LP COMPRESSOR: Nine stage axial flow on inner of two concentric shafts driven by two stage turbine and supported on ball and roller bearings.
HP COMPRESSOR: Seven stage axial flow on outer hollow shaft driven by single stage turbine and running on ball and roller bearings.
COMBUSTION CHAMBER: Eight burner cans located in an annular arrangement and enclosed in a one piece steel casing. Each burner has six duplex fuel nozzles.
TURBINES: Steel casing with hollow guide vanes. Turbine wheels are bolted to the compressor shafts and are supported on ball and roller bearings. A single stage turbine drives the high compressor and a two stage turbine drives the low compressor.
POWER TURBINE: The gas turbine is available with either clockwise or counterclockwise rotation of the power turbine. Desired direction of rotation specified by customer. Power turbine housing is bolted to gas generator turbine housing. The three stage turbine shaft assembly is straddle mounted and supported on ball and roller bearings. The output shaft is bolted to the hub of the power turbine rotor and extends through the exhaust duct.
BEARINGS: Anti-friction ball and roller bearings.
ACCESSORY DRIVE: Starter, fluid power pump, tachometer drives for low compressor, high compressor and free turbine.

LUBRICATION SYSTEM: Return system and scavenge pumps with internal pressure (45 psi)

LUBRICATING OIL SPECIFICATIONS: Type 2 synthetic lube oil PWA-521 MIL-L-23699.

MOUNTING: Horizontal 5 degrees nose up or nose down. 15 degrees either side of vertical. Momentary inclination for periods of 10 seconds; pitch 10 degrees nose up or down and up to a 45 degrees either side of vertical.

STARTING: Pneumatic or hydraulic.

DIMENSIONS:

Length	338 ins
Width	96 ins
Height	115 in

FUEL SPECIFICATIONS:
Light Distillate (Naphtha)   PWA-532(1)
Aviation Grade Kerosene
                      PWA-522(1) MIL-T-5624

PERFORMANCE DATA: FT4 MARINE GAS TURBINE

Rating	Power Output (1)	Special Fuel Consumption (2)
Max Intermittent	48,800 shp	0·42 lb (192 gr)/shp-hr
Max Continuous	44,250 shp	0·42 lb (192 gr)/shp-hr
Normal	39,000 shp	0·43 lb (196 gr)/shp-hr

(1) All ratings at 3,600 rpm shaft speed, 59°F and sea level.
(2) Based on fuel with LHV of 18,500 Btu/lb

OIL CONSUMPTION: 0·4 gal. (1·82 litres)/hr max as measured over a 10-hour period. 0·1 gal. (0·45 litres)/hr service operation avg.

Marine Diesel
                      PWA-527(1) MIL-F-16884
Heavy Distillate
                      PWA-539 MIL-F- 24376(2)
                      or
                      MIL-F-24397(3)

(1) Covered by TPM-FR-1 for series engine
(2) Navy distillate fuel, referee
(3) Navy distillate fuel

UNION OF SOVIET SOCIALIST REPUBLICS

A. IVCHENKO

The design team headed by the late general designer Ivchenko is based in a factory at Zaporojie in the Ukraine, where all prototypes and pre-production engines bearing the "AI" prefix are developed and built. Chief designer is Lotarev and chief engineer Tichienko. The production director is M. Omeltchenko.

First engine with which Ivchenko was associated officially was the 55 hp AI-4G piston-engine used in the Kamov Ka-10 ultra-light helicopter. He later progressed via the widely used AI-14 and AI-26 piston-engines, to become one of the Soviet Union's leading designers of gas-turbines engines.

Two AI-20s in de-rated, marinised form and driving two 3-stage waterjets power the Burevestink, the first Soviet gas-turbine hydrofoil to go into series production, and a single AI-24 drives the integrated lift/propulsion system of the Sormovich 50 passenger ACV.

IVCHENKO

AI-20

Ivchenko's design bureau is responsible for the AI-20 turboprop engine which powers the Antonov An-10, An-12 and Iluyshin Il-18 airliners and the Beriev M-12 Tchaika amphibian.

Six production series of this engine had been built by the Spring of 1966. The first four series, of which manufacture started in 1957 were variants of the basic AI-20 version. They were followed by two major production versions, as follows.

AI-20K. Rated at 3,945 ehp. Used in Il-18V, An-10A and An-12.

AI-20M. Uprated version with T-O rating of 4,190 ehp (4,250 ch e). Used in Il-18D/E, An-10A and An-12.

Conversion of the turboprop as a marine power unit for hydrofoil waterjet propulsion (as on the Burevestnik) involved a number of changes to the engine. In particular it was necessary to hold engine rpm at a constant level during conditions of varying load from the waterjet pump—and it was also necessary to be able to vary the thrust from the waterjet unit from zero to forward or rearwards thrust to facilitate engine starting and vessel manoeuvring.

A 1,750 hp Ivchenko AI-23-CI marine gas-turbine

Constant speed under variable load was achieved by replacing the engine's normal high pressure fuel pump with a special fuel regulator pump—and the waterjet pump was modified to have a variable exit area and was fitted with an air valve enabling a variable amount of air to be passed into the intake just ahead of the pump rotor. With less air passing through the waterjet, unit load on the engine increased, and vice versa if the air flow was increased by opening the air valve.

The fuel regulator pump was designed to maintain engine rpm constant and to regulate output while the AI-20 was driving the waterjet unit. Steady running conditions were shown to be satisfactorily maintained by the engine under all operating conditions—and rpm and turbine temperature were held within the limits laid down for the aircraft turboprop version: engine rpm did not fluctuate outside ±2·5 per cent of its set speed when loading or unloading the waterjet unit.

During development of the marinised AI-20, the normal aircraft propeller and speed governor were removed and the turboprop was bench tested over the full range of its operating conditions. This demonstrated that the engine performed in a stable manner throughout, from slow running to normal rpm. These tests were run initially using aviation kerosene Type TS-1 fuel, and then

diesel fuels Types L and DS.

Following satisfactory results on the bench, the test engine was mounted on a self-propelled floating test bed equipped with a waterjet propulsion unit. Further tests with this configuration were also satisfactorily concluded, including starting checks with varying degrees of submersion of the pump section of the waterjet unit.

Electrical starting of the engine up to slow running speed (equal to approximately 25 per cent of rated rpm) was shown to take 70 to 85 seconds. For starting and ignition at ambient conditions below 10°C, fuel preheating is employed, and modified igniters are fitted. With this equipment, starts have been achieved down to —12°C.

Based on this experience, the marinised AI-20 for the twin-engined Burevestink was rated at 2,700 hp at 13,200 rpm. At this power output, the hydrofoil achieved speeds of up to 60 mph (97 km/hr). Specific fuel consumption was 0·71 to 0·73 lb (320-330 gr)/hp/hr.

Testing with the Burevestnik revealed a number of operating characteristics of the vessel: when the two AI-20s were running while the vessel was moored or manoeuvring, residual exhaust thrust from the turbines occurred and this is required to be balanced by a negative, or reverse thrust from the waterjet by partially closing the unit's nozzle flaps. This increased the load on the engine however, and caused a rise in fuel consumption.

Also, experience showed that with a normal start following a series of wet starts, any fuel which has accumulated in the jet pipe became ignited. This resulted in a sharp rise in turbine temperature and back pressure, and flame emerged from the ejection apertures into the engine compartment and exhaust nozzle. To circumvent this, the ejection apertures were covered with a metal grid, and a spray of water is provided at the exhaust nozzle prior to starting.

Based on an overhaul life for the turboprop AI-20 of several thousand hours, special techniques have been applied to the marinised version to increase its service life. These include the use of high quality assembly procedures for the engine, efficient design of the air intake and exhaust duct, adoption of appropriate procedures for starting and on-loading of the main and auxiliary turbines at all ambient temperature conditions—and by the utilisation of highly-skilled servicing methods of the installation during operation.

The AI-20 is a single-spool turboprop, with a 10-stage axial-flow compressor, cannular combustion chamber with ten flame tubes, and a three-stage turbine, of which the first two stages are cooled. Planetary reduction gearing, with a ratio of 0·08732 : 1, is mounted forward of the annular air intake. The fixed nozzle contains a central bullet fairing. All engine-driven accessories are mounted on the forward part of the compressor casing, which is of magnesium alloy.

The AI-20 was designed to operate reliably in all temperatures from —60°C to +55°C at heights up to 33,000 ft (10,000 m). It is a constant speed engine, the rotor speed being maintained at 21,300 rpm by automatic variation of propeller pitch. Gas temperature after turbine is 560°C in both current versions. TBO of the AI-20K was 4,000 hours in the Spring of 1966.

WEIGHT (Dry):
AI-20K   2,380 lb (1,080 kg)
AI-20M   2,290 lb (1,039 kg)

PERFORMANCE RATINGS:
  Max T-O:
  AI-20K   3,945 ehp (4,000 ch e)
  AI-20M   4,190 ehp (4,250 ch e)
Cruise rating at 390 mph (630 kmh) at 26,000 ft (8,000 m):
  AI-20K   2,220 ehp (2,250 ch e)
  AI-20M   2,663 ehp (2,700 ch e)

SPECIFIC FUEL CONSUMPTION:
  At cruise rating:
  AI-20K   0·472 lb (215 gr) hp/hr
  AI-20M   0·434 lb (197 gr) hp/hr

OIL CONSUMPTION:
  Normal   1·75 Imp pints 1 litre/hr

IVCHENKO
AI-24

In general configuration, this single-spool turboprop engine, which powers the An-24 transport aircraft, is very similar to the earlier and larger AI-20. Production in 1960 and the following data refer to engines of the second series, which were in production in the Spring of 1966.

A single marinized version, developing 1,800 shp, drives the integrated lift/propulsion system of the Sormovich 50-passenger ACV.

An annular ram air intake surrounds the cast light alloy casing for the planetary reduction gear, which has a ratio of 0·08255 : 1. The cast magnesium alloy compressor casing carries a row of inlet guide vanes and the compressor stator vanes and provides mountings for the engine-driven accessories. These include fuel, hydraulic and oil pumps, tacho-generator and propeller governor.

The 10-stage avial-flow compressor is driven by a three-stage axial-flow turbine, of which the first two stages are cooled. An annular combustion chamber is used, with eight injectors and two igniters.

The engine is flat-rated to maintain its nominal output to 11,500 ft (3,500 m). TBO was 3,000 hours in the Spring of 1966.

DIMENSIONS:
  Length overall   95·87 in (2,435 mm)
WEIGHT, Dry: 1,100 lb (499 kg)
PERFORMANCE RATING:
  Max T-O with water injection
                        2,820 ehp (2,859 ch e)

SUDOIMPORT

ADDRESS:

ul. Kaliaevskaja, 5, Moscow K-6, USSR

Russian industry has developed a variety of marine diesel engines, selected models of which have been installed in the Krasnoye Sormovo series of hydrofoil craft. Most popular of these are the 1,100 hp M401 powering the Kometa hydrofoil, and the 1,200 hp M50 powering the Byelorus, Chaika, Meteor, Mir, Raketa, Sputnik, Strela and Vikhr hydrofoils. A third marine diesel engine is the 3D12 with a continuous rating of 300 hp. A version of this engine is installed in the Nevka hydrofoil, now in series production in Leningrad.

These and other marine diesels are available through Sudoimport, USSR marine export, import and repair organisation.

TYPE M 400

TYPE: Water-cooled, 12-cylinder, V-type four-stroke supercharged marine diesel engine.

CYLINDERS: Two banks of six cylinders set at 30°, each bank comprising cast aluminium alloy monobloc with integral head. Pressed-in liner with spiral cooling passages comprises inner alloy steel sleeve with nitrided working surface, and outer carbon steel sleeve. Each monobloc retained on crankcase by 14 holding-down studs. Bore 7·09 in. (180 mm). Stroke 7·87 in (200 mm). Cubic capacity 381 cu in (62·4 litres). Compression ratio 13·5 : 1.

SUPERCHARGING: Single-stage centrifugal supercharger, mechanically driven and providing supercharging pressure of at least 22 lb/in² (1·55 kg/cm²) at rated power.

CRANKCASE: Two-part cast aluminium alloy case with upper half carrying cylinder monoblocs, and transmitting all engine loads.

Sudoimport M400

CYLINDER HEADS: Integral with cylinder monoblocs.

CRANKSHAFT: Six-crank seven-bearing crankshaft in nitrided alloy steel with split steel shells, lead bronze lined with lead-tin alloy bearing surface. Spring damper at rear end reduces torsional vibrations.

CONNECTING RODS: Master and articulated rods, with master connected to crankshaft by split big end with lead bronze lining. Articulated rods connected by pin pressed into eye of master rods.

PISTONS: Forged aluminium alloy with four rings, upper two of which are of trapeziform cross-section. Alloy steel floating gudgeon pin. Piston head specially shaped to form combustion chamber with spherical cylinder head.

CAMSHAFTS: Two camshafts acting direct on valve stems.

VALVES: Four valves in each cylinder, two inlet and two exhaust. Each valve retained on seat by three coil springs.

COOLING: Forced circulation system using fresh water with 1·0 to 1·1 per cent potassium bichromate added. Fresh water pump mounted on forward part of engine. Fresh water, and lubricating oil leaving the engine are cooled by water-to-water and water-to-oil coolers, in turn cooled by sea water circulated by engine-mounted sea water pump.

SUPERCHARGING: Single-stage centrifugal supercharger, mechanically driven and providing supercharging pressure of at least 22 lb/in² (1·55 kg/cm²) at rated power.

LUBRICATION: Comprises delivery pump together with full-flow centrifuge; twin-suction scavenge pump, double gauze-type strainers at inlet and outlet to oil system; and electrically-driven priming pump to prime engine with oil and fuel.

FUEL INJECTION: Closed-type fuel injection with hydraulically-operated valves, giving initial pressure of 2,845 lb/in² (200 kg/cm²). Each injector has eight spray orifices forming 140° conical spray. High pressure 12-plunger fuel injection pump with primary gear pump. Two filters in parallel filter oil to HP pump.

STARTING: Compressed air system with starting cylinder operating at 1,067 to 2,134 lb/in² (75 to 150 kg/cm²), two disc-type air distributors and 12 starting valves.

GOVERNOR: Multi-range indirect-action engine speed governor with resilient gear drive from pump camshaft. Governor designed to maintain pre-set rpm throughout full speed range from minimum to maximum.

EXHAUST SYSTEM: Fresh water-cooled exhaust manifolds fastened to exterior of cylinder blocs. Provision made for fitting thermocouple or piezometer.

REVERSING: Hydraulically-operated reversing clutch fitted to enable prop shaft to run forwards, idle or reverse with constant direction of crankshaft rotation.

MOUNTING: Supports fitted to upper half of crankcase for attaching engine to bedplate.

DIMENSIONS:

Width	48·03 in (1,220 mm)
Height	49·21 in (1,250 mm)
Length	102·36 in (2,600 mm)

PERFORMANCE RATINGS:

Max	1,100 hp at 1,800 rpm
Continuous	1,000 hp at 1,700 rpm

FUEL CONSUMPTION:
At continuous rating
Not over 0·425 lb (193 gr)/hp/hr

OIL CONSUMPTION:
At continuous rating
Not over 0·013 lb (6 gr)/hp/hr

TYPE 3D12

TYPE: Water-cooled, 12-cylinder, V-type, four-stroke marine diesel engine.

CYLINDERS: Two banks of six cylinders in jacketed blocks with pressed-in steel liners. Bore 5·9 in (150 mm). Stroke 7·09 in (180 mm). Cubic capacity 237 cu in (38·8 litres). Compression ratio 14 to 15 : 1.

CRANKCASE: Two-part cast aluminium alloy case with upper half accommodating seven main bearings of steel shell, lead bronze lined type. Lower half carries oil pump, water circulating pump and fuel feed pump.

CYLINDER HEADS: Provided with six recesses to accommodate combustion cham-

Sudoimport 3D12

bers. Each chamber is connected via channels to inlet and outlet ports of cylinder bloc.

CRANKSHAFT: Alloy steel forging with seven journals and six crankpins. Pendulum anti-vibration dampers fitted on first two webs to reduce torsional vibration.

CONNECTING RODS: Master and articulated rods of double-T section forged in alloy steel. Master rod big-end bearings have steel shells, lead bronze lined. Small end bearings of master rods and both bearings of articulated rods have bronze bushes.

PISTONS: Aluminium alloy.

CAMSHAFTS: Carbon steel camshafts with cams and journals hardened by high frequency electrical current.

COOLING: Closed water, forced circulation type incorporating centrifugal pump, self suction sea water pump and tubular water cooler.

LUBRICATION: Forced circulation type with dry sump, incorporating three-section gear pump, oil feed pump, wire-mesh strainer with fine cardboard filtering element and tubular oil cooler.

FUEL INJECTION: Rotary fuel feed pump, twin felt filter, plunger fuel pump with device to stop engine in event of oil pressure drop in main line. Closed-type fuel injectors with slotted filters. Plunger pump carries variable-speed centrifugal governor for crankshaft rpm.

STARTING: Main electrical starting system, with compressed air reserve system.

REVERSE-REDUCTION GEAR: Non-co-axial type with twin-disc friction clutch; and gear-type reduction gear giving optional ratios, forwards, of 2·95 : 1, 2·04 : 1 or 1·33 : 1, and 2·18 : 1 astern.

DIMENSIONS:

Width	41·42 in (1,052 mm)
Height	45·63 in (1,159 mm)
Length	97·01 in (2,464 mm)

WEIGHT, Dry:

Fully equipped	4,189 lb (1,900 kg)

PERFORMANCE RATING:

Continuous	300 hp at 1,500 rpm

FUEL CONSUMPTION:
At continuous rated power
0·388 lb (176 gr)/hp/hr

OIL CONSUMPTION:
At continuous rated power
Not over 0·02 lb (9 gr)/hp/hr

M401A

The M401A, fitted to the new Voskhod and the latest variants of the Kometa and Raketa, is based on the M50. The new engine is more reliable than its predecessor and its development involved the redesigning of a number of units and parts, as well as the manufacturing of components with a higher degree of accuracy, which necessitated the employment of the latest engineering technique.

The engine is manufactured in left hand and right hand models. These differ by the arrangement on the engine housing of the fresh water pump drive and the power take-off drive for the shipboard compressor.

TYPE: Water-cooled, 12-cylinder, V-type four-stroke supercharged marine diesel.

CYLINDERS: Two banks of six cylinders set at 60°. Monobloc is a solid aluminium casting. Pressed into monobloc are six steel sleeves with spiral grooves on the outer surface for the circulation of cooling water. Bore, 7·09 in (180 mm), Stroke, 7·87 in (200 mm). Compression ratio: 13·5 : 0·5.

CRANKCASE: Two piece cast aluminium alloy case with upper half carrying cylinder monoblocs and transmitting all engine loads.

CYLINDER HEADS: Integral with cylinder monobloc.

CRANKSHAFT: Six-crank, seven bearing crankshaft in nitrided alloy steel with split steel shells, lead-tin bronze lined with lead tin alloy bearing surface.

CONNECTING RODS: Master and articulated rods, with master connected to the crankshaft by split big end, lined with lead tin bronze. Articulated rod connected to crankshaft by a pin pressed into its eye ring.

PISTONS: Forged aluminium alloy with five rings. Top two steel rings, one cast iron of rectangular section and the two bottom rings, in cast iron and steel, are oil control rings fitted in a common groove.

CAMSHAFTS: Two, acting directly on valve stems.

VALVES: Four in each cylinder, two inlet

and two exhaust. Each retained on seat by three coil springs.

SUPERCHARGING: Two, Type TK-18H superchargers, each comprising an axial-flow turbine and a centrifugal compressor mounted on a common shaft with a vane diffuser and volute. A silencer can be installed on the compressor air inlet. Turbine casing cooled with fresh water from the diesel engine cooling system.

GOVERNOR: Multi-range indirect action engine speed governor with resilient gear drive from pump camshaft. Designed to maintain pre-set rpm throughout full speed range.

LUBRICATION: Delivery pump with full-flow centrifuge, scavenge pump, double gauge strainers and electrically driven priming pump to power engine with oil and fuel.

COOLING: Double-circuit forced circulation system using fresh water with 1·0 to 1·1% potassium bichromate to GOST2652-71. Fresh water pump mounted on engine. Fresh water and lubricating oil leaving engine are cooled by water-to-water and water-to-oil coolers in turn cooled by sea water circulated by engine-mounted sea water pump.

STARTING: Compressed air system with two disc-type air distributors and twelve starting valves.

REVERSING: Hydraulically operated reversing clutch to enable propeller shaft to

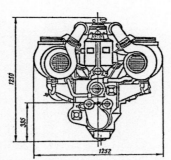 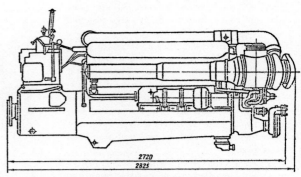

M401A water cooled 12-cylinder, V-type four-stroke supercharged marine diesel

run forwards, idle or reverse. Manual control available in emergency.

Rated power at ahead running under normal atmospheric conditions and at rated rpm, hp	1,000
Rated rpm at ahead running	1,550
Maximum hourly power at maximum rpm, hp	1,100
Maximum rpm at ahead running	1,600
Maximum power at astern running	250
Minimum rpm at astern running (with the diesel engine control lever at reverse stop)	750
Maximum specific fuel consumption at rated power (with operating generator, hydraulic pump and the power take-off for compressor), g/e.h.p.hr	172 + 5%
Maximum specific oil burning losses at rated power, g/e.h.p.hr	5

Fuel

Diesel fuel Grade (GOST 4749—49) Oil MC-20 (GOST 4749—49) with additive (GOST 8312-57) 3% in weight

Sense of power take-off flange rotation (if viewed from turbo-supercharger):

of R.H. diesel engine	clockwise
of L.H. diesel engine	counter-clockwise
Operating life (until major overhaul) hrs.	2,500

Diesel engine dimensions, mm

Length	2,825*/2,720**
Width	1,252
Height	1,250
Weight (dry) with all units and pipe lines mounted, kg	2,000

*With muffler at intake
**Without muffler at intake

A SELECTED
BIBLIOGRAPHY

A SELECTED BIBLIOGRAPHY

AIR CUSHION VEHICLES

ACVs IN NORTH AMERICA
ACV Icing Problems, J. R. Stallabras and T. R. Ringer, National Research Council, Seventh Canadian Symposium on Air Cushion Technology, June 1973.

ACV potential in New York, Leedham, C. (New York City Commissioner for Marine and Aviation) Hoverfoil News, Vol 5, No 6, March 14th 1974.

Aircushion Technology in Canada, 1975, National Research Council of Canada, report NRC Associate Committee on Air-Cushion Technology, 1975.

Air Cushion Technology: the Prospects for Canadian Industry, Dr P. A. Sullivan, Institute for Aerospace Studies, University of Toronto. Sixth CASI Symposium on Air Cushion Technology, Ontario, June 1972.

Air-Cushion Vehicles, Operational use in the Arctic, Ives, G, Petroleum Eng., Vol 45 No 1, January 1974.

Air Cushion Vehicles and Soil Erosion. P. Abeels, International Society for Terrain-Vehicle Systems 5th International Conference, Detroit, Houghton, Michigan, 2-6 June, 1975.

Arctic Development Using Very Large ACVs, J. L. Anderson, NASA Lewis Laboratories. Seventh Canadian Symposium on Air Cushion Technology, June 1973.

Arctic Operational Experience with SR.N6 engaged in Hydrographic Survey and Cushioncraft CC-7, L. R. Colby and G. M. Yeaton, Polar Continental Shelf Project, DEMR. Fourth Canadian Symposium on Air Cushion Technology, 1970. Canadian Aeronautics and Space Institute.

The Arctic Surface Effect Vehicle Program, Kordenbrock, J. V.. and Harry, C. W. 59th Annual Meeting of American Society of Naval Engineers, Washington DC, May, 1976.

Dynamic Performance of an Air-Cushion Vehicle in a Marine Environment, J. A. Fein, A. H. Magnuson and D. D. Moran (Naval Ship Research and Development Center, Bethesda, Md), AIAA/SNAME Advanced Marine Vehicle Conference, San Diego, California, February 25-28 1974.

Development of the Canadian Air-Cushion Vehicle Industry, R. G. Wade, (Ministry of Transport, Ottawa). AIAA/SNAME Advanced Marine Vehicle Conference, San Diego, California, 25-28 February 1974.

Effects of Hovrecraft Operation on Organic Terrain in the Arctic, Gunars Abele, US Army Cold Regions Research and Engineering Laboratory, Hovering Craft, Hydrofoil and Advanced Transit Systems Conference, Brighton May 1974.

Environmental Effects of ACV and other Off-Road Vehicle Operations on Tundra, G. Abele and W. E. Rickard, US Army Cold Region Research and Engineering Laboratory. Seventh Canadian Symposium on Air Cushion Technology, June 1973.

Heavy Goods Transport by Air-Cushion Vehicles. C. A. R. Eastman. The Society of Engineers Journal (UK) Vol. LXIV Nos 2 and 3, Apr/June and July/Sept. 1973.

Hovercraft Operations in the Arctic, the Activities of Voyageur 003 Between Hay River, Northwest Territories, Canada and Umiat, Alaska, N. Ray Sumner Jr, November 1974. Science Applications, Inc 1651 Old Meadow Road, McLean, Virginia 22101, USA.

Icebreaking with Air-Cushion Technology, Report National Research Council of Canada, NRC Associate Committee on Air-Cushion Technology, 1975.

Improvements in Ice-breaking by the use of Air Cushion Technology, R. G. Wade, R. Y. Edwards and J. K. Kim. Eastern Canada Section of SNAME Symposium Ice Tech 75, Montreal, 9-11 April 1975.

Marine Transportation and Air-Cushion Vehicles North of 60. L. R. Montpetit, Canadian Min. & Met. Bulletin. 68, January 1975. p 78-81.

Model Tests of an Arctic Surface Effect Vehicle over Model Ice, E. J. Lecourt, T. Kotras and J. Kordenbrock. Eastern Canadian Section of SNAME Ice Tech 75 Symposium, Montreal, 9-11 April 1975.

NCTL's Voyageur Experience, B. Meade, Northern Transportation Co. Seventh Canadian Symposium on Air Cushion Technology June 1973.

Operational Evaluation of the SK-5 in Alaska, R. A. Liston and B. Hanamoto, US Army Cold Region Research and Engineering Laboratory. Seventh Canadian Symposium on Air Cushion Technology, June 1973.

Requirements for a Canadian ACV Industry, R. G. Wade, Hovermarine (Canada) Ltd, June 1969. Third Canadian Symposium on Air Cushion Technology, Canadian Aeronautics and Space Institute, SC 2.00.

Small Air Cushion Vehicle Operation on Floating Ice under Winter Condition, R. J. Weaver and R. O. Romseier, Dept of the Environment. Seventh Canadian Symposium on Air Cushion Technology. June 1973.

AIR CUSHION LANDING SYSTEMS
ACLS for a commercial transport, T. D. Earl, (Textron Bell Aerospace). Society of Automotive Engineers Meeting 30 April-2 May 1974.

Air-Cushion Landing Systems Development on a Buffalo Aircraft, C. J. Austin. (The De Havilland Aircraft Co of Canada Ltd) CASI Flight Test Symposium, Edmonton, Alberta, 12-13 March 1975.

Elastically Retracting ACLS Trunks, T. D. Earl. (Textron Bell Aerospace). Canadian Aeronautics and Space Journal, Vol 21 No 5 May 1975. p 169-173

Further Developments in Surface Effect Take-Off and Landing System Concepts, A. E. Johnson, F. W. Wilson and W. B. Maguire, NSRDC. Sixth CASI Symposium on Air Cushion Technology. Ontario, June 1972.

Landing on a Cushion of Air, J. H. Brahney, (Wright Patterson Air Force Base), Astronautics & Aeronautics, pp 58-61, February 1976.

The Potential of an Air Cushion Landing Gear in Civil Air Transport, T. D. Earl, Bell Aerosystems Co. Second Canadian Symposium on Air Cushion Technology, 1968. Canadian Aeronautics and Space Institute, $C 2.00.

AIR CUSHION LOAD CARRIERS
A 1,000-ton River Hovercraft, R. A. Shaw, V. E. Barker and D. M. Waters, Hoverprojects Ltd, Hovering Craft, Hydrofoil and Advanced Transit Systems Conference, May, 1974.

Aircraft Recovery, G. M. Parkes, Hovertrailers International Ltd, Hovering Craft, Hydrofoil and Advanced Transit Systems Conference, Brighton, May 1974.

Air Cushion Towed Raft Evaluation Project—Current Trials, J. E. Laframboise, Transportation Development Agency. Seventh Canadian Symposium on Air Cushion Technology, June 1973.

An Amphibious Hover Platform for Civil Engineering uses, D. G. W. Turner, Mackace Ltd. Hovering Craft, Hydrofoil and Advanced Transit Systems Conference, Brighton, May, 1974.

A track laying Air-Cushion Vehicle. R. Wingate Hill, (NSW Dept. of Agriculture, Agricultural Engineering Centre, Glenfield, NSW, Australia) in Journal of Terramechanics, pp 201-216, vol 12. No 3/4, 1975.

Development of a Track Laying Air Cushion Vehicle, J. R. Goulburn and R. B. Steven, University of Belfast. Hovering Craft, Hydrofoil and Advanced Transit Systems Conference, Brighton, May 1974.

Movement of Drill Rigs Using an Air Cushion Platform, R. L. Wheeler, British Hovercraft Corporation. Fourth Canadian Symposium on Air Cushion Technology, June 1970. Canadian Aeronautics and Space Institute.

Movement of Heavy Loads, L. A. Hopkins, Air Cushion Equipment Ltd, Seventh Canadian Symposium on Air Cushion Technology, June 1973.

On the Applications of Air Cushion Technology to Off-Road Transport, Dr J. Y. Wong, Carleton University. Sixth CASI Symposium on Air Cushion Technology, Ontario, June 1972.

River Crossing Problems Posed by the Mackenzie Highway and a Possible Solution, R. G. Wade, Canadian Ministry of Transport. Seventh Canadian Symposium on Air Cushion Technology, June 1973.

The Role of the Non-Self-Propelled Air Cushion Vehicle, L. A. Hopkins, Air Cushion Equipment Ltd. Sixth CASI Symposium on Air Cushion Technology, Ontario, June 1972.

Towed Air Cushion Rafts, J. Doherty, G. Morton and C. R. Silversides (National Research Council of Canada), NRC Associate Committee on Air-Cushion Technology, Ottawa, Canada, 1975.

AIR LUBRICATED HULLS
The Application of the Air Cushion Principle to Very Large Vessels -A Case for Further Research, J. W. Grundy, Naval Architect. Hovering Craft, Hydrofoil and Advanced Transit Systems Conference, Brighton, May 1974.

COMMERCIAL OPERATION
A Successful Operation, E. Jones. (Hoverlloyd Ltd). Second

International Hovering Craft & Hydrofoil Conference, May, 1976, Amsterdam

Air Cushion Vehicles in the Gulf Offshore Oil Industry: A Feasibility Study, J. M. Pruett, (Louisiana State University, Baton Rouge). Final Report on Sea Grant Project (NOAA Contract 04-3-158-19), December 1973.

Air Cushion Vehicles in the Search and Rescue Role, Commander B. W. Mead, Canadian Coast Guard, June 1969. Third Canadian Symposium on Air Cushion Technology, Canadian Aeronautics and Space Institute, $C 2.00.

Air Cushion Vehicles in Support of the Petroleum Industry, Wilfrid J. Eggington, Donald J. Iddins, Aerojet-General Corporation. American Petroleum Institute Meeting: Shreveport, Louisiana. March 1969.

Commercial Operation of Hovercraft, J. Lefeaux BR Seaspeed, Second International Hovering Craft & Hydrofoil Conference, May 1976, Amsterdam.

ACV PROJECTS

ACV Technology Programs at Aerojet-General, R. W. Muir, Aerojet-General Corporation, June 1969. Third Canadian Symposium on Air Cushion Technology, Canadian Aeronautics and Space Institute, $C 2.00.

Control of a Single Propeller Hovercraft, with Particular Reference to BH7, R. L. Wheeler, British Hovercraft Corporation Ltd. Fourth Canadian Symposium on Air Cushion Technology, June 1970. Canadian Aeronautics and Space Institute.

Development of Surface Effect Technology in the US Industry, John B. Chaplin, Bell Aerospace Company. AIAA/SNAME/USN Advanced Marine Vehicles Meeting, Annapolis, Maryland, July 17-19, 1972.

New Advanced Design ACVs, Jean Bertin, Bertin et Cie. Third Canadian Symposium on Air Cushion Technology, June 1969. Canadian Aeronautics and Space Institute, $C 2.00.

Operational Experience on VT1s, R. D. Hunt, Hovercraft Division, Vosper Thornycroft Ltd. Institute of Production Engineers, Second International Hovercraft Conference, April 1971.

The VT.2 100-ton Amphibious Hovercraft, A. Bingham, Vosper Thornycroft Ltd, Second International Hovering Craft & Hydrofoil Conference, May, 1976 Amsterdam.

Voyageur Trials and Operating Experience, T. F. Melhuish, Bell Aerospace, Canada. Seventh Canadian Symposium on Air Cushion Technology, June 1973.

DESIGN

A Comparison of Some Features of High-Speed Marine Craft, A. Silverleaf and F. G. R. Cook, National Physical Laboratory. Royal Institution of Naval Architects, March 1969.

A Linearised Potential Flow Theory for the Motions of Air-Cushion Vehicles in a Seaway, T. K. S. Murthy, Portsmouth Polytechnic. Ninth Symposium on Naval Hydrodynamics, Paris, August 1972.

A method for the preliminary sizing of Lift Fan Systems, Applicable to Large Hovercraft, W. B. Wilson, Webb Institute of Naval Architecture, Glen Cove, New York. Naval Ship Engineering Center of the US Navy, Propulsion Systems Analysis Branch, Technical Report no 6144E-75-126. February 1975.

A Theoretical Note on the Lift Distribution of a Non-Planar Ground Effect Wing, T. Kida and Y. Miyai, (University of Osaka Prefecture, Japan). The Aeronautical Quarterly, Vol 24. August 1973. Part 3.

Development of the Axial-flow Surface Effect Vehicle, A. M. Jackes, AirSeamobile Co, Santa Ana, Calif. Advanced Marine Vehicle meeting AIAA/SNAME/USN, Annapolis, July 1972.

FANS

Aerodynamic Challenges for the Faster Interface Vehicles, P. R. Shipps, Rohr Corporation. Sixth CASI Symposium on Air Cushion Technology, Ontario, June 1972.

The Design of a Ram Wing Vehicle for high speed ground Transportation, E. A. Tan, E. I. Dupont Co., W. P. Goss and D. E. Cromack, University of Massachusetts, Amherst. International Conference on High Speed Ground Transportation, Arizona State University, 7-10 January 1975, Tempe, Arizona.

The Design, Fabrication and Initial Trials of a Light Amphibious Arctic Transporter, J. H. Kennedy and A. M. Garner, Jr, Transportation Technology Inc. Fourth Canadian Symposium on Air Cushion Technology, 1970. Canadian Aeronatics and Space Institute.

Lateral Stability of a Dynamic Ram Air Cushion Vehicle, P. V. Aidala. Transportation Systems Center, Cambridge, Mass. DOT-TSC-FRA-74-6. FRA-ORD/D-75-6. PB-236-516/1WT. August

1974. 72p.

A Method for Generating Aerodynamic Sideforces on ACV Hulls, Dr R. J. Kind, Carleton University. Sixth CASI Symposium on Air Cushion Technology, Ontario, June 1972.

On the Determination of the Hydrodynamic Performance of Air-Cushion Vehicles, S. D. Prokhorov, V. N. Treshchevski, L. D. Volkov, Kryloff Research Institute, Leningrad. Ninth Symposium on, Naval Hydrodynamics, Paris, August 1972.

On the Prediction of Acceleration Response of Air-Cushion Vehicles to Random Seaways and the Distortion Effects of Cushion Inherent in Scale Models, D. R. Lavis and R. V. Bartholemew, Aerojet-General Corporation Advanced Marine Vehicle meeting, AIAA/SNAME/USN, Annapolis, July 1972.

Ram-Wing Surface Effect Boat, Capt R. W. Gallington, USAF, US Air Force Acadamy, Colorado, Advanced Marine Vehicle Meeting AIAA/SNAME/USN Annapolis, July 1972.

Resultats d'Exploitation des Aeroglisseurs Marins "Naviplane", M. P. Guienne, Bertin et Cie. Seventh Canadian Symposium on Air Cushion Technology, June 1973.

Some Aspects of Optimum Design of Lift Fans, T. G. Csaky, NSRDC. Sixth CASI Symposium on Air Cushion Technology, Ontario, June 1972.

Some Design Aspects of Air Cushion Craft, Peter J. Mantle, International Congress of Subsonic Aeronautics, New York Academy of Sciences, April 1967.

Some Design Aspects of an Integrated Lift/Propulsion System, D. Jones, Jones, Kirwan and Associates. Sixth CASI Symposium on Air Cushion Technology, Ontario, June 1972.

Trade-Off Methodology for Evaluation of Design Alternatives of Air Cushion Vehicles, O. Gokcek and J. H. Madden, Aerojet General Corporation. Sixth CASI Symposium on Air Cushion Technology, Ontario, June 1972.

Vortex Shedding from the Ram Wing Vehicle, Technical Progress Report, R. Gallington. (Air Force Acadamy, Colorado) Jan-July 1973. AD-767234. August 1973. Available N. T. I. S.

Design and Operation of Centrifugal, Axial-flow and Crossflow fans. Translated from German, Edited by R. S. Azad and D. R. Scott, Pergamon Press 1973.

EXTERNAL AERODYNAMICS

The External Aerodynamics of Hovercraft, Professor E. J. Andrews College of Aeronautics, Cranfield. Royal Aeronautical Society Rotorcraft Section, April 1969.

INDUSTRIAL APPLICATIONS

Hoverpallets for Material Handling, A. J. I. Poynder, British Hovercraft Corporation. Institution of Production Engineers, International Hovercraft Conference, April 1968.

Industrial Applications of Air Cushion Technology, P. H. Winter, Air Vehicle Developments Ltd, June 1969. Third Canadian Symposium on Air Cushion Technology, Canadian Aeronautics and Space Institute, C 2.00.

LIGHTWEIGHT ACVs

Amphibious Hovercraft: The Little Ones are growing up, M. A. Pinder, Pindair Ltd. Article in "Hovering Craft & Hydrofoil". pp 5-9, vol 14, No 9 June, 1975.

Control and Guidance of Light Amphibious Hovercraft up to a Gross Weight of 5,000 lbs, R. L. Trillo, Robert Trillo Ltd. Seventh Canadian Symposium on Air Cushion Technology, June 1973.

Small Hovercraft Design, P. H. Winter, Air Vehicle Developments. International Hovercraft Conference, 1968, the Institution of Production Engineers (Southampton Section).

Small Hovercraft Structure, A. J. English, Sealand Hovercraft Ltd, Hovering Craft, Hydrofoil and Advanced Transit Systems Conference, Brighton, May 1974.

MILITARY APPLICATIONS and OPERATING EXPERIENCE

ACV Military Applications—Experience and Potential, J. B. Chaplin Bell Aerosystems Company, June 1969. Third Canadian Symposium on Air Cushion Technology, Canadian Aeronautics and Space Institute, $C 2.00.

Air Cushion Vehicles in a Logistical Role, Col H. N. Wood (Ret), US Army Combat Development Command Transportation Agency. Fourth Canadian Symposium on Air Cushion Technology, 1970. Canadian Aeronautics and Space Institute.

BH.7 Mk 2—Experience during the first 2,000 hours of Operation, Cdr L. G. Scovell, Dept of Trade and Industry, UK. Seventh Canadian Symposium on Air Cushion Technology, June 1973.

Development of the SR.N6 Mk 5 Vehicle-carrying Hovercraft, Major M. H. Burton, Dept of Trade and Industry, UK. Seventh

Canadian Symposium on Air Cushion Technology, June 1973.
Military Experience, Commander D. F. Robbins, RN, Interservice Hovercraft Unit. International Hovercraft Conference, April 1968. The Institution of Production Engineers (Southampton Section).
Military Hovercraft, R. Old, British Hovercraft Corporation Ltd, Second International Hovering Craft & Hydrofoil Conference, May 1976, Amsterdam.
A Review of British Army Hovercraft Activity 1967-72, Major G. G. Blakey, Royal Corps of Transports. Sixth CASI Symposium on Air Cushion Technology, Ontario, 1972.
Some Military Applications of Small Hovercraft, G. W. Shepherd, SAS Developments Ltd, Second International Hovering Craft & Hydrofoil Conference, May 1976, Amsterdam.
UK Military Hovercraft, Commander N. T. Bennett, AFC, RN, Interservice Hovercraft Unit. Second International Hovercraft Conference, Institute of Production Engineers, April 1971.
US Army ACV Operations, Major D. G. Moore, US Army Air Cushion Vehicle Unit, June 1969. Third Canadian Symposium on Air Cushion Technology, Canadian Aeronautics and Space Institute, $C 2.00.

LEGISLATION and REGULATIONS
The Air Registration Board and Hovercraft, S. Gardner, Air Registration Board, June 1968, Second Canadian Symposium on Air Cushion Technology, Canadian Aeronautics and Space Institute, $C 2.00.
Canadian Air-Cushion Vehicle Legislation and Regulation, J. Doherty, Ministry of Transport Canada, Paper presented to Ninth Canadian Symposium on Air Cushion Technology, Ottowa, October, 1975.
Lloyd's Register's Requirements for ACVs, A. K. Buckle, Lloyd's Register of Shipping. Second Canadian Symposium on Air Cushion Technology, June 1968. Canadian Aeronautics and Space Institute, $C 2.00.
Operating Legislation for ACVs, Captain J. Doherty, Department of Transport, June 1968. Second Canadian Symposium on Air Cushion Technology. Canadian Aeronautics and Space Institute, $C 2.00.
United States Requirements for Commercial Surface Effect Ships, W. A. Cleary Jr and Lt D. H. Whitten, US Coast Guard. Second Canadian Symposium on Air Cushion Technology, June 1968. Canadian Aeronautics and Space Institute, $C 2.00.

POWERPLANTS
The Selection of the Optimum Powerplant for the Air Cushion Vehicle, R. Messet, United Aircraft of Canada Ltd. Fourth Canadian Symposium on Air Cushion Technology, June 1970. Canadian Aeronautics and Space Institute.
Some Aspects of Free Turbine Engine Hovercraft Control, W. Bloomfield, T. B. Lauriat, AVCO Corporation Lycoming Division. Institute of Production Engineers, Second International Hovercraft Conference, April 1971.

PRODUCTION
Hovercraft from a Shipbuilder, A. E. Bingham, Vosper Thornycroft Ltd., Hovering Craft, Hydrofoil and Advanced Transit Systems Conference, Brighton, May 1974.
The Production of Air Cushion Vehicles, E. F. Gilberthorpe, British Hovercraft Corporation. Institution of Production Engineers (Southampton Section), International Hovercraft Conference, April 1968.

RESEARCH and DEVELOPMENT
Air Appraisal of Present and Future Large Commercial Hovercraft, R. L. Wheeler, British Hovercraft Corporation Ltd., Paper presented to Naval Institution of Naval Architects, October, 1975.
CAA Paper 75017, Report of the ARB Special Committee on Hovercraft Stability and Control, Civil Aviation Authority, London, 1975.
Conceptual Study for a new Winged Surface Effect Vehicle System, J. H. McMasters and R. R. Greer, Naval Engineers Journal, 86 April 1974. p 41-51.
A Decade of Development—The SR.N6 Family of Hovercraft R. L. Wheeler, British Hovercraft Corporation, Hovering Craft, Hydrofoil & Advanced Transit Systems Conference, Brighton, May 1974.
Development of Hovermarine Transport Vehicles, E. G. Tattersall, Hovermarine Transport Ltd. Institute of Production Engineers, Second International Hovercraft Conference, April 1971.
The Development of Marine Hovercraft with special reference to the Construction of the N500., Guienne, M. (SEDAM). Second International Conference Transport-Expo, Paris, 15-20 April 1975.

Development of the Hovergem Range of Commercial Air Cushion Vehicles, G. L. Green, Hovergem Australasia Pty Ltd, Institute of Production Engineers. Second International Hovercraft Conference, April 1971.
The Drag of a Sidewall ACV over calm water, R. Murao, Ministry of Transport, Japan, Second International Hovering Craft Hydrofoil Conference, May, 1976, Amsterdam.
General Survey of the Studies and Testing Techniques that led to the definition of N500 Performance, G. Herrouin, and Y. Boccarodo, SEDAM, France. Second International Hovering Craft and Hydrofoil Conference, May 1976, Amsterdam.
Hovercraft Research and Development, R. L. Wheeler, British Hovercraft Corporation Ltd. Institute of Production Engineers, Second International Hovercraft Conference, April 1971.
Investigation of the static lift capability of a Low-Aspect-Ratio Wing Operating in a powered ground-effect mode, J. K. Huffman, and C. M. Jackson, NASA TM X-3031. July 1974. 32p.
Minimum Induced Drag of a Semi-Circular Ground Effect Wing, H. Mamada. Aichi University of Education and S. Ando. Nagoya University, Japan. Journal of Aircraft, Vol 10 No 11, November 1973.
Recent Developments in Hovercraft Performance Testing, B. J. Russell, Interservice Hovercraft Unit, HMS Daedalus. Hovering Craft, Hydrofoil & Advanced Transit Systems Conference, Brighton May 1974.
Research and Development Work Associated with the Lift and Propulsion of Air Cushion Vehicles, J. G. Russell, Dowty Rotol Ltd, Hovering Craft, Hydrofoil & Advanced Transit Systems Conference, Brighton, May 1974.
Research into the Profitability of the Design and Construction of the N.500, P. Guienne. (SEDAM, France). Second International Hovering Craft & Hydrofoil Conference, May 1976, Amsterdam.
Response of Air:Cushion Vehicles to random seaways and tne inherent distortion in scale models., D. R. Lavis, R. J. Bartholomew, and J. C. Jones, Journal of Hydronautics, Vol 8, July 1974. p 83.
Some Aspects of Hovercraft Dynamics, J. R. Richardson, NPL Hovercraft Unit, Institution of Production Engineers, Second International Hovercraft Conference, April 1971.
Study of Materials and Nonmetallic coatings for erosion and wear resistance, G. Sertour, M. Armbruster, H. Bernard and P. Renard, Soc. Nationale Industrielle Aerospatiale, Paris. (In French). Association Technique Maritime et Aeronatique Bulletin No 74, 1974. p 357-367.

STRUCTURAL DESIGN
A Method of Testing Models of Hovercraft in Open Waters, Prof L. Koblinski and Dr M. Krezelewski, Ship Research Institute, Technical University of Gdansk. Institution of Production Engineers. Second International Hovercraft Conference, April 1971.

SYSTEMS
ACV Design Technology, J. B. Chaplin. Bell Aerosystems Co. Second Canadian Symposium on Air Cushion Technology, 1968 Canadian Aeronautics and Space Institute, $C 2.00.
An Accumulator Control System for Alleviating SES Craft Heave motions in waves, P. Kaplan and T. P. Sargent, Oceanics Inc, and James L. Decker, US Navy Surface Effect Ships Project Office, Washington DC. Advanced Marine Vehicle meeting AIAA/SNAME/USN. Annapolis, July 1972.
Airscrews for Hovercraft, G. K. Ketley, Hawker Siddeley Dynamics Ltd. Second Canadian Symposium on Air Cushion Technology, 1968. Canadian Aeronautics and Space Institute, $C 2.00.
Characterisation and Testing of Skirt Materials, Dr R. C. Tennyson and J. R. McCullough, University of Toronto, Institute for Aerospace Studies. Seventh Canadian Symposium on Air Cushion Technology, June 1973.
The Design and Operating Features of Vosper Thornycroft Skirts, R. Dyke. Vosper Thornycroft Ltd. Second International Hovering Craft & Hydrofoil Conference, May 1976, Amsterdam.
Deterioration of Hovercraft Skirt Components on Craft Operating over Water, M. D. Kelly, J. Morris & E. R. Gardner, Avon Rubber Co. Ltd., Hovering Craft, Hydrofoil and Advanced Transit Systems Conference, Brighton, May 1974.
Evolution of Integrated Lift, Propulsion and Control in the Aeromobile ACV, Dr W. R. Bertelsen, Bertelsen Manufacturing Co, June 1969. Third Canadian Symposium on Air Cushion Technology. Canadian Aeronautics and Space Institute, $C 2.00.
Experience of Using the Gas Turbine Engine for the Propulsion of the Fully Amphibious Air Cushion Vehicle, M. L. Woodward, Rolls-Royce (1971) Ltd. Sixth Canadian Symposium on Air Cushion

Technology, Ontario, June 1972.

The French Technique of Aeroglisseurs Marins, C. Marchetti, SEDAM. Second Canadian Symposium on Air Cushion Technology, June 1968, Canadian Aeronautics and Space Institute, $C 2.00.

Hovercraft Skirts, R. L. Wheeler, British Hovercraft Corporation, Hovering Craft, Hydrofoil and Advanced Transit Systems Conference, Brighton, May 1974.

The influence of Plenum Chamber Obstructions on the Performance of a Hovercraft Lift Fan, G. Wilson, Dr D. J. Myles and G. Gallacher, National Engineering Laboratory, June 1969. Third Canadian Symposium on Air Cushion Technology. Canadian Aeronautics and Space Institute, $C 2.00.

Jets, Props and Air Cushion, Propulsion Technology and Surfaces Effect Ships, Alfred Skolnick, Z. G. Wachnik, Joint Surface Effect Ships Program Office. Gas Turbine Conference and Products Show. The American Society of Mechanical Engineers, March 1968.

Pneumatic Power Transmission Applied to Hovercraft, J. F. Sladey Jr and R. K. Muench, United States Naval Academy and Naval Ship Research and Development Centre. Sixth CASI Symposium on Air Cushion Technology, Ontario, June 1972.

Power Transmission System of Hovercraft MV-PPI, MV-PP5 and MV-PP15, T. Yamada, O. Tamano, T. Morita, K. Horikiri, H. Hirasawa and M. Fujiwasa. Mitsui Shipbuilding & Engineering Co. Proc. International Symposium on Marine Engineering, Tokyo, Japan, 12-15 November 1973. Technical Paper Vol Ser 2-4, p. 13-23. Pub: Marine Engineers Society in Japan, Tokyo, 1973.

Skirt Design for Small Hovercraft, J. A. Eglen, National Association of ACV Enthusiasts, June 1969. Third Canadian Symposium on Air Cushion Technology. Canadian Aeronautics and Space Institute, $C 2.00.

Study of the Performance of a Partially Submerged Propeller, W. T. Lindemuth and R. A. Barr, Hydronautics Inc. Technical Report 760-1, July 1967.

Surface Effect Vehicle Propulsion: A Review of the State of the Art, J. B. Chaplin, R. G. Moore and J. L. Allison, Bell Aerospace, Sixth Canadian Symposium on Air Cushion Technology, Ontario, June 1972.

Water-Jet Propulsion, S. Kuether and F. X. Stora, Tamco Ltd US Army Mobility Equipment, R & D Center. Second Canadian Symposium on Air Cushion Technology, 1968. Canadian Aeronautics and Space Institute, $C 2.00.

Waterjet Propulsion for High Speed Surface Ships, P. Duport ,M. Visconte, J. Merle, SOGREAH. Ninth Symposium on Naval Hydrodynamics, Paris, August 1973.

SURFACE EFFECT SHIPS

American Surface Effect Ship Activities. E. K. Liberatore, Aeromar Corporation. Jane's Surface Skimmers System, Second Edition 1968-69. pp 210-212.

An Analysis of Desired Manoeuvring Characteristics of Large SEVs, W. Zeitfuss Jr and E. N. Brooks Jr, Naval Ship Research and Development Centre, Washington DC. Advanced Marine vehicle meeting, AIAA/SNAME/USN. Annapolis, July 1972.

Crew/Combat System Performance Requirements in the Operational Environment of Surface Effect Ships, A. Skolnick. Naval Engineers Journal, Vol 86 No 6, December 1974. p 15-32.

Current State-of-the-Art of Waterjet Inlet Systems for High Performance Naval Ships, R. A. Barr and N. R. Stark. Hydronautics Inc, Tech. Rep. 7224-5, December 1973.

Domain of the Surface Effect Ship, W. J. Eggington & N. Kobitz, Paper at Eighty-third Annual Meeting of SNAME, New York, November, 1975. Paper NB 11.

Large High Speed Surface Effect Ship Technology, P. J. Mantle Aerojet-General Corporation, Hovering Craft, Hydrofoil & Advanced Transit Systems Conference, Brighton, May 1974.

The Nuclear Powered Ocean-Going SES, E. K. Liberatore, Aeromar Corporation, Jane's Surface Skimmers, 1971-72.

Ocean-Going Surface Effect Ships, W. F. Perkins. Ocean Systems Div, Lockheed Missiles & Space Co, Sunnyvale, Ca. Northern California Section of SNAME and Golden Gate Section of ASNE Meeting at Treasure Island Naval Station, 1974.

On the Wave Resistance of Surface Effect Ships, J. C. Trotinclaux. Paper No 3 at the Eighty-third Annual Meeting of SNAME, New York, November, 1975.

Some Special Problems in Surface Effect Ships, Robert D. Waldo, Aerojet-General Corporation. Journal of Hydronautics. July 1968. American Institute of Aeronautics and Astronautics.

Study of Heave Acceleration/Velocity Control for the Surface Effect Ship, AD-009 302/1WT. U.S. Grant, Naval Postgraduate School, Montery, Cal. December 1974. 222pp.

Surface Effect Ship Habitability Familiarisation, W. F. Clement, and J. J. Shanahan. Systems Technology Inc, Interim Tech. Rep. STI-1041-1. November 1973.

The Surface Effect Ship in the American Merchant Marine, Final Report for the US Department of Commerce, Maritime Administration, Booz-Allen Applied Research Inc.

Surface Effect Ships for Ocean Commerce (SESOC), Final Report, February 1966. The SESOC Advisory Committee, Commerce Technical Advisory Board, US Department of Commerce, Washington DC.

Surface Effect Ships in the Surface Navy, R. C. Truax. US Navy Institute Proceedings, Vol 99 No 12/850. December 1973. p 50-54.

Transocean Surface Effect Ships, Dr A. Skolnik, Director of Technology, Surface Effect Ships Program Office. Proceedings of the IEEE Vol 56, No 4, 1968. Institute of Electrical and Electronics Engineers Inc.

TRACKED AIR CUSHION VEHICLES

Aerotrain Tridim for Urban Transportation, Jean Bertin and Jean Berthelot (Bertin & Cie and Soc. Aerotrain), Hovering Craft, Hydrofoil & Advanced Transit Systems Conference, Brighton, May 1974.

The Air-Cushion at High Speeds, F. Steiner. Societe de l'Aerotrain. Second International Conference Transport-Expo, Paris, 15-20 April 1975.

Applications du Coussin d'Air Aux Transports en Zones Urbaines, André Garnault, Société d l'Aérotrain, June 1973.

Canadian Research Activities Applicable to Tracked Levitated Vehicle Systems, P. L. Eggleton, Transportation Development Agency. Seventh Canadian Symposium on Air Cushion Technology, June 1973.

Current Collection for High-Speed Transit Systems, Messrs Appleton, Bartam, MacMichael & Fletcher, International Research & Development Co Ltd, Second International Hovering Craft & Hydrofoil Conference, May 1976, Amsterdam.

High Speed Ground Transportation, Documentation of Preliminary Engineering, Los Angeles International Airport and the San Fernando Valley, Kaiser Engineers, Los Angeles, California, April 1972.

The Invention and Development of a Suspended Air Cushion Passenger Transport System in France, Maurice Barthalon, ScM, MIT. The Inventor, Journal of the Institute of Patentees and Inventors, Vol 9, No 1, March 1969.

LIM—Suspension Interaction, J. H. Parker and R. J. Charles. Ministry of Transportation & Communications, Ontario, Second Intersociety Conference on Transportation, Denver, Colorado, September 23-27, 1973. ASME Paper No. 73-ICT-116.

Linear Propulsion by Electromagnetic River, Prof E. R. Laithwaite, Imperial College of Science and Technology, Hovering Craft, Hydrofoil & Advanced Transit Systems Conference, Brighton, May 1974.

Metrotran - 2,000, a study of future concepts in Metropolitan Transportation for the year 2,000, Robert A. Wolf. Final Report CAL Internally Supported Project, October 1967. Cornell Aeronautical Laboratory Inc, Cornell University, Buffalo, NY 14221.

A New Linear Air Turbine Vehicle—TACV, Dr Yau Wu, Virginia Polytechnic Institute and State University. Sixth CASI Symposium on Air Cushion Technology, Ontario, June 1972.

The Operational Performance and Economics of URBA, M. E. Barthalon and L. Pascual, Seturba, Hovering Craft, Hydrofoil and Advanced Transit Systems Conference, Brighton, May 1974.

The Pendair Suspension System, D. S. Bliss, Pendair Ltd, Hovering Craft, Hydrofoil and Advanced Transit Systems Conference, Brighton, May 1974.

Problems Poses à Propos des Technologies non Conventionnelles de Transports Rapide au Sol, Jean Bertin, President Directeur Général de la Société de l'Aérotrain, June 1973.

Status of "Transrapid" Development Programme. G. Winkel (Krauss-Maffei, Augsburg), Second Intercity Conference on Transportation, Denver, Colorado, September, 1973.

Tracked ACVs for Urban Applications, N. McQueen and H. R. Ross, Sverdrup & Parcel & Associates Inc, June 1969. Third Canadian Symposium on Air Cushion Technology. Canadian Aeronautics and Space Institute, $C 2.00.

Tracked Air-Cushion Research Vehicle Dynamics Simulation Program User's Manual Final Report, E. Magnani, R. Lee and R. Coppolino, Grumman Aerospace Corp, Bethpage, NY. PB-219 984/2. October 1972.

Tracked Air Cushion Vehicle Research and Development by the US Department of Transportation, A. F. Lampros and C. G. Swanson, Mitre Corporation. Hovering Craft, Hydrofoil and Advanced Transit Systems Conference, Brighton, May 1974.

Tracked Air-Cushion Vehicle Suspension Models: Analysis and

Comparison, D. P. Garg. Duke University, North Carolina and B. E. Platin. MIT, Cambridge. Vehicle System Dynamics (Holland) Vol 2, No 3, November 1973.

ACV PUBLICATIONS, BOOKS and GENERAL LITERATURE
GENERAL INTEREST
Hovercraft, B. Marshall, published by Muller
Hovercraft and Hydrofoils, Roy McLeavy, Blandford Press Ltd, Link House, West Street, Poole, Dorset BH15 1LL, 80pp col. £2·75.
Hovercraft & Hydrofoils Work Like This, Egon Larsen, Published by J. M. Dent.
The Hovercraft Story, Garry Hogg, Published by Abelard-Schuman.
Hydrofoils and Hovercraft, Bill Gunston, Published by Aldus Books.
Jane's Surface Skimmers (Annual) edited by Roy McLeavy, Published by MacDonald & Jane's.
This is the Hovercraft, Hugh Colver, Published by Hamish Hamilton.

TECHNICAL
Hovercraft Design and Construction, Elsley & Devereax. Published by David & Charles.
An Introduction to Hovercraft and Hoverports, Cross & O'Flaherty. Published by Pitman Publishing/Juanita Kalerghi.
Light Hovercraft Design Handbook, edited by Dave Waters. Published by Loughborough University.
Light Hovercraft Handbook, edited by Keith Oakley. Published by The Hover Club of Great Britain (available from G. Porter, 15 Watling Street, Dartford, Kent).
Marine Hovercraft Technology, Robert Trillo. Published by Leonard Hill Books.

HOVERCRAFT PERIODICALS
Air-Cushion and Hydrofoil Systems Bibliography Service, (bi-monthly) Published by Robert Trillo Ltd., Broadlands, Brockenhurst, Hants. SO4 7SX.
Air Cushion Review, (monthly) Published by Aristos Publications, 17 Southampton Road, Paulsgrove, Hants. PO6 4SA.
Hoverfoil News, (fortnightly) Published by Horizon Publications Ltd, Shoemaker's House, Montacute, Somerset TA15 6XQ.
Hovering Craft & Hydrofoil, (monthly) Published by Kalerghi Publications, 51 Welbeck Street, London W1M 7HE.
Light Hovercraft, (monthly) Published by The Hoverclub of Great Britain Ltd, 45 St Andrews Road, Lower Bemerton, Salisbury, Wilts.
UKHS Newsletter, (monthly) Published by The United Kingdom Hovercraft Society, Rochester House, 66 Little Ealing Lane, London W5 4XX.

SPECIAL INTEREST
The Law of Hovercraft, L. J. Kovats. Published by Lloyd's of London Press Ltd. 1975.

HYDROFOILS
BOOKS
Hydrofoils, Christopher Hook and A. C. Kermode. Sir Isaac Pitman & Sons Ltd, London,
Hydrofoil Sailing, A. J. Alexander, J. L. Grogono, Donald J. Nigg. 96 pages. Price £3·00. Kalerghi Publications, 51 Welbeck Street, London WIM 7HE.

PAPERS, ETC.
COMMERCIAL OPERATION
Die Antriebsanlagen von Schnellen Marinefahrzeugen und die Muglichkeit iher Verwendung auf Passágier-Tragflugelbooten, E. Faber, Supramar, Sonderdruck MTZ Motor-technische Zietschrift, published June 1968.
Future of the Commercial Hydrofoil, Baron H. von Schertel, Supramar. Meeting, Business Aspects of Hovercraft and Hydrofoils, London. May 1968.
Jetfoil Progress Report 2: Test and Commercial Service, B. Michael. Boeing Marine Systems, US. Second International Hovering Craft & Hydrofoil Conference, May 1976, Amsterdam.
Operational Experience with USSR Raketa Hydrofoils on the River Thames, H. Snowball. Hovermarine Transport Ltd. Second International Hovering Craft & Hydrofoil Conference, May 1976, Amsterdam.
Operating the PT150 Hydrofoil, J. Presthus. Johns Presthus Rederi. Second International Hovering Craft & Hydrofoil Conference, May 1976, Amsterdam.

Running and Maintenance of Supramar Hydrofoils in Hong Kong, D. Hay and N. J. Matthew, Institute of Marine Engineers, April 1970.
Safety, Reliability and Maintainability of Supramar Commercial Hydrofoils, Baron H. von Schertel, Supramar, 7th Reliability and Maintainability Conference, San Francisco, July 1968.
The US Gets Serious about Hydrofoils, R. B. Aronson, Machine Design, Vol 45 No 25, 18th October 1973.

DESIGN
Bau und Erprobung von Tragflugelbooten, A. Mattl, Supramar, Schweizerischer Technischer Verband, Uzwil, Aarau, 1968.
Bending Flutter and Torsional Flutter of Flexible Hydrofoil Struts, P. K. Beach, Y. N. Liu, US Naval Ship Research and Development Centre. Ninth Symposium on Naval Hydrodynamics, Paris, August 1972.
Canadian Advances in Surface Piercing Hydrofoils, N. E. Jeffrey and M. C. Eames, Defence Research Establishment, Atlantic, Dartmouth, Nova Scotia. Advanced Marine Vehicle Meeting. AIAA/SNAME/USN, Annapolis, July 1972.
A Comparison of Some Features of High-Speed Marine Craft, A. Silverleaf and F. G. R. Cook, National Physical Laboratory Royal Institute of Naval Architects, March 1969.
Design Optimization of Waterjet Propulsion Systems for Hydrofoils, R. P. Gill, M. S. Theseis, Massachusetts Institute of Technology, Cambridge, Mass., May 1972.
Flow Separation, Re-attachment and Ventilation of Foils with Sharp Leading Edge at Low Reynolds Number, R. Hecker, and G. Ober, Naval Ship Research & Development Center Report 4390, III. May 1974. 20pp.
A High-Speed Hydrofoil Strut and Foil Study, R. Wermter, and Y. T. Shen. Naval Ship Research & Development Center, Bethesda, Md. AIAA/SNAME Advanced Marine Vehicle Conference, San Diego, California, 25-28 February 1974. Paper 74-310.
Hydrodynamics and Simulation in the Canadian Hydrofoil Program, R. T. Schmitke and E. A. Jones Defence Research Establishment Atlantic, (Canada). Ninth Symposium on Naval Hydrodynamics, Paris, August 1972.
Hydroelastic Design of Sub-Cavitating and Cavitating Hydrofoil Strut Systems, Naval Ship Research & Development Center, Maryland, USA. NSRDC Report 4257. April 1974.
Hydrofoil Craft Designers Guide, R. Altmann, Hydronautics Inc, Technical Report 744-1, March 1968.
Laminar Boundary-Layer Induced Wave Forces on a Submerged Flat-Plate Hydrofoil, Journal of Hydronautics, Vol 8 No 2. April 1974. p 47-53.
Large Hydrofoil Ships Feasibility Level Characteristics, James R. Greco, Naval Ship Engineering Center, Hyattsville, Md. Advanced marine Vehicle meeting, AIAA/SNAME/USN, Annapolis, July 1972.
100 Passagier-Tragflugelboote mit schnellaufenden Dieselmotoren im Verkehr, E. Fabre, Supramar, Sonderdruck MTZ Motortechnische Zeitschrift, published November 1967.
Prospects for very High Speed Hydrofoils, A. Conolly. San Diego Section of the Society of Naval Architects and Marine Engineers/ The American Society of Navel Engineers joint meeting, 20 November 1974. Avail: Section Librarian, Cder R. Bernhardt, US Coast Guard, Code 240, Box 119, US Naval Station, San Diego, Ca. 92136.
Special Problems in the Design of Supercavitating Hydrofoils, G. F. Dobay and E. S. Baker Naval Ship Research & Development Center, Bethesda, Md. AIAA/SNAME Advanced Marine Vehicle Conference, San Diego, California, 25-28 February 1974. Paper 74-309.
Tragflugelschiff Supramar PT 150 DC, V. Jost (Schiff); E. Faber (Maschine); D. Cebulla (Tragflugel), Supramar. Sonderdruck aus Fachzeitschrift, "Schiff und Hafen", published May 1968.
Typhoon—A Seagoing Vessel on Automatically Controlled Submerged Foils, I. I. Baskalov and V. M. Burlakov, Sudostroyeniye. Hovering Craft & Hydrofoil. October 1972.
A Universal Digital Autopilot for a Hydrofoil Craft, Pierre Dogan and Frederick Gamber, MIT Advanced Marine Vehicle meeting, AIAA/SNAME/USN, Annapolis, July 1972.

NAVAL CRAFT
High Speed and US Navy Hydrofoil Development, D. A. Jewell, Naval Ship Research & Development Center, Bethesda, Md. AIAA/ SNAME Advanced Marine Vehicle Conference, San Diego, California, 25-28 February 1974. Paper 74-307.
HMCS Bras d'Or—Sea Trials and Future Prospects, M. C. Eames and T. G. Drummond, Defence Research Establishment Atlantic,

Canada. Royal Institution of Naval Architects, April 1972.
Military Hydrofoils, Baron H. Von Schertel, Dipl. Ing. Egon Faber, Dipl. Ing. Eugen Schatte, Supramar AG. Jane's Surface Skimmers, 1972-73.
The NATO PHM Programme, Cdr Karl M. Duff, USN, Naval Ship Systems Command, Washington DC. Advanced Marine Vehicle Meeting, AIAA/SNAME/USN, Annapolis, July 1972.
Operational and Development Experience on the US Navy Hydrofoil High Point, D. M. Petrie, The Boeing Company. AIAA/USN Marine Systems and ASW Conference. March 1965.
The Operational Evaluation of the Hydrofoil Concept in US Coast Guard Missions, R. E. Williams, US Coast Guard & Development Center. Second International Hovering Craft & Hydrofoil Conference, May 1976. Amsterdam.
PHM Hullborne Wave Tests, C. J. Stevens. Institute of Technology, Hoboken, New Jersey. Stevens Institute of Technology, Davidson Lab. Rep. R-1759, June 1974. 44pp.
Research on Hydrofoil Craft, Prof. Dr. Siegfried Schuster, Director Berlin Towing Tank. International Hydrofoil Society Winter Meeting, 1971. Hovering Craft and Hydrofoil, December, 1971.
The Role of the Hydrofoil Special Trials Unit (HYSTU) in the US Navy Hydrofoil Program, R. E. Nystrom, US Navy. Second International Hovering Craft & Hydrofoil Conference, May 1976, Amsterdam.
The "Swordfish" Type Hydrofoil Design Criteria and Operational Experience, M. Baldi, Cantiere Navali Riuniti, Italy, Second International Hovering Craft & Hydrofoil Conference, May 1976, Amsterdam.

SEAKEEPING CHARACTERISTICS
Prediction of the Seakeeping Characteristics of Hydrofoil Ships, Irving A. Hirsch, The Boeing Company. Paper 67-352 at the AIAA/SNAME Advanced Marine Vehicles Meeting, Norfolk Va, May 1967.

SYSTEMS
Heaving Motions of Ventilated Trapezoidal Hydrofoils, Tsen, L. F. and M. Guilbaud. (University of Poitiers, France). Fourth Canadian Congress of Applied Mechanics, CANCAM '73, 28 May— 1 June 1973. Ecole Polytechnique, Montreal
The Longitudinal Behaviour of a Hydrofoil Craft in Rough Seas, M. Krezelewki, Institute of Ship Research, Gdansk University, Hovering Craft, Hydrofoil and Advanced Transit Systems Conference, Brighton, May 1974.
On the Design of Propulsion Systems with Z-Drives for Hydrofoils Ships, A. A. Rousetsky, Kryloff Research Institute, Leningrad. Ninth Symposium on Naval Hydrodynamics, Paris, August 1972.

RESEARCH AND DEVELOPMENT
Air-Feed Stabilisation of Hydrofoil Craft, Baron H. von Schertel. Supramar. NATO, Brussels, September 1968.
Betriebserfahrungen mit der Antriebsanlage des Tragflugalschiffes PT 150, E. Faber, Supramar. Sounderdrunk aus MTZ Motortechnische Zeitschrift, published October 1968.
Control of the Hydrofoil Ship, Dr P. Magini and Dr J. Burroughs, Advanced Marine Systems—Alinavi SpA. Journal of the Institute of Navigation, July 1967.
Controls Technology in Hydrofoil Ship Design, J. J. Jamieson, The Boeing Company. Ship Control Systems Symposium, November 1966.
The Design of Waterjet Propulsion Systems for Hydrofoil Craft, J. Levy, Soc Naval Architects and Marine Engineers, Marine Technology, 2, 15-25 41, January 1965.
The Development of Automatic Control Systems for Hydrofoil Craft, R. L. Johnston & W. C. O'Neill, Naval Ship Research Development Centre, Bethesda, Maryland. Hovering Craft, Hydrofoil and Advanced Transit Systems Conference, Brighton, May 1974.
The Economics of an Advanced Hydrofoil System, A. M. Gonnella, W. M. Schultz, Hydrofoil Systems Organisation, The Boeing Company, Hovering Craft & Hydrofoil, November 1970.

The Effect of Nose Radius on the Cavitation Inception Characteristics of Two-Dimensional Hydrofoils, D. T. Valentine. Naval Ship Research & Development Centre Report 3813, VI. July 1974. 46 pp.
An Examination of the Hazards to Hydrofoil Craft from Floating Objects. Christopher Hook. Society of Environmental Engineers Symposium, The Transport Environment, April 1969.
Hydrodynamic Study on Fully Submerged Foils of Hydrofoil Ships in a Sea Way up to 140 kt at Constant Froude Number. Dr de Witt, Supramar. Hovering Craft and Hydrofoil, Vol 8, No 5, February 1969.
Key Problems Associated with Developing the Boeing Model 929-100 Commercial Passenger Hydrofoil, William Shultz, Boeing International Corporation. Hovering Craft, Hydrofoil and Advanced Transit Systems Conference, Brighton, May 1974.
50-knot Hydrofoils We Could Start Building Today, Gene R. Myers The Boeing Company, Aeronautics & Astronautics, June 1970.
The Large Commercial Hydrofoils and its limits in Size and Speed, H. von Schertel. SupramarAG. Second International Hovering Craft & Hydrofoil Conference, May 1976, Amsterdam.
Machinery of the PT 150 DC Hydrofoil, E. Faber, Supramar, Marine Engineer and Naval Architect, January 1968.
Model Resistance Data of Series 65 Hull Forms Applicable to Hydrofoils and Planing Craft, H. D. Holling and E. N. Hubble. Naval Ship Research & Development Center Report 4121, V. May 1974. 431p.
Nine Year's History of the Hitachi-Supramar Hydrofoil Boat, Hovering craft & hydrofoil, November 1970.
PGH Tucumcari: Successful Application of Performance Specification, Gene R. Myers, The Boeing Company, Naval Engineers Journal, June 1970.
Selection of Hydrofoil Waterjet Propulsion Systems, Ross Hatte and Hugh J. Davis, The Boeing Company. Journal of Hydronautics, Vol 1 No 1, 1967. American Institute of Aeronautics and Astronautics.
Stabilisierung von Tragflugelbooten durch Luftspeisung der Flugel, Baron H. von Schertel, Supramar. Tagung der Schiff bautechnischen Gesellschaft, Lucerne, June 5, 1968.
Survey of French Hydrofoil Programs (in French), J. L. Vollot, Bulletin de l'Association Technique Maritime et Aeronautique, No 72, 1972. pp 229-248.
Twenty Years of Hydrofoil Construction & Operation, L. Rodriquez, Cantiere Navaltecnica. Second International Hovering Craft & Hydrofoil Conference, May 1976, Amsterdam.
Waterjet Propulsion for Marine Vehicles, V. E. Johnson, Jr. AIAA Paper 64-306, 1964. American Institute of Aeronautics and Astronautics.
Waterjet Propulsion for Marine Vehicles, J. Traksel and W. E. Beck. AIAA Paper 65-245, 1965. American Institute of Aeronautics and Astronautics.

SAILING SKIMMERS
The Basic Mechanics of Sailing Surface Skimmers and their Future Prospects, Dr Jerzy Wolf, Aviation Institute, Warsaw. Hovering Craft & Hydrofoil, March 1972.
Hydrofoil Ocean Voyager "Williwaw", David A. Keiper, PhD, Hydrofoil Sailing Craft. Third AIAA Symposium on the Aero/Hydronautics of Sailing, November, 1971.
Hydrofoil Sailing, James Grogono, Hovering Craft, Hydrofoil and Advanced Transit Systems Conference, Brighton, May 1974.
A Self-Tending Rig with Feedback and Compass Course, C. Hook, Hovering Craft & Hydrofoil, Vol 14 no. 10, July 1975. pp 26-31.
Why Sailing Hydrofoils?—Christopher Hook. "Ancient Interface IV" Symposium, American Institute of Aeronautics and Astronautics, January 1973.

ACV AND HYDROFOIL
LICENSING AUTHORITIES

ACV and HYDROFOIL LICENSING AUTHORITIES

ARGENTINA
ACVs and Hydrofoils
Prefectura Naval Maritima
  Paseo Colon 533
  Buenos Aires.
  Argentina

AUSTRALIA
ACVs and Hydrofoils
Department of Transport
  Childers Street,
  Turner,
  Australian Capital Territory,
  Australia

AUSTRIA
ACVs and Hydrofoils
Bundesministerium für Handel,
  Gewerbe und Industrie,
  Stubenring 1,
  Vienna 1.
  Austria
  Telephone: 575655

BELGIUM
ACVs and Hydrofoils
Administration de la Marine et de la
  Navigation Interieure,
  30, Rue Belliard,
  B-1040 Bruxelles,
  Belgium
  Telephone: (02) 511 58 90

CANADA
ACVs and Hydrofoils
Chief of Air Cushion Vehicles, Marine Safety
  Division, Ministry of Transport
  Sir Richard Scott Building
  191 Laurier Avenue,
  W. Ottawa,
  Canada

DENMARK
ACVs
Handelsministeriet,
  3 Atdeling,
  Slotsholmsgade 12,
  1216 Copenhagen K,
  Denmark.
Hydrofoils
Generaldirektoratet for Statsbanerne,
  Solvgade 40
  1349 Copenhagen K,
  Denmark.

EIRE
ACVs and Hydrofoils
Department of Transport and Power,
  Kildare Street,
  Dublin 2,
  Eire

FIJI
ACVs and Hydrofoils
Director of Marine,
  Marine Department,
  Suva,
  Fiji.

FINLAND
Board of Navigation,
  Vuorimiehenkatu 1,
  PO Box 158,
  SF-00141 Helsinki 14

FRANCE
ACVs and Hydrofoils
Secrétariat Générale de la Marine Marchande
  3 Place de Fontenoy,
  75700 Paris
  Telephone: (1) 783 40 90
  Telex: 25 823 Minimar Paris

GAMBIA
ACVs and Hydrofoils
Ministry of Works and Communications
  Bathurst,
  Gambia

GERMANY
Hydrofoils and ACVs
See-Berufsgenossenschaft,
  Ships Safety Department,
  Reimerstwiete 2,
  D 2000 Hamburg 11

GHANA
The Shipping Commissioner
  Ministry of Transport and Communications
  PO Box M.38, Accra, Ghana

HELLENIC REPUBLIC
ACVs and Hydrofoils
Ministry of Mercantile Marine,
  Mechant Ships Inspection Service,
  Palaiologou 1 str,
  Piraeus, Greece

HUNGARY
ACVs only
Ministry of Foreign Trade,
  1880 Budapest,
  Honvéd u. 12-15, Hungary

ICELAND
Directorate of Shipping,
  PO Box 484,
  Reykjavik,
  Iceland

INDIA
ACVs and Hydrofoils
Directorate-General of Shipping,
  Bombay,
  India

INDONESIA
ACVs and Hydrofoils
Departemen Perhubungan
  Medan Merdeka, Barat 8,
  Jakarta,
  Indonesia

ISRAEL
ACVs and Hydrofoils
Ministry of Transport,
  Division of Shipping and Ports
  102, Ha'atzmauth Road,
  Haifa,
  Israel

ITALY
ACVs and Hydrofoils
Ministero Della Marina Mercantile,
  Ispettorato Tecnico,
  Viale Asia,
  00100 Roma.

IVORY COAST
ACVs and Hydrofoils
Ministère des Travaux Publics et des Transports,
  B.P. V6,
  Abidjan,
  Republic of the Ivory Coast

JAMAICA
The Collector General's Department,
Newport East.
Kingston,
Jamaica

JAPAN
ACVs and Hydrofoils
Japanese Ministry of Transportation,
  2-1 Kaoumigaseki,
  Chiyoda-ku,
  Tokyo,
  Japan.

KHMER REPUBLIC
(Formerly Cambodia)
ACVs and Hydrofoils
Ministère des Travaux Publics,
  Phnom-Penh,
  Khmer Republic

KUWAIT
ACVs and Hydrofoils
Department of Customs and Ports,
  PO Box 9, Kuwait,
  Arabian Gulf.

LEBANON
ACVs and Hydrofoils
Ministère des Travaux Publics,
  Direction des Transports,
  Beirut, Lebanon.

LUXEMBOURG
AVCs
  Ministère des Transports,
  19-21 Boulevard Royal,
  Luxembourg.
  Telephone: 2 19 21

MALAGASY REPUBLIC
ACVs and Hydrofoils
  Ministère de l'Amina,
  Jement du Territoire,
  Anosy,
  Tananarive,
  Madagascar

MALAWI
The Ministry of Transport and Communications
  Private Bag 322,
  Capital City,
  Lilougwe 3,
  Malawai

MALAYSIA
The Ministry of Communications,
  Jalan Gurney,
  Kuala Lumpur,
  Malaysia
  Telephone: 20 4044
  Cables: Transport

MEXICO
ACVs and Hydrofoils

Departamento de Licencias,
  Direccion de Marina Mercante,
  Dr Mora No 15, 3er Piso,
  Mexico 1, DF

MOROCCO
Ministère des Travaux Publics
  Rabat,
  Morocco

NETHERLANDS
ACVs and Hydrofoils
Directoraat-Generaal van Scheepvaart,
  Afdeling Scheepvaartinspectie,
  Noord-West Buitensingel 2,
  's-Gravenhage (The Hague),
  Netherlands.

NEW ZEALAND
ACVs and Hydrofoils (Certificates of Construction and Performance)
Operating approval and licences:
  Ministry of Transport,
  Marine Division,
  Private Bag,
  Wellington 1,
  New Zealand

NORWAY
ACVs and Hydrofoils
Norwegian Maritime Directorate,
  Thv. Meyersgt 7,
  PO Box 8123,
  Oslo 1,
  Norway.

SOUTH AFRICA
Department of Transport,
  Private Bag X193,
  Pretoria 0001,
  South Africa

SOUTH KOREA
Ministry of Transportation,
  1-3 Do-dong,
  Choong-ku,
  Seoul,
  Republic of Korea

SPAIN
ACVs and Hydrofoils
The Subsecretaria de la Marina Mercante,
  Ruiz de Alarcon No. 1,
  Madrid 14.

SWEDEN
ACVs and Hydrofoils
The National Board of Shipping and Navigation,
  Sjöfartsverket,
  Fack,
  S-601 01 Norrköping,
  Telephone 011/10 84 00

SWITZERLAND
Cantonal licensing authorities for ACVs and Hydrofoils

Lake Zurich
Seepolizei/Schiffahrts Kontrolle des Kautons
  Zürich Seestrasse 87,
  8942 Oberrieden, Switzerland

Seepolizei-und Gewässerschutzkommissariat
  der Stadt Zurich,
  Bellerivestrasse 260,
  8008 Zurich, Switzerland.

Lake Constance
Polizeidepartement des Kantons Thurgau,
  Regierungsgebaude,
  8500 Frauenfeld.
  Polizeidepartement des Kantons St Gallen
  Schiffahrts- und Hafenverwaltung,
  9400 Rorschach

Lake Lucerne
Polizeidepartement des Kantons, Luzern,
  Bahnhofstrasse 17,
  6000 Luzern, Switzerland.

Lake Geneva
Department de Justice et Police Service de
  la Navigation
  Place Bourg-de-Four 1,
  1200 Geneva, Switzerland
Departement de la Justice,
  de la Police et des affaires militaire,
  Service de la police administrative,
  Place Chateau 6,
  1000 Lausanne, Switzerland

Lake Lugano
Ufficio cantonale de polizia,
  VC Ghiringhelli 27b,
  6500 Bellinzona, Switzerland

Lake Thoune and Lake Brienz
Polizeidirektion des Kantons Bern,
  Kramgasse 20,
  3000 Bern, Switzerland

Lake Neuchatel
Departement de Police,
  2000 Neuchatel, Switzerland.

TURKEY
ACVs and Hydrofoils
T.C. Ulastirma Bakanligi,
  Liman ve Deniz Isleri Dairesi Baskanligi,
  Ankara,
  Turkey

UNITED ARAB REPUBLIC
ACVs
The Arab General Organisation for Air
  Transport,
  11 Emad El Din Street,
  Cairo.

UNITED KINGDOM
Hovercraft—Certification and maintenance
Type Certificates. Approval of components and equipment.

Safety and Experimental Certificates; Certificates of Construction and Performance.
Approval of persons or organisations from whom the CAA may at its discretion accept reports touching upon the design, construction, maintenance or repair of hovercraft or elements thereof.
Publication of "British Hovercraft Saftey Requirements", Hovercraft Stability and Control, "Report of the ARB Special Committee on Hovercraft Stability and Control" CAA Paper 75017.

Technical Enquiries to:
Hovercraft Department
  Airworthiness Division
  Civil Aviation Authority,
  Brabazon House
  Redhill, Surrey RH1 1SQ
Telephone: Redhill 65966
Telex: 27100
Cables: Bordair Redhill

Publications:
  Printing and Publication Services,
  Greville House,
  3 Gratton Road,
  Cheltenham,
  Glos. GL50 2BN
Hovercraft and Hydrofoils
  Hovercraft Operating Permits and Hydrofoil Passenger Certificates,
  Department of Trade,
  Marine Division,
  Sunley House,
  90-93 High Holborn,
  London WC1V 6LP

ACVs and Hydrofoils
Operating approval and licences:
  Department of Trade,
  Marine Division,
  Sunley House,
  90-93 High Holborn,
  London WC1V 6LP
  Telephone: 01 405 6911
  Telex: 264084

UNITED STATES OF AMERICA
ACVs and Hydrofoils
  Department of Transportation,
  Commandant (G-MMT-4),
  U.S. Coast Guard,
  Washington, DC 20590, USA

VENEZUELA
Ministerio de Comunicaciones,
  Direccion de Marina Mercante,
  Esquina Carmelitas, Edificio Ramia,
  Caracas, Venezuela,

YUGOSLAVIA
Yugoslave Federal Economic Secretariat,
  Transport Department,
  Bulevar AVNOJ-a 104,
  Belgrade,
  Yugoslavia

UK CIVIL ACV REGISTRATIONS

U.K. HOVERCRAFT REGISTRATIONS — 1976

Registration Number	Craft Type and Production No.	Manufacturer	Operator, Owner or Charterer
GH-2002	VT.1-002	Vosper Thornycroft Ltd	Lombard North Central Ltd
GH-2003	VT.1-003	Vosper Thornycroft Ltd	Lombard North Central Ltd
GH-2004	SR.N4-002	British Hovercraft Corp.	Hoverlloyd Ltd
GH-2005	SR.N4-003	British Hovercraft Corp	Hoverlloyd Ltd
GH-2006	SR.N4-001	British Hovercraft Corp	British Rail Hovercraft Ltd
GH-2007	SR.N4-004	British Hovercraft Corp	British Rail Hovercraft Ltd
GH-2008	SR.N4-005	British Hovercraft Corp	Hoverlloyd Ltd
GH-2009	SR.N5-001*	British Hovercraft Corp	Hoverwork Ltd
GH-2010	SR.N6-022	British Hovercraft Corp	Hovertravel Ltd
GH-2011	SR.N6-024	British Hovercraft Corp	Hovertravel Ltd
GH-2012	SR.N6-026	British Hovercraft Corp	Hovertravel Ltd
GH-2013	SR.N6-130	British Hovercraft Corp	Hovertravel Ltd
GH-2014	SR.N6-009	British Hovercraft Corp	Westland Charters Ltd
GH-2015	SR.N6-011	British Hovercraft Corp	Westland Charters Ltd
GH-2016 (lapsed)	HM.2-004	Hovermarine Transport Ltd	Hellenic Hoverlines
GH-2017 (lapsed)	HM.2-007	Hovermarine Transport Ltd	Hellenic Hoverlines
GH-2018	HM.2-305	Hovermarine Transport Ltd	International Hoverservices
GH-2019	HM.2-312	Hovermarine Transport Ltd	International Hoverservices
GH-2020	HA5 MkIIIW(101)	Hover Air Ltd	Lord Hotham (Contract Hover)
GH-2021	SR.N6-016**	British Hovercraft Corp	British Hovercraft Corp
GH-2022 (lapsed)	SR.N6-028	British Hovercraft Corp	British Hovercraft Corp
GH-2023	HC.2-002	Hovermarine Transport Ltd	Hovermarine Transport Ltd
GH-2024	HM.2-303	Hovermarine Transport Ltd	International Hoverservices
GH-2025	HQ-007	Robin Parkhouse	Messrs Warman & Pott
GH-2026	SH.2-004***	Sealand Hovercraft Ltd	Sealand Hovercraft Ltd
GH-2027	SH.2-005	Sealand Hovercraft Ltd	Mr Kenneth Stuart
GH-2028	HM.2-304	Hovermarine Transport Ltd	Hellenic Hoverlines
GH-2029	SH.2-008***	Sealand Hovercraft Ltd	—
GH-2030	HM.2-319	Hovermarine Transport Ltd	Overseas operator
GH-2031	HR.N6-031	British Hovercraft Corp	British Hovercraft Corp
GH-2032	SH.2-006***	Sealand Hovercraft Ltd	—
GH-2033 (lapsed)	HM.2-320	Hovermarine Transport Ltd	Overseas operator
GH-2034	SH.2-013***	Sealand Hovercraft Ltd	Airgo Ltd
GH-2035	SR.N6-055†	British Hovercraft Corp	Hovertravel Ltd
GH-2036	SH.2-014***	Sealand Hovercraft Ltd	—
GH-2037	SH.2-001***	Sealand Hovercraft Ltd	—
GH-2038	SH.2-016***	Sealand Hovercraft Ltd	—
GH-2039	SH.2-017***	Sealand Hovercraft Ltd	—
GH-2040	SH.2-020***	Sealand Hovercraft Ltd	—
GH-2041	SR.N5-006	British Hovercraft Corp	Hoverwork Ltd
GH-2042	SH.2-025***	Sealand Hovercraft Ltd	—
GH-2043	SH.2-035***	Sealand Hovercraft Ltd	—
GH-2044	HM.2-324	Hovermarine Transport Ltd	Overseas operator
GH-2045	HM.2-325	Hovermarine Transport Ltd	Overseas operator
GH-2046	SR.N6-037	British Hovercraft Corp	British Hovercraft Corp
GH-2047	HM.2-330	Hovermarine Transport Ltd	Overseas operator
GH-2048	HM.2-331	Hovermarine Transport Ltd	Overseas operator
GH-2049	VT.2-001	Vosper Thornycroft Ltd	Vosper Thornycroft Ltd
GH-2050	HM.2-435	Hovermarine Transport Ltd	Charterhouse Japhet Ltd
GH-2051	HM.2-310	Hovermarine Transport Ltd	Secretary of State for Industry

Notes

*   Although originally built by BHC, this craft (GH-2009) was re-built by Air Vehicles Ltd and is known as an SR.N5A.

**   This craft has changed ownership and is now operated by an overseas military force.

***   The ownership of many SH.2 craft is uncertain following the demise of Sealand in mid-1976. New registrations are awaited for them.

†   This craft has been constructed from components from other SR.N6 and SR.N5 hovercraft by Hovertravel, Hoverwork and Air Vehicles personnel under supervision from BHC.

LIST OF LIGHT HOVERCRAFT REGISTERED WITH THE HOVERCLUB OF GREAT BRITAIN

This list, compiled with assistance from the Hoverclub of Great Britain, presents the numbers, names and operators/owners of recreational light hovercraft registered with the Hoverclub of Great Britain Ltd. Some of the craft included in this list have undergone changes in ownership or name since registration and others have been destroyed or scrapped. A secondary list of other light hovercraft, not registered with the Hoverclub, is also presented.

Key:

Craft Ownership/Existance uncertain   *

Craft Destroyed or Scrapped   **

Craft No	*Craft Name*	*Craft Owner/Operator*
01	—	—
02	Guinea Pig**	Grant Wickington
03	Olympic Runner	Ian Massey
	Mistral*	P. Smith & Tony Larosa
04	Mod Rider*	P. Smith
05	Highbury Hoverer*	Keith Oakley
06	Bumbly Two*	Chris Fox Robinson
	Number Six*	Manchester Hoverclub
07	Avenger 1*	Graham Porter
	Hover Hornet*	Capt. John Prendergast
08	Hover Imp	Cecil Blankley
09	Hoverscout Mk 2*	Colin Knight
10	Air Raiser	C. Maddocks
11	Jimbo**	Jim Rowbotham
	Doufa*	Brian Wavell
12	Crested Wren*	W. Parkin
13	—	—
14	Phoop*	Nick Low
15	Unknown*	Ian Hall
16	Caliban 1*	Don Draper
	Bullet**	Barry Oakley
17	Loflya	Mike Weller
18	Blue Streak*	P. Howell
19	K.B.1*	Ken Burtt
20	Poof*	Phil Conron
21	Pinkushion*	Dave McClunan
22	Hoveranne 2*	Keith Oakley
23	G.T.3*	Peter Garbutt
24	Humbug	John Gifford
25	Express Air Rider*	John Vass
	Dair-E-Goes Mk 2	Job's Dairy Sports & Social Club
26	Yellow Peril**	Malcolm Saunders
27	Snoopy	Barry Wilkinson
28	Avenger 1 (as No. 7)	Graham Porter
29	Aries*	R. Aubrey
30	Dunnit	Poundswick School
31	Vulcan*	Ron Shepherd
32	Unknown*	E. Betty
33	Cheshire Cat*	Colin Burley
34	Atlast 2*	Wellington School
	Unknown	H. Ratcliffe
35	Unknown*	Cowes Secondary School
36	Aerostyle*	P. Hall
37	Jet Hover**	John Trulock
38	Blowfly	Terry Brazier
39	114 Squadron ATC*	114 Squadron ATC Ruislip & Norwood
40	J.4**	Hovercraft Development Ltd
41	—	—
42	Project 69*	Teddington Secondary School
	JR.5	Rev. G. Spedding & Jeff Green
43	Express Air Rider*	St. Margaret Mary Secondary School
44	Norvil*	Norton Villiers Ltd.
45	Aquarius*	L. Scarr
46	Nefaettiti*	Venerable Francis Levenson School
47	Cyclone 1	John Scriven
48	Dragonfly*	D. Gubbins
49	Blue Devil*	Robert Dee (Netherlands)
50	Ariel*	J. Adlington & C. Felton
51	Superdocious*	Ernie Lamerton
52	Cyclone 2*	Nigel Beale
53	Horatio*	Mark Prentice
54	Air Lubri-Cat 2*	Roy Barnes
55	Philibuster	Phil Conron
56	Calibug**	Nigel Beale
57	Rocket*	G. R. Stephenson
58	Unknown*	Eric Sangster
59	Aeolus	Brian Wavell
60	Typhoon*	Peter Mayer & Geoff Harding
61	Rowena*	Tony Billing

Craft No	Craft Name	Craft Owner/Operator
62	JD.600*	Job's Dairy Sports & Social Club
63	Daffydol	Ted Naylor
64	Unknown	Rev G. Spedding
65	Simo*	Jack Simpson
66	Ranger 1*	Colin Knight
67	Ranger 1*	P. Smith
68	Vulcan 3*	David Ibbotson
69	Caliban 4*	Geoff Kent
70	Nodis 1	Don Ison
71	Peanuts	David Waters
72	Gee Whizz	Grant Wickington
73	Cyclone 3	Nigel Beale
74	Chinook*	Nick Horn & Alan Bliault
75	Skima 2S	Pindair Ltd
76	Skima 4	Pindair Ltd.
77	Skima	Tony Billing
78	Excalibur*	Bill Gough
79	Unknown*	A. Provost
80	Mistral*	Robert Trillo
81	Gryphon	Ken Kennaby
82	Nodis 1	Don Ison
83	Discorde**	Jim Batten
84	Eureka**	Keith Oakley
85	Vulcan IV	David Ibbotson & Greg Peck
86	Windmill	Warriner School
87	Scarab Noir	Jim Lyne
88	Hoverminx*	Alan Stanley
89	Scarab 1	Graham Nutt
90	Pushover*	Rex Camp
91	Caspar**	Greg Peck
92	Air Lubri-Cat 3*	Roy Barnes
93	—	—
94	Aggro*	Tony Wilcox
95	Pooline	149 (Poole) Squadron ATC
96	Caliban 5*	Geoff Kent
97	Buzzard*	Robert Raven
98	AH.5*	Peter Dance
99	Hoverking Experimental*	Colin Knight
100	—	—
101	Marander**	Aleks Murzyn
102	G.T.4*	Peter Garbutt
103	Tellstar	Malcolm Harris
104	Paddywack	Guy Rackham
105	Hoverfly*	Geoff Kent
106	Snoopy Too	Barry Wilkinson
107	Nimbus*	Graham Porter
108	Arrowspeed*	Richard Cresswell
109	Skyboy	Bob Hall
110	Greenfly**	Bill Baker
111	Blood, Sweat & Tears*	Terry Sherlock
112	Tango	Westfield School
113	—	—
114	Wasp*	Lindsay Gatward
115	—	—
116	Wotsit 6	Geoff Harding
117	Tornado	Alan Stanley
118	Buzzard 2	Lindsay Gatward
119	Tentando	Heles School
120	Marander	Aleks Murzyn
121	Hoverfly 2*	Geoff Kent
122	Jayfour	Mike Turner
123	—	—
124	—	—
125	Ere -'E-Cums	Peter Ball
126	Streaker	Roy Barnes
127	Go-Tune-One	Gordon Harker
128	Swift	Bourne Valley School
129	Scarab III/B	Hoverservices
130	Saturn 1	Bill Sherlock
131	Woodstock	Alan Bliault
132	Swallow	Bourne Valley School
133	Unknown	Rudheath School
134	Aggro II	Tony Wilcox
135	Bluebottle	Richard Cresswell
136	GP Too	Grant Wickington
137	Matilda	Newark School
138	Blue Scarab	Royal Grammar School, Newcastle

Craft No	Craft Name	Craft Owner/Operator
139	Draftee	D. Bennett
140	Bora	Heles School
141	Unknown	Reeds School
142	Unknown	Churchill School
143	Be-off	Dennis Shrimpton
144	Tri-A-Fly	Dave Council
145	Mistrale 1	Nick Low
146	Kipper	Mike Martyn-Jones
147	No-name**	Dennis Wilson
148	Talisman	Lewis Sharp
149	Volitat	Tony Groves
150	Bullet	Geoff Zaizey
151	Torvic	Victor Garman
152	Tempest	Roy Smart
153	Splinter*	Bill Congdon
154	Viking	M. Scott
155	Saturn 2	Derek Preston
156	Grasshopper	13th Nuneaton Scout Group
157	N.R. S.4. (?)	Wrockwardine School
158	Snagglepuss	Keith Smallwood
159	Hum-Bolt	John Gifford
160	Nasus	Barry Oakley
161	Scarab 10	Bill Baker
162	Unknown	B. Howarth
163	Saturn 3	Terry Sherlock
164	Fantasia	Graham Nutt
165	Treboreus	Bob Hall
166	RH.1	Richard Hale School
167	Stardust	Dennis Wilson
168	Red Baron	Heles School
169	Alicart	K. Allen
170	Half Pint	S. Allen
171	Simple Cyclone	Nigel Beale
172	Spirit of Snodland	Keith Oakley
173	Gale Force	R. Lang & K. Norton
174	Barrycuda	Barry Horsman
175	Peek-A-Boo	Roger Peek
176	Armadillo	Roger Porter
177	The Custard Beast	Bill Congdon
178	What's it Called	Churchill School
179	Deep Purple	Alan Vaughn
180	Lynx	Westfield School
181	Milady	Newark School
182	Kestral	Hayes Grammar School
183	Krak-A-Long	Ian & David Cook
184	Nima	Nick Horn
185	Blo-Fly	Roger Lee
186	Stratus	Lindsay Gatward
187	Fantasy	Lindsay Gatward

ADDITIONAL LIGHT HOVERCRAFT NOT REGISTERED WITH THE HOVERCLUB

Dragonfly II	D. Gubbins
Hermione	Mark Prentice
J.5	Peter Gooch
Loughborough Skimmer	Loughborough University of Technology Students Union
Mariner 6	George Eland
May-Fly	C. Woodruff
Orion	Victor Dunn
Nodis 3	Don Ison
Pegasus	George Rainey
Shadowfax	Peter Rudderham
Stockton Skima	Arnold J. Burton
U-One	D. Norman Lee
Wizzard	Manor Court Youth Club

SELECTED AMATEUR
BUILT HOVERCRAFT

B. BAKER

ADDRESS:

1 Stud Farm Cottage, Adderbury,
Near Banbury, Oxon

SCARAB 10

Completed in April 1976, this craft was envisaged as a useful cruising light hovercraft by its builder Bill Baker. In many respects the design is an extension of the successful and versatile series of "Scarab" hovercraft and during the 1976 Hoverclub race meetings it has demonstrated a good performance.

LIFT AND PROPULSION: A single engine of 210 cc, rated at 8 bhp at 5,500 rpm, is employed for lift and drives direct a single 22 in diameter, five-bladed axial fan. For propulsion the craft is fitted with a single Kohler 440 cc engine, rated at 42 bhp at 7,000 rpm. This drives, via a notched belt, a pair of 24 in diameter, five-bladed ducted fans. The lift fan has 30° pitch blades and the twin thrust fan units are fitted with 45° pitch blades. Static thrust for the propulsion system is 165 lbs. Cushion pressure is about 9 lb/ft². The craft carries 20 gallons of fuel.

HULL: The hull is made from glass reinforced plastic with expanded polystyrene foam being used for buoyancy. The foam is encased within the hull and provides 100% buoyancy. A bag skirt using 18 oz/yd² material is fitted.

ACCOMMODATION: Open cockpit for up to three persons sitting in-line on a pillion-type seat.

Bill Baker's large cruising hovercraft, Scarab 10, climbing a bank. This versatile craft can carry up to three people and operate at speeds over 50 mph. *(Photo: Bill Baker)*

CONTROLS: A lever controls the lift engine and a twist-grip mounted on the handle-bars acts as throttle for the propulsion engine. Movement of the handlebars activates a single rudder located in the rear of each thrust duct.

DIMENSIONS:

Length overall	12 ft 0 in (3·65 m)
Width overall	6 ft 6 in (1·98 m)
Height overall, hovering at rest	
	4 ft 10 in (1·47 m)
Height overall, hovering at rest	
	4 ft 0 in (1·21 m)

WEIGHTS:

Empty weight	450 lb (204 kg)
All-up weight	750 lbs (340 kg)
Normal payload	300 lb (136 kg)

PERFORMANCE:

Maximum speed	50 mph over land, 35 knots over water.
Obstacle clearance	10 in (190 mm)
Endurance	6½ hours
Range	+100 n miles

W. B. CONGDON

ADDRESS:

29 Avalon Road, Orpington, Kent

THE CUSTARD BEAST

Completed in June 1976 at an estimated total cost of £800 by Bill Congdon, this yellow painted, light hovercraft has a number of interesting features in its design. These include novel side skirts on extra decks fitted on the stern corners.

LIFT AND PROPULSION: A single Kyoritsu 225 cc engine, rated at 12 bhp at 3,700 rpm, is used for lift and drives direct a 22 in diameter, five-bladed axial fan fitted with 30° pitch blades. Propulsion is provided by a single JLO 440 cc engine rated at about 40 bhp which through toothed belts drives a pair of 24 in diameter, five-bladed ducted fans. These fans use 45° pitch blades and give the craft a static thrust of 140 lbs. The craft has a capacity for 5 gallons of fuel and a cushion pressure of about 10 lbs/ft².

HULL: The glass reinforced plastic hull is fitted with large buoyancy tanks under the side decking. A segmented skirt made from 5 oz/yd² weight polyurethane coated nylon material is employed on the craft.

ACCOMMODATION: Two persons, sitting in line astride a central pillion seat, can be carried.

CONTROLS: A twist grip throttle is fitted for the propulsion engine and a quadrant

"The Custard Beast", built by Bill Congdon of Bromley, Kent, for £800. Craft is seen with cockpit covered up for storage

lever for lift unit throttle. Twin rudders in the craft thrust units are operated for directional control by movement of the handlebars.

DIMENSIONS:

Length overall	11 ft 0 in
Width overall, over extra side sections	
	7 ft 11 in
Height overall, over extra side sections	
	4 ft 3 in
	3 ft 6 in

WEIGHTS:

Empty weight	450 lb
All-up weight	600 lb
Normal payload	150 lb

PERFORMANCE:

Maximum speed	30-35 mph (estimated)
Obstacle clearance	9 in
Endurance	2 hours

R. DEE

ADDRESS:

Sweilandstraat 7, Warmond, The Netherlands

SOMETHING BLUE

This craft is the second to have been built by Robert Dee, a keen Dutch hovercraft builder. The craft shows great promise and took part in the 1974 International Light

Hovercraft Rally at Calais. It was completed in February 1973 and cost in the region of £200 to construct.

LIFT AND PROPULSION: A single JLO 99cc two-stroke engine, rated at 3 bhp at 3,500 rpm, drives direct an 18 in diameter, six-bladed, axial fan fitted with 30° pitch blades of Multi-wing design. Propulsion is provided by a JLO 223cc engine rated at

15½ bhp at 5,300 rpm. This drives via vee-belts, a single 24 in diameter, five-bladed 45° pitch ducted fan. A static thrust figure of 80 lb has been achieved with this unit. Fuel capacity of the craft is 2½ gallons. Cushion pressure is 6 lb/ft².

HULL: The hull and superstructure of the craft are constructed from glass-reinforced plastic (grp), with polyurethane foam filling the hull structure to provide buoyancy. A bag skirt system made from 5 oz/yd² polyurethane-coated nylon material is fitted.

ACCOMMODATION: The craft is a single-seater with an enclosed cockpit.

CONTROLS: For both lift and propulsion engines there are simple throttle levers, and for directional control, a single rudder is fitted in the thrust duct at the rear of the craft. This is activated by a lever in the cockpit.

DIMENSIONS:

Length overall	10 ft 2 in (3·10 m)
Width overall	5 ft 6 in (1·68 m)
Height, hovering	3 ft 8 in (1·12 m)
at rest	3 ft 0 in (0·914 m)

WEIGHTS:

Empty weight	200 lb (90·71 kg)
All-up weight	350 lb (158·75 kg)

PERFORMANCE:

Maximum speed	
land	35 mph (56·33 km/h)
water	30 knots
Obstacle clearance	8 in (203·2 mm)

"Something Blue", a 35 mph single-seater built in the Netherlands by R. Dee

G. HARKER

ADDRESS:
38 Lyndon Avenue, Blackfen, Sidcup, Kent

GO-TUNE-ONE

This craft, the owner's first, was completed in October 1974 at an estimated cost of £400. It has been entered in a number of National Race Meetings organised by the Hover Club.

LIFT AND PROPULSION: A Villiers 250 cc engine, fitted with a Dynastart and rated at 15 bhp at 3,200 rpm, drives a single 24 in diameter axial fan fitted with ten blades at 30° pitch. The 30½ in diameter, ten-bladed ducted propulsion fan which is fitted with 45° pitch blades, is driven by a Hillman Imp 875 cc automotive engine rated at 45 bhp at 5,000 rpm. Transmission is via a chain-drive system. Cushion pressure is about 10 lb/ft². No static thrust figure is yet known. The craft has capacity for 5¼ gallons.

HULL: A frame of Oregon pine is covered with sheets of marine ply, and eight sealed buoyancy tanks filled with expanded polystyrene foam are contained within this structure. A simple bag skirt system is fitted, fabricated in 4 oz/yd² neoprene-coated nylon material.

ACCOMMODATION: Seating is provided for two persons in an open cockpit, side-by-side, bench-style.

Gordon Harker at the controls of his light hovercraft, "Go-Tune-One" at Sherborne Castle in August 1976

CONTROLS: To control the propulsion engine, a foot throttle lever is fitted. A simple hand lever provides variable lift throttle settings. Directional control is maintained by use of a large single rudder mounted on the rear of the propulsion thrust duct.

DIMENSIONS:

Length overall	12 ft 0 in (3·66 m)
Width overall	6 ft 0 in (1·83 m)
Height overall	
hovering	5 ft 2 in (1·57 m)
at rest	4 ft 3 in (1·30 m)

WEIGHTS:

Empty weight	520 lb (235·86 kg)
All-up weight	700 lb (317·5 kg)

PERFORMANCE:

Maximum speed (estimated)	35 mph (56·33 km/h)
Hard structure clearance (approx)	9 in (0·228 mm)
Endurance	3 hours

M. MARTYN JONES

ADDRESS:
47 Rosebank Cottages, Westfield Square, Woking, Surrey

KIPPER

This light hovercraft runabout was built at a cost of about £400 by Mike Martyn-Jones and was completed in May 1975. Since that date the craft has been entered in a number of Hoverclub meetings in various parts of Britain. The craft is designed for use in the hover-cruising role rather than for racing events.

LIFT AND PROPULSION: A single JLO 250cc engine, rated at about 15 bhp, supplies power direct to a 24 in diameter, five-bladed axial fan which uses 30° pitch blades. For propulsion the craft has a JLO 440 cc engine, rated at 40 bhp, and this drives, via /vee-belts, a pair of 24 in diameter ducted fans. These are five-bladed fans using 45° pitch blades. Cushion pressure of the craft loaded is about 10 lb/ft².

HULL: The glass reinforced plastic hull contains large airtight buoyancy chambers amounting to a high percentage excess buoyancy. A loop and segment skirt made from a lightweight material is fitted.

ACCOMMODATION: Seating 'in-line' is available for three persons.

CONTROLS: A twist-grip throttle on the control handlebars governs the thrust unit whilst a simple lever acts as lift throttle. Moving the handlebars activates rudders in the thrust ducts for directional control.

DIMENSIONS:

Length overall	12 ft 6 in (3·81 m)
Width overall	6 ft 6 in (1·98 m)
Height overall, hovering	4 ft 0 in (1·21 m)
Height overall, on pads	3 ft 3 in (0·99 m)

WEIGHTS:
Not available.

PERFORMANCE:

Estimated max speed	35 mph (56·32 km/h)
Obstacle clearance	9 in (228 mm)

NEWARK C. OF E. HIGH SCHOOL

ADDRESS:
Barnby Road, Newark, Nottinghamshire

MILADY

This simple yet successful light hovercraft is the second to be built by pupils of the School, and despite its very modest engine power, the craft has demonstrated a very satisfactory performance over land and water. The hovercraft was completed early in July 1976 and is estimated to have cost only £50 to build.

LIFT AND PROPULSION: A single Rowena Stihl 137 cc engine rated at 8½ bhp provides power for both lift and thrust functions.

The engine drives a single 24 in Multi-wing ducted fan with approximately one-third of the air going into the cushion and two-thirds being used for propulsion. The fan is fitted with five blades, each of 30° pitch.

HULL: The craft has a simple tray-shaped hull made from glass-reinforced plastic with buoyancy bags strapped onto the inner sides of the hull to provide reserve buoyancy. A simple bag skirt design is used on the craft and is fitted to the outer edge of the

hull. The skirt is made from lightweight 6 oz/yd² material.

ACCOMMODATION: Seating is provided for one person in an open cockpit.

CONTROLS: A pair of handlebars provide the craft driver with directional controls for a single rudder in the rear of the thrust duct. The thrust engine is controlled by a twist-grip arrangement on the handlebars.

DIMENSIONS:

Length overall	9 ft 0 in
Width overall	5 ft 0 in
Height hovering	2 ft 10 in
Height at rest	2 ft 6 in

WEIGHTS:

Empty weight	150 lb
All-up weight, one person	300 lb

PERFORMANCE:

Estimated max speed over land and water	25 mph

MESSRS NUTT, LYNE AND BRAN

ADDRESS:
24 Hazel Grove, Wallingford, Oxon, OX10 07A

SCARAB III/B

This light hovercraft, a development of their earliest designs, was completed in April 1975 at an estimated cost of £500 by Graham Nutt, James Lyne and Graham Bran. This team has successfully engineered and raced single and two-seater light hovercraft for several years.

LIFT AND PROPULSION: A single Husqvarna 150 cc engine, rated at 6 bhp at 3,800 rpm, is employed for lift and drives direct a 19 in diameter, five-bladed axial fan. This fan uses 30° pitch Multi-wing fan blades. For propulsion a Kohler 4402AS 440 cc engine, rated at 42 bhp at 7,200 rpm, drives via toothed belts a pair of 24 in diameter, five-bladed ducted fans which use 45° pitch blades and give a static thrust of 160 lbs. Cushion pressure of the craft is estimated to be 7·5 lbs/ft². Fuel capacity is 6 gallons.

HULL: The hull is constructed from sheets of plywood with air-tight compartments and sealed polythene containers providing it with buoyancy. A full-flow bag skirt is fitted which is made from 15 oz/yd² PVC on nylon material.

ACCOMMODATION: In-line seating is provided in an open cockpit for two persons.

CONTROLS: A twist grip engine throttle is located on the handlebars for the thrust engine. Movement of the handlebars provides directional control for the craft through

Twin thrust ducts on Scarab III/B distinguish this high-performance light hovercraft from other Scarab variants *(Photo: Neil MacDonald)*

single rudders in each thrust duct.

DIMENSIONS:

Overall length	11 ft 6 in
Overall width	5 ft 9 in
Height overall, hovering	4 ft 4 in
Height overall, at rest	3 ft 4 in

WEIGHTS:

Empty weight	300 lb
All-up weight, two persons	660 lb
Normal payload	360 lb

PERFORMANCE:

Maximum speed	
50 mph overland, 35 knots over water	
Obstacle clearance	9 in
Range	80 nautical miles
Endurance	2½ hours

R. PEEK

ADDRESS:
14 Bedford Street, Berkhampstead, Herts

PEEK-A-BOO

This attractively painted and well-finished light hovercraft was built by Roger Peek at a cost of about £600 and was completed in July 1976. Operations with the craft during Hoverclub events in 1976 have displayed a promising performance.

LIFT AND PROPULSION: A JLO 250 cc engine, rated at 12 bhp at 6,000 rpm, supplies power directly to a 22 in diameter, five-bladed axial lift fan which has 30° pitch blades. Propulsion is provided by a single JLO 440 cc engine, rated at 42 bhp at 6,700 rpm, which drives through a toothed belt a pair of 24 in diameter, five-bladed, ducted fans. These units, which are fitted with 35° pitch blades, are located close behind the driver's position.

HULL: The hull of the craft is made from glass reinforced plastic which is filled with polyurethane foam in order to give the craft buoyancy of 150% of the craft's all-up weight. The loop and segment skirt fitted used 5 oz/yd² weight neoprene coated nylon material. Estimated cushion pressure of the craft is 10 lb/ft².

ACCOMMODATION: Seating is provided on

"Peek-a-Boo", driven by Roger Peek of Berkhampstead, Herts, operating at speed on the lake at Sherborne Castle, Dorset, in August 1976 *(Photo: Neil MacDonald)*

a central seat for the craft to carry two persons sitting astride.

CONTROLS: Twist-grip throttles are used for both lift and thrust control and are mounted upon a pair of handlebars. Movement of the handlebars operates three rudders located in the rear of each duct.

DIMENSIONS:

Length overall	12 ft 0 in
Width overall	7 ft 1 in
Height overall, hovering	3 ft 8 in
Height overall, at rest	3 ft 0 in

WEIGHTS:

Craft empty weight	200 lb
All-up weight	400 lb
Normal payload	200 lb

PERFORMANCE:

Maximum speed	35-40 mph (est)
Craft fuel capacity	4 gallons
Obstacle clearance	8 in

R. PORTER

ADDRESS:

5 Osborne Road, Warsash, Southampton
Hants. SO3 6GT

ARMADILLO

This well-finished light hovercraft was
built by Roger Porter at an estimated cost
of £600. It was completed in June 1976
and employs several novel features including
control devices.

LIFT AND PROPULSION: A single Saab
96 automotive engine of 850 cc provides power
for the integrated lift/thrust system. Rated
at 42 bhp at 4,000 rpm, the Saab engine
drives via a gearbox a single 42 in diameter
centrifugal fan. This fan has twelve blades
at an angle of 35° and air from the unit is
pumped into the cushion and out through
louvres on the craft's stern. Fuel capacity
is 1½ gallons. Cushion pressure with one
person is about 10 lb/ft².

HULL: The craft is constructed from sheets
of aluminium which are riveted to form the
craft hull and superstructure. Buoyancy is
built into the hull. A bag skirt made from
lightweight material is fitted at the present
time although initially a loop and segment
type was employed. It is intended to
revert to the loop and segment arrangement
in the near future.

ACCOMMODATION: Seating for two persons
sitting side by side is provided in a partially

Armadillo, an aluminium hovercraft built and owned by Roger Porter of Warsash, Southampton.
A Saab 850 cc car engine drives the lift and thrust systems

enclosed cockpit.

CONTROLS: A throttle (centrifugal clutch)
is provided for the engine and twin rudders
which can be independently altered provide
the craft with directional control. These
rudders are activated by a split steering
wheel in the cockpit.

DIMENSIONS:

Length overall	12 ft 0 in
Width overall	6 ft 0 in
Height overall, hovering	3 ft 0 in
Height overall, at rest	2 ft 3 in

WEIGHTS:

Empty weight	400 lbs
All-up weight one person carried	600 lbs
Normal payload	200 lbs

PERFORMANCE:

Max speed	
25 mph overland, 20 knots over water	
Range	10 n miles
Endurance	½ hour
Obstacle clearance	9 in

B. SHERLOCK

ADDRESS:

35 Combewell Close, Garsington, Oxford

SATURN 1

Completed in March 1975 at an estimated
cost of £160, this craft has shown great
promise during the early events of the
Hover Club's 1975 Racing Programme.

LIFT AND PROPULSION: A JLO 98cc
engine, rated at 5 bhp at 3,500 rpm, drives
direct a 19 in diameter, five-bladed, 35°
pitch axial fan. Propulsion is supplied by a
Triumph T100A engine of 500cc, rated at
40 bhp at 6,000 rpm. This drives via toothed
belts, a pair of 24 in diameter, five-bladed,
45° pitch ducted thrust fans. A static
thrust of 170 lbs is obtained with this arrangement. The craft carries three gallons
of fuel. Cushion pressure is estimated at
7 lb/ft².

HULL: Construction of the hull and superstructure is of glass-reinforced plastic with
eight buoyancy chambers built into the hull.
A deep bag skirt system is made from 5 oz/yd²
coated nylon material.

ACCOMMODATION: Side-by-side seating
for two persons is provided in an open cockpit.

CONTROLS: Movement of the control

"Saturn I", driven by Bill Sherlock, has a Triumph 500 cc thrust engine and a ILO lift unit

joystick backwards regulates the thrust
engine and a twist grip operates the lift
engine throttle. A single rudder in each
thrust duct provides the craft with directional
control.

DIMENSIONS:

Length overall	11 ft 0 in	(3·35 m)
Width overall	5 ft 6 in	(1·68 m)
Height, hovering	3 ft 9 in	(1·14 m)
at rest	3 ft 0 in	(0·914 m)

WEIGHTS:

Empty weight	290 lb (131·54 kg)
All-up weight (with two persons)	
	610 lb (276·68 kg)

PERFORMANCE:

Max. speed, estimated	
land	35 mph (56·33 km/h)
water	30 knots
Endurance	2 hours
Obstacle clearance	9 in (228·6 mm)

T. SHERLOCK

ADDRESS:

14 Collinwood Road, Risinghurst, Oxford

SATURN 3

Completed in April 1976 at an estimated
cost of £120, this light hovercraft—the
second to be built by Terry Sherlock—has
proved a good performer during the Hoverclub's 1976 race season.

LIFT AND PROPULSION: A single BSA
Bantam 125cc engine, rated at 6 bhp at
3,300 rpm, provides power for a 19 in (0·48
m) diameter axial fan, fitted with five 30°
pitch blades. Propulsion is supplied by a
single Triumph 5TA 498cc motorcycle engine,
rated at 28 bhp at 6,000 rpm, which drives,
via a toothed belt, a 30 in (0·53 m) diameter,
ten-bladed ducted fan, fitted with 45°

Saturn 3, the Triumph motorcycle-engined hovercraft built by Terry Sherlock of Risinghurst,
Oxford for £120. (Photo: Neil MacDonald)

pitch blades. This arrangement gives the craft a static thrust of 130 lbs. Fuel capacity of the craft is 3 gallons and with one person being carried the craft's cushion pressure is 9 lb/ft².

HULL: The complete hull of the craft, with the exception of the engine frame, constructed from 1 × 1 × 8⅛ in angle iron, is in glass reinforced plastic. Eight separate chambers in the side sections of the craft provide 150% buoyancy. A bag skirt is employed, made from 18 oz/yd² nylon/PVC material.

ACCOMMODATION: The craft can carry two persons sitting astride the central section of the hull.

CONTROLS: A twist-grip throttle is used for the propulsion engine and a choke lever for the lift unit. Engine controls are mounted on handle bars which also activate twin rudders in the thrust duct.

DIMENSIONS:

Length overall	11 ft 0 in (3·35 m)
Width overall	5 ft 6 in (1·67 m)
Height overall, hovering	4 ft 2 in (1·27 m)
Height overall, on pads	3 ft 6 in (1·06 m)

WEIGHTS:

Empty weight	300 lb (136 kg)
All-up weight	550 lb (249·46 kg)
Normal payload	250 lb (113·39 kg)

PERFORMANCE:

Estimated max speed	40 mph (64·37 km/h)
Obstacle clearance	8 in (203 mm)
Endurance	
15 n miles (racing) or 30 n miles (cruising)	

WESTFIELD SCHOOL

ADDRESS:

Stiby Road, Yeovil, Somerset. BA21 3EP

LYNX

Completed on July 10, 1976 at an estimated cost of £120, this light hovercraft was built by pupils of Westfield School and is the second hovercraft which they have constructed. At the BP National Schools Hovercraft Championships in July 1976, the craft was placed first in the Junior Girls competition for single-engined craft, and won various trophies including the Barber Design Award.

LIFT AND PROPULSION: A single Micmar-Talon 246cc motorcycle engine, rated at 18 bhp at 5,700 rpm, provides power for an integrated lift/thrust arrangement. The engine drives via a toothed belt a single 25 in Breeza ducted fan fitted with five 25° pitch blades. A proportion of the air generated by this unit is fed into the skirt and the rest (about 70%) is used for thrust. Fuel capacity is 1½ gallons and the craft has a cushion pressure of 8 lbs/ft².

HULL: Built from pop-riveted aluminium sheets, with large blocks of expanded polystyrene foam along the front and sides for buoyancy. Skirt is of the inflated loop type made in 4 oz/yd² polyurethane-coated nylon material.

ACCOMMODATION: Seating for one person is provided on a pillion-type seat in the open cockpit.

CONTROLS: A brake-type lever acts as throttle for the single engine. A pair of handlebars activate triple rudders located

Lynx, built by pupils of Westfield School at a cost of £120, is a successful single-engined light hovercraft. It was well-placed in the 1976 BP Schools hovercraft competition. (Photo: Westfield School)

at the rear of the thrust duct to control craft heading.

DIMENSIONS:

Length overall	9 ft 0 in (2·74 m)
Width overall	5 ft 0 in (1·52 m)
Height overall, hovering	3 ft 10 in (1·16 m)
Height overall on pads	3 ft 3 in (0·99 m)

WEIGHTS:

Empty weight, est	150 lb (68 kg)
All-up weight	300 lb (136·07 kg)
Max payload	150 lb (68 kg)

PERFORMANCE:

Max speed	20 mph (32·18 km/h) overland
Obstacle clearance	7 in (177 mm)

G. WICKINGTON

ADDRESS:

8 Hardwicke Way, Hamble, Herts

GP Too

This is the third hovercraft built by Grant Wickington, the well-known light hovercraft enthusiast, and was completed in May 1975. The cost was about £50 since the main engine and the fan unit were taken from his first hovercraft, Guinea Pig, (see JSS 72/73) which has now been scrapped.

LIFT AND PROPULSION: A Hillman Imp 875 cc, rated at 40 bhp, supplies power for lift and thrust. The engine, through a centrifugal fan clutch and 4·8:1 reduction gearbox, drives a 3 ft 6½ in diameter centrifugal fan made of light alloy. A proportion of the air flow from the fan is ducted into the cushion system and the remainder is channelled aft to escape through louvres at the stern of the craft. The craft carries three gallons of fuel and has a cushion pressure of about 9 lb/ft².

HULL: The entire hull and superstructure is in light alloy, with 36 airtight buoyancy tanks included in the structure. A simple bag skirt system is employed, made from 4 oz/yd² pvc coated nylon material.

Grant Wickington's light alloy hovercraft "GPTOO" between races at Dodington Park, Avon

ACCOMMODATION: Open cockpit with side-by-side bench seating for two.

CONTROLS: A hand throttle lever controls the Imp engine and for directional control the craft is equipped with a 'Butterfly'-type steering column. This activates three vanes in the rear section of the thrust duct.

DIMENSIONS:
Length overall	13 ft 0 in (3·96 m)
Width overall	6 ft 2 in (1·88 m)
Height overall, hovering	3 ft 0 in (0·914 m)

WEIGHTS:
Empty weight	550 lb (249·46 kg)
All-up weight (one person carried)	710 lb (322·94 kg)

PERFORMANCE:
Max. speed (estimated)-	
land	30 mph (48·28 km/h)
water	25-30 knots

ACV CLUBS AND ASSOCIATIONS

CLUBS AND ASSOCIATIONS

ACV Clubs & Associations
THE HOVERCLUB OF GREAT BRITAIN LTD

As Britain's national organisation for light hovercraft, the Hoverclub exists to encourage the construction and operation of light, recreational hovercraft by private individuals, schools, colleges, universities and other youth groups. The Hoverclub's major role in recent years has been its organisation of several national race meetings at sites throughout Britain. At these events up to thirty light hovercraft may compete for National Championship points over land and water courses at meetings held in the grounds of stately homes, or at reclaimed gravel workings.

In addition to national race meetings, the Hoverclub also performs the important task of providing its own members and prospective hovercraft builders with useful advice and information. This information, largely collected by the Club through the vast range of experience accummulated by its members during twelve years of hovering, is made available through technical articles in the Hoverclub's monthly magazine, "Light Hovercraft", the annually published "Light Hovercraft Handbook", or through various booklets dealing with specific areas of hovercraft construction and operation. Club members can also contact a technical enquiries officer within the Hoverclub.

The "Light Hovercraft Handbook" has been regularly up-dated and expanded since it was first launched a few years ago, and it is now acknowledged as the prime reference book for the design, construction and safe operation of small recreational hovercraft.

A growing activity within the Hoverclub has been the pastime of hovercruising which involves travelling by single or more usually multi-seat light hovercraft along rivers, canals, lochs or coastlines. Many hovercraft constructors see this activity as one offering the ability to explore areas which are not accessible by other means of transport. Hovercruises and holidays have been arranged in Scotland and Wales and other events are planned for the 1976 season.

HOVERCLUB COUNCIL 1976-77

Michael Bentine, President
G. G. Harding, Chairman
K. Oakley, vice-Chairman
M. Drake, Treasurer
C. C. A. Curtis, Hon. Secretary
D. Ison
M. Pinder
K. Kennaby
N. MacDonald
J. Lyne
W. Sherlock

The Hoverclub's main address for initial enquiries related to membership and publication is:

Mrs J. Waddon, Hoverclub Information Officer,
45 St Andrews Road, Lower Bemerton, Salisbury, Wilts

Telephone:
Salisbury 3424

Addresses of the various branches of the Hoverclub throughout Britain are listed below:

CHILTERNS
Mr J. Lyne, Berkshire College of Agriculture
Hall Place, Burchetts Green,
Nr Maidenhead, Berks

EAST ANGLIAN
Mr C. Seager,
33 Acacia Road, Thorpe St Andrews,
Norfolk

ESSEX
Mr E. W. Sangster,
53 Elm View Road, Benfleet, Essex
SS7 5AR

ISLE OF WIGHT
Mr M. Prentice,
1 Kingston Farm Cottages, Kingston Farm
Lane, East Cowes, Isle of Wight

LONDON
Mr B. Horsman,
8 Merivale Grove, Walderslade,
Chatham, Kent

MIDLANDS
Mr D. M. Waters,
99 William Street, Loughborough,
Leicester

NORTH WESTERN
Rev. W. G. Spedding,
14 Avondale Road, Farnworth,
nr Bolton, Lancs

Members of the Hover Club of Japan and their craft at a national race meeting in 1976. (Photo· (Photo: M. Mino)

SCOTTISH
Mr W. S. Sharp
1 Coates Place, Edinburgh, EH3 7AA
SOUTHERN
Mr P. Hampson
1 Rednal House, Greetham Street,
Portsmouth, Hants
SOUTH WESTERN
Mrs D. Stanley
40 Lulworth Avenue, Hamworthy,
Poole, BH15 4DJ, Dorset

National Schools Hovercraft Association

The National Schools Hovercraft Association was formed in 1975 to provide a focal
point for the growing interest from schools
and colleges in building and operating
recreational hovercraft. In the region of
170 schools are registered with the NSHA.
Many have either completed a hovercraft or
are currently engaged in craft construction.
Each year the Schools Association, together
with the British Petroleum Co Ltd and the
Hoverclub of Great Britain, organise a
National Schools Hovercraft Championship.
This competition allows many light hovercraft
built by school groups to be evaluated over
land and water circuits.

SECRETARY:
Mr D. Hale,
Brookmead, Rimpton, Nr Yeovil,
Somerset
TELEPHONE:
Marston Magna 241

THE UNITED KINGDOM HOVERCRAFT SOCIETY

ADDRESS:
Rochester House, 66 Little Ealing Lane,
London W5 4XX
TELEPHONE:
(01) 579 9411
OFFICERS:
Sir Christopher Cockerell, President
R. L. Wheeler, vice-President
J. E. Rapson, Chairman
W. F. S. Woodford, OBE, vice-Chairman
J. Bentley, Treasurer
P. A. Bartlett, Secretary

1976 MANAGEMENT COMMITTEE
J. E. Rapson, Chairman
P. A. Bartlett, Secretary

A. E. Bingham
M. Dawson
P. S. Chennell
M. A. Pinder

N. A. MacDonald
P. H. Winter
W. F. S. Woodford
R. L. Wheeler

Formed in 1971, the United Kingdom
Hovercraft Society (UKHS) is the UK
constituent member of the 'International
Air Cushion Engineering Society'. Its membership is drawn from ACV manufacturers,
ferry operators, design groups, government
departments and agencies, financial and
insurance organisations, consultants, journ-
alists and universities. Membership of the
Society is open to persons engaged in hovercraft related fields in the UK and overseas.
Currently the UKHS has over 200 members.

In addition to its programme of regular
meetings, at which papers are presented on
the technical, commercial, design, operating
and military aspects of hovercraft and air-
cushion devices, the UKHS also produces a
regular monthly "UKHS Newsletter". This
publication contains the latest up-to-date
information on hovercraft activities throughout the world. From time to time the
Society also organises visits to hovercraft
manufacturing or component factories for
its members.

At the Society's headquarters in London a
collection of hovercraft films is held, together
with a library of books, periodicals, papers
and reports on the subject of hovercraft.

THE HOVERCLUB OF AMERICA INC

Following a general meeting of the members
of the American Hovercraft Association on
May 29, 1976, it was agreed to reorganise the
Association into the HoverClub of America,
Inc. Subsequently the HoverClub of America
has been incorporated under the State Laws
of Indiana and six national directors appointed and elected to serve for one year.

In the United States the HoverClub of
America organises race meetings, rallies and
other events for members possessing hovercraft, and also publishes a monthly Newsletter.

DIRECTORS (1976):
Dennis N. Benson
Mike Klare
Paul Esterle
Chris Fitzgerald
Mike Kiester
Woodrow Nasser
OFFICERS:
Paul Esterle, President
Chris Fitzgerald, Vice-President & Public
Relations

Mike Kiester, Secretary & Editor
Dennis N. Benson, Treasurer
Membership of the HoverClub of America,
Inc, is available at US $10·00 pa.
ADDRESS:
The HoverClub of America, Inc.,
Box 234
Uniontown
Ohio 44685, United States of America

INTERNATIONAL FEDERATION OF HOVERCLUBS

HEADQUARTERS:
Hon. Secretary: J. E. C. Bliault,
128 Queens Road, Portsmouth,
Hampshire, PO2 7NE, England.

Affiliated Members

HOVER CLUB OF GREAT BRITAIN LTD
Hon. Sec. C. Curtis, 26 Buckthorne Road,
London, SE4, England.
HOVER CLUB OF AUSTRALIA
Hon. Sec. H. B. Standen, GPO Box 1882,
Brisbane, Queensland 4001, Australia
HOVERCLUB OF AMERICA
Box 234 Uniontown, Ohio, 44685, USA
CLUB FRANCAIS DES AEROGLISSEURS
President: J. Beaudequin, 41-43 Rue Aristide,
45130 Meung sur Loire, France
HOVER CLUB OF TRINIDAD & TOBAGO
President: N. Seal, 1 Richardson Street,
Point Fortin, Trinidad, West Indies.
HOVERCRAFT CLUB OF NEW ZEALAND
Hon. Sec. K. F. Leathem, MacDonald Road,
Pokeno, New Zealand
THE HOVER CLUB OF CANADA
R. Fishlock, 103 Doane Street, Ottawa
K2B 6GY, Ontario, Canada

New Hoverclubs

THE HOVER CLUB OF JAPAN
Information from Masahiro Mino, Senior
Director, Aerodynamics Section, Nihon Uni-
versity at Narashino, 7-1591 Narashinodai,
Funabashi, Chiba-Ken, Japan

THE INTERNATIONAL HYDROFOIL SOCIETY

ADDRESS:
17 Melcombe Court, Dorset Square,
London, NW1
TELEPHONE:
01 935 8678
PRESIDENT:
Peter Dorey
The International Hydrofoil Society pub-
lishes a regular news letter and holds meetings
at which hydrofoil topics are discussed.
PAST PRESIDENT:
Baron Hanns von Schertel

ACV CONSULTANTS

CONSULTANTS IN AIR-CUSHION VEHICLE TECHNOLOGY AND OPERATION

AIR CUSHION EQUIPMENT (1976) LTD

HEAD OFFICE AND WORKS:
15-35 Randolph Street, Shirley, Southampton
TELEPHONE: 0703 776468
TELEX: 477537
CABLES: HOVERACE SOTON
DIRECTORS:
F. B. Hake, Chairman
A. Latham, Marketing Manager
R. Gilbert, Chief Designer
R. Henvest, Works Manager

Besides developing products and systems for its own benefit and that of its associate companies Air Cushion Equipment Ltd also offers a comprehensive design and technical consulting service to any organisation with a load-moving problem. Many such problems have been considered and air cushion systems designed and built to cope with them. New products are also under development for the mechanical handling industry, and also for the civil engineering and construction industries specialising in very heavy and awkward steel and concrete erection projects.

Over the last three years the company has also been investigating new methods of adapting skirt systems for the dense load movement sector of the market and to reduce both the capital and operating costs. The latest product to emerge is known as the ACE "Water Skate" load-carrying pallet which uses water as the cushion fluid and has been tested for operation at 6 bar (87 psi).

AIR VEHICLES LTD

HEAD OFFICE:
1, Sun Hill, Cowes, Isle of Wight.
YARD:
Dinnis' Yard, High Street, Cowes, Isle of Wight.
TELEPHONE: Cowes 3194 & 4739
DIRECTORS:
P. H. Winter, M.Sc
C. D. J. Bland
C. B. Eden
Air Vehicles Ltd, formed in 1968, has a wide experience of all types of hovercraft and hovercraft operation, and can offer a full range of services as consultants.

Particular fields where Air Vehicles Ltd has specialised knowledge are:

1) manufacture and operation of small hovercraft up to 10 seats. Several craft have been built and the latest AV Tiger is also offered for charter.

2) design and construction of ducted propellers. Sizes have ranged from 4 ft 6 in diameter used on AV Tiger, ducts for SR.N6 and two large ducts of 9 ft overall diameter delivered to the US early 1976.

3) design, operation and site surveys for hoverbarges, particularly for ship-to-shore cargo. The first 350 ton hoverbarge on the Yukon River in Alaska was designed and commissioned by Air Vehicles Ltd.

Approved by the Civil Aviation Authority, the company can design and undertake modifications to larger craft. Typical of this work is the conversion to hoverfreighter configuration of SR.N5 and SR.N6. The company also offers two SR.N5 hovercraft for charter as well as the new AV Tiger 8-10 seat hovercraft.

The company's association with Hoverwork Ltd enables it to call on the company's world-wide experience of hovercraft operations. A special feature of Air Vehicles consultancy is a complete on-site survey and a feasibility study of all types of hovercraft which is undertaken for a fixed fee. Several of these have been completed for hoverbarge projects in various parts of the world.

C. R. BRINDLE & ASSOCIATES

ADDRESS:
10 Cliff Road, Cowes, Isle of Wight, PO31 8BN, England
TELEPHONE: (098 382) 2218
C. A. Brindle & Associates provides a consultancy service specialising in marine transport and transportation economics, hydrofoil and hovercraft operation in all parts of the world.
Contractors to British and other Governments.

Work undertaken has included world-wide surveys for potential hovercraft and hydrofoil operation and the technical assessment of specific craft.

Detailed application studies have been carried out in the United Kingdom, United States of America, Canada, Mediterranean, Africa, France, Holland, Scandinavia and the Caribbean.

Practical experience with scheduled commercial services and specialised operations and maintenance in domestic and international fields. Adviser to United Nations Organisation and OECD on maritime operations in developing countries.

BRITISH RAIL HOVERCRAFT LIMITED

HEAD OFFICE
Royal London House, 22/25 Finsbury Square, London EC2P 2BQ
TELEPHONE: (01) 628 3050
Managing Director: J. M. Lefeaux
Commercial and Planning Manager: A. J. Tame
Chief Engineer: P. A. Yerbury
British Rail Hovercraft Limited is the most experienced commercial hovercraft in operation in the world. It is the only company to have operated commercially both amphibious and non-amphibious craft on esturial and open water services.

Studies have been conducted on behalf of clients in many parts of the world and the Company is able to provide a route costing and viability appraisal service based on "real time" operating experience.

LESLIE COLQUHOUN AND ASSOCIATES

HEAD OFFICE:
7 Daryngton Avenue, Birchington, Kent
Telephone: 0843 430 85
Leslie Colquhoun and Associates was formed in 1973 to provide a hovercraft transport consultancy service using the unique experience of L. R. Colquhoun who has been closely associated with the hovercraft industry since 1959. This experience involved the testing, development and marketing of Vickers Ltd. hovercraft projects from 1959-1965, and from 1966-1973 the setting up and running of Hoverlloyd's Ramsgate to Calais hovercraft service with the SR.N6 and SR.N4. Mr Colquhoun was Managing Director of the Company when he resigned in December 1972 to set up the Consultancy.

The Consultancy is contracted to Hoverlloyd and has completed on their behalf a report on the Company's SR.N4 cross channel operations for the S.E.S.P.O. P.M.17 office of the Department of the US Navy.

Further work has been contracted in U.K., France, Hungary, America, Iran and Malaysia.

The Consultancy also provides assistance to International Hoverservices Ltd.

Through a close association with Comasco International Ltd. the Consultancy is involved in pollution and waste disposal schemes using both chemical and incineration processes.

PETER G. FIELDING, CEng, FRAeS

OFFICES:
UNITED KINGDOM:
20 Warmdene Road, Brighton, Sussex, BN1 8NL
TELEPHONE: Brighton 501212
Dock House, Niton Undercliff, Ventnor, Isle of Wight. PO38 2NE
Telephone: Niton 730 252
USA:
1701 North Fort Myer Drive, Suite 908 Arlington, Virginia 22209
Telephone: (703) 528 1092
7910 Woodmont Avenue, Suite 1103, Bethesda, Maryland 20014
Telephone: (301) 656 5991
Consultant in air cushion systems, air cushion operations, and air cushion technology since 1959 to the US Army, the US Navy, US Department of Defense, the Advanced Research Projects Agency-DOD, US Department of Commerce-Maritime Administration, the Office of Naval Research, the US Naval Ships Research

and Development Center, the US Army TRECOM, the Executive Office of the President USA, the US Navy-Chief of Naval Operations, the US Marine Corp, the Institute for Defense Analysis, the Center for Naval Analysis, the Bell Aerosystems Corporation, the Aerojet Corporation, the Research Analysis Corporation, Science Applications Incorporated, Hoverlift Applications Incorporated, Booz-Allen Applied Research Incorporated, Associated Consultants International Inc, and SeaSpan Inc. Services for the above organizations have included state of the art reports, technical and economic analysis, route surveys, environmental impact studies, sub-system analysis, operational plans, test plans, mission studies, advanced technology estimates, test site selection, cost analysis, structural and materials analysis and market research.

RECENTLY COMPLETED ASSIGNMENTS INCLUDE:

1. Review and assessment of the Arctic SEV advanced technology programme for the Advanced Research Projects Agency US Dept of Defense.

2. Analysis of "paddle wheel" propulsion and sealing systems for SES, for S.A. Inc. McLean, Va, USA.

3. "The Surface Effect Vehicle (SEV) in Search and Rescue Missions in Alaska"—for the Research Analysis Corporation, McLean, Va.

4. "An Assessment of the Technological Risk and Uncertainty of Advanced Surface Effect Vehicles (SEV) for the Arctic"—for the US Naval Ships Research and Development Center, Carderock, Md.

5. "An Evaluation of Advanced Surface Effect Vehicle Platforms Performing Military Missions in the Arctic"—for Science Applications Inc, La Jolla, California, and Arlington, Virginia.

6. "An Exhaustive Bibliography of Air Cushion Subjects" for the Research Analysis Corporation, McLean, Virginia.

7. "Preliminary Findings of the Economic Suitabilities of the Surface Effect Ship to Various Routes in the US"—for SEASPAN Inc, Washington, DC.

8. "Appraisal of Heavy Lift Systems for Commercial Applications"—for Hoverlift Applications Inc, Arlington, Virginia.

9. Results and Implications of the Advanced Projects Agency, US Department of Defense, Surface Effect Vehicles Programme—for Science Applications Inc, Arlington, Va, USA.

HOVERCRAFT DEVELOPMENT LTD.

HEAD OFFICE:
Kingsgate House, 66-74 Victoria Street, London, SWIE 6SL
TELEPHONE: 01-828-3400
TELEX: 23580
TECHNICAL OFFICE:
Forest Lodge West, Fawley Road, Hythe, Hants SO4 6ZZ
TELEPHONE: Hythe (Hants) 84 3178 STD Code 84 0703
DIRECTORS:
T. G. Fellows (Chairman)
M. W. Innes
Prof. W. A. Mair
J. E. Rapson
T. A. Coombs
SECRETARY:
P. N. Randell

Hovercraft Development Ltd, was established by the National Research Development Corporation in 1959 to develop and exploit the hovercraft patents of Christopher Cockerell. The Technical Group of the Company was set up in 1960. It provided technical services for the Company's hovercraft manufacturing licensees until that part of HDL was taken over by Mintech (now the Department of Industry) to become a unit of the National Physical Laboratory. The office at Hythe continues to provide technical information for interested parties and particularly for the Company's licensees and for hovercraft operators. It also advises HDL on technical matters associated with development projects and the craft designs of prospective licensees.

HOVERWORK LIMITED

HEAD OFFICE:
12 Lind Street, Ryde, Isle of Wight, PO33 2NR
TELEPHONE: Ryde 5181
CABLES: Hoverwork Ryde
TELEX: 86513 (A/B Hoverwork Ryde)

DIRECTORS:
C. D. J. Bland (Managing)
D. R. Robertson
E. W. H. Gifford
A. C. Smith
R. G. Clarke

Hoverwork Limited is a subsidiary of Hovertravel Limited and was formed in 1966. The company provides crew training and charter facilities for all available types of ACVs, thus bridging the gap between the operators and manufacturers.

Hoverwork and its parent, Hovertravel, own the largest fleet of hovercraft available for charter in the world. Types include the SR.N6, the SR.N6 freighter, SR.N5 passenger/freighter and AV.2. In recent years the company has concentrated on providing craft for seismic, gravity and hydrographic survey work in shallow water areas and terrain impossible to other forms of transport.

The company, jointly with Hovertravel Limited, offers a route feasibility investigation service.

PELLINKHOF CONSULTANCY

Th. Pellinkhof, C.Eng., F.I.Mar.E
ADDRESS: 139c Gloucester Terrace, Bayswater, London, W2 6DX
TELEX: Nedham Ldn 23211—att. Pellinkhof
TELEPHONE: (01) 262 8159

Consultancy in the fields of rapid transit systems, amphibious vehicles and air-cushion applications, including air-supported structures (air domes).

Selection and indication of solutions for various transport problems in developing areas. Also the selection of air-cushion vehicles and hydrofoils to meet specific high-performance and amphibious requirements. Assistance in selection of air-cushion platforms and air-cushion conveyor belts to facilitate cost-saving load moving.

The Netherlands-British foundation of the enterprise ensures a wide area of industrial and technological resources.

R. A. SHAW

(Managing Director Hoverprojects Limited)
ADDRESS:
Fell Brow, Silecroft, Millom, Cumbria, LA18 5LS
TELEPHONE: 0657 2022

Consultancy services to governments, local authorities and private enterprise on all aspects of fast transport with special emphasis on hovercraft and hydrofoils. Services include financial, economic and operational assessments in all conditions and new designs to meet particular requirements.
Contracts have included:

1. A study for the State of Washington to assess the feasibility of introducing hovercraft and hydrofoils into the Puget Sound ferry system.

2. A feasibility appraisal of proposed hovercraft operations in British Columbia.

3. Reporting to a local authority on prospects of establishing a hoverport within their borough.

4. A study for the Greater London Council on fast passenger services on the Thames.

5. Three independent studies on the potential for hovercraft in the Venetian lagoon.

6. Examination of world potential market for hovercraft.

7. Design and Economics of 1000 ton River Hovercraft.

8. Planning and operating consultancy for Airavia Ltd. and Speed Hydrofoils Ltd. for hydrofoils on the River Thames.

ROBERT TRILLO LIMITED

HEAD OFFICE:
Broadlands, Brockenhurst, Hampshire, SO4 7SX.
TELEPHONE: Brockenhurst (05902) 2220.
MANAGING DIRECTOR:
R. L. Trillo, CEng., FIMechE, FRAeS, AFAIAA, AFCASI
Author "Marine Hovercraft Technology" (ISBN 0 249 44036 9) and Editor "Janes' Ocean Technology Yearbook" (ISBN 0 354 00530 8).

Operating since 1969 as a consultancy engaging principally in air-cushion vehicle technology and economics, the firm has worked for industry and government departments in a number of countries and has undertaken transport feasibility studies, preliminary design investigations and experimental investigations. Other work has been concerned with the aerodynamic design of three ducted propeller installations (including the SR.N6 and Skima 12) and the preliminary design of two inflatable hovercraft, one of which is the largest built to date. Research into skirt wear and the design of skirts has also been undertaken. Recent commissions have included work in Canada for the National Research Council, Ottawa, and in Australia for the Department of Aboriginal Affairs; in this context a feasibility study was carried out on the practicality of operating hovercraft between the islands in the coral reef areas in the Torres Strait between Papua New Guinea and Northern Queensland and as a result a successful SR.N5 operation was established. The firm publishes bimonthly bibliography services on air-cushion and hydrofoil systems and on high-speed ground transportation and urban rapid transit systems. (ISSN 0306-0594, ISSN 0306-0586).

REPRESENTATIVES:
Canada:
Vice-Admiral K. L. Dyer, RCN Rtd.,
Dyer & Associates,
Suite 800, 75 Albert Street,
Ottawa,
Ontario K1P 5E7
Denmark:
Mr. Leif Hansen,
A. B. C. Hansen Comp, A/S,
Hauchsvej 14,
DK-1825 Copenhagen V.
Affiliate member of Northern Associates Reg'd., Canada, Canadian Arctic consulting group.

JOHN VASS

ADDRESS:
Beaverbrook Newspapers, Fleet Street, London E.C.4
Telephone: (01) 353 8000
Home: Rosehaugh Farm, Newbarn Lane, Cudham, Kent
Telephone: Biggin Hill 2718
Received first official light hovercraft licence issued by Air Registration Board 1968. Elected first Life Member of Hoverclub of Gt. Britain, 1974. Author "Hovercraft" and "Express Air Rider Handbook" Hovercraft Correspondent, Daily Express. Light Hovercraft consultant, British Petroleum, Air Rider Research Ltd, and McCulloch & Associates, Ontario, Originator of National Schools Hovercraft Contest, (first held 1968).

UNITED STATES
AEROPHYSICS COMPANY

ADDRESS:
3500 Connecticut Avenue, N.W., Washington D.C. 20008
TELEPHONE: (202) 244 7502
OFFICERS:
Dr. Gabriel D. Boehler, President
Mr. William F. Foshag, Chief Engineer
Aerophysics Company was formed in 1957 to conduct fundamental research of the ground effect principle. Dr. Boehler had previously performed private feasibility work with Mr. M. Beardsley. Since then, Aerophysics has undertaken work in various areas of ACV design, including, skirt design, control techniques, parametric analysis, conceptual and design studies, studies of ACV lift air systems including various types of blowers and propulsion systems.

BOOZ-ALLEN & HAMILTON INC.

135 South La Salle Street, Chicago, Illinois 60603
ACTIVITIES:
General Management Consulting,
Computer Systems and Software
Market and Social Science Research
Industrial Engineering Systems
Pollution and Environmental Resources Management
Defence and Space Research
Product, Process and Equipment Development
Transportation and Airport Planning and Engineering

DAVIDSON LABORATORY
STEVENS INSTITUTE OF TECHNOLOGY

HEAD OFFICE:
Castle Point Station Hoboken, New Jersey 07030
Telephone: 201-792-2700
OFFICERS:
Dr. J. P. Breslin, Director
Daniel Savitsky, Assistant Director
Organised in 1935 as the Experimental Towing Tank, the Laboratory is active in basic and applied hydrodynamic research, including smooth water performance and manouvrability; seakeeping, propulsion and control of marine vehicles including ACV and hydrofoil craft. Special model test facilities are available to investigate the dynamic behaviour of ACV and hydrofoil craft in smooth water and waves.

FORRESTAL LABORATORY

ADDRESS:
Princeton University, Princeton, N.J.
OFFICERS:
T. E. Sweeney
ACTIVITIES:
Research prototypes (ACVs)

GIBBS & COX

ADDRESS:
40 Rector Street, New York, N. Y. 10006 Ph: (212) 487-2800
ACTIVITIES:
Project management, coordination and consultation on conceptual and preliminary designs, contract drawings and specifications and construction drawings for commercial or naval ships of the SES/ACV or submerged hydrofoil systems, destroyers, escorts, frigates, corvettes and VTOL/Helo carriers.

GLOBAL MARINE INC

HEAD OFFICE:
811 West 7th Street, Los Angeles, California 90017
TELEPHONE: (213) 680 9550
OFFICERS:
A. J. Field, President
R. B. Thornburg, Senior Vice-President
R. G. Longaker, General Manager
Arctic Engineers & Constructors
1770 St James Place, Suite 504, Houston, Texas 77027
Telephone: 713-626-9773
Global Marine Inc was incorporated in 1959, and is engaged primarily in offshore drilling and engineering. However, in 1968 the company undertook an engineering feasibility study directed towards developing equipment and techniques for drilling in Arctic areas. This engineering study led to the selection of ACT (Air Cushion Transport) units as the most feasible for operating in the area, and it has a continuing design programme directed towards various size ACT (Air Cushion Transport) drilling rigs with various drilling capabilities. This design work is handled by Global Marine Inc (Los Angeles), and the sales and operational aspects, with respect to the Arctic, are handled by Arctic Engineers & Constructors (see above). Arctic Engineers & Constructors is a joint venture between Global Marine and Raymond International, Houston, Texas.
AEC constructed the ACT-100 in Canada in 1971. This unit was test operated in the Arctic during 1971, and was test operated by the Canadian government in connection with the Mackenzie River Highway and by Imperial Oil Ltd. in connection with its offshore winter drilling operations in 1973-74. Design work on larger ACV drilling rigs continues.

HOVERLIFT APPLICATIONS INCORPORATED

HEAD OFFICE:
1651 Old Meadow Road, McLean, Virginia 22101 USA
TELEPHONE: (703) 790-9494
Hoverlift Applications Incorporated is a subsidiary of Science

Applications, Inc. and provides wide ranging engineering consulting services, applications studies, economic analyses and operation of air cushion vehicles. The company also has concentrated expertise and experience in the design and application of air casters, hovertrailers and hoverpallets, tank moving systems, hoverbarges, lighter-than-air vehicles and heavy lift helicopters. Recent work has included participation in the ARPA Arctic SEV Program and feasibility studies for various municipalities in the United States.

HYDRONAUTICS, INCORPORATED

HEAD OFFICE:
.7210 Pindell School Road, Howard County, Laurel, Maryland 20810
TELEPHONE: 301-776-7454
OFFICERS:
Marshall P. Tulin, Chairman of the Board
Phillip Eisenberg, Chairman of the Executive Committee
Virgil E. Johnson, Jr., President
Alex Goodman, Senior Vice-President
Philip A. Weiner, Vice-President and Secretary
Harvey Post, Treasurer

The company was founded in July, 1959, and has undertaken research, development and design of air cushion vehicles, hydrofoil craft and other high speed marine vehicles as well as advanced propulsion systems, under United States Government and industrial contracts. Hydronautics has its own ship model basin and high speed water channel suitable for the evaluation of air cushion vehicles and hydrofoils.

INSTITUTE FOR DEFENSE ANALYSES (IDA)

HEAD OFFICE:
400 Army-Navy Drive, Arlington, Virginia 22202
TELEPHONE: (703) 558 1000
ACTIVITIES:
Performs interdisiplinary studies and analysis for agencies of the US Government, systems analysis, operations research, economics, policy analysis and studies of advanced technology and its applications.

E. K. LIBERATORE COMPANY

ADDRESS:
567 Fairway Road, Ridgewood, N.J. 07450
PERSONNEL:
E. K. Liberatore, Head
John Eller

Formed in 1964, the company specialises in systems engineering, vehicle design and in operations in the fields of ACVs, SESs and VTOL aircraft. Work includes requirements, integration, analysis, design, costing, FAA and other certification, route and market surveys and methodology. Current projects in the areas of helicopter development, steam propulsion, non-expendable energy system and cryogenic waterjet propulsion systems.

GEORGE E. MEESE

ADDRESS:
194 Acton Road, Annapolis, Md USA 21403
TELEPHONE: 301 263 4054
CABLE: Meesmarine Annapolis
ACTIVITIES:
SES structures.

M. ROSENBLATT & SON, INC

HEAD OFFICE:
350 Broadway, New York, 10013 New York
TELEPHONE: (212) 431 6900
OFFICERS:
Lester Rosenblatt, President
E. F. Kaufman, Vice-President and Manager, Western Division
N. M. Maniar, Vice-President and Technical Director
P. W. Nelson, Vice-President
L. M. Schlosberg, Vice-President and Design Manager
F. K. Serim, Vice-President and Manager, Washington Area Branch

BRIEF HISTORY:
The firm was founded in 1947 and has since grown to be one of the largest engineering design firms of its type, specialising in naval architecture and marine engineering. An organisation of experienced engineers, designers and draftsmen has been assembled which is fully capable of providing the engineering, design and research and development services associated with ship and marine vehicle design.

Since its establishment, the company has successfully completed approximately three thousand ship design and related assignments for government and private customers. These assignments embrace work on commercial and naval ships and on almost every type of floating vessel. Merchant vessels include: passenger ships, containerships, oceanographic ships, general cargo ships, bulk carriers, tankers, surface effect ships, drilling platforms, survey vessels, tugs, etc. Naval vessels include: carriers, cruisers, destroyers, frigates, destroyer-escorts, tenders and auxiliaries of all kinds, submarines, LPDs, LPHs, LSTs, LSDs, hydrofoils and patrol craft.

Typical ACV assignments include:

1. ARPA Advanced Surface Effect Vehicles

Conceptual studies, parametric studies and propulsion machinery analysis for phase "O" studies of Advanced Surface Effect Vehicles for Advanced Research Project Agency. Work performed for American Machine and Foundry Company.

2. JSESPO Surface Effect Ship Testcraft

Conceptual and feasibility design studies of candidate SES vehicles for the JSESPO sizing study for second generation SES testcraft in the 1,000 to 3,000-ton range. The work included studies of various candidate versions of SES to identify and evaluate their unique operational and design capabilities; technological assessment of various structural materials and systems; preparation of a proposed development programme with required supporting R&D. Work performed for Joint Surface Effect Ship Program Office.

3. Amphibious Fleet Conceptual Studies

Conceptual design studies of various types of ships for future amphibious fleets, including submarine, displacement, planing hydrofoil and ACV type ships. Studies included technological assessment of performance of the concepts, taking into account various operational capabilities, including speed, propulsion systems, manning, weapons, materials, payloads and costs. Work performed for Stanford Research Institute under basic contract with ONR.

4. The Surface Effect Ship, Advanced Design and Technology

A 283 page text book covering drag, structure, propulsion, transmission, propulsors, stability, lift systems, seals, auxiliaries, weights, parametric analysis, and sample problems. Each topic is discussed including design procedures and equations. The book was prepared for the U.S. Navy Surface Effect Ships Project Office.

5. 2000-ton Surface Effect Ship

Trade-off studies, system design parameters, equipment selection, system diagrams, hull-borne stability in connection with a complete design proposal. The scope of work included hullborne structural design criteria, electrical power generating and distribution, heating, ventilating, air conditioning, hull appurtenances, piping systems, hotel and auxiliary machinery arrangements. Work performed for the Lockheed Missiles and Space Co., and the Surface Effect Ships Project Office.

6. ACV Amphibian

Conceptual design of a 20-ton capacity air cushion lighter, with retractable wheels, for US Army Mobility Equipment Research & Development Center.

STANFORD RESEARCH INSTITUTE

ADDRESS:
Menlo Park, California 09425
TELEPHONE: (415) 326 6200
EXECUTIVES:
Robert S. Ratner, Director Transportation Center

ACTIVITIES:
Operational tradeoff studies; optimising vehicles with missions; demand studies; economic evaluations; system and facilities planning, simulation studies.

MARTIN STEVENS
ADDRESS:
Woodhull Cove, Oldfield Village, Setauket, Long Island, N.Y.
ACTIVITIES:
Mechanical design, drive systems.

SYSTEMS EXPLORATION INC
HEAD OFFICE:
3687 Voltaire Street, San Diego, California 92106
TELEPHONE: (714) 223 8141
REPRESENTATIVES:
Dale K. Beresford
Erwin J. Hauber
ACTIVITIES:
Consultants to the US Navy on ACV and hydrofoil test and development programmes. Developed high aspect ratio displacement (HARD) hydrofoil concept.

WATER RESEARCH COMPANY
HEAD OFFICE:
3003 North Central Avenue, Suite 600, Phoenix, Arizona 85012
TELEPHONE: (602) 265 7722
EXECUTIVES:
Richard R. Greer, President
Dr. John H. McMasters, Chief Engineer
(Members of American Society of Naval Engineers)
The Water Research Company was formed in 1972 to consolidate activities surrounding the patents held or applied for by Richard R. Greer relating to various aspects of water-borne vehicles. The company has subsequently prepared conceptual studies on a class of winged surface effect vessels (WSEV) intended to fill a variety of US Navy and commercial freight applications. The conclusions of this study were published in the Naval Engineers' Journal, April 1974, and further comprehensive conclusions also setting forth energy savings and use of alternate fuels were published in Jane's Surface Skimmers, 1975-76 edition. The company is able to undertake analytical studies on hydrofoil, SES and WIG systems, and can provide contract co-ordinating services for such systems. Present efforts are directed to providing assistance in related research activities and further research studies.

WHEELER INDUSTRIES INC
EXECUTIVE OFFICE:
Board of Trade Building, Suite 403, 1129 20th Street, NW, Washington, DC 20036
Telephone: (202) 659-1867
Telex: 89-663

SYSTEMS RESEARCH CENTER:
Longfellow Building, Suite 800, 1201 Connecticut Avenue NW, Washington, DC 20036
Telephone: (202) 223-1938
OTHER OFFICES:
Hayes Building, Suite 618, 2361 South Jefferson Davis Highway, Arlington, Virginia 20362
Telephone: (703) 521-5005
Presidential Building, Suites 618/635, Prince George's Center, 6525 Belcrest Road, Hyattsville, Maryland 20782
Telephone: (301) 779-2060

OFFICERS:
E. Joseph Wheeler, Jr, President and Chief Executive Officer
George W. Glatis, Vice President, Corporate Development
James W. Wine, Vice President, Energy and Environment
James S. Tassin, Vice President, Contracts and Administration
Samuel A. Mawhood, Director, Advanced Systems Development
Scott E. Terrill, Jr, Director, Systems Research Center
Roy G. Shults, Associate Director, Systems Research Center

Wheeler Industries Inc., is a privatey-owned, small business firm that was founded in 1966 and specialises in systems engineering for ship, air, electronic, and deep ocean systems, as well as oceanographic and environmental research. Since its establishment, the company has continuously provided technical, engineering, and management support, primarily in the ship acquisition areas, to the US Navy. This support has encompassed a wide range including top level management plans, ship acquisition plans, technology assessments and forecasts, subsystem analysis and trade-offs, development and acquisition requirements and specifications, programme budgeting, development of hydrofoil design data, and hydrofoil strut/foil hydrodynamic load criteria and data. Currently, the company has one of the largest high speed surface ship teams in the United States. A team of experienced engineers has been assembled which is fully capable of providing the engineering, technical, design, and management services associated with hydrofoils. During the past year, the company has expanded its organization to provide technical and management services to the US Navy for air cushion vehicles and surface effect ships.

The technical and operational functions and capabilities are coordinated by the System Research Center. Under the Director of the Center, permanently assigned Project Managers (for ship, electronic, and oceanograpjic systems) form engineering task teams for the duration of a contract or included task(s), supported as necessary by technical support (clerical, graphics, editorial, and reproduction) personnel. This approach provides maximum management visibility and control over each task, and provides optimum response to customers while minimising costs.

HYDROFOIL CONSULTANTS

CONSULTANTS IN HYDROFOIL TECHNOLOGY AND OPERATION

SWITZERLAND
Dr. Ing. E. G. Faber
HEAD OFFICE:
Weinberglistrasse 60, CH-Luzern Switzerland
TELEPHONE: National (CH) 04/44 33 20
International +41/44 33 20
TELEX: 78 670 DATAG-CH
Consultant in marine engine plant planning, marine engineering and marine technology; with special emphasis on high-speed and hydrofoil craft.
GENERAL: Feasibility studies, cost estimates, specifications, plant descriptions, project co-ordinations.
CONCEPTUAL AND PRELIMINARY DESIGNS: Engine and auxiliary plants, piping systems and hydraulics, electrical and monitoring systems, ventilation and air conditioning systems, noise insulation.
TECHNICAL EXPERTISE: Speed estimates and hydrodynamics problems, waterjet propulsion, analysis of ship structure, vibration and shock isolation, acceptance tests and damage syrveu.

SUPRAMAR AG
HEAD OFFICE:
Denkmalstrasse 2
6006 Lucerne, Switzerland
TELEPHONE: (041) 36 96 36
TELEX: 78228
MANAGEMENT:
Hussain Najadi, Chairman
Ing. Volker Jost, Technical and Managing Director
Baron Hanns von Schertel, Technical Director
Dipl.-Ing Ernst Jaksch, Design Manager

DESIGN:
Dipl Ing Ernst Jaksch, Manager Foil Design Division
Dipl Ing Georg Chvojka, Manager Marine Engineering Division
Ing Vincent Schweizer, Manager Hull Design Division
Dipl Ing Otto Münch, Manager Controls Division

RESEARCH & DEVELOPMENT:
Baron Hanns von Schertel
Dipl Ing Eugen Schatté, Hydrodynamics and Propulsion
Supramar was founded in Switzerland in 1952 to develop on a commercial basis the hydrofoil system introduced by the Schertel-Sachsenberg Hydrofoil Syndicate and its licensee, the Gebrüder Sachsenberg Shipyard.
From this early date Supramar have provided a consultancy service on a world-wide basis covering not only their hydrofoil vessels but also other aspects of fast marine transportation. Their scientists have delivered papers to most of the world's leading professional bodies.
The company has been under contract to many Governments and military services.

UNITED KINGDOM
C. A. BRINDLE & PARTNERS
See main entry under ACV consultants.

CHRISTOPHER HOOK
ADDRESS:
Burfield Flat, Bosham Lane, Bosham, Sussex
Christopher Hook was responsible for the conception, design and development of the fully submerged hydrofoil which he demonstrated in the USA in 1951 with his Red Bug, and later with Miami-built conversion sets. He became a partner of the late Herr G. Sachsenberg, the pioneer hydrofoil builder and has completed hydrofoil design and consultancy contracts in the USA, Israel, Holland, France, Norway, Italy as well as with Strathclyde University. He is currently developing a self-tending sail rig for sailing hydrofoil craft, comprising sails that tilt to windward and have reefing. In the 1975 version a small wind vane ahead of the sails is coupled with the balanced air rudder with pilot differential interference so that the sail system will be constantly and automatically adjusted to any shift in the apparent wind. The four sail system was inspired by the hang glider. He is the holder of two gold and one silver medal for invention, President of the Republic Prize, France and an Inventaway award.

H. H. SNOWBALL
ADDRESS:
30 Lismore Road, Croydon, Surrey
Founder, in 1968, of Airavia Ltd, the first company to represent Sudoimport hydrofoils in the West. Founder, Speed Hydrofoils Ltd, which introduced Raketa hydrofoils on scheduled services on the River Thames in 1974. Consultant Bataan-Manila Ferry Services, Hydrofoil Exploration Services, etc. Prime negotiator 1968-1975 in conversion of Raketa and Kometa to British Passenger Certificate standards for re-export. Crew training arranged, also feasibility studies of projected hydrofoil routes.

T. PELLINKHOF See main entry under ACV consultants.

UNITED STATES
ATLANTIC HYDROFOILS INC
HEAD OFFICE:
Hancock, New Hampshire 03449
TELEPHONE: (605) 525 4403
DIRECTORS:
John K. Roper
Atlantic Hydrofoils' mechanically-controlled submerged foil system was the first to be approved for use on hydrofoil passenger ferries. The company has completed a number of Technical Reports for the United States Government on hydrofoil design and testing.

DAVIDSON LABORATORY
STEVENS INSTITUTE OF TECHNOLOGY
HEAD OFFICE:
Castle Point Station Hoboken, New Jersey 07030
TELEPHONE: (201) 792 2700
OFFICERS:
J. P. Breslin, Director
Daniel Savitsky, Assistant Director
Organised in 1935 as the Experimental Towing Tank, the Laboratory is active in basic and applied hydrodynamic research, including smooth water performance and manoeuvrability; seakeeping, propulsion and control of marine vehicles including ACV and hydrofoil craft. Special model test facilities are avilable to investigate the dynamic behaviour of ACV and hydrofoil craft in smooth water and waves.

GIBBS & COX
ADDRESS:
40 Rector Street, New York, N.Y. 10006 Ph: (212) 487-2800
6525 Belcrest Road, Hyattsville, Md. 20782 Ph: (301) 277-1919
ACTIVITIES:
Project management, coordination and consultation on conceptual and preliminary designs, contract drawings and specifications and construction drawings for commercial or naval ships of the SES/ACV or submerged hydrofoil systems, destroyers, escorts, frigates, corvettes and VTOL/Helo carriers.

W. A. GRAIG
ADDRESS:
307 Troy Towers, Union City, N. J. 07087, USA
Telephone: (201) 864-3993
W. A. Graig, Ingénieur Civil de l'Aéronautique (Ecole Nationale Superieure de l'Aeronautique, France). Registered Prof. Engineer (Ohio, U.S.A.).
W. A. Graig (formerly Grunberg) is the inventor of the Grunberg foil system, first patented in 1935. His approach provided the basis for the Aquavion series and many other designs, and his influence is still to be found in vessels in production today.
The Grunberg principle of inherent angle of attack variation is fully compatible with Forlanini's concept of area variation. Both can be incorporated in the same structure and in a number of modern hydrofoils the two principles work in association.
Among Mr Graig's recent developments include several foil systems which provide lateral stability without impinging on the original Grunberg concept. Directional control ensures co-ordinated turns.

HOERNER
ADDRESS:
Hoerner Fluid Dynamics
P.O. Box 342
Brick Town, New Jersey 08723, USA

S. F. Hoerner, Dr-Ing habilitatus

Hydrodynamicist of hydrofoils "Sea Legs" and "Victoria", since 1951.

Author of **"Fluid-Dynamic Drag"** (1965) and **"Fluid-Dynamic Lift"** (1975).

HELMUT KOCK
ADDRESS:

3132 Carleton Street, San Diego, California 92106

Helmut Kock designed the Albatross, first hydrofoil in the United States to certificated by the US Coast Guard for passenger services in lakes, bays and sounds. Twenty of these craft were built. A 72 passenger hydrofoil ferry designed by Helmut Kock is to be built for International Hydrolines Inc.

HYDRONAUTICS INCORPORATED
ADDRESS, TELEPHONE AND COMPANY OFFICERS:
See main entry under ACVs in this section.

M. ROSENBLATT & SON. INC
HEAD OFFICE:

350 Broadway, New York, 10013 New York

TELEPHONE: (212) 431 6900

OFFICERS:

Lester Rosenblatt, President

E. F. Kaufman, Vice-President and Manager, Western Division

N. M. Maniar, Vice-President and Technical Director

P. W. Nelson, Vice-President

L. M. Schlosberg, Vice-President and Design Manager

F. K. Sorim, Vice-President and Manager, Washington Area Branch

BRIEF HISTORY:

The firm was founded in 1947 and has since grown to be one of the largest engineering design firms of its type, specialising in naval architecture and marine engineering. An organisation of experienced engineers, designers and draftsmen has been assembled which is fully capable of providing the engineering, design and research and development services associated with ship and marine vehicle design.

Since its establishment, the company has successfully completed approximately three thousand ship design and related assignments for government and private customers. These assignments embrace work on commercial and naval ships and on almost every type of floating vessel. Merchant vessels include: passenger ships, containerships, oceanographic ships, general cargo ships, bulk carriers, tankers, surface effect ships, drilling platforms, survey vessels, tugs, etc. Naval vessels include: carriers, cruisers, destroyers, frigates, destroyer-escorts, tenders and auxiliaries of all kinds, submarines, LPDs, LPHs, LSTs LSDs hydrofoils and patrol craft.

Typical hydrofoil assignments include:

AGEH
Preliminary design and naval architectural services for preparation of proposal for design and construction of 300-ton AG(EH) Hydrofoil Research Vessel—for Lockheed Aircraft Corp.

HYDROFOIL (LVH)
Provided naval architectural services, including development of lines, powering predictions, stability curves and loading criteria for design and development of a 37-foot Landing Force Amphibious Support Vehicle Hydrofoil (LVH)—for Lycoming Division, Avco Corporation.

HYDROFOIL AMPHIBIAN
Conceptual design of a 60-ton capacity hydrofoil lighter with retractable wheels for US Army Mobility Equipment Research and Development Center.

STANFORD RESEARCH INSTITUTE
ADDRESS:

Menlo Park, California 94025

TELEPHONE: (415) 326 6200

EXECUTIVES:

Robert S. Ratner, Director, Transportation Center

ACTIVITIES:

Operational tradeoff studies; optimising vehicles with missions; demand studies; economic evaluations; system and facility planning; simulation studies.

SYSTEMS EXPLORATION, INC.
HEAD OFFICE:

3687 Voltaire Street, San Diego, California 92106

TELEPHONE: (714) 223-8141

REPRESENTATIVES:

Dale K. Beresford

Erwin J. Hauber

ACTIVITIES:

Consultants to the US Navy on ACV and hydrofoil test and development programmes. Developed high aspect ratio displacement (HARD) hydrofoil concept.

WATER RESEARCH COMPANY
HEAD OFFICE:

3003 North Central Avenue, Suite 600, Phoenix, Arizona 85012

TELEPHONE: (602) 265 -7722

EXECUTIVES:

Richard R. Greer, President

Dr. John H. McMasters, Chief Engineer

(Members of American Society of Naval Engineers)

The Water Research Company was formed in 1972 to consolidate activities surrounding the patents held or applied for by Richard R. Greer relating to various aspects of water-borne vehicles. The company has subsequently prepared conceptual studies on a class of winged surface effect vessels (WSEV) intended to fill a variety of US Navy and commercial freight applications. The conclusions of this study were published in the Naval Engineers' Journal, April 1974, and further comprehensive conclusions also setting forth energy savings and use of alternate fuels were published in the Jane's Surface Skimmers 1975-76 edition. The company is able to undertake analytical studies on hydrofoil, SES and WIG systems, and can provide contract co-ordinating services for such systems. Current studies are directed towards providing assistance in related research activities and further research.

WHEELER INDUSTRIES INC
EXECUTIVE OFFICE:

Board of Trade Building, Suite 403, 1129 20th Street, NW Washington, DC 20036

TELEPHONE: (202) 659 1867

TELEX: 98-663

SYSTEMS RESEARCH CENTER:

Longfellow Building, Suite 800, 1201 Connecticut Avenue NW, Washington, DC 20036

TELEPHONE: (202) 223 1938

OTHER OFFICES:

Hayes Building, Suite 618, 2361 South Jefferson Davis Highway, Arlington, Virginia 20362

TELEPHONE: (703) 521 5005

Presidential Building, Suites 618/635, Prince George's Center, 6525 Belcrest Road, Hyattsville, Maryland 20782

TELEPHONE: (301) 779 2060

OFFICERS:

E. Joseph Wheeler, Jr., President and Chief Executive Officer

George W. Glatis, Vice President, Corporate Development

James W. Wine, Vice President, Energy and Environment

James S. Tassin, Vice President, Contracts and Administration

Samuel A. Mawhood, Director, Advanced Systems Development

Scott E. Terrill, Jr., Director, Systems Research Center

Roy G. Shults, Associate Director, Systems Research Center

Wheeler Industries Inc., is a privately-owned, small business firm that was founded in 1966 and specialises in systems engineering for ship, air, electronic, and deep ocean systems, as well as oceanographic and environmental research. Since its establishment, the company has continuously provided technical, engineering, and management support, primarily in the ship acquisition areas, to the US Navy. This support has encompassed a wide range including top level management plans, ship acquisition plans, technology assessments and forecasts, subsystem analyses and trade-offs, development and acquisition requirements and specifications, programme budgeting, development of hydrofoil design data, and hydrofoil strut/foil hydrodynamic load c iteria and data. Currently, the company has one of the largest high speed surface ship teams on the United States. A team of experienced engineers has been assembled which is fully capable of providing the engineering, technical, design, and management services associated with hydrofoils. During the past year, the company has expanded its organisation to provide technical and management services to the US Navy for air cushion vehicles and surface effect ships.

The technical and operational functions and capabilities are co-ordinated by the System Research Center. Under the Director of the Center, permanently assigned Project Managers (for ship, electronic, and oceanographic systems) form engineering task teams for the duration of a contract or included task(s), supported as necessary by technical support (clerical, graphics, editorial, and reproduction) personnel. This approach provides maximum management visibility and control over each task, and provides optimum response to customers while minimising costs.

GLOSSARY

GLOSSARY OF ACV AND HYDROFOIL TERMS

ACS. Abbrev. Automatic control system. See foil systems submerged.

ACV. Air cushion vehicle.

AMPS. Abbrev. Arctic Marine Pipelaying System. Method of laying pipelines in ice-covered Arctic waters employing a skirted air-cushion barge as an icebreaker. System was devised after Arctic Engineers successfully and continuously broke ice up to 27 in (0·68 m) thick using the 250-ton ACT-100 platform. On contact with the ice sheet, the skirt rises above it, maintaining its seal. As the ice sheet enters the cushion zone, the water level beneath it is depressed by the air pressure. Having lost flotation support, the ice becomes a cantilevered ledge and when it reaches its critical length, it breaks off into the water below. The broken ice is then thrust aside by a plough-like deflector.

APU. Auxiliary power unit.

AQL. Abbrev. French. Aeroglisseur á quille laterale. Term employed in France for a ship-size seagoing air-cushion vehicle employing rigid sidewalls and flexible seals fore and aft, to contain the air cushion.

abeam. Another craft or object seen at the side or beam.

actuator. Unit designed to translate sensor information and/or computer instructions into mechanical action. Energy is transferred to control surfaces hydraulically, pneumatically or electrically.

A to N. Abbrev. Aids to navigation.

aeration. See **air entry.**

aerodynamic lift. Lifting forces generated by a vehicle's forward speed through the atmosphere due to the difference in pressure between upper and lower surfaces.

Aerofoil boat. Name given by Dr Alexander M. Lippisch, the inventor and aircraft designer, to his range of aerodynamic ram-wing machines.

aeroglisseur. (French, air-glider). Name given to range of passenger-carrying amphibious ACVs designed in France by Société Bertin & Cie in conjunction with Société D'Études et de Développement des Aéroglisseurs Marins (SEDAM). The name **Aerobac** is given to mixed passenger/car ferries and freighters designed by Bertin and SEDAM.

aeroplane foil system. Arrangement in which the main foil is located forward of the centre of gravity to support 75% to 85% of the load, and the auxiliary foil, supporting the remainder, is located aft as a tail assembly.

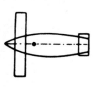

Aeroplane or conventional foil systems. The main foil may be divided into two to facilitate retraction

aerostatic lift. Lift created by a self-generated cushion of pressurised air. The cushion is put under pressure by a fan or fans and contained beneath the vehicle's structure by flexible seals or sidewalls.

aerosuspendu. (French, air-suspended). Form of suction-suspended monorail designed in France by Maurice Barthalon for mass public transportation on urban and suburban routes. The vehicle is suspended from its track by an air lift system in which the pressure is sub-atmospheric. Propulsion is by linear induction motor, q.v.

Aerotrain. Generic name for a range of tracked air cushion vehicles under development in France by Société de l'Aerotrain.

aft. At, near or towards the stern of the craft.

air bleed (hyd). See **air stabilisation.** Occasionally used instead of earation or air entry.

air bleed (ACV). One method of preventing "plough in" on a skirted ACV is to bleed air from the cushion through vent holes on the

Four aerostatic-type air cushion vehicles. Each is supported by air put under pressure by a fan or fans and contained beneath the vehicles by flexible skirts or sidewalls. *Left to right:* the projected 3,000-ton Bell 3KSES; the 220-ton Soviet Aist and *below* (upper picture) the 280-ton BHC SR.N4 Mk III and (lower) Sedam's 240 ton N500

outer front of the skirt to reduce its water drag by air lubrication.

air cushion vehicle. A vehicle capable of being operated so that its weight, including its payload, is wholly or significantly supported on a continuously generated cushion or 'bubble' of air at higher than ambient pressure. The air bubble or cushion is put under pressure by a fan or fans and generally contained beneath the vehicle's structure by flexible skirts or sidewalls. In the United States large or ship size air-cushion vehicles are called **surface effect ships** or **surface effect vessels**. Broadly speaking, there are two main types of air-cushion vehicles, those supported by a self-generated cushion of air and those dependent upon forward speed to develop lift. The former are designated *aerostatic*, and the latter, *aerodynamic*.

Aerodynamic craft include the *ram-wing*, the *channel-flow wing* and the *wing-in-ground-effect*. The *ram-wing* (a) can be likened to a short-span wing with sidewalls attached to its tip. The wing trailing edge and the sidewalls almost touch the water surface. At speed, lifting forces are generated by both the wing and the ram pressure built up beneath. One of the first concepts utilising a *channel-flow* wing (b) was the Columbia, designed in the USA by Vehicle Research Corporation in 1961 (JSS 1967-8 edition). The design featured a peripheral jet sidewall system for use at low speeds and an aerofoil shaped hull to provide lift at high speeds during forward flight. The side curtains of the peripheral jet were to be retained to seal the high pressure "channel" of air developed beneath from the low pressure airflow above and along the sides of the craft, down to the water surface. A 30 ft long manned model of the Columbia was successfully tested in 1964.

The *wing-in-ground-effect* (c) is essentially an aircraft designed to fly at all times in close proximity to the earth's surface, in order to take advantage of the so-called "image" flow that reduces induced drag by about 70%. In the Soviet Union this type of machine is known as an **Ekranoplan.**

Aerostatic-type air cushion vehicles can be divided into two categories—plenum chamber craft and peripheral or annular jet craft. *Plenum chamber craft* (d) employ the most simple of surface effect concepts. Air is forced from the lift fan directly into a recessed base where it forms a cushion which raises the craft. The volume of air pumped into the base is just sufficient to replace the air leaking out beneath the edges.

Variants of this category include the *skirted plenum craft* (e), in which a flexible fabric extension is hung between the metal structure and the surface to give increased obstacle and overwave clearance capability. The Naviplanes and Terraplanes designed by Bertin and SEDAM employ separately fed multiple plenum chambers, each surrounded by lightweight flexible skirts. Skirted plenum chamber types are also favoured by builders of light air cushion vehicles because of their relatively simple design and construction.

Another variant is the *sidewall* ACV (f), in which the cushion air is contained between solid sidewalls or skegs and deflectable seals,

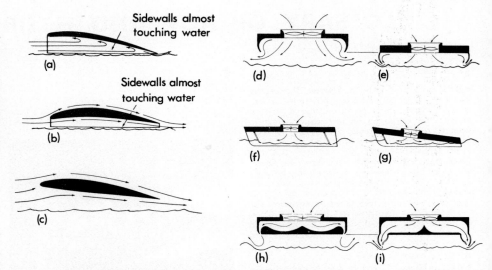

(a) ram wing; (b) channel-flow wing; (c) wing-in-ground effect; (d) plenum chamber; (e) plenum chamber with skirt; (f) captured air bubble; (g) hydrokeel; (h) annular jet; (i) trunked annular jet

either solid or flexible, fore and aft. Stability is provided by the buoyancy of the sidewalls and their planing forces. Sidewall craft are also known as captured air bubble vessels (*CABs*) a term used widely in the United States. One of the derivatives of the sidewall type is the *hydrokeel* (g) which is designed to plane on the after section of its hull and benefit to some degree from air lubrication.

In *peripheral* or *annular jet craft* (h) the ground cushion is generated by a continuous jet of air channelled through ducts or nozzles around the outer periphery of the base. The flexible skirts fitted to this type can take the form either of an extension to the outer wall of the duct or nozzle only, or an extension to both outer and inner walls. In the latter form it is known as a *trunked annular jet* (i).

air entrainment. See **air entry.**

air entry. Entry of air from the atmosphere that raises the low pressures created by the flow due to a foil's cambered surface.

air gap; also daylight gap, daylight clearance and **hover gap.** Distance between the lowest component of the vehicle's understructure, e.g. skirt hem, and the surface when riding on its cushion. **air gap area**: area through which air is able to leak from a cushion.

air pad. Part of an air pallet assembly into which compressed air is introduced and allowed to escape in a continuous flow through communicating holes in the diaphragm.

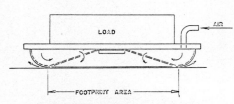

An air pad with a flexible plastic diaphragm

air pallet, also **hoverpallet.** Air cushion supported, load-carrying structure, which bleeds a continuous low pressure volume of air between the structure and the reaction surface, creating an air film.

air-port system, also **thrust port.** See **puff-port.**

air-rider. Alternative generic name for air cushion vehicles or weight carrying structures lifted off the surface by a cushion or film of air.

air stabilised foils. See **foil systems.**

amidships. (1) Midway between the stem and stern of a hull. (2) abbreviated to **midships** and meaning the rudder or helm is in a mid-position.

amphibarge. Name given to a range of amphibious air cushion barges designed in France by SEDAM. The craft can be either self-propelled or towed.

Sedam Amphibarges

Three aerodynamic air cushion vehicles. Like aeroplanes, these craft depend upon forward speed to develop lift. A dynamic air cushion is formed between the vehicle and its supporting surface below. *Left to right*: The Soviet ESKA-1, two-seat river rescue craft; the Lippisch Rheinflugzeugbau X 113 Am and a large Soviet experimental wing-in-ground-effect machine said to have been built at Gorky, and which is undergoing tests

angle of attack. The angle made by the mean chord line of an aero- or hydrofoil with the flow.

angle of incidence. The angle made by the mean chord line of a hydrofoil in relation to the fixed struts or hull.

Aquavion type foil. Adapted from the Grunberg system. About 85% of the load is carried by a mainfoil located slightly aft of the centre of gravity, 10% by a submerged aft stabiliser foil, and the remainder on a pair of planing sub-foils at the bow. The planing subfoils give variable lift in response to wave shapes, whether skimming over them or through them, and so trim the angle of the hull in order to correct the angle of attack of the main foil.

articulated air-cushion vehicle. A modular type load-carrying platform designed by Charles Burr of Bell Aerospace. A number of skirted platforms can be joined to form a variety of ACVs of different load carrying capacities. An application envisaged for craft of this type is the movement of containers and other heavy machinery in the American arctic and middle north.

aspect ratio. (1) the measure of the ratio of a foil's span to its chord. It is defined as

$$\frac{span^2}{total\ foil\ area}$$

(2) for ACVs it is defined as $\frac{cushion\ beam}{cushion\ length}$

athwart, athwartship. Across the hull in a transverse direction from one side of the craft to the other.

axial-flow lift fan. A fan generating an airflow for lift that is parallel to the axis of rotation.

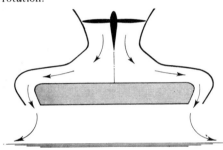

Axial flow lift fan

b.h.p. Brake horse power.

backstrap. A fabric strap used to secure a lift jet exit nozzle in a flexible skirt at the correct angle.

baffle plates. See **fences.**

ballast. Fuel, water or solids used to adjust the centre of gravity or trim of a craft.

ballast system. A method of transferring water or fuel between tanks to adjust fore and aft trim. In Mountbatten class ACVs, four groups of tanks, one at each corner of the craft, are located in the buoyancy tanks. A ring main facilitates the rapid transfer of fuel between the tanks as ballast and also serves as a refuelling line.

ballast tank or box. Box or tank containing the liquids or solids used to trim a craft.

base ventilated foil. A system of forced ventilation designed to overcome the reduction in lift/drag ratio of a foil at supercavitating speeds. Air is fed continuously to the upper surface of the foil un-wetting the surface and preventing the formation of critical areas of decreased pressure. Alternatively the air may be fed into the cavity formed behind a square trailing edge.

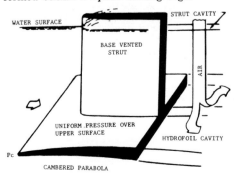

Base ventilated foil

beam. Measurement across a hull at a given point.

Beaufort Scale. A scale of wind forces described by name and range of velocity and classified as from force 0 to force 12, or in the case of strong hurricanes to force 17. Named after Admiral Sir Frances Beaufort, 1774-1857, who was responsible for preparing the scale.

Beaufort Force Number	State of Air	Description	Wind Velocity in Knots
0	calm	Smoke ascends vertically. Sea mirror-like	Less than 1
1	light air	Wind direction shown by smoke. Scale-like ripples on surface but no crests	1-3
2	slight breeze	As force 1, but wavelets more pronounced	4-6
3	gentle breeze	Flags extended. Short pronounced wavelets; crests start to break, scattered white horses	7-10
4	moderate breeze	Small waves, lengthening. Frequent white horses	11-16
5	fresh breeze	Waves more pronounced and longer form. More white horses some spray	17-21
6	strong breeze	Larger waves and extensive white foam crests. Sea breaks with dull rolling noise. Spray	22-27
7	moderate gale	White foam blown in streaks in direction of wind Spindrift appears Noise increases	28-33
8	fresh gale	Moderately high waves breaking into spindrift: well marked foam	34-40
9	strong gale	High waves and dense streaks of foam along direction of wind. Sea begins to roll	41-47
10	whole gale	Sea surface becomes white. Very high waves with over-hanging crests. Rolling of sea heavy. Visibility affected	48-55
11	storm	Waves exceptionally high, visibility affected	56-65
12	hurricane	Air full of foam and spray. Visibility seriously affected	above 65

bilge. Point of the hull where the side and the bottom meet. Also water or fuel accumulated in the bilges.

bilge system. A pumping system devised to dispose of water and other fluids which have accumulated in the bilges. In air-cushion vehicles bilge systems are installed to clear the buoyancy tanks. Small craft generally have a hand operated pump which connects directly to pipes in the tanks. In larger craft, like the 190-ton BHC Mountbatten, because of the large number of buoyancy compartments, four electrically driven pumps are provided, each of which can drain one compartment at a time.

block speed. Route distance divided by block time.

block time, also **trip time.** Journey time between lift off and touchdown.

boating. Expression used to describe an air cushion vehicle when operating in displacement condition. The boating or **semi-hover** mode is used in congested terminal areas, when lift power and spray generation is kept to a minimum. Some craft have water surface contact even at full hover for stability requirements.

bow. Forward part of a craft. The stem.

bow-up. Trim position or attitude when a craft is high at the bow. Can be measured by eye or attitude gyro.

breast, to. To take waves at 90° to their crests.

bridge. Elevated part of the superstructure, providing a clear all round view, from which a craft is navigated and steered.

broach, to. Sudden breaking of the water surface by a foil, or part of a foil, resulting in a loss of lift due to air flowing over the foil's upper surface.

to broach to. Nautical expression meaning to swing sideways in following seas under wave action.

bulkheads. Vertical partitions, either transverse or longitudinal, which divide or subdivide a hull. May be used to separate accommodation areas, strengthen the structure, form tanks or localise fires or flooding.

buoyancy. The reduction in weight of a floating object. If the object floats its weight is equal to (or less than) the weight of fluid displaced.

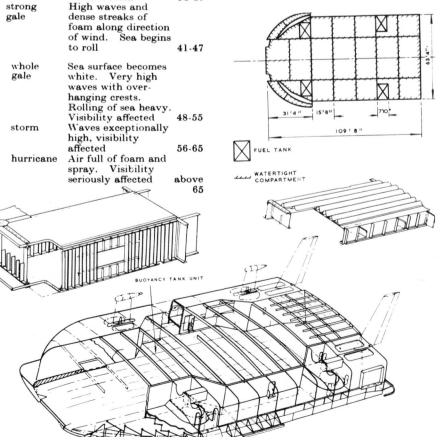

Typical buoyancy tank unit on the SR.N4. The basic structure of the SR.N4 is the buoyancy chamber, built around a grid of longitudinal and transversal frames, which form twenty-four watertight sub-divisions for safety. Below, the SR.N4 buoyancy tank layout

buoyancy chamber. A structure designed in such a way that the total of its own weight and all loads which it supports is equal to (or less than) the weight of the water it displaces.

buoyancy, reserve. Buoyancy in excess of that required to keep an undamaged craft afloat. See **buoyancy.**

buoyancy tubes. Inflatable tubular members providing reserve buoyancy. May be used as fenders if fitted to the outer periphery of a craft.

CAA. (Abbrev.) Civil Aviation Authority.

CAB. Captured Air Bubble. See **air cushion vehicle.**

c.p. Centre of pressure.

CP shifter. A control system which moves the centre of pressure of an air cushion to augment a craft's natural stability in pitch and roll.

CWL. Calm water line.

camber. (1) A convexity on the upper surface of a deck to give it increased strength and/or facilitate draining. (2) The convex form on the upper surface of a foil. The high speed flow over the top surface causes a decrease in pressure and about two-thirds of the lift is provided by this surface.

canard foil system. A foil arrangement in which the main foil of wide span is located near the stern, aft of the centre of gravity, and bears about 65% of the weight, while a small central foil is placed at the bow.

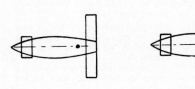

Canard foil configuration. The main foil area may be divided into two to facilitate retraction

captain. Senior crew member aboard a hovercraft. Defined as the person designated by the operator to be in charge of a hovercraft during any journey, under the UK government's "The Hovercraft (Application of Enactments) Order 1972". Equivalent in rank to airliner or ship's captain. Alternative terms: pilot, driver, helmsman, coxswain and ACV operator.

captured air bubble craft (see also **sidewall craft** and **surface effect ship**). Vessel in which the cushion (or air bubble) is contained by rigid sidewalls and flexible bow and stern skirts. Occasionally used for any air cushion craft in which the air cushion (or air bubble) is contained within the cushion periphery with minimal air leakage.

cavitation. Cavitation is the formation of vapour bubbles due to pressure decrease on the upper surface of a foil or the back of a propeller's blades at high speeds, and falls into two categories, unstable and stable. Non-stable cavities or cavitation bubbles of aqueous vapour form near the foil's leading edge and extend down stream expanding and collapsing. At the points of collapse positive pressure peaks may rise to as high as 20,000 psi These cause erosion and pitting of the metal. Cavitation causes an unstable water flow over the foils which results in abrupt changes in lift and therefore discomfort for those aboard the craft.

Foil sections are now being developed which either delay the onset of cavitation by reduced camber, thinner sections, or sweepback, or if the craft is required to operate at supercavitating speeds, stabilise cavitation to provide a smooth transition between sub-cavitating and super-cavitating speeds.

centrifugal flow lift fan. A cushion lift fan which generates an airflow at right angles to the axis of rotation.

chain ties. Chains used to maintain the correct shape of an air jet exit nozzle on a flexible skirt.

chord. The distance between the leading and trailing edges of a foil section measured along the chord line.

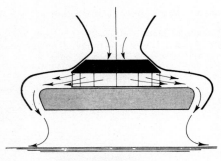

Centrifugal flow lift fan

chord-line. A straight line joining the leading and trailing edges of a foil or propeller blade section.

classification. Seagoing and amphibious craft for commercial application are classified by mode and place of construction, in the manner of the registration system started in the City of London by Edward Lloyd, and continued since 1760 by Lloyd's Register of Shipping. Outside the British Isles classification societies now include Registro Italiano Navale, Germanischer Lloyd, Det Norske Veritas, American Bureau of Shipping and the Japanese Ministry of Transport.

A classification society's surveyors make a detailed examination of craft certificated by them at regular intervals to ensure their condition complies with the particular society's requirements.

continuous nozzle skirt. See **skirt.**

contour, to. The motion of an air cushion vehicle or hydrofoil when more or less following a wave profile.

craft. Boats, ships, air cushion vehicles and hydrofoils of all types, regardless of size.

crew. Those responsible for manning a craft of either boat or ship size, including the officers. The company of an ACV or hydrofoil.

cross-flow. The flow of air, transversally or longitudinally within an air cushion.

cryogenics. Science of refrigeration, associated in particular with temperatures of —260 deg C and lower.

cushion. A volume of higher than ambient pressure air trapped beneath the structure of a vehicle and its supporting surface causing the vehicle to be supported at some distance from the ground.

cushion area. Area of a cushion contained within a skirt or sidewall.

cushion beam. Measurement across an air cushion at a given point.

cushion borne. A craft borne above the sea or land surface by its air cushion.

cushion length. Longitudinal cushion measurement.

cushion length, mean. Defined as:

$$\frac{\text{cushion area}}{\text{cushion beam}}$$

cushion seal. Air curtains, sidewalls, skirts, water-jets or other means employed to contain or seal an air cushion to reduce to a minimum the leakage of trapped air.

cushion thrust. Thrust obtained by the deflection of cushion air.

DWL. Displacement water line.

daylight clearance. See **air gap.**

daylight gap. See **air gap.**

deadrise. The angle with the horizontal made at the keel by the outboard rise of a vessel's hull form at each frame.

Delta wing. A triangular-shaped aircraft wing, as in fourth letter of Greek alphabet Δ, corresponding to D. Designed and developed by Dr. Alexander Lippisch and applied in supersonic configuration on the Me 163B rocket-propelled interceptor, the fastest military aircraft of World War II. More recently the delta wing has been employed by Dr. Lippisch in his series of Aerofoil Boats. Applied also in Soviet Union because of its high aerodynamic qualities and stability for a range of Ekranoplan aerodynamic ram-wings.

Diesel engine. An internal combustion engine which burns a relatively inexpensive oil of similar consistency to light lubricating oil. Invented by Rudolf Diesel, 1858-1913. Fuel oil is pumped into the cylinder then compressed so highly that the heat generated is sufficient to ignite oil subsequently injected, without an electric spark.

diffuser-recirculation. See **recirculation system.**

direct operating cost. Cost of operating a craft, excluding company overheads and indirect costs.

displacement. The weight in tons of water displaced by a floating vessel. Light displacement is the craft weight exclusive of ballast.

ditch, to. An emergency landing on water while under way due to a local navigation hazard, loss of cushion air or failure of a powerplant.

Doppler, navigator. An automatic dead reckoning device which gives a continuous indication of position by integrating the speed derived from measuring the Doppler effect of echoes from directed beams of radiant energy transmitted from the vessel.

down-by-the-head. Trim or sit of a craft with its bow more deeply immersed than the stern. The opposite expression is 'down by the stern'.

drag. (1) ACVs—aerodynamic and hydrodynamic resistances encountered by an air cushion vehicle resulting from aerodynamic profile, gain of momentum of air needed for cushion generation, wave making, wetting or skirt contact.

(2) hydrofoils—hydrodynamic resistances encountered by hydrofoils result from wave making, which is dependent on the craft shape and displacement, frictional drag due to the viscosity of the water, the total wetted surface and induced drag from the foils and transmission shafts and their supporting struts and structure, due to their motion through the water.

draught. Depth between the water surface and the bottom of a craft. Under the Ministry of Transport Merchant Shipping (Construction) rules, 1952, draught is defined as the vertical distance from the moulded base line amidships to the sub-division load waterline.

draught marks. (1) marks on the side of a craft showing the depth to which it can be loaded. (2) figures cut at the stern and stem to indicate draught and trim.

drift angle. Difference between the actual course made and the course steered.

ESKA (Russian). Abbrev. Name given to series of small wing-in-ground-effect machines developed by the Central Laboratory of Lifesaving Technology, Moscow. Shortened form of Ekranolytny Spasatyelny Kater Amphibiya (screen-effect amphibious lifeboat). Also known as **Ekranolyet** or **Nizkolet** (skimmer).

Ekranoplan. (Russian). Composite word based on *ekran*, a screen or curtain, and *plan*, the principal supporting surface of an aeroplane. Employed almost exclusively to describe types of ACVs in the Soviet Union raised above their supporting surfaces by dynamic lift. Western equivalent, wing-in-ground-effect machines (WIG) and aerodynamic ram-wing.

elevator. Moveable aerodynamic control surface used on small hovercraft to provide a degree of fore and aft trim control. Elevator surfaces are normally located in the slipstream of the propulsive units in order to provide some control at low speed.

FWL. Foilborne water line.

fathom. A depth of 6 ft.

fences. Small partitions placed at short intervals down the upper and lower surfaces of a hydrofoil tending to prevent air ventilation passing down to destroy the lift. They are attached in the direction of the flow.

ferry. A craft designed to carry passengers across a channel, estuary, lake, river or strait.

fetch. The number of miles a given wind

Fences on the bow foil of a Supramar hydrofoil

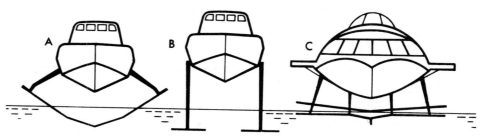

Foil systems in current use. A surface piercing: B submerged and C shallow draught submerged

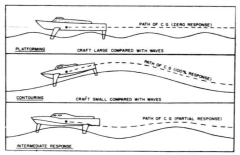

Comparison of platforming and contouring modes, and the intermediate response of a craft equipped with fully submerged, automatically controlled foil system

has been blowing over open water or the distance upwind to the nearest land.

finger skirt. See **skirts.**

fire zone. A compartment containing a fuel supply and ignition source which is walled with fire resisting material and fitted with an independent fire warning and extinguishing system.

fixed annual cost. Major component of a vehicle's direct operating cost. This comprises depreciation, craft insurance and operating and maintenance crew salaries, all of which are incurred regardless of whether the craft is operated or not.

flare. Upward and outward curvature of the freeboard at the bow, presenting additional, rising surface to oncoming waves.

flexible skirt. See **skirt.**

flying bridge. A navigating position atop the wheel or chart house.

foilborne. A hydrofoil is said to be foilborne when the hull is raised completely out of the water and wholly supported by lift from its foil system.

foil flaps. Foils are frequently fitted with (a) trailing edge flaps for lift augmentation during take-off and to provide control forces, (b) upper and lower flaps to raise the cavitation boundary.

foil systems. Foil systems in current use are generally either **surface piercing, submerged** or **semi-submerged.** There are a number of craft with hybrid systems with a combination of submerged and surface piercing foils, recent examples being the Supramar PT.150 and the De Havilland FHE-400.

surface piercing foils are more often than not vee-shaped, the upper parts of the foil forming the tips of the Vee and piercing the surface on either side of the craft. The vee foil, with its marked dihedral is area stabilised and craft employing this configuration can be designed to be inherently stable, and, for stability, geometry dependent.

The forces restoring normal trim are provided by the area of the foil that is submerged. A roll to one side means the immersion of increased foil area, which results in the

generation of extra lift to counter the roll and restore the craft to an even keel.

Equally, a downward pitching movement at the bow means an increase in the submerged area of the forward foil, and the generation of extra lift on this foil, which raises the bow once more. Should the bow foil rise above its normal water level the lift decreases in a similar way to restore normal trim. This type of foil is also known as an **emerging foil system.**

As the vee-foil craft increases its speed, so it generates greater lift and is raised further out of the water—at the same time reducing the wetted area and the lift. The lift must be equal to the weight of the craft, and as the lift depends on the speed and wetted foil area, the hull rides at a pre-determined height above the water level.

ladder foils. Also come under the heading surface piercing, but are rarely used at the present time. This is one of the earliest foil arrangements and was used by Forlanini in his 1905 hydro-aeroplane, which was probably the first really successful hydrofoil. In 1911 Alexander Graham Bell purchased Forlanini's patent specifications and used his ladder system on his Hydrodromes, one of which, the HD-4, set up a world speed record of 61·5 knots in 1919. Early ladder foils, with single sets of foils beneath the hull, fore and aft, lacked lateral stability, but this disadvantage was rectified later by the use of two sets of forward foils, one on each side of the hull. The foils were generally straight and set at right angles to their supporting struts, but were occasionally of vee configuration, the provision of dihedral preventing a sudden change of lift as the foils broke the surface. Both the vee foil and the ladder

systems are self stabilising to a degree. The vee foil has the advantage of being a more rigid, lighter structure and is less expensive.

Primary disadvantages of the conventional surface-piercing systems in comparison with the submerged foil system are: (a) the inability of vee-foil craft without control surfaces to cope with downward orbital velocities at wave crests when overtaking waves in a following sea, a condition which can decrease the foil's angle of attack, reducing lift and cause either wave contact or a stall; (b) on large craft the weight and size of the surface piercing system is considerably greater than that of a corresponding submerged foil system; (c) restoring forces to correct a roll pass above the centre of gravity of the craft, which necessitates the placing of the foils only a short distance beneath the hull. This means a relatively low wave clearance and therefore the vee foil is not suited to routes where really rough weather is encountered.

shallow-draught submerged foil system. This system which incorporates the Grunberg angle of attack variation approach, is employed almost exclusively on hydrofoils designed and built in the Soviet Union and is intended primarily for passenger carrying craft used on long, calm water rivers, canals and inland seas. The system, also known as the immersion depth effect system, was evolved by Dr. Rostislav Alexeyev. It generally comprises two main horizontal foils, one forward, one aft, each carrying approximately half the weight of the vessel. A submerged foil loses lift gradually as it approaches the surface from a depth of about one chord, which prevents it from rising completely to the surface. Means therefore have to be provided to assist take-off and prevent the vessel from sinking back into the displacement mode. Planing subfoils, port and starboard, are therefore provided in the vicinity of the forward struts, and are so located that when they are touching the water surface, the main foils are submerged at a depth of approximately one chord.

submerged foils. These have a greater potential for seakeeping than any other, but are not inherently stable to any degree. The foils are totally immersed and a sonic, mechanical or air stabilisation system has to be installed to maintain the foils at the required depth. The system has to stabilise the craft from take-off to touchdown in heave and all three axes—pitch, roll and yaw. It must also see that the craft makes co-ordinated banked turns in heavy seas to reduce the side loads on the foil struts; ensure that vertical and lateral accelerations are kept

These military hydrofoil designs illustrate three different foil systems. *Left to right:* The De Havilland Canada MP-100, a 100-ton missile craft with its inherently stable 'canard' surface-piercing system, incorporating a trapeze configuration main foil aft; the 83·5 ton Super Flagstaff with incidence-controlled fully submerged foils in "aeroplane" configuration and the Boeing NATO/PHM. The latter has a fully submerged canard system with 32% of the dynamic lift provided by the bow foil and 68% by the aft foil. Lift control is provided by trailing edge flaps on each foil within limits in order to prevent excessive loads on the structure and finally, ensure a smooth ride for the passengers and crew.

The control forces are generated either by deflecting flaps at the trailing edge of the foil or varying the incidence angle of the entire foil surface. Incidence control provides better performance in a high sea state.

A typical sonic electronic automatic control system (ACS) is that devised for the Boeing PCH-1 High Point. The key element is an acoustic height sensor located at the bow. The time lag of the return signal is a measure of the distance of the sensor from the water.

Craft motion input is received from dual sonic ranging devices which sense the height above the water of the bow in relation to a fixed reference; from three rate gyros which measure yaw, pitch and roll; from forward and aft accelerometers which sense vertical acceleration fore and aft and from a vertical gyro which senses the angular position of the craft in both pitch and roll. This information is processed by an electronic computer and fed continuously to hydraulic actuators of the foil control surfaces, which develop the necessary hydrodynamic forces for stability producing forces imposed by wave action manoeuvring and correct flight.

mechanical incidence control. The most successful purely mechanically operated incidence control system is the Hydrofin autopilot principle, designed by Christopher Hook, who pioneered the development of the submerged foil. A fixed, high-riding crash preventer plane is mounted ahead of and beneath the bow.

The fixed plane, which is only immersed when the craft is in a displacement mode, is also used as a platform for mounting a lightweight pitch control sensor which is hinged to the rear.

The sensor rides on the waves and continuously transmits their shape through a connecting linkage to vary the angle of incidence of the main foils as necessary to maintain them at the required depth. A filter system ensures that the craft ignores small waves and that the hull is flown over the crests of waves exceeding the height of the keel over the water.

Two additional sensors, trailing from port and starboard immediately aft of the main struts, provide roll control. The pilot has overriding control through a control column, operated in the same manner as that in an aircraft.

air stabilisation system. A system designed and developed by Baron Hanns von Schertel of Supramar AG, Lucerne. Air from the free atmosphere is fed through air exits to the foil upper surface and under certain conditions the lower surface also (i.e. into the low pressure regions). The airflow decreases the lift and the flow is deflected away from the foil section with an effect similar to that of a deflected flap, the air cavities extending out behind producing a virtual lengthening of the foil profile. Lift is reduced and varied by the quantity of air admitted, this being controlled by a valve actuated by signals from a damped pendulum and a rate gyro. The pendulum causes righting moments at static heeling angles. If exposed to a centrifugal force in turning, it causes a moment, which is directed towards the centre of the turning circle, thereby avoiding outside banking (co-ordinated banking). The rate gyro responds to angular velocity and acts dynamically to dampen rolling motions.

following sea. A sea following the same or similar course to that of the craft.

force time effectiveness. Time to land an effective landing force ashore.

fore peak. The space forward of the fore collision bulkhead, frequently used as storage space.

forward. Position towards the fore end of a craft.

Free power turbine

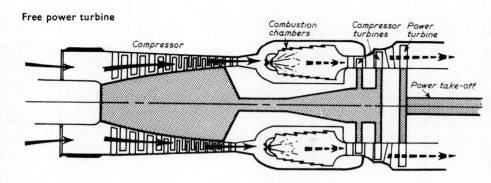

frames. The structure of vertical ribs or girders to which a vessel's outside plates are attached. For identification purposes the frames are numbered consecutively, starting aft.

freeboard. Depth of the exposed or free side of a hull between the water level and the freeboard deck. The degree of freeboard permitted is marked by load lines.

freeboard deck. Deck used to measure or determine loadlines.

free power turbine. A gas-turbine on which the power turbine is on a separate shaft from the compressor and its turbine.

full hover. Expression used to describe the condition of an ACV when it is at its design hoverheight.

g. Gravitational acceleration.

g.r.p. Glass-reinforced plastics.

gas-turbine engine. Engine in which expanding gases are employed to rotate a turbine. Its main elements are a rotary air compressor with an air intake, one or a series of combustion chambers, a turbine and an exhaust outlet.

GEM. Ground effect machine.

gross tonnage. Total tonnage of a vessel, including all enclosed spaces, estimated on the basis of 100 ft² = 1 ton.

ground effect machine. Early generic term for air cushion vehicles of all types.

ground crew and **ground staff.** Those responsible for craft servicing and maintenance. Also those responsible for operational administration.

Grunberg Foil System. First patented in 1936, the Grunberg principle of inherent angle of attack variations comprises a "stabiliser" attached to the bow or a forward projection from the latter, and behind this a 'foil'. Both foil and stabiliser can be "split" into several units. The lift curve of the stabiliser, plotted against its draft, is considerably steeper than its corresponding foil lift curve. Hence as the operational conditions (speed, weight, CG travel) change, the foil sinks or rises relative to the stabiliser, automatically adjusting its angle of attack. The "foil" is set at an appropriate angle of incidence in order to prevent it from approaching the interface. The system is fully compatible with Forlanini's concept of area variation and both can be incorporated in the same structure.

HDL. Hovercraft Development Ltd.

hp. Horsepower.

Hz (abbrev.) Unit of wave frequency employed especially in acoustics and electronics. 1 hertz = 1 cycle per second. Named after Heinrich Hertz (1857-1894), German physicist.

hard chine. Hull design with the topsides and bottom meeting at an angle, rather than curving to a round bilge.

head sea. A sea approaching from the direction steered.

heave. Vertical motion of a craft in response to waves.

heel. (a) To incline or list in a transverse direction while under way. (b) Lower end of a mast or derrick. (c) Point where keel and stern post meet.

Helibarge. System devised by A Walter.

Crowley (USA) combining a helicopter with an air-cushion barge. The downwash of the helicopter rotor pressurises the air-cushion.

hourly running cost. That part of the direct operating cost incurred when the craft is operated, i.e., fuel, maintenance and overhauls.

hoverbarge. Fully buoyant, shallow-draught hovercraft built for freight carrying. Either self-propelled or towed.

hovercraft. (a) Originally a name for craft using the patented peripheral jet principle invented by Sir Christopher Cockerell, in which the air cushion is generated and contained by a jet of air exhausted downward and inward from a nozzle at the periphery at the base of the vehicle. (b) Classification in the USA for skirted plenum chamber and annular jet-designs. (c) In the British Hovercraft Act 1968, a hovercraft is defined as a vehicle which is designed to be supported when in motion wholly or partly by air expelled from the vehicle to form a cushion of which the boundaries include the ground, water or other surface beneath the vehicle.

hoverplatform. Non self-propelled hovercraft designed primarily to convey heavy loads across terrain impassable to wheeled and tracked vehicles under load.

A Mackace 50-ton hoverplatform

hoverport. Defined by the British Hovercraft Act, 1968 as any area, whether land or elsewhere, which is designed, equipped, set apart or commonly used for affording facilities for the arrival and departure of hovercraft.

hover gap. See **air gap.**

hover height. Vertical height between the hard structure of an ACV and the supporting surface when a vehicle is cushion-borne.

hover-listen. Expression covering ACVs employed for anti-submarine warfare while operating at low speeds to detect a target.

hover-pallet. See **air pallet.**

hoversled. Vehicle designed for northern latitudes combining features of an air cushion vehicle with skis or pontoons. The first vehicle of this type was designed in Finland by Mr. Erkki Peri. Because of the contact between the vehicle's skis and the supporting surface beneath, directional control is a great improvement on that of most conventional skirted ACVs while operating over ice and snow.

hovertrailer. A steel structure platform around which is fitted a flexible segmented skirt, cushion lift being provided by fans driven by petrol or diesel engines on the platform. The system, devised by Air Cushion Equipment Ltd and UBM Hover-Systems, is designed to increase the load capacity of tracked and wheeled vehicles many times. In cases where it is impossible for a tow vehicle to operate, the trailer can be winched.

A hovertrailer. Payload at 100 psf is 6.7 tons

hull cresting. Contact of a hydrofoil's hull with the waves in high seas. The term **hull slamming** q.v., or slamming, is used if the hull contact is preceeded by foil broaching.
hull slamming. Contact of a hydrofoil's hull with the water following a foil broach. See **broach, to.**
hump. The "hump" formed on the graph of resistance against the speed of a displacement vessel or ACV. The maximum of the "hump" corresponds to the speed of the wave generated by the hull or air depression.
hump speed. Critical speed at which the curve on a graph of wave making drag of an ACV tends to hump or peak. As speed is increased, the craft over-rides its bow wave; the wave making drag diminishes and the rate of acceleration rapidly increases with no increase in power.

hydrofoils. Small wings, almost identical in section to those of an aircraft, and designed to generate lift. Since water has a density some 815 times that of air, the same lift as an aeroplane wing is obtained for only six of the area (at equal speeds).
hydroskimmer. Name given originally to experimental air cushion vehicles built under contract to the US Navy Bureau of Ships. Preference was given to this name since it gave the craft a sea-service identity.
inclined shaft. A marine drive shaft used in small vee foil and shallow-draught submerged foil craft, with keels only a limited height above the mean water level. The shaft is generally short and inclined at about 12°-14° to the horizontal. On larger craft, designed for operation in higher waves, the need to fly higher necessitates alternative drive arrangements such as the vee drive and Z-drive, the water jet system or even air propulsion.
indirect operating cost. Costs incurred apart from running a craft. Includes advertising, buildings, rents, rates and salaries for terminal staff other than those employed for craft maintenance.
induced wave drag. Drag caused by the hollow depressed in the water by an ACV's air cushion. As the craft moves forward it, building up a bow wave and causing wave drag as in a displacement craft until the hump speed has been passed.
integrated lift-propulsion system. An ACV lift and propulsion system operated by a common power source, the transmission and power-sharing system allowing variation in the division of power.
JP-4. Liquid fuel, based on kerosene, used widely in gas-turbines.
keel. (a) The "backbone" of a hull.
(b) An extension of an ACV's fore-and-aft stability air jet, similar in construction and shape to a skirt, and taking the form of an inflated bag.

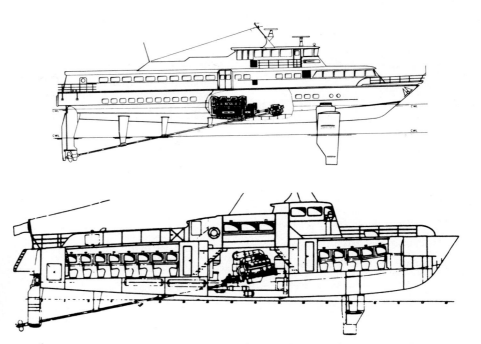

Sectional views showing the inclined shaft (above) on the PT 50 and the vee drive system employed on the PT 150

knitmesh pads. Thick, loosely woven pads, in either metal or plastic wire fitted in the engines air intake to filter out water and solid particles from the engine air.
knot. A nautical mile per hour.
land to. At the end of a run hyfrodoils and ACVs are said to settle "down" or "land".
LIMRV. Abbrev. Linear Induction Motor Research Vehicle.
landing pads, also **hard points.** Strengthened areas of the hull on which an ACV is supported when at rest on land. These may also provide attachment points for towing equipment, lifts and jacks.
leading frequency of sea waves. See **significant wave height.** Sea waves are composed of different frequencies. The sea wave of greatest energy content is called the sea wave of leading frequency.
leakage rate. Rate at which air escapes from an air cushion, measured in cubic metres or cubic feet per second.
lift fan. See also **axial flow lift fan** and **centrifugal flow lift fan.** A fan used to supply air under pressure to an air cushion, and/or to form curtains.

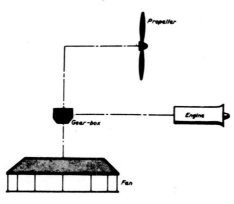

Integrated lift-propulsion system

lift off. An ACV is said to lift off when it rises from the ground on its air cushion.
linear induction motor. Linear induction motors show considerable promise as a means of propulsion for tracked skimmers, and are now under development in France, the United Kingdom, West Germany, Italy, Japan, the United States and USSR. An attractive feature of this method of electric traction is that it does not depend upon the vehicle having contact with the track or guideway.

The motor can be likened to a normal induction motor opened out flat. The "stator" coils are attached to the vehicle,

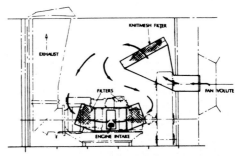

Gas turbine air filtration path on the Vosper Thornycroft VT 1, showing the knitmesh filter pad

while the "rotor" consists of a flat rail of conductive material which is straddled by the stator poles. The variable frequency multiphase AC current required for the linear motor can either be generated aboard the vehicle or collected from an electrified track.

Although the mounting of the stators on the vehicle appears to be preferred in Europe at present they can also be built into the guideway. In this case the rotor, in the form of a reaction rail, would be suspended from the vehicle. It would be of sufficient length to span several of the fixed stators simultaneously to avoid jerking.

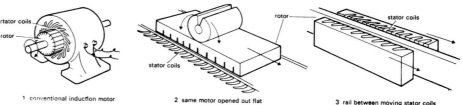

1 conventional induction motor   2 same motor opened out flat   3 rail between moving stator coils

Principle of the linear induction motor

load factor. Relationship between the payload capacity available, and the capacity filled.

logistics. Science of transporting, accommodating and supplying troops.

longitudinal framing. Method of hull construction employing frames set in a fore and aft direction or parallel to the keel.

maglev (abbrev). magnetic levitation.

multiple skirt. System devised by M. Jean Bertin, employing a number of separate flexible skirts for his system of individually fed, multiple air cushions.

nautical mile. A distance of 6,080 ft or one minute of latitude at the equator.

Naviplane. Name for the overwater or amphibious air cushion vehicles developed in France by SEDAM.

net tonnage. Total tonnage of a craft based on cubic capacity of all space available for carrying revenue-producing cargo less allowance for the engine room, crew quarters, water ballast, stores and other areas needed to operate the craft.

orbital motion. Orbital or circular motion of the water particles forming waves. The circular motion decreases in radius with increasing depth. It is the peculiar sequence of the motion that causes the illusion of wave translation. In reality the water moves very little in translation. The circular directions are: up at the wave front, forward at the crest, down at the wave back and back at the trough.

payload weight. Weight of revenue earning load, excluding crew and fuel.

PTO. See **power take-off unit.**

peripheral jet. See **air curtain** and **hovercraft.**

peripheral jet cushion system. A ground cushion generated by a continuous jet of air issued through ducts or nozzles around the outer periphery of the base of a craft. The cushion is maintained at above ambient pressure by the horizontal change of momentum of the curtain.

peripheral trunk. See **skirt.**

pitch. Rotation or oscillation of the hull about a transverse axis in a seaway. Also angle of air or water propeller blades.

pitch angle. Pitch angle a craft adopts relative to a horizontal datum.

platform, to. Approximately level flight of a hydrofoil over waves of a height less than the calm water hull clearance.

plenum. Space or air chamber beneath or surrounding a lift fan or fans through which air under pressure is distributed to a skirt system.

plenum chamber cushion system. The most simple of air cushion concepts. Cushion pressure is maintained by pumping air continuously into a recessed base without the use of a peripheral jet curtain.

"plough in". A bow down attitude resulting from the bow part of the skirt contacting the surface and progressively building up a drag. Unless controlled this can lead to a serious loss of stability and possibly an overturning moment.

With the skirt's front outer edge dragging on the water towards the centre of the craft (known as 'tuck under') there is a marked reduction in righting moment of the cushion pressure. As the downward pitch angle increases, the stern of the craft tends to rise from the surface and excessive yaw angles develop. Considerable deceleration takes place down to hump speed and the danger of a roll over in a small craft is accentuated by following waves which further increase the pitch angle.

Solutions include the provision of vent holes on a skirt's outer front to reduce its drag through air lubrication, and the development of a bag skirt which automatically bulges outwards on contact with the water, thereby delaying tuck under and providing a righting moment.

power take off unit. Unit for transmitting power from the main engine or engines, generally for auxiliary services required while a craft is under way, such as hydraulics, alternators and bilge pumps.

pvc. Polyvinylchloride.

puff ports. Controlled apertures in a skirt system or cushion supply ducting through which air can be expelled to assist control at low speeds.

Puff port arrangement on the BHC SR.N6

ram wing. See **air cushion vehicles.**

recirculation system. An air curtain employing a recirculating air flow, which is maintained within and under the craft.

reliability factor. Percentage relationship between the number of trips scheduled and those achieved.

Ro-Ro. (abbrev USA). Roll-on roll-off. Applied to ships and air cushion vehicles with decks providing straight through loading facilities, i.e. with cargo ramps or loading doors fore and aft.

roll. Oscillation or rotation of a hull about a longitudinal axis.

roll attitude. Angle of roll craft adopts relative to a longitudinal datum.

running time. Time during which all machinery has been in operation, including idling time.

SAR. Abbrev. Search and rescue.

SES. See **surface effect ship.**

SEV. Surface effect vehicle. Currently used in the USA to describe air cushion vehicles of all types. In the Soviet Union, the term is employed to describe large sea- or ocean-going wing-in-ground-effect machines.

Savitsky flap. Hinged vertical control flaps employed for foil lift variation, attached to the trailing edge of the foil struts, and canted out at an angle. The flaps are attached mechanically to the trailing-edge flaps on the foil. At the normal flying height only the lower part of the Savitsky flap is submerged.

As more of the flap becomes submerged due to increased wave height, the moment of the flap increases causing it to raise the the foil flap, thus increasing lift and restoring normal inflight attitude and flying height. The system can be adjusted to react only to lower-frequency layer waves. The system is employed on the Atlantic Hydrofoils Flying Cloud and Sea World. It was invented by Dr Daniel Savitsky of the Davidson laboratory.

seal. See **cushion seal.**

sea state. A scale of sea conditions classified from state 1, smooth, to state 8, precipitous, according to the wind duration, fetch and velocity, also wave length, period and velocity.

semi-submerged propeller. A concept for the installation of a partially submerged, supercavitating propeller on ship-size air cushion vehicles, driven through the sidewall transom. The advantages of this type of installation include considerable drag reduction due to the absence of inclined shafts and their supporting structures, and possibly the elimination of propeller erosion as a result of appendage cavity impingement.

service speed. Cruising speed obtained by an average crew in an average craft on a given route.

set down. To lower an air cushion vehicle onto its landing pads.

skirt. Flexible fabric extension hung between an ACV's metal structure and the surface to give increased obstacle and overwave clearance capability for a small air gap clearance and therefore reduced power requirement. The skirt deflects when encountering waves or solid obstacles, then returns to its normal position, the air gap being increased only momentarily. On peripheral jet ACV's the skirt is a flexible extension of the peripheral jet nozzle with inner and outer skins hung from the inner and outer edges of the air duct and linked

1 WIND VELOCITY			4	5	6	7	8 9	10		20		30		40	50	60 70									
2 BEAUFORT WIND AND DESCRIPTION			1 LIGHT AIR	2 LIGHT BREEZE		3 GENTLE BREEZE			4 MODERATE BREEZE		5 FRESH BREEZE	6 STRONG BREEZE	7 MOD. GALE	8 FRESH GALE	9 STRONG GALE	10	11 STORM								
3 REQUIRED FETCH IN MILES	FETCH IS THE NUMBER OF MILES A GIVEN WIND HAS BEEN BLOWING OVER OPEN WATER								50		100		200		300	400 500 600 700									
4 REQUIRED WIND DURATION IN HOURS	DURATION IS THE TIME A GIVEN WIND HAS BEEN BLOWING OVER OPEN WATER								5		20		25			30		35							

IF THE FETCH AND DURATION ARE AS GREAT AS INDICATED ABOVE, THE FOLLOWING WAVE CONDITIONS WILL EXIST. WAVE HEIGHTS MAY BE UP TO 10% GREATER IF FETCH AND DURATION ARE GREATER

5 WAVE HEIGHT CREST TO TROUGH IN FEET		1		2		4		6	8	10		15	20	25	30	40	50	60	ONLY LINES 7 8 AND 9 ARE APPLICABLE TO SWELLS AS WELL AS TO WAVES
6 SEA STATE AND DESCRIPTION		1 SMOOTH		2 SLIGHT			3 MOD.	4 ROUGH	5 VERY ROUGH		6 HIGH		7 VERY HIGH			8 PRECIPITOUS			
7 WAVE PERIOD IN SECONDS		1		2		3		4		6		8		10		12	14	16 18 20	
8 WAVE LENGTH IN FEET			20		40	60	80 100		150 200		300	400 500	600	800 1000		1400 1800			
9 WAVE VELOCITY IN KNOTS			5			10		15		20		25		30	35	40	45 50 55 60		
10 PARTICLE VELOCITY IN FT/S		1		2			3		4	5		6		8	10	12 14			
11 WIND VELOCITY IN KNOTS			4	5	6	7	8 9 10		20		30		40	50	60 70			

Chart of sea state conditions. Corresponding values lie on a vertical line

together by chain ties or diaphragms so that they form the correct nozzle profile at the hemline.

skirt, bag. Simple skirt design consisting of an inflated bag. Sometimes used as transverse and longitudinal stability skirts.

skirt, finger. Skirt system designed by British Hovercraft Corporation, consisting of a fringe of conically shaped nozzles attached to the base of a bag or loop skirt. Each nozzle or finger fits around an air exit hole and channels cushion air inwards towards the bottom centre of the craft.

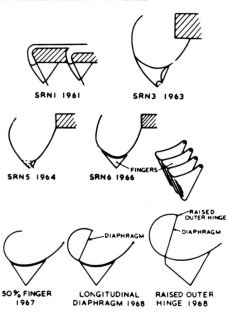

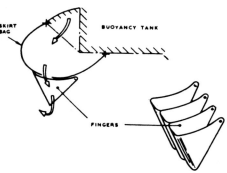

Types of finger skirts developed by British Hovercraft Corporation

skirt, segmented. Conceived by Hovercraft Development Ltd's Technical Group, this skirt system is employed on the HD.2, Vosper Thornycroft VT1, VT2 and many new craft either under design or construction. It is also being employed for industrial applications, including hoverpallets and hovertrailers.

The flexible segments are located around the craft periphery, each being attached to the lower edge of a sheet of light flexible material, which inflates to an arc shape, and also to the craft hard structure.

The system enables the craft to clear high waves and obstacles as the segments occupy a substantial part of the full cushion depth. No stability skirts or other forms of compartmentation are necessary. A smooth ride is provided as the skirt has good response due to low inertia.

The cushion area can be the same as the craft hard structure plan area. The skirt inner attachment points can be reached without jacking the craft up from its off-cushion position, simplifying maintenance.

skirt shifting. A control system in which movement of the centre of area of the cushion is achieved by shifting the skirt along one side, which has the effect of tilting the craft. Pitch and roll trim can be adjusted by this method.

Single shaft gas turbine

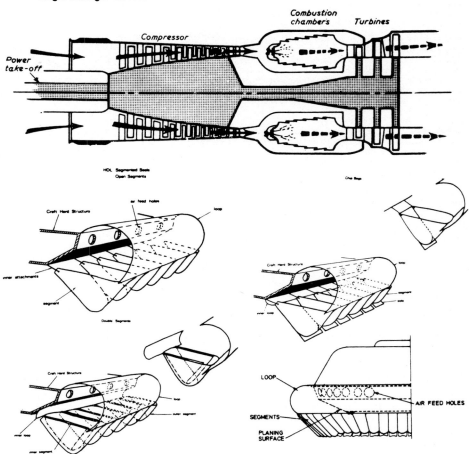

Segmented skirt developed by Hovercraft Development Ltd and employed on the HD.2. The separate segments occupy the full depth of the cushion between the hard structure and the supporting surface

Underside of the SR.N4 showing stability skirts

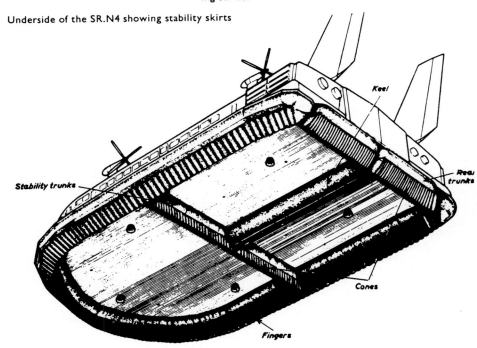

sidewall vessel. An ACV with its cushion air contained between immersed sidewalls or skegs and transverse air curtains or skirts fore and aft. Stability is provided by the buoyancy of the sidewalls and their planing forces.

single shaft gas-turbine. A gas-turbine with a compressor and power turbine on a common shaft.

significant wave height. Sea waves are composed of different frequencies and have different wave heights (energy spectrum).

A wave with the leading frequency of this spectrum and energy content is called the significant wave. It is from this wave that the significant wave height is measured.

split foil. A main foil system with the foil area divided into two, either to facilitate retraction, or to permit the location of the control surfaces well outboard, where foil control and large roll correcting moments can be applied for small changes in lift.

stability curtain. Transverse or longitudinal air curtains dividing an air cushion in order to restrict the cross flow of air within the cushion and increase pitch and roll stability.

stability skirt. A transverse or longitudinal skirt dividing an air cushion so as to restrict cross flow within the cushion and increase pitch or roll stability.

strake. (a) a permanent band of rubber or other hard wearing material along the sides of a craft to protect the structure from chafing against quays, piers and craft alongside. (b) lengths of material fitted externally to a flexible skirt and used to channel air downwards to reduce water drag.

submerged foil system. A foil system employing totally submerged lifting surfaces. The depth of submergence is controlled by mechanical, electronic or pneumatic systems which alter the angle of incidence of the foils or flaps attached to them to provide stability and control. See **foil systems.**

supercavitating foil. A general classification given to foils designed to operate efficiently at high speeds while fully cavitated. Since at very high speeds foils cannot avoid cavitation, sections are being designed which induce the onset of cavitation from the leading edge and cause the cavities to proceed downstream and beyond the trailing edge before collapsing. Lift and drag of these foils is determined by the shape of the leading edge and undersurface.

surf. The crests of waves that break in shallow water on a foreshore.

surface effect ship. Term implying a large ship-size ACV, regardless of specific type.

The various surface effect ship concepts are illustrated. For further definitions see **air cushion vehicles.**

surface piercing a.c.v. A craft with rigid sidewalls that penetrate the water surface. The air cushion is contained laterally by the sidewalls and at the bow and stern by flexible seals. (see sidewall air cushion vehicles or surface effect ships).

surf zone. Area from the outer waves breaking on the shore to the limit of their uprush on a beach.

TLACV. Abbrev. Track-laying air cushion vehicle. Air cushion vehicle employing looped caterpillar-like tracks for propulsion. The air cushion and its seals may be located between the flexible tracks, as in the case of the Soviet MVP-3 series, or it can take the form of a broad belt or track that loops round the complete air cushion. The latter approach is being developed by the Ashby Institute Belfast.

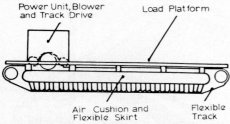

Track laying air cushion vehicle operating on a broad track that loops around the air cushion. This approach is being developed at the Ashby Institute, Belfast

TLRV. Abbrev. Tracked Levitated Research Vehicle.

take-off speed. Speed at which the hull of a hydrofoil craft is raised clear of the water, dynamic foil lift taking over from static displacement or planing of the hull proper.

tandem foils. Foil system in which the area of the forward foils is approximately equal to that of the aft foils, balancing the loading between them.

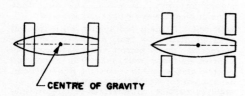

Tandem foil system. The foil areas can be "split" into two to facilitate retraction

terramechanics. Study of the general relationship between the performance of an off-road vehicle and its physical environment.

thickness-chord ratio. Maximum thickness of a foil section in relation to its chord.

thruster. Controlled aperture through which air can be expelled to assist control at low speeds.

Tietjens-type foil. Named after Professor Tietjens, this system was based on a forward swept (surface piercing) main foil located almost amidships and slightly ahead of the centre of gravity. It was intended that the pronounced sweep of the vee foils would result in an increasing area of the foil further forward coming into use to increase the bow up trim of the craft when lift was lost. The considerable length of unsupported hull ahead of the centre of gravity meant the craft was constantly in danger of "digging in" in bad seas and it was highly sensitive to loading arrangements.

transcavitating foil. Thin section foil designed for smooth transition from fully wetted to supercavitating flow. By loading the tip more highly than the root, cavitation is first induced at the foil's tip, then extends spanwise over the foil to the roots as speed increases.

transisting foil. See **transcavitating foil.**

transit foil. See **transcavitating foil.**

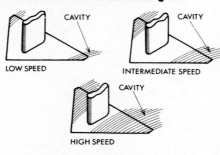

Transit foil operation

transom. The last transverse frame of a ship's structure forming the stern board.

transverse framing. Steel frames running athwartships, from side to side, instead of in a fore and aft direction.

trapped air cushion vehicle. A concept for a skirt-type surface effect ship with 20 ft skirts separated from the water surface by a thin film of air lubrication.

trim. Difference between drafts forward and aft in a displacement vessel and by extension of the general idea. ACV and hydrofoil hull attitude relative to the line of flight.

turnround time. Time from doors open to doors closed between trips.

utilisation. Operating hours timed from doors closed to doors open, including manoeuvring time.

utilisation, annual. Annual total of utilisation time.

variable-pitch propeller. A propeller with blades which can be rotated about their longitudinal axes to provide forward or reverse thrust.

ventilation. See **air entry.**

water wall ACV. A craft employing a curtain of water to retain its air cushion instead of an air curtain.

waterjet propulsion. A term now applied to a propulsion system devised as an alternative to supercavitating propellers for propelling high speed ship systems. Turbines drive pumps located in the hull, and water is pumped through high velocity jets above the water line and directed astern. The system weighs less than a comparable supercavitating propeller system and for craft with normal operating speeds above 45 knots it is thought to be competitive on an annual cost basis. First high speed applications include the Soviet Burevestnik and Chaika hydrofoils the Aerojet-General SES-100A testcraft and two products of the Boeing Company—the PGH-2 hydrofoil gunboat and the NATO PHM Fast Patrol Ship Guided Missile.

Waterjets are also being employed for propulsion at relatively low speeds. In the

SURFACE EFFECT SHIP CONFIGURATIONS

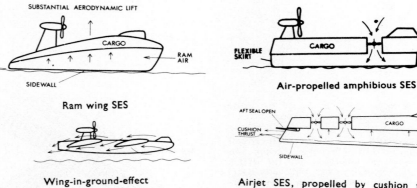

Ram wing SES

Wing-in-ground-effect

Aircat SES with wide buoyant hulls

Hybrid SES with rigid sidewalls and bow skirt

Air-propelled amphibious SES

Airjet SES, propelled by cushion thrust

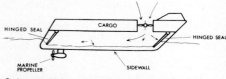

Sidewall SES. Also known as a Captured Air Bubble or CAB Type

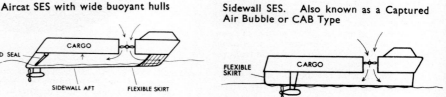

Water propelled, semi-amphibious SES

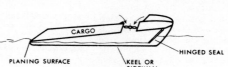

Air lubricated hull or hydrokeel SES

Soviet Union the Zarya shallow-draught waterbus (24 knots) and the Gorkovchanin sidewall ACV are propelled by waterjets. In the USA the PGH-1 and PGH-2 hydrofoils use waterjets for hullborne propulsion. The jet can be turned easily to give side propulsion to facilitate docking which is not so easy for a normal propeller.

wave height. The vertical distance from wave trough to crest or twice the wave amplitude.

wave length. The horizontal distance between adjacent wave crests.

wave velocity. Speed at which a wave form travels along the sea surface. (The water itself remaining without forward movement).

weights. The subject of weights involves definition of format, nomenclature, and units. There are no generally accepted standards with respect to ACV and SES weights, except that small ACVs tend to follow aircraft practice and large types follow ship practice. The hydrofoil concepts are ship orientated. A consistently used format aids in evaluating the concept and permits usage on, or direct comparison with other designs. Format 1, below is according to US Naval practice and is suitable for all sizes of ACVs, SESs, and hydrofoils. The actual terminology used for the totals is optional, so that the nomenclature can be consistent with the size of the vessel. In presenting results, the units (short tons, long tons, metric tons, pounds, etc) should be clearly indicated.

Format 2 is used by the Hovercraft industry in the United Kingdom. This emphasises equipment options, and by breaking down the expendable or useful load, the payload/range performance can be readily determined. It is also useful in defining first costs and operating costs.

winged hull. Alternative name given by Dr Alexander M. Lippisch to his range of aerodynamic ram-wing machines. See also **Aerofoil boat.**

wing-in-ground-effect. See **air cushion vehicle.** An aerodynamic-type air cushion vehicle which depends upon forward speed in order to develop lift. At speed lifting forces are generated both by the wing and a dynamic cushion of air built up beneath the vehicle and its supporting surface.

yaw angle. Rotation or oscillation of a craft about a vertical axis.

yaw-port. See **puff port.**

Z-drive. A drive system normally employed on hydrofoils to transmit power from the engine in the hull to the screw. Power is transmitted through a horizontal shaft leading to a bevel gear over the stern, then via a vertical shaft and a second bevel gear to a horizontal propeller shaft, thus forming a propeller "Z" shape.

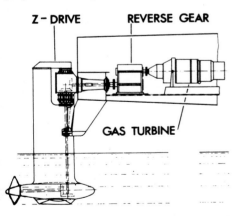

Z-Drive

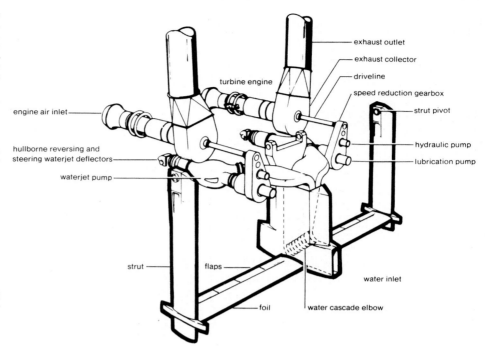

Waterjet propulsion system employed on the Boeing 929-100 Jetfoil, 106-ton, 190-250 passenger hydrofoil fast ferry

HOVERCRAFT WEIGHT TERMS

Format 1

	Group	Typical Items
1	Hull (or structure)	Basic structure, planting, frames, stringers, scantlings, decks, foundations, fittings, superstructure, doors and closures.
2	Propulsion	Engines, turbines, propellers, fans, gearboxes, shafting, drive systems, associated controls, nuclear plant, associated fluids.
3	Electrical	Power generation, switching. lighting, load canters, panels, cable
4	Communication and Control	Communications (internal, external) and navigation equipment, military electronics, computers, displays (note ship controls are in Group 5)
5	Auxiliary Systems	Fuel, heating, ventilation, fresh water, ship controls, rudder, cushion seal (flexible or articulated), plumbing, oil, fire extinguishing, drainage, ballast, mooring, anchoring, hydrofoils distilling plant.
6	Outfit and Furnishings	Hull fittings, marine hardware, ladders, furnishings, boats, rafts, preservers, stowages, lockers, painting, deck covering, hull insulation, commissary equipment, radiation shielding (other than at reactor area)
7	Armament	Weapons, mounts, ammunition stowage, handling systems, special plating
Total: Light Ship or Light Displacement or Empty Weight		(sum of the above items)
Variable Load or Useful Load		Operating personnel and effects, cargo, freight fuel, passengers, baggage, water, ammunition, aircraft, stores, troops, provisions.
Full Load Displacement or Load Displacement or Gross Weight or All Up Weight		(sum of empty weight and useful load)

Format 2

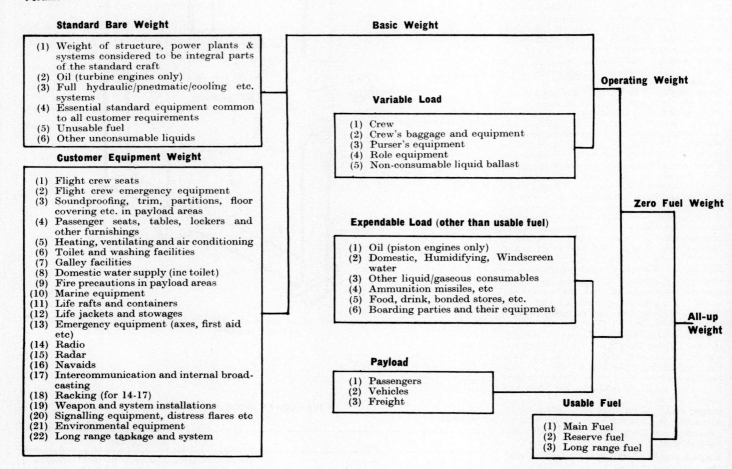

Standard Bare Weight

(1) Weight of structure, power plants & systems considered to be integral parts of the standard craft
(2) Oil (turbine engines only)
(3) Full hydraulic/pneumatic/cooling etc. systems
(4) Essential standard equipment common to all customer requirements
(5) Unusable fuel
(6) Other unconsumable liquids

Customer Equipment Weight

(1) Flight crew seats
(2) Flight crew emergency equipment
(3) Soundproofing, trim, partitions, floor covering etc. in payload areas
(4) Passenger seats, tables, lockers and other furnishings
(5) Heating, ventilating and air conditioning
(6) Toilet and washing facilities
(7) Galley facilities
(8) Domestic water supply (inc toilet)
(9) Fire precautions in payload areas
(10) Marine equipment
(11) Life rafts and containers
(12) Life jackets and stowages
(13) Emergency equipment (axes, first aid etc)
(14) Radio
(15) Radar
(16) Navaids
(17) Intercommunication and internal broadcasting
(18) Racking (for 14-17)
(19) Weapon and system installations
(20) Signalling equipment, distress flares etc
(21) Environmental equipment
(22) Long range tankage and system

Basic Weight

Variable Load

(1) Crew
(2) Crew's baggage and equipment
(3) Purser's equipment
(4) Role equipment
(5) Non-consumable liquid ballast

Expendable Load (other than usable fuel)

(1) Oil (piston engines only)
(2) Domestic, Humidifying, Windscreen water
(3) Other liquid/gaseous consumables
(4) Ammunition missiles, etc
(5) Food, drink, bonded stores, etc.
(6) Boarding parties and their equipment

Payload

(1) Passengers
(2) Vehicles
(3) Freight

Usable Fuel

(1) Main Fuel
(2) Reserve fuel
(3) Long range fuel

Operating Weight

Zero Fuel Weight

All-up Weight

ADDENDA

AIR CUSHION VEHICLES

UNITED KINGDOM
BRITISH HOVERCRAFT CORPORATION

HEAD OFFICE:
  East Cowes
  Isle of Wight
TELEPHONE:
  Cowes 4121
TELEX:
  86190
TELEGRAMS:
  Brithover Cowes Telex
DIRECTORS:
  See main entry.

BHC HOVERLIGHTER

Preliminary details have been released by BHC for a hoverlighter variant of the SR.N4. The rapid increase of trade in many ports in the Middle East has led to serious congestion and expensive delays. Expansion of port facilities is costly, time consuming and in many cases extremely difficult due to urban growth. Hover-lighters offer a unique solution to this problem by providing a rapid link between ships and shore. A simple base can be located clear of the port, but alongside a roadway or railway for offloading onto road vehicles or railway trucks.

The hoverlighter is a flat-decked hover-craft based on the highly successful SR.N4 cross Channel passenger and car ferry craft. Fitted with four machinery modules, each located in a corner of the cargo deck area, the craft would have a bow loading/unloading ramp and a control cabin adjacent to one of the forward modules. Powered by four Rolls Royce Proteus engines the craft will have an unloaded speed of 40-45 knots and loaded could reach speeds of 20 knots.

A typical operation using a fleet of five

BHC's hoverlighter—a flat-decked variant of the SR.N4 with four machinery modules, each located in a corner of the cargo deck area

hoverlighters each with a payload of ap-proximately 200 tons, working a ten-hour day, could move up to 10,000 tonnes daily.

Unloading from the ships would be ship operated cranes or large floating cranes, the containers and other loads would be lifted onto the hoverlighter's deck and placed on wheeled trolleys; these would be positioned on the cargo deck using powerful motor tractors, these same tractors being used to

unload the lighter onshore. A typical loading and unloading sequence would take approxi-mately 30 minutes.

The hoverlighter offers a low cost solution to port congestion. In the longer term the craft could form the backbone of river transport systems where the natural terrain of mudbanks, rapids and shifting sandbanks make the use of conventional freighters impossible.

UNITED STATES
SUPERIOR HOVERCRAFT CORPORATION

HEAD OFFICE:
  PO Box 1214,
  North Bay,
  Ontario,
  Canada P1B 8K4

RESEARCH AND EVALUATION CENTRE:
  Riverbend Road,
  North Bay
  Ontario,
  Canada
TELEPHONE:
  (705) 472 7761
OFFICERS:
  H. R. Irving, President
  A. Robertson, Vice President
  D. J. Murray, Test and Demonstration
    Manager

The first craft to be marketed by Superior Hovercraft Corporation is the Turbo Super Hover Mk 5. The company has built three prototypes, the most recent of which was undergoing winter tests as this edition went to press. Arctic trials are included in the test programme.

TURBO SUPER HOVER Mk. 5

This new multiduty ACV has been designed for a variety of commercial and military applications in the more remote areas of North America and Canada. It carries a driver and up to four passengers or up to 1,000 lb (453 kg) of freight. Built in moulded,

The Turbo Super Hover Mk.5

high impact fibreglass, it is powered by a single 390 hp V8 water-cooled engine and has a top speed over ice and snow of 35-40 mph.

LIFT AND PROPULSION: Integrated system powered by a single 390 hp V8 water-cooled engine with heat exchanger. Mounted inboard, the engine drives two axial-flow fans mounted at opposite ends of a transverse shaft. Both fans are enclosed in ducts to eliminate any danger from moving parts. Airflow is ducted beneath the craft for lift and via outlets aft for thrust. Fuel recom-mended is Hi-Test gasoline. Cushion area

is 160 sq ft. Cushion pressure, 4 psi.
CONTROLS: Craft heading is controlled by multiple rudders in the airjet outlets aft. Driving controls comprise a steering wheel, which actuates the rudders, an electric starter, automatic choke and a throttle lever for lift and thrust. Reverse thrust is applied for braking and stopping.
HULL: Moulded fibreglass and corrosion resistant aluminium construction. Buoyancy, 150%.
ACCOMMODATION: Access to the enclosed cabin is via twin gull-wing doors, one port one starboard.

DIMENSIONS:
Length overall	19 ft 0 in (5·79 m)
Beam overall	11 ft 6 in (3·50 m)
Height, cushionborne	7 ft 8 in (2·33 m)

WEIGHTS:
Gross weight	4,150 lb (1,882 kg)
Empty weight	2,890 lb (1,310 kg)
Payload, freight	1,000 lb (453 kg)

PERFORMANCE:
Max speed	40 mph (64·37 km/h)
Range	125-150 miles (2r01-244 km)
Endurance	4½ hours
Distance for emergency stopping	50 ft (15 m)
Normal stopping distance	150 ft (45 m)
Gradient capability	8·7%

Craft can climb long 20% gradiants and short 30% gradiants, including river banks.

Cabin of the Turbo Super Hover looking aft

Driver's position in the Turbo Super Hover Mk.5

HYDROFOIL OPERATORS

VENEZUELA
TURISMO MARGARITO C.A.

Turismo Margarito has purchased two Boeing Jetfoil 929-100s for operation between Puerto La Cruz and Margarita Island in the Caribbean. Price of the two vessels is understocd to be about $18 million. Each vessel will seat 242 passengers and cruise at about 43 knots. Conventional ferries carry more than 2 million passengers to and from the island annually.

INDEX

Printed in England by Netherwood Dalton & Co. Ltd., Huddersfield

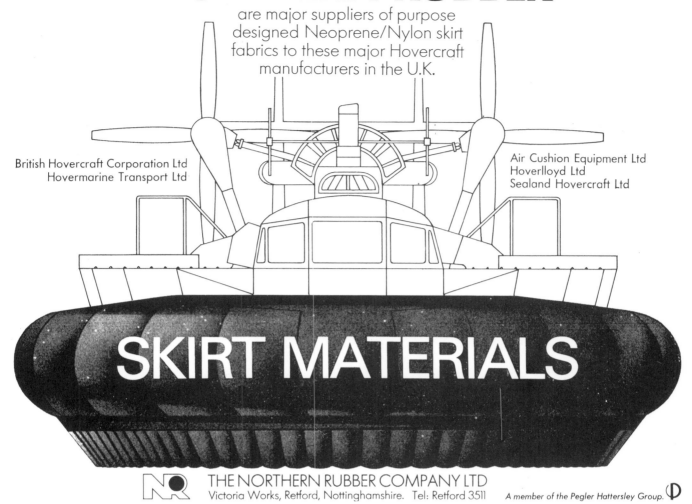
[i]

VT2
60 knots and fully amphibious